Leading Dealers In Fine And Rare Great Britain

www.markbrandon.co.uk

01908 915553

Stanley Gibbons

Great Britain
CONCISE
Stamp Catalogue

2023 edition

STANLEY
GIBBONS
THE HOME OF STAMP COLLECTING

By Appointment to
Her Majesty The Queen
Philatelists
Stanley Gibbons Ltd
London

Published by Stanley Gibbons Publications
Editorial, Sales Offices and Distribution Centre:
7 Parkside, Christchurch Road, Ringwood,
Hants BH24 3SH

First Edition — May 1986
Second Edition — May 1987
Third Edition — May 1988
Fourth Edition — May 1989
Fifth Edition — May 1990
Sixth Edition — May 1991
Seventh Edition — May 1992
Eighth Edition — April 1993
Ninth Edition — April 1994
Tenth Edition — April 1995
11th Edition — April 1996
12th Edition — April 1997
13th Edition — April 1998
14th Edition — April 1999
15th Edition — May 2000
16th Edition — April 2001
17th Edition — April 2002
18th Edition — April 2003
19th Edition — April 2004
20th Edition — May 2005

21st Edition — April 2006
22nd Edition — April 2007
23rd Edition — April 2008
24th Edition — April 2009
24th Edition — reprinted June 2009
25th Edition — May 2010
26th Edition — April 2011
27th Edition — April 2012
28th Edition — April 2013
29th Edition — April 2014
30th Edition — May 2015
31st Edition — May 2016
32nd Edition — June 2017
33rd Edition — May 2018
34th Edition — May 2019
35th Edition — May 2020
35th Edition — reprinted Jan 2021
36th Edition — May 2021
37th Edition — May 2022
38th Edition — May 2023

Printed by
Sterling, Kettering

Contents

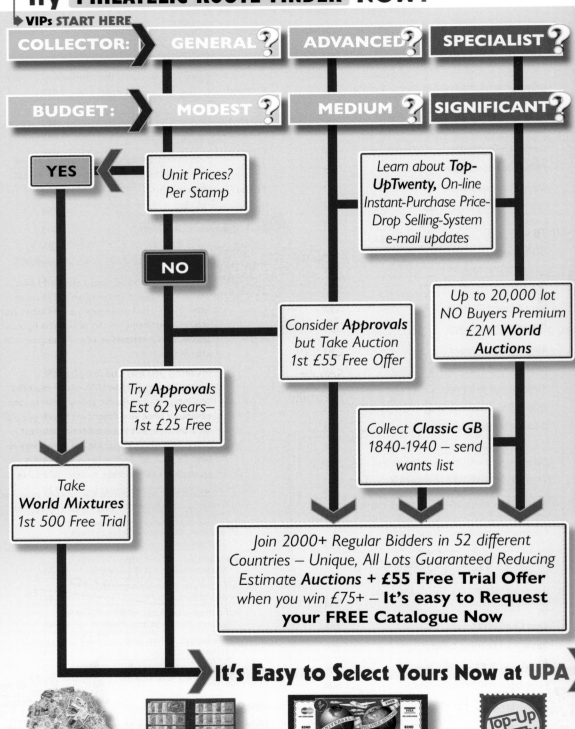

Sometimes Collectors Get a Raw Deal
Determine how You wish to be treated Here ...

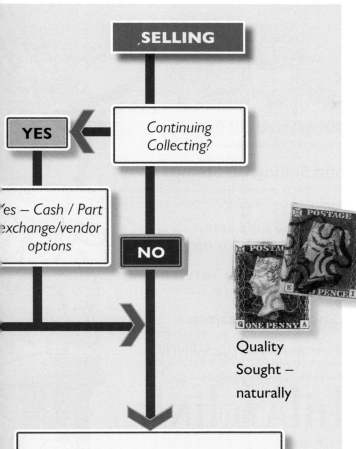

SELLING

YES ← **Continuing Collecting?**

Yes – Cash / Part exchange/vendor options

NO

Quality Sought – naturally

Contact Andrew Now or another member of his specialist Team to discuss the market/selling options:
andrew@upastampauctions.co.uk

☎
01451 861111

'money spent in the wrong way soon mounts up ...'

Successful and enjoyable collecting depends upon understanding the relationship of your budget to your interest.

Offers and services can be confusing can't they, and money spent in the wrong way soon mounts up.

In philately, sometimes it is hard to decide which way to go. Your passion may exceed your resource, so just what may be best for you?

Often, it is not what you collect but how you collect

This is the reason why my team and I have devised this quick and easy philatelic route-map QUIZ which does not ask you what you collect – but helps you to determine by your answers just which type of collecting service may best suit you ...

Presently you may find few philatelic companies other than UPA which can offer you integrated philatelic selling systems, but obviously once you determine which philatelic services best suit your collecting interest – you may have a clearer idea of which way is best to go – depending upon your levels of specialism and philatelic budget, of course

Check out our Philatelic QUIZ right now and see for yourself. To select your choice, visit our website or call my team

Dedicated to De-mystifying Philately

Andrew

Andrew McGavin,
Veteran Philatelic Auctioneer
Philatelic Expert & Author
Managing Director Universal Philatelic Auctions (UPA)

Visit: www.UPAstampauctions.co.uk

opTips OF THE Trade

Fax: 01451 861297 ~ info@upastampauctions.co.uk ~ T: 01451 861111
Participate in this Philatelic Route-Map to Enjoyable Collecting.
Find UPA also on-line at www.top-uptwenty.co.uk
New Instant-Purchase Price-Drop Selling-System

GB Conc 2023

UNIVERSAL SINCE PHILAT...
88th Edition
POSTAL AUCTION
Closing Date:
5pm Tuesday 10th I...
27,934 lots +

Preface

Welcome to the 38th edition of the Great Britain *Concise* Stamp Catalogue, again a very significant year for anyone that collects GB stamps. The sad loss of Her Majesty Queen Elizabeth II in September left a country in mourning, and an end of an era for collectors. Having known no other monarch on their stamps there is the obvious dilemma for many collectors. Do they now have a finishing point for their collections, or do they embark on collecting an exciting new reign? With one of the superb new King Charles III definitives on the front cover you can probably guess exactly how we at Stanley Gibbons feel.

Editorial developments

Apart from the usual 'new issues' we have continued to iron out any discrepancies from our new catalogue production software, and I once again thank all our readers that have made contributions to the accuracy of the catalogue and offered constructive advice. Regular readers will notice we also have made a lot of changes with many new explanatory notes, to improve the consistencies of the listings and the information available for readers. We have also expanded the Machin booklet pane diagrams to include panes for the older NVI Machins and the recent Queen Elizabeth barcode Machins.

I reported briefly last year on the Royal Mail 'Swap Out' scheme which should have seen the nonbarcode Machins demonetised on the 31 January. Unfortunately due to a lot of media hype and a not insignificant amount or inaccurate reporting, the Post Office received a lot of bad publicity and sensibly took the decision to postpone the invalidation date to 31 July.

Use of non-barcoded machin stamps from the 1 August will be deemed invalid and subject to surcharge, and as previously reported, no end date to the 'Swap out' scheme has been announced.

If a new King, and the demise of the Machin wasn't enough, the hot topic of conversation amongst many collectors is undoubtedly the future of Royal Mail. I'm sure you are all aware of the reports that Royal Mail expects to make an annual operating loss of £350m in the year to the end of March 2023. Possibly rising to £450m if customers turn to rivals because of the disruptions to its delivery services. Royal Mail owner International Distributions Services (IDS) have also reported that the recent wave of strikes have cost it £200m so far.

So where does all this leave collectors? With declining demand for delivering letters, parcels are becoming the mainstay of the company. With online payment for smaller parcels being heavily promoted and the inability to use stamps for Parcelforce items, what is the future for stamps and philately within Royal Mail?

Let's just hope that in their efforts to return to profit they don't decide that Philately is surplus to requirements!

Vince Cordell

April 2023

Features of this Catalogue

The Concise Catalogue, now in its 38th year of publication, has established itself as an essential guide for the 'one-country' collector of Great Britain. As the popularity of Great Britain stamps continues to grow — the Concise Catalogue supplies the information you need to enhance your collection.

+ All issues from the Penny Black of 1840 to 30 April 2023 including Regional, Postage Due, Official and Postal Fiscal stamps.
+ All different stamp designs are illustrated.
+ Every basic stamp listed, including those with different watermarks or perforations and those showing graphite lines or phosphor bands.
+ Unmounted mint and mounted mint prices quoted for 1887 'Jubilee' series and all King Edward VII and King George V issues, apart from the Departmental Officials.
+ Missing colours, missing embossing, watermark errors, imperforate errors and phosphor omitted varieties from those stamps normally issued with phosphor bands.
+ Booklet panes, including inverted watermark and phosphor omitted varieties.
+ Gutter Pairs and 'Traffic light' Gutter Pairs listed in mint sets.
+ First Day Covers for Special Issues from 1924 and for King Edward VIII and King George VI definitives. For the present reign the coverage also extends to Prestige Booklet panes and Regionals. All British Post Office special First Day of Issue postmarks are priced on cover.
+ Post Office Picture Cards (PHQ cards) are priced as sets, both mint and used with First Day of Issue postmarks.
+ Presentation, Collector and Gift Packs, including the scarce versions with foreign inscriptions.
+ Quick-reference diagrams for listed Machin decimal booklet panes.
+ Design Index for Commemorative and Special Stamps at the back of the catalogue.
+ Machin and commemorative underprints given separate catalogue numbers.
+ Post Office Yearbooks.
+ Royal Mail Postage Labels priced in mint or used sets and on British Post Office First Day Covers.
+ Royal Mail Post & Go stamps; with notes on machine types, errors, date codes and special inscriptions.
+ Notes on Postage Due bisects based on research by Mr P. Frost.
+ Wartime issues for the Channel Islands.
+ Separate section for Post Office Stamp Booklets with dated editions of King George VI and Queen Elizabeth listed separately.

+ Post Office Label Sheets, popularly known as 'Generic Smilers'.
+ Specimen overprints up to 1970.
+ Helpful introductory section providing definitions and guidance for the collector and including all watermark illustrations shown together to assist identification.
+ Post Office Telegraph Stamps
+ Security Machin priced year and source code tables
+ The following have been added to this edition: 2029a and 2815a.

We would like to thank all those who have assisted in the compilation of this catalogue. Special thanks for amendments to this edition are due to Rowan Baker, Allan Grant, Robert Oliver, John Peart, Ian Rimmer, Kevin Samuels, Paul Taylor and Julian Tremayne.

Great Britain
Philatelic Societies

The Great Britain Philatelic Society.
Hon. Membership Secretary: Linda Hill,
membership@gbps.org.uk

The Modern British Philatelic Circle. Hon. Membership Secretary: A J Wilkins, 3 Buttermere Close, Brierley Hill, West Midlands, DY5 3SD.

Stanley Gibbons Holdings Plc

Stanley Gibbons Limited,
Stanley Gibbons Auctions
399 Strand, London WC2R 0LX
Tel: +44 (0)207 836 8444
E-mail: support@stanleygibbons.com
Website: www.stanleygibbons.com
for all departments, Auction and
Specialist Stamp Departments.

Open Monday–Friday 9.30 a.m. to 6 p.m.
Shop. Open Monday–Saturday 9.30
a.m. to 6 p.m.

Stanley Gibbons Publications,
Mail Order, Gibbons Stamp Monthly
and Philatelic Exporter
7 Parkside, Christchurch Road,
Ringwood, Hampshire BH24 3SH.
Tel: +44 (0)1425 472363
E-mail: support@stanleygibbons.com

Monday–Friday 8.30 a.m. to 5 p.m.

Stanley Gibbons Publications
Overseas Representation
Stanley Gibbons Publications are
represented overseas by the following

Australia
Renniks Publications PTY LTD
Unit 6, 30 Perry St, Matraville,
NSW 2036, Australia
Tel: +612 9695 7055
Website: www.renniks.com

Canada
Unitrade Associates
99 Floral Parkway, Toronto,
Ontario M6L 2C4, Canada
Tel: +1 416 242 5900
Website: www.unitradeassoc.com

Canada
F.v.H. Stamps
102-340 West Cordova Street,
Vancouver, BC, V6B 1E8, Canada
Tel: +1 604 684 8408
Website: www.fvhstamps.com

Denmark
Nordfrim A/S
Kvindevadet 42,
Otterup DK-5450, Denmark
Tel: +45 64 82 1256
Website: www.nordfrim.com

Italy
Ernesto Marini S.R.L.
V. Struppa, 300, Genova, 16165, Italy
Tel: +39 010 802 186
Website: www.ernestomarini.it

Japan
Japan Philatelic
PO Box 2, Suginami-Minami,
Tokyo 168-8081, Japan
Tel: +81 3330 41641
Website: www.yushu.co.jp

Netherlands
Uitgeverij Davo BV
PO Box 411, Ak Deventer, 7400
Netherlands
Tel: +3188 0284300
Website: www.davo.nl

New Zealand
House of Stamps
PO Box 12, Paraparaumu,
New Zealand
Tel: +61 6364 8270
Website: www.houseofstamps.co.nz

New Zealand
Philatelic Distributors
PO Box 863
15 Mount Edgecumbe Street
New Plymouth 4615, New Zealand
Tel: +6 46 758 65 68
Website: www.stampcollecta.com

Singapore
C S Philatelic Agency
Peninsula Shopping Centre #04-29
3 Coleman Street, 179804, Singapore
Tel: +65 6337-1859
Website: www.cs.com.sg

USA
Vidiforms Company Inc
115 North Route 9W, Congers,
New York NY 10920, United States
Tel: +1 845 268 4005
Website: www.showgard.com

USA
Amos Media Company
1660 Campbell Road,
Suite A, Door #9,
Sidney OH 453652480,
United States
Tel: +1 937 498 2111
Website: www.amosmedia.com

General Information

The prices quoted in this catalogue are the estimated selling prices of Stanley Gibbons Ltd at the time of publication. They are, *unless it is specifically stated otherwise*, for examples in very fine condition for the issue concerned. Superb examples are worth more; those of a lower quality considerably less.

All prices are subject to change without prior notice and Stanley Gibbons Ltd may from time to time offer stamps below catalogue price. Individual low value stamps sold at 399, Strand are liable to an additional handling charge. Purchasers of new issues are asked to note that the prices charged for them contain an element for the service rendered and so may exceed the prices shown when the stamps are subsequently catalogued.

No guarantee is given to supply all stamps priced, since it is not possible to keep every catalogued item in stock.

Quotation of prices

The prices in the left-hand column are for unused stamps and those in the right-hand column are for used.

A dagger (†) denotes that the item listed does not exist in that condition and a blank, or dash, that it exists, or may exist, but no market price can be quoted.

Prices are expressed in pounds and pence sterling. One pound comprises 100 pence (£1 = 100p).

The method of notation is as follows: pence in numerals (e.g. 5 denotes five pence); pounds and pence up to £100, in numerals (e.g. 4·25 denotes four pounds and twenty-five pence); prices above £100 expressed in whole pounds with the '£' sign shown.

Unused and Used stamps

The prices for unused stamps of Queen Victoria issued before 1887 are for lightly hinged examples. Unused stamps of the 1887 'Jubilee' issue and from the reigns of King Edward VII and King George V are priced in both unmounted and mounted condition. The only exception is the Departmental Officials, which are priced unused, used and used on cover. Unused prices for King Edward VIII to Queen Elizabeth II issues are for unmounted mint (though when not available, mounted mint stamps are often supplied at a lower price). Prices for used stamps are for fine postally used examples, usually cancelled by a clear operational circular datestamp (See 'Operational Cancellations' in Philatelic Information section).

Prices quoted for bisects on cover or on large piece are for those dated during the period officially authorised.

Minimum price

The minimum price quoted is 10 pence. For individual stamps, prices between 10 pence and 95 pence are provided as a guide for catalogue users. The lowest price *charged* for individual stamps or sets purchased from Stanley Gibbons Ltd is £1.

Set prices

Set prices are generally for one of each value, excluding shades and varieties, but including major colour changes. Where there are alternative shades, etc., the cheapest is usually included. The number of stamps in the set is always stated for clarity.

The mint and used prices for sets containing *se-tenant* pieces are based on the prices quoted for such combinations, and not on those for individual stamps which may be considerably less.

Gutter Pairs

These, and traffic light gutter pairs, are priced as complete sets.

Used on Cover prices

To assist collectors, cover prices are quoted in a third column for postage and Official stamps issued in the reign of Queen Victoria and in boxed notes for the 1887 'Jubilee' issue and for King Edward VII stamps.

The cover should be of non-philatelic origin, bearing the correct postal rate for the period and distance involved and cancelled with the markings normal to the offices concerned. Purely philatelic items have a cover value only slightly greater than the catalogue value for the corresponding used stamps. This applies generally to those high-value stamps used philatelically rather than in the normal course of commerce.

Oversized covers, difficult to accommodate on an album page, should be reckoned as worth little more than the corresponding value of the used stamps. The condition of a cover affects its value. Except for 'wreck covers', serious damage or soiling reduces the value where the postal markings and stamps are ordinary ones. Conversely, visual appeal adds to the value and this can include freshness of appearance, important addresses, old-fashioned but legible handwriting, historic town-names, etc. The prices quoted are a base on which further value would be added to take account of the cover's postal historical importance in demonstrating such things as unusual, scarce or emergency cancels, interesting routes, significant postal markings, combination usage, the development of postal rates, and so on.

However, it should also be noted that multiples of some stamps are frequently more commonly found on cover than single usages and in such cases the cover might be worth less than the price quoted.

First Day Cover prices

Prices are quoted for commemorative first day covers from 1924 British Empire Exhibition pair onwards. These prices are for special covers (from 1937) franked with complete sets and cancelled by ordinary operational postmarks to the end of 1962 or the various standard 'First Day of Issue' markings from 1963.

Prices are provided for King Edward VIII and King George VI definitives on plain covers with operational postmarks of the first day of issue. For some values special covers also exist and these are worth more than the prices quoted.

The Philatelic Bureau and other special 'First Day of Issue' postmarks provided by the Post Office since 1963 are listed under each issue. Prices quoted are for these postmarks used on illustrated covers (from 1964 those produced by the Post Office), franked with complete sets.

The British Post Office did not introduce special First Day of Issue postmarks for definitive issues until the first instalment of the Machin £sd series, issued 5 June 1967, although 'First Day' treatment had been provided for some Regional stamps from 8 June 1964 onwards. Prices for the First Day Covers from 1952 to 1966, showing definitive stamps are for the stamps indicated, used on illustrated envelopes and postmarked with operational cancellations.

From 1967 onwards the prices quoted are for stamps as indicated, used on illustrated envelopes and postmarked with special First Day of Issue handstamps. Other definitives issued during this period were not accepted for 'First Day' treatment by the British Post Office.

Guarantee

All stamps are guaranteed genuine originals in the following terms:

If not as described, and returned by the purchaser, we undertake to refund the price paid to us in the original transaction. If any stamp is certified as genuine by the Expert Committee of the Royal Philatelic Society, London, or by BPA Expertising Ltd, the purchaser shall not be entitled to make any claim against us for any error, omission or mistake in such certificate.

Consumers' statutory rights are not affected by the above guarantee.

The recognised Expert Committees in this country are those of the Royal Philatelic Society, London, 15 Abchurch Lane, London EC4 7BW, and B.P.A. Expertising Ltd, P.O. Box 1141, Guildford, Surrey GU5 0WR. They do not undertake valuations under any circumstances and fees are payable for their services.

Contacting the Catalogue Editor

The Editor is always interested in hearing from people who have new information which will improve or correct the Catalogue. As a general rule he must see and examine the actual stamps before they can be considered for listing; photographs or scans are insufficient evidence, although an initial email to *Thecatalogueeditor@stanleygibbons.com* will determine whether or not an item is likely to be of interest.

Where information is solicited purely for the benefit of the enquirer, the editor cannot undertake to reply if the answer is already contained in these published notes. Email communications are greatly preferred to enquiries by telephone and the editor regrets that he or his staff cannot see personal callers without a prior appointment being made. Correspondence may be subject to delay during the production period of each new edition.

Please note that the following classes of material are outside the scope of this Catalogue:

(a) Non-postal revenue or fiscal stamps.
(b) Postage stamps used fiscally.
(c) Local carriage labels and private local issues.
(d) Punctured postage stamps (perfins).
(e) Bogus or phantom stamps.
(f) Railway or airline letter fee stamps, bus or road transport company labels.

(g) Postal stationery cut-outs.
(h) All types of non-postal labels and souvenirs.
(i) Documentary labels for the postal service, e.g. registration, recorded delivery, airmail etiquettes, etc.
(j) Privately applied embellishments to official issues and privately commissioned items generally.
(k) Stamps for training postal staff.

> We regret we do not give opinions as to the genuineness of stamps, nor do we identify stamps or number them by our Catalogue.

General Abbreviations

Alph	Alphabet
Anniv	Anniversary
Brt	Bright (colour)
C.	Overprinted in carmine
Des	Designer; designed
Dp	Deep (colour)
Eng	Engraver; engraved
Horiz	Horizontal; horizontally
Imp, Imperf	Imperforate
Inscr	Inscribed
L	Left
Litho	Lithographed
Lt	Light (colour)
mm	Millimetres
MS	Miniature sheet
Opt(d)	Overprint(ed)
P, Perf	Perforated
Photo	Photogravure
Pl	Plate
Pr	Pair
Ptd	Printed
Ptg	Printing
PVA	Polyvinyl alcohol (gum)
R	Right
R.	Row
Recess	Recess-printed
T	Type
Typo	Typographed (Letterpress)
Un	Unused
Us	Used
Vert	Vertical; vertically
W or wmk	Watermark
Wmk s	Watermark sideways

(†) = Does not exist.
(—) (or blank price column) = Exists, or may exist, but no market price can be quoted.
/ between colours means 'on' and the colour following is that of the paper on which the stamp is printed.

Printers

BW	Bradbury Wilkinson & Co, Ltd.
Cartor	Cartor S.A., La Loupe, France
DLR	De La Rue & Co, Ltd, London, and (from 1961) Bogota, Colombia. De La Rue Security Print (*formerly Harrison & Sons Ltd*) from 8 September 1997.
Enschedé	Joh. Enschedé en Zonen, Haarlem, Netherlands.
Harrison	Harrison & Sons, Ltd, High Wycombe.
ISP	International Security Printers (Walsall and/or Cartor
JW	John Waddington Security Print, Ltd, Leeds.
PB	Perkins Bacon Ltd, London.
Questa	Questa Colour Security Printers, Ltd.
Waterlow	Waterlow & Sons, Ltd, London.
Walsall	Walsall Security Printers, Ltd.

Philatelic information

Catalogue Numbers

The catalogue number appears in the extreme left column. The boldface Type numbers in the next column are merely cross-reference to illustrations. Catalogue numbers in the *Gibbons Stamp Monthly* Supplements are provisional only and may need to be altered when the lists are consolidated.

Our Catalogue numbers are universally recognised in specifying stamps and as a hallmark of status.

Inverted and other watermark varieties incorporate 'Wi', etc., within the number.

Catalogue Illustrations

Stamps and first day postmarks are illustrated at three-quarters linear size. Stamps not illustrated are the same size and format as the value shown, unless otherwise indicated. Overprints, surcharges and watermarks are normally actual size. Illustrations of varieties are often enlarged to show the detail. Illustrations of miniature sheets have their dimensions, in millimetres, stated with the width given first.

Designers

Designers' names are quoted where known, though space precludes naming every individual concerned in the production of a set. In particular, photographers supplying material are usually named only when they also make an active contribution in the design stage; posed photographs of reigning monarchs are, however, an exception to this rule.

Printing Errors

Errors in printing are of major interest to this Catalogue. Authenticated items meriting consideration would include: background, centre or frame inverted or omitted; centre or subject transposed; error of colour; error or omission of value; double prints and impressions; printed both sides; and so on. Designs *tête-bêche*, whether intentionally or by accident, are listable. Colours only partially omitted are not listed. However, stamps with embossing, phosphor or both omitted and stamps printed on the gummed side are included.

Printing technology has radically improved over the years, during which time gravure and lithography have become predominant. Varieties nowadays are more in the nature of flaws which are almost always outside the scope of this book.

In no catalogue, however, do we list such items as: dry prints, kiss prints, doctor-blade flaws, colour shifts or registration flaws (unless they lead to the complete omission of a colour from an individual stamp), lithographic ring flaws, and so on. Neither do we recognise fortuitous happenings like paper creases or confetti flaws.

Paper Types

All stamps listed are deemed to be on 'ordinary' paper of the wove type and white in colour; only departures from this are normally mentioned.

A coloured paper is one that is coloured right through (front and back of the stamp). In the Catalogue the colour of the paper is given in *italics*, thus:
purple/*yellow* = purple design on yellow paper.

Papers have been made specially white in recent years by, for example, a very heavy coating of chalk. We do not classify shades of whiteness of paper as distinct varieties. The availability of many postage stamps for revenue purposes made necessary some safeguard against the illegitimate re-use of stamps with removable cancellations. This was at first secured by using fugitive inks and later by printing on chalky (chalk-surfaced) paper, both of which made it difficult to remove any form of obliteration without also damaging the stamp design. Stamps which exist on both ordinary and chalk-surfaced papers are separately listed.

The 'traditional' method of indentifying chalk-surfaced papers has been that, when touched with a silver wire, a black mark is left on the paper, and the listings in this catalogue are based on that test. However, the test itself is now largely discredited, for, although the mark can be removed by a soft rubber, some damage to the stamp will result from its use.

The difference between chalk-surfaced and pre-war ordinary papers is fairly clear: chalk-surfaced papers being smoother to the touch and showing a characteristic sheen when light is reflected off their surface. Under good magnification tiny bubbles or pock marks can be seen on the surface of the stamp and at the tips of the perforations the surfacing appears 'broken'. Traces of paper fibres are evident on the surface of ordinary paper and the ink shows a degree of absorption into it.

Initial chalk-surfaced paper printings by De La Rue had a thinner coating than subsequently became the norm. The characteristics described above are less pronounced in these printings.

Perforation Measurement

The gauge of a perforation is the number of holes in a length of 2 cm.

The Gibbons *Instanta* gauge is the standard for measuring perforations. The stamp is viewed against a dark background with the transparent gauge put on top of it. Though the gauge measures to decimal accuracy, perforations read from it are generally quoted in the Catalogue to the nearest half. For example:

Just over perf 12¾ to just under 13¼ .... = perf 13
Perf 13¼ exactly, rounded up .... = perf 13½
Just over perf 13¼ to just under 13¾ .... = perf 13½
Perf 13¾ exactly, rounded up .... = perf 14

However, where classification depends on it, actual quarter-perforations are quoted. Perforations are usually abbreviated (and spoken) as follows, though sometimes they may be spelt out for clarity.

P 14: perforated alike on all sides (read: 'perf 14').

P 14×15: the first figure refers to top and bottom, the second to left and right sides (read: 'perf 14 by 15'). This is a compound perforation.

Such headings as 'P 13×14 (vert) and P 14×13 (horiz)' indicate which perforations apply to which stamp format—vertical or horizontal.

From 1992 onwards most definitive and greetings stamps from both sheets and booklets occur with a large elliptical (oval) hole inserted in each line of vertical perforations as a security measure. The £10 definitive, No. 1658, is unique in having two such holes in the horizontal perforations.

Stamps which have the elliptical perforations hole towards the top in error are normally outside the scope of this catalogue, but in 2013 a booklet was issued in which the entire print run contained Machin stamps in this format. These are listed as U3073 and U3076.

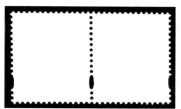

Elliptical Perforations

Perforation Errors

Authenticated errors, where a stamp normally perforated is accidentally issued imperforate, are listed provided no traces of perforations (blind holes or indentations) remain. They must be provided as pairs, both stamps wholly imperforate, and are only priced in that form.

Numerous part-perforated stamps arose from the introduction of the Jumelle Press. This had a rotary perforator with rows of pins on one drum engaging with holes on another. Engagement is only gradual when the perforating unit is started up or stopped, giving rise to perforations 'fading out', a variety mentioned above as not listed.

Stamps from the Jumelle printings sometimes occur imperforate between stamp and sheet margin. Such errors are not listed in this catalogue, but are covered by the volumes of the *Great Britain Specialised Catalogue*.

Pairs described as 'imperforate between' have the line of perforations between the two stamps omitted.

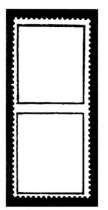

Imperf between
(vertical pair)

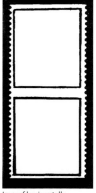

Imperf horizontally
(vertical pair)

Imperf between (horiz pair): a horizontal pair of stamps with perfs all around the edges but none between the stamps.

Imperf between (vert pair): a vertical pair of stamps with perfs all around the edges but none between the stamps. Where several of the rows have escaped perforation the resulting varieties are listable. Thus:

Imperf vert (horiz pair): a horizontal pair of stamps perforated at top and bottom; all three vertical directions are imperf—the two outer edges and between the stamps.

Imperf horiz (vert pair): a vertical pair perforated at left and right edges; all three horizontal directions are imperf—the top, bottom and between the stamps.

Varieties of double, misplaced or partial perforation caused by error or machine malfunction are not listable, neither are freaks, such as perforations placed diagonally from paper folds, nor missing holes caused by broken pins.

Phosphor Issues

Machines which sort mail electronically were introduced progressively and the British Post Office issued the first stamps specially marked for electronic sorting in 1957. This first issue had easily visible graphite lines printed on the back beneath the gum (see Nos. 561/6). They were issued in the Southampton area where the experiment was carried out.

The graphite lines were replaced by phosphor bands, activated by ultraviolet light. The bands are printed on the front of the stamps and show as a matt surface against the usual smooth or shiny appearance of the untreated surface of the paper. The bands show clearly in the top or bottom horizontal margins of the sheet.

The first phosphor issues appeared in 1959 (see Nos. 599/609) and these stamps also had graphite lines on the back. Further details will be found in the listings above No. 599 and 619. From 1962 onwards most commemoratives were issued in versions with or without bands. From 1967 all commemorative stamps had phosphor bands, but from 1972 they were replaced by 'all-over' phosphor covering the entire area of the stamp.

After a considerable period of development a special paper was produced in which the phosphor had been incorporated into the coating. From 15 August 1979 to April 1996 phosphorised paper was accepted for use generally, replacing phosphor bands on most issues for all values except the second class letter rate. Phosphorised paper can only be identified by ultraviolet light. The Stanley Gibbons Ultraviolet Lamp is firmly recommended for use in identifying the phosphor stamps listed in this Catalogue. *Warning.* Never stare at the lighted lamp but follow the manufacturer's instructions. Phosphor bands were reintroduced for all issues from April 1996.

During the years 1967 to 1972, when all issues, except the high values, should have shown phosphor bands, a number of stamps appeared with them omitted in error. These varieties are listed in this Catalogue. Stamps with 'all-over' phosphor omitted can only be detected by the use of an ultraviolet lamp and these varieties are listed in the Stanley Gibbons *Great Britain Specialised Catalogue*. Note that prices are for unmounted mint examples only. Varieties such as double or misplaced bands are not listed in this Catalogue.

Gum Description

All stamps listed are assumed to have gum of some kind and original gum (o.g.) means that which was present on the stamp as issued to the public. Deleterious climates and the presence of certain chemicals can cause gum to crack and, with early stamps, even make the paper deteriorate. Unscrupulous fakers are adept in removing it and regumming the stamp to meet the unreasoning demand often made for 'full o.g.' 'unmounted' or 'never hinged, mint' (NHM) in cases where such a thing is virtually impossible.

The gum normally used on stamps has been gum

arabic until the late 1960's when synthetic adhesives were introduced. Harrison and Sons Ltd for instance used *polyvinyl alcohol*, known to philatelists as PVA (see note above SG 723).

From 1993 many stamps have been issued with self-adhesive gum. Unused prices are for such stamps with backing paper attached, as issued. Initially such stamps were issued with a water-soluble layer of gum allowing used examples to be 'soaked off', but with the 2008 Christmas issue, most self-adhesive stamps are issued without the water-soluble layer of gum, preventing their removal from paper without damage. It is recommended that used stamps from this later period be collected 'on piece'.

Colour Identification

The 200 colours most used for stamp identification are given in the Stanley Gibbons Stamp Colour Key. The Catalogue has used the Colour Key as a standard for describing new issues for some years. The names are also introduced as lists are rewritten, though exceptions are made for those early issues where traditional names have become universally established.

In compound colour names the second is the predominant one, thus:

orange-red = a red tending towards orange.

red-orange = an orange containing more red than usual.

When comparing actual stamps with colour samples in the Colour Key, view in a good north daylight (or its best substitute: fluorescent 'colour-matching' light). Sunshine is not recommended. Choose a solid portion of the stamp design; if available, marginal markings such as solid bars of colour or colour check dots are helpful. Shading lines in the design can be misleading as they appear lighter than solid colour. Furthermore, the listings refer to colours as issued: they may deteriorate into something different through the passage of time.

Shades are particularly significant when they can be linked to specific printings. In general, shades need to be quite marked to fall within the scope of this Catalogue.

Modern colour printing by lithography is prone to marked differences of shade, even within a single run, and variations can occur within the same sheet. Such shades are not listed.

Royal Mail Colour Descriptions

In recent years Royal Mail has introduced its own colour descriptions of definitive stamps, describing, for example, the £1.05 stamp (SG 2935) as 'Gooseberry green' and incorporating this in the sheet margin of the stamp. We do not use these descriptions because they are, in many cases, unfamiliar to collectors and, should a listable change in shade occur in a later printing, we would expect that the sheet margin would continue to bear the original Royal Mail colour description.

Errors of Colour

Major colour errors in stamps or overprints which qualify for listing are: wrong colours; albinos (colourless impressions), where these have Expert Committee certificates; colours completely omitted, but only on unused stamps (if found on used stamps the information is usually footnoted) and with good credentials, missing colours being frequently faked.

Colours only partially omitted are not recognised. Colour shifts, however spectacular, are not listed.

Booklet Stamps

Single stamps from booklets are listed if they are distinguishable in some way (such as watermark or phosphor bands) from similar sheet stamps. Single booklet stamps whose only distinguishing feature is that they are imperforate on one or two adjacent sides are omitted

Booklet panes are listed where they contain stamps of different denominations *se-tenant*, where stamp-size printed labels are included, or where such panes are otherwise identifiable. Booklet panes are placed in the listing under the lowest denomination present.

Booklet panes containing single values issued up to 1970 are also listed in this catalogue. Users should note that prices are for panes with the binding margin intact and full perforations on the other three sides.

In the listing of complete booklets the numbers and prefix letters are the same as used in the Stanley Gibbons *Great Britain Specialised Catalogue*.

Coil Stamps

Stamps only issued in coil form are given full listing. If stamps are issued in both sheets and coils, the coil stamps are listed separately only where there is some feature (e.g. watermark sideways or gum change) by which single stamps can be distinguished. Coil strips containing different values *se-tenant* are also listed.

Booklet Pane with Printed Labels

Se-tenant Pane of Four

Multi-value Coil Strip

Coil join pairs are generally too random and easily faked to permit listing; similarly ignored are coil stamps which have accidentally suffered an extra row of perforations from the claw mechanism in a malfunctioning vending machine.

Gutter pair

Gutter Pairs

In 1988 the recess-printed Castle high value definitives were issued in sheets containing four panes separated by a gutter margin. All modern Great Britain commemoratives and special stamps are produced in sheets containing two panes separated by a blank horizontal or vertical margin known as a gutter. This feature first made its appearance on some supplies of the 1972 Royal Silver Wedding 3p and marked the introduction of Harrison & Sons' new 'Jumelle' stamp-printing press. There are advantages for both the printer and the Post Office in such a layout which has been used for most commemorative issues since 1974.

Traffic Light Gutter Pair

The term 'gutter pair' is used for a pair of stamps separated by part of the blank gutter margin as illustrated above. Most printers include some form of colour check device on the sheet margins, in addition to the cylinder or plate numbers. Harrison & Sons use round 'dabs', or spots of colour, resembling traffic lights. For the period from the 1972 Royal Silver Wedding until the end of 1979 these colour dabs appeared in the gutter margin. There was always one example to every double-pane sheet of stamps. They can also be found in the high value Machin issue printed in photogravure. Gutter pairs showing these 'traffic lights' are priced in complete sets in this catalogue.

From the 2004 Entente Cordiale set, Walsall reintroduced

traffic lights in the gutters of certain sets. Where these extend over more than one section of gutter margin on any value, they are priced in blocks rather than pairs.

Miniature Sheets

A miniature sheet contains a single stamp or set with wide inscribed or decorated margins. The stamps often also exist in normal sheet format. This Catalogue lists, with **MS** prefix, complete miniature sheets which have been issued by the Post Office and which are valid for postal purposes.

Stamps from miniature sheets, not also available in normal sheet format, are not individually listed or priced in this catalogue.

Where such stamps have also appeared in a booklet, and the booklet pane differs in layout or design to the miniature sheet (e.g. 'Britain Alone' (2nd issue), Nos. 3082/5) these stamps are listed separately, but if the booklet pane is the same as the miniature sheet (e.g. 'Astronomy' , Nos. **MS**2315/a) they are only listed as complete miniature sheets or booklet panes.

Miniature Sheet containing a set of stamps

Se-tenant Combinations

Se-tenant means 'joined together'. Some sets include stamps of different design arranged *se-tenant* as blocks or strips and, in mint condition, these are usually collected unsevered as issued. The set prices quoted in this catalogue refer to the unsevered combination plus singles of any other values in the set.

Presentation and Souvenir Packs

Special Packs comprising slip-in cards with printed commemorative inscriptions and notes on the back and with protective covering, were introduced in 1964 for the Shakespeare issue. Definitive issues first appeared in Presentation Packs in 1960. Notes will be found in the listings to describe souvenir books issued on special occasions.

Issues of 1968–1969 (British Paintings to the Prince of Wales Investiture) were also issued in packs with text in

German for sale through the Post Office's German Agency and these are also included.

Collectors packs, first called gift packs, containing commemoratives issued in the preceding 12 months, first appeared in 1967. These are listed and priced.

It should be noted that prices given for presentation packs are for items as originally sold, including any additional inserts, such as questionnaire forms and publicity material.

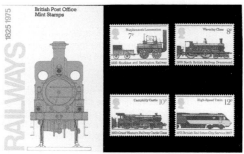

13 August 1975 Public Railways Presentation Pack

Yearbooks

Special Post Office Yearbooks were first available in 1984. They contain all of the commemorative issues for one year in a hardbound book, illustrated in colour complete with slip case. These are listed and priced.

Commemorative First Day Covers

Until 1963 the Post Office did not provide any special first day of issue postmark facilities for collectors. Several philatelic organisations and stamp dealers did produce pictorial covers for the various commemorative issues and collectors serviced these to receive ordinary operational postmarks. Occasionally a special handstamp was produced which coincided with a new stamp issue, or relevant slogan postmarks, like the 1953 'Long Live the Queen' type, were in general use at the time.

On 21 March 1963 the Post Office installed special posting boxes at 11 main post offices so that collectors could obtain 'uniformly high standard' impressions, from normal operational postmarks, for their first day covers. From 7 May 1963 special 'First Day of Issue' slogans (Type A) were applied to mail posted in these special boxes, whose number had, by then, risen to 30. The Philatelic Bureau accepted orders by post for such covers from the issue of 16 May 1963 onwards.

The slogan type was replaced on 23 April 1964 by 'First Day of Issue' handstamps (Type B). These were, initially, of considerable size, but were later replaced by smaller versions (Type C) which remained in use at nearly 200 principal offices until the Christmas issue of 2 November 1998. From 1970 the Bureau postmarks as Type C were inscribed 'British Philatelic Bureau'.

Since 1972 the Post Office has provided for virtually all issues an additional 'alternative' pictorial 'First Day of Issue' cancellation, at a location connected with the issue. Being available from the Bureau, these cancellations are listed in this catalogue.

From 12 January 1999 (Millennium Inventors' Tale issue) the 'alternative' pictorial postmark has been applied to all covers posted in special first day boxes throughout the country, replacing the local, non-pictorial, cancels. A bilingual version is used when the 'alternative' office is in Wales. For collectors who prefer plain postmarks a non-pictorial version of the

'alternative' postmark is available from Royal Mail Special Handstamp Centres.

'First Day of Issue' postmarks of standard or pictorial type have occasionally been provided on a 'one-off' basis for places linked to particular stamp issues, eg Weymouth for the 1975 Sailing set. Such postmarks, which are not available from the Bureau, are footnoted only.

Royal Mail established Special Handstamp Centres in 1990 where all sponsored special handstamps and many 'First Day of Issue' postmarks are now applied.

Pictorial local 'First Day of Issue' postmarks were in use between 1988 and 1998 applied to covers posted in first day boxes and sent to main offices or Special Handstamp Centres. These included Birmingham (1993–98), Durham (1988–98), City of London (1989–98), London (1993–98), Newcastle upon Tyne (1992–94), and St Albans (1995–98). Different designs were used at the Glasgow Handstamp Centre for various places, 1993–98. As these postmarks were not available from the Bureau they are not included in this catalogue.

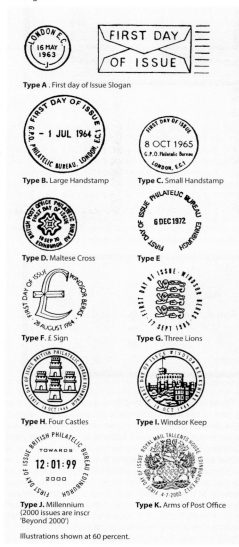

Type A. First day of Issue Slogan

Type B. Large Handstamp

Type C. Small Handstamp

Type D. Maltese Cross

Type E

Type F. £ Sign

Type G. Three Lions

Type H. Four Castles

Type I. Windsor Keep

Type J. Millennium (2000 issues are inscr 'Beyond 2000')

Type K. Arms of Post Office

Illustrations shown at 60 percent.

CANCELLATIONS

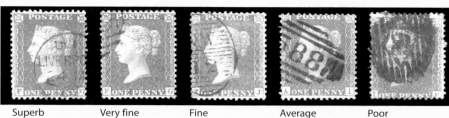

| Superb | Very fine | Fine | Average | Poor |

| Superb | Very fine |

| Fine | Average | Poor |

First day cover prices for modern issues are based on those with a Philatelic Bureau (later, 'Tallents House' postmark.

Operational Cancellations

Early cancellation devices were designed to 'obliterate' the stamp in order to prevent it being reused and this is still an important objective for today's postal administrations. Stamp collectors, on the other hand, prefer postmarks to be lightly applied, clear, and to leave as much as possible of the design visible. Dated, circular cancellations have long been 'the postmark of choice', but the definition of a 'Fine' cancellation will depend upon the types of cancellation in use at the time a stamp was current—it is clearly illogical to seek a circular datestamp on a Penny Black.

'Fine', by definition, will be superior to 'Average', so, in terms of cancellation quality, if one begins by identifying what 'Average' looks like, then one will be half way to identifying 'Fine'. The illustrations will give some guidance on mid-19th century and mid-20th century cancellations of Great Britain, but types of cancellation in general use in each country and in each period will determine the appearance of 'Fine'.

Anything less than 'Fine' will result in a downgrading of the stamp concerned, while a very fine or superb cancellation will be worth a premium.

Post Office Label Sheets

This catalogue lists complete 'Generic Smilers' sheets in a section following the booklet listings. 'Personalised' and 'Corporate' sheets are not listed, neither are identifiable single stamps from label sheets.

2 Small Crown **4** Large Crown **9** (Extends over three stamps) **13** V R

15 Small Garter **16** Medium Garter **17** Large Garter **20** Emblems **33** Spray of Rose **39** Maltese Cross

40 Large Anchor **47** Small Anchor **48** Orb **49** Imperial Crown **100** Simple Cypher **103** Multiple Cypher

110 Single Cypher **111** Block Cypher **117** PUC £1 **125** E 8 R **127**

133 **153** Tudor Crown **165** St. Edward's Crown **179** Multiple Crowns **F5** Double-lined Anchor **F6** Single-lined Anchor

General Types of watermark *as seen through the front of the stamp*

No Value Indicated Stamps

From 22 August 1989 various definitive and special stamps appeared inscribed '2nd', '1st' or 'E' instead of a face value. These were sold at the current minimum rates for these services which were as follows:

Inland Postage Rate	2nd Class	1st Class
5 September 1988	14p.	19p.
2 October 1989	15p.	20p.
17 September 1990	17p.	22p.
16 September 1991	18p.	24p.
1 November 1993	19p.	25p.
8 July 1996	20p.	26p.
26 April 1999	19p.	26p.
17 April 2000	19p.	27p.
8 May 2003	20p.	28p.
1 April 2004	21p.	28p.
7 April 2005	21p.	30p.
3 April 2006	23p.	32p.
2 April 2007	24p.	34p.
7 April 2008	27p.	36p.
6 April 2009	30p.	39p.
6 April 2010	32p.	41p.
4 April 2011	36p.	46p.
30 April 2012	50p.	60p.
31 March 2014	53p.	62p.
30 March 2015	54p.	63p.
29 March 2016	55p.	64p.
27 March 2017	56p.	65p.
26 March 2018	58p.	67p.
25 March 2019	61p.	70p.
23 March 2020	65p.	76p.
1 January 2021	66p.	85p.
4 April 2022	68p.	95p.
3 April 2023	75p.	£1.10

European Airmail Rate	
26 April 1999	30p.
25 October 1999	34p.
27 April 2000	36p.
2 July 2001	37p.
27 March 2003	38p.
1 April 2004	40p.

From June 2004, European Airmail rate stamps reverted to showing a face value.

From 4 April 2022 the European Airmail rate is £1.85.

From 21 August 2006 'Large' letters were charged at a higher rate following the introduction of 'Pricing in Proportion'. Rates as follows:

Inland Postage Rate	2nd Class Large	1st Class Large
21 August 2006	37p.	44p.
2 April 2007	40p.	48p.
7 April 2008	42p.	52p.
6 April 2009	47p.	61p.
6 April 2010	51p.	66p.
4 April 2011	58p.	75p.
30 April 2012	69p.	90p.
31 March 2014	73p.	93p.
30 March 2015	74p.	95p.
29 March 2016	75p.	96p.
27 March 2017	76p.	98p.
26 March 2018	79p.	£1.01
25 March 2019	83p.	£1.06
23 March 2020	88p.	£1.15
1 January 2021	96p.	£1.29
4 April 2022	£1.05	£1.45
3 April 2023	£1.15	£1.60

In 2009 special stamps were introduced for the Recorded Delivery service (renamed Royal Mail Signed For in 2013) and in 2010 for Special Delivery. Rates for these services have increased as follows:

Date	Recorded/ Signed for 1st	Recorded/ Signed for 1st Large	Special Delivery to 100g	Special Delivery to 500g
17 Nov 2009	£1.14	£1.36		
6 April 2010	£1.15	£1.40		
26 Oct 2010	£1.15	£1.40	£5.05	£5.50
4 April 2011	£1.23	£1.52	£5.45	£5.90
30 April 2012	£1.55	£1.85	£5.90	£6.35
2 April 2013	£1.70	£2.00	£6.22	£6.95
31 March 2014	£1.72	£2.03	£6.40	£7.15
30 March 2015	£1.73	£2.05	£6.45	£7.25
29 March 2016	£1.74	£2.06	£6.45	£7.25
27 March 2017	£1.75	£2.08	£6.45	£7.25
26 March 2018	£1.77	£2.11	£6.50	£7.30
25 March 2019	£1.90	£2.26	£6.60	£7.40
23 March 2020	£2.06	£2.45	£6.70	£7.50
1 January 2021	£2.25	£2.69	£6.85	£7.65
4 April 2022	£2.35	£2.85	£6.85	£7.65

Over the same period European and Worldwide rates have increased as follows. Note that the current rate covered by the 'E' denominated stamps is shown in the left-hand column.

	Europe 20g *	World 10g *	Europe 60/100g **	World 20g	World 40/ 60/100g ***
6 April 2009	56p	62p	-	90p	-
6 April 2010	70p	67p	-	97p	£1.46
4 April 2011	68p	76p	-	£1.10	£1.65
30 April 2012	87p			£1.28	£1.90
2 April 2013	88p		-	£1.25	£1.88
31 March 2014	97p		£1.47	£1.28	£2.15
30 March 2015	£1		£1.52	£1.33	£2.25
29 March 2016	£1.05		£1.52	£1.33	£2.25
27 March 2017	£1.17		£1.57	£1.40	£2.27
26 March 2018	£1.25		£1.55	£1.45	£2.25
25 March 2019	£1.35		£1.60	£1.55	£2.30
23 March 2020	£1.42		£1.68	£1.63	£2.42
1 January 2021	£1.70		£1.70	£1.70	£2.55
4 April 2022	£1.85		£1.85	£1.85	£2.55
3 April 2023[1]	£2.20		£2.20	£2.20	£2.20

* The Europe 20g. and Worldwide 10g. rates were combined from 30 April 2012

** The upper weight for the Europe 60g. rate, introduced on 31 March 2014, was increased to 100g. from 30 March 2015

*** The upper weight for the Worldwide 40g. rate was increased to 60g. from 31 March 2014 and 100g. from 30 March 2015

[1] Standard unified international letter rate introduced, all zones up to 100g.

PHQ Card cancelled on First Day of Issue

PHQ Cards

From 1973 the Post Office produced sets of picture cards to accompany commemorative issues which can be sent through the post as postcards. Each card shows an enlarged colour reproduction of one stamp, initially of a single value from one set and subsequently of all values.

The Post Office gives each card a 'PHQ' serial number, hence the term. The cards are usually on sale shortly before the date of issue of the stamps, but there is no officially designated 'first day'. Cards are priced in fine mint condition for complete sets as issued. Used prices are for cards franked with the stamp affixed, on the obverse, as illustrated; the stamp being cancelled with an official postmark for first day of issue.

Watermark Types

Stamps are on unwatermarked paper except where the heading to the set states otherwise.

Watermarks are detected for Catalogue description by one of four methods: (1) holding stamps to the light; (2) laying stamps face down on a dark background; (3) by use of the Morley-Bright Detector, which works by revealing the thinning of the paper at the watermark; or (4) by the more complex electric watermark detectors such as the Stanley Gibbons Detectamark Spectrum.

The diagram above shows how watermark position is described in the Catalogue. Watermarks are usually impressed so that they read normally when looked through from the printed side. However, since philatelists customarily detect watermarks by looking at the back of the stamp, the watermark diagram also makes clear what is actually seen. Note that 'G v R' is only an example and illustrations of the different watermarks employed are shown in the listings. The illustrations are actual size and shown in normal positions (from the front of the stamps).

AS DESCRIBED (Read through front of stamp)		AS SEEN DURING WATERMARK DETECTION (Stamp face down and back examined)
GvR	Normal	Яvꓓ
Яʌꓓ	Inverted	ꓭʌЯ
Яvꓓ	Reversed	GvR
ꓭʌЯ	Inverted and reversed	Яʌꓓ
GvR	Sideways	Яvꓓ
GvR	Sideways inverted	ꓭʌЯ
ꓭʌЯ	Sideways reversed	GvR
ꓭʌЯ	Sideways inverted and reversed	GvR

Watermark Errors and Varieties

Watermark errors are recognised as of major importance. They comprise stamps showing the wrong watermark devices or stamps printed on paper with the wrong watermark. Stamps printed on paper showing broken or deformed bits on the dandy roll, are not listable.

Underprints

From 1982 various values appeared with underprints, printed on the reverse, in blue, over the gum. These were usually from special stamp booklets, sold at a discount by the Post Office, but in 1985 surplus stocks of such underprinted paper were used for other purposes.

In this Catalogue stamps showing underprints are priced mint only. Used examples can be obtained, but care has to be taken in floating the stamps since the devices were printed on top of the gum and will be removed as the gum dissolves.

Underprint Types

1 Star with central dot **2** Double-lined Star **3** Double-lined 'D'

4 Multiple double lined stars

5 Multiple double-lined 'D'
(Types **4/5** are shown ¾ actual size)

Note: Types **4/5** are arranged in a random pattern so that the stamps from the same sheet or booklet pane will show the underprint in a slightly different position to the above. Stamps, when inspected, should be placed the correct way up, face down, when comparing with the illustrations.

Specimen Stamps

From 1847 stamps have been overprinted 'SPECIMEN' for a variety of purposes, including the provision of samples to postmasters, as a security overprint on printers' or official reference copies and, from 1859, on examples of current British stamps sent to the International Bureau of the Univeral Postal Union for distribution to member nations.

Numerous styles were employed for these 'SPECIMEN' overprints, which are now listed in this catalogue up to decimalisation in 1971. The different types are illustrated here. Note that for ease of reference type numbers are the same as those given in the *Stanley Gibbons Great Britain Specialised Catalogue* and 'missing' type numbers may have been used on stamps outside the scope of this catalogue or may refer to 'Cancelled' overprints, which are, likewise, not listed here.

SPECIMEN
1

SPECIMEN
2

SPECIMEN
3

SPECIMEN
4

SPECIMEN
5

SPECIMEN
6

SPECIMEN
7

SPECIMEN
8

SPECIMEN
9

SPECIMEN
10

SPECIMEN
11

SPECIMEN
12

SPECIMEN
13

SPECIMEN
15

SPECIMEN
16

SPECIMEN
17

SPECIMEN
22

SPECIMEN
23

SPECIMEN
26

SPECIMEN
29

SPECIMEN
30

SPECIMEN
31

SPECIMEN
32

'SPECIMEN' stamps are listed with details of the types of 'SPECIMEN' overprints found. The different types are not listed and where more than one type was used the price given is for the cheapest version. Imperforate overprints are also not listed, unless the stamp was normally issued in that form.

More detailed listings will be found in Volumes 1 and 2 of the *Great Britain Specialised Catalogue*.

The Stanley Gibbons Auction
House has been operating
philatelic auctions since 1901.

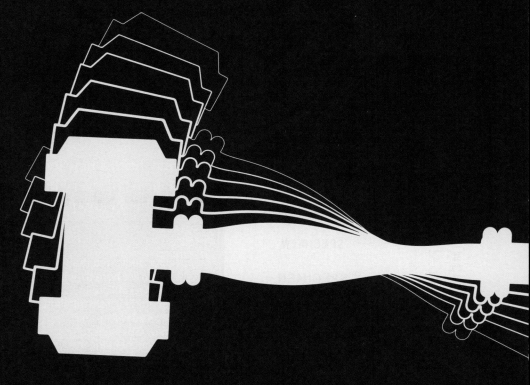

The Stanley Gibbons Auction
House has been operating
philatelic auctions since 1901.
Following the refurbishment
of our auction room, and the
continuing increase of instructions
from third parties, we are looking
for national and international
agents who may be interested in
working with our recognised and
trusted brand as we continue to
expand our
global reach.

We offer uncapped commission,
and our unrivalled team of
in-house experts ensure maximum
realisation from our lots.

If you would be interested in
working with us please email our
Head of Auctions, Tom Hazell at
thazell@stanleygibbons.com

 @StanleyGibbons   /StanleyGibbonsGroup    @StanleyGibbons

Queen Victoria

20 June 1837-22 January 1901

PARLIAMENTARY ENVELOPES

When the Uniform Penny Postage was introduced on 10 January 1840 the free franking privileges of Members of Parliament were abolished. During the same month, special envelopes were introduced for mail posted from the Houses of Parliament and these remained in use until the introduction of stamps and the Mulready stationery in May 1840. Envelopes are priced in used condition only.

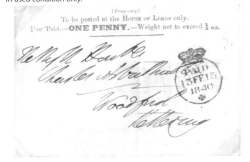

1840 (16 Jan). Inscribed 'Houses of Parliament' in black

PE2	1d. envelope.................................from	£8000
PE3	2d. envelope.................................from	£25000
PE4	4d. envelope.................................from	

1840 (16 Jan). Inscribed 'House of Lords' in vermilion

PE5	1d. envelope.................................from	£12000
PE8	2d. envelope.................................	—

1840 (Jan). Inscribed 'House of Commons' in black

PE9	1d. envelope.................................from	£3000

MULREADY ENVELOPES AND LETTER SHEETS

So called from the name of the designer, William Mulready, were issued concurrently with the first British adhesive stamps.

A large number of letter sheets and much smaller quantity of envelopes were sold by businesses, advertising to promote their services.

1840 (6 May). Letter sheets

ME1	1d. black...	£350	£550
	a. With advertisements printed inside		
	....from	£750	£850
	s. 'SPECIMEN', Type 2....................	£3750	
ME3	2d. blue...	£425	£2400
	a. With advertisements printed inside		
	....from		£3500
	s. 'SPECIMEN', Type 2....................	£5500	

1840 (6 May). Envelopes

ME2	1d. black...	£350	£550
	a. With advertisements printed inside		
	....from	£2500	£3500
	s. 'SPECIMEN', Type 2....................	£3750	
ME4	2d. blue...	£450	£2500
	a. With advertisements printed inside		
	....from		£3500
	s. 'SPECIMEN', Type 2....................	£5500	

LINE-ENGRAVED ISSUES

GENERAL NOTES

Brief notes on some aspects of the line-engraved stamps follow, but for further information and a full specialist treatment of these issues collectors are recommended to consult Volume 1, Part 1 of the Stanley Gibbons *Great Britain Specialised Catalogue*.

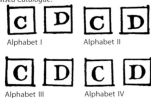

Alphabet I   Alphabet II

Alphabet III   Alphabet IV

Typical Corner Letters of the four Alphabets

Alphabets. Four different styles were used for the corner letters on stamps prior to the issue with letters in all four corners, these being known to collectors as:

Alphabet I. Used for all plates made from 1840 to the end of 1851. Letters small.

Alphabet II. Plates from 1852 to mid-1855. Letters larger, heavier and broader.

Alphabet III. Plates from mid-1855 to end of period. Letters tall and more slender.

Alphabet IV. 1861. 1d. Die II, Plates 50 and 51 only. Letters were hand-engraved instead of being punched on the plate. They are therefore inconsistent in shape and size but generally larger and outstanding.

While the general descriptions and the illustrations of typical letters given above may be of some assistance, only long experience and published aids can enable every stamp to be allocated to its particular Alphabet without hesitation, as certain letters in each are similar to those in one of the others.

Blued Paper. The blueing of the paper of the earlier issues is believed to be due to the presence of prussiate of potash in the printing ink, or in the paper, which, under certain conditions, tended to colour the paper when the sheets were damped for printing. An alternative term is *bleuté* paper.

Corner Letters. The corner letters on the early British stamps were intended as a safeguard against forgery, each stamp in the sheet having a different combination of letters. Taking the first 1d. stamp, printed in 20 horizontal rows of 12, as an example, the lettering is as follows:

Row 1.	A A, A B, A C, etc. to A L.
Row 2.	B A, B B, B C, etc. to B L.
	and so on to
Row 20	T A, T B, T C, etc. to T L.

On the stamps with four corner letters, those in the upper corners are in the reverse positions to those in the lower corners.

Thus in a sheet of 240 (12×20) the sequence is:

Row 1.	A A B A C A		L A
		etc. to	
Row 2.	A A A B A C		A L
	A B B B C B		L B
		etc. to	
	B A B B B C		B L
	and so on to		
	A T B T C T		L T
Row 20.		etc. to	
	T A T B T C		T L

Placing letters in all four corners was not only an added precaution against forgery but was meant to deter unmarked parts of used stamps being pieced together and passed off as an unused whole.

Dies. The first die of the 1d. was used for making the original die of the 2d., both the No Lines and White Lines issues. In 1855 the 1d. Die I was amended by retouching the head and deepening the lines on a transferred impression of the original. This later version, known to collectors as Die II, was used for making the dies for the 1d. and 2d. with letters in all four corners and also for the 1½d.

The two dies are illustrated above No. 17 in the catalogue.

Double letter   Guide line in corner

Guide line through value

Double Corner Letters. These are due to the workman placing his letter-punch in the wrong position at the first attempt, when lettering the plate, and then correcting the mistake; or to a slight shifting of the punch when struck. A typical example is illustrated. If a wrong letter was struck in the first instance, traces of a wrong letter may appear in a corner in addition to the correct one.

Guide Lines and Dots. When laying down the impressions of the design on the early plates, fine vertical and horizontal guide lines were marked on the plates to assist the operative. These were usually removed from the gutter margins, but could not be removed from the stamp impression without damage to the plate, so that in such cases they appear on the printed stamps, sometimes in the corners, sometimes through 'POSTAGE' or the value. Typical examples are illustrated.

Guide dots or cuts were similarly made to indicate the spacing of the guide lines. These too sometimes appear on the stamps.

Ivory Head

'Ivory Head'. The so-called 'ivory head' variety is one in which the Queen's Head shows white on the back of the stamp. It arises from the comparative absence of ink in the head portion of the design, with consequent absence of blueing. (See 'Blued Paper', above).

Line-engraving. In this context 'line-engraved' is synonymous with recess-printing, in which the engraver cuts recesses in a plate and printing (the coloured areas) is from these recesses. 'Line-engraved' is the traditional philatelic description for these stamps; other equivalent terms found are 'engraving in *taille-douce*' (French) or 'in intaglio' (Italian).

Plates. Until the introduction of the stamps with letters in all four corners, the number of the plate was not indicated in the design of the stamp, but was printed on the sheet margin. By long study of identifiable blocks and the minor variation in the design, coupled with the position of the corner letters, philatelists are now able to allot many of these stamps to their respective plates. Specialist collectors often endeavour to obtain examples of a given stamp printed from its different plates and our catalogue accordingly reflects this depth of detail.

Maltese Cross   Type of Town Postmark

Type of Penny Post Cancellation

Example of 1844 type postmark

Postmarks. The so-called Maltese Cross design was the first employed for obliterating British postage stamps and was in use from 1840 to 1844. Being hand-cut, the obliterating stamps varied greatly in detail and some distinctive types can be allotted to particular towns or offices. Local types, such as those used at Manchester, Norwich, Leeds, etc., are keenly sought. A red ink was first employed, but was superseded by black, after some earlier experiments, in February 1841. Maltese Cross obliterations in other colours are rare.

Obliteration of this type, numbered 1 to 12 in the centre, were used at the London Chief Office in 1843 and 1844.

Some straight-line cancellations were in use in 1840 at the Penny Post receiving offices, normally applied on the envelope, the adhesives then being obliterated at the Head Office. They are nevertheless known, with or without Maltese Cross, on the early postage stamps.

In 1842 some offices in south-west England used dated postmarks in place of the Maltese Cross, usually on the back of the letter since they were not originally intended as obliterators. These town postmarks have likewise been found on adhesives.

In 1844 the Maltese Cross design was superseded by numbered obliterators of varied type, one of which is illustrated. They are naturally comparatively scarce on the first 1d. and 2d. stamps.

Like the Maltese Cross they are found in various colours, some of which are rare.

Re-entry

'Union Jack' re-entry

Re-entries. Re-entries on the plate show as a doubling of part of the design of the stamp generally at top or bottom. Many re-entries are very slight while others are most marked. A typical one is illustrated.

The 'Union Jack' re-entry, so-called owing to the effect of the re-entry on the appearance of the corner stars (see illustration) occurs on stamp L K of Plate 75 of the 1d. red, Die I.

T A (T L)   M A (M L)

Varieties of Large Crown Watermark

I   II

Two states of Large Crown Watermark

Watermarks. Two watermark varieties, as illustrated, consisting of crowns of entirely different shape, are found in sheets of the Large Crown paper and fall on stamps lettered M A and T A (or M L and T L when the paper is printed on the wrong side). Both varieties are found on the 1d. rose-red of 1857, while the M A (M L) variety comes also on some plates of the 1d. of 1864 (Nos. 43, 44) up to about Plate 96. On the 2d. the T A (T L) variety is known on plates 8 and 9, and the M A (M L) on later prints of plate 9. These varieties may exist inverted, or inverted reversed on stamps lettered A A and A L and H A and H L, and some are known.

In 1861 a minor alteration was made in the Large Crown watermark by the removal of the two vertical strokes, representing *fleurs-de-lis*, which projected upwards from the uppermost of the three horizontal curves at the base of the Crown. Hence two states are distinguishable, as illustrated.

CONDITION—IMPERFORATE

LINE-ENGRAVED ISSUES

The prices quoted for the 1840 and 1841 imperforate Line engraved issues are for very 'fine' examples. As condition is most important in assessing the value of a stamp, the following definitions will assist collectors in the evaluation of individual examples.

Four main factors are relevant when considering quality.

(a) Impression. This should be clean and the surface free of any rubbing or unnatural blurring which would detract from the appearance.

(b) Margin. This is perhaps the most difficult factor to evaluate. Stamps described as 'fine', the standard adopted in this catalogue for pricing purposes, should have margins of the recognised width, defined as approximately one half of the distance between two adjoining unsevered stamps. Stamps described as 'very fine' or 'superb' should have margins which are proportionately larger than those of a 'fine' stamp. Examples with close margins should not, generally, be classified as 'fine'.

(c) Cancellation. On a 'fine' stamp this should be reasonably clear and not noticeably smudged. A stamp described as 'superb' should have a neat cancellation, preferably centrally placed or to the right.

(d) Appearance. Stamps, at the prices quoted, should always be without any tears, creases, bends or thins and should not be toned on either the front or back. Stamps with such defects are worth only a proportion of the catalogue price.

Average

Fine

Very Fine

Superb

The actual size illustrations of 1840 1d. blacks show the various grades of quality. When comparing these illustrations it should be assumed that they are all from the same plate and that they are free of any hidden defects.

PRINTERS. Nos. 1/53a were recess-printed by Perkins Bacon & Petch, known from 1852 as Perkins Bacon & Co.

STAMPS ON COVER. Prices are quoted, for those Victorian and Edwardian issues usually found used *on cover*. In general these prices refer to single examples of the cheapest versions of each basic stamp, with other shades, plates or varieties, together with unusual frankings and postmarks, being worth more. However multiples of some stamps may be more common than single usages and in this case the covers might be worth considerably less than the price quoted.

1

1a

2 Small Crown

(Eng Charles and Frederick Heath)

1840 (6 May). Letters in lower corners. Wmk Small Crown, W **2**. Imperf.

			Unused	Used	Used on cover
1	**1**	1d. intense black	£17500	£525	
2		1d. black	£12500	£375	£750
		Wi. Watermark inverted	£35000	£2500	
3		1d. grey-black (worn plate)	£16500	£500	

			Unused	Used	Used on cover
4	**1a**	2d. deep full blue	£45000	£1200	
5		2d. blue	£38000	£975	£2750
		Wi. Watermark inverted	£60000	£6000	
6		2d. pale blue	£45000	£1100	

The 1d. stamp in black was printed from Plates 1 to 11. Plate 1 exists in two states (known to collectors as 1a and 1b), the latter being the result of extensive repairs.

Repairs were also made to plates 2, 5, 6, 8, 9, 10 and 11, and certain impressions exist in two or more states.

The so-called 'Royal reprint' of the 1d. black was made in 1864, from Plate 66, Die II, on paper with Large Crown watermark, inverted. A printing was also made in carmine, on paper with the same watermark, upright.

For 1d. black with 'VR' in upper corners see No. V1 under Official Stamps.

The 2d. stamps were printed from Plates 1 and 2.

Plates of 1d. black

	Unused	Used	Used on cover
1a	£18500	£450	£1000
1b	£12500	£400	£750
2	£12500	£375	£750
3	£20000	£500	£1000
4	£13000	£425	£850
5	£12500	£400	£775
6	£13500	£400	£775
7	£13500	£450	£850
8	£16500	£525	£1000
9	£20000	£625	£1200
10	£27500	£950	£3500
11	£22000	£4600	£16000

Varieties of 1d. black

		Unused	Used
a.	On *bleuté* paper (Plates 1 to 8) *from*	—	£775
b.	Double letter in corner *from*	£13000	£400
bb.	Re-entry *from*	£13500	£450
bc.	'PB' re-entry (Plate 5, 3rd state)	—	£8000
c.	Guide line in corner	£13000	£400
cc.	Large letters in each corner (EJ, IL, JC and PA) (Plate 1b) *from*	£13500	£550
d.	Guide line through value	£13000	£450
g.	Obliterated by Maltese Cross		
	In red	†	£425
	In black	†	£375
	In blue	†	£8000
	In magenta	†	£2250
	In yellow	†	—
	In violet	†	£12000
h.	Obliterated by Maltese Cross with number in centre *from*	†	£12000
i.	Obliterated 'Penny Post' in black (without Maltese Cross) *from*	†	£3500
j.	Obliterated by town postmark (without Maltese Cross)		
	In black *from*	†	£15000
	In yellow *from*	†	£40000
	In red *from*	†	£15000
k.	Obliterated by 1844 type postmark in black *from*	†	£1800

Plates of 2d. blue (Plates 1 and 2)

Plate	Unused	Used	Used on cover
1......Shades from	£38000	£975	£2750
2......Shades from	£45000	£1000	£3000

Varieties of 2d. blue

		Unused	Used
a.	Double letter in corner	—	£1100
aa.	Re-entry	—	£1100
b.	Guide lines in corner	—	£1000
c.	Guide lines through value	—	£1100
e.	Obliterated by Maltese Cross		
	In red	†	£1250
	In black	†	£975
	In blue	†	£12000
	In magenta	†	£9000
f.	Obliterated by Maltese Cross with number in centre *from*	†	£14000
g.	Obliterated 'Penny Post' in black (without Maltese Cross) *from*	†	£15000
h.	Obliterated by town postmark (without Maltese Cross) in black *from*	†	£7000
i.	Obliterated by 1844 type postmark		
	In black *from*	†	£2000
	In blue *from*	†	£14000

OFFICIAL STAMP

In 1840 the 1d. black (T 1), with 'V R' in the upper corners, was prepared for official use, but was never issued for postal purposes. Obliterated specimens are those which were used for experimental trials of obliterating inks, or those that passed through the post by oversight.

V1

1840. Prepared for use but not issued; 'V' 'R' in upper corners. Imperf.
V1 **V1** 1d. black.................................... £20000 £22500

1841 (10 Feb). Printed from 'black' plates. Wmk W **2**. Paper more or less blued. Imperf.

			Unused	Used	Used on cover
7	**1**	1d. red-brown (shades)............	£2500	£130	£350
		a. 'PB' re-entry (Plate 5, 3rd state).................................	—	£2250	
		Wi. Watermark inverted (Plates 1b, 8 and 10)...from	—	£6000	

The first printings of the 1d. in red-brown were made from Plates 1b, 2, 5 and 8 to 11 used for the 1d. black.

1d. red-brown from 'black' plates

Plate	Unused	Used	Used on Cover
1b..................	£23000	£375	£650
2....................	£25000	£325	£550
5....................	£9000	£180	£400
8....................	£11000	£275	£500
9....................	£5000	£190	£375
10..................	£2500	£200	£400
11..................	£8500	£130	£350

1841 (late Feb). Plate 12 onwards. Wmk W **2**. Paper more or less blued. Imperf.

		Unused	Used	Used on cover
8	1d. red-brown.................................	£600	35·00	45·00
	s. Optd 'SPECIMEN' (1).................	£2000		
	Wi. Watermark inverted.................	£5000	£400	
8a	1d. red-brown on very blue paper	£700	35·00	
9	1d. pale red-brown (worn plates)..	£675	45·00	
10	1d. deep red-brown.........................	£900	50·00	
11	1d. lake-red....................................	£5250	£850	
12	1d. orange-brown...........................	£2000	£275	

The error 'No letter A in right corner' was due to the omission to insert this letter on stamp B A of Plate 77. The error was discovered some months after the plate was registered and was then corrected.

There are innumerable variations in the colour shade of the 1d. 'red' and those given in the above list represent colour groups each covering a wide range.

Varieties of 1d. red-brown, etc

		Unused	Used
b.	Major re-entry from		£100
c.	Double letter in corner from	£625	40·00
d.	Double Star (Plate 75) 'Union Jack' re-entry	£25000	£2500
e.	Guide line in corner	£625	38·00
f.	Guide line through value	£625	40·00
g.	Thick outer frame to stamp	£625	38·00
h.	Ivory head	£625	38·00
i.	Treasury roulette	£50000	£5000
j.	Left corner letter 'S' inverted (Plates 78, 105, 107) from	—	£180
k.	P converted to R (Plates 30/31, 33, 83, 86/87) from	—	80·00
l.	Obliterated by Maltese Cross		
	In red	†	£2500
	In black	†	60·00
	In blue	†	£650
m.	Obliterated by Maltese Cross with number in centre		
	No. 1	†	£180
	No. 2	†	£180
	No. 3	†	£225
	No. 4	†	£500
	No. 5	†	£180
	No. 6	†	£160
	No. 7	†	£160
	No. 8	†	£160
	No. 9	†	£180
	No. 10	†	£320
	No. 11	†	£350
	No. 12	†	£350
n.	Obliterated 'Penny Post' in black (without Maltese Cross)	†	£1100
o.	Obliterated by town postmark (without Maltese Cross)		
	In black from	†	£700
	In blue from	†	£1800
	In green from	†	£3250
	In yellow from	†	—
	In red from	†	£8000
p.	Obliterated by 1844 type postmark		
	In blue from	†	£250
	In red from	†	£5500
	In green from	†	£2800
	In violet from	†	£3500
	In black from	†	35·00
	In olive-yellow/brown from	†	£2000

Stamps with thick outer frame to the design are from plates on which the frame lines have been straightened or recut, particularly Plates 76 and 90.

For 'Union Jack' re-entry see General Notes to Line-engraved Issues.

In 'P converted to R' the corner letter 'R' is formed from the 'P', the distinctive long tail having been hand-cut.

KEY TO LINE-ENGRAVED ISSUES

SG Nos.	Description	Date	Wmk	Perf	Die	Alphabet
	THE IMPERFORATE ISSUES					
1/3	1d. black	6.5.40	SC	Imp	I	I
4/6	2d. no lines	8.5.40	SC	Imp	I	I
	PAPER MORE OR LESS BLUED					
7	1d. red-brown	2.41	SC	Imp	I	I
8/12	1d. red-brown	2.41	SC	Imp	I	I
8/12	1d. red-brown	4.52	SC	Imp	I	II
13/15	2d. white lines	13.3.41	SC	Imp	I	I
	THE PERFORATED ISSUES					
	ONE PENNY VALUE					
16a	1d. red-brown	1848	SC	Roul	I	I
16b	1d. red-brown	1850	SC	16	I	I
17/18	1d. red-brown	2.54	SC	16	I	II
22	1d. red-brown	1.55	SC	14	I	II
24/25	1d. red-brown	27.2.55	SC	14	II	II
21	1d. red-brown	17.2.55	SC	16	II	II
26	1d. red-brown	24.7.55	LC	16	II	II
29/33	1d. red-brown	10.1.56	LC	14	II	III
37	1d. red-brown	3.1856	LC	14	II	III
	NEW COLOURS ON WHITE PAPER					
38/41	1d. rose-red	3.57	LC	14	II	III
36	1d. rose-red	26.12.57	LC	16	II	III
42	1d. rose-red	9.7.61	LC	14	II	IV
	TWO PENCE VALUE					
19, 20	2d. blue	1.3.54	SC	16	I	I
23	2d. blue	22.2.55	SC	14	I	I
23a	2d. blue	4.7.55	SC	14	I	II
20a	2d. blue	18.8.55	SC	16	I	II
27	2d. blue	20.7.55	LC	16	I	II
34	2d. blue	20.7.55	LC	14	I	II
35	2d. blue	2.7.57	LC	14	I	III
36a	2d. blue	1.2.58	LC	16	I	III
	LETTERS IN ALL FOUR CORNERS					
48/49	½d. rose-red	1.10.70	W 9	14	—	
43/44	1d. rose-red	1.4.64	LC	14	II	
53a	1½d. rosy mauve	1860	LC	14	II	
51/53	1½d. rose-red	1.10.70	LC	14	II	
45	2d. blue	7.58	LC	14	II	
46/47	2d. thinner lines	7.7.69	LC	14	II	

Watermarks: SC = Small Crown, W **2**. LC = Large Crown, W **4**.
Dies: See notes above No. 17 in the catalogue.
Alphabets: See General Notes to this section.

3 White lines added

BH Spectacles variety (Plate 4)

1841 (13 Mar)–**51**. White lines added. Wmk W **2**. Paper more or less blued. Imperf.

			Unused	Used	Used on cover
13	**3**	2d. pale blue..............................	£7500	£110	
14		2d. blue......................................	£5000	90·00	£350
		s. Optd 'SPECIMEN' (1)...........	£5500		
		Wi. Watermark inverted...........	£18000	£875	
15		2d. deep full blue......................	£6500	£110	
15aa		2d. violet-blue (1851)................	£22000	£1500	

The 2d. stamp with white lines was printed from Plates 3 and 4.
No. 15aa came from Plate 4 and the quoted price is for examples on thicker, lavender tinted paper.

Plates of 2d. blue

Plate		Unused	Used
3 shades........from		£5000	£100
4 shades........from		£5000	90·00

Varieties of 2d. blue

		Unused	Used
a.	Guide line in corner	£5250	£110
b.	Guide line through value	£5500	£125
bb.	Double letter in corner	£5500	£125
be	Re-entry	£6500	£225
c.	Ivory head	£5250	£100
d.	Spectacles variety: BH Plate 4 (Later printings)	£11500	£1100
e.	Obliterated by Maltese Cross		
	In red	†	—
	In black	†	£275
	In blue	†	£4000
f.	Obliterated by Maltese Cross with number in centre		
	No. 1	†	£700
	No. 2	†	£700
	No. 3	†	£700
	No. 4	†	£700
	No. 5	†	£850
	No. 6	†	£700
	No. 7	†	£1200
	No. 8	†	£1000
	No. 9	†	£1200
	No. 10	†	£1500
	No. 11	†	£850
	No. 12	†	£550
g.	Obliterated by town postmark (without Maltese Cross)		
	In black from	†	£3000
	In blue from	†	£4500
h.	Obliterated by 1844 type postmark		
	In black from	†	90·00
	In blue from	†	£875
	In red from	†	£20000
	In green from	†	£6000

1841 (Apr). Trial printing (unissued) on Dickinson silk-thread paper. No wmk. Imperf.

16	**1**	1d. red-brown (Plate 11)........................	£4750	†

Eight sheets were printed on this paper, six being gummed, two ungummed, but we have only seen examples without gum.

1848. Wmk W **2**. Rouletted approx 11½ by Henry Archer.

16a	**1**	1d. red-brown (Plates 70, 71)................	£15000	†

1850. Wmk W **2**. Perf 16 by Henry Archer.

			Unused	Used	Used on cover
16b	**1**	1d. red-brown (Alphabet 1) (from Plates 90–94, 96–101, 105, 107, 108, 116)............................from	£3000	£550	£1500
		bWi. Watermark inverted..from	—	£3750	

SEPARATION TRIALS. Although the various trials of machines for rouletting and perforating were unofficial, Archer had the consent of the authorities in making his experiments, and sheets so experimented upon were afterwards used by the Post Office.

As Archer ended his experiments in 1850 and plates with corner letters of Alphabet II did not come into issue until 1852, perforated stamps with corner letters of Alphabet I may safely be assumed to be Archer productions, if genuine.

Die I

Die II

4 Large Crown

Die I: The features of the portrait are lightly shaded and consequently lack emphasis.
Die II: (Die I retouched by William Humphrys): The lines of the features have been deepened and appear stronger. The eye is deeply shaded and made more lifelike. The nostril and lips are more clearly defined, the latter appearing much thicker. A strong downward stroke of colour marks the corner of the mouth. There is a deep indentation of colour between lower lip and chin. The band running from the back of the ear to the chignon has a bolder horizontal line below it than in Die I.

1854–57. Paper more or less blued.

*(a) Wmk Small Crown, W **2**. Perf 16.*

			Unused	Used*	Used on cover
17		1d. red-brown (Die I) (24.2.54)........	£375	35·00	60·00
		a. Imperf three sides (horiz pair).......	†	£6500	
		Wi. Watermark inverted...........	—	£350	
18		1d. yellow-brown (Die I)........	£450	50·00	
19	**3**	2d. deep blue (Plate 4) (1.3.54)........	£4700	£100	£200
		a. Imperf three sides (horiz pair).......	†	—	
		b. Spectacles variety: BH.......		£550	
		s. Optd 'SPECIMEN' (2)...........	£2000		
		Wi. Watermark inverted...........	—	£325	
20		2d. pale blue (Plate 4).............	£5500	£110	
20a		2d. blue (Plate 5) (18.8.55).......	£10000	£350	£550
		aWi. Watermark inverted...........	—	£950	
21	**1**	1d. red-brown (Die II) (17.2.55)........	£550	65·00	£110
		a. Imperf (Plates 2, 14)..........	£1800	£300	
		Wi. Watermark inverted...........			

*(b) Wmk Small Crown, W **2**. Perf 14.*

			Unused	Used*	Used on cover
22	**1**	1d. red-brown (Die I) (20.1.55)........	£1200	£100	£180
		Wi. Watermark inverted...........	—	£400	
23	**3**	2d. blue (Plate 4) (22.2.55).......	£13000	£225	£375
		a. Spectacles variety: BH.......	—	£1000	
		s. Optd 'SPECIMEN' (2)...........	£1700		
		Wi. Watermark inverted...........	£18500	£675	
23a		2d. blue (Plate 5) (4.7.55).......	£14000	£350	£525
		b. Imperf (Plate 5).................			
		aWi. Watermark inverted...........	—	£950	
24	**1**	1d. red-brown (Die II) (27.2.55)........	£700	70·00	£125
		Wi. Watermark inverted...........	£2500	£400	
24a		1d. deep red-brown (very blue paper) (Die II)........	£850	£110	
25		1d. orange-brown (Die II)........	£1900	£225	

*(c) Wmk Large Crown, W **4**. Perf 16.*

			Unused	Used*	Used on cover
26	**1**	1d. red-brown (Die II) (24.7.55)........	£2500	£130	£240
		a. Imperf (Plates 6, 7, 10, 13, 14, 15)..........................from	£4000	£3500	
		Wi. Watermark inverted...........	—	£1500	
27	**3**	2d. blue (Plate 5) (20.7.55).......	£18500	£450	£575
		a. Imperf........................	—	£12000	
		Wi. Watermark inverted...........	—	£1200	

*(d) Wmk Large Crown, W **4**. Perf 14.*

			Unused	Used*	Used on cover
29	**1**	1d. red-brown (Die II) · (10.1.56)........................	£240	22·00	40·00
		a. Imperf (shades) (Plates 22, 24, 25, 32, 43).......from	£3000	£3500	
		s. Optd 'SPECIMEN' (2)...........	£750		
		Wi. Watermark inverted...........	£1000	£150	
30		1d. brick-red (Die II)........	£375	45·00	
31		1d. plum (Die II) (2.56).............	£3500	£900	
32		1d. brown-rose (Die II)........	£375	55·00	
33		1d. orange-brown (Die II) (3.57)........	£725	60·00	
34	**3**	2d. blue (Plate 5) (20.7.55).......	£2800	70·00	£200
		Wi. Watermark inverted...........	—	£325	
35		2d. blue (Plate 6) (2.7.57)........	£3000	70·00	£200
		a. Imperf........................	—	£12000	
		b. Imperf between (vert pair)........	†	£12500	
		Wi. Watermark inverted...........	—	£325	

* Nos. 17/35b **For well-centred, lightly used +125%**

1856–58. Wmk Large Crown, W **4**. Paper no longer blued.

(a) Perf 16.

			Unused	Used*	Used on cover
36	**1**	1d. rose-red (Die II) (26.12.57)	£2800	80·00	£160
		Wi. Watermark inverted..........	—	£750	
36a	**3**	2d. blue (Plate 6) (1.2.58)........	£14500	£325	£550
		aWi. Watermark inverted..........	—	£1000	

(b) Die II. Perf 14.

			Unused	Used*	Used on cover
37	**1**	1d. red-brown (11.56)...............	£2750	£375	£1100
38		1d. pale red (3.57)...................	£425	80·00	
39		1d. pale rose-red (6.57)............	£110	35·00	
40		1d. rose-red (6.57)..................	40·00	8·00	23·00
		a. Imperf...............................	£3750	£2500	
		b. Imperf three sides (horiz pair)...................................	†	—	
		s. Optd 'SPECIMEN' (6, 7, 10).....................................	£200		
		Wi. Watermark inverted..........	£180	85·00	
41		1d. deep rose-red (8.57).........	£140	20·00	

1861. Letters engraved on plate instead of punched (Alphabet IV).

			Unused	Used*	Used on cover
42	**1**	1d. rose-red (Die II) (Plates 50 and 51) (9.7.61)...................	£200	40·00	70·00
		a. Imperf...............................	—	£4500	
		Wi. Watermark inverted..........	£700	£200	

* Nos. 36/42a **For well-centred, lightly used +125%**

The original die (Die I) was used to provide roller dies for the laying down of all the line-engraved stamps from 1840 to 1855. In that year a new master die was laid down (by means of a Die I roller die) and the impression was retouched by hand engraving by William Humphreys. This retouched die, always known to philatelists as Die II, was from that time used for preparing all new roller dies.

One Penny. The numbering of the 1d. plates recommenced at 1 on the introduction of Die II. Plates 1 to 21 were Alphabet II from which a scarce plum shade exists. Corner letters of Alphabet III appear on Plate 22 and onwards. As an experiment, the corner letters were engraved by hand on Plates 50 and 51 in 1856, instead of being punched (Alphabet IV), but punching was again resorted to from Plate 52 onwards. Plates 50 and 51 were not put into use until 1861.

Two Pence. Unlike the 1d. the old sequence of plate numbers continued. Plates 3 and 4 of the 2d. had corner letters of Alphabet I, Plate 5 Alphabet II and Plate 6 Alphabet III. In Plate 6 the white lines are thinner than before.

In both values, varieties may be found as described in the preceding issues – ivory heads, inverted watermarks, re-entries, and double letters in corners.

The change of perforation from 16 to 14 was decided upon late in 1854 since the closer holes of the former gauge tended to cause the sheets of stamps to break up when handled, but for a time both gauges were in concurrent use. Owing to faulty alignment of the impressions on the plates and to shrinkage of the paper when dampened, badly perforated stamps are plentiful in the line-engraved issues.

5

6

Showing position of the plate number on the 1d. and 2d. values (Plate 170 shown)

1864–79. Letters in all four corners. Wmk Large Crown, W **4**. Die II. Perf 14.

			Unused	Used*	Used on cover
43	**5**	1d. rose-red (1.4.64)................	27·00	2·75	8·00
		s. Optd 'SPECIMEN' (1, 6, 8, 9)..............................from			
44		1d. lake-red...........................	27·00	2·75	
		a. Imperf.......................from	£4000	£2500	
		Wi. Watermark inverted..from	£110	35·00	

* Nos. 43/44a **For well-centred, lightly used +200%**

The following plate numbers are known imperf (No. 44a): 72, 79, 80, 81, 82, 83, 84, 85, 86, 87, 88, 90, 91, 92, 93, 96, 97, 98, 100, 101, 102, 103, 104, 105, 107, 108, 109, 112, 113, 114, 116, 117, 120, 121, 122, 136, 137, 142, 146, 148, 158, 162, 164, 166, 171, 174, 191 and 202.

The numbering of this series of 1d. red plates follows after that of the previous 1d. stamp, last printed from Plate 68.

Plates 69, 70, 75, 126 and 128 were prepared for this issue but rejected owing to defects, and stamps from these plates do not exist, so that specimens which appear to be from these plates (like many of those which optimistic collectors believe to be from Plate 77) bear other plate numbers. Owing to faulty engraving or printing it is not always easy to identify the plate number. Plate 77 was also rejected but some stamps printed from it were used. Seven or eight examples have been recorded, of which only three certified examples are believed to exist in private hands. Plates 226 to 228 were made but not used.

Examples of all plates except 77 are known with inverted watermark. The variety of watermark described in the General Notes to this section occurs on stamp M A (or M L) on plates up to about 96 (*Prices from £500 used*).

Re-entries in this issue are few, the best being on stamps MK and TK of Plate 71 and on SL and TL, Plate 83.

Plate	Unused	Used
71..................	55·00	4·00
72..................	60·00	5·00
73..................	60·00	4·00
74..................	60·00	2·75
76..................	55·00	2·75
77..................	—	£600000
78..................	£130	2·75
79..................	48·00	2·75
80..................	65·00	2·75
81..................	65·00	3·00
82..................	£130	5·00
83..................	£155	9·00
84..................	80·00	3·00
85..................	60·00	4·00
86..................	70·00	5·00
87..................	48·00	2·75
88..................	£190	9·50
89..................	60·00	2·75
90..................	60·00	2·75
91..................	75·00	7·00
92..................	55·00	2·75
93..................	70·00	2·75
94..................	65·00	6·00
95..................	60·00	2·75
96..................	65·00	2·75
97..................	60·00	4·50
98..................	70·00	7·00
99..................	75·00	6·00
100................	80·00	3·00
101................	80·00	11·00
102................	65·00	2·75
103................	70·00	4·50
104................	£100	6·00
105................	£130	9·00
106................	75·00	2·75
107................	80·00	9·00
108................	£110	3·00
109................	£120	4·50
110................	80·00	11·00
111................	70·00	3·00
112................	90·00	3·00
113................	70·00	15·00
114................	£325	15·00
115................	£130	3·00
116................	£100	11·00
117................	65·00	2·75
118................	70·00	2·75
119................	65·00	2·75
120................	27·00	2·75
121................	60·00	11·00
122................	27·00	2·75
123................	60·00	2·75
124................	42·00	2·75
125................	60·00	2·75
127................	75·00	3·00
129................	60·00	10·00
130................	75·00	3·00
131................	85·00	20·00
132................	£190	27·00
133................	£160	11·00
134................	27·00	2·75
135................	£130	30·00
136................	£130	24·00
137................	42·00	3·00
138................	32·00	2·75
139................	80·00	20·00
140................	32·00	2·75
141................	£160	11·00
142................	95·00	30·00
143................	80·00	17·00
144................	£130	25·00
145................	48·00	3·00
146................	60·00	7·00
147................	70·00	4·00
148................	60·00	4·00
149................	60·00	7·00
150................	27·00	2·75
151................	80·00	11·00
152................	80·00	7·50
153................	£140	11·00
154................	70·00	2·75
155................	70·00	3·00
156................	65·00	2·75
157................	70·00	2·75

Plate	Unused	Used
158	48·00	2·75
159	48·00	2·75
160	48·00	2·75
161	80·00	9·00
162	70·00	9·00
163	70·00	4·00
164	70·00	4·00
165	65·00	2·75
166	65·00	7·00
167	65·00	2·75
168	70·00	10·00
169	80·00	9·00
170	55·00	2·75
171	27·00	2·75
172	48·00	2·75
173	95·00	11·00
174	50·00	2·75
175	80·00	4·50
176	80·00	3·00
177	60·00	2·75
178	80·00	4·50
179	70·00	3·00
180	80·00	6·50
181	65·00	2·75
182	£130	6·50
183	75·00	4·00
184	48·00	3·00
185	70·00	4·00
186	90·00	3·00
187	70·00	2·75
188	95·00	12·00
189	95·00	8·50
190	70·00	7·00
191	48·00	9·00
192	70·00	2·75
193	48·00	2·75
194	70·00	10·00
195	70·00	10·00
196	70·00	6·50
197	75·00	11·00
198	60·00	7·00
199	75·00	7·00
200	80·00	2·75
201	48·00	6·00
202	80·00	10·00
203	48·00	20·00
204	75·00	3·00
205	75·00	4·00
206	75·00	11·00
207	80·00	11·00
208	75·00	18·00
209	65·00	10·00
210	90·00	15·00
211	95·00	25·00
212	80·00	13·00
213	80·00	13·00
214	90·00	23·00
215	90·00	23·00
216	95·00	23·00
217	95·00	9·00
218	90·00	10·00
219	£130	85·00
220	60·00	9·00
221	95·00	20·00
222	£110	50·00
223	£130	75·00
224	£165	65·00
225	£3000	£700

1858–76 Wmk Large Crown. W **4**. Die II. Perf 14

			Unused	Used*	Used on cover
45	**6**	2d. blue (thick lines) (7.58)	£350	15·00	50·00
		a. Imperf (Plate 9)		£10000	
		s. Optd 'SPECIMEN' (1, 7)	£650		
		Wi. Watermark inverted	£1700	£250	

Plate	Un.	Used
7	£2000	65·00
8	£1850	45·00
9	£350	15·00
12	£3000	£140

46		2d. blue (thin lines) (1.7.69)	£375	27·00	75·00
		s. Optd 'SPECIMEN' (pl. 14, 15) (6, 8, 9, 10)	£250		
		Wi. Watermark inverted	£2250	£300	
47		2d. deep blue (thin lines)	£375	30·00	
		a. Imperf (Plate 13)	£7500		

Plate	Un.	Used
13	£375	30·00
14	£500	38·00
15	£525	38·00

* Nos. 45/47 **For well-centred, lightly used +150%**

Plates 10 and 11 of the 2d. were prepared but rejected. Plates 13 to 15 were laid down from a new roller impression on which the white lines were thinner.

There are some marked re-entries and repairs, particularly on Plates 7, 8, 9 and 12.

The TA (TL) and MA (ML) watermark varieties (described in the General Notes to this section) can be found on plates 8 and 9 (*Prices from £500 used*).

Though the paper is normally white, some printings showed blueing and stamps showing the 'ivory head' may therefore be found.

7   Showing the plate number (9)

9

(Eng Frederick Heath)

1870 (1 Oct)–**79**. Wmk W **9**, extending over three stamps. Perf 14.

			Unused	Used*	Used on cover
48	**7**	½d. rose-red	£110	30·00	70·00
49		½d. rose	£110	30·00	
		a. Imperf (Plates 1, 4, 5, 6, 8, 14)............from	£2400	£2000	
		s. Optd 'SPECIMEN' (various plates) (2, 8, 9, 10)	£225		
		Wi. Watermark inverted	£450	£150	
		Wj. Watermark reversed	£450	£150	
		Wk. Watermark inverted and reversed	£300	£100	

Plate	Un.	Used
1	£325	£100
3	£240	55·00
4	£150	50·00
5	£110	30·00
6	£120	30·00
8	£600	£120
9	£5000	£700
10	£130	30·00
11	£120	30·00
12	£120	30·00
13	£120	30·00
14	£120	30·00
15	£175	50·00
19	£300	65·00
20	£350	85·00

*   Nos. 48/49a **For well-centred, lightly used +200%**

The ½d. was printed in sheets of 480 (24×20) so that the check letters run from

$$\begin{matrix} AA & AX \\ & to \\ TA & TX \end{matrix}$$

Plates 2, 7, 16, 17 and 18 were not completed while Plates 21 and 22, though made, were not used.

Owing to the method of perforating, the outer side of stamps in either the A or X row (ie the left or right side of the sheet) is imperf.

Stamps may be found with watermark inverted or reversed, or without watermark, the latter due to misplacement of the paper when printing.

8   Position of plate numbers

1870 (1 Oct)–**74**. Wmk W **4**. Perf 14.

			Unused	Used*	Used on cover
51	**8**	1½d. rose-red	£500	75·00	£275
		s. Optd 'SPECIMEN' (pl. 1) (2, 6)	£550		
		sa. Optd 'SPECIMEN' (pl. 3) (8, 9, 10)	£300		

			Unused	Used*	Used on cover
52		1½d. lake-red..............................	£600	75·00	
		a. Imperf (Plates 1 and 3)			
		.................................from	£5000	†	
		Wi. Watermark inverted...........	£3000	£500	

	Plate	Un.	Used
	(1)........................	£725	£110
	3........................	£500	75·00

Error of lettering. OP–PC for CP–PC (Plate 1).

53	8	1½d. rose-red..........................	£20000	£2000	£7500

Prepared for use in 1860, but not issued; blued paper.

53a	8	1½d. rosy mauve (Plate 1)..........	£5750	—	
		b. Error of lettering, OP–PC for CP–PC........................	—	†	
		s. Optd 'SPECIMEN' (2, 6)......	£1750		

* Nos. 51/53 **For well-centred, lightly used +125%**

Owing to a proposed change in the postal rates, 1½d. stamps were first printed in 1860, in rosy mauve, No. 53a, but the change was not approved and the greater part of the stock was destroyed, although three or four postally used examples have been recorded.

In 1870 a 1½d. stamp was required and was issued in rose-red. Plate 1 did not have the plate number in the design of the stamps, but on stamps from Plate 3 the number will be found in the frame as shown above. Plate 2 was defective and was not used.

The error of lettering OP–PC on Plate 1 was apparently not noticed by the printer, and therefore not corrected.

EMBOSSED ISSUES

Volume 1, Part 1 of the Stanley Gibbons *Great Britain Specialised Catalogue* gives further detailed information on the embossed issues.

PRICES. The prices quoted are for cut-square stamps with average to fine embossing. Stamps with exceptionally clear embossing are worth more.

10	11

12	13

Position of die number

1847–54. Imperf (For paper and watermark see footnote).

			Unused	Used	Used on cover
54	10	1s. pale green (11.9.47)..........	£24000	£1000	£1900
		s. Optd 'SPECIMEN' (red opt)....................................	£2500		
		sa. Optd 'SPECIMEN' (black opt) (1, 2)...............	£2250		
55		1s. green................................	£24000	£1000	
56		1s. deep green.......................	£28000	£1200	
		i. Die 1 (1847)........................	£24000	£1000	
		ii. Die 2 (1854).......................	£27000	£1100	
57	11	10d. brown (6.11.48)...............	£11500	£1500	£3200
		s. Optd 'SPECIMEN' (1, 2)......	£3000		
		i. Die 1 (1848)........................	£12000	£1500	
		ii. Die 2 (1850).......................	£11500	£1500	
		iii. Die 3 (1853)......................	£11500	£1500	
		iv. Die 4 (1854)......................	£13000	£1750	
		v. Die 5................................			

			Unused	Used	Used on cover
58	12	6d. mauve (1.3.54)..................	£19500	£1000	
		s. Optd 'SPECIMEN' (1, 2)......	£3500		
59		6d. dull lilac (1.3.54)...............	£19500	£1000	£1900
60		6d. purple..............................	£19500	£1000	
		Wi. Watermark inverted...........	£19500	£1000	
		Wj. Watermarked upright.......			
		Wk. Watermark inverted and reversed.........................	£19500	£1000	
61		6d. violet...............................	—	£4000	

The 1s. and 10d. are on 'Dickinson' paper with 'silk' threads. The 6d. is on paper watermarked V R in single-lined letters, W **13**, which may be found in four ways–upright, inverted, upright reversed, and inverted reversed. In this listing the reversed watermark is taken to be 'normal'.

Collectors are reminded that Types **10/12** were also used to print postal stationery. 6d. stamps without watermark and 10d. and 1s. stamps without 'silk' threads come from this source and should not be confused with the adhesives, Nos. 54/61.

The die numbers are indicated on the base of the bust. Only Die 1 (1WW) of the 6d. was used for the adhesive stamps. The 10d. is from Die 1 (WW1 on stamps), and Dies 2 to 4 (2WW, 3WW and 4WW) but the number and letters on stamps from Die 1 are seldom clear and many specimens are known without any trace of them. Because of this the stamp we previously listed as 'No die number' has been deleted. That they are from Die 1 is proved by the existence of blocks showing stamps with and without the die number. The 1s. is from Dies 1 and 2 (WW1, WW2).

The normal arrangement of the 'silk' threads in the paper was in pairs running down each vertical row of the sheets, the space between the threads of each pair being approximately 5 mm and between pairs of threads 20 mm. Varieties due to misplacement of the paper in printing show a single thread on the first stamp from the sheet margin and two threads 20 mm apart on the other stamp of the row. Faulty manufacture is the cause of stamps with a single thread in the middle.

Through bad spacing of the impressions, which were handstruck, all values may be found with two impressions more or less overlapping. Owing to the small margin allowed for variation of spacing, specimens with good margins on all sides are not common.

Double impressions are known of all values.

Later printings of the 6d. had the gum tinted green to enable the printer to distinguish the gummed side of the paper.

SURFACE-PRINTED ISSUES

GENERAL NOTES

Volume 1 of the Stanley Gibbons *Great Britain Specialised Catalogue* gives further detailed information on the surface-printed issues.

'Abnormals'. The majority of the great rarities in the surface printed group of issues are the so-called 'abnormals', whose existence is due to the practice of printing six sheets from every plate as soon as made, one of which was kept for record purposes at Somerset House, while the others were perforated and usually issued. If such plates were not used for general production or if, before they came into full use, a change of watermark or colour took place, the six sheets originally printed would differ from the main issue in plate, colour or watermark and, if issued would be extremely rare.

The abnormal stamps of this class listed in this Catalogue and distinguished, where not priced, by an asterisk (*) are:

No.	
78	3d. Plate 3 (with white dots)
152	4d. vermilion, Plate 16
153	4d. sage-green, Plate 17
109	6d. mauve, Plate 10
124/124a	6d. pale chestnut and 6d. chestnut, Plate 12
145	6d. pale buff, Plate 13
88	9d. Plate 3 (hair lines)
98	9d. Plate 5 (see footnote to No. 98)
99	10d. Plate 1 (Wmk Emblems)
113	10d. Plate 2
91	1s. Plate 3 ('Plate 2')
148/150	1s. green, Plate 14
120	2s. blue, Plate 3

Those which may have been issued, but of which no specimens are known, are 2½d. wmk Anchor, Plates 4 and 5; 3d. wmk Emblems, Plate 5; 3d. wmk Spray, Plate 21, 6d. grey, wmk Spray, Plate 18; 8d. orange, Plate 2; 1s. wmk Emblems, Plate 5; 5s. wmk Maltese Cross, Plate 4.

The 10d. Plate 1, wmk Emblems (No. 99), is sometimes reckoned among the abnormals, but was an error, due to the use of the wrong paper.

Corner Letters. With the exception of the 4d., 6d. and 1s. of 1855–1857, the ½d., 1½d., 2d. and 5d. of 1880, the 1d. lilac of 1881 and the £5 (which had letters in lower corners only, and in the reverse order to the normal), all the surface-printed stamps issued prior to 1887 had letters in all four corners, as in the later line-engraved stamps. The arrangement is the same, the letters running in sequence right across and down the sheets, whether these were divided into panes or not. The corner letters existing naturally depend on the number of stamps in the sheet and their arrangement.

Imprimaturs and Imperforate Stamps. The Post Office retained in their records (now in the National Postal Museum) one imperforate sheet from each plate, known as the Imprimatur (or officially approved) sheet. Some stamps were removed from time to time for presentation purposes and have come on to the market, but these imperforates are not listed as they were not issued. Full details can be found in Volume 1 of the *Great Britain Specialised Catalogue*.

However, other imperforate stamps are known to have been issued and these are listed where it has been possible to prove that they do not come from the Imprimatur sheets. It is therefore advisable to purchase these only when accompanied by an Expert Committee certificate of genuineness.

Plate Numbers. All stamps from No. 75 to No. 163 bear in their designs either the plate number or, in one or two earlier instances, some other indication by which one plate can be distinguished from another. With the aid of these and of the corner letters it is possible to 'reconstruct' a sheet of stamps from any plate of any issue or denomination.

Surface-printing. In this context the traditional designation 'surface-printing' is synonymous with letterpress—the printers' term—as meaning printing from (the surface of) raised type while philatelists often use the expression 'Typo(graphy)', although this is beginning to fall out of favour. It is also called relief printing, as the image is in relief (in French, *en épargne*), unwanted parts of the design having been cut away. Duplicate impressions can be electrotyped or stereotyped from an original die, the resulting clichés being locked together to form the printing plate.

Wing Margins. As the vertical gutters (spaces) between the panes, into which sheets of stamps of most values were divided until the introduction of the Imperial Crown watermark, were perforated through the centre with a single row of holes, instead of each vertical row of stamps on the inner side of the panes having its own line of perforation as is now usual, a proportion of the stamps in each sheet have what is called a 'wing margin' about 5 mm wide on one or either side.

The stamps with 'wing margins' are the watermark Emblems and Spray of Rose series (3d., 6d., 9d., 10d., 1s. and 2s.) with letters D, E, H or I in the south-east corner, and the watermark Garter series (4d. and 8d.) with letters F or G in the south-east corner. Knowledge of this lettering will enable collectors to guard against stamps with wing margin cut down and re-perforated, but note that wing margin stamps of Nos. 62 to 73 are also to be found re-perforated.

PRINTERS. The issues of Queen Victoria, Nos. 62/214, were typo by Thomas De La Rue & Co.

PERFORATIONS. All the surface-printed issues of Queen Victoria are perf 14, with the exception of Nos. 126/129.

KEY TO SURFACE-PRINTED ISSUES 1855–1883

SG Nos.	Description	Watermark	Date of Issue
	NO CORNER LETTERS		
62	4d. carmine	Small Garter	31.7.55
63/65	4d. carmine	Medium Garter	25.2.56
66/66a	4d. carmine	Large Garter	1.57
69/70	6d. lilac	Emblems	21.10.56
71/73	1s. green	Emblems	1.11.56
	SMALL WHITE CORNER LETTERS		
75/77	3d. carmine	Emblems	1.5.62
78	3d. carmine (dots)	Emblems	8.62
79/82	4d. red	Large Garter	15.1.62
83/85	6d. lilac	Emblems	1.12.62
86/88	9d. bistre	Emblems	15.1.62
89/91	1s. green	Emblems	1.12.62
	LARGE WHITE CORNER LETTERS		
92	3d. rose	Emblems	1.3.65
102/103	3d. rose	Spray	7.67
93/94	4d. vermilion	Large Garter	4.7.65
96/97	6d. lilac	Emblems	7.3.65
104/107	6d. lilac	Spray	21.6.67
108/109	6d. lilac	Spray	8.3.69
122/124	6d. chestnut	Spray	12.4.72
125	6d. grey	Spray	24.4.73
98	9d. straw	Emblems	30.10.65
110/111	9d. straw	Spray	3.10.67
99	10d. brown	Emblems	11.11.67
112/114	10d. brown	Spray	1.7.67
101	1s. green	Emblems	19.1.65
115/117	1s. green	Spray	13.7.67
118/120b	2s. blue	Spray	1.7.67
121	2s. brown	Spray	27.2.80
126/127	5s. rose	Cross	1.7.67
128	10s. grey	Cross	26.9.78
129	£1 brown-lilac	Cross	26.9.78
130, 134	5s. rose	Anchor	25.11.82
131, 135	10s. grey-green	Anchor	2.83
132, 136	£1 brown-lilac	Anchor	12.82
133, 137	£5 orange	Anchor	21.3.82

SG Nos.	Description	Watermark	Date of Issue
	LARGE COLOURED CORNER LETTERS		
138/139	2½d. rosy mauve	Anchor	1.7.75
141	2½d. rosy mauve	Orb	1.5.76
142	2½d. blue	Orb	5.2.80
157	2½d. blue	Crown	23.3.81
143/144	3d. rose	Spray	5.7.73
158	3d. rose	Crown	1.81
159	3d. on 3d. lilac	Crown	1.1.83
152	4d. vermilion	Large Garter	1.3.76
153	4d. sage-green	Large Garter	12.3.77
154	4d. brown	Large Garter	15.8.80
160	4d. brown	Crown	9.12.80
145	6d. buff	Spray	15.3.73
146/147	6d. grey	Spray	20.3.74
161	6d. grey	Crown	1.1.81
162	6d. on 6d. lilac	Crown	1.1.83
156a	8d. purple-brown	Large Garter	7.76
156	8d. orange	Large Garter	11.9.76
148/150	1s. green	Spray	1.9.73
151	1s. brown	Spray	14.10.80
163	1s. brown	Crown	24.5.81

Watermarks:	Anchor	W **40**, W **47**
	Cross	W **39**
	Crown	W **49**
	Emblems	W **20**
	Large Garter	W **17**
	Medium Garter	W **16**
	Orb	W **48**
	Small Garter	W **15**
	Spray	W **33**

Please note that all watermark illustrations are *as seen from the front of the stamp*.

14   **15** Small Garter

16 Medium Garter   **17** Large Garter

1855–57. No corner letters.

*(a) Wmk Small Garter, W **15**. Highly glazed, deeply blued paper (31 July 1855).*

			Unused	Used*	Used on cover
62	14	4d. carmine (shades)	£8500	£450	£780
		a. Paper slightly blued	£9000	£450	
		b. White paper	£15000	£1100	
		s. Optd 'SPECIMEN' (2, 3)	£1200		
		Wi. Watermark inverted	£11000	£1200	

*(b) Wmk Medium Garter, W **16**.*
(i) Thick, blued highly glazed paper (25 February 1856).

63	14	4d. carmine (shades)	£14000	£575	£1100
		a. White paper	£12000		
		s. Optd 'SPECIMEN' (2)	£1200		
		Wi. Watermark inverted	—	£1400	

(ii) Ordinary thin white paper (September 1856).

64	14	4d. pale carmine	£13000	£500	£1000
		a. Stamp printed double	†		
		s. Optd 'SPECIMEN' (2)	£1100		
		Wi. Watermark inverted	£17000	£1300	

(iii) Ordinary white paper, specially prepared ink (1 November 1856).

65	14	4d. rose or deep rose	£13000	£525	£1000
		s. Optd 'SPECIMEN' (4)	£1500		
		Wi. Watermark inverted	†	—	

*(c) Wmk Large Garter, W **17**. Ordinary white paper (January 1857).*

66	14	4d. rose-carmine	£2100	£150	£225
		a. Rose	£1750	£150	

*a*Wi. Watermark inverted............	£4800	£400
*a*Wj. Watermark inverted and		
reversed................................		—
b. Thick glazed paper.............	£6500	£375
bWi. Watermark inverted.............		
s. Optd 'SPECIMEN' (2, 7).......	£450	

* Nos. 62/66b **For well-centred, lightly used +125%**

18   19

20 Emblems wmk (normal)

20a Watermark error, three roses and shamrock

20b Watermark error, three roses and thistle

1857.

(d) Wmk Emblems, W 20.

			Unused	Used*	Used on cover
68	**18**	6d. lilac....................................	£1350	£120	£240
69		6d. deep lilac (21.10.56)..........	£1800	£175	
		s. Optd 'SPECIMEN' (2, 4, 7, 8).......................................	£600		
70		6d. pale lilac...........................	£1350	£120	£240
		a. Azure paper........................	£9000	£950	
		b. Thick paper........................	£4000	£350	
		c. Error. Watermark W **20a**....			
		Wi. Watermark inverted..........	£3000	£400	
		Wj. Watermark reversed..........		£475	
		Wk. Watermark inverted and reversed...............................		—	
71	**19**	1s. deep green (1.11.56)..........	£5750	£550	
		s. Optd 'SPECIMEN' (2, 4, 7)...	£975		
72		1s. green................................	£3250	£350	£425
73		1s. pale green.........................	£3250	£350	
		a. Azure paper........................	—	£2000	
		b. Thick paper........................	—	£400	
		c. Imperf................................		†	—
		Wi. Watermark inverted..........	—	£700	
		Wj. Watermark reversed..........	—	£1400	
		Wk. Watermark inverted and reversed...............................			

* Nos. 69/73b **For well-centred, lightly used +125%**

21   22

23   24   25 Plate 2

A. White dots added   B. Hair lines

1862–64. Small uncoloured corner letters. Wmk Large Garter, W **17** (4d.) or Emblems, W **20** (others).

			Unused	Used*	Used on cover
75	**21**	3d. deep carmine-rose (Plate 2) (1.5.62)...................................	£4800	£575	
		s. Optd 'SPECIMEN' (2, 5, 6, 8).....	£500		
76		3d. bright carmine-rose..............	£2700	£350	£600
		a. Error. Watermark W **20b** (stamp TF)..........................		£4000	
		Wi. Watermark inverted...........	£7500	£1200	
77		3d. pale carmine-rose...............	£2700	£350	
		b. Thick paper........................	£4000	£475	
		Wj. Watermark reversed..............		—	
78		3d. rose (with white dots, Type A, Plate 3) (8.62).................	£35000	£14000	
		a. Imperf (Plate 3)..................	£5500		
		s. Optd 'SPECIMEN' (2).............	£2000		
79	**22**	4d. bright red (Plate 3) (15.1.62)..	£2200	£170	
		s. Opt 'SPECIMEN' (2, 5, 6, 8).......	£500		
80		4d. pale red............................	£2000	£140	£300
		Wi. Watermark inverted...........	—	£375	
81		4d. bright red (Hair lines, Type B, Plate 4) (16.10.63)..............	£2300	£185	
		s. Optd 'SPECIMEN' (2).............	£500		
82		4d. pale red (Hair lines, Type B, Plate 4).............................	£2100	£150	£300
		a. Imperf (Plate 4)..................	£2400		
		Wi. Watermark inverted...........	£5500	£400	
83	**23**	6d. deep lilac (Plate 3) (1.12.62)..	£2800	£160	
84		6d. lilac.................................	£2250	£140	£225
		a. Azure paper........................	—	£1400	
		b. Thick paper........................	—	£375	
		c. Error. Shamrock missing from wmk (stamp TF).............		£3000	
		d. Error. Watermark W **20b** (stamp TF)..........................	—	£5500	
		e. Hyphen omitted (KA)**...........		£7750	
		s. Optd 'SPECIMEN' (2, 5, 8).......	£600		
		Wi. Watermark inverted...........	£7000	£450	
		Wj. Watermark reversed..........		£550	
		Wk. Watermark inverted and reversed...............................	£9500		
85		6d. lilac (Hair lines, Plate 4) (20.4.64).............................	£3000	£250	£350
		a. Imperf (watermark inverted)..	£3250		
		b. Imperf and watermark upright................................	£3500		
		c. Thick paper........................	£3250	£280	
		d. Error. Watermark W **20b** (stamp TF)..........................	—		
		s. Optd 'SPECIMEN' (2).............	£600		
		Wi. Watermark inverted...........	£8250	£475	
		Wj. Watermark reversed..........		—	
		Wk. Watermark inverted and reversed...............................		—	
86	**24**	9d. bistre (Plate 2) (15.1.62).......	£5800	£575	£1200
		s. Optd 'SPECIMEN' (2, 6)............	£750		
		Wi. Watermark inverted...........	£10000	£700	
		Wj. Watermark reversed..........	—	£850	
		Wk. Watermark inverted and reversed...............................		—	
87		9d. straw................................	£4000	£475	£1000
		a. On azure paper....................	£6000	£550	
		b. Thick paper........................			
		c. Error. Shamrock missing from wmk (stamp TF).............	†	—	
		d. Error. Watermark W **20b** (stamp TF)..........................	†	—	
		Wi. Watermark inverted...........	£7000	£650	
		Wk. Watermark inverted and reversed...............................	—	£1000	
88		9d. bistre (Hair lines, Plate 3) (5.62)...................................	£32000	£13500	
89	**25**	1s. deep green (Plate No. 1 = Plate 2) (1.12.62).................	£4800	£500	
90		1s. green................................	£3200	£300	£450
		a. 'K' in lower left corner in white circle (stamp KD)......	£20000	£2750	
		awi. Watermark inverted................	—	£4250	

		Unused	Used*	Used on cover
	ab. 'K' normal (stamp KD).............	—	£2200	
	b. On azure paper......................			
	c. Error. Watermark W **20b** (stamp TF)..............................			
	d. Thick paper..............................	—	£375	
	da. Thick paper, 'K' in circle as No. 90a......................................		£3750	
	s. Optd 'SPECIMEN' (2, 5, 8)........	£550		
	Wi. Watermark inverted................	—	£450	
	Wj. Watermark reversed..........			
	Wk. Watermark inverted and reversed....................................	—	£475	
91	1s. deep green (Plate No. 2 = Plate 3)....................................	£35000		
	a. Imperf.....................................	£7250		
	s. Optd 'SPECIMEN' (2)................	£4200		
	Wi. Watermark inverted................	£7250		

* Nos. 75/91 **For well-centred, lightly used +125%**

The 3d. as T **21**, but with network background in the spandrels, was never issued. Optd 'SPECIMEN' *price* £800.

The plates of this issue may be distinguished as follows:

3d.	Plate 2	No white dots.
	Plate 3	White dots as illustration A.
4d.	Plate 3	No hair lines. Roman I next to lower corner letters.
	Plate 4	Hair lines in corners. (Illustration B.) Roman II.
6d.	Plate 3	No hair lines.
	Plate 4	Hair lines in corners.
9d.	Plate 2	No hair lines.
	Plate 3	Hair lines in corners. Beware of faked lines.
1s.	Plate 2	Numbered 1 on stamps.
	Plate 3	Numbered 2 on stamps and with hair lines.

** One used example of No. 84e *on piece* has been recorded, cancelled by a Glasgow Duplex postmark dated 6.1.1863.

The 9d. on azure paper (No. 87a) is very rare, only one confirmed example being known.

The variety 'K' in circle, No. 90a, is believed to be due to a damaged letter having been cut out and replaced. It is probable that the punch was driven in too deeply, causing the flange to penetrate the surface, producing an indentation showing as an uncoloured circle.

The watermark variety 'three roses and a shamrock' illustrated in W **20a** was evidently due to the substitution of an extra rose for the thistle in a faulty watermark bit. It is found on stamp TA of Plate 4 of the 3d. (No. 92a), Plates 1 (No. 70c), 5 and 6 of the 6d. (No. 97c), Plate 4 of the 9d. (No. 98b) and Plate 4 of the 1s. (No. 101a).

Similar problems occurred on stamp TF of the 6d. and 9d. Here the shamrock emblem became detached and used examples are known showing it omitted. It was replaced by a third rose (W **20b**) and this variety exists on the 6d. Plates 3, 4 and 5 (Nos. 84d/85d and 97d), 9d. Plate 4 (Nos. 87d and 98c) and 1s. green Plates 2 and 4 (Nos. 90c and 101ab).

1865–67. Large uncoloured corner letters. Wmk Large Garter, W **17** (4d.) or Emblems, W **20** (others).

			Unused	Used*	Used on cover
92	**26**	3d. rose (Plate 4) (1.3.65)........	£2500	£250	£500
		a. Error. Watermark W **20a**.....	£7000	£1250	
		b. Thick paper........................	£3500	£325	
		s. Optd 'SPECIMEN' (2)...........	£4500		
		Wi. Watermark inverted............	—	£600	
		Wj. Watermark reversed.........			
		Wk. Watermark inverted and reversed..................................			
93	**27**	4d. dull vermilion (4.7.65)........	£650	90·00	
		s. Optd 'SPECIMEN' (pl. 14) (8)..	£525		
94		4d. vermilion..........................	£575	75·00	£140
		a. Imperf (Plates 11, 12)..........	£7000		
		Wi. Watermark inverted............	£575	75·00	
95		4d. deep vermilion..................	£650	90·00	

Plate	Un.	Used
7 (1865).......	£650	£130
8 (1866).......	£600	90·00
9 (1867).......	£600	90·00
10 (1868).......	£825	£150
11 (1869).......	£625	90·00
12 (1870).......	£575	75·00
13 (1872).......	£650	75·00
14 (1873).......	£775	£110

			Unused	Used*	Used on cover
96	**28**	6d. deep lilac (with hyphen) (7.3.65).................................	£1900	£200	
		s. Optd 'SPECIMEN' (pl. 5) (2)	£4750		
97		6d. lilac (with hyphen).............	£1200	£140	£225
		a. Thick paper........................	£1600	£175	
		b. Stamp doubly printed (Plate 6).............................	—	£12000	
		c. Error. Watermark W **20a** (Pl 5, 6)........................*from*	—	£2400	
		d. Error. Watermark W **20b** (Plate 5).............................	—		
		e. Imperf (Plate 5)..................	—		
		Wi. Watermark inverted..........	—	£250	
		Wj. Watermark reversed.........	—		
		Wk. Watermark inverted and reversed..................................	†		

Plate	Un.	Used
5 (1865)........	£1200	£140
6 (1867)........	£3800	£250

			Unused	Used*	Used on cover
98	**29**	9d. straw (Plate 4) (25.10.65)..	£4800	£600	£1400
		a. Thick paper........................	£5800	£850	
		b. Error. Watermark W **20a**....	—	£2500	
		c. Error. Watermark W **20b** (stamp TF)............................			
		s. Optd 'SPECIMEN' (2)............	£925		
		Wi. Watermark inverted............	—	£1800	
99	**30**	10d. red-brown (Plate 1) (11.11.67).............................		†*£55000	
100	**31**	1s. deep green (Plate 4) (19.1.65).................................	£3000	£300	
101		1s. green (Plate 4) (19.1.65)......	£2850	£275	£450
		a. Error. Watermark W **20a**.....		£1700	
		ab. Error. Watermark W **20b**....			
		b. Thick paper........................	£3500	£380	
		c. Imperf between (vertical pair)....................................	—	£12000	
		d. Imperf (watermark inverted)	—		
		s. Optd 'SPECIMEN' (2)............	£650		
		Wi. Watermark inverted............	—	£650	
		Wj. Watermark reversed..........	—	£650	
		Wk. Watermark inverted and reversed..................................	—	£650	

* Nos. 92/101c **For well-centred, lightly used +100%**

From mid-1866 to about the end of 1871 4d. stamps of this issue appeared generally with watermark inverted.

Unused examples of No. 98 from Plate 5 exist, but this was never put to press and all evidence points to such stamps originating from a portion of the Imprimatur sheet which was perforated by De La Rue in 1887 for insertion in albums to be presented to members of the Stamp Committee (*Price* *£15000 *unused*).

The 10d. stamps, No. 99, were printed in error on paper watermarked 'Emblems' instead of on 'Spray of Rose'.

26   27

28 (with hyphen)   28a (without hyphen)

29

30   31

32

33 Spray of Rose

34

1867–80. Large uncoloured corner letters. Wmk Spray of Rose. W **33**.

			Unused	Used*	Used on cover
102	**26**	3d. deep rose (12.7.67)............	£800	£100	
103		3d. rose.................................	£525	60·00	£110
		a. Imperf (Plates 5, 6).....from	£6500		
		s. Optd 'SPECIMEN' (pl. 5) (8)	£275		
		sa. Optd 'SPECIMEN' (pl. 6) (2, 8)...	£300		
		sb. Optd 'SPECIMEN' (pl. 7) (2, 6)...	£300		
		sc. Optd 'SPECIMEN' (pl. 8) (8)	£300		
		sd. Optd 'SPECIMEN' (pl. 10) (2, 8, 9).................................	£275		
		Wi. Watermark inverted.........	£2250	£300	

Plate		Un.	Used
4 (1867)......		£1850	£300
5 (1868)......		£525	70·00
6 (1870)......		£550	70·00
7 (1871)......		£650	70·00
8 (1872)......		£625	60·00
9 (1872)......		£625	70·00
10 (1873)......		£875	£150

			Unused	Used*	Used on cover
104	**28**	6d. lilac (with hyphen) (Plate 6) (21.6.67)...........................	£1900	£185	£250
		a. Imperf......................................		£4800	
		Wi. Watermark inverted.........	—	£350	
105		6d. deep lilac (with hyphen) (Plate 6)...............................	£1900	£185	
106		6d. purple (with hyphen) (Plate 6).............................	£1900	£210	£300
107		6d. bright violet (with hyphen) (Plate 6) (22.7.68)............	£1900	£225	£300
108	**28a**	6d. dull violet (without hyphen) (Plate 8) (8.3.69)..	£1400	£190	£275
		s. Optd 'SPECIMEN' (pl. 8) (1, 8)...	£350		
		Wi. Watermark inverted.........	—	£275	
109		6d. mauve (without hyphen)..	£700	90·00	£140
		a. Imperf (Plate Nos. 8 and 9)...	£9500	£4000	
		s. Optd 'SPECIMEN' (pl. 9) (6, 8)...	£350		
		Wi. Watermark inverted.........	—	£250	

Plate		Un.	Used
8 (1869, mauve)......		£800	£140
9 (1870, mauve)......		£700	90·00
10 (1869, mauve)...			*£37500

			Unused	Used*	Used on cover
110	**29**	9d. straw (Plate No. 4) (3.10.67)............................	£2500	£325	£525
		s. Optd 'SPECIMEN' (2, 8, 9, 10, 11)...............................	£425		
		Wi. Watermark inverted.........	—	£650	
111		9d. pale straw (Plate No. 4)......	£2400	£300	
		a. Imperf (Plate 4)................	£17500		
112	**30**	10d. red-brown (1.7.67)............	£3600	£400	£850
		s. Optd 'SPECIMEN' (2, 5, 6, 8, 9 10, 11)........................	£500		
		Wi. Watermark inverted.........	—	£1000	
113		10d. pale red-brown............	£3600	£400	
114		10d. deep red-brown............	£5000	£600	
		a. Imperf (Plate 1)............	£12000		

Plate		Un.	Used
1 (1867).........		£3600	£400
2 (1867).........		*£38000	*£12500

			Unused	Used*	Used on cover
115	**31**	1s. deep green (13.7.67).........	£1300	70·00	
117		1s. green.................................	£800	45·00	90·00
		a. Imperf between (horiz pair) (Plate 7)......................		—	
		b. Imperf (Plate 4)............	£6500	£5000	
		s. Optd 'SPECIMEN' (pl. 4) (1, 8, 9).......................................	£400		
		sa. Optd 'SPECIMEN' (pl. 5) (2, 6, 8, 9).........................	£425		
		sb. Optd 'SPECIMEN' (pl. 6) (8, 9)..	£425		
		sc. Optd 'SPECIMEN' (pl. 7) (9)	£400		
		Wi. Watermark inverted.........	£2400	£180	

Plate		Un.	Used
4 (1867).........		£975	65·00
5 (1871).........		£800	45·00
6 (1871).........		£1200	45·00
7 (1873).........		£1400	90·00

			Unused	Used*	Used on cover
118	**32**	2s. dull blue (1.7.67)................	£4500	£225	£700
		s. Optd 'SPECIMEN' (2, 5, 8, 9 10, 11)...............................	£600		
		Wi. Watermark inverted.........	—	£950	
119		2s. deep blue............	£5000	£240	
		a. Imperf (Plate 1)................	£17500		
120		2s. pale blue............	£5000	£275	
		aa. Imperf (Plate 1)................	£17500		
120a		2s. cobalt...............	£30000	£3000	
120b		2s. milky blue............	£24000	£2000	

Plate		Un.	Used
1 (1867)........		£4500	£225
3 (1868)........			*£16500

			Unused	Used*	Used on cover
121		2s. brown (Plate No. 1) (27.2.80)................................	£30000	£4250	
		a. Imperf...................................	£30000		
		b. No watermark.......................	†	—	
		s. Optd 'SPECIMEN' (9)............	£3000		
		Wi. Watermark inverted.........	—	£6000	

* Nos. 102/121 **For well-centred, lightly used +75%**

Examples of the 1s. from Plates 5 and 6 without watermark are postal forgeries used at the Stock Exchange Post Office in the early 1870s. (*Prices from £850 pl.5, £2500 pl.6*)

1872–73. Large uncoloured corner letters. Wmk Spray of Rose, W **33**.

			Unused	Used*	Used on cover
122	**34**	6d. deep chestnut (Plate 11) (12.4.72)............................	£1300	£125	
		s. Optd 'SPECIMEN' (2, 6, 8)....	£325		
122a		6d. chestnut (Plate 11) (22.5.72)............................	£800	65·00	£150
		Wi. Watermark inverted.........	—	£325	
122b		6d. pale chestnut (Plate 11) (1872)............................	£800	65·00	
123		6d. pale buff (18.10.72).........	£1100	£140	£250
		Wi. Watermark inverted.........	—	£375	

Plate		Un.	Used
11 (1872, pale buff)..		£1100	£125
12 (1872, pale buff)..		£3400	£350

			Unused	Used*	Used on cover
124		6d. chestnut (Plate 12) (1872)		*£3800	
124a		6d. pale chestnut (Plate 12) (1872)............................		*£3500	
125		6d. grey (Plate 12) (24.4.73)...	£1900	£300	£375
		a. Imperf............	£15000		
		s. Optd 'SPECIMEN' (6, 8, 9)...	£375		
		Wi. Watermark inverted.........	£6250		

* Nos. 122/125 **For well-centred, lightly used +50%**

35   **36**   **37**

38

39 Maltese Cross   **40** Large Anchor

1867–83. Large uncoloured corner letters.
(*a*) Wmk Maltese Cross, W *39*. Perf 15½×15.

			Unused	Used*
126	**35**	5s. rose (1.7.67)......................................	£9500	£675
		s. Optd 'SPECIMEN' (2, 6)......................	£1100	
127		5s. pale rose..	£9500	£675
		a. Imperf (Plate 1).................................	£10000	
		s. Optd 'SPECIMEN' (pl. 2) (8. 9)...........	£1250	

Plate	Un.	Used
1 (1867)........	£9500	£675
2 (1874)........	£15000	£1500

			Un.	Used
128	**36**	10s. greenish grey (Plate 1) (26.9.78)......	£50000	£3000
		s. Optd 'SPECIMEN' (8, 9)...............	£3750	
129	**37**	£1 brown-lilac (Plate 1) (26.9.78)........	£75000	£3750
		s. Optd 'SPECIMEN' (9).....................	£6000	

*(b) Wmk Large Anchor, W **40**. Perf 14.*
(i) Blued paper.

			Un.	Used
130	**35**	5s. rose (Plate 4) (25.11.82)...............	£35000	£3500
		s. Optd 'SPECIMEN' (9).....................	£4500	
		Wi. Watermark inverted........................	—	£18000
131	**36**	10s. grey-green (Plate 1) (2.83)...............	£110000	£4500
		s. Optd 'SPECIMEN' (9).....................	£8500	
132	**37**	£1 brown-lilac (Plate 1) (12.82)............	£140000	£6500
		s. Optd 'SPECIMEN' (9).....................	£11000	
133	**38**	£5 orange (Plate 1) (21.3.82)...............	£60000	£12500
		s. Optd 'SPECIMEN' (9, 11)...............	£3000	

(ii) White paper.

			Un.	Used
134	**35**	5s. rose (Plate 4).............................	£28000	£3250
135	**36**	10s. greenish grey (Plate 1)...............	£130000	£4000
136	**37**	£1 brown-lilac (Plate 1).....................	£160000	£6000
137	**38**	£5 orange (Plate 1)............................	£10000	£3500
		s. Optd 'SPECIMEN' (9, 11, 16).........	£3250	

* Nos. 126/137 **For well-centred, lightly used +75%**

41   **42**   **43**

44   **45**   **46**

47 Small Anchor   **48** Orb

1873–80. Large coloured corner letters.
*(a) Wmk Small Anchor, W **47**.*

			Unused	Used*	Used on cover
138	**41**	2½d. rosy mauve (*blued paper*) (1.7.75)...............................	£900	£190	
		a. Imperf...............................			
		Wi. Watermark inverted..........	£3000	£350	
		s. Optd 'SPECIMEN' (pl. 1) (8)		£350	

Plate	Un.	Used
1 (*blued paper*) (1875)........	£900	£190
2 (*blued paper*) (1875)........	£8000	£1650
3 (*blued paper*) (1875)........	—	£5750

			Un.	Used	
139		2½d. rosy mauve (*white paper*)..	£675	£120	£180
		Wi. Watermark inverted..........	£2750	£250	

Plate	Un.	Used
1 (*white paper*) (1875).........	£675	£120
2 (*white paper*) (1875).........	£675	£120
3 (*white paper*) (1875).........	£1000	£175

Error of Lettering L H—F L for L H—H L (Plate 2).

			Un.	Used
140	**41**	2½d. rosy mauve..........................	£28000	£2750

*(b) Wmk Orb, W **48**.*

			Un.	Used	
141	**41**	2½d. rosy mauve (1.5.76)............	£525	85·00	£125
		s. Optd 'SPECIMEN' (pl. 3) (10)............................	£4200		
		sa. Optd 'SPECIMEN' (pl. 5) (9)	£220		
		sb. Optd 'SPECIMEN' (pl. 6) (8, 9)............................	£220		
		sc. Optd 'SPECIMEN' (pl. 7) (9)	£220		
		sd. Optd 'SPECIMEN' (pl. 10) (9)............................	£220		
		se. Optd 'SPECIMEN' (pl. 16) (9)............................	£220		
		Wi. Watermark inverted..........	£1900	£250	

Plate	Un.	Used
3 (1876)........	£1350	£150
4 (1876)........	£525	85·00
5 (1876)........	£525	85·00
6 (1876)........	£525	85·00
7 (1877)........	£525	85·00
8 (1877)........	£525	85·00
9 (1877)........	£525	85·00
10 (1878)......	£550	85·00
11 (1878)......	£525	85·00
12 (1878)......	£525	85·00
13 (1878)......	£525	85·00
14 (1879)......	£525	85·00
15 (1879)......	£525	85·00
16 (1879)......	£525	85·00
17 (1880)......	£1700	£300

			Un.	Used	
142	**41**	2½d. blue (5.2.80).....................	£575	55·00	90·00
		s. Optd 'SPECIMEN' (pl. 17) (9)............................	£160		
		Wi. Watermark inverted..........	£2100	£275	

Plate	Un.	Used
17 (1880)......	£575	75·00
18 (1880)......	£575	55·00
19 (1880)......	£575	55·00
20 (1880)......	£575	55·00

*(c) Wmk Spray of Rose, W **33**.*

			Un.	Used	
143	**42**	3d. rose (5.7.73).....................	£450	80·00	£120
		s. Optd 'SPECIMEN' (pl. 14) (2)............................	£350		
		sa. Optd 'SPECIMEN' (pl. 17) (8, 9)............................	£250		
		sb. Optd 'SPECIMEN' (pl. 18) (8, 9, 10)............................	£250		
		sc. Optd 'SPECIMEN' (pl. 19) (9, 10)............................	£250		
		Wi. Watermark inverted..........	£1650	£375	
144		3d. pale rose.............................	£450	80·00	

Plate	Un.	Used
11 (1873)......	£450	80·00
12 (1873)......	£525	80·00
14 (1874)......	£525	80·00
15 (1874)......	£450	80·00
16 (1875)......	£450	80·00
17 (1875)......	£525	80·00
18 (1875)......	£525	80·00
19 (1876)......	£450	80·00
20 (1879)......	£850	£140

			Un.	Used	
145	**43**	6d. pale buff (Plate 13) (15.3.73)....	*£25000		
146		6d. deep grey (20.3.74).....................	£600	£120	£150
		s. Optd 'SPECIMEN' (pl. 14) (8, 10)............................	£300		
		sa. Optd 'SPECIMEN' (pl. 15) (8, 9)..	£300		
		sb. Optd 'SPECIMEN' (pl. 16) (9)......	£300		
147		6d. grey....................................	£500	90·00	
		Wi. Watermark inverted.................	£1800	£375	

Plate	Un.	Used
13 (1874)......	£500	90·00
14 (1875)......	£500	90·00
15 (1876)......	£500	90·00
16 (1878)......	£500	90·00
17 (1880)......	£950	£180

			Un.	Used	
148	**44**	1s. deep green (1.9.73)............	£1100	£225	
150		1s. green....................................	£650	£160	£240
		s. Optd 'SPECIMEN' (pl. 11) (8)............................	£450		
		sa. Optd 'SPECIMEN' (pl. 12) (8, 9, 10)............................	£350		
		sb. Optd 'SPECIMEN' (pl. 13) (9)............................	£350		
		Wi. Watermark inverted..........	£2400	£400	

Plate	Un.	Used
8 (1873)........	£825	£175
9 (1874)........	£825	£175
10 (1874)......	£775	£200
11 (1875)......	£775	£175
12 (1875)......	£650	£160
13 (1876)......	£650	£160
14 (—)........		*£40000

151		1s. orange-brown (Plate 13)			
		(14.10.80)......	£4750	£550	£1800
		s. Optd 'SPECIMEN' (9)......	£550		
		Wi. Watermark inverted......	£11000	£1800	

(d) Wmk Large Garter, W 17.

152	**45**	4d. vermilion (1.3.76)......	£3000	£475	£1100
		s. Optd 'SPECIMEN' (pl. 15)...			
		(9)......	£400		
		Wi. Watermark inverted......	—	£1000	

Plate	Un.	Used
15 (1876)......	£3000	£475
16 (1877)......		*£35000

153		4d. sage-green (12.3.77)......	£1400	£300	£600
		s. Optd 'SPECIMEN' (pl. 15)...			
		(9)......	£350		
		sa. Optd 'SPECIMEN' (pl. 16)...			
		(9)......	£350		
		Wi. Watermark inverted......	£3000	£625	

Plate	Un.	Used
15 (1877)......	£1600	£325
16 (1877)......	£1400	£300
17 (1877)......		*£20000

154		4d. grey-brown (Plate 17)			
		(15.8.80)......	£2800	£500	£1700
		a. Imperf......	£15000		
		s. Optd 'SPECIMEN' (9)......	£350		
		Wi. Watermark inverted......	—	£1200	

156	**46**	8d. orange (Plate 1) (11.9.76)..	£1850	£350	£625
		s. Optd 'SPECIMEN' (8, 9)......	£350		
		Wi. Watermark inverted......	—	£900	

*   Nos. 138/156 **For well-centred, lightly used +100%**
** No. 145, No. 150 plate 14, No. 152 plate 16 and No. 153 plate 17 are all 'abnormals' see Surface-printed Issues general notes.

1876 (July). Prepared for use but not issued

			Unused
156*a*	**46**	8d. purple-brown (Plate 1)......	£6000
		s. Optd 'SPECIMEN' (8, 9)......	£4500

49 Imperial Crown

(50)   **(51)**

Surcharges in red

1880–83. Large coloured corner letters. Wmk Imperial Crown, W **49**.

			Unused	Used*	Used on cover
157	**41**	2½d. blue (23.3.81)......	£450	35·00	55·00
		s. Optd 'SPECIMEN' (pl. 23)...			
		(9)......	£175		
		Wi. Watermark inverted......	—	£550	

Plate	Un.	Used
21 (1881)......	£500	45·00
22 (1881)......	£450	45·00
23 (1881)......	£450	35·00

158	**42**	3d. rose (3.81)......	£500	£100	£175
		s. Optd 'SPECIMEN' (pl. 21)...			
		(9)......	£250		
		Wi. Watermark inverted......	—	£600	

Plate	Un.	Used
20 (1881)......	£900	£150
21 (1881)......	£500	£100

159	**42**	3d. on 3d. lilac (surch Type 50) (pl. 21) (1.1.83)......	£650	£160	£450
		s. Optd 'SPECIMEN' (9)......	£300		
		Wi. Watermark inverted......		£850	

160	**45**	4d. grey-brown (8.12.80)......	£450	75·00	£190
		s. Optd 'SPECIMEN' (pl. 17)...			
		(9)......	£250		
		sa. Optd 'SPECIMEN' (pl. 18)...			
		(9)......	£275		
		Wi. Watermark inverted......	—	£650	

Plate	Un.	Used
17 (1880)......	£475	80·00
18 (1882)......	£450	75·00

161	**43**	6d. grey (1.1.81)......	£400	80·00	£120
		s. Optd 'SPECIMEN' (pl. 18)...			
		(9)......	£275		
		Wi. Watermark inverted......	—	£650	

Plate	Un.	Used
17 (1881)......	£425	80·00
18 (1882)......	£400	80·00

162	**42**	6d. on 6d. lilac (surch Type 51) (pl. 18) (1.1.83)......	£675	£150	£425
		a. Slanting dots (various)......from	£2000	£450	
		b. Optd double......	—	£12500	
		s. Optd 'SPECIMEN' (9)......	£300		
		Wi. Watermark inverted......	£3500	£850	

163	**44**	1s. orange-brown (24.5.81)......	£750	£170	£575
		s. Optd 'SPECIMEN' (pl. 13)...			
		(9)......	£350		
		sa. Optd 'SPECIMEN' (pl. 14)...			
		(9)......	£350		
		Wi. Watermark inverted......	£3250	£950	

Plate	Un.	Used
13 (1881)......	£875	£170
14 (1881)......	£750	£170

*   Nos. 157/163 **For well-centred, lightly used +75%**
The 1s. plate 14 (line perf 14) exists in purple but was not issued in this shade (*Price* £15000 *unused*). Examples were included in a few of the Souvenir Albums prepared for members of the Stamp Committee of 1884.

KEY TO SURFACE-PRINTED ISSUES
1880–1900

SG Nos.	Description	Date of Issue
164/165	½d. green	14.10.80
187	½d. slate-blue	1.4.84
197/197e	½d. vermilion	1.1.87
213	½d. blue-green	17.4.1900
166	1d. Venetian red	1.1.80
170/171	1d. lilac, Die I	12.7.81
172/174	1d. lilac, Die II	12.12.81
167	1½d. Venetian red	14.10.80
188	1½d. lilac	1.4.84
198	1½d. purple and green	1.1.87
168/168a	2d. rose	8.12.80
189	2d. lilac	1.4.84
199/200	2d. green and red	1.1.87
190	2½d. lilac	1.4.84
201	2½d. purple on blue paper	1.1.87
191	3d. lilac	1.4.84
202/204	3d. purple on yellow paper	1.1.87
192	4d. dull green	1.4.84
205/205a	4d. green and brown	1.1.87
206	4½d. green and carmine	15.9.92
169	5d. indigo	15.3.81
193	5d. dull green	1.4.84
207	5d. purple and blue, Die I	1.1.87
207a	5d. purple and blue, Die II	1888
194	6d. dull green	1.4.84
208/208a	6d. purple on rose-red paper	1.1.87
195	9d. dull green	1.8.83
209	9d. purple and blue	1.1.87
210/210b	10d. purple and carmine	24.2.90
196	1s. dull green	1.4.84
211	1s. green	1.1.87
214	1s. green and carmine	11.7.1900
175	2s.6d. lilac on blued paper	2.7.83
178/179	2s.6d. lilac	1884
176	5s. rose on blued paper	1.4.84
180/181	5s. rose	1884
177/177a	10s. ultramarine on blued paper	1.4.84
182/183a	10s. ultramarine	1884
185	£1 brown-lilac, wmk Crowns	1.4.84
186	£1 brown-lilac, wmk Orbs	6.1.88
212	£1 green	28.1.91

Note that the £5 value used with the above series is listed as Nos. 133 and 137.

52    **53**

54   **55**   **56**

Normal   Recut tail to 'R'

1880–81. Wmk Imperial Crown, W **49**.

			Unused	Used*	Used on cover
164	**52**	½d. deep green (14.10.80)......	55·00	22·00	30·00
		a. Imperf...............................	£5000		
		b. No watermark..................	£10000		
		s. Optd 'SPECIMEN' (9)..........	60·00		
		Wi. Watermark inverted.........	£2400	£575	
165		½d. pale green.......................	55·00	22·00	
166	**53**	1d. Venetian red (1.1.80).........	35·00	15·00	30·00
		a. Imperf...............................	£4250		
		b. Error. Wmk **48**..................	†	£27000	
		c. Re-cut tail to 'R'.................	£550	£275	
		s. Optd 'SPECIMEN' (9)..........	£100		
		Wi. Watermark inverted..........	—	£350	
167	**54**	1½d. Venetian red (14.10.80)......	£250	60·00	£160
		s. Optd 'SPECIMEN' (9)..........	80·00		
		Wi. Watermark inverted..........	†	—	
168	**55**	2d. pale rose (8.12.80)............	£350	£120	£300
		s. Optd 'SPECIMEN' (9)..........	£110		
		Wi. Watermark inverted..........	£3000	£850	
168a		2d. deep rose.......................	£375	£120	
169	**56**	5d. indigo (15.3.81).................	£725	£175	£325
		a. Imperf...............................	£5500	£3250	
		s. Optd 'SPECIMEN' (9, 12, 13)...	£160		
		Wi. Watermark inverted..........	—	£4800	
164/169	*Set of 5*..................		£1275	£350	

*   Nos. 164/169 **For well-centred, lightly used +75%**

The re-cut tail to 'R' variety occurs on plate 12, in the top right hand corner on stamp lettered GR-RG.

Two used examples of the 1d. value have been reported on the Orb (fiscal) watermark.

57   Die I   Die II

1881. Wmk Imperial Crown, W **49**.

(a) 14 dots in each corner, Die I (12 July).

			Unused	Used*	Used on cover
170	**57**	1d. lilac..............................	£225	45·00	60·00
		s. Optd 'SPECIMEN' (9)..........	70·00		
		Wi. Watermark inverted..........	—	£600	
171		1d. pale lilac........................	£225	45·00	

(b) 16 dots in each corner, Die II (13 December).

172	**57**	1d. lilac..............................	2·75	2·25	4·00
		s. Optd 'SPECIMEN' (9, 12)......	60·00		
		Wi. Watermark inverted..........	60·00	35·00	
172a		1d. bluish lilac......................	£475	£150	
173		1d. deep purple....................	2·75	2·25	
		a. Printed both sides.............	£700	†	
		b. Frame broken at bottom...	£750	£350	
		c. Printed on gummed side....	£700	†	
		d. Imperf three sides (pair)....	£6000	†	
		e. Printed both sides but impression on back inverted.............................	£800	†	
		f. No watermark....................	£6500	†	
		g. Blued paper......................	—		
174		1d. mauve............................	2·75	1·75	
		a. Imperf (pair).....................	£4500		

*   Nos. 170/174 **For well-centred, lightly used +50%**

1d. stamps with the words 'PEARS SOAP' printed on the back in orange, blue or mauve *price from £550, unused*.

The variety 'frame broken at bottom' (No. 173b) shows a white space just inside the bottom frame-line from between the 'N' and 'E' of 'ONE' to below the first 'N' of 'PENNY', breaking the pearls and cutting into the lower part of the oval below 'PEN'.

58   **59**   **60**

1883–84. Large coloured corner letters. Wmk Large Anchor, W **40**.

(a) Blued paper.

			Unused	Used*
175	**58**	2s.6d. lilac (2.7.83)........................	£6000	£1500
		s. Optd 'SPECIMEN' (9)...........	£625	
176	**59**	5s. rose (1.4.84).....................	£12500	£3250
		s. Optd 'SPECIMEN' (9, 11).......	£1600	
177	**60**	10s. ultramarine (1.4.84).........	£40000	£7000
		s. Optd 'SPECIMEN' (9)...........	£2850	
177a		10s. cobalt (5.84)....................	£55000	£10000
		s. Optd 'SPECIMEN' (9)...........	£5500	

(b) White paper.

			Unused	Used*
178	**58**	2s.6d. lilac............................	£600	£160
		s. Optd 'SPECIMEN' (9, 11, 12, 13)...	£425	
179		2s.6d. deep lilac....................	£825	£225
		a. On blued paper.................	£6500	£3000
		Wi. Watermark inverted.........	—	£8750
180	**59**	5s. rose...............................	£1100	£250
		Wi. Watermark inverted.........	†	£9000
181		5s. crimson..........................	£975	£250
		s. Optd 'SPECIMEN' (9, 11, 12, 13)...	£450	
182	**60**	10s. cobalt............................	£35000	£7500
		s. Optd 'SPECIMEN' (9)...........	£3400	
183		10s. ultramarine....................	£2250	£525
		s. Optd 'SPECIMEN' (9, 11, 13).....	£550	
183a		10s. pale ultramarine.............	£2500	£550

*   Nos. 175/183a **For well-centred, lightly used +50%**

For No. 180 perf 12 see note below No. 196.

61

Broken frames, Plate 2

1884 (1 Apr). Wmk Three Imperial Crowns, W **49**.

185	**61**	£1 brown-lilac.............................	£28000	£3000
		a. Frame broken......................	£55000	£5000
		s. Optd 'SPECIMEN' (9, 11, 12).....	£2800	
		Wi. Watermark inverted.........	—	£35000

1888 (Feb). Wmk Three Orbs, W **48**.

186	**61**	£1 brown-lilac.............................	£60000	£4500
		a. Frame broken......................	£100000	£7500
		s. Optd 'SPECIMEN' (11)...........	£6800	

*   Nos. 185/186a **For well-centred, lightly used +50%**

The broken-frame varieties, Nos. 185a and 186a, are on Plate 2 stamps JC and TA, as illustrated. See also No. 212a.

62   **63**   **64**

65 **66**

80 **81** **82**

1883 (1 Aug). (9d.) or **1884** (1 Apr) (others). Wmk Imperial Crown, W **49** (sideways on horiz designs).

			Unused	Used*	Used on cover
187	52	½d. slate-blue	35·00	10·00	20·00
		a. Imperf	£3250		
		s. Optd 'SPECIMEN' (9)	50·00		
		Wi. Watermark inverted	£3000	£350	
188	62	1½d. lilac	£125	45·00	£120
		a. Imperf	£3250		
		s. Optd 'SPECIMEN' (9)	85·00		
		Wi. Watermark inverted	£3000	£280	
189	63	2d. lilac	£230	80·00	£150
		a. Imperf	£4000		
		s. Optd 'SPECIMEN' (9)	85·00		
		Wi. Watermark sideways inverted	—		
190	64	2½d. lilac	95·00	20·00	30·00
		a. Imperf	£4000		
		s. Optd 'SPECIMEN' (9)	85·00		
		Wi. Watermark sideways inverted	£600	—	
191	65	3d. lilac	£280	£100	£180
		a. Imperf	£4000		
		s. Optd 'SPECIMEN' (9)	85·00		
		Wi. Watermark inverted	†	£1200	
192	66	4d. dull green	£580	£210	£350
		a. Imperf	£4000		
		s. Optd 'SPECIMEN' (9)	£190		
193	62	5d. dull green	£580	£210	£350
		a. Imperf	£4500		
		s. Optd 'SPECIMEN' (9)	£190		
194	63	6d. dull green	£625	£240	£380
		a. Imperf	£4500		
		s. Optd 'SPECIMEN' (9)	£220		
		Wi. Watermark sideways inverted	£1400	—	
195	64	9d. dull green (1.8.83)	£1250	£480	£4750
		s. Optd 'SPECIMEN' (9)	£425		
		Wi. Watermark sideways inverted	£2000	£775	
196	65	1s. dull green	£1600	£325	£625
		a. Imperf	£5500		
		s. Optd 'SPECIMEN' (9)	£375		
		Wi. Watermark inverted	—		

187/196 Set of 10 .... £5000 £1600

* Nos. 187/196 **For well-centred, lightly used +100%**

The normal sideways watermark shows the top of the crown pointing to the right *as seen from the back of the stamp*.

The above prices are for stamps in the true dull green colour. Stamps which have been soaked, causing the colour to run, are virtually worthless.

Stamps of the above set and No. 180 are also found perf 12; these are official perforations, but were never issued. A second variety of the 5d. is known with a line instead of a stop under the 'd' in the value; this was never issued and is therefore only known unused (*Price* £25,000).

71 **72** **73**

74 **75** **76**

77 **78** **79**

Die I   Die II

Die I: Square dots to right of 'd'
Die II: Thin vertical lines to right of 'd'

1½d. Deformed leaf (Duty plate 4, R. 19/1)

1887 (1 Jan)–**92**. Jubilee issue. New types. The bicoloured stamps have the value tablets, or the frames including the value tablets, in the second colour. Wmk Imperial Crown, W **49** (Three Crowns on £1).

			Unmtd mint	Mtd mint	Used*
197	71	½d. vermilion	2·50	1·75	1·25
		a. Printed on gummed side	£3000	£2000	
		b. Printed both sides			
		c. Doubly printed	—	£12500	
		d. Imperf (showing bottom margins)	£5500	£4000	
		s. Optd 'SPECIMEN' (9, 10, 12)		35·00	
		Wi. Watermark inverted	90·00	60·00	60·00
197e		½d. orange-vermilion	2·50	1·75	1·20
198	72	1½d. dull purple and pale green	25·00	18·00	8·00
		a. Purple part of design double	—	—	£9000
		b. Deformed leaf	£1100	£800	£450
		s. Optd 'SPECIMEN' (6, 9, 12)		55·00	
		Wi. Watermark inverted	£1600	£1200	£500
199	73	2d. green and scarlet	£550	£425	£260
200		2d. grey-green and carmine	50·00	35·00	15·00
		s. Optd 'SPECIMEN' (6, 9, 12, 13)		60·00	
		Wi. Watermark inverted	£1600	£1200	£525
201	74	2½d. purple/*blue*	45·00	25·00	5·00
		a. Printed on gummed side (Wmk. inverted)	£10000	£8500	
		b. Imperf three sides	—	£6500	
		c. Imperf	—	£8000	
		d. Missing 'd' in value	†	†	£9500
		s. Optd 'SPECIMEN' (6, 9, 12, 13)		75·00	
		Wi. Watermark inverted	£4500	£3500	£1400
202	75	3d. purple/*yellow*	45·00	25·00	5·00
		a. Imperf (wmk inverted)	—	£8000	
		s. Optd 'SPECIMEN' (6, 9, 12)		60·00	
		Wi. Watermark inverted	—		£725
203		3d. deep purple/*yellow*	60·00	30·00	5·00
204		3d. purple/*orange* (1890)	£1300	£800	
205	76	4d. green and purple-brown	60·00	40·00	18·00
		aa. Imperf	—	£9500	
		s. Optd 'SPECIMEN' (6, 9, 10, 12)		60·00	
		Wi. Watermark inverted	£1600	£1200	£650
205a		4d. green and deep brown	60·00	40·00	18·00
206	77	4½d. green and carmine (15.9.92)	17·00	11·00	45·00
		s. Optd 'SPECIMEN' (9, 13)	£500	£400	
		Wi. Watermark inverted			
206a		4½d. green and deep bright carmine	£1000	£750	£650
207	78	5d. dull purple and blue (Die I)	£1100	£800	£120
		s. Optd 'SPECIMEN' (9, 12)	90·00	65·00	
207a		5d. dull purple and blue (Die II) (1888)	60·00	42·00	15·00
		s. Optd 'SPECIMEN' (13)	—		

			Unmtd mint	Mtd mint	Used*
		Wi. Watermark inverted..............		£12500	£1250
208	79	6d. purple/*rose-red*......................	60·00	40·00	15·00
		s. Optd 'SPECIMEN' (9, 10, 12)...		65·00	
		Wi. Watermark inverted..............	£10000	£7500	£2000
208a		6d. deep purple/*rose-red*............	60·00	40·00	15·00
209	80	9d. dull purple and blue..............	£110	75·00	48·00
		s. Optd 'SPECIMEN' (6, 9, 12)...	£100	70·00	
		Wi. Watermark inverted..............	£11000	£8000	£2800
210	81	10d. dull purple and carmine (*shades*) (24.2.90)..............	90·00	60·00	45·00
		aa. Imperf..........................	—	£12500	
		s. Optd 'SPECIMEN' (9, 13, 15)...	£150	£110	
		Wi. Watermark inverted..............	£1300	£9500	£3000
210a		10d. dull purple and deep dull carmine..........................	£800	£625	£250
210b		10d. dull purple and scarlet..........	£170	95·00	65·00
211	82	1s. dull green.......................	£375	£275	80·00
		s. Optd 'SPECIMEN' (9, 10, 12)...	£100	75·00	
		Wi. Watermark inverted..............	£2200	£1700	£975
212	61	£1 green (28.1.91)...................	£5000	£3500	£800
		a. Frame broken....................	£10000	£7500	£2000
		s. Optd 'SPECIMEN' (9, 11, 13, 15, 16)...........................		£1100	
		Wi. Watermark inverted..............	—	£85000	£13000

* Nos. 197/212a **For well-centred, lightly used +50%**

The broken-frame varieties, No. 212a, are on Plate 2 stamps JC or TA, as illustrated above No. 185.

½d. stamps with 'PEARS SOAP' printed on the back in orange, blue or mauve, *price from* £525 *each*.

No used price is quoted for No. 204 as it is not possible to authenticate the paper colour on stamps in used condition.

1900. Colours changed. Wmk Imperial Crown, W **49**.

			Unmtd mint	Mtd mint	Used
213	71	½d. blue-green (17.4.00)..........	2·50	2·00	2·25
		a. Printed on gummed side....	—	†	†
		b. Imperf..........................	£4800		
		s. Optd 'SPECIMEN' (11, 15)...		£650	
214	82	1s. green and carmine (11.7.00)..........................	£140	65·00	£140
		Wi. Watermark inverted..........	£1900	£1100	
		s. Optd 'SPECIMEN' (15)........		£950	
Set of 14.			£950	£650	£375

* 213/214 **For well-centred, lightly used +50%**

The ½d. No. 213, in bright blue, is a colour changeling caused by a constituent of the ink used for some months in 1900.

USED ON COVER PRICES		
No.	197	7·00
No.	198	25·00
No.	200	28·00
No.	201	8·00
No.	202	38·00
No.	205	42·00
No.	206	£100
No.	207	£275
No.	207a	50·00
No.	208	95·00
No.	209	£275
No.	210	£300
No.	211	£190
No.	213	6·50
No.	214	£1000

DEPARTMENTAL OFFICIALS

The following Official stamps were exclusively for the use of certain government departments. Until 1882 official mail used ordinary postage stamps purchased at post offices, the cash being refunded once a quarter. Later the government departments obtained Official stamps by requisition.

Official stamps may have been on sale to the public for a short time at Somerset House but they were not sold from post offices. The system of only supplying the Government departments with stamps was open to abuse so that all official stamps were withdrawn on 13 May 1904.

OVERPRINTS, PERFORATIONS, WATERMARKS. All official stamps were overprinted by Thomas De La Rue & Co. and are perf 14. Except for the 5s., and 10s. on Anchor watermarked paper W **40**, they are on Crown watermarked paper *unless otherwise stated*.

PRICES. Please note that the price columns in this section are for *mounted mint*, *used* and *used on cover* examples. For Government Parcels and Board of Education stamps, they are for *mint* and *used* only.

INLAND REVENUE

These stamps were used by revenue officials in the provinces, mail to and from Head Office passing without a stamp. The London Office used these stamps only for foreign mail.

I.R.   I. R.

OFFICIAL   OFFICIAL

(O1)   (O2)

1882–1901. Stamps of Queen Victoria. Optd with T **O1** (½d. to 1s.) or T **O2** (others).

(a) Issues of 1880–1881.

			Unused	Used*	Used on cover
O1		½d. deep green (1.11.82).................	£135	60·00	£120
O2		½d. pale green (1.11.82).................	90·00	40·00	
		s. Optd 'SPECIMEN' (9).............	£325		
O3		1d. lilac (Die II) (1.10.82)...........	10·00	7·00	30·00
		a. Optd in blue-black.............	£300	£125	
		b. 'OFFICIAL' omitted.............	—	£12500	
		c. Imperf..........................	£4500		
		ca. Imperf, optd in blue-black......	£4500		
		s. Optd 'SPECIMEN' (9, 15).......	£180		
		Wi. Watermark inverted..............	—	£2200	
O4		6d. grey (Plate 18) (3.11.82)............	£575	£140	
		s. Optd 'SPECIMEN' (9, 15).......	£325		

No. O3 with the lines of the overprint transposed is an essay.

(b) Issues of 1884–1888.

O5	52	½d. slate-blue (8.5.85)................	£110	35·00	£135
		s. Optd 'SPECIMEN' (9)...........	£325		
O6	64	2½d. lilac (12.3.85)....................	£525	£180	£1400
		s. Optd 'SPECIMEN' (9)...........	£325		
O7	65	1s. dull green (12.3.85)...............	£6000	£1900	
		s. Optd 'SPECIMEN' (9)...........	£1250		
O8	59	5s. rose (blued paper) (Wmk Anchor) (12.3.85)...............	£17500	£6500	
		a. Raised stop after 'R'............	£18500	£7250	
		s. Optd 'SPECIMEN' (9, 11)......	£2750		
O9		5s. rose (Wmk Anchor) (3.90).........	£12000	£2500	
		a. Raised stop after 'R'............	£14000	£3200	
		b. Optd in blue-black.............	£14000	£3200	
		s. Optd 'SPECIMEN' (9, 11, 13, 16)............................	£1750		
O9c	60	10s. cobalt (blued paper) (Wmk Anchor) (12.3.85)....	£38000	£9500	
		ca. Raised stop after 'R'............			
		cb. cobalt (white paper) (Wmk Anchor).................	£22000	£7750	
		cs. Optd 'SPECIMEN' (11)........	£4500		
O9d		10s. ultramarine (blued paper) (Wmk Anchor) (12.3.85).................	£27000	£8500	
		da. Raised stop after 'R'...........	£27000	£8500	
		ds. Optd 'SPECIMEN' (10).......	£3750		
O10		10s. ultramarine (Wmk Anchor) (3.90).....................	£11500	£3750	
		a. Raised stop after 'R'............	£12500	£4500	
		b. Optd in blue-black............	£12500	£4500	
		s. Optd 'SPECIMEN' (9, 10, 11, 16)............................	£2750		
O11		£1 brown-lilac (Wmk Crowns) (12.3.85).................	£60000	£22000	
		a. Frame broken....................	£85000	—	
		s. Optd 'SPECIMEN' (11)........	£5000		
O12		£1 brown-lilac (Wmk Orbs) (optd in blue-black) (3.90)......................	£85000	£30000	
		a. Frame broken....................	£125000		
		s. Optd 'SPECIMEN' (9, 11).....	£8500		

Nos. O3, O13, O15 and O16 may be found showing worn impressions of the overprint with thicker letters.

(c) Issues of 1887–1892.

O13		½d. vermilion (15.5.88)..................	15·00	7·00	£110
		a. Without 'I.R.'...................	£7000		
		b. Imperf..........................	£7000		
		c. Optd double (imperf)...........	£8000		
		s. Optd 'SPECIMEN' (9, 15)......	£120		
O14		2½d. purple/*blue* (2.92)...............	£175	30·00	£450
		s. Optd 'SPECIMEN' (9, 13, 15)...	£120		
O15		1s. dull green (9.89).................	£1000	£375	£3750
		a. Optd in blue-black.............	£2250		
		s. Optd 'SPECIMEN' (9, 15)......	£260		
O16		£1 green (6.92).....................	£12500	£2500	
		a. No stop after 'R'...............	—	£4000	
		b. Frame broken...................	£20000	£5250	
		s. Optd 'SPECIMEN' (9, 10, 15)...	£2250		

(d) Issues of 1887 and 1900.

O17		½d. blue-green (4.01)................	20·00	15·00	£350
		s. Optd 'SPECIMEN' (15).........	£160		
O18		6d. purple/*rose-red* (1.7.01)........	£625	£150	
		s. Optd 'SPECIMEN' (15, 16).......	£250		
O19		1s. green and carmine (12.01).......	£4250	£1800	
		s. Optd 'SPECIMEN' (15).........	£1100		

* Nos. O1/O19 **For well-centred, lightly used +35%**

OFFICE OF WORKS

These were issued to Head and Branch (local) offices in London and in Branch (local) offices at Birmingham, Bristol, Edinburgh, Glasgow, Leeds, Liverpool, Manchester and Southampton. The overprints on stamps of value 2d. and upwards were created later in 1902, the 2d. for registration fees and the rest for overseas mail.

O.W.

OFFICIAL

(O3)

1896 (24 Mar)–**02**. Stamps of Queen Victoria. Optd with T **O3**.

			Unused	Used*	Used on Cover
O31		½d. vermilion	£350	£150	£800
		s. Optd 'SPECIMEN' (9, 15)	£325		
O32		½d. blue-green (2.02)	£475	£225	
		s. Optd 'SPECIMEN' (15)	£450		
O33		1d. lilac (Die II)	£500	£150	£1000
		s. Optd 'SPECIMEN' (9, 15, 16)	£325		
O34		5d. dull purple and blue (Die II) (29.4.02)	£4000	£1400	
		s. Optd 'SPECIMEN' (16)	£1250		
O35		10d. dull purple and carmine (28.5.02)	£7250	£2250	
		s. Optd 'SPECIMEN' (16)	£2600		

ARMY

Letters to and from the War Office in London passed without postage. The overprinted stamps were distributed to District and Station Paymasters nationwide, including Cox and Co., the Army Agents, who were paymasters to the Household Division.

ARMY   ARMY

OFFICIAL OFFICIAL

(O4)   (O5)

1896 (1 Sept)–**01**. Stamps of Queen Victoria optd with T **O4** (½d., 1d.) or T **O5** (2½d., 6d.).

			Unused	Used*	Used on cover
O41		½d. vermilion	10·00	5·00	65·00
		a. 'OFFICIAI' (R.13/7)	£300	£130	
		b. Lines of opt transposed	£4700		
		s. Optd 'SPECIMEN' (9)	£225		
		Wi. Watermark inverted	£800	£375	
O42		½d. blue-green (6.00)	10·00	15·00	
		s. Optd 'SPECIMEN' (15)	£500		
		Wi. Watermark inverted	£1000	£650	
O43		1d. lilac (Die II)	8·00	7·00	£110
		a. 'OFFICIAI' (R.13/7)	£240	£150	
		s. Optd 'SPECIMEN' (9)	£500		
O44		2½d. purple/*blue*	50·00	35·00	£775
		s. Optd 'SPECIMEN' (9)	£225		
O45		6d. purple/*rose-red* (20.9.01)	£110	60·00	£1700
		s. Optd 'SPECIMEN' (15)	£500		

Nos. O41a and O43a occur in sheets overprinted by Forme 1, this was replaced in February 189 by Forme 2.

GOVERNMENT PARCELS

These stamps were issued to all departments, including Head Office, for use on parcels weighing over 3lb. Below this weight government parcels were sent by letter post to avoid the 55% of the postage paid from accuring to the railway companies, as laid down by parcel-post regulations. Most government parcels stamps suffered heavy postmarks in use.

GOVT PARCELS

(O7)

1883 (1 Aug)–**86**. Stamps of Queen Victoria. Optd with T **O7**.

O61		1½d. lilac (1.5.86)	£400	£100
		a. No dot under 'T'	£775	£175

		b. Dot to left of 'T'		£775	£175
		s. Optd 'SPECIMEN' (9)		£300	
O62	62	6d. dull green (1.5.86)		£3500	£1400
		s. Optd 'SPECIMEN' (9)		£300	
O63	64	9d. dull green		£2750	£1200
		s. Optd 'SPECIMEN' (9)		£300	
O64	44	1s. orange-brown (watermark Crown, pl. 13)		£1750	£300
		a. No dot under 'T'		£2750	£500
		b. Dot to left of 'T'		£2750	£500
		s. Optd 'SPECIMEN' (9)		£325	
O64c		1s. orange-brown (pl. 14)		£3500	£600
		ca. No dot under 'T'		£4500	£850
		cb. Dot to left of 'T'			

1887–90. Stamps of Queen Victoria. Optd with T **O7**.

O65		1½d. dull purple and pale green (29.10.87)	£170	30·00
		a. No dot under 'T'	£260	75·00
		b. Dot to right of 'T'	£260	75·00
		c. Dot to left of 'T'	£260	75·00
		s. Optd 'SPECIMEN' (9, 10, 13, 15)	£300	
O66		6d. purple/*rose-red* (19.12.87)	£275	75·00
		a. No dot under 'T'	£375	£120
		b. Dot to right of 'T'	£375	£120
		c. Dot to left of 'T'	£375	£120
		s. Optd 'SPECIMEN' (9, 13, 15)	£250	
O67		9d. dull purple and blue (21.8.88)	£425	£120
		a. Optd in blue-black	£675	
		s. Optd 'SPECIMEN' (9, 10, 13, 15)	£300	
		Wi. Watermark inverted		
O68		1s. dull green (25.3.90)	£700	£275
		a. No dot under 'T'	£1000	£500
		b. Dot to right of 'T'	£1000	£500
		c. Dot to left of 'T'	£1000	£500
		d. Optd in blue-black	£1200	
		s. Optd 'SPECIMEN' (9, 13, 15)	£300	

1891–1900. Stamps of Queen Victoria. Optd with T **O7**.

O69		1d. lilac (Die II) (18.6.97)	£100	30·00
		a. No dot under 'T'	£160	75·00
		b. Dot to left of 'T'	£160	75·00
		c. Optd inverted	£7500	£3500
		d. Optd inverted. Dot to left of 'T'	£8500	£4500
		s. Optd 'SPECIMEN' (15)	£450	
		Wi. Watermark inverted	—	£500
O70		2d. grey-green and carmine (24.10.91)	£250	50·00
		a. No dot under 'T'	£400	£125
		b. Dot to left of 'T'	£400	£125
		s. Optd 'SPECIMEN' (9, 11, 13, 15, 16)	£300	
O71		4½d. green and carmine (29.9.92)	£400	£275
		b. Dot to right of 'T'		
		Wi. Watermark inverted	—	£9000
		s. Optd 'SPECIMEN' (9, 13, 15)	£300	
O72		1s. green and carmine (11.00)	£650	£275
		a. Optd inverted	†	£15000
		s. Optd 'SPECIMEN' (9, 13, 15)	£400	

* O61/O72 **For well-centred lightly used +100%**
The 'no dot under T' variety occurred on R.12/3 and 20/2. The 'dot to left of T' comes four times in the sheet on R.2/7, 6/7, 7/9 and 12/9. The best example of the 'dot to right of T' is on R.20/1. All three varieties were corrected around 1897.

BOARD OF EDUCATION

BOARD

OF

EDUCATION

(O8)

1902 (19 Feb). Stamps of Queen Victoria. Optd with T **O8**.

			Unused	Used	Used on cover
O81		5d. dull purple and blue (II)	£5750	£1500	£4250
		s. Optd 'SPECIMEN' (15)	£1400		
O82		1s. green and carmine	£12000	£6000	—
		s. Optd 'SPECIMEN' (15)	£3000		

POST OFFICE TELEGRAPH STAMPS

The telegraph system in the United Kingdom was originally operated by private companies, some of which issued their own stamps.

The Post Office took over the service in 1870, producing telegraph forms with impressed 1s. stationery dies and blank forms to which postage stamps were applied.

To assist in the separate accounting of revenues from the postal and telegraph services, special Post Office Telegraph stamps were issued from 1 February 1876 and from 1 May of that year the use of postage stamps to pre-pay telegraph services was prohibited.

Telegraph stamps were in use for little over five years, when it was decided to withdraw them and postage stamps were, once again, used for telegraph services.

PLATE NUMBERS Like the postage stamps of the period, all telegraph stamps showed their plate number within the design. These are listed under their respective values.

WATERMARKS To differentiate them from postage stamps, all telegraph stamps were in horizontal format and the watermarks appear sideways. Apart from the Shamrock watermark, W **T12**, all were as used for postage stamps of the period. For the purposes of this listing, watermark sideways refers to the top of the watermark device pointing to the right of the stamp *as viewed from the gummed side of the stamp*; watermark sideways inverted refers to the top of the device pointing to the left.

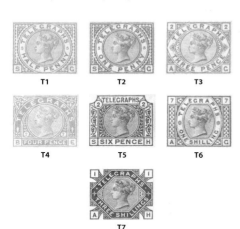

| T1 | T2 | T3 |

| T4 | T5 | T6 |

T7

| T8 | T9 |

T10

T11

T12

1876 (1 Feb)–**81**. Wmks as listed. Perf 15×15½ (5s., 10s., £5), Perf 14 (others).

			Unused	Used
T1	**T1**	½d. orange (W **T12**) (Plate 5) (1.4.80)....	30·00	35·00
		a. Imperf (vertical pair)........................	£2000	

			Unused	Used
		s. Optd 'SPECIMEN' (9)...........................	65·00	
T2	**T2**	1d. red-brown (W **T12**)........................	30·00	28·00
		Wi. Watermark inverted........................	£300	£175
		s. Optd 'SPECIMEN' (9, 10).....................	65·00	

Plate	Un.	Used
Plate 1..........	30·00	28·00
Plate 2..........	35·00	28·00
Plate 3..........	35·00	28·00

T3	**T3**	3d. carmine (W **33** sideways).............	£100	60·00
		Wi. Watermark sideways inverted........	£300	£280
		s. Optd 'SPECIMEN' (9, 10)...................	80·00	

Plate	Un.	Used
Plate 1..........	£100	75·00
Plate 2..........	£100	60·00
Plate 3..........	£125	90·00

T4		3d. carmine (W **49** sideways inverted) (6.6.81).........................	£150	£120

Plate	Un.	Used
Plate 3..........	£150	£120
Plate 4 (watermark sideways)......	£475	£250
Plate 5. (watermark sideways)......	£475	£250

T5	**T4**	4d. sage-green (W **17** sideways inverted) (Plate 1) (1.3.77).........	£150	£125
		a. Imperf (vertical pair).........................	—	—
		wi. Watermark sideways........................	—	—
		s. Optd 'SPECIMEN' (9, 11)...................	75·00	
T6	**T5**	6d. grey (W **33** sideways) (1.3.77)........	£125	80·00
		s. Optd 'SPECIMEN' (9, 11)...................	75·00	

Plate	Un.	Used
Plate 1..........	£125	80·00
Plate 2..........	£300	£160

T7		6d. grey (W **49** sideways inverted) (1.81)............................	£240	£150
		a. Imperf (vertical pair).........................		

T8	**T6**	1s. deep green (W **33** sideways).........	£120	50·00
		Wi. Watermark sideways inverted........	£500	
		s. Optd 'SPECIMEN' (9, 10)...................	£110	

Plate	Un.	Used
Plate 1..........	£180	65·00
Plate 2..........	£140	65·00
Plate 3..........	£140	55·00
Plate 4..........	£200	55·00
Plate 5..........	£120	50·00
Plate 6..........	£120	50·00
Plate 7..........	£350	55·00
Plate 8..........	£180	55·00
Plate 9..........	£180	55·00
Plate 10........	£220	70·00

T9		1s. brown-orange (W **33** sideways) (10.80)............................	£225	£150
		s. Optd 'SPECIMEN' (9)...........................	£120	

Plate	Un.	Used
Plate 10........	£225	£150
Plate 12........	£250	£190

T10		1s. brown-orange (W **49** sideways) (2.81).............................	£250	£200
		a. Imperf (vertical pair).........................	£250	£200
		Wi. Watermark sideways inverted........	£500	
		s. Optd 'SPECIMEN' (12)........................		

Plate	Un.	Used
Plate 11........	£250	£200
Plate 12........	£550	£300

T11	**T7**	3s. slate-blue (W **33** sideways) (Plate 1) (1.3.77)........................	£175	80·00
		Wi. Watermark sideways inverted........	—	£500
		s. Optd 'SPECIMEN' (8, 9, 11)..............	£120	
T12		3s. slate-blue (W **49** sideways inverted) (Plate 1) (8.81).............	£6500	£3800
T13	**T8**	5s. rose (W **39**) (Perf 15×15½).............	£1100	£200
		s. Optd 'SPECIMEN' (8, 9, 10)..............	£250	

Plate	Un.	Used
Plate 1..........	£1100	£200
Plate 2..........	£2250	£375

T14		5s. rose (W **39**) (Perf 14) (Plate 2) (1880)...	£7000	£600
T15		5s. rose (W **40**) (Perf 14) (Plate 3) (5.81)...	£7000	£1100
		s. Optd 'SPECIMEN' (9, 12)...................	£1000	
T16	**T9**	10s. grey-green (W **39**) (Plate 1) (13.77).....	£1750	£450
		s. Optd 'SPECIMEN' (8, 9, 11)..............	£400	
T17	**T10**	£1 brown-lilac (W **T12** sideways×3) (Plate 1) (1.3.77)............................	£8250	£950
		s. Optd 'SPECIMEN' (9)...........................	£900	
T18	**T11**	£5 orange (W **T12** sideways inverted×3), (Plate 1) (1.3.77)...............	£45000	£3200
		s. Optd 'SPECIMEN' (8, 9, 11)..............	£2800	

* Nos. T1/T18 **For well-centred lightly used +75%**

19

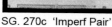

King Edward VII
22 January 1901-6 May 1910

PRINTINGS. Distinguishing De La Rue printings from the provisional printings of the same values made by Harrison & Sons Ltd. or at Somerset House may prove difficult in some cases. For very full guidance Volume 2 of the Stanley Gibbons *Great Britain Specialised Catalogue* should prove helpful.

Note that stamps perforated 15×14 must be Harrison; the 2½d., 3d. and 4d. in this perforation are useful reference material, their shades and appearance in most cases matching the Harrison perf 14 printings.

Except for the 6d. value, all stamps on chalk-surfaced paper were printed by De La Rue.

Of the stamps on ordinary paper, the De La Rue impressions are usually clearer and of a higher finish than those of the other printers. The shades are markedly different except in some printings of the 4d., 6d. and 7d. and in the 5s., 10s. and £1.

Used stamps in good, clean, unrubbed condition and with dated postmarks can form the basis of a useful reference collection, the dates often assisting in the assignment to the printers.

PRICES. For Nos. 215/456a prices are quoted for unmounted mint, mounted mint and used stamps.

USED STAMPS. For well-centred, lightly used examples of King Edward VII stamps, add the following percentages to the used prices quoted below:
De La Rue printings (Nos. 215/266)—3d. values+35%, 4d. orange+100%, 6d.+75%, 7d. and 1s.+25%, all other values+50%.
Harrison printings (Nos. 267/286)—all values and perforations+75%.
Somerset House printings (Nos. 287/320)—1s. values+25%, all other values+50%.

83	84	85	
86	87	88	
89	90	91	
92	93		

94	95	96

97

Deformed tablet (Pl. D4, R. 5/9)

(Des E. Fuchs)

1902 (1 Jan)–**10**. Printed by De La Rue & Co. Wmk Imperial Crown W **49** (½d. to 1s. Three Crowns on £1); Large Anchor, W **40** (2s.6d. to 10s.). Ordinary paper. Perf 14.

			Unmtd mint	Mtd mint	Used
215	**83**	½d. dull blue-green (1.1.02).......	2·75	2·00	1·50
		s. Optd 'SPECIMEN' (15)..........		£350	
		Wi. Watermark inverted............	£3750	£2750	£2000
216		½d. blue-green.........................	2·75	2·00	1·50
217		½d. pale yellowish green			
		(26.11.04).........................	2·75	2·00	1·50
218		½d. yellowish green..................	2·75	2·00	1·50
		a. Pair. No. 218 plus St Andrew's Cross label...........	£275	£175	£200
		aw. Pair. No. 218 Wi plus St Andrew's Cross label...........	£275	£175	£200
		b. Booklet pane. No. 218×5 plus St Andrew's Cross label............	£975	£700	
		bw. Booklet pane. No. 218×5 plus St Andrew's Cross label. Wmk inverted............	£975	£700	
		c. Booklet pane. No. 218×6 (6.06)................	£375	£275	
		cw. Booklet pane. No. 218Wi×6	£375	£275	
		d. Doubly printed (bottom row on one pane) (Control H9)............................	£20000	£15000	
		s. Optd 'SPECIMEN' (17, 22)....		£275	
		Wi. Watermark inverted............	22·00	12·00	9·00
219		1d. scarlet (1.1.02).....................	2·75	2·00	1·50
		a. Booklet pane. No. 219×6 (16.3.04)........................	£325	£250	
		aw. Booklet pane. No. 219Wi×6	£325	£250	
		s. Optd 'SPECIMEN' (15, 16, 17, 22)..........................		£250	
		Wi. Watermark inverted............	8·00	4·00	4·00
220		1d. bright scarlet........................	2·75	2·00	1·50
		a. Imperf (pair)........................	†	£18000	
221	**84**	1½d. dull purple and green (21.3.02)............................	95·00	50·00	24·00
		a. Deformed leaf.......................		£825	£425
		s. Optd 'SPECIMEN' (15)..........		£275	
222		1½d. slate-purple and green........	75·00	45·00	24·00
		Wi. Watermark inverted............	—	—	£900
223		1½d. pale dull purple and green (chalk-surfaced paper) (7.05).............................	75·00	45·00	24·00
		s. Optd 'SPECIMEN' (17)..........		£700	
224		1½d. slate-purple and bluish green (chalk-surfaced paper)................................	75·00	45·00	22·00
225	**85**	2d. yellowish green and carmine-red (25.3.02)..........	£125	70·00	25·00
		Wi. Watermark inverted............	£28000		
		s. Optd 'SPECIMEN' (16).........		£550	
226		2d. grey-green and carmine-red (1904)...........................	£150	85·00	35·00
227		2d. pale grey-green and carmine-red (chalk-surfaced paper) (4.06)..........	45·00	32·00	
		a. Deformed tablet...................		£1000	£750
		s. Optd 'SPECIMEN' (17)..........		£700	
		Wi. Watermark inverted............		£20000	
228		2d. pale grey-green and scarlet (chalk-surfaced paper) (1909)........................	80·00	45·00	32·00
229		2d. dull blue-green and carmine (chalk-surfaced paper) (1907).....................	£180	90·00	50·00
230	**86**	2½d. ultramarine (1.1.02).............	34·00	20·00	15·00
		s. Optd 'SPECIMEN' (15, 17)....		£125	
231		2½d. pale ultramarine.................	34·00	20·00	15·00
		Wi. Watermark inverted............	—	—	£4200

			Unmtd mint	Mtd mint	Used
232	**87**	3d. dull purple/*orange-yellow* (20.3.02)..................	£100	50·00	18·00
		s. Optd 'SPECIMEN' (15).........		£350	
		Wi. Watermark inverted............			
		a. Chalk-surfaced paper (3.06)..................	£450	£250	£100
232b		3d. deep purple/*orange-yellow*	90·00	45·00	18·00
232c		3d. pale reddish purple/*orange-yellow* (chalk-surfaced paper) (3.06)......	£425	£225	85·00
		cs. Optd 'SPECIMEN' (17)...........		£700	
233		3d. dull reddish purple/*yellow* (lemon back) (chalk-surfaced paper)........	£425	£225	85·00
233b		3d. pale purple/*lemon* (chalk-surfaced paper).....................	85·00	45·00	20·00
234		3d. purple/*lemon* (chalk-surfaced paper).....................	85·00	45·00	20·00
235	**88**	4d. green and grey-brown (27.3.02)....................	£125	70·00	35·00
		s. Optd 'SPECIMEN' (16).........		£450	
		Wi. Watermark inverted............			
236		4d. green and chocolate-brown....................	£125	70·00	35·00
		a. Chalk-surfaced paper (1.06).....................	75·00	40·00	20·00
		Wi. watermark inverted............			£9500
238		4d. deep green and chocolate-brown (chalk-surfaced paper) (1.06).....................	75·00	40·00	20·00
239		4d. brown-orange (1.11.09)......	£300	£180	£140
		s. Optd 'SPECIMEN' (17)..........		£700	
240		4d. pale orange (12.09).....	45·00	20·00	18·00
241		4d. orange-red (12.09).....	50·00	25·00	20·00
242	**89**	5d. dull purple and ultramarine (14.5.02)..........	£130	65·00	22·00
		s. Optd 'SPECIMEN' (16)..........		£350	
		a. Chalk-surfaced paper (5.06)........	£120	60·00	22·00
		as. Optd 'SPECIMEN' (17)..........		£700	
243		5d. slate-purple and ultramarine (14.5.02)..........	£130	65·00	22·00
		a. Chalk-surfaced paper (5.06)........	£120	60·00	22·00
		Wi. Watermark inverted............	£5500		
245	**83**	6d. pale dull purple (1.1.02)..	85·00	45·00	22·00
		s. Optd 'SPECIMEN' (15).........		£400	
		a. Chalk-surfaced paper (1.06)........	85·00	45·00	22·00
246		6d. slate-purple..................	85·00	45·00	22·00
		a. Chalk-surfaced paper..........	85·00	45·00	22·00
248		6d. dull purple (chalk-surfaced paper) (1.06).......	85·00	45·00	22·00
		s. Optd 'SPECIMEN' (17)..........		£700	
		Wi. Watermark inverted............	—	—	£3500
249	**90**	7d. grey-black (4.5.10)........	24·00	15·00	22·00
		s. Optd 'SPECIMEN' (17).........		£700	
249a		7d. deep grey-black..................	£170	£120	£100
250	**91**	9d. dull purple and ultramarine (7.4.02)........	£275	£140	75·00
		s. Optd 'SPECIMEN' (16)..........		£450	
		a. Chalk-surfaced paper (6.05)........	£250	£140	75·00
		aWi. Watermark inverted............	—		£3500
251		9d. slate-purple and ultramarine........	£275	£140	75·00
		a. Chalk-surfaced paper (6.05)........	£225	£120	75·00
		as. Optd 'SPECIMEN' (17)..........		£725	
254	**92**	10d. dull purple and carmine (3.7.02)........	£300	£150	75·00
		s. Optd 'SPECIMEN' (16)..........		£500	
		a. No cross on crown...............	£775	£425	£300
		b. Chalk-surfaced paper (9.06).........	£300	£140	75·00
255		10d. slate-purple and carmine (chalk-surfaced paper) (9.06).........	£275	£140	75·00
		a. No cross on crown...............	£725	£450	£275
		s. Optd 'SPECIMEN' (17)..........		£700	
256		10d. dull purple and scarlet (chalk-surfaced paper) (9.10).........	£260	£140	75·00
		a. No cross on crown...............	£725	£425	£250
257	**93**	1s. dull green and carmine (24.3.02)....................	£225	£100	40·00
		s. Optd 'SPECIMEN' (16)..........		£400	
		a. Chalk-surfaced paper (9.05)........	£225	£100	40·00
		as. Optd 'SPECIMEN' (17)..........		£725	
259		1s. dull green and scarlet (chalk-surfaced paper) (9.10)..................	£225	£100	55·00
260	**94**	2s.6d. lilac (5.4.02)...........	£525	£275	£150
		s. Optd 'SPECIMEN' (15, 16)...		£400	
		Wi. Watermark inverted............	£6500	£5000	£3500

			Unmtd mint	Mtd mint	Used
261		2s.6d. pale dull purple (chalk-surfaced paper) (7.10.05)......	£675	£350	£180
		s. Optd 'SPECIMEN' (17)........		£3250	
		Wi. Watermark inverted............	£10000	£7500	£4250
262		2s.6d. dull purple (chalk-surfaced paper).....................	£650	£350	£180
263	**95**	5s. bright carmine (5.4.02)......	£850	£450	£220
		s. Optd 'SPECIMEN' (16, 17).....		£400	
		Wi. Watermark inverted............	—	£65000	£5750
264		5s. deep bright carmine..........	£900	£450	£220
265	**96**	10s. ultramarine (5.4.02).............	£2000	£1000	£500
		s. Optd 'SPECIMEN' (16, 17).....		£500	
		Wi. Watermark inverted............	—	£85000	£40000
266	**97**	£1 dull blue-green (16.2.02)......	£3000	£2000	£825
		s. Optd 'SPECIMEN' (16, 17).....		£1400	
		Wi. Watermark inverted............	—£110000		£24000

USED ON COVER PRICES	
No. 215	2·50
No. 217	2·50
No. 219	2·50
No. 221	50·00
No. 225	50·00
No. 230	25·00
No. 232	35·00
No. 236a	45·00
No. 240	40·00
No. 242	50·00
No. 245	60·00
No. 249	£200
No. 250	£250
No. 254	£224
No. 257	£175
No. 260	£1250
No. 263	£1850

97a

1910 (May). Prepared for use, by De La Rue but not issued. Wmk Imperial Crown, W **49**. Perf 14.

			Unmtd mint	Mtd mint	Used
266a	**97a**	2d. Tyrian plum.........................	—	£90000	
		s. Optd 'SPECIMEN' (17)........	—	£50000	

One example of this stamp is known used, but it was never issued to the public.

1911. Printed by Harrison & Sons. Ordinary paper. Wmk Imperial Crown W **49**.

(a) Perf 14.

			Unmtd mint	Mtd mint	Used
267	**83**	½d. dull yellow-green (3.5.11).	6·00	2·75	4·00
		a. Pair. No. 267×5 plus St Andrew's Cross label..........	£400	£300	£300
		aw. Pair. No. 267Wi×5 plus St Andrew's Cross label..........	£400	£300	£300
		s. Optd 'SPECIMEN' (22)........		£325	
		b. Booklet pane. Five stamps plus St Andrew's Cross label...............	£1250	£800	
		bw. Booklet pane. Five stamps plus St Andrew's Cross label. Wmk inverted	£1250	£800	
		c. Booklet pane. No. 267×6........	£425	£325	
		cw. Booklet pane. No. 267Wi×6........	£425	£325	
		d. Watermark sideways..........	†	†	£25000
		e. Imperf (pair)..........	—	£22500	†
		Wi. Watermark inverted............	£100	60·00	60·00
268		½d. dull green..................	6·00	3·00	4·00
269		½d. deep dull green..................	17·00	11·00	10·00
270		½d. pale bluish green...............	85·00	40·00	40·00
271		½d. bright green (fine impression) (6.11)...............	£425	£275	£170
272		1d. rose-red (3.5.11)...............	18·00	8·00	15·00
		a. No watermark (*brick-red*)..	75·00	50·00	—
		b. Booklet pane. No. 272×6..	£325	£250	
		bw. Booklet pane. No. 272Wi×6........	£325	£250	
		s. Optd 'SPECIMEN' (22)........		£325	
		Wi. Watermark inverted............	90·00	50·00	50·00
273		1d. deep rose-red..................	18·00	8·00	15·00

			Unmtd mint	Mtd mint	Used
274		1d. rose-carmine......................	£100	55·00	50·00
275		1d. aniline pink (5.11).............	£1250	£750	£400
275a		1d. aniline rose......................	£300	£180	£140
276	86	2½d. bright blue (10.7.11)........	£175	65·00	38·00
		Wi. Watermark inverted............	£3000	£2100	£1250
277	87	3d. purple/lemon (12.9.11)........	£275	£150	£250
		s. Optd 'SPECIMEN' (22)........		£450	
277a		3d. grey/lemon......................	£7000	£4500	
278	88	4d. bright orange (12.7.11).....	£225	£120	55·00
		s. Optd 'SPECIMEN' (22)........		£240	
267/278 Set of 5........................			£575	£300	£300

(b) Perf 15×14.

			Unmtd mint	Mtd mint	Used
279	83	½d. dull green (30.10.11).......	65·00	40·00	45·00
		Wi. Watermark inverted.........	†	†	£3500
279a		½d. deep dull green................	90·00	45·00	45·00
280		1d. rose-red (4.10.11).............	80·00	45·00	25·00
281		1d. rose-carmine (4.11.11).......	35·00	15·00	15·00
		Wi. Watermark inverted............	†	†	—
282		1d. pale rose-carmine.............	40·00	22·00	15·00
283	86	2½d. bright blue (14.10.11).......	50·00	22·00	15·00
		s. Optd 'SPECIMEN' (22)........		—	
284		2½d. dull blue.......................	50·00	22·00	15·00
		Wi. Watermark inverted.........	—	—	£3000
285	87	3d. purple/lemon (22.9.11)........	80·00	45·00	15·00
285a		3d. grey/lemon......................	£4250	£3250	
286	88	4d. bright orange (11.11.11).......	60·00	30·00	15·00
279/286 Set of 5........................			£250	£130	90·00

No. 272a was probably a trial printing.

USED ON COVER PRICES	
No. 267	6·00
No. 272	18·00
No. 276	75·00
No. 277	£550
No. 278	£175
No. 279	£100
No. 281	30·00
No. 283	35·00
No. 285	40·00
No. 286	65·00

1911–13. Printed at Somerset House. Ordinary paper. Wmk as 1902–1910. Perf 14.

			Unmtd mint	Mtd mint	Used
287	84	1½d. reddish purple and bright green (13.7.11)......................	90·00	45·00	38·00
288		1½d. dull purple and green..........	60·00	30·00	30·00
289		1½d. slate-purple and green (1.12)............................	65·00	30·00	30·00
290	85	2d. deep dull green and red (8.8.11)......................	60·00	28·00	22·00
		a. Deformed tablet..............		£925	£550
		s. Optd 'SPECIMEN' (22)........		£325	
291		2d. deep dull green and carmine (8.8.11)...............	70·00	30·00	25·00
292		2d. grey-green and bright carmine (carmine shows clearly on back) (11.3.12)..	55·00	28·00	28·00
293	89	5d. dull purple and bright blue (7.8.11)...............	60·00	30·00	22·00
		s. Optd 'SPECIMEN' (22)........		—	
294		5d. deep dull reddish purple and bright blue (7.8.11).......	55·00	30·00	22·00
295	83	6d. royal purple (31.10.11).........	£110	50·00	90·00
296		6d. bright magenta (chalk-surfaced paper) (31.10.11)...	£15000	£10000	†
		s. Optd 'SPECIMEN' (22)........		£4500	
297		6d. dull purple (31.10.11).........	60·00	30·00	22·00
		s. Optd 'SPECIMEN' (22)........		£400	
298		6d. reddish purple (11.11).........	60·00	30·00	28·00
		a. No cross on crown (various shades)...........................		£1800	£1200
299		6d. very deep reddish purple (11.11)..........................	£120	55·00	45·00
300		6d. dark purple (3.12)............	70·00	35·00	28·00
301		6d. dull purple 'Dickinson' coated paper* (3.13)............	£425	£250	£190
		s. Optd 'SPECIMEN' (26)........		£350	
303		6d. deep plum (chalk-surfaced paper) (7.13).................	60·00	30·00	75·00
		a. No cross on crown.............	£1950	£1250	
		s. Optd 'SPECIMEN' (26)........		—	
305	90	7d. slate-grey (1.8.12)............	30·00	15·00	22·00
		s. Optd 'SPECIMEN' (26)........		£350	
306	91	9d. reddish purple and light blue (24.7.11).................	£200	95·00	75·00
		s. Optd 'SPECIMEN' (22)........		£450	
306a		9d. deep dull reddish purple and deep bright blue (9.11).............................	£200	95·00	75·00

			Unmtd mint	Mtd mint	Used
307		9d. dull reddish purple and blue (10.11)...................	£130	60·00	60·00
307a		9d. deep plum and blue (7.13)..	£125	60·00	60·00
308		9d. slate-purple and cobalt-blue (3.12)...................	£350	£160	£110
309	92	10d. dull purple and scarlet (9.10.11)...................	£200	95·00	75·00
		s. Optd 'SPECIMEN' (22)...........		£375	
310		10d. dull reddish purple and aniline pink (5.12)...........	£500	£275	£225
311		10d. dull reddish purple and carmine (5.12)...............	£150	80·00	60·00
		a. No cross on crown.............	£2800	£1800	
312	93	1s. dark green and scarlet (13.7.11)...................	£240	£120	60·00
		s. Optd 'SPECIMEN' (22, 23, 26)...........................		£350	
313		1s. deep green and scarlet (9.10.11)...................	£180	80·00	40·00
		Wi. Watermark inverted............	£240	£150	†
314		1s. green and carmine (15.4.12)...................	£140	60·00	35·00
315	94	2s.6d. dull greyish purple (15.9.11)...................	£1750	£950	£450
		s. Optd 'SPECIMEN' (22)...........		£425	
316		2s.6d. dull reddish purple (5.12)...	£625	£300	£180
		Wi. Watermark inverted............	†	†	—
317		2s.6d. dark purple....................	£675	£325	£190
318	95	5s. carmine (29.2.12).............	£875	£425	£200
		s. Optd 'SPECIMEN' (26)...........		£425	
319	96	10s. blue (14.1.12).................	£2100	£1100	£600
320	97	£1 deep green (3.9.11)...........	£3000	£2000	£750
		s. Optd 'SPECIMEN' (22)...........		£2200	

* No. 301 was on an experimental coated paper which does not respond to the silver test.
Following plate repairs, No. 290a was relocated to R. 5/6 for two Somerset House printings in November and December 1911.

USED ON COVER PRICES	
No. 288	60·00
No. 290	55·00
No. 293	65·00
No. 297	90·00
No. 305	£200
No. 307	£190
No. 311	£225
No. 314	£200
No. 316	£1700
No. 318	£1750

DEPARTMENTAL OFFICIALS

PRICES. Please note that, with the exception of Government Parcels Stamps the price columns in this section are for mounted mint, used and used on cover examples. For Governemtn Parcels Stamps they are for mint and used only.

INLAND REVENUE

These stamps were used by revenue officials in the provinces, mail to and from Head Office passing without a stamp. The London Office used these stamps only for foreign mail.

I.R. **I. R.**

OFFICIAL **OFFICIAL**

(O1) (O2)

1902–04. Stamps of King Edward VII. Optd with T **O1** (½d. to 1s.) or T **O2** (others). Ordinary paper.

			Unused	Used	Used on cover
O20		½d. blue-green (4.2.02)............	32·00	4·50	£150
		s. Optd 'SPECIMEN' (15)........	£425		
O21		1d. scarlet (4.2.02)...............	22·00	3·00	95·00
		s. Optd 'SPECIMEN' (15)........	£425		
O22	86	2½d. ultramarine (19.2.02)........	£1000	£275	
		s. Optd 'SPECIMEN' (15, 16)..	£575		
O23	83	6d. pale dull purple (14.3.04)..	£500000	£300000	
		s. Optd 'SPECIMEN' (16)........	£38000		
O24	93	1s. dull green and carmine (29.4.02)........................	£3750	£900	
		s. Optd 'SPECIMEN' (16)........	£1200		
O25	95	5s. bright carmine (29.4.02).....	£38000	£10000	
		a. Raised stop after 'R'...........	£42000	£12000	
		s. Optd 'SPECIMEN' (16)........	£6500		

			Unused	Used	Used on cover
O26	**96**	10s. ultramarine (29.4.02)........	£85000	£45000	
		a. Raised stop after 'R'............	£95000	£45000	
		s. Optd 'SPECIMEN' (16).........	£20000		
O27	**97**	£1 dull blue-green (29.4.02)...	£50000	£18000	
		s. Optd 'SPECIMEN' (16).........	£12500		

Although an issue date of 4 February has long been recorded, the 1d. is not currently brown used before 24 February and the ½d. before early March 1902.

OFFICE OF WORKS

These were issued to Head and Branch (local) offices in London and to Branch (local) offices at Birmingham, Bristol, Edinburgh, Glasgow, Leeds, Liverpool, Manchester and Southampton. The overprints on stamps of value 2d. and upwards were created later in 1902, the 2d. for registration fees and the rest for overseas mail.

O.W.
OFFICIAL
(O3)

1902 (11 Feb)–**03**. Stamps of King Edward VII. Optd with T **O3**. Ordinary paper.

			Unused	Used	Used on Cover
O36		½d. blue-green (2.02)...............	£575	£180	£2000
		s. Optd 'SPECIMEN' (15).........	£425		
O37		1d. scarlet................................	£575	£180	£425
		s. Optd 'SPECIMEN' (15).........	£425		
O38	**85**	2d. yellowish green and carmine-red (27.4.02)........	£2000	£450	£3250
		s. Optd 'SPECIMEN' (16).........	£850		
O39	**86**	2½d. ultramarine (29.4.02)........	£3500	£675	£4250
		s. Optd 'SPECIMEN' (16).........	£900		
O40	**92**	10d. dull purple and carmine (28.5.03)...........................	£40000	£7000	
		s. Optd 'SPECIMEN' (16).........	£8000		

* O31/O40 **For well-centered, lightly used +25%.**

ARMY

Letters to and from the War Office in London passed without postage. The overprinted stamps were distributed to District and Station Paymasters nationwide, including Cox and Co., the Army Agents, who were paymasters to the Household Division.

ARMY ARMY

OFFICIAL OFFICIAL
(O4) (O6)

1902–03. Stamps of King Edward VII optd with T **O4** (Nos. O48/O50) or T **O6** (No. O52). Ordinary paper.

			Unused	Used	Used on cover
O48		½d. blue-green (11.2.02).................	6·00	2·50	£100
		s. Optd 'SPECIMEN' (15)................	£350		
O49		1d. scarlet (11.2.02).......................	6·00	2·50	£100
		a. 'ARMY' omitted..........................	†	—	
		s. Optd 'SPECIMEN' (15)................	£350		
O50		6d. pale purple (23.8.02)..........	£175	80·00	
		s. Optd 'SPECIMEN' (16).........	£425		
O52		6d. pale dull purple (12.03).............	£2800	£1600	

GOVERNMENT PARCELS

These stamps were issued to all departments, including Head Office, for use on parcels weighing over 3 lb. Below this weight government parcels were sent by letter post to avoid the 55% of the postage paid from accruing to the railway companies, as laid down by parcel-post regulations. Most government parcels stamps suffered heavy postmarks in use.

GOVT
PARCELS
(O7)

1902. Stamps of King Edward VII. Optd with T **O7**. Ordinary paper.

O74		1d. scarlet (30.10.02)........................	75·00	22·00	
		s. Optd 'SPECIMEN' (16).......................	£350		

				Used	Used on cover
O75	**85**	2d. yellowish green and carmine-red (29.4.02)...............................	£225	60·00	
		s. Optd 'SPECIMEN' (15, 16)...........	£350		
O76		6d. pale dull purple (19.2.02)................	£275	60·00	
		a. Opt double, one albino............	£25000		
		s. Optd 'SPECIMEN' (16)................	£350		
O77	**91**	9d. dull purple and ultramarine (28.8.02).................................	£650	£175	
		s. Optd 'SPECIMEN' (16)................	£500		
O78	**93**	1s. dull green and carmine (17.12.02)..	£1350	£300	
		s. Optd 'SPECIMEN' (16)................	£550		

BOARD OF EDUCATION

BOARD
OF
EDUCATION
(O8)

1902 (19 Feb)–**04**. Stamps of King Edward VII. Optd with T **O8**. Ordinary paper.

			Unused	Used	Used on cover
O83		½d. blue-green..........................	£180	45·00	£550
		s. Optd 'SPECIMEN' (15).........	£375		
O84		1d. scarlet.................................	£180	45·00	£550
		s. Optd 'SPECIMEN' (15).........	£375		
O85	**86**	2½d. ultramarine.........................	£5000	£475	
		s. Optd 'SPECIMEN' (15).........	£1100		
O86	**89**	5d. dull purple and ultramarine (6.2.04)............	£30000	£8500	
		s. Optd 'SPECIMEN' (16).........	£7000		
O87	**93**	1s. dull green and carmine (23.12.02)...........................	£160000	—	
		s. Optd 'SPECIMEN' (16).........	£30000		

ROYAL HOUSEHOLD

R.H.
OFFICIAL
(O9)

1902. Stamps of King Edward VII optd with T **O9**. Ordinary paper.

			Unused	Used	Used on cover
O91		½d. blue-green (29.4.02)...................	£375	£200	£1100
		s. Optd 'SPECIMEN' (16).................	£750		
O92		1d. scarlet (19.2.02)........................	£325	£175	£1000
		s. Optd 'SPECIMEN' (15).................	£750		

ADMIRALTY

ADMIRALTY ADMIRALTY

OFFICIAL OFFICIAL
(O10) (O11) (with different 'M')

1903 (1 Apr). Stamps of King Edward VII optd with T **O10**. Ordinary paper.

			Unused	Used	Used on cover
O101		½d. blue-green..........................	30·00	15·00	
		s. Optd 'SPECIMEN' (16).........	£400		
O102		1d. scarlet.................................	20·00	10·00	£300
		s. Optd 'SPECIMEN' (16).........	£400		
O103	**84**	1½d. dull purple and green........	£325	£150	
		s. Optd 'SPECIMEN' (16).........	£500		
O104	**85**	2d. yellowish green and carmine-red......................	£350	£160	
		s. Optd 'SPECIMEN' (16).........	£500		
O105	**86**	2½d. ultramarine.........................	£475	£150	
		s. Optd 'SPECIMEN' (16).........	£500		
O106	**87**	3d. purple/*yellow*.....................	£425	£160	
		s. Optd 'SPECIMEN' (16).........	£500		

1903–04. Stamps of King Edward VII optd with T **O11**. Ordinary paper.

			Unused	Used	Used on cover
O107	**83**	½d. blue-green (9.03).............	60·00	28·00	£500
		s. Optd 'SPECIMEN' (16).........	£400		
O108		1d. scarlet (12.03)...................	60·00	28·00	£160
		s. Optd 'SPECIMEN' (16).........	£400		
O109	**84**	1½d. dull purple and green (2.04).................................	£1900	£650	
O110	**85**	2d. yellowish green and carmine red (3.04).............	£2700	£900	
		s. Optd 'SPECIMEN' (16).........	£750		
O111	**86**	2½d. ultramarine (3.04)..............	£2900	£950	
		s. Optd 'SPECIMEN' (16).........	£950		
O112	**87**	3d. dull purple/*orange-yellow* (12.03)................................	£2600	£400	
		s. Optd 'SPECIMEN' (16).........	£750		

Stamps of various issues perforated with a Crown and initials ('H.M.O.W.', 'O.W.', 'B.T.' or 'S.O.') or with initials only ('H.M.S.O.' or 'D.S.I.R.') have also been used for official purposes, but these are outside the scope of the catalogue.

Detectamark Spectrum Watermark Detector

The Stanley Gibbons Detectamark Spectrum makes it easy to discover those hidden rarities. It's simple to use and the versatile colour settings and adjustable light source provide additional help when identifying the more difficult watermarks.

R2570 £164

KEY FEATURES
- Easy to discover hidden rarities
- Unique multiple colour settings
- It's able to detect watermarks on modern stamps printed on thick, chalk surfaced papers with full gum, which other detectors fail to identify
- No chemicals or solvents are used making this a safe, clean and highly effective
- Lightweight and battery operated

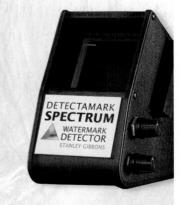

GREAT BRITAIN
POSTAL AUCTIONS

Est. **40** Years

AUCTIONS HELD FIVE TIMES PER YEAR.....CATALOGUES SENT FREE ON REQUEST

(Pl.225)

(SG 177a)

(SG 173g)

(MAGENTA)

(SG 346c)

('CHROME')

('CAMBRIDGE')

Selling your stamp collection?

Warwick and Warwick have an expanding requirement for world collections, single country collections, single items, covers proof material and specialised collections. Our customer base is increasing dramatically and we need an ever-larger supply of quality material to keep pace with demand. The market is currently very strong for G.B. and British Commonwealth and the Far East. If you are considering the sale of your collection, now is the time to act.

FREE VALUATIONS

We will provide a free, professional valuation of your collection, without obligation on your part to proceed. Either we will make you a fair, binding private treaty offer, or we will recommend inclusion of your property in our next public auction.

FREE TRANSPORTATION

We can arrange insured transportation of your collection to our Warwick offices completely free of charge. If you decline our offer, we ask you to cover the return carriage costs only.

FREE VISITS

Visits by our valuers are possible anywhere in the country or abroad, usually within 48 hours, in order to value larger and valuable collections. Please phone for details.

ADVISORY DAYS

We have an ongoing programme of advisory days, in all regions of the United Kingdom, where you can meet us and discuss the sale of your collection. Visit our website for further details.

EXCELLENT PRICES

Because of the strength of our customer base we are in a position to offer prices that we feel sure will exceed your expectations.

ACT NOW

Telephone or email us today
with details of your property.

Warwick & Warwick

Auctioneers and Valuers
www.warwickandwarwick.com

Warwick & Warwick Ltd., Chalon House, Scar Bank
Millers Road, Warwick CV34 5DB England

Tel: (01926) 499031 • Fax: (01926) 491906
Email: info@warwickandwarwick.com

Get the experts on your side!

 /warwickauctions   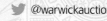 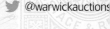 @warwickauctions

King George V

6 May 1910-20 January 1936

Further detailed information on the issues of King George V will be found in Volume 2 of the Stanley Gibbons *Great Britain Specialised Catalogue*.

PRINTERS. Types **98** to **102** were letterpress printed by Harrison & Sons Ltd, with the exception of certain preliminary printings made at Somerset House and distinguishable by the controls 'A.11', 'B.11' or 'B.12' (the Harrison printings do not have a full stop after the letter). The booklet stamps, Nos. 334/337, and 344/345 were printed by Harrison only.

WATERMARK VARIETIES. Many British stamps to 1967 exist without watermark owing to misplacement of the paper, and with either inverted, reversed, or inverted and reversed watermarks. A proportion of the low-value stamps issued in booklets have the watermark inverted in the normal course of printing.

Low values with watermark sideways are normally from stamp rolls used on machines with sideways delivery or, from June 1940, certain booklets.

STAMPS WITHOUT WATERMARK. Stamps found without watermark, due to misplacement of the sheet in relation to the dandy roll, are not listed here but will be found in the *Great Britain Specialised Catalogue*.

The 1½d. and 5d. 1912–1922, and ½d., 2d. and 2½d., 1924–1926, listed here, are from whole sheets completely without watermark.

98 (Hair dark)    **99** (Lion unshaded)    **100** Simple Cypher

For type difference with Types **101**/**102** see notes below the latter.

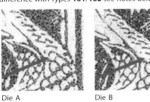

Dies of Halfpenny

Die A. The three upper scales on the body of the right hand dolphin form a triangle; the centre jewel of the cross inside the crown is suggested by a comma.

Die B. The three upper scales are incomplete; the centre jewel is suggested by a crescent.

Die A   Die B

Dies of One Penny

Die A. The second line of shading on the ribbon to the right of the crown extends right across the wreath; the line nearest to the crown on the right hand ribbon shows as a short line at the bottom of the ribbon.

Die B. The second line of shading is broken in the middle; the first line is little more than a dot.

1911–12. Wmk Imperial Crown, W **49**. Perf 15×14.

			Unmtd mint	Mtd mint	Used
321	**98**	½d. pale green (Die A) (22.6.11).....	10·00	5·00	4·00
322		½d. green (Die A) (22.6.11).....	8·00	4·00	4·00
		a. Error. Perf 14 (8.11)..................	—	£16000	£1000
		s. Optd 'SPECIMEN' (22)...............		£800	
		Wi. Watermark inverted.................	£20000	—	£2200

		Unmtd mint	Mtd mint	Used
323	½d. bluish green (Die A)...............	£400	£300	£180
324	½d. yellow-green (Die B)...............	18·00	12·00	1·50
	a. booklet pane No. 324×6 (8.11)............................	£350	£250	
	aw. booklet pane No. 324Wi×6......	£350	£250	
	s. Optd 'SPECIMEN' (22)............		£350	
	Wi. Watermark inverted..............	35·00	20·00	7·50
325	½d. bright green (Die B)...............	13·00	8·00	1·50
	a. Watermark sideways...............	—	—	£5750
326	½d. bluish green (Die B)...............	£260	£160	£100
327	**99** 1d. carmine-red (Die A) (22.6.11)..	10·00	4·50	2·50
	c. Watermark sideways...............	†	†	£17000
	s. Optd 'SPECIMEN' (22)............		£550	
	Wi. Watermark inverted..............	£2200	£1500	£1250
328	1d. pale carmine (Die A) (22.6.11)	25·00	14·00	3·00
	a. No cross on crown..................	£1250	£850	£500
329	1d. carmine (Die B)....................	15·00	10·00	3·00
	a. Booklet pane, No. 329×6 (8.11)............................	£350	£250	
	aw. Booklet pane, No. 329Wi×6....	£350	£250	
	s. Optd 'SPECIMEN' (22)............		£350	
	Wi. Watermark inverted..............	35·00	20·00	7·50
330	1d. pale carmine (Die B).............	15·00	10·00	4·00
	a. No cross on crown..................	£1100	£800	£500
331	1d. rose-pink (Die B)..................	£225	£125	45·00
332	1d. scarlet (Die B) (6.12).............	80·00	45·00	18·00
	a. Booklet pane, No. 332×6 (8.11)............................	£550	£400	
	aw. Booklet pane, No. 332Wi×6....	£550	£400	
	s. Optd 'SPECIMEN' (22)............		£750	
	Wi. Watermark inverted..............	80·00	45·00	18·00
333	1d. aniline scarlet (Die B)............	£375	£240	£110
	a. Booklet pane, No. 333×6........	£2000	£1500	
	aw. Booklet pane, No. 333Wi×6....	£2000	£1500	
	Wi. Watermark inverted..............	£375	£240	£110

For note on the aniline scarlet No. 333 see below No. 343.

1912 (28 Sept). Booklet stamps. Wmk Royal Cypher (Simple), W **100**. Perf 15×14.

			Unmtd mint	Mtd mint	Used
334	**98**	½d. pale green (Die B)...............	90·00	45·00	40·00
335		½d. green (Die B).....................	90·00	45·00	40·00
		a. Booklet pane, No. 334×6 (9.12)...................................	£500	£375	
		aw. Booklet pane, No. 334Wi×6....	£500	£375	
		s. Optd 'SPECIMEN' (22, 26)..		£300	
		Wi. Watermark inverted.............	90·00	45·00	40·00
		Wj. Watermark reversed........	£1750	£1100	£800
		Wk. Watermark inverted and reversed............................	£1750	£1100	£800
336	**99**	1d. scarlet (Die B).....................	40·00	30·00	30·00
		a. Booklet pane, No. 336×6 (9.12)...................................	£400	£275	
		aw. Booklet pane, No. 336Wi×6....	£400	£275	
		s. Optd 'SPECIMEN' (22, 26)..		£325	
		Wi. Watermark inverted.............	40·00	30·00	30·00
		Wj. Watermark reversed..........	£1750	£1100	£800
		Wk. Watermark inverted and reversed............................	—	—	£850
337		1d. bright scarlet (Die B).........	40·00	30·00	30·00

101 (Hair light)    **102** (Lion shaded)    **103** Multiple Cypher

Type differences

½d. In T **98** the ornament above 'P' of 'HALFPENNY' has two thin lines of colour and the beard is undefined. In T **101** the ornament has one thick line and the beard is well defined.

1d. In T **99** the body of the Lion is unshaded and in T **102** it is shaded.

1912 (1 Jan). Wmk Imperial Crown, W **49**. Perf 15×14.

			Unmtd mint	Mtd mint	Used
338	**101**	½d. deep green..........................	28·00	15·00	8·00
339		½d. green.................................	15·00	8·00	4·00
		s. Optd 'SPECIMEN' (26).......		£325	
340		½d. yellow-green......................	15·00	8·00	4·00
		a. No cross on crown.............	£190	£100	55·00
		Wi. Watermark inverted..........	£1750	£1100	£750

			Unmtd mint	Mtd mint	Used
341	**102**	1d. bright scarlet	10·00	5·00	2·00
		a. No cross on crown	£150	£110	55·00
		b. Printed double, one albino	£375	£275	
		Wi. Watermark inverted	£650	£425	£400
342		1d. scarlet	10·00	5·00	2·00
343		1d. aniline scarlet*	£275	£175	£100
		a. No cross on crown	£1750	£1200	

* Our prices for the aniline scarlet 1d. stamps, Nos. 333 and 343, are for the example in which the colour is suffused on the surface of the stamp and shows through clearly on the back. Examples without these characteristics but which show 'aniline' reactions under the quartz lamp are relatively common.

1912 (Aug). Wmk Royal Cypher (Simple), W **100**. Perf 15×14.

			Unmtd mint	Mtd mint	Used
344	**101**	½d. green	14·00	7·00	3·00
		a. No cross on crown	£325	£225	£175
		s. Optd 'SPECIMEN' (26)		£550	
		Wi. Watermark inverted	£600	£375	£275
		Wj. Watermark reversed	£675	£425	£300
		Wk. Watermark inverted and reversed	20·00	12·00	20·00
345	**102**	1d. scarlet	15·00	8·00	4·50
		a. No cross on crown	£175	£100	50·00
		Wi. Watermark inverted	28·00	18·00	25·00
		Wj. Watermark reversed	£200	£125	£125
		Wk. Watermark inverted and reversed	20·00	12·00	20·00

1912 (Sept–Oct). Wmk Royal Cypher (Multiple), W **103**. Perf 15×14.

			Unmtd mint	Mtd mint	Used
346	**101**	½d. green (10.12)	20·00	12·00	8·00
		a. No cross on crown	£300	£200	£150
		b. Imperf	£250	£175	
		c. Watermark sideways	†	†	£4250
		d. Printed on gummed side	—	—	†
		Wi. Watermark inverted	20·00	12·00	20·00
		Wj. Watermark reversed	22·00	15·00	20·00
		Wk. Watermark inverted and reversed	£160	£100	£110
347		½d. yellow-green	20·00	15·00	8·00
348		½d. pale green	25·00	15·00	8·00
349	**102**	1d. bright scarlet	25·00	18·00	10·00
350		1d. scarlet	25·00	18·00	10·00
		a. No cross on crown	£225	£150	60·00
		b. Imperf	£225	£150	
		c. Watermark sideways	£325	£190	£220
		d. Watermark sideways. No cross on crown	£1200	£750	£750
		Wi. Watermark inverted	55·00	30·00	35·00
		Wj. Watermark reversed	55·00	30·00	35·00
		Wk. Watermark inverted and reversed	£1600	£1000	£700

104

105

106

107

108

No. 357a

No. 357ab

No. 357ac

Die I

Die II

Two Dies of the 2d.

Die I. Inner frame line at top and sides close to solid of background. Four complete lines of shading between top of head and oval frame line. These four lines do not extend to the oval itself. White line round 'TWOPENCE' thin.

Die II. Inner frame line farther from solid of background. Three lines between top of head and extending to the oval. White line round 'TWOPENCE' thicker.

(Des Bertram Mackennal (heads) and G. W. Eve (frames). Coinage head (½d., 1½d., 2d., 3d. and 4d.); large medal head (1d., 2½d.); intermediate medal head (5d. to 1s.); small medal head used for fiscal stamps. Dies eng J. A. C. Harrison) (Letterpress by Harrison & Sons Ltd., except the 6d. printed by the Stamping Department of the Board of Inland Revenue, Somerset House. The latter also made printings of the following which can only be distinguished by the controls: ½d. B.13; 1½d. A.12; 2d. C.13; 2½d. A.12; 3d. A.12, B.13, C.13; 4d. B.13; 5d. B.13; 7d. C.13; 8d. C.13; 9d. agate B.13; 10d. C.13; 1s. C.13)

1912–24. Wmk Royal Cypher (Simple), W **100**. Chalk-surfaced paper (6d.). Perf 15×14.

			Unmtd mint	Mtd mint	Used
351	**105**	½d. green (16.1.13)	3·00	1·00	1·00
		a. Partial double print (half of bottom row) (Control G15)	—	£15000	
		b. Gummed both sides	£16000	—	—
		c. Booklet pane, No. 351×6 (4.13)	£140	£120	
		cw. Booklet pane, No. 351Wi×6	£140	£100	
		s. Optd 'SPECIMEN' (23, 26)		£150	
		Wi. Watermark inverted	4·00	3·00	1·50
		Wj. Watermark reversed	80·00	55·00	60·00
		Wk. Watermark inverted and reversed	6·00	4·00	3·50
352		½d. bright green	3·00	1·00	1·00
353		½d. deep green	10·00	5·00	2·00
354		½d. yellow-green	10·00	6·00	3·00
355		½d. very yellow (Cyprus) green (1914)	£11000	£8000	
356		½d. blue-green	60·00	40·00	25·00
357	**104**	1d. bright scarlet (8.10.12)	3·00	1·00	1·00
		a. 'Q' for 'O' (R. 1/4) (Control E14)	£250	£175	£175
		ab. 'Q' for 'O' (R. 4/11) (Control T22)	£450	£350	£190
		ac. Reversed 'Q' for 'O' (R. 15/9) (Control T22)	£400	£300	£240
		ad. Inverted 'Q' for 'O' (R. 20/3)	£550	£375	£240
		b. Tête-bêche (pair)	—	£50000	†
		c. booklet pane, No. 357×6 (4.13)	£175	£120	
		cw. Booklet pane, No. 357Wi×6	£175	£120	
		s. Optd 'SPECIMEN' (23, 26)		£200	
		Wi. Watermark inverted	4·00	2·00	1·00
		Wj. Watermark reversed	£150	95·00	£110
		Wk. Watermark inverted and reversed	6·00	3·00	3·00
358		1d. vermilion	9·00	5·00	2·50
359		1d. pale rose-red	30·00	20·00	5·00
360		1d. carmine-red	20·00	11·00	5·00
361		1d. scarlet-vermilion	£180	£125	50·00
		a. Printed on back	£450	£300	†
362	**105**	1½d. red-brown (15.10.12)	10·00	6·00	1·50
		a. 'PENCF' (R. 15/12)	£400	£300	£250
		b. Booklet pane, No. 362×4 plus two printed labels (2.24)	£800	£600	
		bw. Booklet pane, No. 362Wi×4 plus two printed labels	£775	£600	
		c. Booklet pane, 1½d. (No. 362)×6 (10.18)	£200	£150	

			Unmtd mint	Mtd mint	Used
		cw. Booklet pane, 1½d. (No. 362Wi)×6..........	£200	£150	
		s. Optd 'SPECIMEN' (23, 26)......		£125	
		Wi. Watermark inverted..........	9·00	5·00	2·00
		Wj. Watermark reversed..........	70·00	50·00	50·00
		Wk. Watermark inverted and reversed..........	15·00	8·00	8·00
363		1½d. chocolate-brown..........	20·00	11·00	2·00
		a. No watermark..........	£375	£250	£240
364		1½d. chestnut..........	5·00	3·00	1·00
		a. 'PENCF' (R. 15/12)..........	£175	£125	£110
365		1½d. yellow-brown..........	30·00	20·00	16·00
366	**106**	2d. orange-yellow (Die I) (20.8.12)..........	14·00	8·00	3·00
367		2d. reddish orange (Die I) (11.13)..........	10·00	6·00	3·00
368		2d. orange (Die I)..........	8·00	4·00	3·00
		a. Booklet pane, No. 368×6 (7.20)..........	£425	£350	
		aw. Booklet pane, No. 368Wi×6..	£425	£350	
		s. Optd 'SPECIMEN' (26)..........		£250	
		Wi. Watermark inverted..........	22·00	12·00	12·00
		Wj. Watermark reversed..........	25·00	15·00	15·00
		Wk. Watermark inverted and reversed..........	18·00	10·00	10·00
369		2d. bright orange (Die I)..........	8·00	5·00	3·00
370		2d. orange (Die II) (9.21)..........	8·00	5·00	3·50
		a. Booklet pane, No. 370×6 (8.21)..........	£500	£350	
		aw. Booklet pane, No. 370Wi×6..	£500	£350	
		s. Optd 'SPECIMEN' (15, 23)......		£800	
		Wi. Watermark inverted..........	60·00	40·00	40·00
		Wk. Watermark inverted and reversed..........	£200	£140	£130
371	**104**	2½d. cobalt-blue (18.10.12)..........	22·00	12·00	4·00
371a		2½d. bright blue (1914)..........	22·00	12·00	4·00
372		2½d. blue..........	22·00	12·00	4·00
		s. Optd 'SPECIMEN' (15, 23, 26)..........		£120	
		Wi. Watermark inverted..........	£120	85·00	85·00
		Wj. Watermark reversed..........	£100	65·00	65·00
		Wk. Watermark inverted and reversed..........	45·00	28·00	28·00
373		2½d. indigo-blue* (1920)..........	£4500	£3000	£2500
373a		2½d. dull Prussian blue* (12.20)..........	£1500	£1200	£850
374	**106**	3d. dull reddish violet (9.10.12)..........	22·00	12·00	3·00
375		3d. violet..........	15·00	8·00	3·00
		s. Optd 'SPECIMEN' (15, 23, 26)..........		£250	
		Wi. Watermark inverted..........	£160	95·00	£110
		Wj. Watermark reversed..........	£850	£500	£500
		Wk. Watermark inverted and reversed..........	40·00	30·00	30·00
376		3d. bluish violet (11.13)..........	20·00	9·00	3·00
377		3d. pale violet..........	17·00	10·00	3·00
378		4d. deep grey-green (15.1.13).....	75·00	45·00	25·00
379		4d. grey-green..........	25·00	15·00	2·00
		s. Optd 'SPECIMEN' (15, 23, 26)..........		£125	
		Wi. Watermark inverted..........	50·00	30·00	30·00
		Wj. Watermark reversed..........	£550	£350	£350
		Wk. Watermark inverted and reversed..........	£140	90·00	£100
380		4d. pale grey-green..........	40·00	25·00	5·00
381	**107**	5d. brown (30.6.13)..........	25·00	15·00	5·00
		s. Optd 'SPECIMEN' (15, 23, 26)..........		£250	
		Wi. Watermark inverted..........	£1250	£950	£1000
		Wj. Watermark reversed..........	†	†	—
		Wk. Watermark inverted and reversed..........	£500	£400	£400
382		5d. yellow-brown..........	25·00	15·00	5·00
		a. No watermark..........	£1500	£950	
383		5d. bistre-brown..........	£275	£185	75·00
384		6d. dull purple (1.8.13)..........	45·00	25·00	10·00
		s. Optd 'SPECIMEN' (15, 23, 26)..........		£200	
385		6d. reddish purple (8.13)..........	30·00	15·00	7·00
		a. Perf 14 (9.20)..........	£150	90·00	£110
		Wi. Watermark inverted..........	85·00	50·00	60·00
		Wj. Watermark reversed..........	£5500	£4500	
		Wk. Watermark inverted and reversed..........	£150	£100	£100
386		6d. deep reddish purple..........	90·00	50·00	5·00
387		7d. olive (1.8.13)..........	35·00	20·00	10·00
		s. Optd 'SPECIMEN' (26)..........		£200	
		Wi. Watermark inverted..........	85·00	50·00	60·00
		Wj. Watermark reversed..........	†	†	—
		Wk. Watermark inverted and reversed..........	£6000	£5000	
388		7d. bronze-green (1915)..........	£120	70·00	25·00
389		7d. sage-green (1917)..........	£120	70·00	18·00
390		8d. black/*yellow* (1.8.13)..........	55·00	32·00	11·00
		s. Optd 'SPECIMEN' (26)..........		£250	
		Wi. Watermark inverted..........	£220	£150	£150
		Wj. Watermark reversed..........	£375	£250	£250
		Wk. Watermark inverted and reversed..........	£7000	£5500	

			Unmtd mint	Mtd mint	Used
391		8d. black/*yellow-buff* (granite) (5.17)..........	60·00	40·00	15·00
392	**108**	9d. agate (30.6.13)..........	30·00	15·00	6·00
		a. Printed double, one albino...	—	£1200	†
		s. Optd 'SPECIMEN' (26)..........		£425	
		Wi. Watermark inverted..........	£240	£175	£175
		Wk. Watermark inverted and reversed..........	£240	£175	£175
393		9d. deep agate..........	45·00	25·00	6·00
393a		9d. olive-green (9.22)..........	£225	£110	30·00
		as. Optd 'SPECIMEN' (15, 23)......		£750	
		aWi. Watermark inverted..........	£120	£900	£825
		aWk. Watermark inverted and reversed..........	£1250	£950	£1000
393b		9d. pale olive-green..........	£250	£120	40·00
394		10d. turquoise-blue (1.8.13)..........	40·00	22·00	20·00
		s. Optd 'SPECIMEN' (15, 23, 26)..........		£425	
		Wi. Watermark inverted..........	£3250	£2500	£2500
		Wk. Watermark inverted and reversed..........	£475	£325	£300
394a		10d. deep turquoise-blue..........	£150	90·00	30·00
395		1s. bistre (1.8.13)..........	40·00	20·00	4·00
		s. Optd 'SPECIMEN' (15, 23, 26, 31)..........		£375	
		Wi. Watermark inverted..........	£350	£250	£225
		Wk. Watermark inverted and reversed..........	£120	70·00	70·00
396		1s. bistre-brown..........	55·00	35·00	12·00
		Set of 15..........	£475	£250	95·00

† The impression of No. 361a is set sideways and is very pale. Nos. 362a and 364a occur on Plates 12 and 29 and are known from Controls L18, M18, M19, O19 and Q21. The flaws were corrected by 1921.

* No. 373 comes from Control O20 and also exists on toned paper.
Imperf stamps of this issue exist but may be wartime colour trials.
No. 373a comes from Control R21 and also exists on toned paper, but both are unlike the rare Prussian blue shade of the 1935 2½d. Jubilee issue.
Examples of the 2d., T **106** which were in the hands of philatelists, are known bisected in Guernsey from 27 December 1940 to February 1941.
See also Nos. 418/429.

1913 (Aug.) Wmk Royal Cypher (Multiple), W **103**. Perf 15×14.

			Unmtd mint	Mtd mint	Used
397	**105**	½d. bright green..........	£250	£150	£180
		a. Watermark sideways..........	†	†	£18000
		Wi. Watermark inverted..........	£1200	£900	
398	**104**	1d. dull scarlet..........	£350	£225	£225
		Wi. Watermark inverted..........	£1600	£1100	

Both these stamps were originally issued in rolls only. Subsequently sheets were found, so that horizontal pairs and blocks are known but are of considerable rarity.

NOTE. All illustrations of re-entries on Nos. 399–417 are copyright GB Philatelic Publications Ltd and Bryan Kearsley and are reproduced with their permission

109

110 Single Cypher

A

Major Re-entries on 2s.6d.

No. 400a

Nos. 406/407a

No. 415b

No. 417a

(Des Bertram Mackennal. Dies eng J. A. C. Harrison. Recess)

High values, so-called Sea Horses design T **109**. Background around portrait consists of horizontal lines, Type A. Wmk Single Cypher, W **110**. Perf 11×12.

1913 (30 June). Printed by Waterlow Bros & Layton.

			Unmtd mint	Mtd mint	Used
399	**109**	2s.6d. deep sepia-brown	£850	£400	£200
		s. Optd 'SPECIMEN' (23, 26)		£650	

		Unmtd mint	Mtd mint	Used
400	2s.6d. sepia-brown	£600	£300	£150
	a. Re-entry (Plate 3, R. 2/1)	£2800	£1800	£800
	Wk. Watermark inverted and reversed	†	†	—
401	5s. rose-carmine	£1100	£625	£325
	s. Optd 'SPECIMEN' (26)		£950	
402	10s. indigo-blue (1.8)	£1500	£850	£475
	s. Optd 'SPECIMEN' (23, 26, 29)		£1200	
403	£1 green (1.8.13)	£3750	£2800	£1400
	s. Optd 'SPECIMEN' (23, 26)		£3000	
404	£1 dull blue-green (1.8)	£3800	£2800	£1600

* 399/404 **For well-centred, lightly used +35%**

1915 (Sept–Dec). Printed by De la Rue & Co.

			Unmtd mint	Mtd mint	Used
405	**109**	2s.6d. deep yellow-brown (10.15)	£680	£375	£250
		Wi. Watermark inverted	£1900	£1100	
406		2s.6d. yellow-brown (inc. worn plates)	£550	£325	£225
		a. Re-entry (Plate 3, R. 2/1)	£3000	£2000	£950
		s. Optd 'SPECIMEN' (23)		£1400	
		Wi. Watermark inverted	£1250	£950	£875
		Wj. Watermark reversed	£1250	£950	£900
		Wk. Watermark inverted and reversed	£3500	£2750	
407		2s.6d. grey-brown (inc. worn plates)	£700	£400	£300
		a. Re-entry (Plate 3, R. 2/1)	£3000	£2000	£950
		Wi. Watermark inverted	£1250	£950	£900
		Wj. Watermark reversed	£1250	£950	£900
408		2s.6d. sepia (seal-brown)	£550	£325	£250
		Wi. Watermark inverted	£1250	£950	£900
		Wj. Watermark reversed	£1250	£950	£900
409		5s. bright carmine	£1100	£650	£400
		s. Optd 'SPECIMEN' (23)		£1250	
		Wi. Watermark inverted	£5500	£3250	
		Wj. Watermark reversed	£5250	£3000	
		Wk. Watermark inverted and reversed	—	£14000	†
410		5s. pale carmine (worn plate)	£1400	£800	£500
411		10s. deep blue (12.15)	£4250	£3250	£1000
		s. Optd 'SPECIMEN' (26)		£2800	
412		10s. blue	£3250	£2500	£900
		Wk. Watermark inverted and reversed	—	—	†
413		10s. pale blue	£3500	£3750	£900

* 405/413 **For well-centred, lightly used +45%**

No. 406/407 were produced from the original Waterlow plates as were all De La Rue 5s. and 10s. printings. Examples of Nos. 406/407, 410 and 411 occur showing degrees of plate wear. No. 412Wk. one damaged mint example is recorded.

1918 (Dec)–**19**. Printed by Bradbury Wilkinson & Co, Ltd.

			Unmtd mint	Mtd mint	Used
413a	**109**	2s.6d. olive-brown	£350	£190	£100
		as. Optd 'SPECIMEN' (15, 23, 26, 31, 32)		£1000	
414		2s.6d. chocolate-brown (12.18)	£325	£160	75·00
415		2s.6d. reddish brown	£325	£160	75·00
415a		2s.6d. pale brown	£340	£175	85·00
		b. Major re-entry (Plate 3/5L, R. 1/2)	£1600	£1000	£500
416		5s. rose-red (1.19)	£475	£325	£135
		s. Optd 'SPECIMEN' (15, 23, 26, 31, 32)		£1200	
417		10s. dull grey-blue (1.19)	£850	£475	£175
		a. Re-entry (Plate 1/3L, R.1/1)	£2250	£1800	£1000
		s. Optd 'SPECIMEN' (15, 23, 26, 31, 32)		£1400	
413a/417 and 403 Set of 4			£5800	£4000	£1500

* 413a/417 **For well-centred, lightly used +35%**

DISTINGUISHING PRINTINGS. Note that the £1 value was only printed by Waterlow.

Waterlow and De La Rue stamps measure exactly 22.1 mm vertically. In the De La Rue printings the gum is usually patchy and yellowish, and the colour of the stamp, particularly in the 5s., tends to show through the back. The holes of the perforation are smaller than those of the other two printers, but there is a thick perforation tooth at the top of each vertical side.

In the Bradbury Wilkinson printings the height of the stamp is 22.6–23.1 mm due to the use of curved plates. On most of the 22.6 mm high stamps a minute coloured guide dot appears in the margin just above the middle of the upper frame line.

For (1934) re-engraved Waterlow printings see Nos. 450/452.

UNITED KINGDOM OF GREAT BRITAIN AND NORTHERN IRELAND

111 Block Cypher   **111a**

The watermark T **111a**, as compared with T **111**, differs as follows: Closer spacing of horizontal rows (12½ mm instead of 14½ mm). Letters shorter and rounder. Watermark thicker. The dandy roll to produce watermark T **111a** was provided by Somerset House in connection with experiments in paper composition undertaken during 1924–1925. These resulted in a change from rag only paper to that made from a mixture including esparto and sulphite.

(Letterpress by Waterlow & Sons, Ltd (all values except 6d.) and later, 1934–1935, by Harrison & Sons, Ltd (all values). Until 1934 the 6d. was printed at Somerset House where a printing of the 1½d. was also made in 1926 (identifiable only by control E.26). Printings by Harrisons in 1934–1935 can be identified, when in mint condition, by the fact that the gum shows a streaky appearance vertically, the Waterlow gum being uniformly applied, but Harrisons also used up the balance of the Waterlow 'smooth gum' paper)

1924 (Feb)–26. Wmk Block Cypher, W **111**. Perf 15×14.

			Unmtd mint	Mtd mint	Used
418	105	½d. green	2·00	1·00	1·00
		a. Watermark sideways (5.24)...	18·00	9·00	3·25
		aWi. Watermark sideways inverted	£650	£450	
		b. Doubly printed	£12500	£9500	†
		c. No watermark	£4000	—	—
		d. Booklet pane, No. 418×6 (2.24)	£120	85·00	
		dw. Booklet pane, 418Wi×6	£120	85·00	
		s. Optd 'SPECIMEN' (15, 23, 30, 32)		90·00	
		Wi. Watermark inverted	7·00	3·50	1·00
419	104	1d. scarlet	2·00	1·00	1·00
		a. Watermark sideways	40·00	20·00	15·00
		b. Experimental paper, W **111a** (10.24)	40·00	22·00	
		c. Partial double print, one inverted	—	—	
		d. Inverted 'Q' for 'O' (R. 20/3)	£850	£500	
		e. Booklet pane, No. 419×6 (2.24)	£120	85·00	
		ew. Booklet pane, No. 419Wi×6...	£120	85·00	
		s. Optd 'SPECIMEN' (15, 23, 30, 32)		90·00	
		Wi. Watermark inverted	7·00	4·00	1·50
420	105	1½d. red-brown	2·00	1·00	1·00
		a. Tête-bêche (pair)	£750	£500	£800
		b. Watermark sideways (8.24)...	20·00	10·00	3·50
		bWi. Watermark sideways inverted	—	£900	
		c. Printed on the gummed side	£1000	£650	
		d. Booklet pane, No. 420×4 plus two printed labels (3.24)	£300	£225	
		dw. Booklet pane, No. 420Wi×4 plus two printed labels	£300	£225	
		e. Booklet pane, No. 420×6 (2.24)	70·00	50·00	
		ew. Booklet pane, No. 420Wi×6...	70·00	50·00	
		f. Booklet pane, No. 420b×4 plus two printed labels, watermark sideways	£10000	£7500	
		g. Experimental paper, W **111a** (10.24)	£160	£120	£120
		h. Double impression	—	—	†
		s. Optd 'SPECIMEN' (15, 23, 30, 32)		90·00	
		Wi. Watermark inverted	3·50	2·00	1·00
421	106	2d. orange (Die II) (7.24)	4·00	2·50	2·50
		a. No watermark	£1750	£1200	
		b. Watermark sideways (7.26)...	£210	£100	£100
		c. Partial double print	—	£25000	†
		s. Optd 'SPECIMEN' (23, 32)		£100	
		Wi. Watermark inverted	90·00	55·00	55·00
422	104	2½d. blue (10.10.24)	10·00	5·00	3·00
		a. No watermark	£3000	£2200	
		b. Watermark sideways	†	†	£18000
		s. Optd 'SPECIMEN' (23, 32)		£550	
		Wi. Watermark inverted	£140	90·00	90·00
423	106	3d. violet (10.10.24)	20·00	10·00	2·50
		s. Optd 'SPECIMEN' (23, 32)		£750	

			Unmtd mint	Mtd mint	Used
424		Wi. Watermark inverted	£140	90·00	90·00
		4d. grey-green (10.10.24)	28·00	12·00	2·50
		a. Printed on the gummed side	£5250	£3750	†
		s. Optd 'SPECIMEN' (23, 32)		£650	
		Wi. Watermark inverted	£240	£150	£150
425	107	5d. brown (17.10.24)	40·00	20·00	3·00
		s. Optd 'SPECIMEN' (23, 26, 32)		£140	
		Wi. Watermark inverted	£225	£150	£150
426		6d. reddish purple (chalk-surfaced paper) (9.24)	20·00	12·00	2·50
		Wi. Watermark inverted	90·00	60·00	60·00
		Wk. Watermark inverted and reversed	£650	£425	£400
426a		6d. purple (6.26)	8·00	4·00	1·50
		as. Optd 'SPECIMEN' (23, 26, 32)..		£425	
		aWi. Watermark inverted	£140	90·00	90·00
427	108	9d. olive-green (11.11.24)	40·00	12·00	3·50
		s. Optd 'SPECIMEN' (23, 26, 32)		£140	
		Wi. Watermark inverted	£175	£120	£120
428		10d. turquoise-blue (28.11.24)	85·00	40·00	40·00
		s. Optd 'SPECIMEN' (23, 32)		£750	
		Wi. Watermark inverted	£3250	£2000	£2400
429		1s. bistre-brown (10.24)	50·00	22·00	3·00
		s. Optd 'SPECIMEN' (23, 32)		£550	
		Wi. Watermark inverted	£600	£375	£375
418/429 Set of 12			£250	£110	60·00

The normal sideways watermark shows the top of the Crown pointing to the right, *as seen from the back of the stamp.*

There are numerous shades in this issue.

The 6d. on chalk-surfaced and ordinary papers was printed by both Somerset House and Harrisons. The Harrison printings have streaky gum, differ slightly in shade, and that on chalk-surfaced paper is printed in a highly fugitive ink. The prices quoted are for the commonest (Harrison) printing in each case.

112

Scratch across the Lion's nose (left pane, R. 1/4)

113b Tail to 'N' of 'EXHIBITION' (Left pane, R. 1/5)

(Des H. Nelson. Eng J. A. C. Harrison. Recess Waterlow)

1924–25. British Empire Exhibition. W **111**. Perf 14.

(a) Dated 1924 (23.4.24).

			Unmtd mint	Mtd mint	Used
430	112	1d. scarlet	12·00	10·00	11·00
		a. Scratch across the Lion's nose	£225	£150	85·00
		b. Tail to 'N' of EXHIBITION..	£225	£150	85·00
		s. Optd 'SPECIMEN' (15, 23, 30)		£1100	
431		1½d. brown	20·00	15·00	15·00
		s. Optd 'SPECIMEN' (15, 23, 30)		£1100	
Set of 2			30·00	25·00	26·00
First Day Cover					£450

(b) Dated 1925 (9.5.25).

			Unmtd mint	Mtd mint	Used
432	112	1d. scarlet	25·00	15·00	30·00
		s. Optd 'SPECIMEN' (30)		£1000	
433		1½d. brown	60·00	40·00	70·00
		s. Optd 'SPECIMEN' (30)		£1000	
Set of 2			80·00	55·00	£100
First Day Cover					£1700

113   **114**   **115**

118   **119**   **120**

116 St George and the Dragon

121   **122**

1934–36. W **111**. Perf 15×14.

			Unmtd mint	Mtd mint	Used
439	**118**	½d. green (17.11.34)......................	1·00	50	50
		a. Watermark sideways..............	17·00	10·00	5·00
		aWi. Watermark sideways			
		inverted..................................	£600	£450	£150
		b. Imperf three sides..................	£6000	£4250	
		c. Booklet pane, No. 439×6			
		(1.35).....................................	£120	85·00	
		cw. Booklet pane, No.			
		439Wi×6................................	£130	95·00	
		s. Optd 'SPECIMEN' (23, 32).......		£500	
		Wi. Watermark inverted..............	22·00	11·00	1·50
440	**119**	1d. scarlet (24.9.34)....................	1·00	50	50
		a. Imperf (pair)..........................	£5500	£4000	
		b. Printed on gummed side..........	£1000	£750	
		c. Watermark sideways			
		(30.4.35)................................	40·00	20·00	12·00
		cWi. Watermark sideways			
		inverted..................................	£190	£125	—
		d. Double impression.................	†	†	£18000
		e. Imperf between (pair).............	£10000	£7000	
		f. Imperf (three sides) (pair).......	£7500	£5500	
		g. Booklet pane, No.			
		440×6 (1.35).........................	£120	85·00	
		gw. Booklet pane, No.			
		440Wi×6................................	£130	95·00	
		s. Optd 'SPECIMEN' (23, 32).......		£600	
		Wi. Watermark inverted..............	20·00	9·00	3·00
441	**118**	1½d. red-brown (20.8.34)............	1·00	50	50
		a. Imperf (pair)..........................	£1400	£1000	
		b. Imperf (three sides) (lower			
		stamp in vert pair).................	£5000	£3000	
		c. Imperf between (horiz			
		pair)......................................			
		d. Watermark sideways..............	15·00	10·00	5·00
		dWi. Watermark sideways			
		inverted..................................			
		e. Booklet pane. No. 441×4			
		plus two printed labels			
		(1.35).....................................	£275	£200	
		ew. Booklet pane. No.			
		441Wi×4 plus two			
		printed labels........................	£275	£200	
		f. Booklet pane, No. 441×6			
		(1.35).....................................	42·00	30·00	
		fw. Booklet pane. No.			
		441Wi×6................................	55·00	40·00	
		s. optd 'SPECIMEN' (23, 32).......		£650	
		Wi. Watermark inverted..............	8·00	4·00	1·00
442	**120**	2d. orange (19.1.35)...................	1·50	75	75
		a. Imperf (pair)..........................	£5500	£4000	
		b. Watermark sideways			
		(30.4.35)................................	£225	£125	90·00
		s. Optd 'SPECIMEN' (30, 32).......		—	
443	**119**	2½d. bright blue (18.3.35)...........	2·50	1·50	1·25
		s. Optd 'SPECIMEN' (23).............		£700	
444	**120**	3d. reddish violet (18.3.35).........	3·00	1·50	1·25
		s. Optd 'SPECIMEN' (23, 30).......		£650	
		Wi. Watermark inverted..............	—	—	£9000
445		4d. deep grey-green (2.12.35).....	4·00	2·00	1·25
		s. Optd 'SPECIMEN' (23, 30).......		£400	
		Wi. Watermark inverted..............	†	†	£9000
446	**121**	5d. yellow-brown (17.2.36).........	13·00	6·50	2·75
		s. Optd 'SPECIMEN' (23).............		£650	
447	**122**	9d. deep olive-green (2.12.35).....	20·00	12·00	2·25
		s. Optd 'SPECIMEN' (23).............		£650	
448		10d. turquoise-blue (24.2.36)......	30·00	15·00	10·00
		s. Optd 'SPECIMEN' (23, 32).......		£700	
449		1s. bistre-brown (24.2.36)..........	40·00	15·00	1·25
		a. Double impression..................	—	—	†
		s. Optd 'SPECIMEN' (23, 32).......		£125	
439/449	*Set of 11*...................		95·00	50·00	20·00

The normal sideways watermark shows the top of the Crown pointing to the right, *as seen from the back of the stamp.*

117

Des J. Farleigh) (Types **113** and **115**), E. Linzell (T **114**) and H. Nelson (T **116**). Eng C. G. Lewis (T **113**), T. E. Storey (T **115**), both at the Royal Mint; J. A. C. Harrison, of Waterlow (Types **114** and **116**). Letterpress by Waterlow from plates made at the Royal Mint, except (T **116**), recess by Bradbury Wilkinson from die and plate of their own manufacture

1929 (10 May). Ninth UPU Congress, London.

(a) W **111**. Perf 15×14.

			Unmtd mint	Mtd mint	Used
434	**113**	½d. green........................	3·00	2·25	2·25
		a. Watermark sideways..........	80·00	55·00	50·00
		b. Booklet pane, No. 434×6			
		(5.29)..................................	£250	£200	
		bw. Booklet pane, No.			
		343Wi×6................................	£300	£225	
		Wi. Watermark inverted..........	35·00	15·00	12·00
435	**114**	1d. scarlet...........................	3·00	2·25	2·25
		a. Watermark sideways..........	£140	90·00	90·00
		b. Booklet pane, No. 435×6			
		(5.29)..................................	£250	£200	
		bw. Booklet pane, No.			
		435Wi×6................................	£300	£225	
		Wi. Watermark inverted..........	35·00	15·00	12·00
436		1½d. purple-brown...................	3·00	2·25	1·75
		a. Watermark sideways..........	90·00	60·00	55·00
		b. Booklet pane. No. 436×4			
		plus two printed labels......	£500	£375	
		bw. Booklet pane. No.			
		436Wi×4 plus two			
		printed labels......................	£500	£375	
		c. Booklet pane, No. 436×6			
		(5.29)..................................	85·00	60·00	
		cw. Booklet pane. No.			
		436Wi×6................................	£110	80·00	
		Wi. Watermark inverted..........	15·00	5·00	6·00
437	**115**	2½d. blue...............................	28·00	10·00	10·00
		s. Optd 'SPECIMEN' (32).......		£3000	
		Wi. Watermark inverted..........	£3250	£2200	£950

(b) W **117**. Perf 12.

438	**116**	£1 black...............................	£1100	£750	£600
		s. Optd 'SPECIMEN' (32, red			
		opt)....................................		£3000	
Set of 4 (to 2½d.)..................			35·00	15·00	14·50
First Day Cover (Nos. 434/437) (4 values).............					£675
First Day Cover (Nos. 434/438) (5 values).............					£14000

PRINTERS. All subsequent issues were printed in photogravure by Harrison & Sons Ltd *except where otherwise stated.*

The ½d. imperf three sides, No. 439b, is known in a block of four, from a sheet, to which the bottom pair is imperf at top and sides.

Owing to the need for wider space for the perforations the size of the designs of the ½d. and 2d. were once, and the 1d. and 1½d. twice reduced from that of the first printings.

The format description, size in millimetres and SG catalogue number are given but further details will be found in the *Great Britain Specialised Catalogue*, Volume 2.

Description	Size	SG Nos.	Date of Issue
½d. intermediate format	18.4×22.2	—	19.11.34
½d. small format	17.9×21.7	439	14.2.35
1d. large format	18.7×22.5	—	24.9.34
1d. intermediate format	18.4×22.2	—	1934
1d. small format	17.9×21.7	440	8.2.35
1½d. large format	18.7×22.5	—	20.8.34
1½d. intermediate format	18.4×22.2	—	1934
1½d. small format	17.9×21.7	441	7.2.35
2d. intermediate format	18.4×22.2	—	21.1.35
2d. small format	18.15×21.7	442	1935

There are also numerous minor variations, due to the photographic element in the process.

Examples of 2d., T **120**, which were in the hands of philatelists are known bisected in Guernsey from 27 December 1940 to February 1941.

B

(Eng. J. A. C. Harrison. Recess Waterlow)

1934 (16 Oct). T **109** (re-engraved). Background around portrait consists of horizontal and diagonal lines, Type B. W **110**. Perf 11×12.

			Unmtd mint	Mtd mint	Used
450	**109**	2s.6d. chocolate-brown...............	£150	80·00	40·00
		s. Optd 'SPECIMEN' (23, 30)...		£3250	
451		5s. bright rose-red..................	£400	£175	85·00
		s. Optd 'SPECIMEN' (23, 30)...		£3250	
452		10s. indigo................................	£500	£350	80·00
		s. Optd 'SPECIMEN' (23, 30)...		£3250	
450/452	*Set of 3*....................................		£1000	£575	£190

There are numerous other minor differences in the design of this issue.

123

(Des B. Freedman)

1935 (7 May). Silver Jubilee. W **111**. Perf 15×14.

			Unmtd mint	Mtd mint	Used
453	**123**	½d. green..................................	1·00	1·00	1·00
		a. Booklet pane, No. 453×4			
		(5.35)......................................	70·00	50·00	
		aw. Booklet pane, No.			
		453Wi×4..............................	80·00	60·00	
		s. Optd 'SPECIMEN' (23).........		£1400	
		Wi. Watermark inverted..........	15·00	8·00	3·00
454		1d. scarlet................................	2·00	1·50	2·00
		a. Booklet pane, No. 454×4			
		(5.35)......................................	60·00	45·00	
		aw. Booklet pane, No.			
		454Wi×4, watermark			
		inverted............................	75·00	55·00	
		s. Optd 'SPECIMEN' (23).........		£1400	
		Wi. Watermark inverted..........	15·00	8·00	4·00

			Unmtd mint	Mtd mint	Used
455		1½d. red-brown...........................	1·25	1·00	1·00
		a. Booklet pane, No. 455×4			
		(5.35)......................................	25·00	18·00	
		aw. Booklet pane, No.			
		455Wi×4..............................	30·00	22·00	
		s. Opts 'SPECIMEN' (23).........		£1400	
		Wi. Watermark inverted..........	5·00	3·00	1·50
456		2½d. blue..................................	8·00	5·00	6·50
		s. Optd 'SPECIMEN' (23).........		£1750	
456a		2½d. Prussian blue......................	£15000	£11000	£14000
	Set of 4..		11·00	7·50	9·50
	First Day Cover................................				£650

The 1d., 1½d. and 2½d. values differ from T **123** in the emblem in the panel at right.

Four sheets of No. 456a, printed in the wrong shade, were issued in error by the Post Office Stores Department on 25 June 1935. It is known that three of the sheets were sold from the sub-office at 134 Fore Street, Upper Edmonton, London, between that date and 4 July.

King Edward VIII

20 January-10 December 1936

King George VI

11 December 1936-6 February 1952

Further detailed information on the stamps of King Edward VIII will be found in Volume 2 of the Stanley Gibbons *Great Britain Specialised Catalogue*.

Further detailed information on the stamps of King George VI will be found in Volume 2 of the Stanley Gibbons *Great Britain Specialised Catalogue*.

PRICES. From No. 457 prices quoted in the first column are for stamps in unmounted mint condition.

126 King George VI and Queen Elizabeth   **127**

Colon flaw (Cyl. 7 No dot, R. 10/1, later corrected)

(Des E. Dulac)

1937 (13 May). Coronation. W **127**. Perf 15×14.

461	**126**	1½d. maroon	30	30
		a. Colon flaw	70·00	
		s. Optd 'SPECIMEN' (32)	£750	
First Day Cover				35·00

124   **125**

(Des H. Brown, adapted Harrison using a photo by Hugh Cecil)

1936. W **125**. Perf 15×14.

457	**124**	½d. green (1.9.36)	30	30
		a. Double impression		
		b. Booklet pane. No. 457×6 (10.36)	30·00	
		bw. Booklet pane. No. 457×6, watermark inverted	45·00	
		Wi. Watermark inverted	10·00	5·00
		s. Optd 'SPECIMEN' (30, 32)	£775	
458		1d. scarlet (14.9.36)	60	50
		a. Booklet pane. No. 458×6 (10.36)	25·00	
		aw. Booklet pane. No. 458×6, watermark inverted	40·00	
		Wi. Watermark inverted	9·00	5·00
		s. Optd 'SPECIMEN' (30, 32)	£775	
459		1½d. red-brown (1.9.36)	30	30
		a. Booklet pane. No. 459×4 plus two printed labels (10.36)	£100	
		aw. Booklet pane. No. 459Wi×4 plus two printed labels	£100	
		b. Booklet pane. No. 459×6 (10.36)	15·00	
		bw. Booklet pane. No. 459×6, watermark inverted	15·00	
		c. Booklet pane. No. 459×2	30·00	
		cw. Booklet pane. No. 459×2, watermark inverted	30·00	
		d. Imperf (pair)	—	
		s. Optd 'SPECIMEN' (30, 32)	£775	
		Wi. Watermark inverted	1·00	1·00
460		2½d. bright blue (1.9.36)	30	85
		s. Optd 'SPECIMEN' (30)	£850	
457/460 *Set of 4*			1·25	1·75

First Day Covers

1.9.36	Nos. 457, 459/460	£175
14.9.36	No. 458	£200

128   **129**   **130**

King George VI and National Emblems

(Des Types **128/129**, E. Dulac (head) and E. Gill (frames). T **130**, E. Dulac (whole stamp))

1937–47. W **127**. Perf 15×14.

462	**128**	½d. green (10.5.37)	30	25
		a. Watermark sideways (1.38)	75	60
		ab. Booklet pane. No. 462a×4 (6.40)	£110	
		b. Booklet pane. No462×6 (8.37)	50·00	
		bw. Booklet pane. No. 462Wi×6	80·00	
		c. Booklet pane. No. 462×2 (8.37)	£120	
		cw. Booklet pane. No. 462Wi×2	£120	
		s. Optd 'SPECIMEN' (32)		
		Wi. Watermark inverted	10·00	60
463		1d. scarlet (10.5.37)	30	25
		a. Watermark sideways (2.38)	20·00	9·00
		ab. Booklet pane. No. 463a×4 (6.40)	£175	
		b. Booklet pane. No. 463×6 (2.38)	65·00	
		bw. Booklet pane. No. 463×6	£275	
		c. Booklet pane. No. 463×2 (2.38)	£125	
		cw. Booklet pane. No. 463Wi×2	£125	
		s. Optd 'SPECIMEN' (9, 32)		
		Wi. Watermark inverted	40·00	3·00
464		1½d. red-brown (30.7.37)	30	25
		a. Watermark sideways (2.38)	1·25	1·25
		b. Booklet pane. No. 464×4 plus two printed labels (8.37)	£140	
		bw. Booklet pane. No464Wi×4 plus two printed labels	£140	
		c. Booklet pane. No. 464×6 (8.37)	60·00	
		cw. Booklet pane. No. 464Wi×6	£100	
		d. Booklet pane. No. 464×2 (1.38)	35·00	
		dw. Booklet pane. No. 464Wi×2	50·00	
		e. Imperf three sides (pair)	£5000	
		s. Optd 'SPECIMEN' (9, 32)		
		Wi. Watermark inverted	15·00	1·25
465		2d. orange (31.1.38)	1·25	50
		a. Watermark sideways (2.38)	75·00	40·00
		b. Bisected (*on cover*)	†	60·00
		c. Booklet pane. No. 465×6 (6.40)	£175	
		cw. Booklet pane. No. 465Wi×6	£425	
		s. Optd 'SPECIMEN' (9, 26)	£325	
		Wi. Watermark inverted	60·00	22·00

466		2½d. ultramarine (10.5.37)............................	40	25
		a. *Watermark sideways* (6.40)...................	75·00	35·00
		b. *Tête-bêche* (horiz pair).........................	—	
		c. Booklet pane. No. 466×6 (6.40)...........	£150	
		cw. Booklet pane. No. 466Wi×6..............	£375	
		Wi. Watermark inverted...............................	55·00	22·00
467		3d. violet (31.1.38)......................................	5·00	1·00
		s. Optd 'SPECIMEN' (9, 26, 30)................	£300	
468	**129**	4d. grey-green (21.11.38)........................	60	75
		a. Imperf (pair)...	£6750	
		b. Imperf three sides (horiz pair)..............	£7000	
		s. Optd 'SPECIMEN' (9, 23).......................	£200	
469		5d. brown (21.11.38).................................	3·50	85
		a. Imperf (pair)...	£6500	
		b. Imperf three sides (horiz pair)..............	£6750	
		s. Optd 'SPECIMEN' (9, 23).......................	£250	
470		6d. purple (30.1.39)...................................	1·50	60
		s. Optd 'SPECIMEN' (9, 23).......................		
471	**130**	7d. emerald-green (27.2.39)...................	5·00	60
		a. Imperf three sides (horiz pair)..............	£6500	
		s. Optd 'SPECIMEN' (9, 23).......................	£250	
472		8d. bright carmine (27.2.39)......................	7·50	80
		s. Optd 'SPECIMEN' (9, 23).......................	£250	
473		9d. deep olive-green (1.5.39).....................	6·50	80
		s. Optd 'SPECIMEN' (9, 23).......................	£250	
474		10d. turquoise-blue (1.5.39)......................	7·00	80
		aa. Imperf (pair)...		
		s. Optd 'SPECIMEN' (9, 23).......................	£250	
474a		11d. plum (29.12.47)..................................	3·00	2·75
		as. Optd 'SPECIMEN' (30)...........................	£275	
475		1s. bistre-brown (1.5.39)...........................	9·00	75
		s. Optd 'SPECIMEN' (9, 23, 30)................	£160	
462/475 *Set of 15*..			45·00	10·00

First Day Covers

10.5.37	Nos. 462/463, 466	45·00
30.7.37	Nos. 464	45·00
31.1.38	Nos. 465, 467	£100
21.11.38	Nos. 468/469	65·00
30.1.39	No. 470	60·00
27.2.39	Nos. 471/472	85·00
1.5.39	Nos. 473/474, 475	£500
29.12.47	No. 474a	55·00

For later printings of the lower values in apparently lighter shades and different colours, see Nos. 485/490 and 503/508.

No. 465b was authorised for use in Guernsey from 27 December 1940 until February 1941.

Nos. 468b and 469b are perforated at foot only and each occurs in the same sheet as Nos. 468a and 469a.

No. 471a is also perforated at foot only, but occurs on the top row of a sheet.

131 **132**

133

Mark in shield (R. 1/7) Gashed diadem (R. 2/7)

Gashed crown (R. 5/5) Broken stem (R. 1/4)

Blot on scroll Scratch on scroll (R. 4/6)
(R. 2/5)

(Des E. Dulac (T **131**) and the Honourable G. R. Bellew (T **132**). Eng J. A. C. Harrison. Recess Waterlow)

1939–48. W **133**. Perf 14.

476	**131**	2s.6d. brown (4.9.39).........................	£100	8·00
		aa. Mark in shield...............................	£190	85·00
		ab. Gashed diadem.............................	£190	85·00
		ac. Gashed crown...............................	£190	85·00
		as. Optd *SPECIMEN* (23)..................	£300	
476b		2s.6d. yellow-green (9.3.42)................	15·00	1·50
		bs. Optd *SPECIMEN* (9, 23, 26, 30)......	£300	1·50
477		5s. red (21.8.39).................................	20·00	2·00
		s. Optd *SPECIMEN* (9, 23, 26, 30).....	£300	
478	**132**	10s. dark blue (30.10.39)..................	£260	22·00
		aa. Broken stem..................................	£275	80·00
		ab. Blot on scroll................................	£275	80·00
		ac. Scratch on scroll...........................	£350	£100
		s. Optd *SPECIMEN* (23)....................	£500	
478b		10s. ultramarine (30.11.42)................	45·00	5·00
		bs. Optd *SPECIMEN* (9, 23, 30)........	£425	
478c		£1 brown (1.10.48)............................	25·00	26·00
		cs. Optd *SPECIMEN* (30)...................	—	
476/478c *Set of 6*..			£425	60·00

First Day Covers

21.8.39	No. 477	£875
4.9.39	No. 475	£1800
30.10.39	No. 478	£3250
9.3.41	No. 476b	£1750
30.11.41	No. 478b	£3750
1.10.48	No. 478c	£375

The 10s. dark blue was pre-released in Northern Ireland on 3 October 1939.

134 Queen Victoria and King George VI

(Des H. L. Palmer)

1940 (6 May). Centenary of First Adhesive Postage Stamps. W **127**. Perf 14½×14.

479	**134**	½d. green..	30	75
		s. Optd 'SPECIMEN' (9, 23, 30).............	£750	
480		1d. scarlet..	1·00	75
		s. Optd 'SPECIMEN' (9, 23, 30).............	£750	
481		1½d. red-brown......................................	50	1·50
		s. Optd 'SPECIMEN' (9, 23, 30).............	£750	
482		2d. orange...	1·00	75
		a. Bisected (*on cover*)...........................	†	50·00
		s. Optd 'SPECIMEN' (9, 23, 30).............	£750	
483		2½d. ultramarine....................................	2·25	50
		s. Optd 'SPECIMEN' (9, 23, 30).............	£750	
484		3d. violet..	3·00	3·50
		s. Optd 'SPECIMEN' (9, 23, 30).............	£750	
479/484 *Set of 6*..			8·75	4·25
First Day Cover..			55·00	

No. 482a was authorised for use in Guernsey from 27 December 1940 until February 1941.

1941–42. Head as Nos. 462/467, but with lighter background to provide a more economic use of the printing ink. W **127**. Perf 15×14.

485	**128**	½d. pale green (1.9.41).........................	30	30
		a. *Tête-bêche* (horiz pair)......................	—	
		b. Imperf (pair)..	£6250	
		c. Booklet pane. No. 485×6 (3.42).........	30·00	

	cw. Booklet pane. No. 485Wi×6..................	45·00	
	d. Booklet pane. No. 485×4 (1948)..........	—	
	e. Booklet pane. No. 485×2 (12.47)..........	15·00	
	s. Optd *SPECIMEN* (23)......................	£750	
	Wi. Watermark inverted................................	4·00	50
486	1d. pale scarlet (11.8.41)..............................	30	30
	a. Watermark sideways (10.42)...................	5·00	4·50
	b. Imperf (pair)..	£6000	
	c. Imperf three sides (horiz pair)..............	£6250	
	d. Booklet pane. No. 486×4 (1948)..........	—	
	e. Booklet pane. No. 486×2 (12.47).........	40·00	
	f. Imperf between (vert pair)...................	£4500	
	s. Optd *SPECIMEN* (23)......................	£750	
487	1½d. pale red-brown (28.9.42).....................	60	80
	a. Booklet pane. No. 487×4 (1948)..........	—	
	b. Booklet pane. No. 487×2 (12.47).........	15·00	
	s. Optd *SPECIMEN* (23)......................	£750	
488	2d. pale orange (6.10.41).............................	50	50
	a. Watermark sideways (6.42)....................	28·00	20·00
	b. *Tête-bêche* (horiz pair)........................	£14000	
	c. Imperf (pair)..	£5750	
	d. Imperf pane*..	£12000	
	e. Booklet pane. No. 488×6 (3.42)............	30·00	
	ew. Booklet pane. No. 488Wi×6.................	30·00	
	s. Optd *SPECIMEN* (23)......................	£750	
	Wi. Watermark inverted................................	4·00	1·00
489	2½d. light ultramarine (21.7.41)..................	30	30
	a. Watermark sideways (8.42)....................	15·00	12·00
	b. *Tête-bêche* (horiz pair)........................	—	
	c. Imperf (pair)..	£3500	
	d. Imperf pane*..	£9000	
	e. Imperf three sides (horiz pair)..............	£5750	
	f. Booklet pane. No. 489×6 (3.42)............	20·00	
	fw. Booklet pane. No. 489Wi×6.................	20·00	
	s. Optd *SPECIMEN* (23)......................	£750	
	Wi. Watermark inverted................................	1·50	1·00
490	3d. pale violet (3.11.41)..............................	2·50	1·00
	s. Optd 'SPECIMEN' (32)......................	£750	
485/490 *Set of 6*..		3·50	2·75

* Imperf panes show one row of perforations either at the top or bottom of the pane of six.

First Day Covers

21.7.41	No. 489	45·00	
11.8.41	No. 486	25·00	
1.9.41	No. 485	25·00	
6.10.41	No. 488	60·00	
3.11.41	No. 490	£110	
28.9.42	No. 487	55·00	

135 Symbols of Peace and Reconstruction

136 Symbols of Peace and Reconstruction

Extra porthole aft (Cyl. 11 No dot, R. 16/1)

Extra porthole fore (Cyl. 8 Dot, R. 5/6)

Seven berries (Cyl. 4 No dot, R. 12/5)

(Des H. L. Palmer (T **135**) and R. Stone (T **136**))

1946 (11 June). Peace. W **127**. Perf 15×14.

491	**135**	2½d. ultramarine...................................	20	20
		a. Extra porthole aft...........................	95·00	
		b. Extra porthole fore...........................	£160	
		s. Optd *SPECIMEN* (9, 30).............	£600	
492	**136**	3d. violet...	20	50
		a. Seven berries.................................	35·00	
		s. Optd *SPECIMEN* (9, 30).............	£600	
491/492 *Set of 2*...			40	50
First Day Cover..				65·00

137 King George VI and Queen Elizabeth

138 King George VI and Queen Elizabeth

(Des G. Knipe and Joan Hassall from photographs by Dorothy Wilding)

1948 (26 Apr). Royal Silver Wedding. W **127**. Perf 15×14 (2½d.) or 14×15 (£1).

493	**137**	2½d. ultramarine.............................	35	20
		s. Optd *SPECIMEN* (30).............	£600	
494	**138**	£1 blue..	40·00	40·00
		s. Optd *SPECIMEN* (30).............	£600	
493/494 *Set of 2*..			40·00	40·00
First Day Cover...				£425

1948 (10 May). Stamps of 1d. and 2½d. showing seaweed-gathering were on sale at eight Head Post Offices in Great Britain, but were primarily for use in the Channel Islands and are listed there (see Nos. C1/C2, after Royal Mail Post & Go Stamps).

139 Globe and Laurel Wreath

140 Speed

141 Olympic Symbol

142 Winged Victory

White blob on Lands End (Cyl. 3 No dot R. 7/3)

Spot below '9' (Cyl. 3 No dot R. 8/4)

Crown flaw (Cyl. 1 No dot, R. 20/2, later retouched)

(Des P. Metcalfe (T **139**), A. Games (T **140**), S. D. Scott (T **141**) and E. Dulac (T **142**))

1948 (29 July). Olympic Games. W **127**. Perf 15×14.

495	**139**	2½d. ultramarine.............................	50	10
		s. Optd 'SPECIMEN' (26)..............	£500	
496	**140**	3d. violet..	50	50
		a. Crown flaw..................................	75·00	
		s. Optd 'SPECIMEN' (26)..............	£500	
497	**141**	6d. bright purple............................	3·25	75
		s. Optd 'SPECIMEN' (26)..............	£500	
498	**142**	1s. brown.......................................	4·50	2·00
		a. White blob on Lands End.............	95·00	
		b. Spot below '9'.............................	95·00	
		s. Optd 'SPECIMEN' (26)..............	£500	
495/498 *Set of 4*..			8·00	3·00
First Day Cover...				50·00

143 Two Hemispheres

144 UPU Monument, Bern

145 Goddess Concordia, Globe and Points of Compass

146 Posthorn and Globe

Lake in Asia (Cyl. 3 Dot, R. 14/1)

Lake in India (Cyl. 2 No dot, R. 8/2)

Retouched background to '1/-' (R. 8/5)

(Des Mary Adshead (T **143**), P. Metcalfe (T **144**), H. Fleury (T **145**) and the Honourable G. R. Bellew (T **146**))

1949 (10 Oct). 75th Anniversary of Universal Postal Union. W **127**. Perf 15×14.

499	**143**	2½d. ultramarine..........................	25	10
		a. Lake in Asia............................	£145	
		b. Lake in India..........................	£100	
		s. Optd 'SPECIMEN' (30).............	—	
500	**144**	3d. violet..................................	25	50
		s. Optd 'SPECIMEN' (30).............	—	
501	**145**	6d. bright purple........................	50	75
		s. Optd 'SPECIMEN' (30).............	—	
502	**146**	1s. brown..................................	1·00	1·25
		a. Retouched background to '1/-'.....	75·00	
		s. Optd 'SPECIMEN' (30).............	—	
499/502 *Set of 4*..			1·50	2·50
First Day Cover				80·00

1950–52. 4d. as No. 468 and others as Nos. 485/489, but colours changed. W **127**. Perf 15×14.

503	**128**	½d. pale orange (3.5.51).................	30	30
		a. Imperf (pair)..........................	£5250	
		b. *Tête-bêche* (horiz pair)............	—	
		c. Imperf pane*..........................	£9750	
		d. Booklet pane. No. 503×6 (5.51).....	10·00	
		dw. Booklet pane. 503Wi×6............	10·00	
		e. Booklet pane. No. 503×4 (5.51).....	15·00	
		ew. Booklet pane. 503Wi×4............	15·00	
		f. Booklet pane. No. 503×2 (5.51).....	15·00	
		Wi. Watermark inverted................	50	50
504		1d. light ultramarine (3.5.51)...........	30	30
		a. Watermark sideways (5.51).........	1·10	1·25
		b. Imperf (pair)..........................	£3500	
		c. Imperf three sides (horiz pair)......	£5000	
		d. Booklet pane. No. 504×3 plus three printed labels (3.52)...............	18·00	
		dw. Booklet pane. No. 504Wi×3 plus three printed labels....................	18·00	
		e. Booklet pane. No. 504Wi×3 plus three printed labels. Partial *tête-bêche* pane.....................	£6500	
		f. Booklet pane. No. 504×6 (1.53).....	40·00	
		fw. Booklet pane. 504Wi×6.............	45·00	
		g. Booklet pane. No. 504×4 (5.51).....	20·00	
		gw. Booklet pane. 504Wi×4............	35·00	
		h. Booklet pane. No. 504×2 (5.51).....	15·00	
		Wi. Watermark inverted................	4·50	2·50

505		1½d. pale green (3.5.51)..................	65	60
		a. Watermark sideways (9.51).........	3·25	5·00
		b. Booklet pane. No. 505×6 (3.52).....	30·00	
		bw. Booklet pane. 505Wi×6............	40·00	
		c. Booklet pane. No. 505×4 (5.51).....	15·00	
		cw. Booklet pane. No. 505Wi×4.......	20·00	
		d. Booklet pane. No. 505×2 (5.51).....	15·00	
		Wi. Watermark inverted................	6·00	1·00
506		2d. pale red-brown (3.5.51).............	75	40
		a. Watermark sideways (5.51).........	1·75	2·00
		b. *Tête-bêche* (horiz pair)............	—	
		c. Imperf three sides (horiz pair)......	£6000	
		d. Booklet pane. No. 506×6 (5.51).....	40·00	
		dw. Booklet pane. No. 506Wi×6.......	40·00	
		Wi. Watermark inverted................	6·00	6·50
507		2½d. pale scarlet (3.5.51)................	60	40
		a. Watermark sideways (5.51).........	1·75	1·75
		b. *Tête-bêche* (horiz pair)............	—	
		c. Booklet pane. No. 507×6 (5.51).....	8·00	
		cw. Booklet pane. No. 507Wi×6.......	10·00	
		Wi. Watermark inverted................	2·00	1·25
508	**129**	4d. light ultramarine (2.10.50).........	2·00	1·75
		a. Double impression....................	†	£7000
503/508 *Set of 6*..			4·00	3·25

* BOOKLET ERRORS. Those listed as imperf panes show one row of perforations either at the top or at the bottom of the pane of six.
No. 504c is perforated at foot only and only occurs in the same sheet as No. 504b.
No. 506c is also perforated at foot only.

First Day Covers

2.10.50	No. 508	£125
3.5.51	Nos. 503/507	55·00

147 HMS *Victory*

148 White Cliffs of Dover

149 St George and the Dragon

150 Royal Coat of Arms

(Des Mary Adshead (Types **147**/**148**), P. Metcalfe (Types **149**/**150**). Recess Waterlow)

1951 (3 May). W **133**. Perf 11×12.

509	**147**	2s.6d. yellow-green.....................	7·50	1·00
		s. Optd 'SPECIMEN' (30).............	£1000	
510	**148**	5s. red....................................	35·00	1·00
		s. Optd 'SPECIMEN' (30).............	£1000	
511	**149**	10s. ultramarine.........................	15·00	7·50
		s. Optd 'SPECIMEN' (30).............	£1000	
512	**150**	£1 brown..................................	45·00	18·00
		s. Optd 'SPECIMEN' (30).............	£1000	
509/512 *Set of 4*..			£100	25·00
First Day Cover..				£950

151 Commerce and Prosperity

152 Festival Symbol

(Des E. Dulac (T **151**), A. Games (T **152**))

1951 (3 May). Festival of Britain. W **127**. Perf 15×14.

513	**151**	2½d. scarlet..............................	20	15
514	**152**	4d. ultramarine..........................	30	35
513/514 *Set of 2*..			40	40
First Day Cover..				40·00

Queen Elizabeth II Special Issues 2006-2011

❖ Mint sets ❖ Gutters ❖ Traffic Light Gutters ❖
❖ Cylinder Blocks ❖ NVI Sheets of 30 ❖

❖ First Day Covers ❖ PHQ Cards Mint & FDI (Front) ❖
❖ Miniature Sheets ❖ Prestige Stamp Booklets ❖ Smiler Sheets ❖

❖ Various Special Handstamps Available ❖

Please allow me to Quote you a Price
Email: mygbwantslist@gmail.com
Michael Parker, 32 Aydon Road, Sunderland SR5 3FB

Queen Elizabeth II Specialised Definitives

❖ Security Machins ❖ Barcode Machins ❖
❖ Cartor Regionals ❖ Barcode Regionals ❖

For the Collector of: ❖ Singles ❖ Cylinder Blocks ❖ Date Blocks ❖
❖ Cylinder Booklets (NVI'S-PM'S-Christmas) ❖ Plain & Cylinder Barcode Booklets ❖

❖ Various Grid Position's & Security Backing Papers Available ❖

Please allow me to Quote you a Price
Email: mygbwantslist@gmail.com
Michael Parker, 32 Aydon Road, Sunderland SR5 3FB

Embassy Philatelists

RETAIL LISTS & POSTAL AUCTIONS PRODUCED MONTHLY
CATALOGUE SENT FREE ON REQUEST
1000's OF ITEMS TO VIEW AND BUY ON OUR WEBSITE

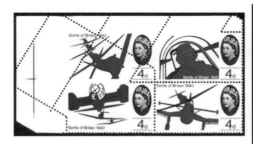 

Embassy Philatelists

P.O. BOX 1553, GUILDFORD, GU1 9YT
Tel: 01483 811 168
Email: info@embassystamps.co.uk

Est. **40** Years

www.embassystamps.co.uk

Leading Dealers In Fine And Rare Great Britain

www.markbrandon.co.uk

 01908 915553

Queen Elizabeth II

6 February 1952-8 September 2022

Further detailed information on the stamps of Queen Elizabeth II will be found in Volumes 3, 4 and 5 of the Stanley Gibbons *Great Britain Specialised Catalogue*.

153 Tudor Crown | **154**

155 | **156** | **157**

158 | **159** | **160**

Queen Elizabeth II and National Emblems

1½d. Extra white dot below 'd' at left (Cyl. 13 dot, R. 17/10) | **1½d.** Butterfly flaw (Cyl. 6 dot, R. 19/1)

I | II

Two types of the 2½d.

Type I: In the frontal cross of the diadem, the top line is only half the width of the cross.

Type II: The top line extends to the full width of the cross and there are signs of strengthening in other parts of the diadem.

(Des Enid Marx (T **154**), M. Farrar-Bell (Types **155**/**156**), G. Knipe (T **157**), Mary Adshead (T **158**), E. Dulac (Types **159**/**160**). Portrait by Dorothy Wilding)

1952–54. W **153**. Perf 15×14.

515	**154**	½d. orange-red (31.8.53)........................	25	15
		Wi. Watermark inverted (3.54)...............	2·00	2·00
		l. Booklet pane No. 515×6 (3.54)........	4·00	
		lWi. Booklet pane No. 515Wi×6 (3.54)...	4·00	
		m. Booklet pane No. 515×4 (22.7.54).....	8·00	
		mWi. Booklet pane No. 515Wi×4 (22.7.54).............	10·00	
		n. Booklet pane No. 515×2 (22.9.53)...	5·00	
516		1d. ultramarine (31.8.53)..................	30	20
		Wi. Watermark inverted (3.54)..............	6·00	3·00
		l. Booklet pane No. 516×6 (3.54).........	35·00	
		lWi. Booklet pane No. 516Wi×6 (3.54)....	75·00	
		la. Booklet pane. No. 516×3 plus three printed labels....................	50·00	
		laWi. Booklet pane. No. 516Wi×3 plus three printed labels..........	50·00	
		m. Booklet pane No. 516×4 (22.7.54).....	12·00	
		mWi. Booklet pane No. 516Wi×4 (22.7.54)............	45·00	
		n. Booklet pane No. 516×2 (2.9.53).....	5·00	
517		1½d. green (5.12.52)......................	25	20
		a. Watermark sideways (15.10.54).......	1·25	1·25
		c. Extra dot..................................	28·00	
		d. Butterfly flaw. Cyl. 6 dot (block of 6).............................	£800	
		Wi. Watermark inverted (5.53).............	1·25	1·25
		l. Booklet pane No. 517×6 (5.53)........	4·00	
		lWi. Booklet pane No. 517Wi×6 (5.53)...	4·00	
		lbWi. Imperf pane*...........................		
		m. Booklet pane No. 517×4 (22.7.54).....	12·00	
		mWi. Booklet pane No. 517Wi×4 (22.7.54)............	15·00	
		n. Booklet pane No. 517×2 (2.9.53).....	9·00	
518		2d. red-brown (31.8.53)....................	30	20
		a. Watermark sideways (8.10.54)........	2·00	2·00
		Wi. Watermark inverted (3.54).............	30·00	22·00
		l. Booklet pane No. 518×6 (3.54).........	60·00	
		lWi. Booklet pane No. 518Wi×6 (3.54)...	£200	
519	**155**	2½d. carmine-red (Type I) (5.12.52)..........	30	15
		a. Watermark sideways (15.11.54).......	12·00	12·00
		b. Type II (booklets) (5.53)...............	1·25	1·25
		bWi. Watermark inverted (5.53)............	1·00	1·00
		l. Booklet pane No. 519b×6 (Type II) (5.53)............................	6·00	
		lWi. Booklet pane No. 519bWi×6 (Type II) (5.53).....................	4·50	
520	**156**	3d. deep lilac (18.1.54)...................	1·50	90
521		4d. ultramarine (2.11.53)................	3·25	1·25
522	**157**	5d. brown (6.7.53).......................	1·00	3·50
523		6d. reddish purple (18.1.54)...........	4·00	1·00
		a. Imperf three sides (pair).................	£3750	
524		7d. bright green (18.1.54)...............	9·50	5·50
525	**158**	8d. magenta (6.7.53)....................	1·25	85
526		9d. bronze-green (8.2.54).................	23·00	4·75
527		10d. Prussian blue (8.2.54)...............	18·00	4·75
528		11d. brown-purple (8.2.54)..............	35·00	15·00
529	**159**	1s. bistre-brown (6.7.53)...............	80	50
530	**160**	1s.3d. green (2.11.53)..................	4·50	3·25
531	**159**	1s.6d. grey-blue (2.11.53)..............	14·00	3·75
515/531 *Set of 17*..................................			£100	40·00

*   BOOKLET ERRORS. This pane of six stamps is completely imperf. Stamps with sideways watermark come from left-side delivery coils and stamps with inverted watermark are from booklets.

See also Nos. 540/556, 561/566, 570/594 and 599/618a. For stamps as Types **154**/**155** and **157**/**160** with face values in decimal currency see Nos. 2031/2033, 2258/2259, **MS**2326, **MS**2367, 2378/2379 and 3329.

First Day Covers

5.12.52	Nos. 517, 519	28·00
6.7.53	Nos. 522, 525, 526	60·00
31.8.53	Nos. 515/516, 518	60·00
2.11.53	Nos. 521, 530/531	£200
18.1.54	Nos. 520, 523/524	£125
8.2.54	Nos. 526/528	£250

161 | **162**

163 | **164**

(Des E. Fuller (2½d.), M. Goaman (4d.), E. Dulac (1s.3d.), M. Farrar-Bell (1s.6d.). Portrait (except 1s.3d.) by Dorothy Wilding)

1953 (3 June). Coronation. W **153**. Perf 15×14.

532	**161**	2½d. carmine-red......................	20	20
533	**162**	4d. ultramarine......................	80	40
534	**163**	1s.3d. deep yellow-green.............	3·00	1·00
535	**164**	1s.6d. deep grey-blue...............	6·50	2·00
Set of 4...................................			10·00	3·50
First Day Cover...........................				75·00

For a £1 value as T **163** see Nos. **MS**2147 and 2380.

165 St Edward's Crown

The paper of De La Rue printings is uniformly white, identical with that of Waterlow printings from February 1957 onwards, but earlier Waterlow printings are on paper which is creamy by comparison.

In this and later issues of Types **166/169** the dates of issue given for changes of watermark or paper are those on which supplies were first sent by the Supplies Department to Postmasters.

A used example of No. 538a has been reported with watermark inverted.

166 Carrickfergus Castle

167 Caernarvon Castle

168 Edinburgh Castle

169 Windsor Castle

(Des L. Lamb. Portrait by Dorothy Wilding. Eng Harold J. Bard and Benjamin Savinson (lettering). Recess Waterlow (until 31.12.57) and De La Rue (subsequently))

1955–58. W **165**. Perf 11×12.

536	**166**	2s.6d. black-brown (23.9.55)......................	15·00	2·00
		a. De La Rue printing (17.7.58)............	30·00	2·50
		Wi. Watermark inverted........................	†	£3000
537	**167**	5s. rose-carmine (23.9.55).....................	40·00	4·00
		a. De La Rue printing. *Scarlet-vermilion* (30.4.58)........................	65·00	10·00
538	**168**	10s. ultramarine (1.9.55).......................	90·00	14·00
		a. De La Rue printing. *Dull ultramarine* (25.4.58)........................	£225	22·00
539	**169**	£1 black (1.9.55).................................	£140	35·00
		a. De La Rue printing (28.4.58)............	£350	65·00
		Set of 4 (Nos. 536/539)..........................	£250	50·00
		Set of 4 (Nos. 536a/539a).......................	£600	90·00
		First Day Cover (Nos. 538/539) (1.9.55)............		£850
		First Day Cover (Nos. 536/537) (23.9.55)...........		£650

See also Nos. 595/598a and 759/762.

For stamps inscribed in decimal currency see Nos. **MS**2530 and 3221.

On 1 January 1958, the contract for printing the high values, Types **166** to **169**, was transferred to De La Rue & Co, Ltd. The work of the two printers is very similar, but the following notes will be helpful to those attempting to identify Waterlow and De La Rue stamps of the W **165** issue.

The De La Rue sheets are printed in pairs and have a '-|' or '|-' shaped guide-mark at the centre of one side-margin, opposite the middle row of perforations, indicating left and right-hand sheets respectively.

The Waterlow sheets have a small circle (sometimes crossed) instead of a '|-' and this is present in both side-margins opposite the sixth row of stamps, though one is sometimes trimmed off. Short dashes are also present in the perforation gutter between the marginal stamps marking the middle of the four sides and a cross is at the centre of the sheet. The four corners of the sheet have two lines forming a right-angle as trimming marks, but some are usually trimmed off. All these gutter marks and sheet trimming marks are absent in the De La Rue printings. De La Rue used the Waterlow die and no alterations were made to it, so that no difference exists in the design or its size, but the making of new plates at first resulted in slight but measurable variations in the width of the gutters between stamps, particularly the horizontal, as follows:

	Waterlow	De La Rue
Horiz gutters, mm	3.8 to 4.0	3.4 to 3.8

Later De La Rue plates were however less distinguishable in this respect.

For a short time in 1959 the De La Rue 2s.6d. appeared with one dot in the bottom margin below the first stamp.

It is possible to sort singles with reasonable certainty by general characteristics. The individual lines of the De La Rue impression are cleaner and devoid of the whiskers of colour of Waterlow's, and the whole impression lighter and softer.

Owing to the closer setting of the horizontal rows the strokes of the perforating comb are closer; this results in the topmost tooth on each side of De La Rue stamps being narrower than the corresponding teeth in Waterlow's which were more than normally broad.

Shades also help. The 2s.6d. De La Rue is a warmer, more chocolate shade than the blackish brown of Waterlow; the 5s. a lighter red with less carmine than Waterlow's; the 10s. more blue and less ultramarine; the £1 less intense black.

1½d. Two white dots extending upwards from shamrock at left appearing as rabbit's ears. Occurs in booklets in position 2 or 5 in pane of 6

1½d. Butterfly flaw (Cyl. 14 dot, R.19/1)

1½d. Butterfly flaw (Cyl. 15 dot, R. 19/1)

2½d. 'Swan's head' flaw. Top of '2' is extended and curled. Occurs in booklets in positions 1 and 4 in pane of 6

1955–58. W **165**. Perf 15×14.

540	**154**	½d. orange-red (booklets 9.55, sheets 12.12.55).................................	20	15
		Wi. Watermark inverted (9.55).................	45	40
		l. Booklet pane No. 540×6 (9.55).........	2·50	
		lWi. Booklet pane No. 540Wi×6 (9.55).....	4·00	
		lc. Part perf pane*................................	£3250	
		lcWi. Part perf pane*................................	£3250	
		m. Booklet pane No. 540×4 (5.7.56)......	8·00	
		mWi. Booklet pane No. 540Wi×4 (5.7.56)..	8·00	
		n. Booklet pane No. 540×2 (11.57).......	25·00	
541		1d. ultramarine (19.9.55)......................	30	15
		b. *Tête-bêche* (horiz pair).....................		
		Wi. Watermark inverted (9.55).................	65	60
		l. Booklet pane No. 541×6 (8.55).........	5·00	
		lWi. Booklet pane No. 541Wi×6 (8.55).....	5·00	
		la. Booklet pane. No. 541×3 plus three printed labels........................	18·00	
		laWi. Booklet pane. No. 541Wi×3 plus three printed labels..................	18·00	
		m. Booklet pane No. 541×4 (5.7.56)......	10·00	
		mWi. Booklet pane No. 541Wi×4 (5.7.56)..	10·00	
		n. Booklet pane No. 541×2 (11.57).......	25·00	
542		1½d. green (booklet 8.55, sheets 11.10.55).................................	25	30
		a. Watermark sideways (7.3.56).............	35	70
		b. *Tête-bêche* (horiz pair).....................	—	
		c. Extra dot....................................	28·00	
		d. Rabbit's ears...............................	42·00	
		e. Butterfly flaw (Cyl. 14 dot) block of 6..................................	90·00	
		f. Butterfly flaw (Cyl. 15 dot) block of 6..................................	75·00	
		Wi. Watermark inverted (8.55).................	75	70
		l. Booklet pane No. 542×6 (8.55).........	3·50	
		lWi. Booklet pane No. 542Wi×6 (8.55).....	5·00	
		m. Booklet pane No. 542×4 (5.7.56)......	12·00	
		mWi. Booklet pane No. 542Wi×4 (5.7.56)..	12·00	
		n. Booklet pane No. 542×2 (11.57).......	30·00	
543		2d. red-brown (6.9.55)..........................	25	35
		aa. Imperf between (vert pair)................	£4750	
		a. Watermark sideways (31.7.56)............	55	70
		ab. Imperf between (horiz pair)...............	£4750	
		Wi. Watermark inverted (9.55).................	11·00	9·00
		l. Booklet pane No. 543×6 (9.55).........	30·00	
		lWi. Booklet pane No. 543Wi×6 (9.55).....	90·00	
543b		2d. light red-brown (17.10.56)................	30	20

		ba. *Tête-bêche* (horiz pair).........................	£3250	
		bWi. Watermark inverted (1.57).................	9·00	7·00
		d. Watermark sideways (5.3.57).............	8·00	7·00
		bl. Booklet pane No. 543*b*×6 (1.57).......	15·00	
		blb. Imperf pane*.......................................	£3750	
		blc. Part perf pane*....................................	£3750	
		blWi. Booklet pane No. 543*bWi*×6 (1.57).	40·00	
		blbWi. Imperf pane*...................................		
544	**155**	2½d. carmine-red (Type I) (28.9.55)...........	30	25
		a. Watermark sideways (Type I)		
		(23.3.56)...	1·50	1·75
		b. Type II (booklets 9.55, sheets 1957).	45	45
		ba. *Tête-bêche* (horiz pair)......................	£3250	
		bd. Swan's head flaw..............................	95·00	
		bWi. Watermark inverted (9.55)...............	55	70
		bl. Booklet pane No. 544*b*×6 (Type II)		
		(9.55)...	3·50	
		blb. Imperf pane*.......................................	£3750	
		blc. Part perf pane*....................................	£3250	
		blWi. Booklet pane No. 544*bWi*×6 (Type		
		II) (9.55)...	3·50	
		blbWi. Imperf pane*...................................	£3750	
		blcWi. Part perf pane*................................	£3250	
545		3d. deep lilac (17.7.56).............................	40	25
		aa. *Tête-bêche* (horiz pair)......................	£3000	
		a. Imperf three sides (pair).....................	£2750	
		b. Watermark sideways (22.11.57).......	18·00	17·00
		Wi. Watermark inverted (1.10.57)..........	1·25	1·25
		l. Booklet pane No. 545×6 (1.10.57)....	5·00	
		lWi. Booklet pane No. 545Wi×6		
		(1.10.57)..	10·00	
		m. Booklet pane No. 545×4 (22.4.59)...	60·00	
		mWi. Booklet pane No. 545Wi×4		
		(22.4.59)..	75·00	
546	**156**	4d. ultramarine (14.11.55).......................	1·25	45
547	**157**	5d. brown (21.9.55)................................	6·00	6·00
548		6d. reddish purple (20.12.55)...................	4·50	1·25
		aa. Imperf three sides (pair).....................	£5250	
		a. Deep claret (8.5.58)...........................	4·50	1·40
		ab. Imperf three sides (pair).....................	£5250	
549		7d. bright green (23.4.56).........................	50·00	10·00
550	**158**	8d. magenta (21.12.55)...........................	7·00	1·25
551		9d. bronze-green (15.12.55)......................	20·00	2·75
552		10d. Prussian blue (22.9.55)......................	20·00	2·75
553		11d. brown-purple (28.10.55)....................	1·00	1·10
554	**159**	1s. bistre-brown (3.11.55)........................	22·00	65
555	**160**	1s.3d. green (27.3.56)...............................	30·00	1·60
556	**159**	1s.6d. grey-blue (27.3.56).........................	23·00	1·60
		Set of 18...	£160	27·00

* BOOKLET ERRORS. Those listed as imperf panes show one row of perforations either at top or bottom of the booklet pane; those as part perf panes have one row of three stamps imperf on three sides. The dates given for Nos. 540/556 are those on which they were first issued by the Supplies Department to postmasters.

In December 1956 a completely imperforate sheet of No. 543*b* was noticed by clerks in a Kent post office, one of whom purchased it against PO regulations. In view of this irregularity we do not consider it properly issued.

Types of 2½d. In this issue, in 1957, Type II formerly only found in stamps from booklets, began to replace Type I on sheet stamps.

170 Scout Badge and 'Rolling Hitch

171 Scouts coming to Britain

172 Globe within a Compass

(Des Mary Adshead (2½d.), P. Keely (4d.), W. H. Brown (1s.3d.))

1957 (1 Aug). World Scout Jubilee Jamboree. W **165**. Perf 15×14.

557	**170**	2½d. carmine-red......................................	20	20
558	**171**	4d. ultramarine......................................	50	50
559	**172**	1s.3d. green...	3·00	2·00
		Set of 3..	3·50	2·50
		First Day Cover..		25·00

173

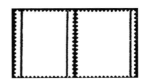

½d. to 1½d., 2½d., 3d., 2d.

Graphite line arrangements (Stamps viewed from back)

(Adapted F. Langfield)

1957 (12 Sep). 46th Inter-Parliamentary Union Conference. W **165**. Perf 15×14.

560	**173**	4d. ultramarine..	40	40
		First Day Cover..		£150

GRAPHITE-LINED ISSUES. These were used in connection with automatic sorting machinery, first introduced experimentally at Southampton in December 1957.

The graphite lines were printed in black on the back, beneath the gum; two lines per stamp, except for the 2d.

In November 1959 phosphor bands were introduced (see notes after No. 598).

1d. Extra stop before '1d.' at right. Occurs in sideways delivery coils (Roll No. 2). This was retouched on No. 571.

1d. Stop below 'd' at left missing. Occurs on sideays delivery coils (Roll No. 3). The dot was added for No. 571.

1957 (19 Nov). Graphite-lined issue. Two graphite lines on the back, except 2d. value, which has one line. W **165**. Perf 15×14.

561	**154**	½d. orange-red..	50	40
562		1d. ultramarine.......................................	70	60
		a. Extra stop..	40·00	
		b. Stop omitted......................................	40·00	
563		1½d. green...	2·00	1·75
		a. Both lines at left.................................	£1600	£600
564		2d. light red-brown.................................	2·50	2·50
		a. Line at left..	£700	£250
565	**155**	2½d. carmine-red (Type II)..........................	8·50	7·00
566		3d. deep lilac..	1·40	1·25
		Set of 6..	14·00	12·00
		First Day Cover..		90·00

No. 564a results from a misplacement of the line and horizontal pairs exist showing one stamp without line. No. 563a results from a similar misplacement.

See also Nos. 587/594.

176 Welsh Dragon

177 Flag and Games Emblem

178 Welsh Dragon

3d. Short scale (Cyl. 2 Dot, R. 1/1)   **3d.** Shoulder flaw (Cyl. 2 Dot, R. 12/2)

(Des R. Stone (3d.), W. H. Brown (6d.), P. Keely (1s.3d.))

1958 (18 July). Sixth British Empire and Commonwealth Games, Cardiff. W **165**. Perf 15×14.

567	**176**	3d. deep lilac	10	10
		a. Short scale	40·00	
		b. Shoulder flaw	40·00	
568	**177**	6d. reddish purple	30	30
569	**178**	1s.3d. green	1·00	1·00
Set of 3			1·20	1·20
First Day Cover				75·00

179 Multiple Crowns   **½d.** 'd' at right joined to shamrock by white line. Occurs on vertical delivery coils (Roll No. 11)

1958–65. W **179**. Perf 15×14.

570	**154**	½d. orange-red (25.11.58)	10	10
		a. Watermark sideways (26.5.61)	75	75
		d. 'd' joined to shamrock	30·00	
		Wi. Watermark inverted (11.58)	1·50	1·50
		k. Chalk-surfaced paper (15.7.63)	2·50	2·75
		kWi. Watermark inverted	2·75	3·00
		l. Booklet pane No. 570×6 (11.58)	5·50	
		lWi. Booklet pane No. 570Wi×6 (11.58).	5·50	
		m. Booklet pane No. 570×4 (13.8.59)	6·00	
		mWi. Booklet pane 570Wi×4 (13.8.59)	6·00	
		mb. Booklet pane. No. 570a×4	10·00	
		mk. Booklet pane. No. 570k×3 *se-tenant* with 574k	9·00	
		mkWi. Booklet pane. No. 570kWi×3 *se-tenant* with No. 574Wi (15.7.63)	9·00	
		mn. Booklet pane No. 570a×2 *se-tenant* with 574g×2 (1.7.64)	2·25	
571		1d. ultramarine (booklets 11.58, sheets 24.3.59)	10	10
		aa. Imperf (vert pair from coil)	£4500	
		a. Watermark sideways (26.5.61)	1·50	1·50
		d. *Tête-bêche* (horiz pair)	£2750	
		Wi. Watermark inverted (11.58)	50	50
		l. Booklet pane No. 571×6 (11.58)	7·00	
		lb. Imperf pane*	£4500	
		lc. Part perf pane*	£3500	
		lWi. Booklet pane No. 571Wi×6 (11.58).	7·00	
		lbWi. Imperf pane*	£4500	
		lcWi. Part perf pane*	£3500	
		m. Booklet pane No. 571×4 (13.8.59).	8·00	
		mWi. Booklet pane No. 571Wi×4 (13.8.59)	8·00	
		mb. Booklet pane. 571a×4 (26.5.61)	12·00	
		mn. Booklet pane. 571a×2 *se-tenant* with 575a×2 (1d. values at left) (16.8.65)	12·00	
		mna. Booklet pane. 1d. values at right	13·00	
572		1½d. green (booklets 12.58, sheets 30.8.60)	10	15
		b. Watermark sideways (26.5.61)	9·00	9·00
		c. *Tête-bêche* (horiz pair)	£2750	
		Wi. Watermark inverted (12.58)	1·50	1·25
		l. Booklet pane No. 572×6 (12.58)	10·00	
		lc. Part perf pane*	£5000	
		lWi. Booklet pane No. 572Wi×6 (12.58).	12·00	
		m. Booklet pane No. 572×4 (13.8.59).	10·00	
		mWi. Booklet pane No. 572Wi×4 (13.8.59)	12·00	
		mb. Booklet pane. No. 572b×4	35·00	
573		2d. light red-brown (4.12.58)	10	10
		a. Watermark sideways (3.4.59)	1·00	1·00
		Wi. Watermark inverted (10.4.61)	£140	70·00
		l. Booklet pane No. 573×6 (10.4.61).	£100	
		lWi. Booklet pane No. 573Wi×6 (10.4.61)	£900	
574	**155**	2½d. carmine-red (Type II) (booklets 11.58, sheets 15.9.59)	10	20

		b. *Tête-bêche* (horiz pair)	—	
		d. Swan's head flaw	£100	
		Wi. Watermark inverted (Type II) (11.58)	4·50	3·00
		e. Watermark sideways (Type I) (10.11.60)	40	60
		ea. Imperf strip of 6	—	
		f. Type I (wmk upright) (4.10.61)	70	70
		g. Watermark sideways (Type II) (1.7.64)	70	1·25
		k. Chalk-surfaced paper (Type II) (15.7.63)	50	80
		kWi. Do. Watermark inverted (15.7.63)...	75	1·25
		l. Booklet pane No. 574×6 (Type II) (11.58)	17·00	
		lb. Imperf pane*	—	
		lc. Part perf pane*	£3000	
		lWi. Booklet pane No. 574Wi×6 (Type II) (11.58)		
		mk. Booklet pane No. 574k×4 (Type II) (15.7.63)	2·00	
		mkWi. Booklet pane No. 574kWi×4 (Type II) (15.7.63)	2·00	
575		3d. deep lilac (booklets 11.58, sheets 8.12.58)	20	15
		a. Watermark sideways (24.10.58)	50	55
		d. Phantom 'R' (Cyl 41 no dot)	£375	
		da. Do. First retouch	30·00	
		db. Do. Second retouch	30·00	
		e. Phantom 'R' (Cyl 37 no dot)	55·00	
		ea. Do. Retouch	20·00	
		Wi. Watermark inverted (11.58)	50	55
		l. Booklet pane No. 575×6 (11.58)	3·50	
		lb. Imperf pane*	£3250	
		lc. Part perf pane*	£3000	
		lWi. Booklet pane No. 575Wi×6 (11.58).	4·00	
		lcWi. Part per pane*	£3000	
		m. Booklet pane No. 575a×4 (2.11.60)...	25·00	
		mWi. Booklet pane No. 575Wi×4 (2.11.60)	25·00	
		mb. Booklet pane. No. 575a×4 (26.5.61)	5·00	
576	**156**	4d. ultramarine (29.10.58)	45	35
		a. Deep ultramarine†† (28.4.65)	15	15
		ab. Watermark sideways (31.5.65)	70	55
		ae. Double impression	—	
		al. Booklet pane No. 576×6 (21.6.65)	6·00	
		alb. Imperf pane*	£3750	
		alc. Part perf pane*	£3500	
		aWi. Watermark inverted (21.6.65)	60	75
		alWi. Booklet pane No. 576aWi×4 (21.6.65)	12·00	
		am. Booklet pane. No. 576ab×4 (16.8.65)	7·00	
577		4½d. chestnut (9.2.59)	10	25
		a. Phantom frame	£100	
578	**157**	5d. brown (10.11.58)	30	40
579		6d. deep claret (23.12.58)	30	25
		a. Imperf three sides (pair)	£4000	
		b. Imperf (pair)	£4500	
580		7d. bright green (26.11.58)	50	45
581	**158**	8d. magenta (24.2.60)	60	40
582		9d. bronze-green (24.3.59)	60	40
583		10d. Prussian blue (18.11.58)	1·00	50
584	**159**	1s. bistre-brown (30.10.58)	75	30
585	**160**	1s.3d. green (17.6.59)	75	30
586	**159**	1s.6d. grey-blue (16.12.58)	5·00	40
Set of 17 (one of each value)			9·00	4·25
First Day Cover (No. 577) (9.2.59)				£250
*Presentation Pack**			£275	

*   BOOKLET ERROR. See note after No. 556.

**   This was issued in 1960 and comprises Nos. 542, 553, 570/571 and 573/586. It exists in two forms: (a) inscribed '10s6d' for sale in the UK and (b) inscribed '$1.80' for sale in the USA.

††   This 'shade' was brought about by making more deeply etched cylinders, resulting in apparent depth of colour in parts of the design. There is no difference in the colour of the ink.

Sideways watermark. The 2d., 2½d., 3d. and 4d. come from coils and the ½d., 1d., 1½d., 2½d., 3d. and 4d. come from booklets. In coil stamps the sideways watermark shows the top of the watermark to the left *as seen from the front of the stamp*. In the booklet stamps it comes equally to the left or right.

Nos. 570k and 574k only come from 2s. Holiday Resort experimental undated booklets issued in 1963, in which one page contained 1×2½d. *se-tenant* with 3×½d. (See No. 570mk).

No. 574l comes from coils, and the Holiday Resort experimental booklets dated 1964 comprising four panes each containing two of these 2½d. stamps *se-tenant* vertically with two ½d. No. 570a. (See No. 570mn).

No. 574b comes from a booklet.

No. 574d is from a booklet with watermark upright.

Nos. 574e and 574ea come from sideways delivery coils

No. 574f comes from sheets bearing cylinder number 42 and vertical delivery coils

In 1964 No. 575 was printed from cylinder number 70 no dot and dot on an experimental paper which is distinguishable by an additional watermark letter 'T' lying on its side, which occurs about four times in the sheet, usually in the side margins, 48,000 sheets were issued.

No. 575 is known imperforate and *tête-bêche*. These came from booklet sheets which were not issued (*price £70 per pair*).

Phantom 'R' varieties

Nos. 575d and 615aa (Cyl 41 no dot)

No. 575da

No. 575e (Cyl 37 no dot)

Phantom Frame variety Nos. 577a and 616ba

3d. An incomplete marginal rule revealed an 'R' on cyls 37 and 41 no dot below R. 20/12. It is more noticeable on cyl 41 because of the wider marginal rule. The 'R' on cyl 41 was twice retouched, the first being as illustrated here (No. 575da) and traces of the 'R' can still be seen in the second retouch.

No. 575d is best collected in a block of four or six with full margins in order to be sure that it is not 615a with phosphor lines removed.

The retouch on cyl 37 (575ea) is not easily identified: there is no trace of the 'R' but the general appearance of that part of the marginal rule is uneven.

4½d. An incomplete marginal rule revealed a right-angled shape frame line on cyl. 8 no dot below R. 20/12. It occurs on ordinary and phosphor.

DOLLIS HILL TRIAL STAMPS. From 1957 to 1972 trials were carried out at the Post Office Research Station, Dollis Hill, London, to determine the most efficient method of applying phosphor to stamps in connection with automatic letter sorting. Stamps were frequently applied to 'live' mail to test sorting machinery.

The 2d. light red-brown and 3d. deep lilac stamps from these trials exist on unwatermarked paper, prices from £300 (2d.), £350 (3d.), mint or used.

WHITER PAPER. On 18 May 1962 the Post Office announced that a whiter paper was being used for the current issue (including Nos. 595/598). This is beyond the scope of this catalogue, but the whiter papers are listed in Vol. 3 of the *Stanley Gibbons Great Britain Specialised Catalogue*.

1958 (24 Nov)–**61**. Graphite-lined issue. Two graphite lines on the back, except 2d. value, which has one line. W **179**. Perf 15×14.

587	**154**	½d. orange-red (15.6.59)............................	9·00	9·00
		Wi. Watermark inverted (4.8.59)............	3·25	4·00
		l. Booklet pane No. 587×6 (4.8.59).......	65·00	
		lWi. Booklet pane No. 587Wi×6 (4.8.59)	25·00	
588		1d. ultramarine (18.12.58).......................	2·00	1·50
		a. Misplaced graphite lines (7.61)*......	80	1·25
		b. Three graphite lines..........................	65·00	60·00
		Wi. Watermark inverted (4.8.59)............	1·50	2·00
		l. Booklet pane No. 588×6 (4.8.59).......	30·00	
		lWi. Booklet pane No. 588Wi×6 (4.8.59)	20·00	
589		1½d. green (4.8.59)....................................	90·00	80·00
		Wi. Watermark inverted (4.8.59)............	75·00	60·00
		l. Booklet pane No. 589×6 (4.8.59).......	£500	
		lWi. Booklet pane No. 589Wi×6 (4.8.59)	£250	
590		2d. light red-brown (24.11.58)................	10·00	3·50
		a. One line at exteme left as seen from back.....................................	£1250	
591	**155**	2½d. carmine-red (Type II) (9.6.59).........	12·00	10·00
		Wi. Watermark inverted (21.8.59)...........	65·00	50·00
		l. Booklet pane No. 591×6 (Type II) (21.8.59)...	£120	
		lWi. Booklet pane No. 591Wi×6 (Type II) (21.8.59)...................................	£400	
592		3d. deep lilac (24.11.58)..........................	90	65
		a. Misplaced graphite lines (5.61)*......	£550	£425
		b. One graphite line..............................	£2500	£2500
		c. Three graphite lines*........................	£150	£120
		Wi. Watermark inverted (4.8.59)............	1·00	1·25
		l. Booklet pane No. 592×6 (4.8.59).......	6·00	
		lWi. Booklet pane No. 592Wi×6 (4.8.59)	7·00	
593	**156**	4d. ultramarine (29.4.59).........................	5·50	5·00
		a. Misplaced graphite lines (1961)*.....	£2400	
594		4½d. chestnut (3.6.59)..............................	6·50	5·00
Set of 8 (cheapest)..			£110	70·00

*	No. 588a (in coils), and Nos. 592a/592c and 593a (all in sheets) result from the use of a residual stock of graphite-lined paper. As the use of graphite lines had ceased, the register of the lines in relation to the stamps was of no importance and numerous misplacements occurred – two lines close together, one line only, etc. No. 588a refers to two lines at left or right; No. 592a refers to stamps with two lines only at left and both clear of the perforations No. 592b refers to stamps with a single line and Nos. 588b, 592c and 593a to stamps with two lines at left (with left line down perforations) and traces of a third line down the opposite perforations.

Nos. 587/589 were only issued in booklets or coils.

No. 592Wi was included in 4s.6d. booklets, Nos. L15 and L16, dated April and June 1959. These represent production dates not issue dates.

166 Carrickfergus Castle

167 Caernarvon Castle

168 Edinburgh Castle

169 Windsor Castle

(Recess D.L.R. (until 31.12.62), then B.W.)

1959–68. W **179**. Perf 11×12.

595	**166**	2s.6d. black-brown (22.7.59)..................	10·00	75
		Wi. Watermark inverted........................	—	£3250
		a. B.W. printing (1.7.63)........................	35	40
		aWi. Watermark inverted.......................	£4000	£325
		k. Chalk-surfaced paper (30.5.68).......	50	1·50
596	**167**	5s. scarlet-vermilion (15.6.59)...............	45·00	2·00
		Wi. Watermark inverted........................	£9000	£600
		a. B.W. ptg. *Red* (shades) (3.9.63).......	1·25	50
		ab. Printed on the gummed side..........	£1600	
		aWi. Watermark inverted.......................	£400	£300
597	**168**	10s. blue (21.7.59)..................................	55·00	5·00
		a. B.W. ptg. *Bright ultramarine* (16.10.63)...	4·50	4·50
		aWi. Watermark inverted.......................	—	£3250
598	**169**	£1 black (30.6.59)..................................	£120	12·00
		Wi. Watermark inverted........................	—	£3000
		a. B.W. printing (14.11.63)....................	13·00	8·00
		aWi. Watermark inverted.......................	£15000	£3750
		k. Chalk-surfaced paper.......................	£5250	
Set of 4 (Nos. 595/598)..			£195	17·00
Set of 4 (Nos. 595a/598a)....................................			15·00	11·00
Presentation Pack (1960)* from............................			£1400	

*	This exists in three forms: (a) inscribed 'S6.50' for sale in the USA; (b) without price for sale in the UK; inscribed '£1 18s' for sale in the UK.

The B.W. printings have a marginal Plate Number. They are generally more deeply engraved than the D.L.R. showing more of the Diadem detail and heavier lines on Her Majesty's face. The vertical perf is 11.9 to 12 against D.L.R. 11.8.

See also Nos. 759/762.

PHOSPHOR BAND ISSUES. These are printed on the front and are wider than graphite lines. They are not easy to see but show as broad vertical bands at certain angles to the light.

Values representing the rate for printed papers (and when this was abolished in 1968 for second issue class mail) have one band and others two, three or four bands as stated, according to the size and format.

In the small size stamps the bands are on each side with the single band at left (*except where otherwise stated*). In the large size commemorative stamps the single band may be at left, centre or right, varying in different designs. The bands are vertical on both horizontal and vertical designs *except where otherwise stated*.

The phosphor was originally applied by letterpress but later usually by photogravure and sometimes using flexography, a relief printing process using rubber cylinders.

Three different types of phosphor have been used, distinguishable by the colour emitted under an ultraviolet lamp, the first being green, then blue and then violet. Different sized bands are also known. All these are fully listed in Vol. 3 of the Stanley Gibbons *Great Britain Specialised Catalogue*.

Varieties. Misplaced and missing phosphor bands are known but such varieties are beyond the scope of this Catalogue.

1959 (18 Nov). Phosphor-Graphite issue. Two phosphor bands on front and two graphite lines on back, except 2d. value, which has one band on front and one line on back.

(a) W **165**. Perf 15×14.

599	**154**	½d. orange-red..	4·25	4·25
600		1d. ultramarine...	11·00	11·00
601		1½d. green..	4·50	4·50

(b) W **179**. Perf 15×14.

605	**154**	2d. light red-brown (1 band)...................	6·00	4·25
		a. Error. W **165**..................................	£200	£175
606	**155**	2½d. carmine-red (Type II).......................	22·00	18·00
607		3d. deep lilac...	12·00	8·00
608	**156**	4d. ultramarine...	20·00	16·00
609		4½d. chestnut..	30·00	20·00
Set of 8...			£100	80·00
Presentation Pack...			£300	

Examples of the 2½d., No. 606, exist showing watermark W **165**, but this was not officially issued.

The Presentation Pack was issued in 1960 and comprises two each of Nos. 599/609. It exists in two forms: (a) inscribed '3s 8d' for sale in the UK and (b) inscribed '50c' for sale in the USA.

1960 (22 June)–**67**. Phosphor issue. Two phosphor bands on front, except where otherwise stated. W **179**. Perf 15×14.

610	**154**	½d. orange-red..	10	15
		a. Watermark sideways (14.7.61).........	15·00	15·00
		b. 'd' joined to shamrock......................	25·00	
		Wi. Watermark inverted (14.8.60).........	1·50	1·50
		l. Booklet pane No. 610×6 (14.8.60)....	7·00	
		lWi. Booklet pane No. 610Wi×6		
		(14.8.60)...	10·00	
		ma. Booklet pane No. 610a×4..................	45·00	
611		1d. ultramarine...	10	10
		a. Watermark sideways (14.7.61).........	1·10	1·10
		Wi. Watermark inverted (14.8.60).........	65	65
		l. Booklet pane No. 611a×4..................	10·00	
		lWi. Booklet pane No. 611Wi×6 (14.8.60)	7·00	
		mb. Booklet pane No. 611a×4 (14.7.61)	18·00	
		mm. Booklet pane No. 611a×2 *se-tenant* with 615d×2† (16.8.65)........	18·00	
		mma. Booklet pane No. 611a×2 *se-tenant* with 615da×2(16.8.65).......	18·00	
		mn. Booklet pane No. 611a×2 *se-tenant* with 615b×2†† (11.67)......	10·00	
		mna. Ditto. 1d. values at right..................	10·00	
612		1½d. green..	15	15
		a. Watermark sideways (14.7.61).........	20·00	20·00
		Wi. Watermark inverted (14.8.60).........	25·00	22·00
		l. Booklet pane No. 612×6 (14.8.60)...	55·00	
		lWi. Booklet pane No. 612Wi×6 (14.8.60)	£150	
		mb. Booklet pane No. 612a×4..................	80·00	
613		2d. light red-brown (1 band)...................	22·00	22·00
613*a*		2d. light red-brown (2 bands) (4.10.61)	10	15
		aa. Imperf three sides*** (pair).............	£4500	
		ab. Watermark sideways (6.4.67)...........	1·00	1·00
614	**155**	2½d. carmine-red (Type II) (2 bands)**...	40	30
		Wi. Watermark inverted (14.8.60).........	£175	£175
		l. Booklet pane No. 614×6 (Type II) (14.8.60).....................................	£120	
		lWi. Booklet pane No. 614Wi×6 (Type II) (14.8.60).....................	£1200	
614*a*		2½d. carmine-red (Type II) (1 band) (4.10.61).....................................	60	75
		aWi. Watermark inverted (3.62)...............	50·00	42·00
		al. Booklet pane No. 614a×6 (Type II) (3.62)...	£110	
		alWi. Booklet pane No. 614aWi×6 (Type II) (3.62)......................................	£300	
614*b*		2½d. carmine-red (Type I) (1 band) (4.10.61).....................................	45·00	40·00
615		3d. deep lilac (2 bands)..........................	60	55
		aa. Phantom 'R' (Cyl 41 no dot)............	55·00	
		Wi. Watermark inverted (14.8.60).........	50	90
		a. Imperf three sides (horiz pair)........	£2000	
		b. Watermark sideways (14.7.61).........	1·75	1·75
		l. Booklet pane No. 615×6 (14.8.60)...	8·00	
		lWi. Booklet pane No. 615Wi×6 (14.8.60)...	8·00	
		bm. Booklet pane No. 615b×4..................	30·00	
615*c*		3d. deep lilac (1 band at right) (29.4.65)	60	55
		ca. Band at left......................................	60	70
		cWi. Watermark inverted (band at right) (2.67)..................................	8·00	7·00
		cWia. Watermark inverted (band at left) (2.67)..................................	80·00	80·00
		cl. Booklet pane No. 615c×4 and No. 615ca×2 (2.67)...........................	35·00	
		clWi. Booklet pane No. 615cWi×4 and No. 615caWi×2 (2.67)...................	£120	
		d. Watermark sideways (band at right) (16.8.65)..............................	5·50	5·00
		da. Watermark sideways (band at left).	5·50	5·00
		e. One centre band (8.12.66)..............	40	45
		eWi. Watermark inverted (8.67)..............	4·00	4·00

		ea. Wmk sideways (19.6.67)...................	1·00	1·00
		el. Booklet pane No. 615ce×6 (8.67).....	7·00	
		elWi. Booklet pane No. 615ceWi×6 (8.67)	24·00	
		em. Booklet pane. No. 615ea×4..............	30·00	
616	**156**	4d. ultramarine...	3·50	3·50
		a. Deep ultramarine (28.4.65).............	25	25
		ab. Wmk sideways..................................	1·10	1·10
		aWi. Watermark inverted (21.6.65)...........	75	75
		al. Booklet pane No. 616a×6 (21.6.65)	3·50	
		alc. Part perf pane*..................................	£3500	
		alWi. Booklet pane No. 616aWi×6 (21.6.65)...	3·50	
		alcWi. Part perf pane*..................................	£3500	
		am. Booklet pane. No. 616ab×4..............	15·00	
616*b*		4½d. chestnut (13.9.61).............................	55	30
		ba. Phantom frame..................................	£100	
616*c*	**157**	5d. brown (9.6.67)....................................	55	35
617		6d. purple..	55	30
617*a*		7d. bright green (15.2.67)........................	70	50
617*b*	**158**	8d. magenta (28.6.67)..............................	70	55
617*c*		9d. bronze-green (29.12.66)...................	70	65
617*d*		10d. Prussian blue (30.12.66)...................	1·00	1·00
617*e*	**159**	1s. bistre-brown (28.6.67)......................	1·00	35
618	**160**	1s.3d. green...	1·90	2·50
618*a*	**159**	1s.6d. grey-blue (12.12.66)........................	2·00	2·00
Set of 17 (one of each value).................................			10·50	8·00

** No. 614 had two bands on the creamy paper was originally from cylinder 50 dot and no dot. When the change in postal rates took place in 1965 it was re-issued from cylinder 57 dot and no dot on the whiter paper. Some of these latter were also released in error in districts of South-east London in September 1964. The shade of the re-issue is slightly more carmine.

***No. 613aa comes from the bottom row of a sheet which is imperf at bottom and both sides.

† Booklet pane No. 611mm shows the 1d. stamps at left and No. 611mna the 1d. stamps at right.

†† Booklet pane No. 611mn comes from 2s. booklets of January and March 1968. The two bands on the 3d. stamp were intentional because of the technical difficulties in producing one band and two band stamps *se-tenant*.

The automatic facing equipment was brought into use on 6 July 1960 but the phosphor stamps may have been released a few days earlier.

The stamps with watermark sideways are from booklets except Nos. 613ab and 615cea which are from coils. No. 616ab comes from both booklets and coils.

The Phosphor-Graphite stamps had the phosphor applied by letterpress but the Phosphor issue can be divided into those with the phosphor applied letterpress and others where it was applied by photogravure. Moreover the photogravure form can be further divided into those which phosphoresce green, blue or violet under ultraviolet light, All these are fully listed in Volume 3 of the Stanley Gibbons *Great Britain Specialised Catalogue*.

No. 615aa (Phantom 'R'), see illustration and footnote following No. 586.

Unlike previous one-banded phosphor stamps, No. 615c has a broad band extending over two stamps so that alternate stamps have the band at left or right (*same prices either way*). No. 615cWi comes from the 10s. phosphor booklet of February 1967 and No. 615ceWi comes from the 10s. phosphor booklets of August 1967 and February 1968.

180 Postboy of 1660

181 Posthorn of 1660

3d. Broken mane (Cyl. 1 No dot, R. 17/2)

(Des R. Stone (3d.), Faith Jaques (1s.3d.))

1960 (7 July). Tercentenary of Establishment of General Letter Office. W **179** (sideways on 1s.3d.). Perf 15×14 (3d.) or 14×15 (1s.3d.).

619	**180**	3d. deep lilac...	20	20
		a. Broken mane....................................	70·00	
620	**181**	1s.3d. green...	1·60	1·75
Set of 2...			1·60	1·75
First Day Cover..				50·00

182 Conference Emblem   **182a** Conference Emblem

(Des R. Stone (emblem, P. Rahikainen))

1960 (19 Sep). First Anniversary of European Postal and Telecommunications Conference. Chalk-surfaced paper. W **179**. Perf 15×14.

621	**182**	6d. bronze-green and purple................	1·00	20
622	**182a**	1s.6d. brown and blue..........................	5·50	2·25
Set of 2			6·00	2·25
First Day Cover..				50·00

SCREENS. Up to this point all photogravure stamps were printed in a 200 screen (200 dots per linear inch), but all later commemorative stamps are a finer 250 screen. Exceptionally No. 622 has a 200 screen for the portrait and a 250 screen for the background.

183 Thrift Plant   **184** 'Growth of Savings'

185 Thrift Plant

(Des P. Gauld (2½d.), M. Goaman (others))

1961 (28 Aug). Centenary of Post Office Savings Bank. Chalk-surfaced paper. W **179** (sideways on 2½d.) Perf 14×15 (2½d.) or 15×14 (others).

623A	**183**	2½d. black and red..................................	10	10
		a. Black omitted..................................	—	
624A	**184**	3d. orange-brown and violet................	10	10
		b. Perf through side sheet margin......	35·00	38·00
		a. Orange-brown omitted...................	£500	
625A	**185**	1s.6d. red and blue...............................	1·00	1·25
623A	**183**	2½d. black and red..................................	10	10
		a. Black omitted..................................	—	
624A	**184**	3d. orange-brown and violet................	10	10
		a. Orange-brown omitted...................	£500	
		b. Perf through side sheet margin......	35·00	38·00
625A	**185**	1s.6d. red and blue...............................	1·00	1·25
623A/625A Set of 3...			1·00	1·25
First Day Cover...				45·00

B. 'Thrissell' Machine.

623B	**183**	2½d. black and red..................................	1·50	1·50
624B	**184**	3d. orange-brown and violet................	30	30
		a. Orange-brown omitted...................	£1200	

Timson   Thrissell

Timson   Thrissell

2½d. TIMSON. Cyls 1E-1F. Deeply shaded portrait (brownish black).
2½d. THRISSELL. Cyls 1D-1B or 1D (dot)-1B (dot). Lighter portrait (grey-black).
3d. TIMSON. Cyls 3D-3E. Clear, well-defined portrait with deep shadows and bright highlights.
3d. THRISSELL. Cyls 3C-3B or 3C (dot)-3B (dot). Dull portrait, lacking in contrast.

Sheet marginal examples without single extension perf hole on the short side of the stamp are always 'Timson', as are those with large punch-hole not coincident with printed three-sided box guide mark.
The 3d. 'Timson' perforated completely through the right hand side margin comes from a relatively small part of the printing perforated on a sheet-fed machine.
Normally the 'Timsons' were perforated in the reel, with three large punch-holes in both long margins and the perforations completely through both short margins. Only one punch-hole coincides with the guide-mark.
The 'Thrissells' have one large punch-hole in one long margin, coinciding with guide-mark and one short margin imperf (except sometimes for encroachments).

186 CEPT Emblem   **187** Doves and Emblem

188 Doves and Emblem

(Des M. Goaman (Doves T. Kurpershoek))

1961 (18 Sept). European Postal and Telecommunications (CEPT) Conference, Torquay. Chalk-surfaced paper. W **179**. Perf 15×14.

626	**186**	2d. orange, pink and brown..................	10	10
		a. Orange omitted...............................	£8000	
		b. Pink omitted....................................		
627	**187**	4d. buff, mauve and ultramarine...........	10	10
628	**188**	10d. turquoise, pale green and Prussian blue.....................................	20	20
		a. Pale green omitted...........................	£14000	
		b. Turquoise omitted...........................	£5000	
Set of 3..			30	30
First Day Cover...				4·00

189 Hammer Beam Roof, Westminster Hall   **190** Palace of Westminster

(Des Faith Jaques)

1961 (25 Sept). Seventh Commonwealth Parliamentary Conference. Chalk-surfaced paper. W **179** (sideways on 1s.3d.) Perf 15×14 (6d.) or 14×15 (1s.3d.).

629	**189**	6d. purple and gold	10	10
		a. Gold omitted	£1500	
630	**190**	1s.3d. green and blue	1·25	1·25
		a. Blue (Queen's head) omitted	£18000	
		b. Green omitted	—	
Set of 2			1·25	1·25
First Day Cover				25·00

191 Units of Productivity   **192** National Productivity

193 Unified Productivity

3d. Lake in Scotland (Cyls. 2A-2B Dot, R. 1/3)

3d. Kent omitted (Cyls. 2C-2B No dot, R. 18/2)

3d. Lake in Yorkshire (Cyls. 2C-2B Dot, R. 19/1)

(Des D. Gentleman)

1962 (14 Nov). National Productivity Year. Chalk-surfaced paper. W **179** (inverted on 2½d. and 3d.). Perf 15×14.

631	**191**	2½d. myrtle-green and carmine-red (*shades*)	10	10
		a. *Blackish olive and carmine-red*	25	15
		p. One phosphor band. *Blackish olive and carmine-red*	60	50
632	**192**	3d. light blue and violet (*shades*)	25	25
		a. Light blue (Queen's head) omitted	£3800	
		b. Lake in Scotland	£150	
		c. Kent omitted	70·00	
		p. Three phosphor bands	1·50	80
		d. Lake in Yorkshire	35·00	
633	**193**	1s.3d. carmine, light blue and deep green	80	80
		a. Light blue (Queen's head) omitted	£8000	
		p. Three phosphor bands	35·00	22·00
Set of 3 (Ordinary)			1·00	1·00
Set of 3 (Phosphor)			35·00	22·00
First Day Cover (Ordinary)				45·00
First Day Cover (Phosphor)				£125

194 Campaign Emblem and Family   **195** Children of Three Races

(Des M. Goaman)

1963 (21 Mar). Freedom from Hunger. Chalk-surfaced paper. W **179** (inverted). Perf 15×14.

634	**194**	2½d. crimson and pink	10	10
		p. One phosphor band	3·00	1·25

635	**195**	1s.3d. bistre-brown and yellow	1·00	1·00
		p. Three phosphor bands	30·00	23·00
Set of 2 (Ordinary)			1·00	1·00
Set of 2 (Phosphor)			30·00	23·00
First Day Cover (Ordinary)				25·00
First Day Cover (Phosphor)				40·00

196 'Paris Conference'

(Des R. Stone)

1963 (7 May). Paris Postal Conference Centenary. Chalk-surfaced paper. W **179** (inverted). Perf 15×14.

636	**196**	6d. green and mauve	20	20
		a. Green omitted	£3000	
		p. Three phosphor bands	3·00	2·75
First Day Cover (Ordinary)				7·50
First Day Cover (Phosphor)				30·00

197 Posy of Flowers   **198** Woodland Life

3d. 'Caterpillar' flaw (Cyl. 3B Dot, R. 3/2)

(Des S. Scott (3d.), M. Goaman (4½d.))

1963 (16 May). National Nature Week. Chalk-surfaced paper. W **179**. Perf 15×14.

637	**197**	3d. yellow, green, brown and black	10	10
		a. 'Caterpillar' flaw	75·00	
		p. Three phosphor bands	30	30
		pa. 'Caterpillar' flaw	75·00	
638	**198**	4½d. black, blue, yellow, magenta and brown-red	15	15
		p. Three phosphor bands	1·40	1·40
Set of 2 (Ordinary)			20	20
Set of 2 (Phosphor)			1·50	1·50
First Day Cover (Ordinary)				12·00
First Day Cover (Phosphor)				35·00

Special First Day of Issue Postmark

London EC (Type A) (*ordinary*)	12·00
London EC (Type A) (*phosphor*)	35·00

This postmark was used on First Day Covers serviced by the Philatelic Bureau.

199 Rescue at Sea   **200** 19th-century Lifeboat

201 Lifeboatmen

(Des D. Gentleman)

1963 (31 May). Ninth International Lifeboat Conference, Edinburgh. Chalk-surfaced paper. W **179**. Perf 15×14.

639	**199**	2½d. blue, black and red	10	10
		p. One phosphor band	50	60
640	**200**	4d. red, yellow, brown, black and blue	20	20
		p. Three phosphor bands	50	60
641	**201**	1s.6d. sepia, yellow and grey-blue	1·50	1·50
		p. Three phosphor bands	48·00	28·00
Set of 3 (Ordinary)			1·50	1·50
Set of 3 (Phosphor)			48·00	28·00
First Day Cover (Ordinary)				20·00
First Day Cover (Phosphor)				55·00

Special First Day of Issue Postmark

London (*ordinary*)	65·00
London (*phosphor*)	85·00

This postmark was used on First Day Covers serviced by the Philatelic Bureau.

202 Red Cross 203

204

(Des H. Bartram)

1963 (15 Aug). Red Cross Centenary Congress. Chalk-surfaced paper. W **179**. Perf 15×14.

642	**202**	3d. red and deep lilac	25	25
		a. Red omitted	£9000	
		p. Three phosphor bands	1·10	1·00
		pa. Red omitted	—	
643	**203**	1s.3d. red, blue and grey	1·25	1·25
		p. Three phosphor bands	35·00	30·00
644	**204**	1s.6d. red, blue and bistre	1·25	1·25
		p. Three phosphor bands	35·00	27·00
Set of 3 (Ordinary)			2·50	2·50
Set of 3 (Phosphor)			65·00	55·00
First Day Cover (Ordinary)				20·00
First Day Cover (Phosphor)				60·00

Special First Day of Issue Postmark

London E.C. (*ordinary*)	80·00
London E.C. (*phosphor*)	£110

This postmark was used on First Day Covers serviced by the Philatelic Bureau.

205 Commonwealth Cable

(Des P. Gauld)

1963 (3 Dec). Opening of COMPAC (Trans-Pacific Telephone Cable). Chalk-surfaced paper. W **179**. Perf 15×14.

645	**205**	1s.6d. blue and black	1·25	1·25
		a. Black omitted	£4500	
		p. Three phosphor bands	7·25	7·00
First Day Cover (Ordinary)				12·00
First Day Cover (Phosphor)				35·00

Special First Day of Issue Postmark

Philatelic Bureau, London EC 1 (Type A) (*ordinary*)	12·00
Philatelic Bureau, London EC 1 (Type A) (*phosphor*)	35·00

Special First Day of Issue Postmark

London EC 1 (Type A) (*ordinary*)	12·00
London EC 1 (Type A) (*phosphor*)	35·00

PRESENTATION PACKS. Special Packs comprising slip-in cards with printed commemorative inscriptions and descriptive notes on the back and with protective covering, were introduced in 1964 with the Shakespeare issue. These are listed and priced. Issues of 1968–1969 (British Paintings to the Prince of Wales Investiture) were also issued in packs with text in German for sale through the Post Office's German Agency and these are also quoted. Subsequently, however, the packs sold in Germany were identical with the normal English version with the addition of a separate printed insert card with German text. These, as also English packs with Japanese and Dutch printed cards for sale in Japan and the Netherlands respectively, are listed in Vols. 3 and 5 of the Stanley Gibbons *Great Britain Specialised Catalogue*.

206 Puck and Bottom (*A Midsummer Night's Dream*) 207 Feste (*Twelfth Night*)

208 Balcony Scene (*Romeo and Juliet*) 209 Eve of Agincourt (*Henry V*)

210 Hamlet contemplating Yorick's Skull (*Hamlet*) and Queen Elizabeth II

(Des D. Gentleman. Photo Harrison & Sons (3d., 6d., 1s.3d., 1s.6d.). Des C. and R. Ironside. Eng Nigel Alan Dow. Recess B.W. (2s.6d.))

1964 (23 Apr). Shakespeare Festival. Chalk-surfaced paper. W **179**. Perf 11×12 (2s.6d.) or 15×14 (others).

646	**206**	3d. yellow-bistre, black and deep violet-blue (*shades*)	10	10
		p. Three phosphor bands	25	25
647	**207**	6d. yellow, orange, black and yellow-olive (*shades*)	20	20
		p. Three phosphor bands	75	75
648	**208**	1s.3d. cerise, blue-green, black and sepia (*shades*)	40	40
		Wi. Watermark inverted	£1500	
		p. Three phosphor bands	2·00	2·00
		pWi. Watermark inverted	£400	
649	**209**	1s.6d. violet, turquoise, black and blue (*shades*)	60	60
		Wi. Watermark inverted		£1300
		p. Three phosphor bands	2·50	2·50
650	**210**	2s.6d. deep slate-purple (*shades*)	1·25	1·25
		Wi. Watermark inverted	£1000	
Set of 5 (Ordinary)			2·00	2·00
Set of 4 (Phosphor) (Nos. 646p/649p)			5·00	5·00
First Day Cover (Ordinary)				5·00
First Day Cover (Phosphor)				9·00
Presentation Pack (Ordinary)			12·00	

The 3d. is known with yellow-bistre missing in the top two-thirds of the figures of Puck and Bottom. This occurred in the top row only of a sheet.

Special First Day of Issue Postmarks

Stratford-upon-Avon, Warwicks (*ordinary*)	15·00
Stratford-upon-Avon, Warwicks (*phosphor*)	22·00

This postmark was used on First Day Covers serviced by the Philatelic Bureau, as well as on covers posted at Stratford PO.

211 Flats near Richmond Park (Urban Development) 212 Shipbuilding Yards, Belfast (Industrial Activity)

213 Beddgelert Forest Park, (Snowdonia Forestry)

214 Nuclear Reactor, Dounreay (Technological Development)

2½d. Short line under 2½d. (Cyl. 3D, various positions)

(Des D. Bailey)

1964 (1 July). 20th International Geographical Congress, London. Chalk-surfaced paper. W **179**. Perf 15×14.

651	**211**	2½d. black, olive-yellow, olive-grey and turquoise-blue...	10	10
		p. One phosphor band...	40	50
		a. Short line under 2½d...	14·00	
652	**212**	4d. orange-brown, red-brown, rose, black and violet...	30	30
		a. Violet (face value) omitted...	£225	
		c. Violet and red-brown (dock walls) omitted...	£425	
		d. Red brown (dock walls) omitted...	—	
		Wi. Watermark inverted...	£750	
		p. Three phosphor bands...	1·25	1·25
653	**213**	8d. yellow-brown, emerald, green and black...	80	80
		a. Green (lawn) omitted...	£12000	
		Wi. Watermark inverted...	£2200	
		p. Three phosphor bands...	2·50	3·50
654	**214**	1s.6d. yellow-brown, pale pink, black and brown...	1·40	1·40
		Wi. Watermark inverted...	55·00	
		p. Three phosphor bands...	28·00	22·00
		Set of 4 (Ordinary)...	2·00	2·00
		Set of 4 (Phosphor)...	30·00	25·00
		First Day Cover (Ordinary)...		10·00
		First Day Cover (Phosphor)...		35·00
		Presentation Pack (Ordinary)...	£100	

A used example of the 4d. is known with the red-brown omitted.

Special First Day of Issue Postmark

GPO Philatelic Bureau, London EC 1 (Type B) (*ordinary*)................. 10·00
GPO Philatelic Bureau, London EC 1 (Type B) (*phosphor*)................. 35·00

215 Spring Gentian

216 Dog Rose

217 Honeysuckle

218 Fringed Water Lily

3d. Broken petal (Cyl. 3A, Dot, R. 1/2)

9d. Line through 'INTER' (Cyl. 2A No Dot, R. 1/1)

(Des M. and Sylvia Goaman)

1964 (5 Aug). Tenth International Botanical Congress, Edinburgh. Chalk-surfaced paper. W **179**. Perf 15×14.

655	**215**	3d. violet, blue and sage-green...	25	25
		a. Blue omitted...	£11000	
		b. Sage-green omitted...	£13500	
		c. Broken petal...	65·00	
		p. Three phosphor bands...	40	40
		pc. Broken petal...	65·00	
656	**216**	6d. apple-green, rose, scarlet and green...	30	30
		p. Three phosphor bands...	2·50	2·75
657	**217**	9d. lemon, green, lake and rose-red...	80	80
		a. Green (leaves) omitted...	£12000	
		b. Line through 'INTER'...	65·00	
		Wi. Watermark inverted...	75·00	
		p. Three phosphor bands...	4·50	4·50
		pb. Line through 'INTER'...	65·00	
658	**218**	1s.3d. yellow, emerald, reddish violet and grey-green...	1·25	1·25
		a. Yellow (flowers) omitted...	—	
		Wi. Watermark inverted...	£2500	
		p. Three phosphor bands...	25·00	20·00
		Set of 4 (Ordinary)...	2·00	2·00
		Set of 4 (Phosphor)...	30·00	25·00
		First Day Cover (Ordinary)...		10·00
		First Day Cover (Phosphor)...		35·00
		Presentation Pack (Ordinary)...	£125	

Unissued Goaman designs of the 3d and 9d values on perforated and gummed paper are known.

Special First Day of Issue Postmark

GPO Philatelic Bureau, London EC 1 (Type B) (*ordinary*)................. 10·00
GPO Philatelic Bureau, London EC 1 (Type B) (*phosphor*)................. 35·00

219 Forth Road Bridge

220 Forth Road and Railway Bridges

(Des A. Restall)

1964 (4 Sept). Opening of Forth Road Bridge. Chalk-surfaced paper. W **179**. Perf 15×14.

659	**219**	3d. black, blue and reddish violet...	10	10
		p. Three phosphor bands...	50	50
660	**220**	6d. blackish lilac, light blue and carmine-red...	20	20
		a. Light blue omitted...	£3000	
		Wi. Watermark inverted...	5·00	
		p. Three phosphor bands...	2·25	2·25
		pWi. Watermark inverted...	£800	
		Set of 2 (Ordinary)...	25	25
		Set of 2 (Phosphor)...	2·50	2·50
		First Day Cover (Ordinary)...		3·00
		First Day Cover (Phosphor)...		10·00
		Presentation Pack (Ordinary)...	£325	

Special First Day of Issue Postmarks

GPO Philatelic Bureau, London EC 1 (Type B) (*ordinary*)............... 15·00
GPO Philatelic Bureau, London EC 1 (Type B) (*phosphor*)............... 20·00
North Queensferry, Fife (*ordinary*)..................................... 50·00
North Queensferry, Fife (*phosphor*)..................................... £130
South Queensferry, West Lothian (*ordinary*)........................... 40·00
South Queensferry, West Lothian (*phosphor*)........................... 95·00

221 Sir Winston Churchill

(Des D. Gentleman and Rosalind Dease, from photograph by Karsh)

1965 (8 Jul). Churchill Commemoration. Chalk-surfaced paper. W **179**. Perf 15×14.

I. 'REMBRANDT' Machine.

661	**221**	4d. black and olive-brown...	15	15
		Wi. Watermark inverted...	3·00	
		p. Three phosphor bands...	20	20

II. 'TIMSON' Machine.

661a		4d. black and olive-brown...	50	50

III. 'L. & M. 4' Machine.

662		1s.3d. black and grey...	45	45
		Wi. Watermark inverted...	£140	
		p. Three phosphor bands...	1·00	1·00
		Set of 2 (Ordinary)...	60	60
		Set of 2 (Phosphor)...	1·10	1·10
		First Day Cover (Ordinary)...		4·75

First Day Cover (Phosphor)... 5·00
Presentation Pack (Ordinary).. 40·00
The 1s.3d. shows a closer view of Churchill's head.

Two examples of the 4d. value exist with the Queen's head omitted, one due to something adhering to the cylinder and the other due to a paper fold. The stamp also exists with Churchill's head omitted, also due to a paper fold.

Rembrandt

Timson

4d. REMBRANDT. Cyls 1A-1B dot and no dot. Lack of shading detail on Churchill's portrait. Queen's portrait appears dull and coarse. This is a rotary machine which is sheet-fed.

4d. TIMSON. Cyls 5A-6B no dot. More detail on Churchill's portrait, furrow on forehead, his left eyebrow fully drawn and more shading on cheek. Queen's portrait lighter and sharper. This is a reel-fed two-colour 12 in. wide rotary machine and the differences in impressions are due to the greater pressure applied by this machine.

1s.3d. Cyls 1A-1B no dot. The 'Linotype and Machinery No. 4' machine is an ordinary sheet-fed rotary press machine. Besides being used for printing the 1s.3d. stamps it was also employed for overprinting the phosphor bands on both values.

Two examples of the 4d. value exist with the Queen's head omitted, one due to something adhering to the cylinder and the other due to a paper fold. The stamp also exists with Churchill's head omitted, also due to a paper fold.

Special First Day of Issue Postmark
GPO Philatelic Bureau, London EC 1 (Type B) (ordinary)................ 4·75
GPO Philatelic Bureau, London EC 1 (Type B) (phosphor)............... 5·00
A first Day of Issue handstamp was provided at Bladon, Oxford, for this issue.

700th Anniversary of Parliament
222 Simon de Montfort's Seal

223 Parliament Buildings (after engraving by Hollar, 1647)

(Des S. Black (6d.), R. Guyatt (2s.6d.))

1965 (19 July). 700th Anniversary of Simon de Montfort's Parliament. Chalk-surfaced paper. W **179**. Perf 15×14.

663	**222**	6d. olive-green....................................	10	10
		p. Three phosphor bands.....................	50	50
664	**223**	2s.6d. black, grey and pale drab.................	40	40
		Wi. Watermark inverted.........................	60·00	
Set of 2 (Ordinary)..			40	40
First Day Cover (Ordinary)...				6·00
First Day Cover (Phosphor)..				20·00
Presentation Pack (Ordinary)...................................			65·00	

Special First Day of Issue Postmark
GPO Philatelic Bureau, London EC 1 (Type B) (ordinary)................ 6·00
A First Day of Issue handstamp was provided at Evesham, Worcs., for this issue.

224 Bandsmen and Banner   **225** Three Salvationists

(Des M. Farrar-Bell (3d.), G. Trenaman (1s.6d.))

1965 (9 Aug). Salvation Army Centenary. Chalk-surfaced paper. W **179**. Perf 15×14.

665	**224**	3d. indigo, grey-blue, cerise, yellow and brown.......................................	10	10
		p. One phosphor band.........................	20	20
666	**225**	1s.6d. red, blue, yellow and brown............	60	60
		p. Three phosphor bands......................	90	90
Set of 2 (Ordinary)..			60	60
Set of 2 (Phosphor)...			1·00	1·00
First Day Cover (Ordinary)...				10·00
First Day Cover (Phosphor)..				22·00

The Philatelic Bureau did not provide First Day Cover services for Nos. 665/670.

226 Lister's Carbolic Spray   **227** Lister and Chemical Symbols

(Des P. Gauld (4d.), F. Ariss (1s.))

1965 (1 Sept). Centenary of Joseph Lister's Discovery of Antiseptic Surgery. Chalk-surfaced paper. W **179**. Perf 15×14.

667	**226**	4d. indigo, brown-red and grey-black..	10	10
		a. Brown-red (tube) omitted...............	£475	
		b. Indigo omitted................................	£3000	
		p. Three phosphor bands.....................	25	25
		pa. Brown-red (tube) omitted...............	£2750	
668	**227**	1s. black, purple and new blue............	40	40
		Wi. Watermark inverted.......................	£675	
		p. Three phosphor bands.....................	1·00	1·00
		pWi. Watermark inverted.......................	£550	
Set of 2 (Ordinary)..			45	45
Set of 2 (Phosphor)...			1·10	1·10
First Day Cover (Ordinary)...				5·00
First Day Cover (Phosphor)..				9·00

228 Trinidad Carnival Dancers   **229** Canadian Folk Dancers

(Des D. Gentleman and Rosalind Dease)

1965 (1 Sept). Commonwealth Arts Festival. Chalk-surfaced paper. W **179**. Perf 15×14.

669	**228**	6d. black and orange..............................	10	10
		p. Three phosphor bands......................	40	40
670	**229**	1s.6d. black and light reddish violet..........	40	40
		p. Three phosphor bands......................	1·25	1·25
Set of 2 (Ordinary)..			45	45
Set of 2 (Phosphor)...			1·50	1·50
First Day Cover (Ordinary)...				7·00
First Day Cover (Phosphor)..				14·00

230 Flight of Supermarine Spitfires   **231** Pilot in Hawker Hurricane Mk I

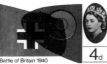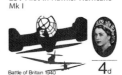

232 Wing-tips of Supermarine Spitfire and Messerschmitt Bf 109   **233** Supermarine Spitfires attacking Heinkel He-111H Bomber

234 Supermarine Spitfire attacking Junkers Ju 87B Stuka Dive-bomber

235 Hawker Hurricanes Mk I over Wreck of Dornier Do-17Z Bomber

236 Anti-aircraft Artillery in Action

237 Air Battle over St Paul's Cathedral

(Des D. Gentleman and Rosalind Dease (4d.×6 and 1s.3d.), A. Restall (9d.))

1965 (13 Sept). 25th Anniversary of Battle of Britain. Chalk-surfaced paper. W **179**. Perf 15×14.

671	**230**	4d. yellow-olive and black	25	25
		a. Block of 6. Nos. 671/676	2·50	2·50
		p. Three phosphor bands	40	40
		pa. Block of 6. Nos. 671p/676pb	3·75	3·75
672	**231**	4d. yellow-olive, olive-grey and black	25	25
		p. Three phosphor bands	40	40
673	**232**	4d. red, new blue, yellow-olive, olive-grey and black	25	25
		p. Three phosphor bands	40	40
674	**233**	4d. olive-grey, yellow-olive and black	25	25
		p. Three phosphor bands	40	40
675	**234**	4d. olive-grey, yellow-olive and black	25	25
		p. Three phosphor bands	40	40
676	**235**	4d. olive-grey, yellow-olive, new blue and black	25	25
		a. New blue omitted	†	£3000
		p. Three phosphor bands	40	40
677	**236**	9d. bluish violet, orange and slate purple	1·75	1·75
		Wi. Watermark inverted	£100	
		p. Three phosphor bands	2·00	2·00
678	**237**	1s.3d. light grey, deep grey, black, light blue and bright blue	1·75	1·75
		a. Face value omitted*	£1100	
		Wi. Watermark inverted	£190	
		p. Three phosphor bands	2·00	2·00
		pWi. Watermark inverted	5·00	
Set of 8 (Ordinary)			5·50	5·50
Set of 8 (Phosphor)			7·00	7·00
First Day Cover (Ordinary)				10·00
First Day Cover (Phosphor)				15·00
Presentation Pack (Ordinary)			40·00	

* No. 678a is caused by a 12 mm downward shift of black which resulted in the value being omitted from the top row of one sheet.

Nos. 671/678 were issued together *se-tenant* in blocks of six (3×2) within the sheet.

No. 676a is only known commercially used *on cover* from Truro.

Special First Day of Issue Postmark

GPO Philatelic Bureau, London EC 1 (Type C) (*ordinary*)	10·00
GPO Philatelic Bureau, London EC 1 (Type C) (*phosphor*)	15·00

238 Tower and Georgian Buildings

239 Tower and Nash Terrace, Regent's Park

(Des C. Abbott)

1965 (8 Oct). Opening of Post Office Tower. Chalk-surfaced paper. W **179** (sideways on 3d.). Perf 14×15 (3d.) or 15×14 (1s.3d.).

679	**238**	3d. olive-yellow, new blue and bronze-green	10	10
		a. Olive-yellow (Tower) omitted	£4250	£2000
		p. One phosphor band at right	15	15
		pa. Band at left	15	15
		pb. Horiz pair. Nos. 679p/679pa	30	50

680	**239**	1s.3d. bronze-green, yellow-green and blue	20	20
		Wi. Watermark inverted	£175	
		p. Three phosphor bands	30	30
		pWi. Watermark inverted	£200	
Set of 2 (Ordinary)			25	25
Set of 2 (Phosphor)			40	40
First Day Cover (Ordinary)				2·50
First Day Cover (Phosphor)				4·75
Presentation Pack (Ordinary)			12·50	
Presentation Pack (Phosphor)				12·50

The one phosphor band on No. 679p was produced by printing broad phosphor bands across alternate vertical perforations. Individual stamps show the band at right or left.

Special First Day of Issue Postmark

GPO Philatelic Bureau, London EC 1 (Type C) (*ordinary*)	2·50
GPO Philatelic Bureau, London EC 1 (Type C) (*phosphor*)	4·75

The Philatelic Bureau did not provide First Day Cover services for Nos. 681/684.

240 UN Emblem

241 ICY Emblem

3d. Broken circle (Cyl. 1A Dot, R. 11/4) **3d.** Lake in Russia (Cyl. 1A Dot, R. 19/3)

(Des J. Matthews)

1965 (25 Oct). 20th Anniversary of UNO and International Co-operation Year. Chalk-surfaced paper. W **179**. Perf 15×14.

681	**240**	3d. black, yellow-orange and light blue	10	10
		a. Broken circle	65·00	
		b. Lake in Russia	65·00	
		p. One phosphor band	25	25
		pa. Broken circle	65·00	
		pb. Lake in Russia	65·00	
682	**241**	1s.6d. black, bright purple and light blue	35	35
		Wi. Watermark inverted	£2250	
		p. Three phosphor bands	1·00	1·00
Set of 2 (Ordinary)			40	40
Set of 2 (Phosphor)			1·10	1·10
First Day Cover (Ordinary)				5·00
First Day Cover (Phosphor)				9·00

242 Telecommunications Network

243 Radio Waves and Switchboard

1s.6d. Red pin with arm (Cyl. 1D, R. 1/4)

(Des A. Restall)

1965 (15 Nov). International Telecommunications Union Centenary. Chalk-surfaced paper. W **179**. Perf 15×14.

683	**242**	9d. red, ultramarine, deep slate, violet, black and pink	20	20
		Wi. Watermark inverted	30·00	
		p. Three phosphor bands	75	75
		pWi. Watermark inverted	£110	
684	**243**	1s.6d. red, greenish blue, indigo, black and light pink	40	40
		a. Light pink omitted	£2000	£1800
		b. Red pin with arm	—	
		Wi. Watermark inverted	—	
		p. Three phosphor bands	2·00	2·00
		pb. Red pin with arm	35·00	
Set of 2 (Ordinary)			50	50
Set of 2 (Phosphor)			2·50	2·50
First Day Cover (Ordinary)				8·00
First Day Cover (Phosphor)				13·00

Originally scheduled for issue on 17 May 1965, supplies from the Philatelic Bureau were sent in error to reach a dealer on that date and another dealer received his supply on 27 May.

244 Robert Burns (after Skirving chalk drawing)

245 Robert Burns (after Nasmyth portrait)

(Des G. Huntly)

1966 (25 Jan). Burns Commemoration. Chalk-surfaced paper. W **179**. Perf 15×14.

685	**244**	4d. black, deep violet-blue and new blue	10	10
		p. Three phosphor bands	20	20
686	**245**	1s.3d. black, slate-blue and yellow-orange	20	20
		p. Three phosphor bands	90	90
Set of 2 (Ordinary)			25	25
Set of 2 (Phosphor)			1·00	1·00
First Day Cover (Ordinary)				1·20
First Day Cover (Phosphor)				3·50
Presentation Pack (Ordinary)			40·00	

Special First Day of Issue Postmarks

Alloway, Ayrshire (*ordinary*)	12·00
Alloway, Ayrshire (*phosphor*)	15·00
Ayr (*ordinary*)	12·00
Ayr (*phosphor*)	15·00
Dumfries (*ordinary*)	12·00
Dumfries (*phosphor*)	15·00
Edinburgh (*ordinary*)	12·00
Edinburgh (*phosphor*)	15·00
Glasgow (*ordinary*)	12·00
Glasgow (*phosphor*)	15·00
Kilmarnock, Ayrshire (*ordinary*)	12·00
Kilmarnock, Ayrshire (*phosphor*)	15·00

A special Philatelic Bureau was set up in Edinburgh to deal with First Day Covers of this issue. The Bureau serviced covers to receive the above postmarks, and other versions were applied locally. The locally applied handstamps were 38–39 mm in diameter, the Bureau postmarks, applied by machine 35 mm. The Ayr, Edinburgh, Glasgow and Kilmarnock postmarks are similar in design to that for Alloway. Similar handstamps were also provided at Greenock and Mauchline, but the Bureau did not provide a service for these.

246 Westminster Abbey

247 Fan Vaulting, Henry VII Chapel

(Des Sheila Robinson. Photo Harrison (3d.). Des and eng Nigel Alan Dow (portrait) and Frederick Warner of Bradbury Wilkinson. Recess (2s.6d.))

1966 (28 Feb). 900th Anniversary of Westminster Abbey. Chalk-surfaced paper (3d.). W **179**. Perf 15×14 (3d.) or 11×12 (2s.6d.).

687	**246**	3d. black, red-brown and new blue	10	10
		p. One phosphor band	10	10
688	**247**	2s.6d. black	30	30
Set of 2			30	30
First Day Cover (Ordinary)				2·50

First Day Cover (Phosphor)		8·00
Presentation Pack (Ordinary)	40·00	

Special First Day of Issue Postmark

GPO Philatelic Bureau, London EC 1 (Type B) (*ordinary*)	2·50

The Bureau did not provide a First Day Cover service for the 3d. phosphor stamp.

248 View near Hassocks, Sussex

249 Antrim, Northern Ireland

250 Harlech Castle, Wales

251 Cairngorm Mountains Scotland

4d. Green flaw on tree trunk (Cyl. 1B Dot, R. 3/4)

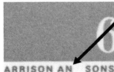

6d. 'AN' for 'AND' (Cyl. 1A No dot, R. 10/3)

1s.3d. Broken 'D' (Cyl. 2B, R. 14/2)

(Des L. Rosoman. Queen's portrait, adapted by D. Gentleman from coinage)

1966 (2 May). Landscapes. Chalk-surfaced paper. W **179**. Perf 15×14.

689	**248**	4d. black, yellow-green and new blue	10	10
		a. Green flaw	40·00	
		p. Three phosphor bands	10	10
		pa. Green flaw	35·00	
690	**249**	6d. black, emerald and new blue	10	10
		a. 'AN' for 'AND'	65·00	
		Wi. Watermark inverted	6·00	
		p. Three phosphor bands	10	10
		pa. 'AN' for 'AND'	65·00	
		pWi. Watermark inverted	£170	
691	**250**	1s.3d. black, greenish yellow and greenish blue	15	15
		a. Broken 'D'	35·00	
		p. Three phosphor bands	15	15
		pa. Broken 'D'	35·00	
692	**251**	1s.6d. black, orange and Prussian blue	15	15
		Wi. Watermark inverted	22·00	
		p. Three phosphor bands	15	15
Set of 4 (Ordinary)			40	40
Set of 4 (Phosphor)			40	40
First Day Cover (Ordinary)				3·50
First Day Cover (Phosphor)				4·50

Blocks of four of Nos. 689 and 690 are known with the Queen's head and face value omitted on one stamp and a partial omission on the second, due to a paper fold (*Price per block* £10,000)

Special First Day of Issue Postmark

GPO Philatelic Bureau, London EC 1 (Type B) (*ordinary*)	3·50
GPO Philatelic Bureau, London EC 1 (Type B) (*phosphor*)	4·50

First Day of Issue handstamps were provided at Lewes, Sussex; Coleraine, Co. Londonderry; Harlech, Merioneth and Grantown-on-Spey, Morayshire, for this issue.

252 Players with Ball

253 Goalmouth Mêlée

254 Goalkeeper saving Goal

(Des D. Gentleman (4d.), W. Kempster (6d.), D. Caplan (1s.3d.). Queen's portrait adapted by D. Gentleman from coinage)

1966 (1 June). World Cup Football Championship. Chalk-surfaced paper. W **179** (sideways on 4d.). Perf 14×15 (4d.) or 15×14 (others).

693	**252**	4d. red, reddish purple, bright blue, flesh and black	10	10
		p. Two phosphor bands	10	10
694	**253**	6d. black, sepia, red, apple green and blue	10	10
		a. Black omitted	£160	
		b. Apple-green omitted	£4500	
		c. Red omitted	£7000	
		Wi. Watermark inverted	5·00	
		p. Three phosphor bands	10	10
		pa. Black omitted	£1800	
695	**254**	1s.3d. black, blue, yellow, red and light yellow-olive	15	15
		a. Blue omitted	£300	
		Wi. Watermark inverted	£150	
		p. Three phosphor bands	15	15
		pWi. Watermark inverted	2·00	
Set of 3 (Ordinary)			30	30
Set of 3 (Phosphor)			30	30
First Day Cover (Ordinary)				9·00
First Day Cover (Phosphor)				11·50
Presentation Pack (Ordinary)			30·00	

Special First Day of Issue Postmark

GPO Philatelic Bureau, London EC 1 Type C) (ordinary)	9·00
GPO Philatelic Bureau, London EC 1 Type C) (phosphor)	11·50

A First Day of Issue handstamp was provided at Wembley, Middx, for this issue.

		ab. Black (value), etc. omitted* (block of four)	£10000	
		c. Black only omitted*	—	
		aWi. Watermark inverted (block of four)	18·00	
		p. Three phosphor bands	10	10
		pWi. Watermark inverted	20·00	
		pa. Block of 4. Nos. 696p/699p	40	40
		paWi. Watermark inverted (block of four)	85·00	
697	**256**	4d. black, greenish yellow, grey, emerald-green, bright blue and bistre	10	10
		b. Black '4d' only omitted	£2000	
		Wi. Watermark inverted	4·00	
		p. Three phosphor bands	10	10
		pWi. Watermark inverted	20·00	
698	**257**	4d. red, greenish yellow, black, grey, bistre, reddish brown and emerald-green	10	10
		a. Black only omitted*	4·00	
		Wi. Watermark inverted	4·00	
		p. Three phosphor bands	10	10
		pWi. Watermark inverted	20·00	
699	**258**	4d. black, reddish brown, greenish yellow, grey and bistre**	10	10
		b. Black '4d' only omitted***	£2000	
		Wi. Watermark inverted	4·00	
		p. Three phosphor bands	10	10
		pWi. Watermark inverted	20·00	
Set of 4 (Ordinary)			40	40
Set of 4 (Phosphor)			40	40
First Day Cover (Ordinary)				3·50
First Day Cover (Phosphor)				4·50
Presentation Pack (Ordinary)			15·00	

*   In No. 696ab the blue, bistre and reddish brown are also omitted but in No. 696c and 698a only the black is omitted.

** In No. 699 the black was printed over the bistre.

*** A partial omission caused by a dry print affecting only the face value on the last column of the sheet.

Nos. 696/699 were issued together *se-tenant* in blocks of four within the sheet.

Nos. 697b and 699b are the result of a partial impression of the black, rendering the '4d' only omitted.

Other colours omitted, and the stamps affected:

d.	Greenish yellow (Nos. 696/699)	£600
pd.	Greenish yellow (Nos. 696p/699p)	£1100
e.	Red (Nos. 696 and 698)	£600
f.	Emerald-green (Nos. 696/698)	£140
pf.	Emerald-green (Nos. 696p/698p)	£140
g.	Bright blue (Nos. 696/697)	£450
pg.	Bright blue (Nos. 696p and 697p)	£2500
h.	Bistre (Nos. 696/699)	£125
ph.	Bistre (Nos. 696p/699p)	£1100
j.	Reddish brown (Nos. 698/699)	£100
pj.	Reddish brown (Nos. 698p and 699p)	£140

The prices quoted are for each stamp.

Special First Day of Issue Postmark

GPO Philatelic Bureau, London EC 1 (Type C) (ordinary)	3·50
GPO Philatelic Bureau, London EC 1 (Type C) (phosphor)	4·50

255 Black-headed Gull

256 Blue Tit

257 European Robin

258 Blackbird

(Des J. Norris Wood)

1966 (8 Aug). British Birds. Chalk-surfaced paper. W **179**. Perf 15×14.

696	**255**	4d. grey, black, red, emerald-green, bright blue, greenish yellow and bistre	10	10
		Wi. Watermark inverted	4·00	
		a. Block of 4. Nos. 696/699	40	40

259 Cup Winners

1966 (18 Aug). England's World Cup Football Victory. Chalk-surfaced paper. W **179** (sideways). Perf 14×15.

700	**259**	4d. red, reddish purple, bright blue, flesh and black	10	10
First Day Cover				7·50

These stamps were only put on sale at post offices in England, the Channel Islands and the Isle of Man, and at the Philatelic Bureau in London and also, on 22 August, in Edinburgh on the occasion of the opening of the Edinburgh Festival as well as at Army post offices at home and abroad.

The Philatelic Bureau did not service First Day Covers for this stamp, but a First Day of Issue handstamp was provided inscribed 'Harrow & Wembley' to replace the 'Wembley Middx', postmark of the initial issue.

260 Jodrell Bank Radio Telescope

261 British Motor cars

262 SRN 6 Hovercraft

263 Windscale Reactor

6d. Broken 'D' (Cyl. 1C, R. 19/6)

(Des D. and A. Gillespie (4d., 6d.), A. Restall (others))

1966 (19 Sept). British Technology. Chalk-surfaced paper. W **179**. Perf 15×14.

701	**260**	4d. black and lemon...............................	10	10
		p. Three phosphor bands........................	10	10
702	**261**	6d. red, deep blue and orange.................	10	10
		a. Red (Mini cars) omitted.....................	£10000	
		b. Deep blue (Jaguar and inscr) omitted	£8000	
		c. Broken 'D'......................................	35·00	
		p. Three phosphor bands........................	10	10
		pc. Broken 'D'.....................................	35·00	
703	**262**	1s.3d. black, orange-red, slate and light greenish blue	15	15
		p. Three phosphor bands........................	20	20
704	**263**	1s.6d. black, yellow-green, bronze-green, lilac and deep blue	15	15
		p. Three phosphor bands........................	20	20
Set of 4 (Ordinary)..			40	40
Set of 4 (Phosphor)..			50	50
First Day Cover (Ordinary)....................................				2·50
First Day Cover (Phosphor)...................................				2·50
Presentation Pack (Ordinary)................................			20·00	

Special First Day of Issue Postmark

GPO Philatelic Bureau, Edinburgh 1 (Type C) (*ordinary*).................		2·50
GPO Philatelic Bureau, Edinburgh 1 (Type C) (*phosphor*)...............		2·50

264

265

266

267

268

269

270 Norman Ship

271 Norman Horsemen attacking Harold's Troops

1s.3d. Club flaw (Cyl. 1A No dot, R. 7/2)

(All the above are scenes from the Bayeux Tapestry)

(Des D. Gentleman. Photo. Queen's head die-stamped (6d., 1s.3d.))

1966 (14 Oct). 900th Anniversary of Battle of Hastings. Chalk-surfaced paper. W **179** (sideways on 1s.3d.). Perf 15×14.

705	**264**	4d. black, olive-green, bistre, deep blue, orange, magenta, green, blue and grey..................................	10	10
		a. Strip of 6. Nos. 705/710...................	60	60
		ab. Imperforate strip of 6......................	£1500	
		aWi. Strip of 6. Watermark inverted........	45·00	
		Wi. Watermark inverted.........................	7·00	
		p. Three phosphor bands........................	10	10
		pa. Strip of 6. Nos. 705p/710p...............	60	60
		pWi. Watermark inverted........................	3·00	
		paWi. Strip of 6. Watermark inverted........	20·00	
706	**265**	4d. black, olive-green, bistre, deep blue, orange, magenta, green, blue and grey..................................	10	10
		Wi. Watermark inverted.........................	7·00	
		p. Three phosphor bands........................	10	10
		pWi. Watermark inverted........................	2·00	
707	**266**	4d. black, olive-green, bistre, deep blue, orange, magenta, green, blue and grey..................................	10	10
		Wi. Watermark inverted.........................	7·00	
		p. Three phosphor bands........................	10	10
		pWi. Watermark inverted........................	3·00	
708	**267**	4d. black, olive-green, bistre, deep blue, magenta, green, blue and grey..................................	10	10
		Wi. Watermark inverted.........................	7·00	
		p. Three phosphor bands........................	10	10
		pWi. Watermark inverted........................	3·00	
709	**268**	4d. black, olive-green, bistre, deep blue, orange, magenta, green, blue and grey..................................	10	10
		Wi. Watermark inverted.........................	7·00	
		p. Three phosphor bands........................	10	10
		pWi. Watermark inverted........................	3·00	
710	**269**	4d. black, olive-green, bistre, deep blue, orange, magenta, green, blue and grey..................................	10	10
		Wi. Watermark inverted.........................	7·00	
		p. Three phosphor bands........................	10	10
		pWi. Watermark inverted........................	3·00	
711	**270**	6d. black, olive-green, violet, blue, green and gold............................	10	10
		Wi. Watermark inverted.........................	42·00	
		p. Three phosphor bands........................	10	10
		pWi. Watermark inverted........................	75·00	
712	**271**	1s.3d. black, lilac, bronze-green, rosine, bistre-brown and gold..................	20	30
		a. Lilac omitted...................................	£2750	
		b. Club flaw.......................................	28·00	
		Wi. Watermark sideways inverted (top of crown pointing to right)*.............	50·00	
		p. Four phosphor bands.........................	20	40
		pa. Lilac omitted..................................	£950	
		pb. Club flaw......................................	28·00	

pWi. Watermark sideways inverted (top of crown pointing to right)*	50·00	
Set of 8 (Ordinary)	85	1·00
Set of 8 (Phosphor)	85	1·00
First Day Cover (Ordinary)	2·00	
First Day Cover (Phosphor)	3·25	
Presentation Pack (Ordinary)	8·50	

* The normal sideways watermark shows the tops of the Crowns pointing to the left, *as seen from the back of the stamp.*

Nos. 705/710 show battle scenes and they were issued together *se-tenant* in horizontal strips of six within the sheet.

Other colours omitted in the 4d. values and the stamps affected:

b.	Olive-green (Nos. 705/710)	40·00
pb.	Olive-green (Nos. 705p/710p)	40·00
c.	Bistre (Nos. 705/710)	40·00
pc.	Bistre (Nos. 705p/710p)	40·00
d.	Deep blue (Nos. 705/710)	50·00
pd.	Deep blue (Nos. 705p/710p)	50·00
e.	Orange (Nos. 705/707 and 709/710)	40·00
pe.	Orange (Nos. 705p/707p and 709p/710p)	40·00
f.	Magenta (Nos. 705/710)	40·00
pf.	Magenta (Nos. 705p/710p)	40·00
g.	Green (Nos. 705/710)	38·00
pg.	Green (Nos. 705p/710p)	38·00
h.	Blue (Nos. 705/710)	30·00
ph.	Blue (Nos. 705p/710p)	40·00
j.	Grey (Nos. 705/710).	30·00
pj.	Grey (Nos. 705p/710p)	40·00
pk.	Magenta and green (Nos. 705p/710p)	—

The prices quoted are for each stamp.

Nos. 705 and 709, with grey and blue omitted, have been seen commercially used, posted from Middleton-in-Teesdale.

The 6d. phosphor is known in a yellowish gold as well as the reddish gold as used in the 1s.3d.

Three examples of No. 712 in a right-hand top corner block of 10 (2×5) are known with the Queen's head omitted as a result of a double paper fold prior to die-stamping. The perforation is normal. Of the other seven stamps, four have the Queen's head misplaced and three are normal.

MISSING GOLD HEADS. The 6d. and 1s.3d. were also issued with the die-stamped gold head omitted but as these can also be removed by chemical means we are not prepared to list them unless a way is found of distinguishing the genuine stamps from the fakes which will satisfy the Expert Committees.

The same remarks apply to Nos. 713/714.

Special First Day of Issue Postmark

GPO Philatelic Bureau, Edinburgh 1 (Type C) (*ordinary*)	2·00
GPO Philatelic Bureau, Edinburgh 1 (Type C) (*phosphor*)	3·25

A First Day of Issue handstamp was provided at Battle, Sussex, for this issue.

272 King of the Orient   **273** Snowman

3d. Missing 'T' (Cyl. 1E No dot, R. 6/2)

(Des Tasveer Shemza (3d.), J. Berry (1s.6d.) (winners of children's design competition). Photo, Queen's head die-stamped)

1966 (1 Dec). Christmas, Children's Paintings. Chalk-surfaced paper. W **179** (sideways on 3d.). Perf 14×15.

713	**272**	3d. black, blue, green, yellow, red and gold	10	10
		a. Queen's head double	—	†
		ab. Queen's head double, one albino	£350	
		b. Green omitted		£2500
		c. Missing 'T'	25·00	
		p. One phosphor band at right	10	10
		pa. Band at left	10	10
		pb. Horiz pair. Nos. 713p/713pa	20	20
		pc. Missing 'T'	45·00	
714	**273**	1s.6d. blue, red, pink, black and gold	10	10
		a. Pink (hat) omitted	£1800	
		Wi. Watermark inverted	30·00	
		p. Two phosphor bands	10	10
		pWi. Watermark inverted	90·00	
Set of 2 (Ordinary)			20	20
Set of 2 (Phosphor)			20	20
First Day Cover (Ordinary)			70	
First Day Cover (Phosphor)			70	
Presentation Pack (Ordinary)			10·00	

No. 713a refers to stamps showing two impressions, one directly below the other, both with embossing. Examples showing two partial strikes on opposite sides of the stamp, caused by a colour shift are common.

The single phosphor band on No. 713p was produced by printing broad phosphor bands across alternate perforations. Individual stamps show the band at right or left.

Special First Day of Issue Postmarks

GPO Philatelic Bureau, Edinburgh 1 (Type C) (*ordinary*)	70
GPO Philatelic Bureau, Edinburgh 1 (Type C) (*phosphor*)	70
Bethlehem, Llandeilo, Carms (Type C) (*ordinary*)	2·00
Bethlehem, Llandeilo, Carms (Type C) (*phosphor*)	2·00

274 Sea Freight   **275** Air Freight

1s.6d. Broken undercarriage leg (Cyl. 2, No dot, R. 13/6)

(Des C. Abbott)

1967 (20 Feb). European Free Trade Association (EFTA). Chalk-surfaced paper. W **179**. Perf 15×14.

715	**274**	9d. deep blue, red, lilac, green, brown, new blue, yellow and black	10	10
		a. Black (Queen's head, etc.), brown, new blue and yellow omitted	£900	
		b. Lilac omitted	£130	
		c. Green omitted	£130	
		d. Brown (rail trucks) omitted	80·00	
		e. New blue omitted	£130	
		f. Yellow omitted	£130	
		Wi. Watermark inverted	£140	
		p. Three phosphor bands	10	10
		pb. Lilac omitted	£180	
		pc. Green omitted	£130	
		pd. Brown omitted	80·00	
		pe. New blue omitted	£130	
		pf. Yellow omitted	£140	
		pWi. Watermark inverted	£1200	
716	**275**	1s.6d. violet, red, deep blue, brown, green, blue-grey, new blue, yellow and black	10	10
		a. Red omitted		
		b. Deep blue omitted	£425	
		c. Brown omitted	£130	
		d. Blue-grey omitted	£130	
		e. New blue omitted	£130	
		f. Yellow omitted	£130	
		g. Green omitted	£2000	
		h. Broken undercarriage leg	40·00	

p. Three phosphor bands.....................	10	10
pa. Red omitted..	—	
pb. Deep blue omitted..............................	£130	
pc. Brown omitted....................................	80·00	
pd. Blue-grey omitted...............................	£130	
pf. New blue omitted................................	£130	
ph. Broken undercarriage leg...................	40·00	
pWi. Watermark inverted..........................	50·00	
Set of 2 (Ordinary)...................................	20	20
Set of 2 (Phosphor).................................	20	20
First Day Cover (Ordinary).......................		5·00
First Day Cover (Phosphor)......................		5·00
Presentation Pack (Ordinary)..................	20·00	

Special First Day of Issue Postmark

GPO Philatelic Bureau, Edinburgh 1 (Type C) (*ordinary*).................	5·00
GPO Philatelic Bureau, Edinburgh 1 (Type C) (*phosphor*)..............	5·00

276 Hawthorn and Bramble

277 Larger Bindweed and Viper's Bugloss

278 Ox-eye Daisy, Coltsfoot and Buttercup

279 Bluebell, Red Campion and Wood Anemone

280 Dog Violet

281 Primroses

(Des Reverend W. Keble Martin (Types **276/279**), Mary Grierson (others))

1967 (24 Apr). British Wild Flowers. Chalk-surfaced paper. W **179**. Perf 15×14.

717	**276**	4d. grey, lemon, myrtle-green, red, agate and slate-purple.....	10	10
		a. Block of 4. Nos. 717/720.....................	40	40
		aWi. Block of 4. Watermark inverted.........	9·00	
		b. Grey double*.......................................		
		c. Red omitted...	£2750	
		f. Slate-purple omitted............................	£3250	
		Wi. Watermark inverted............................	2·00	
		p. Three phosphor bands........................	10	10
		pa. Block of 4. Nos. 717p/720p................	40	40
		paWi. Block of 4. Watermark inverted.......	9·00	
		pd. Agate omitted....................................	£2000	
		pf. Slate-purple omitted..........................	£425	
		pWi. Watermark inverted..........................	2·00	
718	**277**	4d. grey, lemon, myrtle-green, red, agate and violet..............	10	10
		b. Grey double*.......................................		
		Wi. Watermark inverted............................	2·00	
		p. Three phosphor bands........................	10	10
		pd. Agate omitted....................................	£2000	
		pe. Violet omitted....................................		
		pWi. Watermark inverted..........................	2·00	
719	**278**	4d. grey, lemon, myrtle-green, red and agate.................	10	10
		b. Grey double*.......................................		
		Wi. Watermark inverted............................	2·00	
		p. Three phosphor bands........................	10	10
		pd. Agate omitted....................................	£2000	
		pWi. Watermark inverted..........................	2·00	
720	**279**	4d. grey, lemon, myrtle-green, reddish purple, agate and violet........	10	10
		b. Grey double*.......................................		
		c. Reddish purple omitted........................	£1500	
		d. Value omitted†....................................	£7250	
		Wi. Watermark inverted............................	2·00	
		p. Three phosphor bands........................	10	10
		pd. Agate omitted....................................	£2000	
		pe. Violet omitted....................................		
		pWi. Watermark inverted..........................	2·00	
721	**280**	9d. lavender-grey, green, reddish violet and orange-yellow................	15	15
		Wi. Watermark inverted............................	1·25	
		p. Three phosphor bands........................	15	15

722	**281**	1s.9d. lavender-grey, green, greenish yellow and orange................	15	15
		p. Three phosphor bands........................	15	15
Set of 6 (Ordinary)....................................			50	50
Set of 6 (Phosphor)..................................			50	50
First Day Cover (Ordinary)........................				1·25
First Day Cover (Phosphor).......................				7·00
Presentation Pack (Ordinary)...................			20·00	
Presentation Pack (Phosphor).................			20·00	

* The double impression of the grey printing affects the Queen's head, value and inscription.

† No. 720d was caused by something obscuring the face value on R. 14/6 during the printing of one sheet.

Nos. 717/720 were issued together *se-tenant* in blocks of four within the sheet.

Special First Day of Issue Postmark

GPO Philatelic Bureau, Edinburgh 1 (Type C) (*ordinary*).................	1·20
GPO Philatelic Bureau, Edinburgh 1 (Type C) (*phosphor*)..............	7·00

PHOSPHOR BANDS. Issues from No. 723 are normally with phosphor bands only, except for the high values but most stamps have appeared with the phosphor bands omitted in error. Such varieties are listed under 'y' numbers and are priced unused only. See also further notes after 1971–1996 Decimal Machin issue.

PHOSPHORISED PAPER. Following the adoption of phosphor bands the Post Office started a series of experiments involving the addition of the phosphor to the paper coating before the stamps were printed. No. 743c was the first of these experiments to be issued for normal postal use. See also notes after 1971–1996 Decimal Machin issue.

PVA GUM. Polyvinyl alcohol was introduced by Harrisons in place of gum arabic in 1968. As it is almost invisible a small amount of pale yellowish colouring was introduced to make it possible to check that the stamps had been gummed. Although this can be distinguished from gum arabic in unused stamps there is, of course, no means of detecting it in used examples. Where the two forms of gum exist on the same stamps, the PVA type are listed under 'v' numbers, except in the case of the 1d. and 4d. (vermilion), both one centre band, which later appeared with gum arabic and these have 'g' numbers. 'v' and 'g' numbers are priced unused only. All stamps printed from No. 763 onwards were issued with PVA gum only *except where otherwise stated.*

It should be further noted that gum arabic is shiny in appearance, and that, normally, PVA gum has a matt appearance. However, depending upon the qualities of the paper ingredients and the resultant absorption of the gum, occasionally, PVA gum has a shiny appearance. In such cases, especially in stamps from booklets, it is sometimes impossible to be absolutely sure which gum has been used except by testing the stamps chemically which destroys them. Therefore, whilst all gum arabic is shiny it does not follow that all shiny gum is gum arabic.

282   **282a**

Two types of the 2d.

I. Value spaced away from left side of stamp (cylinders 1 no dot and dot).

II. Value close to left side from new multipositive used for cylinders 5 no dot and dot onwards. The portrait appears in the centre, thus conforming to the other values.

Three types of the Machin head, known as Head A, B or C, are distinguished by specialists. These are illustrated in Vol. 3 of the *Great Britain Specialised Catalogue.*

(Des after plaster cast by Arnold Machin)

1967 (5 June)–**70**. Chalk-surfaced paper. Two phosphor bands *except where otherwise stated.* PVA gum except Nos. 725m, 728, 729, 731, 731a, 740, 742/742a, 743/743a and 744/744a. No wmk. Perf 15×14.

723	**282**	½d. orange-brown (5.2.68).......................	10	10
		y. Phosphor omitted...............................	30·00	
724		1d. light olive (*shades*) (2 bands) (5.2.68).................	10	10
		a. Imperf (coil strip)†...............................	£3000	
		b. Part perf pane*...................................	£4000	
		c. Imperf pane*.......................................	£4250	
		d. Uncoated paper (1970)**....................	£150	
		y. Phosphor omitted...............................	4·00	
		l. Booklet pane. No. 724×2 *se-tenant* with 730×2 (6.4.68).............	3·00	
		ly. Booklet pane. Phosphor omitted......	90·00	

	m. Booklet pane. No. 724×4 se-tenant with 734×2 (6.1.69)................	3·50	
	my. Booklet pane. Phosphor omitted....	£225	
	n. Booklet pane. No. 724×6, 734×3, 734b×3 and 735×3 se-tenant (1.12.69)....................	8·50	
	na. Booklet pane. Uncoated paper**......	£3000	
	ny. Booklet pane. Phosphor omitted......	£225	
	s. Optd 'SPECIMEN' (14 mm).............	£250	
725	1d. yellowish olive (16.9.68)........	45	45
	g. Gum arabic (27.8.69).................	1·00	
	l. Booklet pane. No. 725×4 se-tenant with 732×2........................	4·00	
	ly. Booklet pane. Phosphor omitted....	35·00	
	m. Coil strip. No. 728×2 se-tenant with 729, 725g and 733g (27.8.69)........	2·50	
726	2d. lake-brown (Type I) (2 bands) (5.2.68)...........................	10	10
	y. Phosphor omitted..................	40·00	
727	2d. lake-brown (Type II) (2 bands) (1969)...........................	10	10
	y. Phosphor omitted..................	2·00	
728	2d. lake-brown (Type II) (1 centre band) (27.8.69)..................	35	40
729	3d. violet (shades) (1 centre band) (8.8.67)...........................	10	10
	a. Imperf (vert pair).................	£950	
	y. Phosphor omitted..................	4·00	
	v. PVA gum (shades) (12.3.68)........	1·00	
	vy. Phosphor omitted................	4·00	
730	3d. violet (2 bands) (6.4.68)........	10	15
	a. Uncoated paper**.................	£6000	
731	4d. deep sepia (shades) (2 bands)......	10	10
	y. Phosphor omitted..................	4·00	
	a. Deep olive-brown.................	1·00	1·00
	ay. Phosphor omitted................	6·00	
	b. Part perf pane*...................	£3250	
	v. PVA gum (shades) (22.1.68)........	1·00	
	vy. Phosphor omitted................	4·00	
732	4d. deep olive-brown (shades) (1 centre band) (16.9.68).............	10	10
	a. Part perf pane*...................	£3500	
	l. Booklet pane. Two stamps plus two printed labels................	1·00	
	ly. Booklet pane. Phosphor omitted......	60·00	
733	4d. bright vermilion (1 centre band) (6.1.69)...........................	10	10
	a. Tête-bêche (horiz pair)..........	£4000	
	b. Uncoated paper**.................	20·00	
	y. Phosphor omitted..................	4·00	
	l. Booklet pane. Two stamps plus two printed labels (3.3.69)........	1·00	
	ly. Booklet pane. Phosphor omitted......	75·00	
	g. Gum arabic (27.8.69).................	1·00	
	gy. Phosphor omitted................	£175	
	s. Optd 'SPECIMEN' (14 mm).............	45·00	
734	4d. bright vermilion (1 band at left) (6.1.69)...........................	65	75
	a. Uncoated paper**.................	£425	
	s. Optd 'SPECIMEN' (14 mm).............	£275	
	b. One band at right (1.12.69)........	1·00	1·00
	bs. optd 'SPECIMEN' (14 mm)........	£275	
	ba. Ditto. Uncoated paper**..........	£425	
735	5d. royal blue (shades) (1.7.68)........	10	10
	a. Imperf pane*.....................	£2750	
	b. Part perf pane*...................	£2000	
	c. Imperf (pair)††..................	£350	
	d. Uncoated paper**.................	40·00	
	y. Phosphor omitted..................	6·00	
	e. Deep blue........................	1·00	1·00
	ey. Phosphor omitted................	6·00	
	s. Optd 'SPECIMEN' (14 mm).............	60·00	
736	6d. bright reddish purple (shades) (5.2.68)...........................	10	10
	y. Phosphor omitted..................	35·00	
	a. Bright magenta...................	9·00	9·00
	b. Claret...........................	1·25	1·25
	by. Phosphor omitted................	45·00	
737	**282a** 7d. bright emerald (1.7.68)........	25	25
	y. Phosphor omitted..................	£100	
738	8d. bright vermilion (1.7.68)........	10	15
	y. Phosphor omitted..................	£450	
739	8d. light turquoise-blue (6.1.69)........	25	25
	y. Phosphor omitted..................	80·00	
740	9d. myrtle-green (8.8.67)........	25	25
	y. Phosphor omitted..................	60·00	
	v. PVA gum (29.11.68)................	1·00	
	vy. Phosphor omitted................	£120	
741	**282** 10d. drab (1.7.68)........	25	25
	a. Uncoated paper**.................	85·00	
	y. Phosphor omitted..................	85·00	
742	1s. light bluish violet (shades)........	20	20
	y. Phosphor omitted..................	£120	
	a. Pale bluish violet...............	1·00	1·00
	av. PVA gum (26.4.68)................	1·00	
	avy. Phosphor omitted...............	12·00	
743	1s.6d. greenish blue and deep blue (shades) (8.8.67)..................	25	25

	a. Greenish blue omitted...........	£160	
	y. Phosphor omitted..................	15·00	
	v. PVA gum (28.8.68)................	1·00	
	va. Greenish blue omitted...........	£100	
	vy. Phosphor omitted................	22·00	
	vb. Prussian blue and indigo........	7·00	7·00
	vby. Phosphor omitted...............	18·00	
	c. Phosphorised paper (Prussian blue and indigo) (10.12.69)........	30	35
	ca. Prussian blue omitted...........	£450	
744	1s.9d. dull orange and black (shades)........	25	25
	y. Phosphor omitted..................	65·00	
	a. Bright orange and black..........	1·00	1·00
	av. PVA gum (16.11.70)...............	2·50	
723/744	*Set of 16* (one of each value and colour).............	2·00	2·25
	Presentation Pack (one of each value) (1968).............	7·00	
	Presentation Pack (German) (1969).............	90·00	

*   BOOKLET ERRORS. See note after No. 556.
** Uncoated paper. This does not respond to the chalk test, and may be further distinguished from the normal chalk-surfaced paper by the fibres which clearly show on the surface, resulting in the printing impression being rougher, and by the screening dots which are not so evident. The 1d., 4d. and 5d. come from the £1 Stamps for Cooks Booklet (1969); the 3d. and 10d. from sheets (1969). The 20p. and 50p. high values (Nos. 830/831) exist with similar errors.

†   No. 724a occurs in a vertical strip of four, top stamp perforated on three sides, bottom stamp imperf three sides and the two middle stamps completely imperf.

†† No. 735c comes from the original state of cylinder 15 which is identifiable by the screening dots which extend through the gutters of the stamps and into the margins of the sheet. This must not be confused with imperforate stamps from cylinder 10, a large quantity of which was stolen from the printers early in 1970.

The 1d. with centre band and PVA gum (No. 725) only came in the September 1968 10s. booklet (No. XP6). The 1d., 2d. and 4d. with centre band and gum arabic (Nos. 725g, 728 and 733g respectively) only came in the coil strip (No. 725m).

The 3d. (No. 730) appeared in booklets on 6.4.68, from coils during December 1968 and from sheets in January 1969.

The 4d. with one side band at left (No. 734) came from 10s. (band at left) and £1 (band at left or right) booklet se-tenant panes, and the 4d. with one side band at right (No. 734b) came from the £1 booklet se-tenant panes only.

Gum. The 1d. (No. 725), 3d. (No. 729), 4d. (Nos. 731 and 733), 9d., 1s., 1s.6d. and 1s.9d. exist with gum arabic as well as PVA gum; the 2d. (No. 728) and coil strip (No. 725m) exist only with gum arabic, while the remainder have PVA gum only.

The 4d. (No. 731) in shades of washed-out grey are colour changelings which we understand are caused by the concentrated solvents used in modern dry cleaning methods.

For decimal issue, see Nos. X841, etc.

First Day Covers

5.6.67	Nos. 731, 742, 744	2·00	
8.8.67	Nos. 729, 740, 743	2·00	
5.2.68	Nos. 723/724, 726, 736	2·25	
1.7.68	Nos. 735, 737/738, 741	3·00	

283 *Master Lambton* (Sir Thomas Lawrence)   **284** *Mares and Foals in a Landscape* (George Stubbs)

285 *Children Coming Out of School* (L. S. Lowry)

(Des S. Rose)

1967 (10 July). British Paintings (1st series). Chalk-surfaced paper. Two phosphor bands. No wmk. Perf 14×15 (4d.) or 15×14 (others).

748	**283**	4d. rose-red, lemon, brown, black, new blue and gold............	10	10
		a. Gold (value and Queen's head) omitted................	£200	

		b. New blue omitted	£8500	
		y. Phosphor omitted	7·00	
749	**284**	9d. Venetian red, ochre, grey-black, new-blue, greenish yellow and black	10	10
		a. Black (Queen's head and value) omitted	£775	
		ab. Black (Queen's head only) omitted.	£1200	
		y. Phosphor omitted	£500	
750	**285**	1s.6d. greenish yellow, grey, rose, new blue, grey-black and gold	10	10
		a. Gold (Queen's head) omitted	£200	
		b. New blue omitted	£200	
		c. Grey (clouds and shading) omitted	£120	
		y. Phosphor omitted	£300	
Set of 3			30	30
First Day Cover				1·00
Presentation Pack			20·00	

See also Nos. 771/774.

Special First Day of Issue Postmark

GPO Philatelic Bureau, Edinburgh 1 (Type C)...................... 2·00

A First Day of Issue handstamp was provided at Bishop Auckland, Co. Durham, for this issue.

286 *Gipsy Moth IV*

(Des M. and Sylvia Goaman)

1967 (24 July). Sir Francis Chichester's World Voyage. Chalk-surfaced paper. Three phosphor bands. No wmk. Perf 15×14.

751	**286**	1s.9d. black, brown-red, light emerald and blue	10	10
First Day Cover				40

Special First Day of Issue Postmark

GPO Philatelic Bureau, Edinburgh 1	2·50
Greenwich, London SE10	2·50
Plymouth, Devon	2·50

The Philatelic Bureau and Greenwich postmarks are similar in design to that for Plymouth. A First Day of Issue handstamp was provided at Chichester, Sussex for this date.

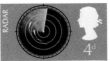

287 Radar Screen

288 *Penicillium notatum*

289 Vickers VC-10 Jet Engines

290 Television Equipment

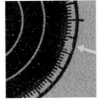

4d. Broken scale (Cyl. 1c, R. 10/2)

(Des C. Abbott (4d., 1s.), Negus-Sharland team (others))

1967 (19 Sept). British Discovery and Invention. Chalk-surfaced paper. Three phosphor bands (4d.) or two phosphor bands (others). W **179** (sideways on 1s.9d.). Perf 14×15 (1s.9d.) or 15×14 (others).

752	**287**	4d. greenish yellow, black and vermilion	10	10
		a. Broken scale	45·00	
		y. Phosphor omitted	5·00	
753	**288**	1s. blue-green, light greenish blue, slate-purple and bluish violet	10	10
		Wi. Watermark inverted	20·00	
		y. Phosphor omitted	10·00	
754	**289**	1s.6d. black, grey, royal blue, ochre and turquoise-blue	10	10
		Wi. Watermark inverted	£325	
		y. Phosphor omitted	£600	
755	**290**	1s.9d. black, grey-blue, pale olive-grey, violet and orange	10	10
		a. Pale olive-grey omitted	—	£3500
		b. Orange (Queen's head) omitted	£600	
		y. Phosphor omitted	£600	
Set of 4			40	40
First Day Cover				70
Presentation Pack			9·00	

Special First Day of Issue Postmark

GPO Philatelic Bureau, Edinburgh (Type C)....................... 70

> **WATERMARK.** All issues from this date are on unwatermarked paper *unless otherwise stated.*

291 *The Adoration of the Shepherds* (School of Seville)

292 *Madonna and Child* (Murillo)

293 *The Adoration of the Shepherds* (Louis le Nain)

(Des S. Rose)

1967. Christmas, Paintings. Chalk-surfaced paper. One phosphor band (3d.) or two phosphor bands (others). Perf 15×14 (1s.6d.) or 14×15 (others).

756	**291**	3d. olive-yellow, rose, blue, black and gold (27.11)	10	10
		a. Gold (value and Queen's head) omitted	90·00	
		ab. Gold (Queen's head only) omitted..	£1100	
		ac. Gold (value only) omitted	£1100	
		b. Printed on the gummed side	£500	
		c. Rose omitted	£2750	
		d. Olive-yellow omitted	—	
		y. Phosphor omitted	1·00	
757	**292**	4d. bright purple, greenish yellow, new blue, grey-black and gold (18.10)	10	10
		a. Gold (value and Queen's head) omitted	70·00	
		ab. Gold (Queen's head only) omitted..	£2500	
		b. Gold ('4D' only) omitted	£1300	
		c. Greenish yellow (Child, robe and Madonna's face) omitted	£3750	
		d. Greenish yellow and gold omitted.	£8000	
		y. Phosphor omitted	£175	

758	**293**	1s.6d. bright purple, bistre, lemon, black, orange-red, ultramarine and gold (27.11)......................		15	15
		a. Gold (value and Queen's head) omitted...............................	£8000		
		ab. Gold (value only) omitted...............	£1500		
		ac. Gold (Queen's head only) omitted..	£1500		
		b. Ultramarine omitted.......................	£500		
		c. Lemon omitted...............................	£9000		
		y. Phosphor omitted...........................	12·00		
		Set of 3..		30	30
		First Day Covers (2)...........................			3·00

Distinct shades exist of the 3d. and 4d. values but are not listable as there are intermediate shades. For the 4d., stamps from one machine show a darker background and give the appearance of the yellow colour being omitted, but this is not so and these should not be confused with the true missing yellow No. 757c.

No. 757b comes from stamps in the first vertical row of a sheet.

The 3d. and 4d. values are known imperforate. They are of proof status.

Special First Day of Issue Postmarks

GPO Philatelic Bureau, Edinburgh 1 (4d.) (18 October) (Type C)...	1·00
GPO Philatelic Bureau, Edinburgh 1 (3d., 1s.6d.) (27 November) (Type C)............	2·00
Bethlehem, Llandeilo, Carms (4d.) (18 October) (Type C).............	2·00
Bethlehem, Llandeilo, Carms (3d., 1s.6d.) (27 November) (Type C)............	3·00

Gift Pack

1967 (27 Nov). Comprises Nos. 715p/722p and 748/758

CP758c	Gift Pack....................................	2·25

166 Carrickfergus Castle   **167** Caernarvon Castle

168 Edinburgh Castle   **169** Windsor Castle

(Recess Bradbury Wilkinson)

1967–68. No wmk. White paper. Perf 11×12.

759	**166**	2s.6d. black-brown (1.7.68)........................	10	20
760	**167**	5s. red (10.4.68).................................	50	50
761	**168**	10s. bright ultramarine (10.4.68).............	4·50	2·00
762	**169**	£1 black (4.12.67).............................	6·50	2·00
		Set of 4..	10·00	4·25

PVA GUM. All the following issues from this date have PVA gum *except where footnotes state otherwise*

294 Tarr Steps, Exmoor   **295** Aberfeldy Bridge

296 Menai Bridge   **297** M4 Viaduct

(Des A. Restall (9d.), L. Rosoman (1s.6d.), J. Matthews (others))

1968 (29 Apr). British Bridges. Chalk-surfaced paper. Two phosphor bands. Perf 15×14.

763	**294**	4d. black, bluish violet, turquoise-blue and gold....................		10	10
		a. Printed on gummed side................	35·00		
		y. Phosphor omitted...........................	10·00		
764	**295**	9d. red-brown, myrtle-green, ultramarine, olive-brown, black and gold....................		10	15
		a. Gold (Queen's head) omitted..........	£225		
		b. Ultramarine omitted........................	†	£3750	
		y. Phosphor omitted...........................	15·00		
765	**296**	1s.6d. olive-brown, red-orange, bright green, turquoise-green and gold....		15	20
		a. Gold (Queen's head) omitted..........	£300		
		b. Red-orange (rooftops) omitted........	£300		
		y. Phosphor omitted...........................	50·00		
766	**297**	1s.9d. olive-brown, greenish yellow, dull green, deep ultramarine and gold....		15	25
		a. Gold (Queen's head) omitted..........	£275		
		y. Phosphor omitted...........................	10·00		
		ya. Gold (Queen's head) and Phosphor omitted...............	£900		
		Set of 4..		45	65
		First Day Cover..................................			90
		Presentation Pack...............................		5·25	

No. 764b is only known on First day covers posted from Canterbury, Kent or the Philatelic Bureau, Edinburgh.

Used examples of the 1s.6d. and 1s.9d. are known with both the gold and the phosphor omitted.

Special First Day of Issue Postmarks

GPO Philatelic Bureau, Edinburgh 1.................................	2·25
Bridge, Canterbury, Kent...	10·00
Aberfeldy, Perthshire (Type A) (9d. value only).....................	10·00
Menai Bridge, Anglesey (Type A) (1s.6d. value only).................	10·00

The Bridge, Canterbury, postmark is similar in design to that for the Philatelic Bureau.

298 'TUC' and Trades Unionists   **299** Mrs Emmeline Pankhurst (statue)

300 Sopwith Camel and English Electric Lightning Fighters   **301** Captain Cook's *Endeavour* and Signature

(Des D. Gentleman (4d.), C. Abbott (others))

1968 (29 May). Anniversaries (1st series). Events described on stamps. Chalk-surfaced paper. Two phosphor bands. Perf 15×14.

767	**298**	4d. emerald, olive, blue and black........		10	10
		y. Phosphor omitted...........................	40·00		
768	**299**	9d. reddish violet, bluish grey and black....................		10	10
		y. Phosphor omitted...........................	10·00		
769	**300**	1s. olive-brown, blue, red, slate-blue and black....................		15	20
		y. Phosphor omitted...........................	10·00		
770	**301**	1s.9d. yellow-ochre and blackish brown...		20	25
		y. Phosphor omitted...........................	£190		
		Set of 4..		50	60
		First Day Cover..................................			2·50
		Presentation Pack...............................		5·00	

See also Nos. 791/795 and 819/823.

Special First Day of Issue Postmarks

GPO Philatelic Bureau, Edinburgh 1 (Type C)......................	3·00
Manchester (4d. value only)...	1·00
Aldeburgh, Suffolk (9d. value only)..................................	2·00
Hendon, London NW 4 (1s. value only).............................	3·00
Whitby, Yorkshire (1s.9d. value only)................................	4·00

The Philatelic Bureau postmark was used on sets of four, but the other postmarks were only available on single stamps.

302 *Queen Elizabeth I* (unknown artist)

303 *Pinkie* (Sir Thomas Lawrence)

304 *Ruins of St Mary le Port* (John Piper)

305 *The Hay Wain* (John Constable)

(Des S. Rose)

1968 (12 Aug). British Paintings (2nd series). Queen's head embossed. Chalk-surfaced paper. Two phosphor bands. Perf 15×14 (1s.9d.) or 14×15 (others).

771	**302**	4d. black, vermilion, greenish yellow, grey and gold..................	10	10
		a. Gold (value and Queen's head) omitted......................	£250	
		b. Vermilion omitted*..................	£550	
		c. Embossing omitted................	90·00	
		y. Phosphor omitted.................	1·50	
		ya. Gold (value and Queen's head) omitted and Phosphor omitted......	£2750	
772	**303**	1s. mauve, new blue, greenish yellow, black, magenta and gold............	10	15
		a. Gold (value and Queen's head) omitted..................	£5000	
		b. Gold (value and Queen's head), embossing and phosphor omitted	£500	
		c. Embossing omitted.................		
		y. Phosphor omitted.................	7·00	
773	**304**	1s.6d. slate, orange, black, mauve, greenish yellow, ultramarine and gold..................	15	20
		a. Gold (value and Queen's head) omitted................	£250	
		b. Embossing omitted...............	£275	
		y. Phosphor omitted................	10·00	
774	**305**	1s.9d. greenish yellow, black, new blue, red and gold................	15	20
		a. Gold (value and Queen's head) and embossing omitted.............	£750	
		b. Red omitted................	£5250	
		c. Embossing omitted...............	£140	
		y. Phosphor omitted................	20·00	
		Set of 4..	45	60
		First Day Cover.............................		1·00
		Presentation Pack (PO Pack No. 1).......	4·50	
		Presentation Pack (German)...............	30·00	

* The effect of this is to leave the face and hands white and there is more yellow and olive in the costume.

No. 774a is only known with the phosphor also omitted.

The 4d. also exists with the value only omitted resulting from a colour shift.

Special First Day of Issue Postmark

GPO Philatelic Bureau, Edinburgh 1 (Type C)..................... 2·00

Gift Pack

1968 (16 Sept). Comprises Nos. 763/774.

CP774c	Gift Pack................................	3·00	
CP774d	Gift Pack (German)..................	80·00	

Collectors Pack

1968 (1 Sept). Comprises Nos. 752/758 and 763/774.

CP774e	Collectors Pack (Pack No. 3)........	2·50

306 Boy and Girl with Rocking Horse

307 *Girl with Doll's House*

308 *Boy with Train Set*

(Des Rosalind Dease. Head printed in gold and then embossed)

1968 (25 Nov). Christmas, Children's Toys. Chalk-surfaced paper. One centre phosphor band (4d.) or two phosphor bands (others). Perf 15×14 (4d.) or 14×15 (others).

775	**306**	4d. black, orange, vermilion, ultramarine, bistre and gold...........	10	10
		a. Gold omitted........................	£3000	
		b. Vermilion omitted*...............	£450	
		c. Ultramarine omitted..............	£425	
		d. Bistre omitted......................	†	—
		e. Orange omitted.....................	†	—
		f. Embossing omitted................	6·00	
		y. Phosphor omitted................	5·00	
		ya. Embossing and Phosphor omitted		
776	**307**	9d. yellow-olive, black, brown, yellow, magenta, orange, turquoise-green and gold..............	15	15
		a. Yellow omitted....................	£150	
		b. Turquoise-green (dress) omitted....	£1200	
		c. Embossing omitted................	6·00	
		y. Phosphor omitted................	10·00	
		ya. Embossing and Phosphor omitted	10·00	
777	**308**	1s.6d. ultramarine, yellow-orange, bright purple, blue-green, black and gold......................	15	20
		a. Embossing omitted................	15·00	
		y. Phosphor omitted................	15·00	
		Set of 3.....................................	35	40
		First Day Cover............................		1·00
		Presentation Pack (PO Pack No. 4)........	9·00	
		Presentation Pack (German)...............	30·00	

No. 775c is only known with phosphor also omitted.

Two machines were used for printing for the 4d. value:

Stamps from cylinders 1A-1B-2C-1D-1E in combination with 1F, 2F or 3F (gold) were printed entirely on the Rembrandt sheet-fed machine. They invariably have the Queen's head level with the top of the boy's head and the sheets are perforated through the left side margin.

Stamps from cylinders 2A-2B-3C-2D-2E in combination with 1F, 2F, 3F or 4F (gold) were printed on the reel-fed Thrissell machine in five colours (its maximum colour capacity) and subsequently sheet-fed on the Rembrandt machine for the Queen's head and the embossing. The position of the Queen's head is generally lower than on the stamps printed at one operation but it varies in different parts of the sheet and is not, therefore, a sure indication for identifying single stamps. Another small difference is that the boy's grey pullover is noticeably 'moth-eaten' in the Thrissell printings and is normal on the Rembrandt. The Thrissell printings are perforated through the top margin.

Special First Day of Issue Postmarks

GPO Philatelic Bureau, Edinburgh 1 (Type C).....................	1·00
Bethlehem, Llandeilo, Carms (Type C).............................	2·50

309 RMS *Queen Elizabeth 2*

310 Elizabethan Galleon

311 East Indiaman

312 *Cutty Sark*

313 SS *Great Britain*

314 RMS *Mauretania*

(Des D. Gentleman)

1969 (15 Jan). British Ships. Chalk-surfaced paper. Two vertical phosphor bands at right (1s.), one horizontal phosphor band (5d.) or two phosphor bands (9d.). Perf 15×14.

778	**309**	5d. black, grey, red and turquoise.........	10	10
		a. Black (Queen's head, value, hull and inscr) omitted...........................	£2500	
		b. Grey (decks, etc.) omitted.................	£180	
		c. Red (inscription) omitted..................	£180	
		y. Phosphor omitted.............................	5·00	
		ya. Red and phosphor omitted.............	£140	
779	**310**	9d. red, blue, ochre, brown, black and grey...	10	10
		a. Strip of 3. Nos. 779/781....................	40	50
		ab. Red and blue omitted......................	£2250	
		ac. Blue omitted....................................	£2250	
		y. Phosphor omitted.............................	12·00	
		ya. Strip of 3. Nos. 779/781. Phosphor omitted..	40·00	
780	**311**	9d. ochre, brown, black and grey.........	10	10
		y. Phosphor omitted.............................	12·00	
781	**312**	9d. ochre, brown, black and grey.........	10	10
		y. Phosphor omitted.............................	12·00	
782	**313**	1s. brown, black, grey, green and greenish yellow...............................	15	15
		a. Pair. Nos. 782/783...........................	50	60
		ab. Greenish yellow omitted.................	£2750	
		y. Phosphor omitted.............................	32·00	
		ya. Pair. Nos. 782/783. Phosphor omitted..	65·00	
783	**314**	1s. red, black, brown, carmine and grey..	15	15
		a. Carmine (hull overlay) omitted.......	£16000	
		b. Red (funnels) omitted.......................	£12000	
		c. Carmine and red omitted..................	£12000	
		y. Phosphor omitted.............................	32·00	
Set of 6..			80	1·00
First Day Cover..				1·50
Presentation Pack (PO Pack No. 5).......................			3·00	
Presentation Pack (German).................................			38·00	

The 9d. and 1s. values were arranged in horizontal strips of three and pairs respectively throughout the sheet.

No. 779ab is known only with the phosphor also omitted.

Special First Day of Issue Postmark

GPO Philatelic Bureau, Edinburgh 1 (Type C)..................................... 1·75

315 Concorde in Flight

316 Plan and Elevation Views

317 Concorde's Nose and Tail

(Des M. and Sylvia Goaman (4d.), D. Gentleman (9d., 1s.6d.))

1969 (3 Mar). First Flight of Concorde. Chalk-surfaced paper. Two phosphor bands. Perf 15×14.

784	**315**	4d. yellow-orange, violet, greenish blue, blue-green and pale green....	10	10
		a. Violet (value etc.) omitted...............	£575	
		b. Yellow-orange omitted......................	£575	
		y. Phosphor omitted.............................	2·00	
		ya. Yellow-orange and phosphor omitted..	£575	
785	**316**	9d. ultramarine, emerald, red and grey-blue...	15	15
		a. Face value and inscr omitted..........	—	
		y. Phosphor omitted.............................	£140	
786	**317**	1s.6d. deep blue, silver-grey and light blue..	15	15
		a. Silver-grey omitted...........................	£575	
		y. Phosphor omitted.............................	10·00	
Set of 3..			35	35
First Day Cover..				4·00
Presentation Pack (PO Pack No. 6).......................			7·50	
Presentation Pack (German).................................			75·00	

No. 785a is caused by a colour shift of the grey-blue. On the only known example the top of the Queen's head appears across the perforations at foot.

No. 786a affects the Queen's head which appears in the light blue colour.

Special First Day of Issue Postmarks

GPO Philatelic Bureau, Edinburgh (Type C).. 4·00
Filton, Bristol (Type C)... 12·00

318 Queen Elizabeth II (See also T **357**)

(Des after plaster cast by Arnold Machin. Eng Robert Goodbehear and Nigel Alan Dow (portrait) and J. G. Heymes (background and lettering). Recess Bradbury Wilkinson)

1969 (5 Mar). Perf 12.

787	**318**	2s.6d. brown...	20	20
788		5s. crimson-lake.......................................	85	25
789		10s. deep ultramarine..............................	3·00	3·75
790		£1 bluish black...	1·75	75
Set of 4..			5·00	4·50
First Day Cover..				6·50
Presentation Pack (PO Pack No. 7).......................			16·00	
Presentation Pack (German).................................			55·00	

Special First Day of Issue Postmarks

GPO Philatelic Bureau (Type C)... 12·00
Windsor, Berks (Type C)... 18·00

For decimal issue, see Nos. 829/831b and notes after No. 831b.

319 Page from *Daily Mail*, and Vickers FB-27 Vimy Aircraft

320 Europa and CEPT Emblems

321 ILO Emblem

322 Flags of NATO Countries

323 Vickers FB-27 Vimy Aircraft
and Globe showing Flight

(Des P. Sharland (5d., 1s., 1s.6d.), M. and Sylvia Goaman (9d., 1s.9d.))

1969 (2 Apr). Anniversaries (2nd series). Events described on stamps. Chalk-surfaced paper. Two phosphor bands. Perf 15×14.

791	**319**	5d. black, pale sage-green, chestnut and new blue..............	10	10
		y. Phosphor omitted.........................	£180	
792	**320**	9d. pale turquoise, deep blue, light emerald-green and black..............	10	15
		y. Phosphor omitted..........................	18·00	
		a. Uncoated paper*............................	£1500	
		ay. Phosphor omitted.........................	—	
793	**321**	1s. bright purple, deep blue and lilac. .	15	20
		y. Phosphor omitted..........................	15·00	
794	**322**	1s.6d. red, royal blue, yellow-green, black, lemon and new blue..............	15	20
		e. Black omitted................................	£100	
		f. Yellow-green (from flags) omitted..	70·00	
		fy. Yellow-green and phosphor omitted.................................	70·00	
		g. Lemon (from flags) omitted.............	9·00 †	£3000
		y. Phosphor omitted..........................	9·00	
795	**323**	1s.9d. yellow-olive, greenish yellow and pale turquoise-green..............	25	30
		a. Uncoated paper*............................	£275	
		y. Phosphor omitted..........................	10·00	
Set of 5............			65	80
First Day Cover............				1·10
Presentation Pack (PO Pack No. 9)............			4·50	
Presentation Pack (German)............			50·00	

* Uncoated paper. The second note after No. 744 also applies here. No. 794g is only known used on First Day Cover from Liverpool. A trial of the 9d value in green and red is known.

Special First Day of Issue Postmarks
GPO Philatelic Bureau, Edinburgh (Type C)........................ 1·10

324 Durham Cathedral

325 York Minster

326 St Giles, Edinburgh

327 Canterbury Cathedral

328 St Paul's Cathedral

329 Liverpool Metropolitan Cathedral

(Des P. Gauld)

1969 (28 May). British Architecture (1st series). Cathedrals. Chalk-surfaced paper. Two phosphor bands. Perf 15×14.

796	**324**	5d. grey-black, orange, pale bluish violet and black..............	10	10
		a. Block of 4. Nos. 796/799......................	40	50
		ab. Block of 4. Uncoated paper†..................	£850	
		b. Pale bluish violet omitted..................	£6000	
797	**325**	5d. grey-black, pale bluish violet, new blue and black..............	10	10
		b. Pale bluish violet omitted..................	£6000	
798	**326**	5d. grey-black, purple, green and black..	10	10
		c. Green omitted*............................	90·00	
799	**327**	5d. grey-black, green, new blue and black..............	10	10
800	**328**	9d. grey-black, ochre, pale drab, violet and black..............	15	20

		a. Black (value) omitted..........................	£200	
		y. Phosphor omitted.............................	45·00	
801	**329**	1s.6d. grey-black, pale turquoise, pale reddish violet, pale yellow-olive and black..............	20	25
		a. Black (value) omitted..........................	£1500	
		b. Black (value) double..........................	£375	
		y. Phosphor omitted.............................	20·00	
Set of 6............			70	85
First Day Cover............				1·00
Presentation Pack (PO Pack No. 10)............			5·50	
Presentation Pack (German)............			35·00	

* The missing green on the roof top is known on R. 2/5, R. 8/5 and R. 10/5 but all are from different sheets and it only occurred in part of the printing, being 'probably caused by a batter on the impression cylinder'. Examples are also known with the green partly omitted.

† Uncoated paper. The second note after No. 744 also applies here. Nos. 796/799 were issued together se-tenant in blocks of four throughout the sheet.

Special First Day of Issue Postmark
GPO Philatelic Bureau, Edinburgh (Type C)........................ 1·00

330 The King's Gate, Caernarvon Castle

331 The Eagle Tower, Caernarvon Castle

332 Queen Eleanor's Gate, Caernarvon Castle

333 Celtic Cross, Margam Abbey

334 HRH The Prince of Wales (after photograph by G. Argent)

(Des D. Gentleman)

1969 (1 July). Investiture of HRH The Prince of Wales. Chalk-surfaced paper. Two phosphor bands. Perf 14×15.

802	**330**	5d. deep olive-grey, light olive-grey, deep grey, light grey, red, pale turquoise-green, black and silver...	10	10
		a. Strip of 3. Nos. 802/804....................	30	50
		b. Black (value and inscr) omitted.......	£500	
		c. Red omitted*............................	£850	
		d. Deep grey omitted**..........................	£350	
		e. Pale turquoise-green omitted.........	£850	
		f. Light grey (marks on walls, window frames etc) omitted..........	£4500	
		y. Phosphor omitted...........................	5·00	
		ya. Strip of 3. Nos. 802/804. Phosphor omitted..........................	15·00	
803	**331**	5d. deep olive-grey, light olive-grey, deep grey, light grey, red, pale turquoise-green, black and silver...	10	10
		b. Black (value and inscr) omitted.......	£500	
		c. Red omitted*............................	£850	

		d. Deep grey omitted**	£350	
		e. Pale turquoise-green omitted	£850	
		f. Light grey omitted	£4500	—
		y. Phosphor omitted	5·00	
804	**332**	5d. deep olive-grey, light olive-grey, deep grey, light grey, red, pale turquoise-green, black and silver…	10	10
		b. Black (value and inscr) omitted	£500	
		c. Red omitted*	£850	
		d. Deep grey omitted**	£350	
		e. Pale turquoise-green omitted	£850	
		f. Light grey omitted	£4500	
		y. Phosphor omitted	5·00	
805	**333**	9d. deep grey, light grey, black and gold	15	20
		y. Phosphor omitted	25·00	
806	**334**	1s. blackish yellow-olive and gold	15	20
		y. Phosphor omitted	45·00	
Set of 5			55	80
First Day Cover				1·00
Presentation Pack† (PO Pack No. 11)			3·00	
Presentation Pack (German)			35·00	
Presentation Pack (Welsh)			35·00	

* The 5d. value is also known with the red misplaced downwards and where this occurs the red printing does not take very well on the silver background and in some cases is so faint it could be mistaken for a missing red. However, the red can be seen under a magnifying glass and caution should therefore be exercised when purchasing copies of Nos. 802c/804c.

** The deep grey affects the dark portions of the windows and doors.

† In addition to the generally issued Presentation Pack a further pack in different colours and with all texts printed in both English and Welsh was made available exclusively through Education Authorities for free distribution to all schoolchildren in Wales and Monmouthshire.

Nos. 802/804 were issued together *se-tenant* in strips of three throughout the sheet.

No. 803f is also known commercially used *on cover*.

Special First Day of Issue Postmarks

GPO Philatelic Bureau, Edinburgh (Type C)	1·00
Day of Investiture, Caernarvon	1·50

335 Mahatma Gandhi

1s.6d. 'Tooth' flaw (Cyl. 2A, R. 20/3)

(Des B. Mullick)

1969 (13 Aug). Gandhi Centenary Year. Chalk-surfaced paper. Two phosphor bands. Perf 15×14.

807	**335**	1s.6d. black, green, red-orange and grey	25	30
		a. Tooth flaw	40·00	
		b. Printed on the gummed side	£850	
		y. Phosphor omitted	10·00	
First Day Cover				3·25

Special First Day of Issue Postmark

GPO Philatelic Bureau, Edinburgh (Type C)	3·25

Collectors Pack

1969 (15 Sept). Comprises Nos. 775/786 and 791/807.

CP807b	Collectors Pack (Pack No. 12)	10·00

336 National Giro 'G' Symbol

337 Telecommunications, International Subscriber Dialling

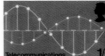

338 Telecommunications, Pulse Code Modulation

339 Postal Mechanisation, Automatic Sorting

(Des D. Gentleman. Litho De La Rue)

1969 (1 Oct). Post Office Technology Commemoration. Chalk-surfaced paper. Two phosphor bands. Perf 13½×14.

808	**336**	5d. new blue, greenish blue, lavender and black	10	10
		y. Phosphor omitted	8·00	
809	**337**	9d. emerald, violet-blue and black	10	10
810	**338**	1s. emerald, lavender and black	15	15
		y. Phosphor omitted	£325	
811	**339**	1s.6d. bright purple, light blue, grey-blue and black	20	20
Set of 4			50	50
First Day Cover				75
Presentation Pack (PO Pack No. 13)			5·00	

Special First Day of Issue Postmark

GPO Philatelic Bureau, Edinburgh (Type C)	75

340 Herald Angel

341 The Three Shepherds

342 The Three Kings

(Des F. Wegner. Queen's head (and stars 4d., 5d. and scrollwork 1s.6d.) printed in gold and then embossed)

1969 (26 Nov). Christmas. Traditional Religious Themes. Chalk-surfaced paper. Two phosphor bands (5d., 1s.6d.) or one centre band (4d.). Perf 15×14.

812	**340**	4d. vermilion, new blue, orange, bright purple, light green, bluish violet, blackish brown and gold	10	10
		a. Gold (Queen's head etc.) omitted	£6000	
		b. Centre band 3½ mm	30	20
813	**341**	5d. magenta, light blue, royal blue, olive-brown, green, greenish yellow, red and gold	10	10
		a. Light blue (sheep, etc.) omitted	£100	
		b. Red omitted*	£1800	
		c. Gold (Queen's head) omitted	£950	
		d. Green omitted	£300	
		e. Olive-brown, red and gold omitted	£8000	
		f. Embossing omitted	25·00	
		y. Phosphor omitted	5·00	
814	**342**	1s.6d. greenish yellow, bluish violet, deep slate, orange, green, new blue and gold	15	15
		a. Gold (Queen's head etc.) omitted	£130	
		b. Deep slate (value) omitted	£425	
		c. Greenish yellow omitted	£400	
		e. New blue omitted	£120	
		f. Embossing omitted	12·00	
		y. Phosphor omitted	6·00	
		ya. Embossing and phosphor omitted	12·00	
Set of 3			30	30
First Day Cover				70
Presentation Pack (PO Pack No. 14)			3·00	

* The effect of the missing red is shown on the hat, leggings and purse which appear as dull orange.

No. 812 has one centre band 8 mm wide but this was of no practical use in the automatic facing machines and after about three-quarters of the stamps had been printed the remainder were printed with a 3½ mm band (No. 812b).

No. 813e was caused by a paper fold and also shows the phosphor omitted.

Used copies of the 5d. have been seen with the olive-brown or greenish yellow (tunic at left) omitted.

Special First Day of Issue Postmarks

PO Philatelic Bureau, Edinburgh (Type C)	70
Bethlehem, Llandeilo, Carms (Type C)	1·00

343 Fife Harling

344 Cotswold Limestone

345 Welsh Stucco

346 Ulster Thatch

5d. Lemon omitted from left chimney (Cyl. 1H, R. 12/2)

(Des D. Gentleman (5d., 9d.), Sheila Robinson (1s., 1s.6d.))

1970 (11 Feb). British Rural Architecture. Chalk-surfaced paper. Two phosphor bands. Perf 15×14.

815	**343**	5d. grey, grey-black, black, lemon, greenish blue, orange-brown, ultramarine and green	10	10
		a. Lemon omitted	£140	
		b. Grey (Queen's head and cottage shading) omitted	—	
		c. Greenish blue (door) omitted	†	£3000
		d. Grey black (inscription and face value) omitted	£10000	
		e. Grey black (face value only) omitted	£8000	
		f. Green omitted (cobblestones)		
		g. Lemon omitted from left chimney	35·00	
		y. Phosphor omitted	2·00	
816	**344**	9d. orange-brown, olive-yellow, bright green, black, grey-black and grey	15	15
		y. Phosphor omitted	30·00	
817	**345**	1s. deep blue, reddish lilac, drab and new blue	15	15
		a. New blue omitted	£110	
		y. Phosphor omitted	15·00	
818	**346**	1s.6d. greenish yellow, black, turquoise-blue and lilac	20	25
		a. Turquoise-blue omitted	£9000	
		y. Phosphor omitted	5·00	
Set of 4			55	60
First Day Cover				85
Presentation Pack (PO Pack No. 15)			3·00	

Used examples of the 5d. exist, one of which is *on piece*, with the greenish blue colour omitted.

Special First Day of Issue Postmark

British Philatelic Bureau, Edinburgh (Type C)	85

347 Signing the Declaration of Arbroath

348 Florence Nightingale attending Patients

349 Signing of International Co-operative Alliance

350 Pilgrims and *Mayflower*

351 Sir William Herschel, Francis Baily, Sir John Herschel and Telescope

(Des F. Wegner (5d., 9d. and 1s.6d.), Marjorie Saynor (1s., 1s.9d.). Queen's head printed in gold and then embossed)

1970 (1 Apr). Anniversaries (3rd series). Events described on stamps. Chalk-surfaced paper. Two phosphor bands. Perf 15×14.

819	**347**	5d. black, yellow-olive, blue, emerald, greenish yellow, rose-red, gold and orange-red	10	10
		a. Gold (Queen's head) omitted	£180	
		b. Emerald omitted	£400	
		y. Phosphor omitted	£375	
820	**348**	9d. ochre, deep blue, carmine, black, blue-green, yellow-olive, gold and blue	10	10
		a. Ochre omitted	£400	
		b. Embossing omitted	15·00	
		y. Phosphor omitted	7·00	
821	**349**	1s. green, greenish yellow, brown, black, cerise, gold and light blue	15	15
		a. Gold (Queen's head) omitted	80·00	
		b. Green and embossing omitted	£120	
		c. Green omitted	£120	
		d. Brown omitted	£250	
		e. Embossing omitted	12·00	
		y. Phosphor omitted	10·00	
		ya. Brown and phosphor missing	£250	
		yb. Embossing and phosphor missing	22·00	
822	**350**	1s.6d. greenish yellow, carmine, deep yellow-olive, emerald, black, blue, gold and sage-green	20	20
		a. Gold (Queen's head) omitted	£300	
		b. Emerald omitted	£150	
		c. Embossing omitted	6·00	
		y. Phosphor omitted	9·00	
823	**351**	1s.9d. black, slate, lemon, gold and bright purple	20	20
		a. Lemon (trousers and document) omitted	£4750	£3500
		b. Embossing omitted	75·00	
		y. Phosphor omitted	9·00	
Set of 5			70	70
First Day Cover				95
Presentation Pack (PO Pack No. 16)			4·00	

No. 823a is known mint, or used on First Day Cover postmarked London WC.

Special First Day of Issue Postmark

British Philatelic Bureau, Edinburgh (Type C)	95

First Day of Issue handstamps were provided at Arbroath, Angus, Billericay, Essex; Boston, Lincs and Rochdale, Lancs for this issue.

352 Mr Pickwick and Sam Weller (*Pickwick Papers*)

353 Mr and Mrs Micawber (*David Copperfield*)

354 David Copperfield and Betsy Trotwood (*David Copperfield*)

355 Oliver Asking for More (*Oliver Twist*)

356 Grasmere (from engraving by J. Farrington, RA)

(Des Rosalind Dease. Queen's head printed in gold and then embossed)

1970 (3 June). Literary Anniversaries (1st series). Death Centenary of Charles Dickens (novelist) (5d.×4) and Birth Bicentenary of William Wordsworth (poet) (1s.6d.). Chalk-surfaced paper. Two phosphor bands. Perf 14×15.

824	**352**	5d. black, orange, silver, gold and magenta	10	10
		a. Block of 4. Nos. 824/827	40	60
		ab. Imperf (block of four)	£1200	
		ac. Silver (inscr) omitted (block of four)	—	
825	**353**	5d. black, magenta, silver, gold and orange	10	10
826	**354**	5d. black, light greenish blue, silver, gold and yellow-bistre	10	10
		b. Yellow-bistre (value) omitted	£4250	
827	**355**	5d. black, yellow-bistre, silver, gold and light greenish blue	10	10
		b. Yellow-bistre (background) omitted	£9000	
		c. Light greenish blue (value) omitted*	£650	
		d. Light greenish blue and silver (inscr at foot) omitted	£10000	
828	**356**	1s.6d. yellow-olive, black, silver, gold and bright blue	15	20
		a. Gold (Queen's head) omitted	£6000	
		b. Silver ('Grasmere') omitted	£200	
		c. Bright blue (face value) omitted	£9000	
		d. Bright blue and silver omitted	£11000	
		e. Embossing omitted	6·00	
		y. Phosphor omitted	5·00	
		ya. Embossing and phosphor omitted	22·00	
Set of 5			50	70
First Day Cover				90
Presentation Pack (PO Pack No. 17)			4·00	

* No. 827c (unlike No. 826b) comes from a sheet on which the colour was only partially omitted so that, although No. 827 was completely without the light greenish blue colour, it was still partially present on No. 826.

Nos. 824/827 were issued together *se-tenant* in blocks of four throughout the sheet.

Essays exist of Nos. 824/827 showing the Queen's head in silver and with different inscriptions. (*Price* £13,000 *per block of 4*).

Special First Day of Issue Postmarks

British Philatelic Bureau, Edinburgh (Type C)	90
Cockermouth, Cumberland (Type C) (No. 828 only)	90
Rochester, Kent (Type C) (Nos. 824/827)	90

A First Day of Issue handstamp was provided at Broadstairs, Kent, for this issue.

NOTE. For Nos. 829/831*b* and Types **356a** and **357** see Decimal Machin Definitive section.

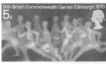

358 Runners

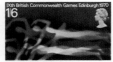

359 Swimmers

360 Cyclists

(Des A. Restall. Litho D.L.R.)

1970 (15 July). Ninth British Commonwealth Games. Chalk-surfaced paper. Two phosphor bands. Perf 13½×14.

832	**358**	5d. pink, emerald, greenish yellow and deep yellow-green	10	10
		a. Greenish yellow omitted	£6000	
		y. Phosphor omitted	£200	
833	**359**	1s.6d. light greenish blue, lilac, bistre-brown and Prussian blue	15	15
		y. Phosphor omitted	60·00	
834	**360**	1s.9d. yellow-orange, lilac, salmon and deep red-brown	15	15
Set of 3			45	45
First Day Cover				75
Presentation Pack (PO Pack No. 19)			3·00	

Special First Day of Issue Postmark

British Philatelic Bureau, Edinburgh (Type C) ..... 1·00

Collectors Pack

1970 (14 Sept). Comprises Nos. 808/828 and 832/834.

CP834*a*   Collectors Pack (Pack No. 20) ..... 15·00

361 1d. Black (1840)

362 1s. Green (1847)

363 4d. Carmine (1855)

(Des D. Gentleman)

1970 (18 Sept). Philympia 70 Stamp Exhibition. Chalk-surfaced paper. Two phosphor bands. Perf 14×14½.

835	**361**	5d. grey-black, brownish bistre, black and dull purple	10	10
		a. Dull purple (Queen's head) omitted	—	
		y. Phosphor omitted	8·00	
836	**362**	9d. light drab, bluish green, stone, black and dull purple	15	15
		y. Phosphor omitted	15·00	
837	**363**	1s.6d. carmine, light drab, black and dull purple	20	20
		y. Phosphor omitted	5·00	
Set of 3			40	40
First Day Cover				75
Presentation Pack (PO Pack No. 21)			3·00	

Special First Day of Issue Postmark

British Post Office Philatelic Bureau, Edinburgh (Type D) ..... 1·00

364 Shepherds and Apparition of the Angel

365 Mary, Joseph and Christ in the Manger

366 The Wise Men bearing gifts

(Des Sally Stiff after *De Lisle Psalter*. Queen's head printed in gold and then embossed)

1970 (25 Nov). Christmas, *Robert de Lisle Psalter*. Chalk-surfaced paper. One centre phosphor band (4d.) or two phosphor bands (others). Perf 14×15.

838	**364**	4d. brown-red, turquoise-green, pale chestnut, brown, grey-black, gold and vermilion		10	10
		a. Embossing omitted		50·00	
		y. Phosphor omitted		90·00	
839	**365**	5d. emerald, gold, blue, brown-red, ochre, grey-black and violet		10	10
		a. Gold (Queen's head) omitted		†	£2750
		b. Emerald omitted		£120	
		c. Imperf (pair)		£300	
		d. Ochre omitted		£3000	†
		e. Embossing omitted		15·00	
		y. Phosphor omitted		5·00	
840	**366**	1s.6d. gold, grey-black, pale turquoise-green, salmon, ultramarine, ochre and yellow-green		15	15
		a. Salmon omitted		£190	
		b. Ochre omitted		£120	
		c. Embossing omitted		35·00	
		y. Phosphor omitted		12·00	
		ya. Embossing and phosphor omitted		60·00	
Set of 3				30	30
First Day Cover					40
Presentation Pack (PO Pack No. 22)				4·00	

Special First Day of Issue Postmark

British Post Office Philatelic Bureau, Edinburgh (Type D)	50
Bethlehem, Llandeilo, Carms	1·00

NOTE. Nos. 841/880 are no longer used. For 1971–1996 definitives in decimal currency with conventional perforations on all sides, see Nos. X841/X1058, T **367**, see Decimal Machin Definitives section.

(New Currency. 100 new pence = £1)

368 *A Mountain Road* (T. P. Flanagan) **369** *Deer's Meadow* (Tom Carr)

370 *Slieve na brock* (Colin Middleton)

(Des Stuart Rose)

1971 (16 June). Ulster 1971 Paintings. Multicoloured Chalk-surfaced paper. Two phosphor bands. Perf 15×14.

881	**368**	3p. *A Mountain Road* (T. P. Flanagan)		10	10
		y. Phosphor omitted		6·00	
		a. Venetian red omitted		—	
882	**369**	7½p. *Deer's Meadow* (Tom Carr)		15	20
		a. Pale olive-grey omitted*		£350	
		y. Phosphor omitted		25·00	
883	**370**	9p. *Slieve na brock* (Colin Middleton)		20	20
		a. Orange (*flowers*) omitted		£2250	
		y. Phosphor omitted		15·00	
Set of 3				40	45
First Day Cover					75
Presentation Pack (PO Pack No. 26a)				3·00	

* This only affects the boulder in the foreground, which appears whitish and it only applied to some stamps in the sheet.

Special First Day of Issue Postmarks

British Post Office Philatelic Bureau, Edinburgh (Type D, see Introduction)	1·10
Belfast	3·00

First Day of Issue handstamps, in the same design as that for Belfast, were provided at Armagh, Ballymena, Coleraine, Cookstown, Enniskillen, Londonderry, Newry, Omagh and Portadown for this issue.

371 John Keats (150th Death Anniversary) **372** Thomas Gray (Death Bicentenary)

373 Sir Walter Scott (Birth Bicentenary)

(Des Rosalind Dease. Queen's head printed in gold and then embossed)

1971 (28 July). Literary Anniversaries (2nd series). Multicoloured Chalk-surfaced paper. Two phosphor bands. Perf 15×14.

884	**371**	3p. John Keats		10	10
		a. Gold (Queen's head) omitted		£225	
		y. Phosphor omitted		5·00	
885	**372**	5p. Thomas Gray		15	20
		a. Gold (Queen's head) omitted		£900	
		y. Phosphor omitted		35·00	
886	**373**	7½p. Sir Walter Scott		20	20
		b. Embossing omitted		40·00	
		y. Phosphor omitted		22·00	
Set of 3				40	45
First Day Cover					75
Presentation Pack (PO Pack No. 32)				3·00	

Special First Day of Issue Postmarks

British Post Office Philatelic Bureau, Edinburgh (Type D, see Introduction)	1·00
London EC	3·00

374 Servicemen and Nurse of 1921 **375** Roman Centurion

376 Rugby Football, 1871

(Des F. Wegner)

1971 (25 Aug). Anniversaries (4th series). Events described on stamps. Multicoloured Chalk-surfaced paper. Two phosphor bands. Perf 15×14.

887	**374**	3p. Servicemen and Nurse of 1921		10	10
		a. Deep blue omitted*		£875	
		b. Red-orange (nurse's cloak) omitted		£700	
		c. Olive-brown (faces, etc.) omitted		£600	
		d. Black omitted		—	
		e. Grey omitted		—	
		f. Olive-green omitted		—	
		y. Phosphor omitted		3·00	

888	375	7½p. Roman Centurion	15	20
		a. Grey omitted	£280	
		b. Ochre omitted	—	
		y. Phosphor omitted	18·00	
889	376	9p. Rugby Football, 1871	20	20
		a. Olive-brown omitted	£250	
		b. New blue omitted	£4750	
		c. Myrtle-green omitted	—	£2750
		d. Lemon (jerseys) omitted	£5000	£3000
		y. Phosphor omitted	£350	
Set of 3			40	45
First Day Cover				1·00
Presentation Pack (PO Pack No. 32A)			3·00	

* The effect of the missing deep blue is shown on the sailor's uniform, which appears as grey.

Special First Day of Issue Postmarks

British Post Office Philatelic Bureau, Edinburgh (Type D, see	
Introduction)	1·10
Maidstone	5·00
Twickenham	5·00
York	5·00

377 Physical Sciences Building, University College of Wales, Aberystwyth

378 Faraday Building, Southampton University

379 Engineering Department, Leicester University

380 Hexagon Restaurant, Essex University

(Des N. Jenkins)

1971 (22 Sept). British Architecture (2nd series). Modern University Buildings. Multicoloured Chalk-surfaced paper. Two phosphor bands. Perf 15×14.

890	377	3p. University College of Wales, Aberystwyth	10	10
		a. Lemon omitted	†	—
		b. Black (windows) omitted	£7000	
		y. Phosphor omitted	9·00	
891	378	5p. Southampton University	25	20
		y. Phosphor omitted	75·00	
892	379	7½p. Leicester University	20	30
		y. Phosphor omitted	15·00	
893	380	9p. Essex University	30	40
		a. Pale lilac omitted		
		y. Phosphor omitted	20·00	
Set of 4			55	75
First Day Cover				80
Presentation Pack (PO Pack No. 33)			5·00	

Mint examples of the 5p. exist with a larger 'P' following the face value. No. 890a is only known used on commercial cover from Wantage. No. 890b is only a partial omission with traces of black on the wall at the far right.

Special First Day of Issue Postmarks

British Post Office Philatelic Bureau, Edinburgh (Type D, see	
Introduction)	1·00
Aberystwyth	4·00
Colchester	4·00
Leicester	4·00
Southampton	4·00

Collectors Pack

1971 (29 Sept). Comprises Nos. 835/840 and 881/893.

CP893a	Collectors Pack (Pack No. 34)	20·00

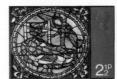

381 Dream of the Wise Men

382 Adoration of the Magi

383 Ride of the Magi

(Des Clarke-Clements-Hughes design team, from stained-glass windows, Canterbury Cathedral. Queen's head printed in gold and then embossed)

1971 (13 Oct). Christmas, Stained-glass Windows. Multicoloured Ordinary paper. One centre phosphor band (2½p.) or two phosphor bands (others). Perf 15×14.

894	381	2½p. Dream of the Wise Men	10	10
		a. Imperf (pair)	£500	
		b. Embossing omitted	—	
895	382	3p. Adoration of the Magi	10	10
		a. Gold (Queen's head) omitted	£1500	
		b. Carmine-rose omitted	£4250	
		c. Lemon (window panels) omitted	£225	
		d. New blue omitted	†	£2500
		e. Reddish violet (tunics etc) omitted	£4500	
		f. Carmine-rose and lemon omitted		£4000
		g. Reddish violet and embossing omitted		£3250
		h. Embossing omitted	15·00	
		y. Phosphor omitted	5·00	
		ya. Embossing and phosphor omitted	£100	
896	383	7½p. Ride of the Magi	20	20
		a. Gold (Queen's head) omitted	£175	
		b. Lilac omitted	£900	
		c. Emerald omitted	£550	
		d. Lemon omitted		£3000
		f. Embossing omitted	50·00	
		g. Embossing double	50·00	
		y. Phosphor omitted	12·00	
		ya. Embossing and phosphor omitted	35·00	
		yb. Phosphor on back but omitted on front	55·00	
Set of 3			35	35
First Day Cover				80
Presentation Pack (PO Pack No. 35)			2·25	

A used example of No. 894 has been reported with gold (Queen's head) omitted.

Special First Day of Issue Postmarks

British Post Office Philatelic Bureau, Edinburgh (Type D, see	
Introduction)	1·00
Bethlehem, Llandeilo, Carms.	4·00
Canterbury	4·00

WHITE CHALK-SURFACED PAPER. From No. 897 all issues, with the exception of Nos. 904/908, were printed on fluorescent white paper, giving a stronger chalk reaction than the original cream paper.

384 Sir James Clark Ross

385 Sir Martin Frobisher

386 Henry Hudson   **387** Robert Falcon Scott

(Des Marjorie Saynor. Queen's head printed in gold and then embossed)

1972 (16 Feb). British Polar Explorers. Multicoloured Two phosphor bands. Perf 14×15.

897	**384**	3p. Sir James Clark Ross......	10	10
		a. Gold (Queen's head) omitted......	£175	
		b. Slate-black (hair, etc.) omitted......	£5250	
		c. Lemon omitted......	£8000	
		d. Embossing omitted......	45·00	
		e. Gold (Queen's head) and embossing omitted......	£250	
		y. Phosphor omitted......	5·00	
		ya. Embossing and phosphor omitted	35·00	
898	**385**	5p. Sir Martin Frobisher......	10	15
		a. Gold (Queen's head) omitted......	£300	
		b. Embossing omitted......	25·00	
		y. Phosphor omitted......	12·00	
		ya. Gold and phosphor omitted......	£325	
		yb. Embossing and phosphor omitted		
899	**386**	7½p. Henry Hudson......	10	15
		a. Gold (Queen's head) omitted......	£300	
		y. Phosphor omitted......	18·00	
900	**387**	9p. Robert Falcon Scott......	20	25
		y. Phosphor omitted......	£350	
Set of 4			45	60
First Day Cover				85
Presentation Pack (PO Pack No. 39)......			4·00	

An example of the 3p. is known used *on piece* with the flesh colour omitted.

Special First Day of Issue Postmarks

Philatelic Bureau, Edinburgh......	85
London WC......	2·00

388 Statuette of Tutankhamun   **389** 19th-century Coastguard

390 Ralph Vaughan Williams and Score

(Des Rosalind Dease (3p.), F. Wegner (7½p.), C. Abbott (9p.). Queen's head printed in gold and then embossed (7½p., 9p.))

1972 (26 Apr). Anniversaries (5th series). Events described on stamps. Multicoloured Two phosphor bands. Perf 15×14.

901	**388**	3p. Statuette of Tutankhamun......	10	10
		a. Face value omitted......	—	
902	**389**	7½p. 19th-century Coastguard......	20	20
		a. Embossing omitted......	£225	
		y. Phosphor omitted......	£275	
903	**390**	9p. Ralph Vaughan Williams......	20	25
		a. Gold (Queen's head) omitted......	£1800	
		b. Brown (facial features) omitted......	£2500	
		c. Deep slate omitted......	—	
		d. Embossing omitted......	—	
		y. Phosphor omitted......	35·00	
Set of 3			45	50
First Day Cover				85
Presentation Pack (PO Pack No. 40)......			2·25	

Special First Day of Issue Postmarks

Philatelic Bureau, Edinburgh......	95
London EC......	1·50

391 St Andrew's, Greensted-juxta-Ongar, Essex   **392** All Saints, Earls Barton, Northants

393 St Andrew's, Letheringsett, Norfolk   **394** St Andrew's, Helpringham, Lincs

395 St Mary the Virgin, Huish Episcopi, Somerset

(Des R. Maddox. Queen's head printed in gold and then embossed)

1972 (21 June). British Architecture (3rd series). Village Churches. Multicoloured Ordinary paper. Two phosphor bands. Perf 14×15.

904	**391**	3p. St Andrew's, Greensted-juxta-Ongar......	10	10
		a. Gold (Queen's head) omitted......	£225	
		b. Orange-vermilion omitted......		£2250
		c. Embossing omitted......	35·00	
		y. Phosphor omitted......	8·00	
		ya. Gold (Queen's head) and phosphor omitted......	£325	
		yb. Embossing and phosphor omitted	22·00	
905	**392**	4p. All Saints, Earls Barton......	10	10
		a. Gold (Queen's head) omitted......	£3250	
		b. Violet-blue omitted......	£250	
		c. Embossing omitted......	12·00	
		y. Phosphor omitted......	20·00	
		yb. Embossing and phosphor omitted	60·00	
906	**393**	5p. St Andrew's, Letheringsett......	10	20
		a. Gold (Queen's head) omitted......	£275	
		b. Red omitted......	†	£2750
		c. Embossing omitted......	50·00	
		y. Phosphor omitted......	25·00	
907	**394**	7½p. St Andrew's, Helpringham......	15	20
		y. Phosphor omitted......	20·00	
		ya. Embossing and phosphor omitted	50·00	
908	**395**	9p. St Mary the Virgin, Huish Episcopi..	15	20
		a. Embossing omitted......	22·00	
		y. Phosphor omitted......	15·00	
Set of 5			55	80
First Day Cover				1·25
Presentation Pack (PO Pack No. 41)......			4·75	

Nos. 905a and 906a only exist with the phosphor omitted.

Special First Day of Issue Postmarks

Philatelic Bureau, Edinburgh......	1·40
Canterbury......	2·50

Belgica 72 Souvenir Pack

1972 (24 June). Comprises Nos. 894/896 and 904/908.
CP908*b*   Souvenir Pack............................ 3·75
    This pack was specially produced for sale at the Belgica '72 Stamp Exhibition, held in Brussels between 24 June and 9 July. It contains information on British stamps with a religious theme with text in English, French and Flemish, and was put on sale at Philatelic Bureaux in Britain on 26 June.

396 Microphones, 1924–1969   **397** Horn Loudspeaker

398 TV Camera, 1972   **399** Oscillator and Spark Transmitter, 1897

(Des D. Gentleman)

1972 (13 Sept). Broadcasting Anniversaries. 75th Anniversary of Marconi and Kemp's Radio Experiments. Perf 15×14

909	**396**	3p. Microphones, 1924–1969...............	10	10
		a. Greenish yellow (terminals) omitted.....................	£3500	
910	**397**	5p. Horn Loudspeaker............................	10	10
		y. Phosphor omitted............................	10·00	
		ya. Phosphor on back but omitted on front......................	45·00	
911	**398**	7½p. TV Camera, 1972............................	15	20
		a. Brownish slate (Queen's head) omitted.....................	†	£2750
		y. Phosphor omitted............................	12·00	
912	**399**	9p. Oscillator and Spark Transmitter.....	15	20
		a. Brownish slate (Queen's head) omitted.....................	£4000	
		y. Phosphor omitted............................	13·00	
		ya. Phosphor on back but omitted on front......................	£100	
Set of 4......................			45	55
First Day Cover......................				1·25
Presentation Pack (PO Pack No. 43)......................			3·25	

    In addition to the generally issued Presentation Pack a further pack exists inscribed '1922–1972'. This pack of stamps commemorating the 50th Anniversary of the BBC was specially produced as a memento of the occasion for the BBC staff. It was sent with the good wishes of the Chairman and Board of Governors, the Director-General and Board of Management. The pack contains Nos. 909/911 only (*Price* £35).
    No. 911a is only found in First Day Covers posted from the Philatelic Bureau in Edinburgh.

Special First Day of Issue Postmarks
Philatelic Bureau, Edinburgh................................ 1·40
London W1.. 3·00

400 Angel holding Trumpet   **401** Angel playing Lute

402 Angel playing Harp

(Des Sally Stiff. Photo and embossing)

1972 (18 Oct). Christmas, Angels. Multicoloured One centre phosphor band (2½p.) or two phosphor bands (others). Perf 14×15.

913	**400**	2½p. Angel holding Trumpet........................	10	10
		a. Gold omitted.............................	£950	
		b. Embossing omitted.............................	15·00	
		c. Deep grey omitted.............................	£2000	
		y. Phosphor omitted.............................	15·00	
914	**401**	3p. Angel playing Lute.............................	10	10
		a. Red-brown omitted.............................	£750	
		b. Bright green omitted.............................	£225	
		c. Bluish violet omitted.............................	£225	
		d. Lavender omitted.............................	—	
		e. Gold omitted.............................	£950	
		f. Embossing omitted.............................	10·00	
		y. Phosphor omitted.............................	8·00	
		ya. Embossing and phosphor omitted......	15·00	
915	**402**	7½p. Angel playing Harp.............................	20	20
		a. Ochre omitted.............................	£200	
		b. Blackish violet (shadow) omitted........	—	
		c. Embossing omitted.............................	20·00	
		y. Phosphor omitted.............................	15·00	
		ya. Embossing and phosphor omitted......	30·00	
Set of 3......................			35	35
First Day Cover......................				85
Presentation Pack (PO Pack No. 44)......................			2·00	

    The gold printing on the 3p. is from two cylinders: 1E and 1F. Examples have been seen with the gold of the 1F cylinder omitted, but these are difficult to detect on single stamps.

Special First Day of Issue Postmarks
Philatelic Bureau, Edinburgh................................ 1·00
Bethlehem, Llandeilo, Carms................................ 3·00

403 Queen Elizabeth and Duke of Edinburgh   **403a** Queen Elizabeth and Duke of Edinburgh

I. Jumelle Machine   II. Rembrandt Machine

    The 3p. JUMELLE has a lighter shade of the brownish black than the 3p. REMBRANDT. It also has the brown cylinders less deeply etched, which can be distinguished in the Duke's face which is slightly lighter, and in the Queen's hair where the highlights are sharper.
3p. REMBRANDT. Cylinders 3A-1B-11C no dot. Sheets of 100 (10×10).
3p. JUMELLE. Cylinders 1A-1B-3C dot and no dot. Sheets of 100 (two panes 5×10, separated by gutter margin).

(Des J. Matthews from photo by N. Parkinson)

1972 (20 Nov). Royal Silver Wedding. Multicoloured 'All-over' phosphor (3p.) or without phosphor (20p.). Perf 14×15.

I. Rembrandt Machine.

916	**403**	3p. Queen Elizabeth and Duke of Edinburgh..	20	20
		a. Silver omitted.................................	£600	
917	**403a**	20p. Queen Elizabeth and Duke of Edinburgh..	60	60

II. Jumelle Machine.

918	**403**	3p. Queen Elizabeth and Duke of Edinburgh..	50	50
Set of 2..			75	75
Gutter Pair (No. 918).....................................			1·50	
Traffic Light Gutter Pair................................			20·00	
First Day Cover..				60
Presentation Pack (PO Pack No. 45).............			2·00	
Presentation Pack (Japanese)......................			3·00	
Souvenir Book...			1·25	

The souvenir book is a 12 page booklet containing photographs of the Royal Wedding and other historic events of the royal family and accompanying information.

Special First Day of Issue Postmarks

Philatelic Bureau, Edinburgh..	70
Windsor, Berks...	2·50

Collectors Pack

1972 (20 Nov). Comprises Nos. 897/917.

CP918a	Collectors Pack (Pack No. 47).................	12·00

404 Europe   **404a**

404b

(Des P. Murdoch)

1973 (3 Jan). Britain's Entry into European Communities. Multicoloured Two phosphor bands. Perf 14×15.

919	**404**	3p. Europe (lilac background)..............	10	10
920	**404a**	5p. Europe (new blue jigsaw pieces)...	15	20
		a. Pair. Nos. 920/921............................	35	45
921	**404b**	5p. Europe (light emerald-green jigsaw pieces)................................	15	20
Set of 3..			40	45
First Day Cover..				70
Presentation Pack (PO Pack No. 48).............			4·00	

Nos. 920/921 were printed horizontally *se-tenant* throughout the sheet.

Special First Day of Issue Postmarks

Philatelic Bureau, Edinburgh..	80

405 Oak Tree

(Des D. Gentleman)

1973 (28 Feb). Tree Planting Year. British Trees (1st issue). Multicoloured Two phosphor bands. Perf 15×14.

922	**405**	9p. Oak Tree...	15	15
		a. Brownish black (value and inscr) omitted...................................	£600	
		b. Brownish grey (Queen's head) omitted...................................	£550	
		y. Phosphor omitted.............................	90·00	
First Day Cover..				40
Presentation Pack (PO Pack No. 49).............			1·25	
See also No. 949.				

Special First Day of Issue Postmarks

Philatelic Bureau, Edinburgh..	50

CHALK-SURFACED PAPER. The following issues are printed on chalk-surfaced paper but where 'all-over' phosphor has been applied there is no chalk reaction except in the sheet margins outside the phosphor area.

406 David Livingstone   **407** Henry M. Stanley

408 Sir Francis Drake   **409** Walter Raleigh

410 Charles Sturt

(Des Marjorie Saynor. Queen's head printed in gold and then embossed)

1973 (18 Apr). British Explorers. Multicoloured. 'All-over' phosphor. Perf 14×15.

923	**406**	3p. David Livingstone............................	10	10
		a. Pair. Nos. 923/924...........................	20	20
		b. Gold (Queen's head) omitted..........	£125	
		c. Turquoise-blue (background and inscr) omitted..................................	£950	
		d. Light orange-brown omitted...........	£800	
		e. Embossing omitted...........................	35·00	
924	**407**	3p. Henry M Stanley...............................	10	10
		b. Gold (Queen's head) omitted..........	£125	
		c. Turquoise-blue (background and inscr) omitted..................................	£950	
		d. Light orange-brown omitted...........	£800	
		e. Embossing omitted...........................	35·00	
925	**408**	5p. Sir Francis Drake..............................	20	20
		a. Gold (Queen's head) omitted..........	£250	
		b. Grey-black omitted...........................	£1800	
		c. Sepia omitted....................................	£2750	
		d. Embossing omitted...........................	9·00	

926	**409**	7½p. Walter Raleigh......................	20	20
		a. Gold (Queen's head) omitted...........	£4000	
		b. Ultramarine (eyes) omitted.............	—	—
927	**410**	9p. Charles Sturt.........................	20	20
		a. Gold (Queen's head) omitted...........	£225	
		b. Brown-grey printing double....*from*	£300	
		c. Grey-black omitted.....................	£3750	
		d. Brown-red (rivers on map) omitted...........................	£650	
		e. Embossing omitted........................	40·00	
	Set of 5...........		75	75
	First Day Cover.........			90
	Presentation Pack (PO Pack No. 50)..................		2·25	

Nos. 923/924 were issued horizontally *se-tenant* throughout the sheet.

Caution is needed when buying missing gold heads in this issue as they can be removed by using a hard eraser, etc., but this invariably affects the 'all-over' phosphor. Genuine examples have the phosphor intact. Used examples off cover cannot be distinguished as much of the phosphor is lost in the course of floating.

In the 5p. value the missing grey-black affects the doublet, which appears as brownish grey, and the lace ruff, which is entirely missing.

In the 5p. value the missing sepia effects only Drake's hair, which appears much lighter.

The double printing of the brown-grey (cylinder 1F) on the 9p., is a most unusual type of error to occur in a multicoloured photogravure issue. Two sheets are known and it is believed that they stuck to the cylinder and went through a second time. This would result in the following two sheets missing the colour but at the time of going to press this error has not been reported. The second print is slightly askew and more prominent in the top half of the sheets. Examples from the upper part of the sheet showing a clear double impression of the facial features are worth a substantial premium over the price quoted.

Special First Day of Issue Postmarks

Philatelic Bureau, Edinburgh.. 1·00

First Day of Issue handstamps were provided at Blantyre, Glasgow, and Denbigh for this issue.

411

412

413

(Types **411**/**413** show sketches of W. G. Grace by Harry Furniss)

(Des E. Ripley. Queen's head printed in gold and then embossed)

1973 (16 May). County Cricket 1873–1973. 'All-over' phosphor. Perf 14×15.

928	**411**	3p. black, ochre and gold......................	10	10
		a. Gold (Queen's head) omitted...........	£3750	
		b. Embossing omitted........................	25·00	
929	**412**	7½p. black, light sage-green and gold....	30	30
		b. Embossing omitted........................	35·00	
930	**413**	9p. black, cobalt and gold......................	40	40
		b. Embossing omitted........................	85·00	
	Set of 3...........		75	75
	First Day Cover.........			1·25
	Presentation Pack (PO Pack No. 51)..........		3·25	
	Souvenir Book..........		3·50	
	PHQ Card (No. 928) (1)..................		35·00	£150

Nos. 928/930 with two phosphor bands are known.

The souvenir book is a 24 page illustrated booklet containing a history of County Cricket with text by John Arlott.

The PHQ Card did not become available until mid-July. The used price quoted is for an example used in July or August 1973.

Special First Day of Issue Postmarks

Philatelic Bureau, Edinburgh.......... 1·40

Lords, London NW........................... 3·00

414 Self-portrait (Reynolds)

415 Self-portrait (Raeburn)

416 *Nelly O'Brien* (Reynolds)

417 *Reverend R. Walker (The Skater)* (Raeburn)

(Des S. Rose. Queen's head printed in gold and then embossed)

1973 (4 July). British Paintings (3rd series). 250th Birth Anniversary of Sir Joshua Reynolds and 150th Death Anniversary of Sir Henry Raeburn. Multicoloured 'All-over' phosphor. Perf 14×15.

931	**414**	3p. Self-portrait (Reynolds)....................	10	10
		a. Gold (Queen's head) omitted...........	£120	
		c. Gold (Queen's head) and embossing omitted..................	£140	
932	**415**	5p. Self-portrait (Raeburn).....................	15	15
		a. Gold (Queen's head) omitted...........	£140	
		b. Greenish yellow omitted..................	£650	
		c. Embossing omitted........................	30·00	
933	**416**	7½p. *Nelly O'Brien* (Reynolds)..................	15	15
		a. Gold (Queen's head) omitted...........	£225	
		b. Cinnamon omitted........................	£9500	
		c. Embossing omitted........................	25·00	
934	**417**	9p. *Reverend R. Walker (The Skater)* (Raeburn).....................	20	20
		b. Brownish rose omitted....................	£175	
		c. Embossing omitted........................	£150	
	Set of 4...........		50	50
	First Day Cover.........			80
	Presentation Pack (PO Pack No. 52)..................		1·75	

Special First Day of Issue Postmarks

Philatelic Bureau, Edinburgh.. 1·80

418 Court Masque Costumes

419 St Paul's Church, Covent Garden

420 Prince's Lodging, Newmarket

421 Court Masque Stage Scene

(Des Rosalind Dease. Litho and typo Bradbury Wilkinson)

1973 (15 Aug). 400th Birth Anniversary of Inigo Jones (architect and designer). Multicoloured 'All-over' phosphor. Perf 15×14.

935	**418**	3p. Court Masque Costumes................	10	10
		a. Pair. Nos. 935/936............................	20	25
		ab. Face values omitted.....................	—	
		ac. Deep mauve ptg double (pair)........	£3750	
		c. 9mm phosphor band*.....................	20·00	
936	**419**	3p. St Paul's Church, Covent Garden.....	10	10
937	**420**	5p. Prince's Lodging, Newmarket..........	15	15
		a. Pair. Nos. 937/938............................	30	35

		c. 9mm phosphor band*....................	20·00	
938	**421**	5p. Court Masque Stage Scene.............	15	15
Set of 4..........			40	50
First Day Cover..........				70
Presentation Pack (PO Pack No. 53)......................................			1·60	
PHQ Card (No. 936) (2)..........			95·00	95·00

* On part of the printings for both values the 'all-over' phosphor band missed the first vertical row and a 9 mm phosphor band was applied to correct this.

The 3p. and 5p. values were printed horizontally *se-tenant* within the sheet.

No. 935ab is caused by the omission of virtually all the black printing from one horizontal row.

Special First Day of Issue Postmarks
Philatelic Bureau, Edinburgh.. 80

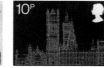

422 Palace of Westminster seen from Whitehall
423 Palace of Westminster seen from Millbank

(Des R. Downer. Recess and typo Bradbury Wilkinson)

1973 (12 Sept). 19th Commonwealth Parliamentary Conference. Multicoloured 'All-over' phosphor. Perf 15×14.

939	**422**	8p. Palace of Westminster seen from Whitehall..........	15	15
940	**423**	10p. Palace of Westminster seen from Millbank..........	20	20
Set of 2..........			30	30
First Day Cover..........				55
Presentation Pack (PO Pack No. 54)..........			1·50	
Souvenir Book..........			3·50	
PHQ Card (No. 939) (3)..........			18·00	70·00

The souvenir book is a 12 page booklet containing a history of the Palace of Westminster.

Special First Day of Issue Postmarks
Philatelic Bureau, Edinburgh.. 1·60

424 Princess Anne and Captain Mark Phillips
424a Princess Anne and Captain Mark Phillips

(Des C. Clements and E. Hughes from photo by Lord Lichfield)

1973 (14 Nov). Royal Wedding. 'All-over' phosphor. Perf 15×14.

941	**424**	3½p. Princess Anne and Captain Mark Phillips..........	10	10
		a. Imperf (horiz pair)..........	£3750	
942	**424a**	20p. deep brown and silver....................	35	25
		a. Silver omitted..........	£4750	
Set of 2..........			40	30
Set of 2 Gutter Pairs..........			80	
Set of 2 Traffic Light Gutter Pairs..........			65·00	
First Day Cover..........				40
Presentation Pack (PO Pack No. 56)..........			1·25	
PHQ Card (No. 941) (4)..........			3·75	20·00

Special First Day of Issue Postmarks
Philatelic Bureau, Edinburgh..........	1·25
Westminster Abbey, London SW1..........	3·50
Windsor, Berks..........	3·50

425   **426**

427   **428**

429   **430**

(Types **425**/**430** show scenes from the carol *Good King Wenceslas*)

(Des D. Gentleman)

1973 (28 Nov). Christmas, Good King Wenceslas. Multicoloured One centre phosphor band (3p.) or 'All-over' phosphor (3½p.). Perf 15×14.

943	**425**	3p. King Wenceslas sees peasant..........	15	15
		a. Strip of 5. Nos. 943/947..........	90	1·10
		ab. Rosy mauve omitted (strip of 5)......	£6000	
		b. Imperf (horiz strip of 5)....................	£3000	
		c. Black (face value) omitted*..............	£4500	
		g. Gum arabic..........	20	
		ga. Strip of 5. Nos. 943g/947g..........	1·20	
		gb. Imperf (strip of 5. Nos. 943g/947g)	£3250	
944	**426**	3p. Page tells king about peasant..........	15	15
		g. Gum arabic..........	20	
945	**427**	3p. King and page set out..........	15	15
		g. Gum arabic..........	20	
946	**428**	3p. King encourages page..........	15	15
		g. Gum arabic..........	20	
947	**429**	3p. King and page give food to peasant..........	15	15
		g. Gum arabic..........	20	
948	**430**	3½p. Peasant, King and page..........	15	15
		a. Imperf (pair)..........	£350	
		b. Grey-black (value, inscr, etc.) omitted..........	£150	
		c. Salmon-pink omitted..........	£100	
		d. Blue (leg, robes) omitted..........	£250	
		e. Rosy mauve (robe at right) omitted..........	£125	
		f. Blue and rosy mauve omitted........	£400	
		g. Bright rose-red (King's robe) omitted..........	£150	
		h. Red-brown (logs, basket, etc.) omitted..........		
		i. Turquoise-green (leg, robe, etc.) omitted..........	£3000	
		j. Gold (background) omitted..........	†	—
Set of 6..........			95	1·10
First Day Cover..........				1·25
Presentation Pack (PO Pack No. 57)..........			1·75	

The 3p. values depict the carol *Good King Wenceslas* and were printed horizontally *se-tenant* within the sheet.

Examples of No. 948j are only known used *on covers* from Gloucester. The 3½p. has also been seen with the lavender-grey omitted used *on piece*.

No. 948h is only known used. The true error shows the pile of logs at night completely omitted.

The 3p. and 3½p. are normally with PVA gum with added dextrin, but the 3½p. also exists with normal PVA gum.

* No. 943c is known in a corner marginal strip of five showing a progressive dry print of black leaving a total omission on the first stamp. Adjacent similar strips of five all show traces of black.

Special First Day of Issue Postmarks
Philatelic Bureau, Edinburgh..........	1·25
Bethlehem, Llandeilo, Carms..........	2·75

Collectors Pack

1973 (28 Nov). Comprises Nos. 919/948.

CP948*k*		Collectors Pack (Pack No. 58).................	11·50

431 Horse Chestnut

(Des D. Gentleman)

1974 (27 Feb). British Trees (2nd issue). Multicoloured 'All-over' phosphor. Perf 15×14.

949	**431**	10p. Horse Chestnut...................................		20	15
		Gutter Pair..		40	
		Traffic Light Gutter Pair.................................		45·00	
		First Day Cover..			40
		Presentation Pack (PO Pack No. 59)................		1·10	
		PHQ Card (5)..		80·00	80·00

The pack number is stated to be 58 on the reverse but the correct number is 59.

Special First Day of Issue Postmarks

Philatelic Bureau, Edinburgh.. 50

432 First Motor Fire Engine, 1904

433 Prizewinning Fire Engine, 1863

434 First Steam Fire Engine, 1830

435 Fire Engine, 1766

(Des D. Gentleman)

1974 (24 Apr). Bicentenary of the Fire Prevention (Metropolis) Act. Multicoloured 'All-over' phosphor. Perf 15×14.

950	**432**	3½p. First Motor Fire Engine, 1904...........		10	10
		a. Imperf (pair).................................		£500	
951	**433**	5½p. Prizewinning Fire Engine, 1863........		10	10
952	**434**	8p. First Steam Fire Engine, 1830...........		15	20
953	**435**	10p. Fire Engine, 1766............................		20	20
		Set of 4...		50	55
		Set of 4 Gutter Pairs..................................		1·00	
		Set of 4 Traffic Light Gutter Pairs.................		36·00	
		First Day Cover..			1·10
		Presentation Pack (PO Pack No. 60)................		1·50	
		PHQ Card (No. 950) (6)...............................		65·00	70·00

The 3½p. exists with ordinary PVA gum.

Special First Day of Issue Postmarks

Philatelic Bureau, Edinburgh.. 1·60

436 P & O Packet, *Peninsular*, 1888

437 Farman HF. III Biplane, 1911

438 Airmail-blue Van and Post Box, 1930

439 Imperial Airways Short S.21 Flying Boat *Maia*, 1937

5½p. 'Bomb burst' damage to wheels at left (Cyl. 1C, R. 6/4)

(Des Rosalind Dease)

1974 (12 June). Centenary of Universal Postal Union. Multicoloured 'All-over' phosphor. Perf 15×14.

954	**436**	3½p. P & O Packet, *Peninsular*, 1888.........		10	10
955	**437**	5½p. Farman HF. III Biplane, 1911..............		10	10
		a. 'Bomb burst'..................................		50·00	
956	**438**	8p. Airmail-blue Van and Post box, 1930..		10	10
957	**439**	10p. Imperial Airways Short S.21 Flying Boat *Maia*, 1937..........................		15	15
		Set of 4...		40	40
		Set of 4 Gutter Pairs..................................		80	
		Set of 4 Traffic Light Gutter Pairs.................		28·00	
		First Day Cover..			60
		Presentation Pack (PO Pack No. 64)................		2·00	

Special First Day of Issue Postmark

Philatelic Bureau, Edinburgh.. 70

440 Robert the Bruce

441 Owain Glyndwr

442 Henry V

443 The Black Prince

(Des F. Wegner)

1974 (10 July). Medieval Warriors. Multicoloured 'All-over' phosphor. Perf 15×14.

958	**440**	4½p. Robert the Bruce.............................		10	10
959	**441**	5½p. Owain Glyndwr...............................		15	15
960	**442**	8p. Henry V..		15	15
961	**443**	10p. The Black Prince..............................		15	15
		Set of 4...		50	50
		Set of 4 Gutter Pairs..................................		1·00	
		Set of 4 Traffic Light Gutter Pairs.................		40·00	
		First Day Cover..			1·25
		Presentation Pack (PO Pack No. 65)................		1·60	
		PHQ Cards (set of 4) (7).............................		12·00	30·00

Imperforate pairs of No. 961 are known and thought to be of proof status (*Price £700 per pair*).

Special First Day of Issue Postmark

Philatelic Bureau, Edinburgh.. 1·75

444 Churchill in Royal Yacht Squadron Uniform

445 Prime Minister, 1940

446 Secretary for War and Air, 1919

447 War Correspondent, South Africa, 1899

(Des C. Clements and E. Hughes)

1974 (9 Oct). Birth Centenary of Sir Winston Churchill. Multicoloured 'All-over' phosphor. Perf 14×15.

962	**444**	4½p. Churchill in Royal Yacht Squadron Uniform	10	10
963	**445**	5½p. Prime Minister, 1940	20	15
964	**446**	8p. Secretary for War and Air, 1919	30	30
965	**447**	10p. War Correspondent, South Africa, 1899	30	30
Set of 4			80	75
Set of 4 Gutter Pairs			1·60	
Set of 4 Traffic Light Gutter Pairs			22·00	
First Day Cover				80
Presentation Pack (PO Pack No. 66)			1·75	
PHQ Card (No. 963) (8)			2·75	15·00
Souvenir Book			1·50	

The souvenir book consists of an illustrated folder containing a biography of Sir Winston.

Nos. 962/965 come with PVA gum containing added dextrin, but the 8p. also exists with normal PVA.

Special First Day of Issue Postmark

Philatelic Bureau, Edinburgh	1·75
Blenheim, Woodstock, Oxford	4·00
House of Commons, London SW	4·00

448 Adoration of the Magi (York Minster, *circa* 1355)

449 The Nativity (St Helen's Church, Norwich, *circa* 1480)

450 Virgin and Child (Ottery St Mary Church, *circa* 1350)

451 Virgin and Child (Worcester Cathedral, *circa* 1224)

(Des Peter Hatch Partnership)

1974 (27 Nov). Christmas, Church Roof Bosses. Multicoloured. One phosphor band (3½p.) or 'All-over' phosphor (others). Perf 15×14.

966	**448**	3½p. York Minster	10	10
		a. Light stone (background shading) omitted	—	
		y. Phosphor omitted	12·00	
967	**449**	4½p. St Helen's Church, Norwich	10	10
968	**450**	8p. Ottery St Mary Church	10	10
969	**451**	10p. Worcester Cathedral	15	15
Set of 4			40	40
Set of 4 Gutter Pairs			80	
Set of 4 Traffic Light Gutter Pairs			24·00	
First Day Cover				70
Presentation Pack (PO Pack No. 67)			1·50	

The phosphor band on the 3½p. was first applied down the centre of the stamp but during the printing this was deliberately placed to the right between the roof boss and the value; however, intermediate positions, due to shifts, are known.

Two used examples of the 3½p. have been reported with the light brown colour omitted.

Special First Day of Issue Postmarks

Philatelic Bureau, Edinburgh	80
Bethlehem, Llandeilo, Carms	1·75

Collectors Pack

1974 (27 Nov). Comprises Nos. 949/969.

CP969a	Collectors Pack (Pack No. 68)	4·75

452 Invalid in Wheelchair

(Des P. Sharland)

1975 (22 Jan). Health and Handicap Funds. 'All-over' phosphor. Perf 15×14.

970	**452**	4½p.+1½p. Invalid in Wheelchair	15	15
Gutter Pair			30	
Traffic Light Gutter Pair			2·25	
First Day Cover				30

Special First Day of Issue Postmark

Philatelic Bureau, Edinburgh	40

 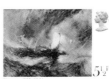

453 Peace – Burial at Sea

454 Snow Storm: Steam-boat off a Harbour's Mouth

455 The Arsenal, Venice

456 St Laurent

(Des S. Rose)

1975 (19 Feb). Birth Bicentenary of J. M. W. Turner (painter). Multicoloured 'All-over' phosphor. Perf 15×14.

971	**453**	4½p. *Peace – Burial at Sea*	10	10
972	**454**	5½p. *Snow Storm: Steam-boat off a Harbour's Mouth*	10	10
973	**455**	8p. *The Arsenal, Venice*	10	10
974	**456**	10p. *St Laurent*	15	15
Set of 4			40	40
Set of 4 Gutter Pairs			80	
Set of 4 Traffic Light Gutter Pairs			5·50	
First Day Cover				50
Presentation Pack (PO Pack No. 69)			1·50	
PHQ Card (No. 972) (9)			18·00	20·00

Special First Day of Issue Postmarks

London WC	1·50
Philatelic Bureau, Edinburgh	75

457 Charlotte Square, Edinburgh

458 The Rows, Chester

459 Royal Observatory, Greenwich

460 St George's Chapel, Windsor

461 National Theatre, London

(Des P. Gauld)

1975 (23 Apr). European Architectural Heritage Year. Multicoloured 'All-over' phosphor. Perf 15×14.

975	**457**	7p. Charlotte Square, Edinburgh..........	10	10
		a. Pair. Nos. 975/976........................	20	20
976	**458**	7p. The Rows, Chester............................	10	10
977	**459**	8p. Royal Observatory, Greenwich.......	10	10
978	**460**	10p. St George's Chapel, Windsor..........	15	15
979	**461**	12p. National Theatre, London................	20	20
Set of 5..			60	60
Set of 5 Gutter Pairs......................................			1·25	
Set of 5 Traffic Light Gutter Pairs................			14·00	
First Day Cover...				80
Presentation Pack (PO Pack No. 70)...............			1·50	
PHQ Cards (Nos. 975/977) (10).......................			4·75	10·00

Nos. 975/976 were printed horizontally *se-tenant* within the sheet.

Special First Day of Issue Postmark

Philatelic Bureau, Edinburgh.. 1·75

462 Sailing Dinghies   **463** Racing Keel Yachts

464 Cruising Yachts   **465** Multihulls

(Des A. Restall. Recess and photo)

1975 (11 June). Sailing. Multicoloured 'All-over' phosphor. Perf 15×14.

980	**462**	7p. Sailing Dinghies................................	10	10
981	**463**	8p. Racing Keel Yachts...........................	10	10
		a. Black omitted..............................	75·00	
982	**464**	10p. Cruising Yachts.................................	15	15
983	**465**	12p. Multihulls...	20	20
Set of 4..			50	50
Set of 4 Gutter Pairs.....................................			1·00	
Set of 4 Traffic Light Gutter Pairs................			18·00	
First Day Cover...				70
Presentation Pack (PO Pack No. 71)...............			1·25	
PHQ Card (No. 981) (11).................................			2·75	8·00

On No. 981a the recess-printed black colour is completely omitted.

Special First Day of Issue Postmark

Philatelic Bureau, Edinburgh.. 1·25

A First Day of Issue handstamp was provided at Weymouth for this issue.

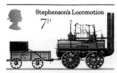

1825 Stockton and Darlington Railway   1876 North British Railway Drummond

466 Stephenson's *Locomotion*,   **467** *Abbotsford*, 1876
1825

468 *Caerphilly Castle*, 1923   **469** High Speed Train, 1975

(Des B. Craker)

1975 (13 Aug). 150th Anniversary of Public Railways. Multicoloured 'All-over' phosphor. Perf 15×14.

984	**466**	7p. Stephenson's *Locomotion*, 1825......	10	10
985	**467**	8p. *Abbotsford*, 1876............................	20	20
986	**468**	10p. *Caerphilly Castle*, 1923....................	20	20
987	**469**	12p. High Speed Train, 1975.....................	30	30
Set of 4..			70	70
Set of 4 Gutter Pairs.....................................			1·40	
Set of 4 Traffic Light Gutter Pairs................			7·50	
First Day Cover...				90
Presentation Pack (PO Pack No. 72)..............			2·00	
PHQ Cards (set of 4) (12)..............................			30·00	30·00
Souvenir Book...			1·60	

The souvenir book is an eight page booklet containing a history of the railways.

Special First Day of Issue Postmarks

Philatelic Bureau, Edinburgh...................................	1·00
Darlington, Co. Durham...	4·00
Shildon, Co. Durham..	5·00
Stockton-on-Tees, Cleveland...................................	4·00

470 Palace of Westminster

(Des R. Downer)

1975 (3 Sept). 62nd Inter-Parliamentary Union Conference. Multicoloured 'All-over' phosphor. Perf 15×14.

988	**470**	12p. Palace of Westminster......................	20	20
Gutter Pair..			40	
Traffic Light Gutter Pair.................................			2·25	
First Day Cover...				30
Presentation Pack (PO Pack No. 74)...............			85	

Special First Day of Issue Postmark

Philatelic Bureau, Edinburgh.. 40

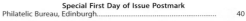

471 Emma and Mr   **472** Catherine
Woodhouse (*Emma*)   Morland (*Northanger Abbey*)

473 Mr Darcy (*Pride   **474** Mary and Henry
and Prejudice*)   Crawford (*Mansfield Park*)

(Des Barbara Brown)

1975 (22 Oct). Birth Bicentenary of Jane Austen (novelist). Multicoloured 'All-over' phosphor. Perf 14×15.

989	**471**	8½p. Emma and Mr Woodhouse..............	10	10
990	**472**	10p. Catherine Morland...........................	15	15
991	**473**	11p. Mr Darcy..	15	15
992	**474**	13p. Mary and Henry Crawford..............	25	20
Set of 4..			60	55
Set of 4 Gutter Pairs...			1·25	
Set of 4 Traffic Light Gutter Pairs......................			7·00	
First Day Cover..				75
Presentation Pack (PO Pack No. 75)....................			7·00	
PHQ Cards (set of 4) (13).................................			9·50	15·00

Special First Day of Issue Postmarks

Philatelic Bureau, Edinburgh................................		85
Steventon, Basingstoke, Hants.............................		1·50

475 Angels with Harp and Lute

476 Angel with Mandolin

477 Angel with Horn

478 Angel with Trumpet

(Des R. Downer)

1975 (26 Nov). Christmas, Angels. Multicoloured One phosphor band (6½p.), phosphor-inked background (8½p.), 'All-over' phosphor (others). Perf 15×14.

993	**475**	6½p. Angels with Harp and Lute..............	10	10
994	**476**	8½p. Angel with Mandolin......................	10	10
995	**477**	11p. Angel with Horn............................	20	15
996	**478**	13p. Angel with Trumpet.......................	20	20
Set of 4..			45	50
Set of 4 Gutter Pairs...			1·10	
Set of 4 Traffic Light Gutter Pairs......................			5·00	
First Day Cover..				75
Presentation Pack (PO Pack No. 76)....................			1·50	

The 6½p. exists with both ordinary PVA gum and PVA containing added dextrin.

Special First Day of Issue Postmarks

Philatelic Bureau, Edinburgh................................		60
Bethlehem, Llandeilo, Dyfed................................		1·00

Collectors Pack

1975 (26 Nov). Comprises Nos. 970/996.

CP996a	Collectors Pack (Pack No. 77)................	4·25

479 Housewife

480 Policeman

481 District Nurse

482 Industrialist

(Des P. Sharland)

1976 (10 Mar). Telephone Centenary. Multicoloured 'All-over' phosphor. Perf 15×14.

997	**479**	8½p. Housewife....................................	10	10
		a. Deep rose (vase and picture frame) omitted...................................	£4750	
		b. Imperf (pair).................................	£1500	
998	**480**	10p. Policeman.....................................	15	15
999	**481**	11p. District Nurse................................	15	15
1000	**482**	13p. Industrialist..................................	25	20
Set of 4..			60	55
Set of 4 Gutter Pairs...			1·25	
Set of 4 Traffic Light Gutter Pairs......................			11·00	
First Day Cover..				60
Presentation Pack (PO Pack No. 78)....................			1·40	

Special First Day of Issue Postmark

Philatelic Bureau, Edinburgh................................		70

483 Hewing Coal (Thomas Hepburn)

484 Machinery (Robert Owen)

485 Chimney Cleaning (Lord Shaftesbury)

486 Hands clutching Prison Bars (Elizabeth Fry)

(Des D. Gentleman)

1976 (28 Apr). Social Reformers. Multicoloured 'All-over' phosphor. Perf 15×14.

1001	**483**	8½p. Hewing Coal (Thomas Hepburn)....	10	10
1002	**484**	10p. Machinery (Robert Owen)...............	15	15
1003	**485**	11p. Chimney Cleaning (Lord Shaftesbury)..................................	15	15
1004	**486**	13p. Hands clutching Prison Bars (Elizabeth Fry)...............................	25	20
Set of 4..			60	55
Set of 4 Gutter Pairs...			1·25	
Set of 4 Traffic Light Gutter Pairs......................			5·00	
First Day Cover..				60
Presentation Pack (PO Pack No. 79)....................			1·25	
PHQ Card (No. 1001) (14).................................			2·75	9·00

Special First Day of Issue Postmark

Philatelic Bureau, Edinburgh................................		70

487 Benjamin Franklin (bust by Jean-Jacques Caffieri)

(Des P. Sharland)

1976 (2 June). Bicentenary of American Revolution. Multicoloured 'All-over' phosphor. Perf 14×15.

1005	**487**	11p. Benjamin Franklin............................	20	20
Gutter Pair...			40	
Traffic Light Gutter Pair.....................................			2·25	
First Day Cover..				50
Presentation Pack (PO Pack No. 80)....................			65	
PHQ Card (15)..			2·25	8·00

Special First Day of Issue Postmark

Philatelic Bureau, Edinburgh................................		60

488 'Elizabeth of Glamis'

489 'Grandpa Dickson'

490 'Rosa Mundi'

491 'Sweet Briar'

(Des Kristin Rosenberg)

1976 (30 June). Centenary of Royal National Rose Society. Multicoloured 'All-over' phosphor. Perf 14×15.

1006	488	8½p. 'Elizabeth of Glamis'........................	10	10
1007	489	10p. 'Grandpa Dickson'............................	15	15
1008	490	11p. 'Rosa Mundi'....................................	15	15
1009	491	13p. 'Sweet Briar'....................................	25	20
		a. Value omitted*................................	—	
Set of 4...			60	55
Set of 4 Gutter Pairs..			1·25	
Set of 4 Traffic Light Gutter Pairs....................			6·00	
First Day Cover..				60
Presentation Pack (PO Pack No. 81)................			1·50	
PHQ Cards (set of 4) (16)................................			14·00	15·00

* During repairs to the cylinder the face value on R.1/9 was temporarily covered with copper. This covering was inadvertently left in place during printing, but the error was discovered before issue and most examples were removed from the sheets. Two mint and one used example have so far been reported, but only one of the mint remains in private hands.

Special First Day of Issue Postmark

Philatelic Bureau, Edinburgh...	70

492 Archdruid

493 Morris Dancing

494 Scots Piper

495 Welsh Harpist

(Des Marjorie Saynor)

1976 (4 Aug). British Cultural Traditions. Multicoloured 'All-over' phosphor. Perf 14×15.

1010	492	8½p. Archdruid..	10	10
1011	493	10p. Morris Dancing................................	15	15
1012	494	11p. Scots Piper.......................................	15	15
1013	495	13p. Welsh Harpist..................................	25	20
Set of 4...			60	55
Set of 4 Gutter Pairs..			1·25	
Set of 4 Traffic Light Gutter Pairs....................			6·00	

First Day Cover...		60
Presentation Pack (PO Pack No. 82)...........................	1·25	
PHQ Cards (set of 4) (17)..	7·50	12·00

The 8½p. and 13p. commemorate the 800th anniversary of the Royal National Eisteddfod.

Special First Day of Issue Postmarks

Philatelic Bureau, Edinburgh...	70
Cardigan, Dyfed...	1·25

496 Woodcut from *The Canterbury Tales*

497 Extract from *The Tretyse of Love*

498 Woodcut from *The Game and Playe of Chesse*

499 Early Printing Press

(Des R. Gay. Queen's head printed in gold and then embossed)

1976 (29 Sept). 500th Anniversary of British Printing. Multicoloured 'All-over' phosphor. Perf 14×15.

1014	496	8½p. Woodcut from *The Canterbury Tales*...........................	10	10
1015	497	10p. Extract from *The Tretyse of Love*......	15	15
1016	498	11p. Woodcut from *The Game and Playe of Chesse*...............................	15	15
1017	499	13p. Early Printing Press.........................	25	25
Set of 4...			60	60
Set of 4 Gutter Pairs..			1·25	
Set of 4 Traffic Light Gutter Pairs....................			6·00	
First Day Cover..				65
Presentation Pack (PO Pack No. 83)................			1·25	
PHQ Cards (set of 4) (18)................................			6·00	9·00

Special First Day of Issue Postmarks

Philatelic Bureau, Edinburgh...	75
London SW1..	1·00

500 Virgin and Child

501 Angel with Crown

502 Angel appearing to Shepherds

503 The Three Kings

(Des Enid Marx)

1976 (24 Nov). Christmas, English Medieval Embroidery. Multicoloured One phosphor band (6½p.) or 'All-over' phosphor (others). Perf 15×14.

1018	500	6½p. Virgin and Child..............................	10	10
		a. Imperf (pair).....................................	£425	
1019	501	8½p. Angel with Crown...........................	15	15
1020	502	11p. Angel appearing to Shepherds........	15	15

		a. Uncoated paper*............................	75·00	30·00
1021	**503**	13p. The Three Kings........................	20	20
Set of 4..			55	55
Set of 4 Gutter Pairs..................................			1·10	
Set of 4 Traffic Light Gutter Pairs..............			4·50	
First Day Cover...				60
Presentation Pack (PO Pack No. 87).........			1·40	
PHQ Cards (set of 4) (19).........................			1·80	5·00

* See footnote after No. 744.

Special First Day of Issue Postmarks

Philatelic Bureau, Edinburgh................................		70
Bethlehem, Llandeilo, Dyfed.................................		1·25

Collectors Pack

1976 (24 Nov). Comprises Nos. 997/1021.

CP1021*a*	Collectors Pack (Pack No. 88)..............	5·50	

504 Lawn Tennis

505 Table Tennis

506 Squash

507 Badminton

(Des A. Restall)

1977 (12 Jan). Racket Sports. Multicoloured Phosphorised paper. Perf 15×14.

1022	**504**	8½p. Lawn Tennis...................................	10	10
		a. Imperf (horiz pair).......................	£1100	
1023	**505**	10p. Table Tennis..............................	15	15
1024	**506**	11p. Squash......................................	15	15
		a. Imperf (horiz pair).......................	£3250	
1025	**507**	13p. Badminton.................................	20	20
Set of 4..			55	55
Set of 4 Gutter Pairs..................................			1·10	
Set of 4 Traffic Light Gutter Pairs..............			5·50	
First Day Cover...				60
Presentation Pack (PO Pack No. 89).........			1·50	
PHQ Cards (set of 4) (20).........................			3·50	8·00

Special First Day of Issue Postmark

Philatelic Bureau, Edinburgh................................		70

For Nos. 1026/1028 and T **508** see Decimal Machin Definitives section	

509 Steroids, Conformational Analysis

510 Vitamin C, Synthesis

511 Starch, Chromatography

512 Salt, Crystallography

(Des J. Karo)

1977 (2 Mar). Royal Institute of Chemistry Centenary. Multicoloured 'All-over' phosphor. Perf 15×14.

1029	**509**	8½p. Steroids, Conformational Analysis..	10	10
		a. Imperf (horiz pair).......................	£3000	
1030	**510**	10p. Vitamin C, Synthesis...................	15	15
1031	**511**	11p. Starch, Chromatography.............	15	15

1032	**512**	13p. Salt, Crystallography...................	20	20
Set of 4..			55	55
Set of 4 Gutter Pairs..................................			1·10	
Set of 4 Traffic Light Gutter Pairs..............			5·50	
First Day Cover...				60
Presentation Pack (PO Pack No. 92).........			1·50	
PHQ Cards (set of 4) (21).........................			3·50	8·00

Special First Day of Issue Postmark

Philatelic Bureau, Edinburgh................................		70

513

514

515

516

Types **513/516** differ in the decorations of 'ER'.

(Des R. Guyatt)

1977 (11 May–15 June). Silver Jubilee. Multicoloured 'All-over' phosphor. Perf 15×14.

1033	**513**	8½p. Pale turquoise-green background..	10	10
		a. Imperf (pair)................................	£650	
1034		9p. Lavender background (15.6.77).....	20	20
1035	**514**	10p. Ochre background......................	10	10
		a. Imperf (pair)................................	£2000	
1036	**515**	11p. Rose-pink background................	25	30
		a. Imperf (pair)................................	£2000	
1037	**516**	13p. Bistre-yellow background.............	25	30
		a. Imperf (pair)................................	£1300	
Set of 5..			80	85
Set of 5 Gutter Pairs..................................			1·60	
Set of 5 Traffic Light Gutter Pairs..............			8·00	
First Day Covers (2)...................................				90
Presentation Pack (PO Pack No. 94) (Nos. 1033, 1035/1037)...............................			1·00	
PHQ Cards (set of 5) (22).........................			5·50	10·00
Souvenir Book...				

The Souvenir book is a 16 page booklet containing a history of the Queen's reign.

Special First Day of Issue Postmarks

Philatelic Bureau, Edinburgh (Nos. 1033, 1035/1037) (11.5.77)......		50
Philatelic Bureau, Edinburgh (No. 1034) (15.6.77)...........................		50
Windsor, Berks (Nos. 1033, 1035/1037) (11.5.77)............................		1·00
Windsor, Berks (No. 1034) (15.6.77)..		50

517 Gathering of Nations

(Des P. Murdoch. Recess and photo)

1977 (8 June). Commonwealth Heads of Government Meeting, London. Multicoloured 'All-over' phosphor. Perf 14×15.

1038	**517**	13p. Gathering of Nations........................	20	20
Gutter Pair..			40	
Traffic Light Gutter Pair..............................			1·75	
First Day Cover...				40
Presentation Pack (PO Pack No. 95).........			45	
PHQ Card (23)...			1·25	1·50

Special First Day of Issue Postmarks

Philatelic Bureau, Edinburgh................................		45
London SW..		55

518 Hedgehog

519 Brown Hare

520 Red Squirrel

521 Otter

522 Badger

(Des P. Oxenham)

1977 (5 Oct). British Wildlife. Multicoloured 'All-over' phosphor. Perf 14×15.

1039	**518**	9p. Hedgehog......................................	15	20
		a. Horiz strip of 5. Nos. 1039/1043......	70	95
		b. Imperf (vert pair).............................	£2000	
		c. Imperf (horiz pair. Nos. 1039/1040)...................................	£2000	
1040	**519**	9p. Brown Hare....................................	15	20
1041	**520**	9p. Red Squirrel...................................	15	20
1042	**521**	9p. Otter...	15	20
1043	**522**	9p. Badger..	15	20
		Set of 5...	70	95
		Gutter Strip of 10.....................................	1·40	
		Traffic Light Gutter Strip of 10...................	5·00	
		First Day Cover...		1·00
		Presentation Pack (PO Pack No. 96)...............	1·00	
		PHQ Cards (set of 5) (25)...........................	1·50	2·50

Nos. 1039/1043 were printed horizontally *se-tenant* within the sheet.

Special First Day of Issue Postmark

Philatelic Bureau, Edinburgh...		1·10

523 'Three French Hens, Two Turtle Doves and a Partridge in a Pear Tree'

524 'Six Geese-a-laying, Five Gold Rings, Four Colly Birds'

525 'Eight Maids-a-milking, Seven Swans-a-swimming'

526 'Ten Pipers piping, Nine Drummers drumming'

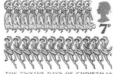

527 'Twelve Lords a-leaping, Eleven Ladies dancing'

528 'A Partridge in a Pear Tree'

(Des D. Gentleman)

1977 (23 Nov). Christmas, *The Twelve Days of Christmas*. Multicoloured One centre phosphor band (7p.) or 'All-over' phosphor (9p.). Perf 15×14.

1044	**523**	7p. 'Three French Hens, Two Turtle Doves and a Partridge in a Pear Tree'......................	10	10
		a. Horiz strip of 5. Nos. 1044/1048......	50	50
		ab. Imperf (strip of 5. Nos. 1044/1048).	£180	
1045	**524**	7p. 'Six Geese-a-laying, Five Gold Rings, Four Colly Birds'.....................	10	10
1046	**525**	7p. 'Eight Maids-a-milking, Seven Swans-a-swimming'........................	10	10
1047	**526**	7p. 'Ten Pipers piping, Nine Drummers drumming'......................	10	10
1048	**527**	7p. 'Twelve Lords a-leaping, Eleven Ladies dancing'.............................	10	10
1049	**528**	9p. 'A Partridge in a Pear Tree'..............	10	20
		a. Imperf (pair)...................................	£850	
		Set of 6...	60	70
		Set of 6 Gutter Pairs..................................	1·25	
		Traffic Light Gutter Pairs............................	3·75	
		First Day Cover...		75
		Presentation Pack (PO Pack No. 97)...............	90	
		PHQ Cards (set of 6) (26)...........................	1·50	2·50

Nos. 1044/1048 were printed horizontally *se-tenant* within the sheet.

Special First Day of Issue Postmarks

Philatelic Bureau, Edinburgh...		75
Bethlehem, Llandeilo, Dyfed...		80

Collectors Pack

1977 (23 Nov). Comprises Nos. 1022/1025 and 1029/1049.

CP1049*b*		Collectors Pack (Pack No. 98)..............	3·75

529 Oil. North Sea

530 Coal. Modern Pithead Production Platform

531 Natural Gas. Flame Rising from Sea

532 Electricity. Nuclear Power Station and Uranium Atom

(Des P. Murdoch)

1978 (25 Jan). Energy Resources. Multicoloured 'All-over' phosphor. Perf 14×15.

1050	**529**	9p. Oil..	10	10
1051	**530**	10½p. Coal..	15	15
1052	**531**	11p. Natural Gas...................................	15	15
1053	**532**	13p. Electricity......................................	20	20
		Set of 4...	55	55
		Set of 4 Gutter Pairs..................................	1·10	
		Set of 4 Traffic Light Gutter Pairs................	4·50	
		First Day Cover...		60
		Presentation Pack (PO Pack No. 99)...............	85	
		PHQ Cards (set of 4) (27)...........................	1·50	2·50

Special First Day of Issue Postmark
Philatelic Bureau, Edinburgh.. 70

533 The Tower of London   **534** Holyroodhouse

535 Caernarvon Castle   **536** Hampton Court Palace

(Des R. Maddox (stamps), J. Matthews (miniature sheet))

1978 (1 Mar). British Architecture (4th series), Historic Buildings. Multicoloured 'All-over' phosphor. Perf 15×14.

1054	**533**	9p. The Tower of London.......................	10	10
1055	**534**	10½p. Holyroodhouse............................	15	15
1056	**535**	11p. Caernarvon Castle.......................	15	15
1057	**536**	13p. Hampton Court Palace...................	20	20
Set of 4.............................			55	55
Set of 4 Gutter Pairs.................			1·10	
Set of 4 Traffic Light Gutter Pairs......			4·25	
First Day Cover....................				60
Presentation Pack (PO Pack No. 100)......			75	
PHQ Cards (set of 4) (28)............			1·50	2·50
MS1058 121×89mm. Nos. 1054/1057 (sold at 53½p.)......			70	70
	a. Imperforate........................		£7250	
	b. Light yellow-olive (Queen's head) omitted........		£10000	
	c. Rose-red (Union Jack on 9p.) omitted...		£4250	
	d. Orange-yellow omitted...............		£5750	
	e. New blue (Union Jack on 9p.) omitted...			
First Day Cover....................				85

The premium on No. **MS**1058 was used to support the London 1980 International Stamp Exhibition.

No. **MS**1058d is most noticeable on the 10½p. (spheres absent on towers) and around the roadway and arch on the 13p.

Special First Day of Issue Postmarks
Philatelic Bureau, Edinburgh (stamps)........................ 80
Philatelic Bureau, Edinburgh (miniature sheet)............... 95
London EC (stamps).. 90
London EC (miniature sheet)............................... 1·00

537 State Coach   **538** St Edward's Crown

539 The Sovereign's Orb   **540** Imperial State Crown

(Des J. Matthews)

1978 (31 May). 25th Anniversary of Coronation. Multicoloured 'All-over' phosphor. Perf 14×15.

1059	**537**	9p. State Coach...........................	15	20
1060	**538**	10½p. St Edward's Crown..................	20	20
1061	**539**	11p. The Sovereign's Orb................	20	20
1062	**540**	13p. Imperial State Crown...............	25	25
Set of 4.............................			70	75
Set of 4 Gutter Pairs.................			1·40	
Set of 4 Traffic Light Gutter Pairs......			4·25	
First Day Cover (Philatelic Bureau, Edinburgh)..........				80
Presentation Pack (PO Pack No. 101)......			85	
PHQ Cards (set of 4) (29)............			1·50	2·25
Souvenir Book........................			1·25	

The souvenir book is a 16 page booklet illustrated with scenes from the Coronation.

Special First Day of Issue Postmarks
Philatelic Bureau, Edinburgh.......................... 85
London SW1.. 95

541 Shire Horse   **542** Shetland Pony

543 Welsh Pony   **544** Thoroughbred

(Des P. Oxenham)

1978 (5 July). Horses. Multicoloured 'All-over' phosphor. Perf 15×14.

1063	**541**	9p. Shire Horse.........................	10	10
	a. Imperf (vert pair)...............		—	
1064	**542**	10½p. Shetland Pony...................	15	15
1065	**543**	11p. Welsh Pony......................	15	15
1066	**544**	13p. Thoroughbred...................	20	20
Set of 4.............................			55	55
Set of 4 Gutter Pairs.................			1·10	
Set of 4 Traffic Light Gutter Pairs......			4·50	
First Day Cover (Philatelic Bureau, Edinburgh)......				60
Presentation Pack (PO Pack No. 102)......			75	
PHQ Cards (set of 4) (30)............			1·00	1·75

Special First Day of Issue Postmarks
Philatelic Bureau, Edinburgh.......................... 65
Peterborough....................................... 75

545 Penny-farthing and 1884 Safety Bicycle   **546** 1920 Touring Bicycles

547 1978 Small-wheel Bicycles   **548** 1978 Road Racers

(Des F. Wegner)

1978 (2 Aug). Centenaries of Cyclists' Touring Club and British Cycling Federation. Multicoloured 'All-over' phosphor. Perf 15×14.

1067	**545**	9p. Penny-farthing and 1884 Safety Bicycle........	10	10
	a. Imperf (pair)....................		£325	
1068	**546**	10½p. 1920 Touring Bicycles............	15	15
1069	**547**	11p. 1978 Small-wheel Bicycles.........	15	15

1070	**548**	13p. 1978 Road racers................................	20	20
		a. Imperf (pair)........................	£900	
Set of 4........................			55	55
Set of 4 Gutter Pairs........................			1·10	
Set of 4 Traffic Light Gutter Pairs........................			4·25	
First Day Cover (Philatelic Bureau, Edinburgh)................				60
Presentation Pack (PO Pack No. 103)........................			75	
PHQ Cards (set of 4) (31)........................			1·00	1·75

Special First Day of Issue Postmarks
Philatelic Bureau, Edinburgh.. 65
Harrogate, North Yorkshire.. 75

549 Singing Carols round the Christmas Tree

550 The Waits

551 18th-century Carol Singers

552 *The Boar's Head Carol*

(Des Faith Jaques)

1978 (22 Nov). Christmas, Carol singers. Multicoloured One centre phosphor band (7p.) or 'All-over' phosphor (others). Perf 15×14.

1071	**549**	7p. Singing Carols round the Christmas Tree........................	10	10
		a. Imperf (pair)........................	£375	
1072	**550**	9p. The Waits........................	15	15
		a. Imperf (pair)........................	£875	
1073	**551**	11p. 18th-century Carol Singers.............	15	15
		a. Imperf (horiz pair)........................	£950	
1074	**552**	13p. *The Boar's Head Carol*........................	20	20
Set of 4........................			55	55
Set of 4 Gutter Pairs........................			1·10	
Set of 4 Traffic Light Gutter Pairs........................			4·00	
First Day Cover........................				60
Presentation Pack (PO Pack No. 104)........................			75	
PHQ Cards (set of 4) (32)........................			1·00	1·75

Special First Day of Issue Postmarks
Philatelic Bureau, Edinburgh.. 65
Bethlehem, Llandeilo, Dyfed.. 70

Collectors Pack

1978 (22 Nov). Comprises Nos. 1050/1057 and 1059/1074.
CP1074*a*   Collectors Pack (Pack No. 105)............ 3·75

553 Old English Sheepdog

554 Welsh Springer Spaniel

555 West Highland Terrier

556 Irish Setter

(Des P. Barrett)

1979 (7 Feb). Dogs. Multicoloured 'All-over' phosphor. Perf 15×14.

1075	**553**	9p. Old English Sheepdog.....................	10	10
1076	**554**	10½p. Welsh Springer Spaniel..................	15	15
1077	**555**	11p. West Highland Terrier....................	15	15
		a. Imperf (horiz pair)........................	£2250	
1078	**556**	13p. Irish Setter........................	20	20
Set of 4........................			55	55

Set of 4 Gutter Pairs........................		1·10	
Set of 4 Traffic Light Gutter Pairs........................		4·00	
First Day Cover........................			60
Presentation Pack (PO Pack No. 106)........................		70	
PHQ Cards (set of 4) (33)........................		80	1·50

Special First Day of Issue Postmarks
Philatelic Bureau, Edinburgh.. 65
London.. 75

557 Primroses

558 Daffodils

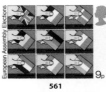

559 Bluebells

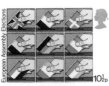

560 Snowdrops

(Des P. Newcombe)

1979 (21 Mar). Spring Wild Flowers. Multicoloured 'All-over' phosphor. Perf 14×15.

1079	**557**	9p. Primroses........................	10	10
		a. Imperf (vert pair)........................	£475	
1080	**558**	10½p. Daffodils........................	15	15
		a. Imperf (vert pair)........................	£1300	
1081	**559**	11p. Bluebells........................	15	15
		a. Imperf (horiz pair)........................	£1300	
1082	**560**	13p. Snowdrops........................	20	20
		a. Imperf (horiz pair)........................	£1000	
Set of 4........................			55	55
Set of 4 Gutter Pairs........................			1·10	
Set of 4 Traffic Light Gutter Pairs........................			4·00	
First Day Cover........................				60
Presentation Pack (PO Pack No. 107)........................			70	
PHQ Cards (set of 4) (34)........................			80	1·25

Special First Day of Issue Postmark
Philatelic Bureau, Edinburgh.. 65

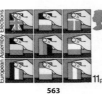

561

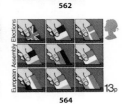

562

563

564

(Des S. Cliff)

1979 (9 May). First Direct Elections to European Assembly. Multicoloured (colours of backgrounds to flag panels given) Phosphorised paper. Perf 15×14.

1083	**561**	9p. dull ultramarine........................	10	10
1084	**562**	10½p. chestnut........................	15	15
1085	**563**	11p. grey-green........................	15	15
1086	**564**	13p. brown........................	20	20
Set of 4........................			55	55
Set of 4 Gutter Pairs........................			1·10	
Set of 4 Traffic Light Gutter Pairs........................			4·00	

First Day Cover.. 60
Presentation Pack (PO Pack No. 108)............................ 70
PHQ Cards (set of 4) (35)...................................... 80   1·25
Nos. 1083/1086 show Hands placing National Flags in Ballot Boxes.

Special First Day of Issue Postmarks

Philatelic Bureau, Edinburgh.. 65
London SW.. 70

565 Saddling Mahmoud for   **566** The Liverpool Great National
the Derby, 1936 (Sir Alfred   Steeple Chase, 1839 (aquatint by
Munnings)   F. C. Turner)

567 The First Spring Meeting,   **568** Racing at Dorsett Ferry,
Newmarket, 1793 (J. N.   Windsor, 1684 (Francis Barlow)
Sartorius)

(Des S. Rose)

1979 (6 June). Horse Racing Paintings Bicentenary of the Derby (9p.).
Multicoloured 'All-over' phosphor. Perf 15×14.
1087   **565**   9p. Saddling Mahmoud for the Derby,
                       1936.. 10   10
1088   **566**   10½p. The Liverpool Great National
                       Steeple Chase, 1839...................... 15   15
1089   **567**   11p. The First Spring Meeting,
                       Newmarket, 1793........................... 15   15
1090   **568**   13p. Racing at Dorsett Ferry, Windsor,
                       1684.. 20   20
Set of 4.. 55   55
Set of 4 Gutter Pairs.. 1·10
Set of 4 Traffic Light Gutter Pairs.............................. 4·50
First Day Cover... 60
Presentation Pack (PO Pack No. 109)............................ 70
PHQ Cards (set of 4) (36)...................................... 80   1·25

Special First Day of Issue Postmarks

Philatelic Bureau, Edinburgh.. 65
Epsom, Surrey... 70

569 The Tale of Peter   **570** The Wind in the
Rabbit (Beatrix Potter)   Willows (Kenneth
                               Grahame)

571 Winnie-the-Pooh   **572** Alice's Adventures
(A. A. Milne)   in Wonderland (Lewis
                               Carroll)

(Des E. Hughes)

1979 (11 July). International Year of the Child. Children's Book Illustrations.
Multicoloured 'All-over' phosphor. Perf 14×15.
1091   **569**   9p. The Tale of Peter Rabbit................... 15   15
1092   **570**   10½p. The Wind in the Willows................. 20   20
1093   **571**   11p. Winnie-the-Pooh............................. 20   20
1094   **572**   13p. Alice's Adventures in Wonderland..... 25   25
Set of 4.. 75   75
Set of 4 Gutter Pairs.. 1·50
Set of 4 Traffic Light Gutter Pairs.............................. 3·75
First Day Cover... 80
Presentation Pack (PO Pack No. 110)............................ 1·00
PHQ Cards (set of 4) (37)...................................... 80   1·40
Nos. 1091/1094 depict original illustrations from four books.

Special First Day of Issue Postmark

Philatelic Bureau, Edinburgh.. 85
First Day of Issue handstamps were provided at Hartfield, East Sussex
and Stourbridge, West Midlands for this issue.

573 Sir Rowland Hill   **574** Postman, circa
                            1839

575 London Postman,   **576** Woman and
circa 1839   Young Girl with
                            Letters, 1840

(Des E. Stemp)

1979 (22 Aug–24 Oct). Death Centenary of Sir Rowland Hill. Multicoloured
'All-over' phosphor. Perf 14×15.
1095   **573**   10p. Sir Rowland Hill............................. 15   15
                       a. Imperf (horiz pair)...................... £275
1096   **574**   11½p. Postman, circa 1839..................... 15   15
1097   **575**   13p. London Postman, circa 1839............ 20   20
1098   **576**   15p. Woman and Young Girl with
                       Letters, 1840.................................. 25   25
Set of 4.. 70   70
Set of 4 Gutter Pairs.. 1·40
Set of 4 Traffic Light Gutter Pairs.............................. 3·75
First Day Cover... 75
Presentation Pack (PO Pack No. 111)............................ 80
PHQ Cards (set of 4) (38)...................................... 50   1·25
MS1099 89×121 mm. Nos. 1095/1098 (sold at 59½p.)
     (24.10.79)... 70   75
           a. Imperforate...................................... £2750
           b. Brown-ochre (15p. background, etc.)
              omitted... £3750
           c. Gold (Queen's head) omitted................... £450
           d. Brown-ochre, myrtle-green and gold
              omitted... £12000
           e. Bright blue (13p. background, etc.)
              omitted... £6500
           f. Myrtle-green (10p. (background), 15p.)
              omitted... £4250
           g. Pale greenish yellow omitted.................. £700
           h. Rosine omitted..................................... £1200
           i. Bistre-brown omitted............................. £1300
           j. Grey-black and pale greenish yellow
              omitted.. —
First Day Cover... 80
The premium on No. **MS**1099 was used to support the London 1980
International Stamp Exhibition.
Examples of No. **MS**1099 showing face values on the stamps of 9p.,
10½p., 11p. and 13p., with a sheet price of 53½p., were prepared, but
not issued.

Special First Day of Issue Postmarks

Special First Day of Issue Postmarks

Philatelic Bureau, Edinburgh (stamps) (22.8.79)	80
Philatelic Bureau, Edinburgh (miniature sheet) (24.10.79)	85
London EC (stamps) (22.8.79)	80
London EC (miniature sheet) (24.10.79)	85

First Day of Issue handstamps were provided at Kidderminster, Worcestershire on 22 August (pictorial) and 24 October (Type C) and at Sanquhar, Dumfriesshire on 22 August and 24 October (both Type C).

577 Policeman on the Beat

578 Policeman directing Traffic

579 Mounted Policewoman

580 River Patrol Boat

(Des B. Sanders)

1979 (26 Sept). 150th Anniversary of Metropolitan Police. Multicoloured Phosphorised paper. Perf 15×14.

1100	**577**	10p. Policeman on the Beat	15	15
1101	**578**	11½p. Policeman directing Traffic	15	15
1102	**579**	13p. Mounted Policewoman	20	20
1103	**580**	15p. River Patrol Boat	25	25
Set of 4			70	70
Set of 4 Gutter Pairs			1·40	
Set of 4 Traffic Light Gutter Pairs			3·75	
First Day Cover				75
Presentation Pack (PO Pack No. 112)			80	
PHQ Cards (set of 4) (39)			50	1·25

Special First Day of Issue Postmarks

Philatelic Bureau, Edinburgh	80
London SW	80

581 The Three Kings

582 Angel appearing to the Shepherds

583 The Nativity

584 Mary and Joseph travelling to Bethlehem

585 The Annunciation

(Des F. Wegner)

1979 (21 Nov). Christmas, Nativity Scenes. Multicoloured One centre phosphor band (8p.) or phosphorised paper (others). Perf 15×14.

1104	**581**	8p. The Three Kings	10	10
		a. Imperf (pair)	£500	
1105	**582**	10p. Angel appearing to the Shepherds	15	15
		a. Imperf between (vert pair)	—	
		b. Imperf (pair)	£500	
1106	**583**	11½p. The Nativity	15	15
1107	**584**	13p. Mary and Joseph travelling to Bethlehem	20	20
1108	**585**	15p. The Annunciation	20	20
Set of 5			75	75
Set of 5 Gutter Pairs			1·50	
Set of 5 Traffic Light Gutter Pairs			4·50	
First Day Cover				80
Presentation Pack (PO Pack No. 113)			80	
PHQ Cards (set of 5) (40)			50	1·25

Special First Day of Issue Postmarks

Philatelic Bureau, Edinburgh	85
Bethlehem, Llandeilo, Dyfed	85

Collectors Pack

1979 (21 Nov). Comprises Nos. 1075/1098 and 1100/1108.

CP1108a	Collectors Pack (Pack No. 114)	4·50

586 Common Kingfisher

587 Dipper

588 Moorhen

589 Yellow Wagtails

(Des M. Warren)

1980 (16 Jan). Centenary of Wild Bird Protection Act. Multicoloured Phosphorised paper. Perf 14×15.

1109	**586**	10p. Common Kingfisher	15	15
1110	**587**	11½p. Dipper	15	15
1111	**588**	13p. Moorhen	20	20
1112	**589**	15p. Yellow Wagtails	20	20
Set of 4			60	60
Set of 4 Gutter Pairs			1·25	
First Day Cover				65
Presentation Pack (PO Pack No. 115)			70	
PHQ Cards (set of 4) (41)			50	1·00

Special First Day of Issue Postmarks

Philatelic Bureau, Edinburgh	70
Sandy, Beds	75

590 *Rocket* approaching Moorish Arch, Liverpool

591 First and Second Class Carriages passing through Olive Mount Cutting

592 Third Class Carriage and Sheep Truck crossing Chat Moss

593 Horsebox and Carriage Truck near Bridgewater Canal

594 Goods Truck and Mail Coach at Manchester

12p. Grey step and dot above (Cyl. 1A, R. 8/4)

(Des D. Gentleman)

1980 (12 Mar). 150th Anniversary of Liverpool and Manchester Railway. Multicoloured Phosphorised paper. Perf 15×14.

1113	**590**	12p. *Rocket*................................	15	10
		a. Strip of 5. Nos. 1113/1117................	75	60
		ab. Imperf (horiz strip of 5. Nos. 1113/1117)................	£2750	
		ac. Lemon omitted (horiz strip of 5. Nos. 1113/1117)................	£12000	
1114	**591**	12p. First and Second Class Carriages.....	15	10
1115	**592**	12p. Third Class Carriage and Sheep Truck................	15	10
1116	**593**	12p. Horsebox and Carriage Truck..........	15	10
		a. Grey step................................	30·00	
1117	**594**	12p. Goods Truck and Mail-Coach..........	15	10
Set of 5................			75	60
Gutter Block of 10................			1·50	
First Day Cover................				70
Presentation Pack (PO Pack No. 116)................			85	
PHQ Cards (set of 5) (42)................			50	1·25

Nos. 1113/1117 were printed together, *se-tenant*, in horizontal strips of five throughout the sheet.

Special First Day of Issue Postmarks

Philatelic Bureau, Edinburgh................	75
Liverpool................	80
Manchester................	80

Montage of London Buildings

During the printing of No. 1118 the die was re-cut resulting in the following two types:

Type I (original). Top and bottom lines of shading in portrait oval broken. Hatched shading below left arm of Tower Bridge and hull of ship below right arm. Other points: Hatched shading on flag on Westminster Abbey, bottom right of Post Office Tower and archway of entrance to Westminster Abbey.

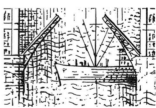

Type II (re-engraved). Lines in oval unbroken. Solid shading on bridge and ship. Also solid shading on flag, Post Office Tower and archway.

(Des J. Matthews. Eng G. Holt. Recess)

1980 (9 Apr–7 May). London 1980 International Stamp Exhibition. Phosphorised paper. Perf 14½×14.

1118	**595**	50p. agate (I)................................	75	70
		a. Type II................................	75	70
Gutter Pair................			1·50	
First Day Cover................				75
Presentation Pack (PO Pack No. 117)................			85	
PHQ Card (43)................			20	80
MS1119 90×123 mm. No. 1118a (*sold at 75p.*) (7.5.80).....			75	95
		a. Error. Imperf................................	£2000	
First Day Cover................				95

Examples of No. 1118 are known in various shades of green.

Such shades result from problems with the drying of the printed sheets on the press, but are not listed as similar colours can be easily faked.

No. **MS**1119 was sold at 75p., the premium being used for the exhibition.

Special First Day of Issue Postmarks

Philatelic Bureau, Edinburgh (stamp) (9.4.80)	80
Philatelic Bureau, Edinburgh (miniature sheet) (7.5.80)	1·00
London SW (stamp) (9.4.80)	1·00
London SW (miniature sheet) (7.5.80)	1·00

596 Buckingham Palace

597 The Albert Memorial

598 Royal Opera House

599 Hampton Court

600 Kensington Palace

(Des Sir Hugh Casson)

1980 (7 May). London Landmarks. Multicoloured Phosphorised paper. Perf 14×15.

1120	**596**	10½p. Buckingham Palace	10	10
1121	**597**	12p. The Albert Memorial	15	15
		a. Imperf (vert pair)	—	
1122	**598**	13½p. Royal Opera House	20	15
		a. Imperf (pair)	£1800	
1123	**599**	15p. Hampton Court	20	20
1124	**600**	17½p. Kensington Palace	25	20
		a. Silver (Queen's head) omitted	£450	
Set of 5			85	75
Set of 5 Gutter Pairs			4·25	
First Day Cover				80
Presentation Pack (PO Pack No. 118)			90	
PHQ Cards (set of 5) (43)			60	1·10

No. 1124a shows the Queen's head in pale greenish yellow, this colour being printed beneath the silver for technical reasons.

Special First Day of Issue Postmarks

Philatelic Bureau, Edinburgh	85
Kingston-upon-Thames	85

601 Charlotte Brontë (*Jane Eyre*)

602 George Eliot (*The Mill on the Floss*)

603 Emily Brontë (*Wuthering Heights*)

604 Mrs Gaskell (*North and South*)

Normal

Missing jewel (R.3/3)

(Des Barbara Brown)

1980 (9 July). Famous Authoresses. Multicoloured Phosphorised paper. Perf 15×14.

1125	**601**	12p. Charlotte Brontë	15	15
		Ea. Missing 'p' in value (R. 4/6)	25·00	
		b. Missing jewel	25·00	
1126	**602**	13½p. George Eliot	15	15
		a. Pale blue omitted	£1600	
1127	**603**	15p. Emily Brontë	25	25
1128	**604**	17½p. Mrs Gaskell	30	30
		a. Imperf and slate-blue omitted (pair)	£750	
Set of 4			75	75
Set of 4 Gutter Pairs			1·50	
First Day Cover				80
Presentation Pack (PO Pack No. 119)			80	
PHQ Cards (set of 4) (44)			50	1·00

Nos. 1125/1128 show authoresses and scenes from novels.
Nos. 1125/1126 also include the Europa CEPT emblem.

Special First Day of Issue Postmarks

Philatelic Bureau, Edinburgh	85
Haworth, Keighley, W. Yorks	90

605 Queen Elizabeth the Queen Mother

(Des J. Matthews from photograph by N. Parkinson)

1980 (4 Aug). 80th Birthday of Queen Elizabeth the Queen Mother. Multicoloured Phosphorised paper. Perf 14×15.

1129	**605**	12p. Queen Elizabeth the Queen Mother	25	25
		a. Imperf (horiz pair)	£900	
Gutter Pair			50	
First Day Cover				50
PHQ Card (45)			20	40

Special First Day of Issue Postmarks

Philatelic Bureau, Edinburgh	60
Glamis Castle, Forfar	65

606 Sir Henry Wood

607 Sir Thomas Beecham

608 Sir Malcolm   **609** Sir John Barbirolli
Sargent

(Des P. Gauld)

1980 (10 Sept). British Conductors. Multicoloured Phosphorised paper.
Perf 14×15.

1130	**606**	12p. Sir Henry Wood	15	15
1131	**607**	13½p. Sir Thomas Beecham	15	15
1132	**608**	15p. Sir Malcolm Sargent	25	25
1133	**609**	17½p. Sir John Barbirolli	30	30
Set of 4			75	75
Set of 4 Gutter Pairs			1·50	
First Day Cover				80
Presentation Pack (PO Pack No. 120)			80	
PHQ Cards (set of 4) (46)			60	1·00

Special First Day of Issues

Postmarks Philatelic Bureau, Edinburgh		85
London SW		90

610 Running   **611** Rugby

612 Boxing   **613** Cricket

(Des R. Goldsmith. Litho Questa)

1980 (10 Oct). Sport Centenaries. Multicoloured Phosphorised paper.
Perf 14×14½.

1134	**610**	12p. Running	15	15
		a. Gold (Queen's head) omitted	—	
1135	**611**	13½p. Rugby	15	15
1136	**612**	15p. Boxing	25	25
		a. Gold (Queen's head) omitted	—	
1137	**613**	17½p. Cricket	30	30
Set of 4			75	75
Set of 4 Gutter Pairs			1·50	
First Day Cover				80
Presentation Pack (PO Pack No. 121)			80	
PHQ Cards (set of 4) (47)			60	1·00

Centenaries: 12p. Amateur Athletics Association; 13½p. Welsh Rugby
Union; 15p. Amateur Boxing Association; 17½p. First England–Australia
Test Match.
Nos. 1134a and 1136a were caused by paper folds.

Special First Day of Issue Postmarks

Philatelic Bureau, Edinburgh		85
Cardiff		90

614 Christmas Tree   **615** Candles

616 Apples and Mistletoe   **617** Crown, Chains and Bell

618 Holly

(Des J. Matthews)

1980 (19 Nov). Christmas. Multicoloured One centre phosphor band (10p.)
or phosphorised paper (others). Perf 15×14.

1138	**614**	10p. Christmas Tree	10	10
		a. Imperf (horiz pair)	£1000	
1139	**615**	12p. Candles	15	15
1140	**616**	13½p. Apples and Mistletoe	15	15
		a. Imperf (pair)	£1400	
1141	**617**	15p. Crown, Chains and Bell	25	25
1142	**618**	17½p. Holly	25	25
Set of 5			80	80
Set of 5 Gutter Pairs			1·60	
First Day Cover				85
Presentation Pack (PO Pack No. 122)			85	
PHQ Cards (set of 5) (48)			75	1·00

Special First Day of Issue Postmarks

Philatelic Bureau, Edinburgh		90
Bethlehem, Llandeilo, Dyfed		95

Collectors Pack

1980 (19 Nov). Comprises Nos. 1109/1118 and 1120/1142.
CP1142a   Collectors Pack (Pack No. 123)............ 5·50

619 St Valentine's Day   **620** Morris Dancers

621 Lammastide   **622** Medieval Mummers

(Des F. Wegner)

1981 (6 Feb). Folklore. Multicoloured Phosphorised paper. Perf 15×14.

1143	**619**	14p. St Valentine's Day	20	20
1144	**620**	18p. Morris Dancers	20	20
1145	**621**	22p. Lammastide	30	35
1146	**622**	25p. Medieval Mummers	40	45
Set of 4			1·00	1·10
Set of 4 Gutter Pairs			2·00	
First Day Cover				1·10

Presentation Pack (PO Pack No. 124)...................	1·10	
PHQ Cards (set of 4) (49).........................	60	1·20

Types **619/620** also include the Europa CEPT emblem.

Special First Day of Issue Postmarks

Philatelic Bureau, Edinburgh.........................		1·25
London WC...		1·25

623 Blind Man with Guide Dog

624 Hands spelling 'Deaf' in Sign Language

625 Disabled Man in Wheelchair

626 Disabled Artist with Foot painting

(Des J. Gibbs)

1981 (25 Mar). International Year of the Disabled. Multicoloured. Phosphorised paper. Perf 15×14.

1147	**623**	14p. Blind Man with Guide Dog..............	20	20
		a. Imperf (pair).............................	£450	
1148	**624**	18p. Hands spelling 'Deaf'...................	20	20
1149	**625**	22p. Disabled Man in Wheelchair...........	35	35
1150	**626**	25p. Disabled Artist with Foot painting..	45	45
Set of 4..			1·10	1·10
Set of 4 Gutter Pairs....................................			2·25	
First Day Cover..				1·20
Presentation Pack (PO Pack No. 125)...................			1·25	
PHQ Cards (set of 4) (50).........................			60	1·25

All known examples of No. 1147a are creased.

Special First Day of Issue Postmarks

Philatelic Bureau, Edinburgh.........................		1·25
Windsor...		1·25

627 Small tortoiseshell

628 Large Blue

629 Peacock

630 Chequered Skipper

(Des G. Beningfield)

1981 (13 May). Butterflies. Multicoloured Phosphorised paper. Perf 14×15.

1151	**627**	14p. Small tortoiseshell...........................	20	20
		a. Imperf (pair).............................	£3750	
1152	**628**	18p. Large Blue..................................	20	20
1153	**629**	22p. Peacock....................................	35	35
1154	**630**	25p. Chequered Skipper........................	45	45
Set of 4..			1·10	1·10
Set of 4 Gutter Pairs....................................			2·25	
First Day Cover..				1·20

Presentation Pack (PO Pack No. 126)...................	1·25	
PHQ Cards (set of 4) (51).........................	60	1·25

Special First Day of Issue Postmarks

Philatelic Bureau, Edinburgh.........................		1·25
London SW...		1·25

631 Glenfinnan, Scotland

632 Derwentwater, England

633 Stackpole Head, Wales

634 Giant's Causeway, Northern Ireland

635 St Kilda, Scotland

(Des M. Fairclough)

1981 (24 June). 50th Anniversary of National Trust for Scotland. British Landscapes. Multicoloured Phosphorised paper. Perf 15×14.

1155	**631**	14p. Glenfinnan, Scotland........................	20	20
1156	**632**	18p. Derwentwater, England.....................	20	20
1157	**633**	20p. Stackpole Head, Wales......................	25	25
1158	**634**	22p. Giant's Causeway, Northern Ireland..	35	35
1159	**635**	25p. St Kilda, Scotland............................	45	45
Set of 5..			1·25	1·25
Set of 5 Gutter Pairs....................................			2·50	
First Day Cover..				1·40
Presentation Pack (PO Pack No. 127)...................			1·40	
PHQ Cards (set of 5) (52).........................			75	1·40

Special First Day of Issue Postmarks

Philatelic Bureau, Edinburgh.........................		1·40
Glenfinnan..		1·40
Keswick...		1·40

636 Prince Charles and Lady Diana Spencer

(Des J. Matthews from photograph by Lord Snowdon)

1981 (22 July). Royal Wedding. Multicoloured Phosphorised paper. Perf 14×15.

1160	**636**	14p. Prince Charles and Lady Diana Spencer...................	25	20
1161		25p. Prince Charles and Lady Diana Spencer...................	40	35
Set of 2..			60	50
Set of 2 Gutter Pairs....................................			1·25	
First Day Cover..				1·20
Presentation Pack (PO Pack No. 127a).................			1·10	
Souvenir Book..			1·25	
PHQ Cards (set of 2) (53).........................			30	70

The souvenir book is a 12 page illustrated booklet with a set of mint stamps in a sachet attached to the front cover.

Special First Day of Issue Postmarks
Philatelic Bureau, Edinburgh.. 1·25
Caernarfon, Gwynedd.. 1·50
London EC.. 1·30

637 'Expeditions'

638 'Skills'

639 'Service'

640 'Recreation'

(Des P. Sharland. Litho J.W.)

1981 (12 Aug). 25th Anniversary of Duke of Edinburgh's Award Scheme. Multicoloured Phosphorised paper. Perf 14.

1162	**637**	14p. 'Expeditions'....................................	20	20
1163	**638**	18p. 'Skills'...	20	20
1164	**639**	22p. 'Service'..	35	35
1165	**640**	25p. 'Recreation'....................................	45	45
Set of 4..			1·10	1·10
Set of 4 Gutter Pairs...			2·25	
First Day Cover..				1·25
Presentation Pack (PO Pack No. 128)...................			1·25	
PHQ Cards (set of 4) (54)...			60	1·25

Special First Day of Issue Postmarks
Philatelic Bureau, Edinburgh.. 1·25
London W2... 1·50

641 Cockle-dredging from *Linsey II*

642 Hauling in Trawl Net

643 Lobster Potting

644 Hoisting Seine Net

(Des B. Sanders)

1981 (23 Sept). Fishing Industry. Multicoloured Phosphorised paper. Perf 15×14.

1166	**641**	14p. Cockle-dredging from *Linsey II*........	20	20
1167	**642**	18p. Hauling in Trawl Net.......................	20	20
1168	**643**	22p. Lobster Potting................................	35	35
1169	**644**	25p. Hoisting Seine Net...........................	45	45
Set of 4..			1·10	1·10
Set of 4 Gutter Pairs...			2·25	
First Day Cover..				1·25
Presentation Pack (PO Pack No. 129)...................			1·25	
PHQ Cards (set of 4) (55)...			60	1·25

Nos. 1166/1169 were issued on the occasion of the centenary of the Royal National Mission to Deep Sea Fishermen.

Special First Day of Issue Postmarks
Philatelic Bureau, Edinburgh.. 1·25
Hull.. 1·50

645 Father Christmas

646 Jesus Christ

647 Flying Angel

648 Joseph and Mary arriving at Bethlehem

649 Three Kings approaching Bethlehem

(Des Samantha Brown (11½p.), Tracy Jenkins (14p.), Lucinda Blackmore (18p.), Stephen Moore (22p.), Sophie Sharp (25p.))

1981 (18 Nov). Christmas. Children's Pictures. Multicoloured One phosphor band (11½p.) or phosphorised paper (others). Perf 15×14.

1170	**645**	11½p. Father Christmas.............................	20	20
1171	**646**	14p. Jesus Christ.....................................	20	20
1172	**647**	18p. Flying Angel.....................................	20	20
1173	**648**	22p. Joseph and Mary arriving at Bethlehem..	30	30
1174	**649**	25p. Three Kings approaching Bethlehem..	40	40
Set of 5..			1·25	1·25
Set of 5 Gutter Pairs...			2·50	
First Day Cover..				1·40
Presentation Pack (PO Pack No. 130)...................			1·25	
PHQ Cards (set of 5) (56)...			75	1·40

Special First Day of Issue Postmarks
Philatelic Bureau, Edinburgh.. 1·50
Bethlehem, Llandeilo, Dyfed.. 1·50

Collectors Pack

1981 (18 Nov). Comprises Nos. 1143/1174.
CP1174*a*   Collectors Pack (Pack No. 131)........... 7·25

650 Charles Darwin and Giant Tortoises

651 Darwin and Marine Iguanas

652 Darwin, Cactus Ground Finch and Large Ground Finch

653 Darwin and Prehistoric Skulls

(Des D. Gentleman)

1982 (10 Feb). Death Centenary of Charles Darwin. Multicoloured Phosphorised paper. Perf 15×14.

1175	**650**	15½p. Charles Darwin and Giant Tortoises......	20	20
1176	**651**	19½p. Darwin and Marine Iguanas............	25	25
1177	**652**	26p. Darwin, Cactus Ground Finch and Large Ground Finch..........	35	35
1178	**653**	29p. Darwin and Prehistoric Skulls..........	50	50
Set of 4..........			1·25	1·25
Set of 4 Gutter Pairs..........			2·50	
First Day Cover..........				1·25
Presentation Pack (PO Pack No. 132)..........			1·25	
PHQ Cards (set of 4) (57)..........			60	1·25

Special First Day of Issue Postmarks

Philatelic Bureau, Edinburgh..........		1·50
Shrewsbury..........		1·50

654 Boys' Brigade   **655** Girls' Brigade

656 Boy Scout Movement   **657** Girl Guide Movement

(Des B. Sanders)

1982 (24 Mar). Youth Organisations. Multicoloured Phosphorised paper. Perf 14×15.

1179	**654**	15½p. Boys' Brigade..........	20	20
1180	**655**	19½p. Girls' Brigade..........	25	25
1181	**656**	26p. Boy Scout Movement..........	35	35
1182	**657**	29p. Girl Guide Movement..........	50	50
Set of 4..........			1·25	1·25
Set of 4 Gutter Pairs..........			2·50	
First Day Cover..........				1·40
Presentation Pack (PO Pack No. 133)..........			1·40	
PHQ Cards (set of 4) (58)..........			60	1·40

Nos. 1179/1182 were issued on the occasion of the 75th anniversary of the Boy Scout Movement; the 125th birth anniversary of Lord Baden-Powell and the centenary of the Boys' Brigade (1983).

Special First Day of Issue Postmarks

Edinburgh Philatelic Bureau..........		1·50
Glasgow..........		1·50
London SW..........		1·50

658 Ballerina   **659** Harlequin

660 Hamlet   **661** Opera Singer

(Des A. George)

1982 (28 Apr). Europa. British Theatre. Multicoloured Phosphorised paper. Perf 14×15.

1183	**658**	15½p. Ballerina..........	20	20
1184	**659**	19½p. Harlequin..........	25	25
1185	**660**	26p. Hamlet..........	35	35
1186	**661**	29p. Opera Singer..........	50	50
Set of 4..........			1·25	1·25
Set of 4 Gutter Pairs..........			2·50	
First Day Cover..........				1·40
Presentation Pack (PO Pack No. 134)..........			1·40	
PHQ Cards (set of 4) (59)..........			60	1·40

Special First Day of Issue Postmarks

Philatelic Bureau, Edinburgh..........		1·50
Stratford-upon-Avon..........		1·50

662 Henry VIII and *Mary Rose*   **663** Admiral Blake and *Triumph*

664 Lord Nelson and HMS *Victory*   **665** Lord Fisher and HMS *Dreadnought*

666 Viscount Cunningham and HMS *Warspite*

(Des Marjorie Saynor. Eng Czesław Slania. Recess and photo)

1982 (16 June). Maritime Heritage. Multicoloured Phosphorised paper. Perf 15×14.

1187	**662**	15½p. Henry VIII and *Mary Rose*..........	20	20
		a. Imperf (pair)..........	£1500	
		b. Black (ship and waves) omitted.........	—	£1250
1188	**663**	19½p. Admiral Blake and *Triumph*..........	25	25
1189	**664**	24p. Lord Nelson and HMS *Victory*..........	35	35
1190	**665**	26p. Lord Fisher and HMS *Dreadnought*....	40	40
		a. Imperf (pair)..........	£2750	
1191	**666**	29p. Viscount Cunningham and HMS *Warspite*..........	50	50
Set of 5..........			1·60	1·60
Set of 5 Gutter Pairs..........			3·25	
First Day Cover..........				1·75
Presentation Pack (PO Pack No. 136)..........			1·75	
PHQ Cards (set of 5) (60)..........			75	1·75

Nos. 1187/1191 were issued on the occasion of Maritime England Year, the Bicentenary of the Livery Grant by the City of London to the Worshipful Company of Shipwrights and the raising of the *Mary Rose* from Portsmouth Harbour.

Special First Day of Issue Postmarks

Philatelic Bureau, Edinburgh..........		1·90
Portsmouth..........		1·90

667 'Strawberry Thief'
(William Morris)

668 Untitled (Steiner
and Co)

669 'Cherry Orchard'
(Paul Nash)

670 'Chevron' (Andrew
Foster)

(Des Peter Hatch Partnership)

1982 (23 July). British Textiles. Multicoloured Phosphorised paper. Perf 14×15.

1192	**667**	15½p. 'Strawberry Thief' (William Morris)..	20	20
		a. Imperf (horiz pair)............................	£1300	
1193	**668**	19½p. Untitled (Steiner and Co).................	25	25
		a. Imperf (vert pair).............................	£2500	
1194	**669**	26p. 'Cherry Orchard' (Paul Nash)............	35	35
1195	**670**	29p. 'Chevron' (Andrew Foster)...............	50	50
Set of 4................			1·25	1·25
Set of 4 Gutter Pairs....			2·50	
First Day Cover.........				1·40
Presentation Pack (PO Pack No. 137)........			1·40	
PHQ Cards (set of 4) (61)................			60	1·40

Nos. 1192/1195 were issued on the occasion of the 250th birth anniversary of Sir Richard Arkwright (inventor of spinning machine).

Special First Day of Issue Postmarks

Philatelic Bureau, Edinburgh...	1·50
Rochdale..	1·50

671 Development of Communications

672 Technological Aids

(Des Delaney and Ireland)

1982 (8 Sept). Information Technology. Multicoloured Phosphorised paper. Perf 14×15.

1196	**671**	15½p. Development of Communications.	25	25
		a. Imperf (pair).................................	£250	
1197	**672**	26p. Technological Aids........................	35	35
		a. Imperf (pair).................................	£1500	
Set of 2................			55	55
Set of 2 Gutter Pairs....			1·10	
First Day Cover.........				60
Presentation Pack (PO Pack No. 138)........			60	
PHQ Cards (set of 2) (62)................			30	60

Special First Day of Issue Postmarks

Philatelic Bureau, Edinburgh...	60
London WC...	60

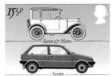

673 Austin Seven and Metro

674 Ford Model T and Escort

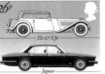

675 Jaguar SS 1 and XJ6

676 Rolls-Royce Silver Ghost
and Silver Spirit

(Des S. Paine. Litho Questa)

1982 (13 Oct). British Motor Cars. Multicoloured. Phosphorised paper. Perf 14½×14.

1198	**673**	15½p. Austin Seven and Metro.................	20	20
1199	**674**	19½p. Ford Model T and Escort................	25	25
		a. Rose-red, grey and black printings double.............	£900	
		b. Black printed double....................	£2000	
1200	**675**	26p. Jaguar SS 1 and XJ6......................	35	35
1201	**676**	29p. Rolls-Royce Silver Ghost and Silver Spirit........	50	50
		a. Black printing quadruple...............	£600	
		b. Bright orange, carmine-red, grey and black printings double..........	£1100	
		c. Black printing quadruple grey printing triple and purple and carmine printings double.........	£1100	
Set of 4................			1·25	1·25
Set of 4 Gutter Pairs....			2·50	
First Day Cover.........				1·40
Presentation Pack (PO Pack No. 139)........			1·40	
PHQ Cards (set of 4) (63)................			60	1·40

The price for Nos. 1199b is for a complete doubling of both cars, examples showing doubling of only one car or parts of two cars are worth less.

Special First Day of Issue Postmarks

Philatelic Bureau, Edinburgh...	1·40
Birmingham..	1·50
Crewe..	1·50

677 While Shepherds Watched

678 The Holly and the Ivy

679 I Saw Three Ships

680 We Three Kings

681 Good King Wenceslas

(Des Barbara Brown)

1982 (17 Nov). Christmas. Carols. Multicoloured One phosphor band (12½p.) or phosphorised paper (others). Perf 15×14.

1202	**677**	12½p. While Shepherds Watched.................	20	20

1203	**678**	15½p. *The Holly and the Ivy*............................	20	20
		a. Imperf (pair)..	£1800	
1204	**679**	19½p. *I Saw Three Ships*...............................	25	25
		a. Imperf (pair)..	£2250	
1205	**680**	26p. *We Three Kings*...................................	35	30
1206	**681**	29p. *Good King Wenceslas*........................	50	50
Set of 5...			1·40	1·40
Set of 5 Gutter Pairs...............................			2·75	
First Day Cover.......................................				1·50
Presentation Pack (PO Pack No. 140).....			1·50	
PHQ Cards (set of 5) (64)........................			75	1·50

Special Day of Issue Postmarks

Philatelic Bureau, Edinburgh..		1·60
Bethlehem, Llandeilo, Dyfed..		1·60

Collectors Pack

1982 (17 Nov). Comprises Nos. 1175/1206.

CP1206*a*	Collectors Pack (Pack No. 141)............	12·00

682 Atlantic Salmon

683 Northern Pike

684 Brown Trout

685 Eurasian Perch

(Des A. Jardine)

1983 (26 Jan). British River Fish. Multicoloured Phosphorised paper. Perf 15×14.

1207	**682**	15½p. Atlantic Salmon..............................	20	20
		a. Imperf (pair)..	£1000	
1208	**683**	19½p. Northern Pike.................................	25	25
1209	**684**	26p. Brown Trout....................................	35	35
		a. Imperf (pair)..	£1500	
1210	**685**	29p. Eurasian Perch................................	50	50
Set of 4...			1·25	1·25
Set of 4 Gutter Pairs...............................			2·50	
First Day Cover.......................................				1·40
Presentation Pack (PO Pack No. 142).....			1·40	
PHQ Cards (set of 4) (65)........................			60	1·40

All known examples of No. 1209a are creased.

Special First Day of Issue Postmarks

Philatelic Bureau, Edinburgh..		1·50
Peterborough..		1·60

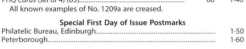

686 Tropical Island

687 Desert

688 Temperate Farmland

689 Mountain Range

(Des D. Fraser)

1983 (9 Mar). Commonwealth Day. Geographical Regions. Multicoloured Phosphorised paper. Perf 14×15.

1211	**686**	15½p. Tropical Island...................................	20	20
1212	**687**	19½p. Desert..	25	25
1213	**688**	26p. Temperate Farmland......................	35	35
1214	**689**	29p. Mountain Range............................	50	50
Set of 4...			1·25	1·25
Set of 4 Gutter Pairs...............................			2·50	
First Day Cover.......................................				1·40
Presentation Pack (PO Pack No. 143).....			1·40	
PHQ Cards (set of 4) (66)........................			60	1·40

Special First Day of Issue Postmarks

Philatelic Bureau, Edinburgh..		1·50
London SW..		1·50

690 Humber Bridge

691 Thames Flood Barrier

692 *Iolair* (oilfield emergency support vessel)

(Des M. Taylor)

1983 (25 May). Europa. Engineering Achievements. Multicoloured Phosphorised paper. Perf 15×14.

1215	**690**	16p. Humber Bridge..............................	20	20
1216	**691**	20½p. Thames Flood Barrier......................	30	30
1217	**692**	28p. *Iolair*..	50	50
Set of 3...			90	90
Set of 3 Gutter Pairs...............................			1·75	
First Day Cover.......................................				1·00
Presentation Pack (PO Pack No. 144).....			1·00	
PHQ Cards (set of 3) (67)........................			40	1·00

Special First Day of Issue Postmarks

Philatelic Bureau, Edinburgh..		1·00
Hull..		1·10

693 Musketeer and Pikeman, The Royal Scots (1633)

694 Fusilier and Ensign, The Royal Welch Fusiliers (mid-18th-century)

695 Riflemen, 95th Rifles (The Royal Green Jackets) (1805)

696 Sergeant (khaki service) and Guardsman (full dress), The Irish Guards (1900)

697 Paratroopers, The
Parachute Regiment
(1983)

(Des E. Stemp)

1983 (6 July). British Army Uniforms. Multicoloured Phosphorised paper.
Perf 14×15.

1218	**693**	16p. The Royal Scots	20	20
1219	**694**	20½p. The Royal Welch Fusiliers	25	25
1220	**695**	26p. The Royal Green Jackets	35	35
		a. Imperf (pair)	£2250	
1221	**696**	28p. The Irish Guards	40	40
		a. Imperf (pair)	£2000	
1222	**697**	31p. The Parachute Regiment	50	50
Set of 5			1·60	1·60
Set of 5 Gutter Pairs			3·25	
First Day Cover				1·75
Presentation Pack (PO Pack No. 145)			1·75	
PHQ Cards (set of 5) (68)			75	1·75

Nos. 1218/1222 were issued on the occasion of the 350th anniversary of
the Royal Scots, the senior line regiment of the British Army.

Special First Day of Issue Postmarks

| Philatelic Bureau, Edinburgh | 1·90 |
| Aldershot | 1·90 |

698 20th-century
Garden, Sissinghurst

699 19th-century
Garden, Biddulph
Grange

700 18th-century
Garden, Blenheim

701 17th-century
Garden, Pitmedden

(Des Liz Butler. Litho J.W.)

1983 (24 Aug). British Gardens. Multicoloured. Phosphorised paper. Perf
14.

1223	**698**	16p. Sissinghurst	20	20
1224	**699**	20½p. Biddulph Grange	25	25
1225	**700**	28p. Blenheim	35	35
1226	**701**	31p. Pitmedden	50	50
Set of 4			1·25	1·25
Set of 4 Gutter Pairs			2·50	
First Day Cover				1·40
Presentation Pack (PO Pack No. 146)			1·40	
PHQ Cards (set of 4) (69)			60	1·40

Nos. 1223/1226 were issued on the occasion of the death bicentenary
of 'Capability' Brown (landscape gardener).

Special First Day of Issue Postmarks

| Philatelic Bureau, Edinburgh | 1·40 |
| Oxford | 1·50 |

702 Merry-go-round

703 Big Wheel, Helter-skelter
and Performing Animals

704 Side Shows

705 Early Produce Fair

(Des A. Restall)

1983 (5 Oct). British Fairs. Multicoloured Phosphorised paper. Perf 15×14.

1227	**702**	16p. Merry-go-round	20	20
1228	**703**	20½p. Big Wheel, Helter-skelter and		
		Performing Animals	25	25
1229	**704**	28p. Side Shows	35	35
1230	**705**	31p. Early Produce Fair	50	50
Set of 4			1·25	1·25
Set of 4 Gutter Pairs			2·50	
First Day Cover				1·40
Presentation Pack (PO Pack No. 147)			1·40	
PHQ Cards (set of 4) (70)			60	1·40

Nos. 1227/1230 were issued to mark the 850th anniversary of St
Bartholomew's Fair, Smithfield, London.

Special First Day of Issue Postmarks

| Philatelic Bureau, Edinburgh | 1·40 |
| Nottingham | 1·40 |

706 Christmas Post (pillar box)

707 The Three Kings (chimney
pots)

708 World at Peace (Dove and
Blackbird)

709 Light of Christmas (street
lamp)

710 Christmas Dove (hedge
sculpture)

(Des T. Meeuwissen)

1983 (16 Nov). Christmas. Multicoloured. One phosphor band (12½p.) or
phosphorised paper (others). Perf 15×14.

1231	**706**	12½p. Christmas Post (pillar box)	20	20
		a. Imperf (horiz pair)	£1200	
1232	**707**	16p. The Three Kings (chimney pots)	20	20
		a. Imperf (pair)	£1100	
1233	**708**	20½p. World at Peace (Dove and		
		Blackbird)	25	25
1234	**709**	28p. Light of Christmas (street lamp)	35	35
1235	**710**	31p. Christmas Dove (hedge sculpture)	50	50
Set of 5			1·50	1·50
Set of 5 Gutter Pairs			3·00	

First Day Cover			1·50
Presentation Pack (PO Pack No. 148)		1·50	
PHQ Cards (set of 5) (71)		75	1·50

Special First Day of Issue Postmarks
Philatelic Bureau, Edinburgh		1·50
Bethlehem, Llandeilo, Dyfed		1·50

Collectors Pack

1983 (16 Nov). Comprises Nos. 1207/1235.
CP1235*a*	Collectors Pack (Pack No. 149)	13·50

711 Arms of the College of Arms

712 Arms of King Richard III (founder)

713 Arms of the Earl Marshal of England

714 Arms of the City of London

(Des J. Matthews)

1984 (17 Jan). 500th Anniversary of College of Arms. Multicoloured. Phosphorised paper. Perf 14½.

1236	**711**	16p. Arms of the College of Arms	25	25
1237	**712**	20½p. Arms of King Richard III (founder)	30	30
1238	**713**	28p. Arms of the Earl Marshal of England	40	40
1239	**714**	31p. Arms of the City of London	50	50
		a. Imperf (horiz pair)	£5750	
Set of 4			1·25	1·25
Set of 4 Gutter Pairs			2·50	
First Day Cover				1·50
Presentation Pack (PO Pack No. 150)			1·50	
PHQ Cards (set of 4) (72)			60	1·50

Special First Day of Issue Postmarks
Philatelic Bureau, Edinburgh		1·50
London EC		1·50

715 Highland Cow

716 Chillingham Wild Bull

717 Hereford Bull

718 Welsh Black Bull

719 Irish Moiled Cow

(Des B. Driscoll)

1984 (6 Mar). British Cattle. Multicoloured Phosphorised paper. Perf 15×14.

1240	**715**	16p. Highland Cow	25	25
		a. Imperf (vert pair)	£5750	
1241	**716**	20½p. Chillingham Wild Bull	30	30
1242	**717**	26p. Hereford Bull	35	35
1243	**718**	28p. Welsh Black Bull	40	40
1244	**719**	31p. Irish Moiled Cow	50	50
		a. Imperf (pair)		
Set of 5			1·60	1·60
Set of 5 Gutter Pairs			3·25	
First Day Cover				1·75
Presentation Pack (PO Pack No. 151)			1·75	
PHQ Cards (set of 5) (73)			75	1·75

Nos. 1240/1244 were issued on the occasion of the centenary of the Highland Cattle Society and the bicentenary of the Royal Highland and Agricultural Society of Scotland.

Special First Day of Issue Postmarks
Philatelic Bureau, Edinburgh		1·75
Oban, Argyll		1·90

720 Garden Festival Hall, Liverpool

721 Milburngate Centre, Durham

722 Bush House, Bristol

723 Commercial Street Development, Perth

(Des R. Maddox and Trickett and Webb Ltd)

1984 (10 Apr). Urban Renewal. Multicoloured Phosphorised paper. Perf 15×14.

1245	**720**	16p. Garden Festival Hall, Liverpool	25	25
1246	**721**	20½p. Milburngate Centre, Durham	30	30
		a. Imperf (horiz pair)	£3750	
1247	**722**	28p. Bush House, Bristol	40	40
1248	**723**	31p. Commercial Street Development, Perth	50	50
		a. Imperf (pair)	£3000	
Set of 4			1·25	1·25
Set of 4 Gutter Pairs			2·50	
First Day Cover				1·50
Presentation Pack (PO Pack No. 152)			1·50	
PHQ Cards (set of 4) (74)			60	1·50

Nos. 1245/1248 were issued on the occasion of 150th anniversaries of the Royal Institute of British Architects and the Chartered Institute of Building, and to commemorate the first International Gardens Festival, Liverpool.

Special First Day of Issue Postmarks
Philatelic Bureau, Edinburgh		1·50
Liverpool		1·50

724 CEPT 25th Anniversary Logo

725 Abduction of Europa

(Des J. Larrivière (T **724**), F. Wegner (T **725**))

1984 (15 May). 25th Anniversary of CEPT (Europa) (T **724**) and Second Elections to European Parliament (T **725**). Multicoloured Phosphorised paper. Perf 15×14.

1249	**724**	16p. CEPT 25th Anniversary Logo	30	30
		a. Horiz pair. Nos. 1249/1250	60	60
		ab. Imperf (horiz pair)	£2500	
1250	**725**	16p. Abduction of Europa	30	30
1251	**724**	20½p. CEPT 25th Anniversary Logo	35	35
		a. Horiz pair. Nos. 1251/1252	70	70

		ab. Imperf (horiz pair)............................	£2750	
1252	**725**	20½p. Abduction of Europa......................	35	35
Set of 4..			1·25	1·25
Set of 2 Gutter Blocks of 4..................................			2·50	
First Day Cover..				1·40
Presentation Pack (PO Pack No. 153)...................			1·40	
PHQ Cards (set of 4) (75).....................................			60	1·40

Nos. 1249/1250 and 1251/1252 were each printed together, *se-tenant*, in horizontal pairs throughout the sheets.

Special First Day of Issue Postmarks

Philatelic Bureau, Edinburgh..	1·40
London SW..	1·50

726 Lancaster House

(Des P. Hogarth)

1984 (5 June). London Economic Summit Conference. Multicoloured Phosphorised paper. Perf 14×15.

1253	**726**	31p. Lancaster House...............................	50	50
Gutter Pair..			1·00	
First Day Cover...				60
PHQ Card (76)...			20	60

Special First Day of Issue Postmarks

Philatelic Bureau, Edinburgh..	60
London SW..	60

727 View of Earth from *Apollo 11*

728 Navigational Chart of English Channel

729 Greenwich Observatory

730 Sir George Airy's Transit Telescope

(Des H. Waller. Litho Questa)

1984 (26 June). Centenary of the Greenwich Meridian. Multicoloured Phosphorised paper. Perf 14×14½.

1254	**727**	16p. View of Earth from *Apollo 11*...........	25	25
		a. Black printing double........................	†	£975
1255	**728**	20½p. Navigational Chart of English Channel..	30	30
1256	**729**	28p. Greenwich Observatory....................	40	40
1257	**730**	31p. Sir George Airy's Transit Telescope....	50	50
Set of 4..			1·25	1·25
Set of 4 Gutter Pairs..			2·50	
First Day Cover..				1·50
Presentation Pack (PO Pack No. 154)...................			1·50	
PHQ Cards (set of 4) (77).....................................			60	1·50

On Nos. 1254/1257 the Meridian is represented by a scarlet line.

Special First Day of Issue Postmarks

Philatelic Bureau, Edinburgh..	1·60
London SE10...	1·75

731 Bath Mail Coach, 1784

732 Attack on Exeter Mail, 1816

733 Norwich Mail in Thunderstorm, 1827

734 Holyhead and Liverpool Mails leaving London, 1828

735 Edinburgh Mail Snowbound, 1831

(Des K. Bassford and S. Paine. Eng C. Slania. Recess and photo)

1984 (31 July). Bicentenary of First Mail Coach Run, Bath and Bristol to London. Multicoloured Phosphorised paper. Perf 15×14.

1258	**731**	16p. Bath Mail Coach, 1784.....................	25	25
		a. Horiz strip of 5. Nos. 1258/1262......	1·25	1·25
		ab. Imperf (horiz pair. Nos. 1261/1262)...................................	£2750	
1259	**732**	16p. Attack on Exeter Mail, 1816.............	25	25
1260	**733**	16p. Norwich Mail in Thunderstorm, 1827...	25	25
1261	**734**	16p. Holyhead and Liverpool Mails leaving London, 1828........................	25	25
1262	**735**	16p. Edinburgh Mail Snowbound, 1831....	25	25
Set of 5..			1·25	1·25
Gutter Block of 10...			2·50	
First Day Cover..				1·40
Presentation Pack (PO Pack No. 155)...................			1·40	
Souvenir Book..			3·25	
PHQ Cards (set of 5) (78).....................................			75	1·40

Nos. 1258/1262 were printed together, *se-tenant*, in horizontal strips of five throughout the sheet.

No. 1258ab also includes No. 1260 perforated at left only.

The souvenir book is a 24 page illustrated booklet with a set of mint stamps in a sachet attached to the front cover.

Special First Day of Issue Postmarks

Philatelic Bureau, Edinburgh..	1·40
Bristol..	1·40

736 Nigerian Clinic

737 Violinist and Acropolis, Athens

738 Building Project, Sri Lanka

739 British Council Library, Middle East

(Des F. Newell and J. Sorrell)

1984 (25 Sept). 50th Anniversary of the British Council. Multicoloured Phosphorised paper. Perf 15×14.

1263	**736**	17p. Nigerian Clinic	25	25
1264	**737**	22p. Violinist and Acropolis, Athens	30	30
1265	**738**	31p. Building Project, Sri Lanka	40	40
1266	**739**	34p. British Council Library, Middle East	50	50
Set of 4			1·40	1·40
Set of 4 Gutter Pairs			2·75	
First Day Cover				1·50
Presentation Pack (PO Pack No. 156)			1·50	
PHQ Cards (set of 4) (79)			60	1·50

Special First Day of Issue Postmarks

Philatelic Bureau, Edinburgh		1·50
London SW		1·50

740 The Holy Family

741 Arrival in Bethlehem

742 Shepherd and Lamb

743 Virgin and Child

744 Offering of Frankincense

(Des Yvonne Gilbert)

1984 (20 Nov). Christmas. Multicoloured One phosphor band (13p.) or phosphorised paper (others). Perf 15×14.

1267	**740**	13p. The Holy Family	25	25
		u. Underprint Type **4**	60	
1268	**741**	17p. Arrival in Bethlehem	25	25
		a. Imperf (pair)	£2500	
1269	**742**	22p. Shepherd and Lamb	30	30
1270	**743**	31p. Virgin and Child	40	40
1271	**744**	34p. Offering of Frankincense	50	50
Set of 5			1·60	1·60
Set of 5 Gutter Pairs			3·25	
First Day Cover				1·75
Presentation Pack (PO Pack No. 157)			1·75	
PHQ Cards (set of 5) (80)			75	1·75

Examples of No. 1267u from the 1984 Christmas booklet (No. FX7) show a random pattern of blue double-lined stars printed on the reverse over the gum.

Special First Day of Issue Postmarks

Philatelic Bureau, Edinburgh		1·90
Bethlehem, Llandeilo, Dyfed		1·90

Collectors Pack

1984 (20 Nov). Comprises Nos. 1236/1271.
CP1271*a* Collectors Pack (Pack No. 158)........... 16·00

Post Office Yearbook

1984 Comprises Nos. 1236/1271 in 24 page hardbound book with slip case, illustrated in colour
YB1271*a* Yearbook................................... 42·00

745 'Flying Scotsman'

746 'Golden Arrow'

747 'Cheltenham Flyer'

748 'Royal Scot'

749 'Cornish Riviera'

(Des Terrance Cuneo)

1985 (22 Jan). Famous Trains. Multicoloured Phosphorised paper. Perf 15×14.

1272	**745**	17p. 'Flying Scotsman'	25	25
		a. Imperf (pair)	£2000	
1273	**746**	22p. 'Golden Arrow'	30	30
1274	**747**	29p. 'Cheltenham Flyer'	40	40
1275	**748**	31p. 'Royal Scot'	40	40
1276	**749**	34p. 'Cornish Riviera'	50	50
Set of 5			1·75	1·75
Set of 5 Gutter Pairs			3·50	
First Day Cover				1·90
Presentation Pack (PO Pack No. 159)			1·90	
PHQ Cards (set of 5) (81)			75	1·90

Nos. 1272/1276 were issued on the occasion of the 150th anniversary of the Great Western Railway Company.

Special First Day of Issue Postmarks

Philatelic Bureau, Edinburgh		2·00
Bristol		2·25

750 Buff tailed bumblebee

751 Seven spotted Ladybird

752 Wart-biter bush-cricket

753 Stag Beetle

Emperor Dragonfly

754 Emperor
dragonfly

(Des G. Beningfield)

1985 (12 Mar). Insects. Multicoloured Phosphorised paper. Perf 14×15.

1277	**750**	17p. Buff tailed bumblebee....................	25	25
1278	**751**	22p. Seven spotted Ladybird..................	30	30
1279	**752**	29p. Wart-biter bush-cricket.................	40	40
1280	**753**	31p. Stag beetle..............................	40	40
1281	**754**	34p. Emperor dragonfly.......................	50	50
		a. Imperf (vert pair).......................	—	
	Set of 5..		1·75	1·75
	Set of 5 Gutter Pairs..		3·50	
	First Day Cover..			1·90
	Presentation Pack (PO Pack No. 160)...................		1·90	
	PHQ Cards (set of 5) (82).....................................		75	1·90

Nos. 1277/1281 were issued on the occasion of the centenaries of the Royal Entomological Society of London's Royal Charter, and of the Selborne Society.

Special First Day of Issue Postmarks

Philatelic Bureau, Edinburgh...	1·90
London SW...	2·00

SEVENTEEN·PENCE

WATER·MUSIC
George Frideric Handel

755 *Water Music* (George Frederick Handel)

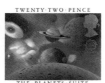

TWENTY·TWO·PENCE

THE·PLANETS·SUITE
Gustav Holst

756 *The Planets Suite* (Gustav Holst)

THIRTY·ONE·PENCE

THE·FIRST·CUCKOO
Frederick Delius

757 *The First Cuckoo* (Frederick Delius)

THIRTY·FOUR·PENCE

SEA·PICTURES
Edward Elgar

758 *Sea Pictures* (Edward Elgar)

(Des W. McLean)

1985 (14 May). Europa. European Music Year. British Composers. Multicoloured Phosphorised paper. Perf 14×14½.

1282	**755**	17p. *Water Music* (George Frederick Handel)...................................	25	25
		a. Imperf (vert pair)........................	£2750	
1283	**756**	22p. *The Planets Suite* (Gustav Holst).......	30	30
		a. Imperf (pair)..............................	£2500	
1284	**757**	31p. *The First Cuckoo* (Frederick Delius)..	45	45
1285	**758**	34p. *Sea Pictures* (Edward Elgar).............	55	55
	Set of 4..		1·40	1·40
	Set of 4 Gutter Pairs..		2·75	
	First Day Cover..			1·50
	Presentation Pack (PO Pack No. 161)...................		1·50	
	PHQ Cards (set of 4) (83).....................................		60	1·50

Nos. 1282/1285 were issued on the occasion of the 300th birth anniversary of Handel.

Special First Day of Issue Postmarks

Philatelic Bureau, Edinburgh...	1·50
Worcester...	1·75

759 RNLI Lifeboat and Signal Flags

760 Beachy Head Lighthouse and Chart

761 *Marecs A* Communications Satellite and Dish Aerials

762 Buoys

(Des F. Newell and J. Sorrell. Litho J.W.)

1985 (18 June). Safety at Sea. Multicoloured Phosphorised paper. Perf 14.

1286	**759**	17p. RNLI Lifeboat and Signal Flags........	25	25
1287	**760**	22p. Beachy Head Lighthouse and Chart..	30	30
1288	**761**	31p. *Marecs A* Communications Satellite and Dish Aerials.................	45	45
1289	**762**	34p. Buoys.......................................	55	55
	Set of 4..		1·40	1·40
	Set of 4 Gutter Pairs..		2·75	
	First Day Cover..			1·50
	Presentation Pack (PO Pack No. 162)...................		1·50	
	PHQ Cards (set of 4) (84).....................................		60	1·50

Nos. 1286/1289 were issued on the occasion of the bicentenary of the unimmersible lifeboat and the 50th anniversary of Radar.

Special First Day of Issue Postmarks

Philatelic Bureau, Edinburgh...	1·50
Eastbourne..	1·50

763 Datapost Motorcyclist, City of London

764 Rural Postbus

765 Parcel Delivery in Winter

766 Town Letter Delivery

(Des P. Hogarth)

1985 (30 July). 350 Years of Royal Mail Public Postal Service. Multicoloured Phosphorised paper. Perf 14×15.

1290	**763**	17p. Datapost Motorcyclist....................	25	25
		a. Imperf on 3 sides (vert pair)............	£1000	
		u. Underprint Type **5**......................	50	
1291	**764**	22p. Rural Postbus..............................	30	30
		a. Imperf (vert pair).......................	—	
1292	**765**	31p. Parcel Delivery in Winter.................	45	45
		a. Imperf..	£1400	
1293	**766**	34p. Town Letter Delivery.....................	55	55
		a. Imperf between (vert pair)...............	£750	
		b. Imperf (vert pair)........................	—	
	Set of 4..		1·40	1·40
	Set of 4 Gutter Pairs..		2·75	
	First Day Cover..			1·50

Presentation Pack (PO Pack No. 163).................................... 1·50
PHQ Cards (set of 4) (85).. 60   1·50

No. 1290a shows perforation indentations at right, but is imperforate at top, bottom and on the left-hand side.

Examples of No. 1290u from the 1985 £1·70 booklet (*sold at £1·53*) (No. FT4) show a blue double-lined D in a random pattern, on the reverse over the gum.

Special First Day of Issue Postmarks

Philatelic Bureau, Edinburgh.. 1·50
Bagshot, Surrey.. 1·50

767 King Arthur and Merlin

768 Lady of the Lake

769 Queen Guinevere and Sir Lancelot

770 Sir Galahad

(Des Yvonne Gilbert)

1985 (3 Sept). Arthurian Legends. Multicoloured Phosphorised paper. Perf 15×14.

1294	**767**	17p. King Arthur and Merlin.....................	25	25
		a. Imperf (pair)............................	£2750	
1295	**768**	22p. Lady of the Lake..............................	30	30
1296	**769**	31p. Queen Guinevere and Sir Lancelot	45	45
1297	**770**	34p. Sir Galahad...................................	55	55
Set of 4...............			1·40	1·40
Set of 4 Gutter Pairs............			2·75	
First Day Cover..............				1·50
Presentation Pack (PO Pack No. 164)...................			1·50	
PHQ Cards (set of 4) (86)..............			60	1·50

Nos. 1294/1297 were issued on the occasion of the 500th anniversary of the printing of Sir Thomas Malory's *Morte d'Arthur*.

Trials are known with face value and inscription in a different typeface.

Special First Day of Issue Postmarks

Philatelic Bureau, Edinburgh.. 1·50
Tintagel, Cornwall... 1·50

771 Peter Sellers (from photo by Bill Brandt)

772 David Niven (from photo by Cornell Lucas)

773 Charlie Chaplin (from photo by Lord Snowdon)

774 Vivien Leigh (from photo by Angus McBean)

775 Alfred Hitchcock (from photo by Howard Coster)

(Des K. Bassford)

1985 (8 Oct). British Film Year. Multicoloured Phosphorised paper. Perf 14½.

1298	**771**	17p. Peter Sellers...	25	25
1299	**772**	22p. David Niven...	30	30
1300	**773**	29p. Charlie Chaplin....................................	45	45
1301	**774**	31p. Vivien Leigh...	50	50
1302	**775**	34p. Alfred Hitchcock...................................	55	55
Set of 5...............			1·90	1·90
Set of 5 Gutter Pairs............			3·75	
First Day Cover..............				2·10
Presentation Pack (PO Pack No. 165)...................			2·10	
Souvenir Book..............			4·75	
PHQ Cards (set of 5) (87)..............			75	2·10

The souvenir book is a 24 page illustrated booklet with a set of mint stamps in a sachet attached to the front cover.

Special First Day of Issue Postmarks

Philatelic Bureau, Edinburgh.. 2·10
London WC... 2·10

776 Principal Boy

777 Genie

778 Dame

779 Good Fairy

780 Pantomime Cat

(Des A. George)

1985 (19 Nov). Christmas. Pantomime Characters. Multicoloured One phosphor band (12p.) or phosphorised paper (others). Perf 15×14.

1303	**776**	12p. Principal Boy.....................................	20	20
		a. Imperf (pair)............................	£850	
		u. Underprint Type **4**...........................	50	
1304	**777**	17p. Genie..	25	25
		a. Imperf (pair)............................	£2500	
1305	**778**	22p. Dame..	30	30
1306	**779**	31p. Good Fairy...	40	40
1307	**780**	34p. Pantomime Cat....................................	50	50
Set of 5...............			1·40	1·40
Set of 5 Gutter Pairs............			2·75	
First Day Cover..............				1·60
Presentation Pack (PO Pack No. 166)...................			1·60	
PHQ Cards (set of 5) (88)..............			75	1·60
Christmas Folder (contains No. 1303×50)............			25·00	

Examples of No. 1303u from the 1985 Christmas booklet (No. FX8) show a random pattern of blue double-lined stars printed on the reverse over the gum.

Special First Day of Issue Postmarks

Philatelic Bureau, Edinburgh.. 1·60
Bethlehem, Llandeilo, Dyfed.. 1·75

Collectors Pack

1985 (19 Nov). Comprises Nos. 1272/1307.
CP1307*a*   Collectors Pack (Pack No. 167)............   16·00

Post Office Yearbook

1985. Comprises Nos. 1272/1307 in 32 page hardbound book with slip
case, illustrated in colour
YB1307*a*   Yearbook...   30·00

781 **Light Bulb and North Sea**
Oil Drilling Rig (Energy)

782 **Thermometer and**
Pharmaceutical Laboratory
(Health)

783 **Garden Hoe Steelworks**
(Steel)

784 **Loaf of Bread and**
Cornfield (Agriculture)

(Des K. Bassford. Litho Questa)

1986 (14 Jan). Industry Year. Multicoloured Phosphorised paper. Perf
14½×14.

1308	**781**	17p. Light Bulb and North Sea Oil Drilling Rig (Energy)......................	25	25
1309	**782**	22p. Thermometer and Pharmaceutical Laboratory (Health)...............	30	30
1310	**783**	31p. Garden Hoe Steelworks (Steel)........	45	45
1311	**784**	34p. Loaf of Bread and Cornfield (Agriculture)....................................	55	55
Set of 4..........			1·40	1·40
Set of 4 Gutter Pairs..........			2·75	
First Day Cover..........				1·60
Presentation Pack (PO Pack No. 168)..........			1·60	
PHQ Cards (set of 4) (89)..........			60	1·60

Special First Day of Issue Postmarks

Philatelic Bureau, Edinburgh...   1·60
Birmingham...   1·60

785 **Dr Edmond Halley as**
Comet

786 *Giotto* **Spacecraft**
approaching Comet

787 **'Maybe Twice in a**
Lifetime'

788 **Comet orbiting Sun and**
Planets

(Des R. Steadman)

1986 (18 Feb). Appearance of Halley's Comet. Multicoloured Phosphorised
paper. Perf 15×14.

1312	**785**	17p. Dr Edmond Halley as Comet...........	25	25
		Imperf (pair)		
1313	**786**	22p. *Giotto* Spacecraft approaching Comet.............................	30	30
1314	**787**	31p. 'Maybe Twice in a Lifetime'............	45	45
		Imperf (pair)		
1315	**788**	34p. Comet orbiting Sun and Planets.....	55	55
Set of 4..........			1·40	1·40
Set of 4 Gutter Pairs..........			2·75	
First Day Cover..........				1·60

Presentation Pack (PO Pack No. 168*).................................   1·60
PHQ Cards (set of 4) (90)..   60   1·60
*   The presentation pack was incorrectly numbered 168.

Special First Day of Issue Postmarks

Philaelic Bureau, Edinburgh..   1·60
London SE10...   1·75

789 **Queen Elizabeth in 1928,**
1942 and 1952

790 **Queen Elizabeth in 1958,**
1973 and 1982

(Des J. Matthews)

1986 (21 Apr). 60th Birthday of Queen Elizabeth II. Phosphorised paper.
Perf 15×14.

1316	**789**	17p. Queen Elizabeth in 1928, 1942 and 1952. Grey-black, turquoise-green, bright green, green and dull blue.	30	40
		a. Pair. Nos. 1316/1317..........	80	1·00
1317	**790**	17p. Queen Elizabeth in 1958, 1973 and 1982. Grey-black, dull blue, greenish blue and indigo................	30	40
1318	**789**	34p. Queen Elizabeth in 1928, 1942 and 1952. Grey-black, deep dull purple, yellow-orange and red........	60	75
		a. Pair. Nos. 1318/1319..........	1·40	1·75
1319	**790**	34p. Queen Elizabeth in 1958, 1973 and 1982. Grey-black, olive-brown, yellow-brown, olive-grey and red.	60	75
Set of 4..........			2·00	2·50
Set of 2 Gutter Blocks of 4..........			4·00	
First Day Cover..........				2·60
Presentation Pack (PO Pack No. 170)..........			2·10	
Souvenir Book..........			3·75	
PHQ Cards (set of 4) (91)..........			60	2·60

Nos. 1316/1317 and 1318/1319 were each printed together, *se-tenant*,
in horizontal pairs throughout the sheet.

The souvenir book is a special booklet, fully illustrated and containing
a mint set of stamps.

Special First Day of Issue Postmarks

Philatelic Bureau, Edinburgh..   2·75
Windsor...   2·75

791 **Barn Owl**   792 **Pine Marten**

793 **Wild Cat**   794 **Natterjack Toad**

(Des K. Lilly)

1986 (20 May). Europa. Nature Conservation. Endangered Species.
Multicoloured Phosphorised paper. Perf 14½×14.

1320	**791**	17p. Barn Owl...	25	25
1321	**792**	22p. Pine Marten....................................	30	30
1322	**793**	31p. Wild Cat...	45	45
1323	**794**	34p. Natterjack Toad..............................	55	55
Set of 4..........			1·50	1·50
Set of 4 Gutter Pairs..........			3·00	
First Day Cover..........				1·60
Presentation Pack (PO Pack No. 171)..........			1·60	
PHQ Cards (set of 4) (92)..........			60	1·60

Special First Day of Issue Postmarks
Philatelic Bureau, Edinburgh... 1·60
Lincoln.. 1·75

795 Peasants working in Fields

796 Freemen working at Town Trades

797 Knight and Retainers

798 Lord at Banquet

(Des Tayburn Design Consultancy)

1986 (17 June). 900th Anniversary of *Domesday Book*. Multicoloured Phosphorised paper. Perf 15×14.

1324	**795**	17p. Peasants working in Fields...............	25	25
1325	**796**	22p. Freemen working at Town Trades...	30	30
1326	**797**	31p. Knight and Retainers........................	45	45
1327	**798**	34p. Lord at Banquet.................................	55	55
Set of 4			1·50	1·50
Set of 4 Gutter Pairs			3·00	
First Day Cover				1·60
Presentation Pack (PO Pack No. 172)			1·60	
PHQ Cards (set of 4) (93)			60	1·60

Special First Day of Issue Postmarks
Philatelic Bureau, Edinburgh... 1·60
Gloucester.. 1·60

799 Athletics

800 Rowing

801 Weightlifting

802 Rifle Shooting

803 Hockey

(Des N. Cudworth)

1986 (15 July). 13th Commonwealth Games, Edinburgh and World Hockey Cup for Men, London (34p.). Multicoloured Phosphorised paper. Perf 15×14.

1328	**799**	17p. Athletics...	25	25
1329	**800**	22p. Rowing..	30	30
		a. imperf (pair).......................................		—
1330	**801**	29p. Weightlifting.......................................	45	45
1331	**802**	31p. Rifle Shooting.....................................	45	45
1332	**803**	34p. Hockey..	55	55
		a. Imperf (pair).......................................	£2750	
Set of 5			1·75	1·75
Set of 5 Gutter Pairs			3·50	
First Day Cover				1·90

Presentation Pack (PO Pack No. 173).................................... 1·90
PHQ Cards (set of 5) (94)................................ 75   1·90
No. 1332 also marked the centenary of the Hockey Association.

Special First Day of Issue Postmarks
Philatelic Bureau, Edinburgh... 1·90
Head Post Office, Edinburgh... 1·90

804 Prince Andrew and Miss Sarah Ferguson (from photo by Gene Nocon)

805 Prince Andrew and Miss Sarah Ferguson (from photo by Gene Nocon)

(Des J. Matthews)

1986 (22 July). Royal Wedding. Multicoloured. One phosphor band (12p.) or phosphorised paper (17p.). Perf 14×15.

1333	**804**	12p. Prince Andrew and Miss Sarah Ferguson...	25	25
1334	**805**	17p. Prince Andrew and Miss Sarah Ferguson...	40	40
		a. Imperf (pair).......................................	£700	
Set of 2			60	60
Set of 2 Gutter Pairs			1·25	
First Day Cover				70
Presentation Pack (PO Pack No. 174)			75	
PHQ Cards (set of 2) (95)			30	75

Special First Day of Issue Postmarks
Philatelic Bureau, Edinburgh... 70
London, SW1.. 75

806 Stylised Cross on Ballot Paper

(Des J. Gibbs. Litho Questa)

1986 (19 Aug). 32nd Commonwealth Parliamentary Association Conference. Multicoloured. Phosphorised paper. Perf 14×14½.

1335	**806**	34p. Stylised Cross on Ballot Paper.........	50	50
		a. Imperf between (vert pair)..............	—	
Gutter Pair			1·00	
First Day Cover				55
PHQ Card (96)			15	55

Special First Day of Issue Postmarks
Philatelic Bureau, Edinburgh... 55
London, SW1.. 55

807 Lord Dowding and Hawker Hurricane Mk I

808 Lord Tedder and Hawker Typhoon IB

809 Lord Trenchard and de Havilland DH.9A

810 Sir Arthur Harris and Avro Type 683 Lancaster

811 Lord Portal and de Havilland DH.98 Mosquito

(Des B. Sanders)

1986 (16 Sept). History of the Royal Air Force. Multicoloured Phosphorised paper. Perf 14½.

1336	**807**	17p. Lord Dowding and Hawker Hurricane Mk I	25	25
		a. Imperf (pair)	£1800	
1337	**808**	22p. Lord Tedder and Hawker Typhoon IB	35	35
		a. Face value omitted*	£550	
		b. Queen's head omitted*	£550	
1338	**809**	29p. Lord Trenchard and de Havilland DH.9A	45	45
1339	**810**	31p. Sir Arthur Harris and Avro Type 683 Lancaster	50	50
1340	**811**	34p. Lord Portal and de Havilland DH.98 Mosquito	55	55
Set of 5			2·00	2·00
Set of 5 Gutter Pairs			4·00	
First Day Cover				2·10
Presentation Pack (PO Pack No. 175)			2·10	
PHQ Cards (set of 5) (97)			75	2·10

Nos. 1336/1340 were issued to celebrate the 50th anniversary of the first RAF Commands.
* Nos. 1337a/1337b come from three consecutive sheets on which the stamps in the first vertical row are without the face value and those in the second vertical row the Queen's head.

Special First Day of Issue Postmarks

Philatelic Bureau, Edinburgh	2·10
Farnborough	2·10

812 The Glastonbury Thorn

813 The Tanad Valley Plygain

814 The Hebrides Tribute

815 The Dewsbury Church Knell

816 The Hereford Boy Bishop

(Des Lynda Gray)

1986 (18 Nov–2 Dec). Christmas. Folk Customs. Multicoloured One phosphor band (12p., 13p.) or phosphorised paper (others). Perf 15×14.

1341	**812**	12p. The Glastonbury Thorn	25	25
		a. Imperf (pair)	£1500	
1342		13p. The Glastonburg Thorn	25	25
		u. Underprint Type **4** (2.12)	50	
1343	**813**	18p. The Tanad Valley Plygain	30	30
1344	**814**	22p. The Hebrides Tribute	40	40
1345	**815**	31p. The Dewsbury Church Knell	45	45
1346	**816**	34p. The Hereford Boy Bishop	50	50
Set of 6			1·90	1·90
Set of 6 Gutter Pairs			3·75	
First Day Covers (2)				2·40
Presentation Pack (PO Pack No. 176) (Nos. 1342/1346)			2·00	
PHQ Cards (set of 5) (98) (Nos. 1342/1346)			75	1·75
Christmas Folder (contains No. 1342u×36)			18·00	

No. 1341 represented a discount of 1p, available between 2 and 24 December 1986, on the current second class postage rate.

Special First Day of Issue Postmarks

Philatelic Bureau, Edinburgh (Nos. 1342/1346) (18.11.86)	1·90
Bethlehem, Llandeilo, Dyfed (Nos. 1342/1346) (18.11.86)	2·00
Philatelic Bureau, Edinburgh (Nos. 1341) (2.12.86)	50

Collectors Pack

1986 (18 Nov). Comprises Nos. 1308/1340 and 1342/1346.

CP1346a	Collectors Pack (Pack No. 177)	16·00

Post Office Yearbook

1986 (18 Nov). Comprises Nos. 1308/1346 in 32 page hardbound book with slip case, illustrated in colour

YB1346a	Yearbook	23·00

817 North American Blanket Flower

818 Globe Thistle

819 Echeveria

820 Autumn Crocus

(Adapted J. Matthews)

1987 (20 Jan). Flower Photographs by Alfred Lammer. Multicoloured Phosphorised paper. Perf 14½×14.

1347	**817**	18p. North American Blanket Flower	25	25
1348	**818**	22p. Globe Thistle	30	30
1349	**819**	31p. Echeveria	45	45
		a. Imperf (pair)	£3250	
1350	**820**	34p. Autumn Crocus	55	55
Set of 4			1·50	1·50
Set of 4 Gutter Pairs			3·00	
First Day Cover				1·60
Presentation Pack (PO Pack No. 178)			1·60	
PHQ Cards (set of 4) (99)			60	1·60

Special First Day of Issue Postmarks

Philatelic Bureau, Edinburgh	1·60
Richmond, Surrey	1·75

105

821 *The Principia Mathematica*

822 *Motion of Bodies in Ellipses*

823 *Optick Treatise*

824 *The System of the World*

(Des Sarah Godwin)

1987 (24 Mar). 300th Anniversary of *The Principia Mathematica* by Sir Isaac Newton. Multicoloured Phosphorised paper. Perf 14×15.

1351	**821**	18p. *The Principia Mathematica*...............	25	25
		a. Imperf (pair).................................	£3250	
1352	**822**	22p. *Motion of Bodies in Ellipses*............	30	30
1353	**823**	31p. *Optick Treatise*..............................	45	45
1354	**824**	34p. *The System of the World*................	55	55
Set of 4..			1·50	1·50
Set of 4 Gutter Pairs.......................................			3·00	
First Day Cover..				1·60
Presentation Pack (PO Pack No. 179)..............			1·60	
PHQ Cards (set of 4) (100)............................			60	1·60

Special First Day of Issue Postmarks

Philatelic Bureau, Edinburgh...		1·60
Woolsthorpe, Lincs...		1·75

825 Willis Faber and Dumas Building, Ipswich

826 Pompidou Centre, Paris

827 Staatsgalerie, Stuttgart

828 European Investment Bank, Luxembourg

(Des B. Tattersfield)

1987 (12 May). Europa. British Architects in Europe. Multicoloured Phosphorised paper. Perf 15×14.

1355	**825**	18p. Willis Faber and Dumas Building, Ipswich..	25	25
1356	**826**	22p. Pompidou Centre, Paris....................	30	30
1357	**827**	31p. Staatsgalerie, Stuttgart...................	45	45
		a. Imperf (horiz pair)...........................	£3250	
1358	**828**	34p. European Investment Bank, Luxembourg......................................	55	55
Set of 4..			1·50	1·50
Set of 4 Gutter Pairs.......................................			3·00	
First Day Cover..				1·60
Presentation Pack (PO Pack No. 180)..............			1·60	
PHQ Cards (set of 4) (101)............................			50	1·60

Special First Day of Issue Postmarks

Philatelic Bureau, Edinburgh...		1·60
Ipswich..		1·60

829 Brigade Members with Ashford Litter, 1887

830 Bandaging Blitz Victim, 1940

831 Volunteer with fainting Girl, 1965

832 Transport of Transplant Organ by Air Wing, 1987

(Des Debbie Cook. Litho Questa)

1987 (16 June). Centenary of St John Ambulance Brigade. Multicoloured Phosphorised paper. Perf 14×14½.

1359	**829**	18p. Brigade Members with Ashford Litter, 1887...	25	25
		a. Black printing double.......................	†	£500
		b. Black printing triple.........................	†	£800
1360	**830**	22p. Bandaging Blitz Victim, 1940..........	30	30
1361	**831**	31p. Volunteer with fainting Girl, 1965...	45	45
1362	**832**	34p. Transport of Transplant Organ by Air Wing, 1987.................................	55	55
Set of 4..			1·50	1·50
Set of 4 Gutter Pairs.......................................			3·00	
First Day Cover..				1·60
Presentation Pack (PO Pack No. 181)..............			1·60	
PHQ Cards (set of 4) (102)............................			60	1·60

Special First Day of Issue Postmarks

Philatelic Bureau, Edinburgh...		1·60
London, EC1...		1·60

833 Arms of the Lord Lyon King of Arms

834 Scottish Heraldic Banner of Prince Charles

835 Arms of Royal Scottish Academy of Painting, Sculpture and Architecture

836 Arms of Royal Society of Edinburgh

(Des J. Matthews)

1987 (21 July). 300th Anniversary of Revival of Order of the Thistle. Multicoloured Phosphorised paper. Perf 14½.

1363	**833**	18p. Arms of the Lord Lyon King of Arms...	25	25
1364	**834**	22p. Scottish Heraldic Banner of Prince Charles.......................................	30	30

1365	**835**	31p. Arms of Royal Scottish Academy of Painting, Sculpture and Architecture......	45	45
1366	**836**	34p. Arms of Royal Society of Edinburgh......	55	55
Set of 4......			1·50	1·50
Set of 4 Gutter Pairs......			3·00	
First Day Cover......				1·60
Presentation Pack (PO Pack No. 182)......			1·60	
PHQ Cards (set of 4) (103)......			60	1·60

Special First Day of Issue Postmarks

Philatelic Bureau, Edinburgh......	1·60
Rothesay, Isle of Bute......	1·75

837 Crystal Palace, *Monarch of the Glen* (Landseer) and Grace Darling

838 *Great Eastern, Beeton's Book of Household Management* and Prince Albert

839 Albert Memorial, Ballot Box and Disraeli

840 Diamond Jubilee Emblem, Newspaper Placard for Relief of Mafeking and Morse Key

(Des M. Dempsey. Eng C. Slania. Recess and photo)

1987 (8 Sept). 150th Anniversary of Queen Victoria's Accession. Multicoloured Phosphorised paper. Perf 15×14.

1367	**837**	18p. Crystal Palace, *Monarch of the Glen* (Landseer) and Grace Darling......	25	25
1368	**838**	22p. *Great Eastern, Beeton's Book of Household Management* and Prince Albert......	30	30
1369	**839**	31p. Albert Memorial, Ballot Box and Disraeli......	45	45
1370	**840**	34p. Diamond Jubilee Emblem, Newspaper Placard for Relief of Mafeking and Morse Key......	55	55
Set of 4......			1·50	1·50
Set of 4 Gutter Pairs......			3·00	
First Day Cover......				1·60
Presentation Pack (PO Pack No. 183)......			1·60	
PHQ Cards (set of 4) (104)......			60	1·60

Special First Day of Issue Postmarks

Philatelic Bureau, Edinburgh......	1·60
Newport, Isle of Wight......	1·60

841 Pot by Bernard Leach

842 Pot by Elizabeth Fritsch

843 Pot by Lucie Rie

844 Pot by Hans Coper

(Des T. Evans)

1987 (13 Oct). Studio Pottery. Multicoloured Phosphorised paper. Perf 14½×14.

1371	**841**	18p. Pot by Bernard Leach......	25	25
1372	**842**	26p. Pot by Elizabeth Fritsch......	35	35
1373	**843**	31p. Pot by Lucie Rie......	45	45
1374	**844**	34p. Pot by Hans Coper......	55	55
		a. Imperf (vert pair)......	£2500	
Set of 4......			1·50	1·50
Set of 4 Gutter Pairs......			3·00	
First Day Cover......				1·60
Presentation Pack (PO Pack No. 184)......			1·60	
PHQ Cards (set of 4) (105)......			60	1·60

Special First Day of Issue Postmarks

Philatelic Bureau, Edinburgh......	1·60
St Ives, Cornwall......	1·60

845 Decorating the Christmas Tree

846 Waiting for Father Christmas

847 Sleeping Child and Father Christmas in Sleigh

848 Child reading

849 Child playing Recorder and Snowman

(Des M. Foreman)

1987 (17 Nov). Christmas. Multicoloured One phosphor band (13p.) or phosphorised paper (others). Perf 15×14.

1375	**845**	13p. Decorating the Christmas Tree......	20	20
		u. Underprint Type **4**......	50	
1376	**846**	18p. Waiting for Father Christmas......	25	25
1377	**847**	26p. Sleeping Child and Father Christmas in Sleigh......	30	30
1378	**848**	31p. Child reading......	40	40
1379	**849**	34p. Child playing Recorder and Snowman......	50	50
Set of 5......			1·50	1·50
Set of 5 Gutter Pairs......			3·00	
First Day Cover......				1·60
Presentation Pack (PO Pack No. 185)......			1·60	
PHQ Cards (set of 5) (106)......			75	1·60
Christmas Folder (contains No. 1375u×36)......			18·00	

Examples of the 13p. value from special folders, containing 36 stamps and sold for £4·60, show a blue underprint of double-lined stars printed on the reverse over the gum.

Special First Day of Issue Postmarks

Philatelic Bureau, Edinburgh......	1·60
Bethlehem, Llandeilo, Dyfed......	1·75

Collectors Pack

1987 (17 Nov). Comprises Nos. 1347/1379.
CP1379a   Collectors Pack (Pack No. 186)...... 16·00

Post Office Yearbook

1987 (17 Nov). Comprises Nos. 1347/1379 in 32 page hardbound book with slip case, illustrated in colour
YB1379a   Yearbook...... 13·00

850 Short-spined Sea scorpion ('Bull-rout') (Jonathan Couch)

851 Yellow Water Lily (Major Joshua Swatkin)

852 Whistling ('Bewick's') Swan (Edward Lear)

853 *Morchella esculenta* (James Sowerby)

(Des. E. Hughes)

1988 (19 Jan). Bicentenary of Linnean Society. Archive Illustrations. Multicoloured Phosphorised paper. Perf 15×14.

1380	**850**	18p. Short-spined Sea scorpion ('Bull-rout')......	25	25
1381	**851**	26p. Yellow Water Lily........................	35	35
1382	**852**	31p. Whistling ('Bewick's') Swan..........	45	45
		a. Imperf (horiz pair)....................	£2500	
1383	**853**	34p. *Morchella esculenta*.................	60	60
Set of 4..			1·50	1·50
Set of 4 Gutter Pairs.......................			3·00	
First Day Cover...............................				1·60
Presentation Pack (PO Pack No. 187)......			1·60	
PHQ Cards (set of 4) (107)................			60	1·60

Special First Day of Issue Postmarks

Philatelic Bureau, Edinburgh.......................	1·75
London, W1..	1·75

854 Revd William Morgan (Bible translator, 1588)

855 William Salesbury (New Testament translator, 1567)

856 Bishop Richard Davies (New Testament translator, 1567)

857 Bishop Richard Parry (editor of Revised Welsh Bible, 1620)

(Des K. Bowen)

1988 (1 Mar). 400th Anniversary of Welsh Bible. Multicoloured Phosphorised paper. Perf 14½×14.

1384	**854**	18p. Revd William Morgan....................	25	25
		a. Imperf (vert pair)......................	£2250	
1385	**855**	26p. William Salesbury....................	35	35
1386	**856**	31p. Bishop Richard Davies..............	45	45
1387	**857**	34p. Bishop Richard Parry...............	60	60
Set of 4..			1·50	1·50
Set of 4 Gutter Pairs.......................			3·00	
First Day Cover...............................				1·60
Presentation Pack (PO Pack No. 188)......			1·60	
PHQ Cards (set of 4) (108)................			60	1·60

Special First Day of Issue Postmarks

Philatelic Bureau, Edinburgh.......................	1·75
Ty Mawr, Wybrnant, Gwynedd......................	1·75

858 Gymnastics (Centenary of British Amateur Gymnastics Association)

859 Downhill Skiing (Ski Club of Great Britain)

860 Tennis (Centenary of Lawn Tennis Association)

861 Football (Centenary of Football League)

(Des J. Sutton)

1988 (22 Mar). Sports Organisations. Multicoloured Phosphorised paper. Perf 14½.

1388	**858**	18p. Gymnastics.................................	25	25
		a. Imperf (pair)............................	£2250	
1389	**859**	26p. Downhill Skiing........................	35	35
1390	**860**	31p. Tennis.......................................	45	45
1391	**861**	34p. Football....................................	60	60
Set of 4..			1·50	1·50
Set of 4 Gutter Pairs.......................			3·00	
First Day Cover...............................				1·60
Presentation Pack (PO Pack No. 189)......			1·60	
PHQ Cards (set of 4) (109)................			50	1·60

Special First Day of Issue Postmarks

Philatelic Bureau, Edinburgh.......................	1·75
Wembley..	1·75

862 *Mallard* and Mailbags on Pick-up Arms

863 Loading Transatlantic Mail on Liner *Queen Elizabeth*

864 Glasgow Tram No. 1173 and Pillar Box

865 Imperial Airways Handley Page HP.45 *Horatius* and Airmail Van

(Des M. Dempsey)

1988 (10 May). Europa. Transport and Mail Services in 1930s.' Multicoloured Phosphorised paper. Perf 15×14.

1392	**862**	18p. *Mallard* and Mailbags on Pick-up Arms..	25	25
1393	**863**	26p. Loading Transatlantic Mail on Liner *Queen Elizabeth*..........	35	35
1394	**864**	31p. Glasgow Tram No. 1173 and Pillar Box..	45	45
1395	**865**	34p. Imperial Airways Handley Page HP.45 *Horatius* and Airmail Van.......	60	60
Set of 4..			1·50	1·50
Set of 4 Gutter Pairs.......................			3·00	
First Day Cover...............................				1·60
Presentation Pack (PO Pack No. 190)......			1·60	
PHQ Cards (set of 4) (110)................			60	1·60

Trials exist with alternative face values; 19p, 27p, 32p and 35p.

866 Early Settler and Sailing Clipper

867 Queen Elizabeth II with British and Australian Parliament Buildings

868 W. G. Grace (cricketer) and Tennis Racquet

869 Shakespeare, John Lennon (entertainer) and Sydney Opera House

(Des G. Emery. Litho Questa)

1988 (21 June). Bicentenary of Australian Settlement. Multicoloured Phosphorised paper. Perf 14½.

1396	866	18p. Early Settler and Sailing Clipper.........	25	25
		a. Horiz pair. Nos. 1396/1397..................	55	55
1397	867	18p. Queen Elizabeth II with British and Australian Parliament Buildings.........	25	25
1398	868	34p. W. G. Grace and Tennis Racquet.........	50	50
		a. Horiz pair. Nos. 1398/1399..................	1·10	1·10
1399	869	34p. Shakespeare, John Lennon and Sydney Opera House........................	50	50
Set of 4..			1·50	1·50
Set of 2 Gutter Blocks of 4..			3·00	
First Day Cover...				1·60
Presentation Pack (PO Pack No. 191)........................			1·60	
Souvenir Book..			6·00	
PHQ Cards (set of 4) (111)..			60	1·60

Nos. 1396/397 and 1398/1399 were each printed together, *se-tenant*, in horizontal pairs throughout the sheets, each pair showing a background design of the Australian flag.

The 40 page souvenir book contains the British and Australian sets which were issued on the same day in similar designs.

870 Spanish Galeasse off The Lizard

871 English Fleet leaving Plymouth

872 Engagement off Isle of Wight

873 Attack of English Fire-ships, Calais

874 Armada in Storm, North Sea

(Des G. Evernden)

1988 (19 July). 400th Anniversary of Spanish Armada. Multicoloured Phosphorised paper. Perf 15×14.

1400	870	18p. Spanish Galeasse off The Lizard......	25	25
		a. Horiz strip of 5. Nos. 1400/1404......	1·40	1·40
1401	871	18p. English Fleet leaving Plymouth.......	25	25
1402	872	18p. Engagement off Isle of Wight..........	25	25
1403	873	18p. Attack of English Fire-ships, Calais..	25	25
		a. '88' for '1988' in imprint (strip of 5)..	35·00	
1404	874	18p. Armada in Storm, North Sea...........	25	25
		a. '988' for '1988' in imprint (strip of 5)..	35·00	
Set of 5..			1·40	1·40
Gutter Block of 10...			2·75	
First Day Cover...				1·50
Presentation Pack (PO Pack No. 192)........................			1·50	
PHQ Cards (set of 5) (112)..			75	1·50

Nos. 1400/1404 were printed together, *se-tenant*, in horizontal strips of five throughout the sheet, forming a composite design.

On R. 3/10 the imprint reads 88, with traces of the 9 visible, on R. 4/4 it reads 988, both on the Dot pane. Both were quickly retouched to show 1988

875 'The Owl and the Pussy-cat'

876 'Edward Lear as a Bird' (self-portrait)

877 'Cat' (from alphabet book)

878 'There was a Young Lady whose Bonnet...' (limerick)

(Des M. Swatridge and S. Dew)

1988 (6–27 Sept). Death Centenary of Edward Lear (artist and author). Multicoloured Phosphorised paper. Perf 15×14.

1405	875	19p. 'The Owl and the Pussy-cat'............	25	25
1406	876	27p. 'Edward Lear as a Bird' (self-portrait)...	35	35
1407	877	32p. 'Cat' (from alphabet book)..............	45	45
1408	878	35p. 'There was a Young Lady whose Bonnet...' (limerick)............................	60	60
Set of 4..			1·50	1·50
Set of 4 Gutter Pairs...			3·00	
First Day Cover...				1·60
Presentation Pack (PO Pack No. 193)........................			1·60	
PHQ Cards (set of 4) (113)..			60	1·60
MS1409 122×90 mm. Nos. 1405/1408 (*sold at £1·35*) (27.9.88)...			3·25	3·50
First Day Cover...				3·75

The premium on No. **MS**1409 was used to support the Stamp World London 90 International Stamp Exhibition.

Special First Day of Issue Postmarks
Philatelic Bureau, Edinburgh (stamps) (6.9.88)............................... 1·75
Philatelic Bureau, Edinburgh (miniature sheet) (27.9.88)............... 3·75
London N7 (stamps) (6.9.88).. 1·75
London N22 (miniature sheet) (27.9.88).. 3·75

879 Carrickfergus Castle

880 Caernarfon Castle

881 Edinburgh Castle

882 Windsor Castle

(Des from photos by Prince Andrew, Duke of York. Eng C. Matthews. Recess Harrison)

1988 (18 Oct). Ordinary paper. Perf 15×14.

1410	**879**	£1 Carrickfergus Castle. Bottle green...	3·50	25
1411	**880**	£1·50 Caernarfon Castle. Maroon.............	3·75	50
1412	**881**	£2 Edinburgh Castle. Indigo................	6·50	75
1413	**882**	£5 Windsor Castle. Deep brown..........	17·00	1·50
Set of 4			28·00	2·75
Set of 4 Gutter Pairs (vert or horiz)......................			60·00	
First Day Cover..				16·00
Presentation Pack (PO Pack No. 18)....................			30·00	

For similar designs, but with silhouette of Queen's head see Nos. 1611/1614 and 1993/1996.

Special First Day of Issue Postmarks

(For illustrations see Introduction).....................................	
Philatelic Bureau Edinburgh (Type H)................................	16·00
Windsor, Berkshire (Type 1)...	20·00

883 Journey to Bethlehem

884 Shepherds and Star

885 Three Wise Men

886 Nativity

887 The Annunciation

(Des L. Trickett)

1988 (15 Nov). Christmas. Christmas Cards. Multicoloured One phosphor band (14p.) or phosphorised paper (others). Perf 15×14.

1414	**883**	14p. Journey to Bethlehem......................	25	25
		a. Error. '13p.' instead of '14p'..............	£7500	
		b. Imperf (pair)..	£1500	
1415	**884**	19p. Shepherds and Star.........................	25	25
		a. Imperf (pair)..	£850	
1416	**885**	27p. Three Wise Men...............................	35	35
1417	**886**	32p. Nativity..	40	40
1418	**887**	35p. The Annunciation............................	55	55
Set of 5...			1·60	1·60
Set of 5 Gutter Pairs...			3·25	
First Day Cover..				1·75
Presentation Pack (PO Pack No. 194)..................			1·75	
PHQ Cards (set of 5) (114)...................................			75	1·75

Examples of No. 1414a were found in some 1988 Post Office Yearbooks.

Special First Day of Issue Postmarks

Philatelic Bureau, Edinburgh...	1·75
Bethlehem, Llandeilo, Dyfed...	1·90

Collectors Pack

1988 (15 Nov). Comprises Nos. 1380/1408, 1414/1418.
CP1418a	Collectors Pack (Pack No. 195)............	16·00

Post Office Yearbook

1988 (15 Nov). Comprises Nos. 1380/1404, **MS**1409, 1414/1418 in 32 page hardbound book with slip case, illustrated in colour
YB1418a	Yearbook..	13·00

888 Atlantic Puffin

889 Avocet

890 Oystercatcher

891 Northern Gannet

(Des D. Cordery)

1989 (17 Jan). Centenary of Royal Society for the Protection of Birds. Multicoloured Phosphorised paper. Perf 14×15.

1419	**888**	19p. Atlantic Puffin..................................	25	25
1420	**889**	27p. Avocet...	35	35
1421	**890**	32p. Oystercatcher...................................	45	45
1422	**891**	35p. Northern Gannet..............................	60	60
Set of 4...			1·50	1·50
Set of 4 Gutter Pairs...			3·00	
First Day Cover..				1·60
Presentation Pack (PO Pack No. 196)..................			1·60	
PHQ Cards (set of 4) (115)...................................			60	1·60

Special First Day of Issue Postmarks

Philatelic Bureau, Edinburgh...	1·75
Sandy, Bedfordshire..	1·75

892 Rose

893 Cupid

894 Yachts

895 Fruit

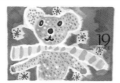

896 Teddy Bear

(Des P. Sutton)

1989 (31 Jan). Greetings Stamps. Multicoloured Phosphorised paper. Perf 15×14.

1423	**892**	19p. Rose	50	60
		a. Booklet pane. Nos. 1423/1427×2 plus 12 half stamp-size labels	24·00	
		b. Horiz strip of 5. Nos. 1423/1427	10·00	12·00
1424	**893**	19p. Cupid	50	60
1425	**894**	19p. Yachts	50	60
1426	**895**	19p. Fruit	50	60
1427	**896**	19p. Teddy Bear	50	60
Set of 5			10·00	12·00
First Day Cover				12·00

Nos. 1423/1427 were printed together, *se-tenant*, in horizontal strips of five, two such strips forming the booklet pane with 12 half stamp-size labels.

Nos. 1423/1427 were only issued in £1·90 booklet No. FY1.

Special First Day of Issue Postmarks

Philatelic Bureau, Edinburgh	12·00
Lover, Salisbury, Wilts	12·00

897 Fruit and Vegetables   **898** Meat Products

899 Dairy Products   **900** Cereal Products

(Des Sedley Place Ltd)

1989 (7 Mar). Food and Farming Year. Multicoloured Phosphorised paper. Perf 14×14½.

1428	**897**	19p. Fruit and Vegetables	25	25
1429	**898**	27p. Meat Products	35	35
1430	**899**	32p. Dairy Products	45	45
1431	**900**	35p. Cereal Products	60	60
Set of 4			1·50	1·50
Set of 4 Gutter Pairs			3·00	
First Day Cover				1·60
Presentation Pack (PO Pack No. 197)			1·60	
PHQ Cards (set of 4) (116)			60	1·60

Special First Day of Issue Postmarks

Philatelic Bureau, Edinburgh	1·60
Stoneleigh, Kenilworth, Warwicks	1·75

901 Mortarboard (150th Anniversary of Public Education in England)   **902** Cross on Ballot Paper (Third Direct Elections to European Parliament)

903 Posthorn (26th Postal, Telegraph and Telephone International Congress, Brighton)   **904** Globe (Inter-Parliamentary Union Centenary Conference, London)

(Des Lewis Moberly from firework set-pieces. Litho Questa)

1989 (11 Apr). Anniversaries. Multicoloured Phosphorised paper. Perf 14×14½.

1432	**901**	19p. Mortarboard	25	25
		a. Horiz pair. Nos. 1432/1433	60	60
1433	**902**	19p. Cross on Ballot Paper	25	25
1434	**903**	35p. Posthorn	50	50
		a. Horiz pair. Nos. 1434/1435	1·10	1·10
1435	**904**	35p. Globe	50	50
Set of 4			1·50	1·50
Set of 2 Gutter Strips of 4			3·00	
First Day Cover				1·60
Presentation Pack (PO Pack No. 198)			1·60	
PHQ Cards (set of 4) (117)			60	1·60

Nos. 1432/1433 and 1434/1435 were each printed together, *se-tenant*, in horizontal pairs throughout the sheets.

Stamps as No. 1435, but inscribed 'ONE HUNDREDH CONFERNCE' were prepared but not issued.

Special First Day of Issue Postmarks

Philatelic Bureau, Edinburgh	1·60
London SW	1·75

905 Toy Train and Aeroplanes   **906** Building Bricks

907 Dice and Board Games   **908** Toy Robot, Boat and Doll's House

(Des D. Fern)

1989 (16 May). Europa. Games and Toys. Multicoloured Phosphorised paper. Perf 14×15.

1436	**905**	19p. Toy Train and Aeroplanes	25	25
1437	**906**	27p. Building Bricks	35	35
1438	**907**	32p. Dice and Board Games	45	45
1439	**908**	35p. Toy Robot, Boat and Doll's House	60	60
Set of 4			1·50	1·50
Set of 4 Gutter Strips			3·00	
First Day Cover				1·60
Presentation Pack (PO Pack No. 199)			1·60	
PHQ Cards (set of 4) (118)			60	1·60

Special First Day of Issue Postmarks
Philatelic Bureau, Edinburgh.. 1·75
Leeds.. 1·75

909 Ironbridge,
Shropshire

910 Tin Mine, St
Agnes Head, Cornwall

911 Cotton Mills, New
Lanark, Strathclyde

912 Pontcysyllte
Aqueduct, Clwyd

912a Horizontal versions of Types **909/912**

(Des R. Maddox)

1989 (4–25 July). Industrial Archaeology. Multicoloured Phosphorised
paper. Perf 14×15.

1440	**909**	19p. Ironbridge, Shropshire........................	25	25
1441	**910**	27p. Tin Mine, St Agnes Head, Cornwall....	35	35
1442	**911**	32p. Cotton Mills, New Lanark,		
		Strathclyde..	45	45
1443	**912**	35p. Pontcysyllte Aqueduct, Clwyd...........	60	60
Set of 4...			1·50	1·50
Set of 4 Gutter Pairs..			3·00	
First Day Cover..				1·60
Presentation Pack (PO Pack No. 200)................			1·60	
PHQ Cards (set of 4) (119)...............................			50	1·60
MS1444 **912a** 122×90 mm. Horizontal versions of				
Types **909/912** (sold at £1·40) (25.7.89)........			3·00	3·00
First Day Cover..				3·00

The premium on No. **MS**1444 was used to support the Stamp World
London 90 International Stamp Exhibition.

Special First Day of Issue Postmarks
Philatelic Bureau, Edinburgh (stamps) (4.7.89).................. 1·75
Philatelic Bureau, Edinburgh (miniature sheet) (25.7.89)...... 3·00
Telford (stamps) (4.7.89)... 1·75
New Lanark (miniature sheet) (25.7.89)........................ 3·25

For Nos. 1445/1452 see Decimal Machin Definitives section.

915 Snowflake (×10)

916 *Calliphora
erythrocephala* (×5) (fly)

 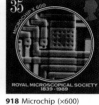

917 Blood Cells (×500)

918 Microchip (×600)

(Des K. Bassford. Litho Questa)

1989 (5 Sept). 150th Anniversary of Royal Microscopical Society.
Multicoloured Phosphorised paper. Perf 14½×14.

1453	**915**	19p. Snowflake..................................	25	25
1454	**916**	27p. *Calliphora erythrocephala*.................	35	35
1455	**917**	32p. Blood Cells.................................	45	45
1456	**918**	35p. Microchip...................................	60	60
Set of 4...			1·50	1·50
Set of 4 Gutter Pairs..			3·00	
First Day Cover..				1·60
Presentation Pack (PO Pack No. 201)................			1·60	
PHQ Cards (set of 4) (120)...............................			60	1·60

Special First Day of Issue Postmarks
Philatelic Bureau, Edinburgh.. 1·65
Oxford.. 1·75

919 Royal Mail Coach

920 Escort of Blues and
Royals

921 Lord Mayor's
Coach

922 Passing St Paul's

923 Blues and Royals
Drum Horse

(Des P. Cox)

1989 (17 Oct). Lord Mayor's Show, London. Multicoloured. Phosphorised paper. Perf 14×15.

1457	**919**	20p. Royal Mail Coach.............................	25	25
		a. Horiz strip of 5. Nos. 1457/1461.....	1·40	1·40
		ab. Imperf (horiz strip of 5. Nos. 1457/1461)................................	£4500	
		ac. Imperf (horiz strip of 4. Nos. 1457/1460)................................	£4000	
		ad. Imperf (horiz strip of 3. Nos. 1457/1459)................................	£3000	
1458	**920**	20p. Escort of Blues and Royals..............	25	25
1459	**921**	20p. Lord Mayor's Coach.........................	25	25
1460	**922**	20p. Passing St Paul's..............................	25	25
1461	**923**	20p. Blues and Royals Drum Horse.........	25	25
Set of 5			1·40	1·40
Gutter Strip of 10			2·75	
First Day Cover				1·50
Presentation Pack (PO Pack No. 202)			1·50	
PHQ Cards (set of 5) (121)			75	1·50

Nos. 1457/1461 were printed together, *se-tenant*, in horizontal strips of five throughout the sheet.

This issue commemorates the 800th anniversary of the installation of the first Lord Mayor of London.

Nos. 1457ab/1457ad come from a sheet partly imperf at left.

Stamps of Types **919/923**, but each with face value of 19p., were prepared but not issued. One mint *se-tenant* strip has been recorded.

See also No. 2957.

Special First Day of Issue Postmarks

Philatelic Bureau, Edinburgh...	1·40
London, EC4...	1·50

924 14th-century Peasants from Stained-glass Window

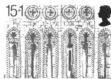

925 Arches and Roundels, West Front

926 Octagon Tower

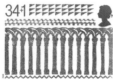

927 Arcade from West Transept

928 Triple Arch from West Front

(Des D. Gentleman)

1989 (14 Nov). Christmas. 800th Anniversary of Ely Cathedral. Multicoloured One phosphor band (15p., 15p.+1p.) or phosphorised paper (others). Perf 15×14.

1462	**924**	15p. 14th-century Peasants from Stained-glass Window..................	25	25
1463	**925**	15p.+1p. Arches and Roundels, West Front	25	35
		a. Imperf (pair)...................................	£1400	
1464	**926**	20p.+1p. Octagon Tower...........................	35	35
		a. Imperf (pair)...................................	£1400	
1465	**927**	34p.+1p. Arcade from West Transept.........	45	45
1466	**928**	37p.+1p. Triple Arch from West Front........	60	60
Set of 5			1·75	1·75
Set of 5 Gutter Pairs			3·50	
First Day Cover				1·90
Presentation Pack (PO Pack No. 203)			1·90	
PHQ Cards (set of 5) (122)			75	1·90

Trials are known showing different values and including an additional design.

Special First Day of Issue Postmarks

Philatelic Bureau, Edinburgh.......................................	1·90
Bethlehem, Llandeilo, Dyfed..	1·90
Ely..	1·90

Collectors Pack

1989 (14 Nov). Comprises Nos. 1419/1422, 1428/1443 and 1453/1466.

CP1466a	Collectors Pack (Pack No. 204)............	15·50

Post Office Yearbook

1989 (14 Nov). Comprises Nos. 1419/1422, 1428/1444 and 1453/1466 in hardbound book with slip case, illustrated in colour

YB1466a	Yearbook...	14·00

929 Queen Victoria and Queen Elizabeth II

(Des J. Matthews (after Wyon and Machin))

1990 (10 Jan–12 June). 150th Anniversary of the Penny Black.

(a) Photo Harrison. Perf 15×14.

1467	**929**	15p. bright blue....................................	30	30
		a. Imperf (pair)..................................	£950	
		l. Booklet pane. No. 1467×10 with horizontal edges of pane imperf (30.1.90)..	4·75	
1468		15p. bright blue (1 side band at left) (30.1.90)..	3·75	3·75
		a. Band at right (20.3.90).....................	1·75	1·75
		l. Booklet pane. No. 1468×2 and 1470 plus label...............................	9·75	
1468a		bright blue (1 side band) (30.1.90)..	1·75	1·75
1469		20p. brownish black and cream (phosphorised paper).........................	40	40
		a. Imperf (pair)..................................	£950	
		l. Booklet pane. No. 1469×5 plus label with vertical edges of pane imperf (30.1.90).............................	5·00	
		m. Booklet pane. No. 1469×10 with horizontal edges of pane imperf (30.1.90)..	5·25	
		n. Booklet pane. No. 1469×6 with margins all round (20.3.90)..............	1·50	
		r. Booklet pane. No. 1469×4 with three edges of pane imperf (17.4.90)..	3·75	
1470		20p. brownish black and cream (2 bands) (30.1.90)..............................	80	80
1471		29p. deep mauve (phosphorised paper)..	55	55
1472		29p. deep mauve (2 bands) (20.3.90)......	3·75	3·75
1473		34p. deep bluish grey (phosphorised paper)..	70	70
1474		37p. rosine (phosphorised paper)...........	75	75

(b) Litho Walsall. Perf 14 (from booklets).

1475	**929**	15p. bright blue (30.1.90).......................	50	50
		l. Booklet pane. No. 1475×4 with three edges of pane imperf............	3·00	
		m. Booklet pane. No. 1475×10 with three edges of pane imperf (12.6.90)..	5·50	
1476		20p. brownish black and cream (phosphorised paper) (30.1.90)........	50	50
		l. Booklet pane. No. 1476×5 plus label with vertical edges of pane imperf...	8·00	
		m. Booklet pane. No. 1476×4 with three edges of pane imperf............	4·00	
		n. Booklet pane. No. 1476×10 with three edges of pane imperf (12.6.90)..	8·00	

(c) Litho Questa. Perf 15×14 (from booklets).

1477	**929**	15p. bright blue (17.4.90).......................	85	85
1478		20p. brownish black (phosphorised paper) (17.4.90)................................	85	85
Set of 5 (Nos. 1467, 1469, 1471, 1473/1474)			2·50	2·50
First Day Cover (Nos. 1467, 1469, 1471, 1473/1474)				2·75
Presentation Pack (PO Pack No. 21) (Nos. 1467, 1469, 1471, 1473/1474)			2·90	

Nos. 1475/1476 do not exist perforated on all four sides, but come with either one or two adjacent sides imperforate.

Nos. 1468, 1468*a*, 1470, 1472 and 1475/1478 were only issued in stamp booklets, Nos. JA1 to JD3.

Nos. 1468*a*, 1470 and 1472 occur in the *se-tenant* pane from the 1990 London Life £5 booklet (No. DX11). This pane is listed as No. X906m.

For illustrations showing the difference between photogravure and lithography see beneath T **367**.

For No. 1469 in miniature sheet see Nos. **MS**1501 and **MS**3965.

For No. 1476 with one elliptical hole on each vertical side see Nos. 2133 and 2955.

For T **929** redrawn with '1st' face value see No. 2133*a* and 2956.

Colour trials are known denominated 19p. in several colours.

Special First Day of Issue Postmark
Philatelic Bureau, Edinburgh (in red).. 2·75
Windsor, Berks (Type G, see Introduction) (in red)........................... 2·75

930 Kitten   **931** Rabbit

932 Duckling   **933** Puppy

(Des T. Evans. Litho Questa)

1990 (23 Jan). 150th Anniversary of Royal Society for Prevention of Cruelty to Animals. Multicoloured Phosphorised paper. Perf 14×14½.

1479	**930**	20p. Kitten......................................	30	30
		a. Silver (Queen's head and face		
		value) omitted................................	£650	
1480	**931**	29p. Rabbit.....................................	45	45
		a. Imperf (horiz pair)........................	£2250	
1481	**932**	34p. Duckling.................................	55	55
		a. Silver (Queen's head and face		
		value) omitted................................	£1000	
1482	**933**	37p. Puppy......................................	65	65
Set of 4..			1·75	1·75
Set of 4 Gutter Pairs..................................			3·50	
First Day Cover..				1·90
Presentation Pack (PO Pack No. 205)......			1·90	
PHQ Cards (set of 4) (123).......................			80	1·90

Special First Day of Issue Postmarks
Philatelic Bureau, Edinburgh.. 2·00
Horsham.. 2·25

934 Teddy Bear   **935** Dennis the Menace

936 Punch   **937** Cheshire Cat

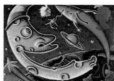   

938 The Man in the Moon   **939** The Laughing Policeman

   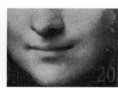

940 Clown   **941** *Mona Lisa*

942 Queen of Hearts   **943** Stan Laurel (comedian)

(Des Michael Peters and Partners Ltd)

1990 (6 Feb). Greetings Stamps. Smiles. Multicoloured Two phosphor bands. Perf 15×14.

1483	**934**	20p. Teddy Bear................................	60	70
		a. Booklet pane. Nos. 1483/1492		
		with margins all round......................	11·50	12·50
1484	**935**	20p. Dennis the Menace.....................	60	70
1485	**936**	20p. Punch.......................................	60	70
1486	**937**	20p. Cheshire Cat..............................	60	70
1487	**938**	20p. The Man in the Moon..................	60	70
1488	**939**	20p. The Laughing Policeman..............	60	70
1489	**940**	20p. Clown.......................................	60	70
1490	**941**	20p. *Mona Lisa*................................	60	70
1491	**942**	20p. Queen of Hearts.........................	60	70
1492	**943**	20p. Stan Laurel................................	60	70
Set of 10..			11·50	12·50
First Day Cover..				13·00

Nos. 1483/1492 were only issued in £2 booklet No. KX1.

The design of Nos. 1483, 1485/1487, 1489 and 1492 extend onto the pane margin.

For Types **934**/**943** inscribed (1st), see Nos. 1550/1559.

SET PRICES. Please note that set prices for booklet greetings stamps are for complete panes. Sets of single stamps are worth considerably less.

Special First Day of Issue Postmarks
Philatelic Bureau, Edinburgh.. 12·50
Giggleswick, North Yorkshire.. 12·50

944 Alexandra Palace (Stamp World London 90 Exhibition)

945 Glasgow School of Art

946 British Philatelic Bureau, Edinburgh

947 Templeton Carpet Factory, Glasgow

(Des P. Hogarth)

1990 (6–20 Mar). Europa (Nos. 1493 and 1495) and Glasgow 1990 European City of Culture (Nos. 1494 and 1496). Multicoloured Phosphorised paper. Perf 14×15.

1493	**944**	20p. Alexandra Palace (Stamp World London 90 Exhibition)......................	25	25
		a. Booklet pane. No. 1493×4 with margins all round (20.3)...................	1·40	
1494	**945**	20p. Glasgow School of Art......................	35	35
1495	**946**	29p. British Philatelic Bureau, Edinburgh.......................	45	45
1496	**947**	37p. Templeton Carpet Factory, Glasgow.......................	60	60
Set of 4..			1·50	1·50
Set of 4 Gutter Pairs......................................			3·00	
First Day Cover..				1·60
Presentation Pack (PO Pack No. 206)...........			1·60	
PHQ Cards (set of 4) (124)...........................			80	1·60

Booklet pane No. 1493a comes from the £5 London Life booklet No. DX11.

Special First Day of Issue Postmarks

Philatelic Bureau, Edinburgh...	1·75
Glasgow..	1·75

948 Export Achievement Award

949 Technological Achievement Award

(Des S. Broom. Litho Questa)

1990 (10 Apr). 25th Anniversary of Queen's Awards for Export and Technology. Multicoloured Phosphorised paper. Perf 14×14½.

1497	**948**	20p. Export Achievement Award............	25	25
		a. Horiz pair. Nos. 1497/1498..............	60	60
1498	**949**	20p. Technological Achievement Award.......................................	25	25
1499	**948**	37p. Export Achievement Award............	50	50
		a. Horiz pair. Nos. 1499/1500..............	1·10	1·10
1500	**949**	37p. Technological Achievement Award.......................................	50	50
Set of 4..			1·50	1·50
Set of 2 Gutter Strips of 4.............................			3·00	
First Day Cover..				1·60
Presentation Pack (PO Pack No. 207)...........			1·60	
PHQ Cards (set of 4) (125)...........................			80	1·60

Nos. 1497/1498 and 1499/1500 were each printed together, se-tenant, in horizontal pairs throughout the sheets.

Special First Day of Issue Postmarks

Philatelic Bureau, Edinburgh...	1·75
London, SW..	1·75

949a Stamp World London '90

(Des Sedley Place Design Ltd. Eng C. Matthews. Recess and photo Harrison)

1990 (3 May). Stamp World London '90 International Stamp Exhibition. Sheet 122×89 mm containing No. 1469. Phosphorised paper. Perf 15×14.

MS1501 **949a** 20p. brownish black and cream (sold at £1)..		2·40	2·40
a. Error. Imperf........................		—	
b. Black (recess-printing) omitted..............		—	
c. Black (recess-printing) inverted..............		—	
First Day Cover..			2·50
Souvenir Book (Nos. 1467, 1469, 1471, 1473/1474 and **MS**1501).......................................		8·50	

The premium on No. **MS**1501 was used to support the Stamp World London '90 International Stamp Exhibition.

In No. **MS**1501 only the example of the 20p. is perforated.

No. **MS**1501b shows an albino impression on the reverse. The 1d. black and Sea horse background are omitted due to one sheet becoming attached to the underside of another prior to recess printing.

No. **MS**1501c shows the recess part of the design inverted in relation to the photogravure of T **929**.

For the single 20p stamp, see No. 1469. For the same stamp redrawn with '1st' face value or with one elliptical hole on each vertical side see Nos. 2133 and 2955/2956.

Special First Day of Issue Postmarks

Philatelic Bureau, Edinburgh (in red)...................................	2·50
City of London (in red)...	2·50

A First Day of Issue handstamp as Type B was provided at Alexandra Palace, London N22 for this issue.

950 Cycad and Sir Joseph Banks Building

951 Stone Pine and Princess of Wales Conservatory

952 Willow Tree and Palm House

953 Cedar Tree and Pagoda

(Des P. Leith)

1990 (5 June). 150th Anniversary of Kew Gardens. Multicoloured Phosphorised paper. Perf 14×15.

1502	**950**	20p. Cycad and Sir Joseph Banks Building............	25	25
1503	**951**	29p. Stone Pine and Princess of Wales Conservatory..........	35	35
1504	**952**	34p. Willow Tree and Palm House...........	45	45
1505	**953**	37p. Cedar Tree and Pagoda...................	60	60
Set of 4............			1·50	1·50
Set of 4 Gutter Pairs............			3·00	
First Day Cover...........				1·60
Presentation Pack (PO Pack No. 208)...................			1·60	
PHQ Cards (set of 4) (126)................			80	1·60

Special First Day of Issue Postmarks

Philatelic Bureau, Edinburgh...............	1·75
Kew, Richmond...............	1·75

954 Thomas Hardy and Clyffe Clump, Dorset

(Des J. Gibbs)

1990 (10 July). 150th Birth Anniversary of Thomas Hardy (author). Multicoloured Phosphorised paper. Perf 14×15.

1506	**954**	20p. Thomas Hardy....................	30	30
		a. Imperf (pair)................	£3000	
Gutter Pair............			60	
First Day Cover...........				40
Presentation Pack (PO Pack No. 209)...................			55	
PHQ Card (127)............			20	40

Special First Day of Issue Postmarks

Philatelic Bureau, Edinburgh...............	60
Dorchester...............	60

955 Queen Elizabeth the Queen Mother

956 Queen Elizabeth

957 Elizabeth, Duchess of York

958 Lady Elizabeth Bowes-Lyon

(Des J. Gorham from photographs by N. Parkinson (20p.), Dorothy Wilding (29p.), B. Park (34p.), Rita Martin (37p.))

1990 (2 Aug). 90th Birthday of Queen Elizabeth the Queen Mother. Multicoloured Phosphorised paper. Perf 14×15.

1507	**955**	20p. Queen Elizabeth the Queen Mother..........	40	40
1508	**956**	29p. Queen Elizabeth................	60	60
1509	**957**	34p. Elizabeth, Duchess of York.......	90	90
1510	**958**	37p. Lady Elizabeth Bowes-Lyon...........	1·10	1·10
Set of 4............			2·75	2·75
Set of 4 Gutter Pairs............			5·50	
First Day Cover...........				2·90

Presentation Pack (PO Pack No. 210)....................		2·90
PHQ Cards (set of 4) (128)...............	80	2·90

For these designs with Queen's head and frame in black see Nos. 2280/2283.

Special First Day of Issue Postmarks

Philatelic Bureau, Edinburgh...............	3·00
Westminster, SW1...............	3·00

For Nos. 1511/1516 see Decimal Machin Definitives section.

959 Victoria Cross   **960** George Cross

961 Distinguished Service Cross and Distinguished Service Medal

962 Military Cross and Military Medal

963 Distinguished Flying Cross and Distinguished Flying Medal

(Des J. Gibbs and J. Harwood)

1990 (11 Sept). Gallantry Awards. Multicoloured Phosphorised paper. Perf 14×15 (vert) or 15×14 (horiz).

1517	**959**	20p. Victoria Cross.....................	35	35
1518	**960**	20p. George Cross....................	35	35
1519	**961**	20p. Distinguished Service Cross and Distinguished Service Medal..........	35	35
		a. Imperf (pair)................	£1000	
1520	**962**	20p. Military Cross and Military Medal...	35	35
1521	**963**	20p. Distinguished Flying Cross and Distinguished Flying Medal............	35	35
Set of 5............			1·50	1·50
Set of 5 Gutter Pairs............			3·00	
First Day Cover...........				1·60
Presentation Pack (PO Pack No. 211)...................			1·60	
PHQ Cards (set of 5) (129)............			1·00	1·60

For T **959** with 'all-over' phosphor and Perf 14×14½ see No. 2666.

Special First Day of Issue Postmarks

Philatelic Bureau, Edinburgh...............	1·75
Westminster, SW1...............	1·75

964 Armagh Observatory, Jodrell Bank Radio Telescope and La Palma Telescope

965 Newton's Moon and Tides Diagram and Early Telescopes

966 Greenwich Old Observatory and Early Astronomical Equipment

967 Stonehenge, Gyroscope and Navigation by Stars

(Des J. Fisher. Litho Questa)

1990 (16 Oct). Astronomy. Multicoloured Phosphorised paper. Perf 14×14½.

1522	**964**	22p. Armagh Observatory, Jodrell Bank Radio Telescope and La Palma Telescope........................	25	25
		a. Gold (Queen's head) omitted..........	£675	
1523	**965**	26p. Newton's Moon and Tides Diagram and Early Telescopes.........	35	35
1524	**966**	31p. Greenwich Old Observatory and Early Astronomical Equipment.......	45	45
1525	**967**	37p. Stonehenge, Gyroscope and Navigation by Stars.........................	60	60
Set of 4...			1·50	1·50
Set of 4 Gutter Pairs..			3·00	
First Day Cover..				1·60
Presentation Pack (PO Pack No. 212).....................			1·60	
PHQ Cards (set of 4) (130).....................................			80	1·60

Nos. 1522/1525 marked the centenary of the British Astronomical Association and the bicentenary of the Armagh Observatory.

Special First Day of Issue Postmarks

Philatelic Bureau, Edinburgh...	1·75
Armagh...	1·75

968 Building a Snowman

969 Fetching the Christmas Tree

970 Carol Singing

971 Tobogganing

972 Ice Skating

(Des J. Gorham and A. Davidson)

1990 (13 Nov). Christmas. Multicoloured One phosphor band (17p.) or phosphorised paper (others). Perf 15×14.

1526	**968**	17p. Building a Snowman.........................	25	25
		a. Imperf (pair)......................................	£1300	
		b. Booklet pane of 20...........................	5·00	
1527	**969**	22p. Fetching the Christmas Tree............	25	25
		a. Imperf (horiz pair)............................	£1300	
1528	**970**	26p. Carol Singing..................................	35	35
1529	**971**	31p. Tobogganing...................................	45	40
1530	**972**	37p. Ice skating......................................	60	60
Set of 5...			1·75	1·75
Set of 5 Gutter Pairs..			3·50	
First Day Cover..				1·90
Presentation Pack (PO Pack No. 213).....................			1·90	
PHQ Cards (set of 5) (131).....................................			1·00	1·90

Booklet pane No. 1526b has the horizontal edges of the pane imperforate.

Special First Day of Issue Postmarks

Philatelic Bureau, Edinburgh...	1·90
Bethlehem, Llandeilo, Dyfed..	1·90

Collectors Pack

1990 (13 Nov). Comprises Nos. 1479/1482, 1493/1510 and 1517/1530.

CP1530a Collectors Pack (Pack No. 214)...........	18·00

Post Office Yearbook

1990 (13 Nov). Comprises Nos. 1479/1482, 1493/1500, 1502/1510, 1517/1530 in hardbound book with slip case

YB1530a Yearbook..	18·00

973 King Charles Spaniel

974 A Pointer

975 Two Hounds in a Landscape

976 A Rough Dog

977 Fino and Tiny

(Des Carroll, Dempsey and Thirkell Ltd)

1991 (8 Jan). Dogs. Paintings by George Stubbs. Multicoloured Phosphorised paper. Perf 14×14½.

1531	**973**	22p. King Charles Spaniel.........................	25	25
		a. Imperf (pair)......................................	£1100	
1532	**974**	26p. A Pointer...	30	30
1533	**975**	31p. Two Hounds in a Landscape.............	40	40
		a. Imperf (pair)......................................	£1800	
1534	**976**	33p. A Rough Dog...................................	45	45
1535	**977**	37p. Fino and Tiny..................................	60	60
Set of 5...			1·75	1·75
Set of 5 Gutter Pairs..			3·50	
First Day Cover..				2·00
Presentation Pack (PO Pack No. 215).....................			2·00	
PHQ Cards (set of 5) (132).....................................			1·00	2·00

Special First Day of Issue Postmarks

Philatelic Bureau, Edinburgh...	2·25
Birmingham..	2·25

978 Thrush's Nest

979 Shooting Star and Rainbow

980 Magpies and Charm Bracelet

981 Black Cat

982 Common Kingfisher with Key

983 Mallard and Frog

984 Four-leaf Clover in Boot and Match Box

985 Pot of Gold at End of Rainbow

986 Heart-shaped Butterflies

987 Wishing Well and Sixpence

(Des T. Meeuwissen)

1991 (5 Feb). Greetings Stamps. Good Luck. Multicoloured Two phosphor bands. Perf 15×14.

1536	**978**	(1st) Thrush's Nest	1·20	1·00
		a. Booklet pane. Nos. 1536/1545 plus 12 half stamp-size labels with margins on 3 sides	13·50	
1537	**979**	(1st) Shooting Star and Rainbow	1·20	1·00
1538	**980**	(1st) Magpies and Charm Bracelet	1·20	1·00
1539	**981**	(1st) Black Cat	1·20	1·00
1540	**982**	(1st) Common Kingfisher with Key	1·20	1·00
1541	**983**	(1st) Mallard and Frog	1·20	1·00
1542	**984**	(1st) Four-leaf clover in Boot and Match Box	1·20	1·00
1543	**985**	(1st) Pot of Gold at End of Rainbow	1·20	1·00
1544	**986**	(1st) Heart-shaped Butterflies	1·20	1·00
1545	**987**	(1st) Wishing Well and Sixpence	1·20	1·00
Set of 10			10·50	9·00
First Day Cover				9·25

Nos. 1536/1545 were only issued in £2·20 booklet, No. KX2 (sold at £2·40 from 16 September 1991)

The backgrounds of the stamps form a composite design.

Special First Day of Issue Postmarks

Philatelic Bureau, Edinburgh		9·50
Greetwell, Lincs		9·50

988 Michael Faraday (inventor of electric motor) (Birth Bicentenary)

989 Charles Babbage (computer science pioneer) (Birth Bicentenary)

990 Radar Sweep of East Anglia (50th Anniversary of Operational Radar Network)

991 Gloster Whittle E28/39 over East Anglia (50th Anniversary of First Flight of Sir Frank Whittle's Jet Engine)

(Des P. Till (Nos. 1546/1547), J. Harwood (Nos. 1548/1549))

1991 (5 Mar). Scientific Achievements. Multicoloured Phosphorised paper. Perf 14×15.

1546	**988**	22p. Michael Faraday	35	35
		a. Imperf (pair)	£300	
1547	**989**	22p. Charles Babbage	35	35
1548	**990**	31p. Radar Sweep of East Anglia	55	55
1549	**991**	37p. Gloster Whittle E28/39 over East Anglia	65	65
Set of 4			1·75	1·75
Set of 4 Gutter Pairs			3·50	
First Day Cover				1·90
Presentation Pack (PO Pack No. 216)			1·90	
PHQ Cards (set of 4) (133)			50	1·90

Special First Day of Issue Postmarks

Philatelic Bureau, Edinburgh		2·00
South Kensington, London, SW7		2·00

992 Teddy Bear

(Des Michael Peters and Partners Ltd)

1991 (26 Mar). Greetings Stamps. Smiles. As Nos. 1483/1492, but inscribed '1st' as T **992**. Multicoloured Two phosphor bands. Perf 15×14.

1550	**992**	(1st) Teddy Bear	1·20	1·00
		a. Booklet pane. Nos. 1550/1559 plus 12 half stamp-size labels with margins on 3 sides	13·50	
1551	**935**	(1st) Dennis the Menace	1·20	1·00
1552	**936**	(1st) Punch	1·20	1·00
1553	**937**	(1st) Cheshire Cat	1·20	1·00
1554	**938**	(1st) The Man in the Moon	1·20	1·00
1555	**939**	(1st) The Laughing Policeman	1·20	1·00
1556	**940**	(1st) Clown	1·20	1·00
1557	**941**	(1st) Mona Lisa	1·20	1·00
1558	**942**	(1st) Queen of Hearts	1·20	1·00
1559	**943**	(1st) Stan Laurel	1·20	1·00
Set of 10			10·50	9·00
First Day Cover				9·25

Nos. 1550/1559 were originally issued in £2·20 booklet, No. KX3 (sold at £2·40 from 16 September 1991 and at £2·50 from 1 November 1993).

The designs of Nos. 1550, 1552/1554, 1556 and 1559 extend onto the pane margin.

The stamps were re-issued in sheets of ten, printed in photogravure by Questa, each with *se-tenant* label on 22 May 2000 in connection with 'customised' stamps available at Stamp Show 2000. The labels show either a pattern of ribbons at £2·95 (No. LS1), or a personal photograph for £5·95.

A similar sheet, but printed in lithography by Questa instead of in photogravure, appeared on 3 July 2001 (No. LS5). Stamps from this sheet were perforated 14½×14 instead of the previous 15×14. Sheets showing greetings on the labels were available from the Bureau or Postshops at £2·95 each or with personal photographs at £12·95 for two.

Similar sheets each containing ten examples of Nos. 1550/1551 and 1555/1557 were only available with personal photograph. From 29 October 2001 sheets with personal photographs could also be purchased, on an experimental basis, from photo-booths situated at six post offices.

On 1 October 2002 three further sheets appeared printed in lithography by Questa. One contained Nos. 1550/1551 each×10 with greetings labels and cost £5·95 (No. LS9). Both designs were also available in sheets of 20 with personal photographs at £14·95 a sheet.

> **SET PRICES.** Please note that set prices for booklet greetings stamps are for complete panes. Sets of single stamps are worth considerably less.

Special First Day of Issue Postmarks

Philatelic Bureau, Edinburgh	9·50
Laugherton, Lincs	9·50

993 Man Looking at Space **994** Man Looking at Space

995 Space Looking at Man **996** Space Looking at Man

(Des J. M. Folon)

1991 (23 Apr). Europa. Europe in space. Multicoloured. Phosphorised paper. Perf 14½×14.

1560	**993**	22p. Man Looking at Space	35	35
		a. Horiz pair. Nos 1560/1561	75	75
1561	**994**	22p. Man Looking at Space	35	35
1562	**995**	37p. Space Looking at Man	65	65
		a. Horiz pair. Nos 1562/1563	1·40	1·40
1563	**996**	37p. Space Looking at Man	65	65
Set of 4			1·90	1·90
Set of 2 Gutter Pairs of 4			3·75	
First Day Cover				2·10
Presentation Pack (PO Pack No. 217)			2·10	
PHQ Cards (set of 4) (134)			80	2·10

Nos. 1560/1561 and 1562/1563 were each printed together, *se-tenant*, in horizontal pairs throughout the sheets, each pair forming a composite design.

Special First Day of Issue Postmarks

Philatelic Bureau, Edinburgh	2·10
Cambridge	2·25

997 Fencing **998** Hurdling

999 Diving **1000** Rugby

(Des Huntley Muir Partners)

1991 (11 June). World Student Games, Sheffield (Nos.1564/1566) and World Cup Rugby Championship, London (No. 1567). Multicoloured. Phosphorised paper. Perf 14½×14.

1564	**997**	22p. Fencing	35	35
1565	**998**	26p. Hurdling	45	45
1566	**999**	31p. Diving	55	55
1567	**1000**	37p. Rugby	75	75
Set of 4			1·90	1·90
Set of 4 Gutter Pairs			3·75	
First Day Cover				2·10
Presentation Pack (PO Pack No. 218)			2·10	
PHQ Cards (set of 4) (135)			80	2·10

Special First Day of Issue Postmarks

Philatelic Bureau, Edinburgh	2·10
Sheffield	2·25

1001 'Silver Jubilee' **1002** 'Mme Alfred Carrière'

1003 *Rosa moyesii* **1004** 'Harvest Fayre'

1005 'Mutabilis'

(Des Yvonne Skargon. Litho Questa)

1991 (16 July). Ninth World Congress of Roses, Belfast. Multicoloured. Phosphorised paper. Perf 14½×14.

1568	**1001**	22p. 'Silver Jubilee'	30	30
		a. Silver (Queen's head) omitted	£1800	
		b. Black printing double	£1500	£150
1569	**1002**	26p. 'Mme Alfred Carrière'	35	35
1570	**1003**	31p. *Rosa moyesii*	40	40
		a. Silver (Queen's head) omitted	—	£3500
1571	**1004**	33p. 'Harvest Fayre'	55	55
1572	**1005**	37p. 'Mutabilis'	65	65
Set of 5			2·00	2·00
Set of 5 Gutter Pairs			4·00	
First Day Cover				2·25
Presentation Pack (PO Pack No. 219)			2·25	
PHQ Cards (set of 5) (136)			60	2·25

Special First Day of Issue Postmarks

Philatelic Bureau, Edinburgh	2·25
Belfast	2·50

1006 Iguanodon

1007 Stegosaurus

1008 Tyrannosaurus

1009 Protoceratops

1010 Triceratops

(Des B. Kneale)

1991 (20 Aug). 150th Anniversary of Dinosaurs' Identification by Owen. Multicoloured Phosphorised paper. Perf 14½×14.

1573	**1006**	22p. Iguanodon.................................	35	35
		a. Imperf (pair).......................	£1200	
1574	**1007**	26p. Stegosaurus...........................	40	40
1575	**1008**	31p. Tyrannosaurus......................	45	45
1576	**1009**	33p. Protoceratops.......................	60	60
1577	**1010**	37p. Triceratops...........................	75	75
Set of 5...			2·25	2·25
Set of 5 Gutter Pairs.......................................			4·50	
First Day Cover..				2·75
Presentation Pack (PO Pack No. 220)..............			3·00	
PHQ Cards (set of 5) (137)...............................			1·00	2·50

Special First Day of Issue Postmarks

Philatelic Bureau, Edinburgh...	2·75
Plymouth..	3·00

1011 Map of 1816

1012 Map of 1906

1013 Map of 1959

1014 Map of 1991

(Des H. Brown. Recess (eng C. Matthews) and litho Harrison (24p.), litho Harrison (28p.), Questa (33p., 39p.))

1991 (17 Sept). Bicentenary of Ordnance Survey. Maps of Hamstreet, Kent. Multicoloured. Phosphorised paper. Perf 14½×14.

1578	**1011**	24p. Map of 1816........	35	35
		a. Black (litho) printing treble and magenta printing double...............	£750	
		b. Black (litho) and magenta printing double....................	£1000	
		c. Black (litho) printing double...........	£1000	
1579	**1012**	28p. Map of 1906........	45	45
1580	**1013**	33p. Map of 1959........	55	55
1581	**1014**	39p. Map of 1991........	75	75
Set of 4...			1·90	1·90
Set of 4 Gutter Pairs...........................			3·75	
First Day Cover....................................				2·00
Presentation Pack (PO Pack No. 221)......			2·25	
PHQ Cards (set of 4) (138)....................			80	2·00

Mint examples of T **1012** exist with a face value of 26p. (*Price* £4000).

Special First Day of Issue Postmarks

Philatelic Bureau, Edinburgh...	2·00
Southampton...	2·25

1015 Adoration of the Magi

1016 Mary and Jesus in Stable

1017 Holy Family and Angel

1018 The Annunciation

1019 The Flight into Egypt

(Des D. Driver)

1991 (12 Nov). Christmas. Illuminated Letters from Acts of Mary and Jesus Manuscript in Bodleian Library, Oxford. Multicoloured One phosphor band (18p.) or phosphorised paper (others). Perf 15×14.

1582	**1015**	18p. Adoration of the Magi....................	25	25
		a. Imperf (pair)...................	—	
		b. Booklet pane of 20..........	5·00	
1583	**1016**	24p. Mary and Jesus in Stable................	30	30
1584	**1017**	28p. Holy Family and Angel....................	40	40
1585	**1018**	33p. The Annunciation..........................	55	55
		a. Imperf (pair)...................	—	
1586	**1019**	39p. The Flight into Egypt.....................	70	70
Set of 5...			1·90	1·90
Set of 5 Gutter Pairs...........................			3·75	
First Day Cover....................................				2·00
Presentation Pack (PO Pack No. 222)......			2·10	
PHQ Cards (set of 5) (139)....................			60	2·00

Booklet pane No. 1582b has margins at left, top and bottom.

Special First Day of Issue Postmarks

Philatelic Bureau, Edinburgh...	2·00
Bethlehem, Landeilo, Dyfed..	2·00

Collectors Pack

1991 (12 Nov). Comprises Nos. 1531/1535, 1546/5419 and 1560/1586.

CP1586a	Collectors Pack (Pack No. 223)............	18·00

Post Office Yearbook

1991 (13 Nov). Comprises Nos. 1531/1535, 1546/1549 and 1560/1586 in hardbound book with slip case

YB1586a	Yearbook.................................	16·00

1020 Fallow Deer in Scottish Forest

1021 Hare on North Yorkshire Moors

1022 Fox in the Fens

1023 Redwing and Home Counties Village

1024 Welsh Mountain Sheep in Snowdonia

(Des J. Gorham and K. Bowen)

1992 (14 Jan–25 Feb). The Four Seasons. Wintertime. Multicoloured One phosphor band (18p.) or phosphorised paper (others). Perf 15×14.

1587	**1020**	18p. Fallow Deer in Scottish Forest........	25	25
1588	**1021**	24p. Hare on North Yorkshire Moors......	30	30
		a. Imperf (pair)...................................	£325	
1589	**1022**	28p. Fox in the Fens.................................	45	45
1590	**1023**	33p. Redwing and Home Counties		
		Village....................................	55	55
1591	**1024**	39p. Welsh Mountain Sheep in		
		Snowdonia.........................	70	70
		a. Booklet pane. No. 1591×4 with		
		margins all round (25.2.92)...........	2·75	
Set of 5..			2·00	2·00
Set of 5 Gutter Pairs...			4·00	
First Day Cover..				2·10
Presentation Pack (PO Pack No. 224)............................			2·25	
PHQ Cards (set of 5) (140)..			1·00	2·10

Booklet pane No. 1591a comes from the £6 Cymru-Wales booklet No. DX13.

Special First Day of Issue Postmarks

Philatelic Bureau, Edinburgh..	2·10
Brecon..	2·10

1025 Flower Spray

1026 Double Locket

1027 Key

1028 Model Car and Cigarette Cards

1029 Compass and Map

1030 Pocket Watch

1031 1854 1d. Red Stamp and Pen

1032 Pearl Necklace and Pen

1033 Marbles

1034 Bucket, Spade and Starfish

(Des Trickett and Webb Ltd)

1992 (28 Jan). Greetings Stamps. Memories. Multicoloured Two phosphor bands. Perf 15×14.

1592	**1025**	(1st) Flower Spray..	1·20	1·00
		a. Booklet pane. Nos. 1592/1601		
		plus 12 half stamp-size labels		
		with margins on 3 sides..................	13·50	
1593	**1026**	(1st) Double Locket..................................	1·20	1·00
1594	**1027**	(1st) Key..	1·20	1·00
1595	**1028**	(1st) Model Car and Cigarette Cards......	1·20	1·00
1596	**1029**	(1st) Compass and Map............................	1·20	1·00
1597	**1030**	(1st) Pocket Watch....................................	1·20	1·00
1598	**1031**	(1st) 1854 1d. Red Stamp and Pen..........	1·20	1·00
1599	**1032**	(1st) Pearl Necklace and Pen....................	1·20	1·00
1600	**1033**	(1st) Marbles..	1·20	1·00
1601	**1034**	(1st) Bucket, Spade and Starfish.............	1·20	1·00
Set of 10...			10·50	9·25
First Day Cover..				9·50
Presentation Pack (PO Pack No. G1)..................................			13·50	

Nos. 1592/1601 were only issued in £2·40 booklet, No. KX4 (sold at £2·50 from 1 November 1993 and at £2·60 from 8 July 1996).

The backgrounds of the stamps form a composite design.

Special First Day of Issue Postmarks

Philatelic Bureau, Edinburgh..	9·50
Whimsey, Gloucestershire..	9·50

1035 Queen Elizabeth in Coronation Robes and Parliamentary Emblem

1036 Queen Elizabeth in Garter Robes and Archiepiscopal Arms

1037 Queen Elizabeth with Baby Prince Andrew and Royal Arms

1038 Queen Elizabeth at Trooping the Colour and Service Emblems

1039 Queen Elizabeth and
Commonwealth Emblem

(Des Why Not Associates. Litho Questa)

1992 (6 Feb). 40th Anniversary of Accession. Two phosphor bands. Perf
14½×14.

1602	**1035**	24p. Queen Elizabeth in Coronation Robes and Parliamentary Emblem	40	50
		a. Horiz strip of 5. Nos. 1602/1606.....	2·75	3·00
1603	**1036**	24p. Queen Elizabeth in Garter Robes and Archiepiscopal Arms................	40	50
1604	**1037**	24p. Queen Elizabeth with Baby Prince Andrew and Royal Arms.................	40	50
1605	**1038**	24p. Queen Elizabeth at Trooping the Colour and Service Emblems.........	40	50
1606	**1039**	24p. Queen Elizabeth and Commonwealth Emblem................	40	50
Set of 5...........			2·75	3·00
Gutter Block of 10...........			5·50	
First Day Cover...........				3·25
Presentation Pack (PO Pack No. 225)...................			3·25	
PHQ Cards (set of 5) (141)...........			1·00	3·25

Nos. 1602/1606 were printed together, *se-tenant*, in horizontal strips of
five throughout the sheet.

Special First Day of Issue Postmarks

Philatelic Bureau, Edinburgh...........		3·25
Buckingham Palace, London SW1...........		3·50

1040 Tennyson in 1888
and *The Beguiling of Merlin*
(Sir Edward Burne-Jones)

1041 Tennyson in 1856
and *April Love* (Arthur
Hughes)

1042 Tennyson in
1864 and *I am Sick
of the Shadows* (John
Waterhouse)

1043 Tennyson as a Young
Man and *Mariana* (Dante
Gabriel Rossetti)

(Des Irene von Treskow)

1992 (10 Mar). Death Centenary of Alfred, Lord Tennyson (poet).
Multicoloured Phosphorised paper. Perf 14½×14.

1607	**1040**	24p. Tennyson in 1888 and *The Beguiling of Merlin*...........	35	35
1608	**1041**	28p. Tennyson in 1856 and *April Love*....	50	50
1609	**1042**	33p. Tennyson in 1864 and *I am Sick of the Shadows*...........	60	60
1610	**1043**	39p. Tennyson as a Young Man and *Mariana*...........	75	75
Set of 4...........			2·00	2·00
Set of 4 Gutter Pairs...........			4·00	
First Day Cover...........				2·25
Presentation Pack (PO Pack No. 226)...................			2·25	
PHQ Cards (Set of 4) (142)...........			80	2·25

Special First Day of Issue Postmarks

Philatelic Bureau, Edinburgh...........		2·25
Isle of Wight...........		2·25

CARRICKFERGUS CASTLE

1044 Carrickfergus Castle

CAERNARFON CASTLE

1044a Caernarfon Castle

EDINBURGH CASTLE

1044b Edinburgh Castle

CARRICKFERGUS CASTLE

1044c Carrickfergus Castle

WINDSOR CASTLE

1044d Windsor Castle

Original head

Re-etched
head

In 1994 the £1, £1·50, £2 and £5 were issued with the Queen's head re-
etched, showing a pattern of diagonal lines, as opposed to the horizontal
and diagonal lines of the original versions.

CASTLE

Harrison Plates (Nos. 1611/1614)

CASTLE

Enschedé Plates (Nos. 1993/1996)

(Des from photos by Prince Andrew, Duke of York. Eng C. Matthews.
Recess Harrison)

1992 (24 Mar)–**95**. Designs as Nos. 1410/1413, but showing Queen's head
in silhouette as T **1044**. Perf 15×14 (with one elliptical hole in each
vertical side).

1611	**1044**	£1 Carrickfergus Castle (bottle green and gold†)...........	5·50	50
		r. Re-etched cylinder (1994)...........	8·00	3·00
1612	**1044a**	£1·50 Caernarfon Castle (maroon and gold†)...........	6·00	75
		r. Re-etched cylinder (1994)...........	8·00	1·50

1613	**1044b**	£2 Edinburgh Castle (indigo and gold†)...............................	8·00	1·00
		r. Re-etched cylinder (1994)............	12·00	2·50
1613a	**1044c**	£3 Carrickfergus Castle (reddish violet and gold†) (22.8.95)...	19·00	1·75
1614	**1044d**	£5 Windsor Castle (deep brown and gold†)...........................	18·00	2·00
		a. Gold† (Queen's head) omitted.....	£575	
		r. Re-etched cylinder (1994)............	22·00	4·00

Set of 5...	50·00	5·50
Set of 5 Gutter Pairs (vert or horiz).................	£100	
Set of 4 re-etched cylinders (1994)...................	50·00	8·00
Set of 4 gutter pairs re-etched cylinders (1994)..................	£100	
First Day Cover (Nos. 1611/1613, 1614)..............		20·00
First Day Cover (No. 1613a).............................		6·00
Presentation Pack (PO Pack No. 27) (Nos. 1611/1613, 1614)...........................	38·00	
Presentation Pack (PO Pack No. 33) (No. 1613a).................	20·00	
PHQ Cards (D2–D5)†† (Nos. 1611/1613, 1614).................	80	6·00
PHQ Card (D8) (No. 1613a).............................	20	2·00

† The Queen's head on these stamps is printed in optically variable ink which changes colour from gold to green when viewed from different angles.

†† The PHQ Cards for this issue did not appear until 16 February 1993. The Bureau FDI cancellation is 3 March 1993 (the date of issue of the £10).

The £1·50 (5 March 1996), £2 (2 May 1996), £3 (February 1997) and £5 (17 September 1996) subsequently appeared on PVA (white gum) instead of the tinted PVAD previously used.

See also Nos. 1410/1413 and 1993/1996.

Special First Day of Issue Postmarks (for illustrations see Introduction)

Philatelic Bureau, Edinburgh (Type H) (£1, £1·50, £2, £5)...............	20·00
Windsor, Berkshire (Type I) (£1, £1·50, £2, £5).....................	20·00
Philatelic Bureau, Edinburgh (Type H) (£3)...........................	6.00
Carrickfergus, Antrim (as Type I) (£3).................................	7.00

1045 British Olympic Association Logo (Olympic Games, Barcelona)

1046 British Paralympic Association Symbol (Paralympics '92, Barcelona)

1047 Santa Maria (500th Anniversary of Discovery of America by Columbus)

1048 Kaisei (Japanese cadet brigantine) (Grand Regatta Columbus, 1992)

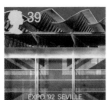

1049 British Pavilion, EXPO '92, Seville

(Des K. Bassford (Nos. 1615/1616, 1619), K. Bassford and S. Paine. Eng C. Matthews (Nos. 1617/1618). Litho Questa (Nos. 1615/1616, 1619) or recess and litho Harrison (Nos. 1617/1618))

1992 (7 Apr). Europa. International Events. Multicoloured Phosphorised paper. Perf 14×14½.

1615	**1045**	24p. British Olympic Association Logo..	30	30
		a. Horiz pair. Nos. 1615/1616..............	80	80
1616	**1046**	24p. British Paralympic Association Symbol.................................	30	30
1617	**1047**	24p. Santa Maria..	40	40
		a. Cream omitted...................................		
1618	**1048**	39p. Kaisei...	65	65
1619	**1049**	39p. British Pavilion, EXPO '92, Seville....	65	65

Set of 5...	2·25	2·25
Set of 3 Gutter Pairs and a Gutter Strip of 4........................	4·50	
First Day Cover..		2·50
Presentation Pack (PO Pack No. 227)................................	2·50	
PHQ Cards (set of 5) (143).......................................	1·00	2·50

Nos. 1615/1616 were printed together, se-tenant, in horizontal pairs throughout the sheet.

Special First Day of Issue Postmarks

Philatelic Bureau, Edinburgh..	2·50
Liverpool...	2·50

1050 Pikeman   **1051** Drummer

1052 Musketeer   **1053** Standard-bearer

(Des J. Sancha)

1992 (16 June). 350th Anniversary of the Civil War. Multicoloured Phosphorised paper. Perf 14½×14.

1620	**1050**	24p. Pikeman...	35	35
		a. Imperf (pair)...................................	£300	
1621	**1051**	28p. Drummer..	45	45
1622	**1052**	33p. Musketeer..	55	55
1623	**1053**	39p. Standard-bearer..............................	70	70

Set of 4...	1·90	1·90
Set of 4 Gutter Pairs.......................................	3·75	
First Day Cover..		2·00
Presentation Pack (PO Pack No. 228)................................	2·00	
PHQ Cards (set of 4) (144).......................................	80	2·00

Special First Day of Issue Postmarks

Philatelic Bureau, Edinburgh..	2·00
Banbury, Oxfordshire...	2·00

1054 The Yeomen of the Guard   **1055** The Gondoliers

1056 The Mikado   **1057** The Pirates of Penzance

1058 *Iolanthe*

(Des Lynda Gray)

1992 (21 July). 150th Birth Anniversary of Sir Arthur Sullivan (composer). Gilbert and Sullivan Operas. Multicoloured One phosphor band (18p.) or phosphorised paper (others). Perf 14½×14.

1624	**1054**	18p. *The Yeomen of the Guard*........	25	25
1625	**1055**	24p. *The Gondoliers*........................	30	30
		a. Imperf (pair).............................	£375	
1626	**1056**	28p. *The Mikado*...........................	40	40
1627	**1057**	33p. *The Pirates of Penzance*........	55	55
1628	**1058**	39p. *Iolanthe*...............................	70	70
Set of 5..			2·00	2·00
Set of 5 Gutter Pairs................................			4·00	
First Day Cover..				2·25
Presentation Pack (PO Pack No. 229).........			2·25	
PHQ Cards (set of 5) (145)........................			1·00	2·25

Special First Day of Issue Postmarks

Philatelic Bureau, Edinburgh..	2·25
Birmingham...	2·25

1059 'Acid Rain Kills'

1060 'Ozone Layer'

1061 'Greenhouse Effect'

1062 'Bird of Hope'

24p. Large full stop after '4' (Dot cyl. R. 10/6)

(Des Christopher Hall (24p.), Lewis Fowler (28p.), Sarah Warren (33p.), Alice Newton-Mold (39p.). Adapted Trickett and Webb Ltd)

1992 (15 Sept). Protection of the Environment. Children's Paintings. Multicoloured Phosphorised paper. Perf 14×14½.

1629	**1059**	24p. 'Acid Rain Kills'......................	35	35
		a. Large full stop after '4'.............	20·00	
1630	**1060**	28p. 'Ozone Layer'........................	40	40
1631	**1061**	33p. 'Greenhouse Effect'...............	55	55
1632	**1062**	39p. 'Bird of Hope'........................	70	70
Set of 4..			1·75	1·75
Set of 4 Gutter Pairs................................			3·50	
First Day Cover..				1·90
Presentation Pack (PO Pack No. 230).........			2·00	
PHQ Cards (set of 4) (146)........................			80	1·90

Special First Day of Issue Postmarks

Philatelic Bureau, Edinburgh (in green)........................	2·00
Torridon (in green)...	2·10

1063 European Star

(Des D. Hockney)

1992 (13 Oct). Single European Market. Multicoloured Phosphorised paper. Perf 15×14.

1633	**1063**	24p. European Star........................	40	40
Gutter Pair..			80	
First Day Cover..				75
Presentation Pack (PO Pack No. 231).........			80	
PHQ Card (147)..			20	50

Special First Day of Issue Postmarks

Philatelic Bureau, Edinburgh..	75
Westminster...	1·00

1064 Angel Gabriel, St James's, Pangbourne

1065 Madonna and Child, St Mary's, Bibury

1066 King with Gold, Our Lady and St Peter, Leatherhead

1067 Shepherds, All Saints, Porthcawl

1068 Kings with Frankincense and Myrrh, Our Lady and St Peter, Leatherhead

(Des Carroll, Dempsey and Thirkell Ltd from windows by Karl Parsons (18p., 24p., 33p.) and Paul Woodroffe (28p. 39p.))

1992 (10 Nov). Christmas. Stained-glass Windows. Multicoloured One centre band (18p.) or phosphorised paper (others). Perf 15×14.

1634	**1064**	18p. Angel Gabriel.........................	25	25
		a. Booklet pane of 20...................	5·00	
		b. Imperf (pair)............................	£200	
1635	**1065**	24p. Madonna and Child................	30	30
1636	**1066**	28p. King with Gold.......................	40	40
1637	**1067**	33p. Shepherds.............................	55	55
1638	**1068**	39p. Kings with Frankincense and Myrrh..	70	70
Set of 5..			2·00	2·00
Set of 5 Gutter Pairs................................			4·00	
First Day Cover..				2·10
Presentation Pack (PO Pack No. 232).........			2·25	
PHQ Cards (set of 5) (148)........................			1·00	2·25

Booklet pane No. 1634a comes from a special £3 Christmas booklet and has margins at left, top and bottom.

Special First Day of Issue Postmarks

Philatelic Bureau, Edinburgh..	2·10
Bethlehem, Llandeilo, Dyfed...	2·10
Pangbourne...	2·25

Collectors Pack

1992 (10 Nov). Comprises Nos. 1587/1591, 1602/1610 and 1615/1638.

CP1638*a*	Collectors Pack (Pack No. 233)............	19·00	

Post Office Yearbook

1992 (11 Nov). Comprises Nos. 1587/1591, 1602/1610 and 1615/1638 in hardbound book with slip case, illustrated in colour

YB1638*a* Yearbook.. 19·00

1069 Mute Swan Cob and St Catherine's Chapel, Abbotsbury

1070 Cygnet and Decoy

1071 Swans and Cygnet

1072 Eggs in Nest and Tithe Barn, Abbotsbury

1073 Young Swan and the Fleet

(Des D. Gentleman)

1993 (19 Jan). 600th Anniversary of Abbotsbury Swannery. Multicoloured One phosphor band (18p.) or phosphorised paper (others). Perf 14×15.

1639	**1069**	18p. Mute Swan Cob............................	30	30
1640	**1070**	24p. Cygnet...	50	50
1641	**1071**	28p. Swans and Cygnet.........................	80	80
1642	**1072**	33p. Eggs in Nest.................................	1·00	1·00
1643	**1073**	39p. Young Swan..................................	1·40	1·40

Set of 5... 3·75 3·75
Set of 5 Gutter Pairs.. 7·50
First Day Cover.. 4·00
Presentation Pack (PO Pack No. 234)................................. 4·00
PHQ Cards (set of 5) (149)... 1·00 4·00

Special First Day of Issue Postmarks

Philatelic Bureau, Edinburgh.. 4·00
Abbotsbury, Dorset.. 4·00

1074 Long John Silver and Parrot (*Treasure Island*)

1075 Tweedledum and Tweedledee (*Alice Through the Looking-Glass*)

1076 William (*William* books)

1077 Mole and Toad (*The Wind in the Willows*)

1078 Teacher and Wilfrid (*The Bash Street Kids*)

1079 Peter Rabbit and Mrs Rabbit (*The Tale of Peter Rabbit*)

1080 Snowman (*The Snowman*) and Father Christmas (*Father Christmas*)

1081 The Big Friendly Giant and Sophie (*The BFG*)

1082 Bill Badger and Rupert Bear

1083 Aladdin and the Genie

(Des Newell and Sorell)

1993 (2 Feb–10 Aug). Greetings Stamps. Gift Giving. Multicoloured Two phosphor bands. Perf 15×14 (with one elliptical hole in each horizontal side).

1644	**1074**	(1st) Long John Silver and Parrot............	1·20	1·00
		a. Booklet pane. Nos. 1644/1653........	13·50	
1645	**1075**	(1st) Tweedledum and Tweedledee.......	1·20	1·00
1646	**1076**	(1st) William....................................	1·20	1·00
1647	**1077**	(1st) Mole and Toad............................	1·20	1·00
1648	**1078**	(1st) Teacher and Wilfrid.....................	1·20	1·00
1649	**1079**	(1st) Peter Rabbit and Mrs Rabbit (Mrs Rabbit in blue dress).....................	1·20	1·00
		a. Peter Rabbit and Mrs Rabbit (Mrs Rabbit in lilac dress) (10.8.93)........	1·25	1·40
		b. Booklet pane. No. 1649a×4 with margins all round (10.8.93)............	5·00	
1650	**1080**	(1st) Snowman and Father Christmas....	1·20	1·00
1651	**1081**	(1st) The Big Friendly Giant and Sophie	1·20	1·00
1652	**1082**	(1st) Bill Badger and Rupert Bear...........	1·20	1·00
1653	**1083**	(1st) Aladdin and the Genie...................	1·20	1·00

Set of 10.. 10·50 9·25
First Day Cover.. 9·50
Presentation Pack (PO Pack No. G2)................................... 13·50
PHQ Cards (set of 10) (GS1).. 2·00 9·50

Nos. 1644/1653 were issued in £2·40 booklet, No. KX5 (*sold at £2·50 from 1 November 1993*), together with a pane of 20 half stamp-sized labels. The stamps and labels were affixed to the booklet cover by a common gutter margin

No. 1649a and booklet pane 1649b come from the £6 (£5·64) Beatrix Potter booklet No. DX15.

Special First Day of Issue Postmarks

Philatelic Bureau, Edinburgh (No. 1644a) (2.2.93)............................. 9·50
Greetland (No. 1644a) (2.2.93).. 9·50
Philatelic Bureau, Edinburgh (No. 1649b) (10.8.93)......................... 5·50
Keswick (No. 1649b) (10.8.93).. 5·50

SET PRICES. Please note that set prices for booklet greetings stamps are for complete panes. Sets of single stamps are worth considerably less.

1084 Decorated Enamel Dial

1085 Escapement, Remontoire and Fusée

1086 Balance, Spring and Temperature Compensator

1087 Back of Movement

(Des H. Brown and D. Penny. Litho Questa)

1993 (16 Feb). 300th Birth Anniversary of John Harrison (inventor of the marine chronometer). Details of 'H4' Clock. Multicoloured Phosphorised paper. Perf 14½×14.

1654	**1084**	24p. Decorated Enamel Dial	30	30
1655	**1085**	28p. Escapement, Remontoire and Fusée	45	45
1656	**1086**	33p. Balance, Spring and Temperature Compensator	55	55
1657	**1087**	39p. Back of Movement	70	70
Set of 4			1·75	1·75
Set of 4 Gutter Pairs			3·50	
First Day Cover				2·00
Presentation Pack (PO Pack No. 235)			2·00	
PHQ Cards (set of 4) (150)			80	2·00

Special First Day of Issue Postmarks

Philatelic Bureau, Edinburgh		2·00
Greenwich		2·25

1088 Britannia

(Des B. Craddock, adapted Roundel Design Group. Litho (silver die-stamped, Braille symbol for 'TEN' embossed) Questa)

1993 (2 Mar). Granite paper. Multicoloured Perf 14×14½ (with two elliptical holes in each horizontal side).

1658	**1088**	£10 Britannia	40·00	12·00
		a. Silver omitted	£2750	
		b. Braille symbol for 'TEN' omitted	£160	
		c. Fluorescent 'Ten Pounds'*	65·00	25·00
First Day Cover				18·00
Presentation Pack (D1)			45·00	
PHQ Card (D1)			5·00	25·00

* Examples from Plate 2A also show 'Ten Pounds' at the bottom right-hand corner under UV light (No. 1658c).

The paper used for No. 1658 contains fluorescent coloured fibres which, together with the ink used on the shield, react under UV light.

Special First Day of Issue Postmarks

Philatelic Bureau, Edinburgh		18·00
Windsor		20·00

1089 *Dendrobium hellwigianum*

1090 *Paphiopedilum Maudiae* 'Magnificum'

1091 *Cymbidium lowianum*

1092 *Vanda Rothschildiana*

1093 *Dendrobium vexillarius* var *albiviride*

(Des Pandora Sellars)

1993 (16 Mar). 14th World Orchid Conference, Glasgow. Multicoloured One phosphor band (18p.) or phosphorised paper (others). Perf 15×14.

1659	**1089**	18p. *Dendrobium hellwigianum*	30	30
		a. Imperf (pair)	£2750	
1660	**1090**	24p. *Paphiopedilum Maudiae* 'Magnificum'	35	35
1661	**1091**	28p. *Cymbidium lowianum*	45	45
1662	**1092**	33p. *Vanda Rothschildiana*	50	50
		a. Copyright logo and '1993' omitted (R. 10/6, dot pane)	20·00	20·00
1663	**1093**	39p. *Dendrobium vexillarius* var *albiviride*	60	60
Set of 5			2·00	2·00
Set of 5 Gutter Pairs			4·00	
First Day Cover				2·25
Presentation Pack (PO Pack No. 236)			2·25	
PHQ Cards (set of 5) (151)			1·00	2·25

Special First Day of Issue Postmarks

Philatelic Bureau, Edinburgh		2·25
Glasgow		2·40

For Nos. 1664/1672 and Y1667/Y1803 see Decimal Machin Definitives section.

1094 *Family Group* (bronze sculpture) (Henry Moore)

1095 *Kew Gardens* (lithograph) (Edward Bawden)

1096 *St Francis and the Birds* (Stanley Spencer)

1097 *Still Life: Odyssey I* (Ben Nicholson)

(Des. A. Dastor)

1993 (11 May). Europa. Contemporary Art. Multicoloured Phosphorised paper. Perf 14×14½.

1767	**1094**	24p. Family Group (bronze sculpture) (Henry Moore).................................	35	35
1768	**1095**	28p. Kew Gardens (lithograph) (Edward Bawden)...............................	50	50
1769	**1096**	33p. St Francis and the Birds (Stanley Spencer)................................	60	60
1770	**1097**	39p. Still Life: Odyssey I (Ben Nicholson)	70	70
	Set of 4..		2·00	2·00
	Set of 4 Gutter Pairs..........................		4·00	
	First Day Cover...................................			2·25
	Presentation Pack (PO Pack No. 237)................		2·25	
	PHQ Cards (set of 4) (152)................		80	2·25

Special First Day of Issue Postmarks
British Philatelic Bureau, Edinburgh............................... 2·25
London SW .... 2·40

1098 Emperor Claudius (from gold coin)

1099 Emperor Hadrian (bronze head)

1100 Goddess Roma (from gemstone)

1101 Christ (Hinton St Mary mosaic)

(Des J. Gibbs)

1993 (15 June). Roman Britain. Multicoloured Phosphorised paper with two phosphor bands. Perf 14×14½.

1771	**1098**	24p. Emperor Claudius............................	35	35
1772	**1099**	28p. Emperor Hadrian............................	50	50
1773	**1100**	33p. Goddess Roma...............................	60	60
1774	**1101**	39p. Christ...	70	70
	Set of 4..		2·00	2·00
	Set of 4 Gutter Pairs..........................		4·00	
	First Day Cover...................................			2·25
	Presentation Pack (PO Pack No. 238)................		2·25	
	PHQ Cards (set of 4) (153)................		80	2·25

Special First Day of Issue Postmarks
Philatelic Bureau, Edinburgh............................... 2·40
Caerllion... 2·40

1102 Midland Maid and other Narrow Boats, Grand Junction Canal

1103 Yorkshire Lass and other Humber Keels, Stainforth and Keadby Canal

1104 Valley Princess and other Horse-drawn Barges, Brecknock and Abergavenny Canal

1105 Steam Barges, including Pride of Scotland, and Fishing Boats, Crinan Canal

(Des T. Lewery. Litho Questa)

1993 (20 July). Inland Waterways. Multicoloured Two phosphor bands. Perf 14½×14.

1775	**1102**	24p. Narrow Boats, Grand Junction Canal.....................................	35	35
1776	**1103**	28p. Humber Keels, Stainforth and Keadby Canal..............................	50	50
1777	**1104**	33p. Horse-drawn Barges, Brecknock and Abergavenny Canal.................	60	60
1778	**1105**	39p. Steam Barges and Fishing Boats, Crinan Canal...............................	70	70
	Set of 4..		2·00	2·00
	Set of 4 Gutter Pairs..........................		4·00	
	First Day Cover...................................			2·25
	Presentation Pack (PO Pack No. 239)................		2·25	
	PHQ Cards (set of 4) (154)................		50	2·25

Nos. 1775/1778 commemorate the bicentenary of the Acts of Parliament authorising the canals depicted.

Special First Day of Issue Postmarks
Philatelic Bureau, Edinburgh............................... 2·40
Gloucester... 2·40

1106 Horse Chestnut

1107 Blackberry

1108 Hazel

1109 Rowan

1110 Pear

(Des Charlotte Knox)

1993 (14 Sept). The Four Seasons. Autumn. Fruits and Leaves. Multicoloured One phosphor band (18p.) or phosphorised paper (others). Perf 15×14.

1779	**1106**	18p. Horse Chestnut............................	30	30
1780	**1107**	24p. Blackberry.....................................	35	35
1781	**1108**	28p. Hazel...	45	45
1782	**1109**	33p. Rowan...	50	50
1783	**1110**	39p. Pear...	60	60
	Set of 5..		2·00	2·00
	Set of 5 Gutter Pairs..........................		4·00	
	First Day Cover...................................			2·25
	Presentation Pack (PO Pack No. 240)................		2·25	
	PHQ Cards (set of 5) (155)................		1·00	2·25

Special First Day of Issue Postmarks
Philatelic Bureau, Edinburgh............................... 2·40
Taunton... 2·50

SHERLOCK HOLMES & DR WATSON "THE REIGATE SQUIRE"

1111 The Reigate Squire

SHERLOCK HOLMES & SIR HENRY "THE HOUND OF THE BASKERVILLES"

1112 The Hound of the Baskervilles

SHERLOCK HOLMES & LESTRADE
"THE SIX NAPOLEONS"

SHERLOCK HOLMES & MYCROFT
"THE GREEK INTERPRETER"

1113 The Six
Napoleons

1114 The Greek
Interpreter

SHERLOCK HOLMES & MORIARTY
"THE FINAL PROBLEM"

1115 The Final Problem

(Des A. Davidson. Litho Questa)

1993 (12 Oct). Sherlock Holmes. Centenary of the Publication of *The Final Problem*. Multicoloured Phosphorised paper. Perf 14×14½.

1784	**1111**	24p. *The Reigate Squire*	30	30
		a. Horiz strip of 5. Nos. 1784/1788	1·90	2·40
1785	**1112**	24p. *The Hound of the Baskervilles*	30	30
1786	**1113**	24p. *The Six Napoleons*	30	30
1787	**1114**	24p. *The Greek Interpreter*	30	30
1788	**1115**	24p. *The Final Problem*	30	30
Set of 5			1·90	2·40
Gutter strip of 10			3·75	
First Day Cover				2·50
Presentation Pack (PO Pack No. 241)			2·75	
PHQ Cards (set of 5) (156)			1·00	2·50

Nos. 1784/1788 were printed together, *se-tenant*, in horizontal strips of five throughout the sheet.

Special First Day of Issue Postmarks

Philatelic Bureau, Edinburgh		2·50
London NW1		2·75

A First Day of Issue handstamp was provided at Autumn Stampex, London SW1, for this issue.

> For No. 1789, T **1116**, see Decimal Machin Definitives section.

1117 Bob Cratchit and Tiny Tim   **1118** Mr and Mrs Fezziwig

1119 Scrooge   **1120** The Prize Turkey

1121 Mr Scrooge's Nephew

(Des Q. Blake)

1993 (9 Nov). Christmas. 150th Anniversary of Publication of *A Christmas Carol* by Charles Dickens. Multicoloured. One phosphor band (19p.) or phosphorised paper (others). Perf 15×14.

1790	**1117**	19p. Bob Cratchit and Tiny Tim	30	30
		a. Imperf (pair)	£2500	
1791	**1118**	25p. Mr and Mrs Fezziwig	40	40
1792	**1119**	30p. Scrooge	50	50
1793	**1120**	35p. The Prize Turkey	55	55
1794	**1121**	41p. Mr Scrooge's Nephew	65	65
Set of 5			2·10	2·10
Set of 5 Gutter Pairs			4·25	
First Day Cover				2·50
Presentation Pack (PO Pack No. 242)			2·75	
PHQ Cards (set of 5) (157)			1·00	2·25

Special First Day of Issue Postmarks

Philatelic Bureau, Edinburgh		2·50
Bethlehem, Llandeilo		2·50

A First Day of Issue handstamp (pictorial) was provided at the City of London for this issue.

Collectors Pack

1993 (9 Nov). Comprises Nos. 1639/1643, 1654/1657, 1659/1663, 1767/1788 and 1790/1794.

CP1794*a*	Collectors Pack (Pack No. 243)	22·00

Post Office Yearbook

1993 (9 Nov). Comprises Nos. 1639/1643, 1654/1657, 1659/1663, 1767/1788 and 1790/1794 in hardbound book with slip case, illustrated in colour

YB1794*a*	Yearbook	20·00

1122 Class 5 No. 44957
and Class B1 No. 61342 on
West Highland Line

1123 Class A1 No. 60149
Amadis at Kings Cross

1124 Class 4 No. 43000 on
Turntable at Blyth North

1125 Class 4 No. 42455
near Wigan Central

1126 Class Castle No. 7002
Devizes Castle on Bridge
crossing Worcester and
Birmingham Canal

(Des B. Delaney)

1994 (18 Jan). The Age of Steam. Railway Photographs by Colin Gifford. Multicoloured One phosphor band (19p.) or phosphorised paper with two bands (others). Perf 14½.

1795	**1122**	19p. Class 5 No. 44957 and Class B1		
		No. 61342...............................	30	30
1796	**1123**	25p. Class A1 No. 60149 *Amadis*...........	40	40
1797	**1124**	30p. Class 4 No. 43000 on Turntable......	50	50
1798	**1125**	35p. Class 4 No. 42455..........................	60	60
1799	**1126**	41p. Class Castle No. 7002 *Devizes*		
		Castle on Bridge..........................	70	70
Set of 5..			2·25	2·25
Set of 5 Gutter Pairs....................................			4·50	
First Day Cover...				2·50
Presentation Pack (PO Pack No. 244)............			3·00	
PHQ Cards (set of 5) (158)...........................			1·00	2·50

Nos. 1796/1799 are on phosphorised paper and also show two phosphor bands.

Special First Day of Issue Postmarks

Philatelic Bureau, Edinburgh..	2·50
York...	2·50

A First Day of Issue handstamp (pictorial) was provided at Bridge of Orchy for this issue.

1127 Dan Dare and the Mekon

1128 The Three Bears

1129 Rupert Bear

1130 Alice (*Alice in Wonderland*)

1131 Noggin and the Ice Dragon

1132 Peter Rabbit posting Letter

1133 Red Riding Hood and the Wolf

1134 Orlando Marmalade Cat

1135 Biggles

1136 Paddington Bear on Station

(Des Newell and Sorrell)

1994 (1 Feb). Greetings Stamps. Messages. Multicoloured Two phosphor bands. Perf 15×14 (with one elliptical hole in each vertical side).

1800	**1127**	(1st) Dan Dare and the Mekon................	1·20	1·00
		a. Booklet pane. Nos. 1800/1809........	13·50	
1801	**1128**	(1st) The Three Bears.............................	1·20	1·00
1802	**1129**	(1st) Rupert Bear...................................	1·20	1·00

1803	**1130**	(1st) Alice (*Alice in Wonderland*)..............	1·20	1·00
1804	**1131**	(1st) Noggin and the Ice Dragon.............	1·20	1·00
1805	**1132**	(1st) Peter Rabbit posting Letter............	1·20	1·00
1806	**1133**	(1st) Red Riding Hood and the Wolf......	1·20	1·00
1807	**1134**	(1st) Orlando Marmalade Cat.................	1·20	1·00
1808	**1135**	(1st) Biggles...	1·20	1·00
1809	**1136**	(1st) Paddington Bear on Station............	1·20	1·00
Set of 10...			10·50	9·00
First Day Cover..				9·25
Presentation Pack (PO Pack No. G3)............			13·50	
PHQ Cards (set of 10) (GS2).......................			2·00	9·25

Nos. 1800/1809 were issued in £2·50 stamp booklet, No. KX6 (*sold at £2·60 from 8 July 1996*), together with a pane of 20 half stamp-sized labels. The stamps and labels were attached to the booklet cover by a common gutter margin.

Special First Day of Issue Postmarks

Philatelic Bureau, Edinburgh..	9·25
Penn, Wolverhampton...	9·25

1137 Castell Y Waun (Chirk Castle), Clwyd, Wales

1138 Ben Arkle, Sutherland, Scotland

1139 Mourne Mountains, County Down, Northern Ireland

1140 Dersingham, Norfolk, England

1141 Dolwyddelan, Gwynedd, Wales

1994 (1 Mar–26 July). 25th Anniversary of Investiture of the Prince of Wales. Paintings by Prince Charles. Multicoloured One phosphor band (19p.) or phosphorised paper (others). Perf 15×14.

1810	**1137**	19p. Castell Y Waun (Chirk Castle),		
		Clwyd, Wales..................................	30	30
1811	**1138**	25p. Ben Arkle, Sutherland, Scotland.....	35	35
1812	**1139**	30p. Mourne Mountains, County		
		Down, Northern Ireland.................	45	45
		a. Booklet pane. No. 1812×4 with		
		margins all round (26.7.94).......	1·75	1·75
1813	**1140**	35p. Dersingham, Norfolk, England.......	60	60
1814	**1141**	41p. Dolwyddelan, Gwynedd, Wales......	70	70
Set of 5..			2·25	2·25
Set of 5 Gutter Pairs....................................			4·50	
First Day Cover...				2·40
Presentation Pack (PO Pack No. 245)............			2·50	
PHQ Cards (set of 5) (159)...........................			1·00	2·50

Booklet pane No. 1812a comes from the £6·04 Northern Ireland booklet No. DX16.

Special First Day of Issue Postmarks

Philatelic Bureau, Edinburgh..	2·50
Caernarfon..	2·50

1142 Bather at Blackpool

1143 Where's my Little Lad?

1144 Wish You were Here!

1145 Punch and Judy Show

1146 The Tower Crane Machine

(Des M. Dempsey and B. Dare. Litho Questa)

1994 (12 Apr). Centenary of Picture Postcards. Multicoloured One side band (19p.) or two phosphor bands (others). Perf 14×14½.

1815	**1142**	19p. Bather at Blackpool......................	30	30
1816	**1143**	25p. Where's my Little Lad?..................	35	35
1817	**1144**	30p. Wish You were Here!....................	45	45
1818	**1145**	35p. Punch and Judy Show..................	60	60
1819	**1146**	41p. The Tower Crane Machine.............	70	70
Set of 5...			2·25	2·25
Set of 5 Gutter Pairs................................			4·50	
First Day Cover.......................................				2·40
Presentation Pack (PO Pack No. 246)........			2·40	
PHQ Cards (set of 5) (160)......................			1·00	2·40

Special First Day of Issue Postmarks

Philatelic Bureau, Edinburgh.............................	2·50
Blackpool...	2·50

1147 British Lion and French Cockerel over Tunnel

1148 Symbolic Hands over Train

(Des G. Hardie (T **1147**), J.-P. Cousin (T **1148**))

1994 (3 May). Opening of Channel Tunnel. Multicoloured Phosphorised paper. Perf 14×14½.

1820	**1147**	25p. British Lion and French Cockerel....	30	35
		a. Horiz pair. Nos. 1820/1821..............	1·00	1·10
1821	**1148**	25p. Symbolic Hands over Train.............	30	35
1822	**1147**	41p. British Lion and French Cockerel....	50	60
		a. Horiz pair. Nos. 1822/1823.............	1·00	1·75
		ab. Imperf (horiz pair).......................	£1800	
1823	**1148**	41p. Symbolic Hands over Train.............	50	60
Set of 4...			2·25	2·50
First Day Cover.......................................				2·75
First Day Covers (2) (UK and French stamps).........				6·00
Presentation Pack (PO Pack No. 247)........			2·75	

Presentation Pack (UK and French Stamps)........ 15·00
Souvenir Book.. 32·00
PHQ Cards (set of 4) (161)......................... 60 2·50

Nos. 1820/1821 and 1822/1823 were printed together, *se-tenant*, in horizontal pairs throughout the sheets.

Stamps in similar designs were also issued by France. These are included in the joint presentation pack and souvenir book.

Special First Day of Issue Postmarks

Philatelic Bureau, Edinburgh.............................	2·75
Folkestone...	3·00

1149 Groundcrew replacing Smoke Canisters on Douglas Boston of 88 Sqn

1150 HMS *Warspite* (battleship) shelling Enemy Positions

1151 Commandos landing on Gold Beach

1152 Infantry regrouping on Sword Beach

1153 Tank and Infantry advancing, Ouistreham

(Des K. Bassford from contemporary photographs. Litho Questa)

1994 (6 June). 50th Anniversary of D-Day. Multicoloured Two phosphor bands. Perf 14½×14.

1824	**1149**	25p. Groundcrew replacing Smoke Canisters on Douglas Boston..........	35	30
		a. Horiz strip of 5. Nos. 1824/1828.....	2·10	1·75
1825	**1150**	25p. HMS *Warspite* shelling Enemy Positions......................................	35	30
1826	**1151**	25p. Commandos landing on Gold Beach...	35	30
1827	**1152**	25p. Infantry regrouping on Sword Beach...	35	30
1828	**1153**	25p. Tank and Infantry advancing, Ouistreham....................................	35	30
Set of 5...			2·10	1·75
Gutter block of 10..................................			4·25	
First Day Cover.......................................				1·90
Presentation Pack (PO Pack No. 248)........			2·40	
PHQ Cards (set of 5) (162)......................			1·00	1·90

Nos. 1824/1828 were printed together, *se-tenant*, in horizontal strips of five throughout the sheet.

Special First Day of Issue Postmarks

Philatelic Bureau, Edinburgh.............................	2·00
Portsmouth..	2·00

1154 The Old Course, St Andrews

1155 The 18th Hole, Muirfield

1156 The 15th Hole ('Luckyslap'), Carnoustie

1157 The 8th Hole ('The Postage Stamp'), Royal Troon

1158 The 9th Hole, Turnberry

(Des P. Hogarth)

1994 (5 July). Scottish Golf Courses. Multicoloured One phosphor band (19p.) or phosphorised paper (others). Perf 14½×14.

1829	**1154**	19p. The Old Course, St Andrews..........	30	30
1830	**1155**	25p. The 18th Hole, Muirfield................	35	35
1831	**1156**	30p. The 15th Hole ('Luckyslap'), Carnoustie.......................	45	45
1832	**1157**	35p. The 8th Hole ('The Postage Stamp'), Royal Troon.....................	60	60
1833	**1158**	41p. The 9th Hole, Turnberry..................	70	70
Set of 5.............			2·10	2·10
Set of 5 Gutter Pairs.............			4·25	
First Day Cover.............				2·25
Presentation Pack (PO Pack No. 249).............			2·40	
PHQ Cards (set of 5) (163).............			1·00	2·25

Nos. 1829/1833 commemorate the 250th anniversary of golf's first set of rules produced by the Honourable Company of Edinburgh Golfers.

Special First Day of Issue Postmarks
Philatelic Bureau, Edinburgh.. 2·25
Turnberry... 2·50

AMSER HAF/SUMMERTIME *Llanelwedd*
1159 Royal Welsh Show, Llanelwedd

SUMMERTIME *Wimbledon*
1160 All England Tennis Championships, Wimbledon

SUMMERTIME *Cowes*
1161 Cowes Week

SUMMERTIME *Lord's*
1162 Test Match, Lord's

SUMMERTIME *Braemar*
1163 Braemar Gathering

(Des M. Cook)

1994 (2 Aug). The Four Seasons. Summertime. Multicoloured One phosphor band (19p.) or phosphorised paper (others). Perf 15×14.

1834	**1159**	19p. Royal Welsh Show, Llanelwedd......	30	30
1835	**1160**	25p. All England Tennis Championships, Wimbledon..........	35	35
1836	**1161**	30p. Cowes Week.............................	45	45
1837	**1162**	35p. Test Match, Lord's....................	60	60
1838	**1163**	41p. Braemar Gathering.....................	70	70
Set of 5.............			2·10	2·10
Set of 5 Gutter Pairs.............			4·25	
First Day Cover.............				2·25
Presentation Pack (PO Pack No. 250).............			2·40	
PHQ Cards (set of 5) (164).............			1·00	2·25

Special First Day of Issue Postmarks
Philatelic Bureau, Edinburgh.. 2·25
Wimbledon... 2·25

1164 Ultrasonic Imaging

1165 Scanning Electron Microscopy

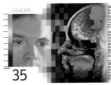

1166 Magnetic Resonance Imaging

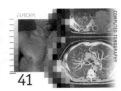

1167 Computed Tomography

(Des P. Vermier and J.-P. Tibbles. Gravure Enschedé)

1994 (27 Sept). Europa. Medical Discoveries. Multicoloured Phosphorised paper. Perf 14×14½.

1839	**1164**	25p. Ultrasonic Imaging.........................	40	40
		a. Imperf (vert pair).......................	£2500	
1840	**1165**	30p. Scanning Electron Microscopy.......	50	50
1841	**1166**	35p. Magnetic Resonance Imaging........	60	60
1842	**1167**	41p. Computed Tomography....................	70	70
Set of 4.............			2·00	2·00
Set of 4 Gutter Pairs.............			4·00	
First Day Cover.............				2·25
Presentation Pack (PO Pack No. 251).............			2·40	
PHQ Cards (set of 4) (165).............			80	2·25

Special First Day of Issue Postmarks
Philatelic Bureau, Edinburgh.. 2·25
Cambridge.. 2·25

1168 Mary and Joseph

1169 Three Wise Men

1170 Mary with Doll   **1171** Shepherds

1172 Angels

(Des Yvonne Gilbert)

1994 (1 Nov). Christmas. Children's Nativity Plays. Multicoloured One phosphor band (19p.) or phosphorised paper (others). Perf 15×14.

1843	**1168**	19p. Mary and Joseph............................	30	30
		a. Imperf (pair)......................................	95·00	
1844	**1169**	25p. Three Wise Men.............................	35	35
1845	**1170**	30p. Mary with Doll...............................	45	45
		a. Imperf (pair)......................................	—	
1846	**1171**	35p. Shepherds......................................	55	60
1847	**1172**	41p. Angels...	65	70
Set of 5..			2·00	2·10
Set of 5 Gutter Pairs...			4·00	
First Day Cover..				2·25
Presentation Pack (PO Pack No. 252)........................			2·25	
PHQ Cards (set of 5) (166)..			1·00	2·25

Special First Day of Issue Postmarks

Philatelic Bureau, Edinburgh..		2·25
Bethlehem, Llandeilo...		2·25

Collectors Pack

1994 (14 Nov). Comprises Nos. 1795/1847.

CP1847a	Collectors Pack (Pack No. 253)...........	27·00	

Post Office Yearbook

1994 (14 Nov). 1795/1799 and 1810/1847 in hardbound book with slip case, illustrated in colour

YB1847a	Yearbook..................................	20·00

1173 Sophie (black cat)

1174 Puskas (Siamese) and Tigger (tabby)

1175 Chloe (ginger cat)

1176 Kikko (tortoiseshell) and Rosie (Abyssinian)

1177 Fred (black and white cat)

(Des Elizabeth Blackadder. Litho Questa)

1995 (17 Jan). Cats. Multicoloured One phosphor band (19p.) or two phosphor bands (others). Perf 14½×14.

1848	**1173**	19p. Sophie...	30	30
1849	**1174**	25p. Puskas and Tigger.........................	40	40
1850	**1175**	30p. Chloe..	50	50
1851	**1176**	35p. Kikko and Rosie.............................	60	60
1852	**1177**	41p. Fred..	70	70
Set of 5..			2·25	2·25
Set of 5 Gutter Pairs...			4·50	
First Day Cover..				2·50
Presentation Pack (PO Pack No. 254)........................			2·50	
PHQ Cards (set of 5) (167)..			1·00	2·50

Special First Day of Issue Postmarks

Philatelic Bureau, Edinburgh..		2·50
Kitts Green..		2·50

1178 Dandelions

1179 Chestnut Leaves

1180 Garlic Leaves

1181 Hazel Leaves

1182 Spring Grass

1995 (14 Mar). The Four Seasons. Springtime. Plant Sculptures by Andy Goldsworthy. Multicoloured One phosphor band (19p.) or two phosphor bands (others). Perf 15×14.

1853	**1178**	19p. Dandelions......................................	30	30
1854	**1179**	25p. Chestnut Leaves.............................	35	35
1855	**1180**	30p. Garlic Leaves.................................	45	45
1856	**1181**	35p. Hazel Leaves..................................	55	55
1857	**1182**	41p. Spring Grass..................................	65	65
Set of 5..			2·00	2·00
Set of 5 Gutter Pairs...			4·00	
First Day Cover..				2·25
Presentation Pack (PO Pack No. 255)........................			2·40	
PHQ Cards (set of 5) (168)..			1·00	2·25

Special First Day of Issue Postmarks

Philatelic Bureau, Edinburgh..		2·40
Springfield...		2·40

1183 *La Danse à la Campagne* (Renoir)

1184 *Troilus and Criseyde* (Peter Brookes)

1185 *The Kiss* (Rodin)

1186 *Girls on the Town* (Beryl Cook)

1187 *Jazz* (Andrew Mockett)

1188 *Girls performing a Kathak Dance* (Aurangzeb period)

1189 *Alice Keppel with her Daughter* (Alice Hughes)

1190 *Children Playing* (L. S. Lowry)

1191 *Circus Clowns* (Emily Firmin and Justin Mitchell)

1192 *Decoration from All the Love Poems of Shakespeare* (Eric Gill)

(Des Newell and Sorrell. Litho Walsall)

1995 (21 Mar). Greetings Stamps. Greetings in Art. Multicoloured Two phosphor bands. Perf 14½×14 (with one elliptical hole in each vertical side).

1858	1183	(1st) *La Danse à la Campagne*................	1·20	1·00
		a. Booklet pane. Nos. 1858/1867.......	13·50	
		ab. Silver (Queen's head and '1ST') and phosphor omitted..................	£5000	
1859	1184	(1st) *Troilus and Criseyde*....................	1·20	1·00
1860	1185	(1st) *The Kiss*..................................	1·20	1·00
1861	1186	(1st) *Girls on the Town*....................	1·20	1·00
1862	1187	(1st) *Jazz*..	1·20	1·00
1863	1188	(1st) *Girls performing a Kathak Dance*.....	1·20	1·00
1864	1189	(1st) *Alice Keppel with her Daughter*.......	1·20	1·00
1865	1190	(1st) *Children Playing*....................	1·20	1·00
1866	1191	(1st) *Circus Clowns*.......................	1·20	1·00
1867	1192	(1st) *Decoration from All the Love Poems of Shakespeare*.......	1·20	1·00
Set of 10..			10·50	9·00
First Day Cover..				9·25
Presentation Pack (PO Pack No. G4)...................			13·50	
PHQ Cards (set of 10) (GS3)...............................			2·00	9·25

Nos. 1858/1867 were issued in £2·50 stamp booklet, No. KX7 (*sold at £2·60 from 8 July 1996*), together with a pane of 20 half stamp-sized labels.

The stamps and labels were attached to the booklet cover by a common gutter margin.

No. 1858ab exists on first day covers bearing the Philatelic Bureau Edinburgh First Day of Issue postmark.

Special First Day of Issue Postmarks

Philatelic Bureau, Edinburgh...............................	9·25
Lover..	9·25

1193 Fireplace Decoration, Attingham Park, Shropshire

1194 Oak Seedling

1195 Carved Table Leg, Attingham Park

1196 St David's Head, Dyfed, Wales

1197 Elizabethan Window, Little Moreton Hall, Cheshire

(Des T. Evans)

1995 (11–25 Apr). Centenary of The National Trust. Multicoloured One phosphor band (19p.), two phosphor bands (25p., 35p.) or phosphorised paper (30p., 41p.). Perf 14×15.

1868	1193	19p. Fireplace Decoration.......................	30	30
1869	1194	25p. Oak Seedling..................................	35	35
		a. Booklet pane. No. 1869×6 with margins all round (25.4.96)............	2·00	
1870	1195	30p. Carved Table Leg...........................	45	45
1871	1196	35p. St David's Head.............................	55	55
1872	1197	41p. Elizabethan Window.......................	65	65
Set of 5..			2·00	2·00
Set of 5 Gutter Pairs...			4·00	
First Day Cover..				2·25
Presentation Pack (PO Pack No. 256)...................			2·40	
PHQ Cards (set of 5) (169)..................................			1·00	2·25

Booklet pane No. 1869a comes from the £6 National Trust booklet No. DX17.

Special First Day of Issue Postmarks

Philatelic Bureau, Edinburgh...............................	2·40
Alfriston...	2·40

1198 British Troops and French Civilians celebrating

1199 Symbolic Hands and Red Cross

1200 St Paul's Cathedral and Searchlights

1201 Symbolic Hand releasing Peace Dove

1202 Symbolic Hands

(Des J. Gorham (Nos. 1873, 1875), J-M. Folon (others))

1995 (2 May). Europa. Peace and Freedom. Multicoloured One phosphor band (Nos. 1873/1874) or two phosphor bands (others). Perf 14½×14.

1873	**1198**	19p. British Troops and French Civilians celebrating..........................	35	35
1874	**1199**	19p. Symbolic Hands and Red Cross......	35	35
1875	**1200**	25p. St Paul's Cathedral and Searchlights.................................	45	45
1876	**1201**	25p. Symbolic Hand releasing Peace Dove..................................	45	45
		a. Imperf (vert pair)............................	—	
1877	**1202**	30p. Symbolic Hands.........................	60	60
		Set of 5...	2·00	2·00
		Set of 5 Gutter Pairs...........................	4·00	
		First Day Cover...................................		2·25
		Presentation Pack (PO Pack No. 257)......	2·40	
		PHQ Cards (set of 5) (170)...................	60	2·25

Nos. 1873 and 1875 commemorate the 50th anniversary of the end of the Second World War.

No. 1874 commemorate the 125th anniversary of the British Red Cross Society.

For No. 1875 with the face value expressed as '1st' see No. **MS**2547.

Nos. 1876/1877 commemorate the 50th anniversary of the United Nations.

Nos. 1876/1877 include the EUROPA emblem.

Special First Day of Issue Postmarks

Philatelic Bureau, Edinburgh...	2·40
London SW..	2·40

A First Day of Issue handstamp (pictorial) was provided at London EC4 for this issue.

1203 *The Time Machine*

1204 *The First Men in the Moon*

1205 *The War of the Worlds*

1206 *The Shape of Things to Come*

(Des Siobhan Keaney. Litho Questa)

1995 (6 June). Science Fiction. Novels by H. G. Wells. Multicoloured Two phosphor bands. Perf 14½×14.

1878	**1203**	25p. *The Time Machine*..............................	40	40
1879	**1204**	30p. *The First Men in the Moon*.................	50	50
1880	**1205**	35p. *The War of the Worlds*......................	60	60
1881	**1206**	41p. *The Shape of Things to Come*...........	70	70
		Set of 4...	2·00	2·00
		Set of 4 Gutter Pairs.............................	4·00	
		First Day Cover...................................		2·25
		Presentation Pack (PO Pack No. 258)......	2·40	
		PHQ Cards (set of 4) (171)...................	50	2·25

Nos. 1878/1881 commemorate the centenary of publication of Wells's *The Time Machine*.

Special First Day of Issue Postmarks

Philatelic Bureau, Edinburgh...	2·40
Wells..	2·40

1207 The Swan, 1595

1208 The Rose, 1592

1209 The Globe, 1599

1210 The Hope, 1613

1211 The Globe, 1614

(Des C. Hodges. Litho Walsall)

1995 (8 Aug). Reconstruction of Shakespeare's Globe Theatre. Multicoloured Two phosphor bands. Perf 14½.

1882	**1207**	25p. The Swan, 1595.............................	40	30
		a. Horiz strip of 5. Nos. 1882/1886.....	2·00	2·25
1883	**1208**	25p. The Rose, 1592.............................	40	30
1884	**1209**	25p. The Globe, 1599............................	40	30
1885	**1210**	25p. The Hope, 1613.............................	40	30
1886	**1211**	25p. The Globe, 1614............................	40	30
		Set of 5...	2·00	2·25
		Gutter Strip of 10.................................	4·00	
		First Day Cover...................................		2·40
		Presentation Pack (PO Pack No. 259)......	2·40	
		PHQ Cards (set of 5) (172)...................	1·00	2·40

Nos. 1882/1886 were issued together, *se-tenant*, in horizontal strips of five throughout the sheet with the backgrounds forming a composite design.

Special First Day of Issue Postmarks

Philatelic Bureau, Edinburgh...	2·50
Stratford-upon-Avon...	2·50

1212 Sir Rowland Hill and Uniform Penny Postage Petition

1213 Hill and Penny Black

1214 Guglielmo Marconi and Early Wireless

1215 Marconi and Sinking of *Titanic* (liner)

(Des The Four Hundred, Eng C. Slania. Recess and litho Harrison)

1995 (5 Sept). Pioneers of Communications. Multicoloured One phosphor band (19p.) or phosphorised paper (others). Perf 14½×14.

1887	**1212**	19p. Sir Rowland Hill and Uniform Penny Postage Petition....................	40	40
1888	**1213**	25p. Hill and Penny Black......................	50	50
		a. Silver (Queen's head and face value) omitted................................	£550	
1889	**1214**	41p. Guglielmo Marconi and Early Wireless..............................	65	65
1890	**1215**	60p. Marconi and Sinking of *Titanic* (liner)......................	75	75
Set of 4...			2·10	2·10
Set of 4 Gutter Pairs...			4·25	
First Day Cover...				2·25
Presentation Pack (PO Pack No. 260)....................			2·50	
PHQ Cards (set of 4) (173).................................			80	2·25

Nos. 1887/1888 mark the birth bicentenary of Sir Rowland Hill. Nos. 1889/1890 the centenary of the first radio transmissions.

Special First Day of Issue Postmarks

Philatelic Bureau, Edinburgh...	2·25
London EC...	2·25

HAROLD WAGSTAFF
RUGBY LEAGUE 1895-1995
1216 Harold Wagstaff

GUS RISMAN
RUGBY LEAGUE 1895-1995
1217 Gus Risman

JIM SULLIVAN
RUGBY LEAGUE 1895-1995
1218 Jim Sullivan

BILLY BATTEN
RUGBY LEAGUE 1895-1995
1219 Billy Batten

BRIAN BEVAN
RUGBY LEAGUE 1895-1995
1220 Brian Bevan

(Des C. Birmingham)

1995 (3 Oct). Centenary of Rugby League. Multicoloured One phosphor band (19p.) or two phosphor bands (others). Perf 14½×14.

1891	**1216**	19p. Harold Wagstaff..............................	30	30
1892	**1217**	25p. Gus Risman....................................	35	35
1893	**1218**	30p. Jim Sullivan...................................	45	45
1894	**1219**	35p. Billy Batten....................................	55	55
1895	**1220**	41p. Brian Bevan...................................	65	65
Set of 5...			2·10	2·10
Set of 5 Gutter Pairs...			4·25	
First Day Cover...				2·25
Presentation Pack (PO Pack No. 261)....................			2·40	
PHQ Cards (set of 5) (174).................................			1·00	2·25

Special First Day of Issue Postmarks

Philatelic Bureau, Edinburgh...	2·25
Huddersfield...	2·25

A First Day of Issue handstamp (pictorial) was provided at Headingly, Leeds for this issue.

1221 European Robin in Mouth of Pillar Box

1222 European Robin on Railings and Holly

1223 European Robin on Snow-covered Milk Bottles

1224 European Robin on Road Sign

1225 European Robin on Door Knob and Christmas Wreath

(Des K. Lilly)

1995 (30 Oct). Christmas. Christmas Robins. Multicoloured One phosphor band (19p.) or two phosphor bands (others). Perf 15×14.

1896	**1221**	19p. Robin in Mouth of Pillar Box...........	30	30
1897	**1222**	25p. Robin on Railings.........................	35	40
1898	**1223**	30p. Robin on Milk Bottles....................	50	55
1899	**1224**	41p. Robin on Road Sign.......................	60	65
1900	**1225**	60p. Robin on Door Knob......................	75	80
Set of 5...			2·25	2·50
Set of 5 Gutter Pairs...			4·50	
First Day Cover...				2·75
Presentation Pack (PO Pack No. 262)....................			2·50	
PHQ Cards (set of 5) (175).................................			1·00	2·75

The 19p. value was re-issued on 3 October 2000 in sheets of 20, each with a *se-tenant* label showing Christmas greetings (*sold for* £3·99) (No. LS2) or a personal photograph (*sold for* £7·99). These sheets were printed in gravure by Questa and were sold by the Philatelic Bureau and selected philatelic outlets.

Similar sheets were available from 9 October 2001 when the price for a personalised version was increased to £8·75. These could also be purchased, on an experimental basis, from photo-booths at six post offices.

Special First Day of Issue Postmarks

Philatelic Bureau, Edinburgh...	2·90
Bethlehem, Llandeilo...	2·90

Year Pack

1995 (30 Oct). Comprises Nos. 1848/1900.

CP1900*a*	Year Pack (Pack No. 263).......................	25·00

Post Office Yearbook

1995 (30 Oct). Comprises Nos. 1848/1857 and 1868/1900 in hardback book with slip case, illustrated in colour

YB1900*a*	Yearbook...	20·00

1226 Opening Lines of *To a Mouse* and Fieldmouse

1227 *O my Luve's like a red, red rose* and Wild Rose

1228 *Scots, wha hae wi Wallace bled* and Sir William Wallace

1229 *Auld Lang Syne* and Highland Dancers

(Des Tayburn Design Consultancy. Litho Questa)

1996 (25 Jan). Death Bicentenary of Robert Burns (Scottish poet) . Multicoloured One phosphor band (19p.) or two phosphor bands (others). Perf 14½.

1901	**1226**	19p. Opening Lines of *To a Mouse* and Fieldmouse......	40	40
1902	**1227**	25p. *O my Luve's like a red, red rose* and Wild Rose......	50	50
1903	**1228**	41p. *Scots, wha hae wi Wallace bled* and Sir William Wallace............	65	70
1904	**1229**	60p. *Auld Lang Syne* and Highland Dancers.........	75	80
Set of 4.........			2·00	2·25
Set of 4 Gutter Pairs.........			4·00	
First Day Cover.........				2·40
Presentation Pack (PO Pack No. 264).........			2·40	
PHQ Cards (set of 4) (176).........			80	2·40

Special First Day of Issue Postmarks

Philatelic Bureau, Edinburgh.........		2·50
Dumfries.........		2·50

1230 'MORE! LOVE' (Mel Calman)

1231 'Sincerely' (Charles Barsotti)

1232 'Do you have something for the HUMAN CONDITION?' (Leo Cullum)

1233 'MENTAL FLOSS' (Mel Calman)

1234 '4.55 P.M.' (Charles Barsotti)

1235 'Dear lottery prize winner' (Larry)

1236 'I'm writing to you because....' (Mel Calman)

1237 'FETCH THIS, FETCH THAT' (Charles Barsotti)

1238 'My day starts before I'm ready for it' (Mel Calman)

1239 'THE CHEQUE IN THE POST' (Jack Ziegler)

(Des M. Wolff. Litho Walsall)

1996 (26 Feb–11 Nov). Greetings Stamps. Cartoons. Multicoloured 'All over' phosphor. Perf 14½×14 (with one elliptical hole in each vertical side).

1905	**1230**	(1st) 'MORE! LOVE'.........	1·20	1·00
		a. Booklet pane. Nos. 1905/1914......	13·50	

		p. Two phosphor bands (11.11.96).....	2·50	2·50
		pa. Booklet pane. Nos. 1905p/1914p..	24·00	24·00
1906	**1231**	(1st) 'Sincerely'.........	1·20	1·00
		p. Two phosphor bands (11.11.96).....	2·50	2·50
1907	**1232**	(1st) 'Do you have something for the HUMAN CONDITION?'.........	1·20	1·00
		p. Two phosphor bands (11.11.96).....	2·50	2·50
1908	**1233**	(1st) 'MENTAL FLOSS'.........	1·20	1·00
		p. Two phosphor bands (11.11.96).....	2·50	2·50
1909	**1234**	(1st) '4.55 P.M.'.........	1·20	1·00
		p. Two phosphor bands (11.11.96).....	2·50	2·50
1910	**1235**	(1st) 'Dear lottery prize winner'.........	1·20	1·00
		p. Two phosphor bands (11.11.96).....	2·50	2·50
1911	**1236**	(1st) 'I'm writing to you because....'.........	1·20	1·00
		p. Two phosphor bands (11.11.96).....	2·50	2·50
1912	**1237**	(1st) 'FETCH THIS, FETCH THAT'.........	1·20	1·00
		p. Two phosphor bands (11.11.96).....	2·50	2·50
1913	**1238**	(1st) 'My day starts before I'm ready for it' (Mel Calman).........	1·20	1·00
		p. Two phosphor bands (11.11.96).....	2·50	2·50
1914	**1239**	(1st) 'THE CHEQUE IN THE POST' (Jack Ziegler).........	1·20	1·00
		p. Two phosphor bands (11.11.96).....	2·50	2·50
Set of 10 (Nos. 1905/1914).........			10·50	9·00
Set of 10 (Nos. 1905p/1914p).........			24·00	24·00
First Day Cover (Nos. 1905/1914).........				9·50
Presentation Pack (PO Pack No. G5) (Nos. 1905/1914)....			13·50	
PHQ Cards (set of 10) (GS4).........			2·00	9·50

Nos. 1905/1914 were issued in £2·50 stamp booklets, Nos. KX8/KX8a (sold at £2·60 from 8 July 1996), together with a pane of 20 half stamp-sized labels. The stamps and labels were attached to the booklet cover by a common gutter margin.

These designs were re-issued on 18 December 2001 in sheets of ten, each with a *se-tenant* label showing cartoon comments (sold for £2·95) (No. LS6). They were re-issued again on 29 July 2003 in sheets of 20 (sold for £6·15) containing two of each design, each stamp accompanied by a half stamp-size label showing a crossword grid (clues printed on the bottom sheet margin) (No. LS13). Sheets of 20 with personal photographs on the labels and a crossword puzzle in the bottom sheet margin were also available, at £14·95 a sheet from Royal Mail, Edinburgh and Post Office philatelic outlets, or £15 a sheet from photo-booths.

All these sheets were printed in lithography by Questa with two phosphor bands and perforated 14½×14 (without elliptical holes), and were available from the philatelic bureau and other selected philatelic outlets.

Special First Day of Issue Postmarks

Philatelic Bureau, Edinburgh.........	9·50
Titterhill, Haytons Bent, Ludlow.........	9·50

1240 'Muscovy Duck'

1241 'Lapwing'

1242 'White-fronted Goose'

1243 'Bittern'

1244 'Whooper Swan'

(Des Moseley Webb)

1996 (12 Mar). 50th Anniversary of the Wildfowl and Wetlands Trust. Bird Paintings by C. F. Tunnicliffe. Multicoloured One phosphor band (19p.) or phosphorised paper (others). Perf 14×14½.

1915	**1240**	19p. 'Muscovy Duck'.........	30	30
1916	**1241**	25p. 'Lapwing'.........	35	35

1917	**1242**	30p. 'White-fronted Goose'......................	45	45
1918	**1243**	35p. 'Bittern'......................................	55	55
1919	**1244**	41p. 'Whooper Swan'...........................	65	65
Set of 5...			2·10	2·10
Set of 5 Gutter Pairs..........................			4·25	
First Day Cover...................................				2·40
Presentation Pack (PO Pack No. 265)......			2·50	
PHQ Cards (set of 5) (177)..................			1·00	2·40

Special First Day of Issue Postmarks

Philatelic Bureau, Edinburgh.........................	2·50
Slimbridge, Gloucester...............................	2·75

1245 The Odeon, Harrogate

1246 Laurence Olivier and Vivien Leigh in *Lady Hamilton* (film)

1247 Old Cinema Ticket

1248 Pathé News Still

1249 Cinema Sign, The Odeon, Manchester

(Des The Chase, Gravure Harrison)

1996 (16 Apr). Centenary of Cinema. Multicoloured One phosphor band (19p.) or two phosphor bands (others). Perf 14×14½.

1920	**1245**	19p. The Odeon, Harrogate....................	30	30
1921	**1246**	25p. Laurence Olivier and Vivien Leigh in *Lady Hamilton*............................	35	35
1922	**1247**	30p. Old Cinema Ticket.........................	45	45
1923	**1248**	35p. Pathé News Still...........................	60	60
1924	**1249**	41p. Cinema Sign, The Odeon, Manchester........................	70	70
Set of 5...			2·25	2·25
Set of 5 Gutter Pairs..........................			4·50	
First Day Cover...................................				2·40
Presentation Pack (PO Pack No. 266)......			2·50	
PHQ Cards (set of 5) (178)..................			1·00	2·40

Special First Day of Issue Postmarks

Philatelic Bureau, Edinburgh.........................	2·50
London, WC2...	2·50

1250 Dixie Dean

1251 Bobby Moore

1252 Duncan Edwards

1253 Billy Wright

1254 Danny Blanchflower

(Des H. Brown. Litho Questa)

1996 (14 May). European Football Championship. Multicoloured One phosphor band (19p.) or two phosphor bands (others). Perf 14½×14.

1925	**1250**	19p. Dixie Dean......................................	30	30
		a. Booklet pane. No. 1925×4 with margins all round...........................	1·50	
1926	**1251**	25p. Bobby Moore..................................	40	40
		a. Booklet pane. No. 1926×4 with margins all round...........................	2·00	
1927	**1252**	35p. Duncan Edwards..............................	50	50
		a. Booklet pane. Nos. 1927/1929, each×2, with margins all round......	3·50	
1928	**1253**	41p. Billy Wright....................................	60	60
1929	**1254**	60p. Danny Blanchflower........................	90	90
Set of 5...			2·50	2·50
Set of 5 Gutter Pairs..........................			5·00	
First Day Cover...................................				2·75
Presentation Pack (PO Pack No. 267)......			2·75	
PHQ Cards (set of 5) (179)..................			1·00	2·75

Booklet panes Nos. 1925a, 1926a and 1927a come from the £6·48 European Football Championship booklet, No. DX18.

Special First Day of Issue Postmarks

Philatelic Bureau, Edinburgh...........................	2·75
Wembley...	2·75

1255 Athlete on Starting Blocks

1256 Javelin

1257 Basketball

1258 Swimming

1259 Athlete celebrating and Olympic Rings

(Des N. Knight. Litho Questa)

1996 (9 July). Olympic and Paralympic Games, Atlanta. Multicoloured Two phosphor bands. Perf 14½×14.

1930	**1255**	26p. Athlete on Starting Blocks..............	30	30
		a. Horiz strip of 5. Nos. 1930/1934.....	2·00	2·10
1931	**1256**	26p. Javelin...	30	30
1932	**1257**	26p. Basketball.....................................	30	30
1933	**1258**	26p. Swimming......................................	30	30

1934 **1259** 26p. Athlete celebrating and Olympic
Rings 30 30
Set of 5.. 2·00 2·10
Gutter Strip of 10... 4·00
First Day Cover.. 2·50
Presentation Pack (PO Pack No. 268)................ 2·50
PHQ Cards (set of 5) (180)................................ 1·00 2·50
Nos. 1930/1934 were printed together, *se-tenant*, in horizontal strips of
five throughout the sheet.
For these designs with face value expressed as '1st' see No. **MS**2554.

Special First Day of Issue Postmarks

Philatelic Bureau, Edinburgh.. 2·50
Much Wenlock.. 2·75

1260 Professor Dorothy   **1261** Dame Margot
Hodgkin (scientist)   Fonteyn (ballerina)

1262 Dame Elisabeth Frink   **1263** Dame Daphne du
(sculptress)   Maurier (novelist)

1264 Dame Marea
Hartman (sports
administrator)

(Des Stephanie Nash Gravure Harrison)

1996 (6 Aug). Europa. Famous Women. Multicoloured One phosphor band
(20p.) or two phosphor bands (others). Perf 14½.
1935 **1260** 20p. Professor Dorothy Hodgkin............ 30 30
1936 **1261** 26p. Dame Margot Fonteyn..................... 35 35
     a. Imperf (horiz pair)........................... £400
1937 **1262** 31p. Dame Elisabeth Frink..................... 50 50
1938 **1263** 37p. Dame Daphne du Maurier.............. 60 60
1939 **1264** 43p. Dame Marea Hartman..................... 70 70
Set of 5.. 2·25 2·25
Set of 5 Gutter Pairs.. 4·50
First Day Cover.. 2·50
Presentation Pack (PO Pack No. 269)................ 2·75
PHQ Cards (set of 5) (181)................................ 1·00 2·50
Nos. 1936/1937 include the EUROPA emblem.

Special First Day of Issue Postmarks

Philatelic Bureau, Edinburgh.. 2·50
Fowey.. 2·75

1265 *Muffin the Mule*   **1266** *Sooty*

1267 *Stingray*   **1268** *The Clangers*

1269 *Dangermouse*

(Des Tutssels. Gravure Harrison (No. 1940a) or Enschedé (others))

1996 (3 Sept)–**97**. 50th Anniversary of Children's Television. Multicoloured
One phosphor band (20p.) or two phosphor bands (others). Perf
14½×14.
1940 **1265** 20p. *Muffin the Mule*............................. 30 30
     a. Perf 15×14 (23.9.97)......................... 65 65
     ab. Booklet pane. No. 1940a×4 with
       margins all round........................... 2·75
1941 **1266** 26p. *Sooty*... 35 35
1942 **1267** 31p. *Stingray*.. 50 50
1943 **1268** 37p. *The Clangers*................................ 60 60
1944 **1269** 43p. *Dangermouse*.............................. 70 70
Set of 5.. 2·25 2·25
Set of 5 Gutter Pairs.. 4·50
First Day Cover.. 2·75
Presentation Pack (PO Pack No. 270)................ 3·00
PHQ Cards (set of 5) (182)................................ 1·00 2·75
Booklet pane No. 1940ab comes from the 1997 £6·15 BBC stamp booklet,
No. DX19.

Special First Day of Issue Postmarks

Philatelic Bureau, Edinburgh.. 2·75
Alexandra Palace, London.. 2·75

1270 Triumph TR3   **1271** MG TD

1272 Austin-Healey 100   **1273** Jaguar XK120

1274 Morgan Plus 4

(Des S. Clay. Gravure Harrison)

1996 (1 Oct). Classic Sports Cars. Multicoloured One phosphor band (20p.)
or two phosphor bands (others). Perf 14½.
1945 **1270** 20p. Triumph TR3.................................... 30 30
1946 **1271** 26p. MG TD... 50 50
     a. Imperf (pair)..................................... £2500
1947 **1272** 37p. Austin-Healey 100.......................... 60 65
     a. Imperf (pair)..................................... £900

1948	**1273**	43p. Jaguar XK120	70	75
		a. Imperf (horiz pair)	£1400	
1949	**1274**	63p. Morgan Plus 4	90	95
Set of 5			2·75	3·00
Set of 5 Gutter Pairs			5·50	
First Day Cover				3·25
Presentation Pack (PO Pack No. 271)			3·00	
PHQ Cards (set of 5) (183)			1·00	3·25

On Nos. 1946/1949 the right-hand phosphor band on each stamp is three times the width of that on the left.

Special First Day of Issue Postmarks

| Philatelic Bureau, Edinburgh | 3·25 |
| Beaulieu, Brockenhurst | 3·25 |

A pictorial First Day of Issue handstamp was provided at London E1 for this issue.

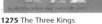

1275 The Three Kings

1276 The Annunciation

1277 The Journey to Bethlehem

1278 The Nativity

1279 The Shepherds

(Des Laura Stoddart, Gravure Harrison)

1996 (28 Oct). Christmas. Multicoloured One phosphor band (2nd) or two phosphor bands (others). Perf 15×14.

1950	**1275**	(2nd) The Three Kings	60	35
1951	**1276**	(1st) The Annunciation	70	55
1952	**1277**	31p. The Journey to Bethlehem	50	65
1953	**1278**	43p. The Nativity	50	75
1954	**1279**	63p. The Shepherds	70	95
Set of 5			2·75	3·00
Set of 5 Gutter Pairs			5·50	
First Day Cover				3·25
Presentation Pack (PO Pack No. 272)			3·25	
PHQ Cards (set of 5) (184)			1·00	3·25

Special First Day of Issue Postmarks

| Philatelic Bureau, Edinburgh | 3·00 |
| Bethlehem, Llandeilo | 3·00 |

Year Pack

1996 (28 Oct). Comprises Nos. 1901/1954.

| CP1954*a* | Year Pack (Pack No. 273) | 27·50 |

Post Office Yearbook

1996 (28 Oct). Comprises Nos. 1901/1904 and 1915/1954 in hardback book with slip case, illustrated in colour

| YB1954*a* | Yearbook | 21·00 |

1280 *Gentiana acaulis* (Georg Ehret)

1281 *Magnolia grandiflora* (Ehret)

1282 *Camellia japonica* (Alfred Chandler)

1283 *Tulipa* (Ehret)

1284 *Fuchsia, Princess of Wales* (Augusta Withers)

1285 *Tulipa gesneriana* (Ehret)

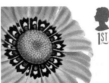

1286 *Gazania splendens* (Charlotte Sowerby)

1287 *Iris latifolia* (Ehret)

1288 *Hippeastrum rutilum* (Pierre-Joseph Redouté)

1289 *Passiflora caerulea* (Ehret)

(Des Tutssels. Litho Walsall)

1997 (6 Jan). Greeting Stamps. 19th-century Flower Paintings. Multicoloured Two phosphor bands. Perf 14½×14 (with one elliptical hole in each vertical side).

1955	**1280**	(1st) *Gentiana acaulis*	1·20	1·00
		a. Booklet pane. Nos. 1955/1964	13·50	
		ab. Gold, blue-green and phosphor omitted	—	
1956	**1281**	(1st) *Magnolia grandiflora*	1·20	1·00
1957	**1282**	(1st) *Camellia japonica*	1·20	1·00
1958	**1283**	(1st) *Tulipa*	1·20	1·00
1959	**1284**	(1st) Fuchsia, Princess of Wales	1·20	1·00
1960	**1285**	(1st) *Tulipa gesneriana*	1·20	1·00
1961	**1286**	(1st) *Gazania splendens*	1·20	1·00
1962	**1287**	(1st) *Iris latifolia*	1·20	1·00
1963	**1288**	(1st) *Hippeastrum rutilum*	1·20	1·00
1964	**1289**	(1st) *Passiflora caerulea*	1·20	1·00
Set of 10			10·50	9·00
First Day Cover				9·50
Presentation Pack (PO Pack No. G6)			13·50	
PHQ Cards (set of 10) (GS5)			2·00	9·50

Nos. 1955/1964 were issued in £2·60 stamp booklets Nos. KX9/KX12 together with a pane of 20 half-sized labels. The stamps and labels were attached to the booklet cover by a common gutter margin.

Nos. 1955/1964 were re-issued on 21 January 2003 in se-tenant sheets of 20, each accompanied by a label showing further flowers (*sold at* £5·95) (No. LS11) or personal photographs (*sold at* £14·95). These stamps were printed in lithography by Questa and are without elliptical holes in the perforations.

For booklet stamps in designs as Nos. 1955, 1958 and 1962 and perforated 15×14, printed by Enschedé see Nos. 2463/2465.

See also Nos. 2942/2943.

Special First Day of Issue Postmarks

| Philatelic Bureau, Edinburgh | 9·50 |
| Kew, Richmond, Surrey | 9·50 |

1290 King Henry VIII

1291 Catherine of Aragon

1292 Anne Boleyn

1293 Jane Seymour

1294 Anne of Cleves

1295 Catherine Howard

1296 Catherine Parr

(Des Kate Stephens from contemporary paintings. Gravure Harrison)

1997 (21 Jan). 450th Death Anniversary of King Henry VIII. Multicoloured Two phosphor bands. Perf 15 (No. 1965) or 14×15 (others).

1965	**1290**	26p. King Henry VIII	50	50
		a. Imperf (vert pair)	£3500	
1966	**1291**	26p. Catherine of Aragon	50	50
		a. Horiz strip of 6. Nos. 1966/1971	3·00	3·00
1967	**1292**	26p. Anne Boleyn	50	50
1968	**1293**	26p. Jane Seymour	50	50
1969	**1294**	26p. Anne of Cleves	50	50
1970	**1295**	26p. Catherine Howard	50	50
1971	**1296**	26p. Catherine Parr	50	50
Set of 7			3·25	3·25
Set of 1 Gutter Pair and a Gutter Strip of 12			6·50	
First Day Cover				3·75
Presentation Pack (PO Pack No. 274)			4·75	
PHQ Cards (set of 7) (185)			1·40	3·75

Nos. 1966/1971 were printed together, se-tenant, in horizontal strips of six throughout the sheet.

Special First Day of Issue Postmarks

Philatelic Bureau, Edinburgh		3·75
Hampton Court, East Molesey		4·00

1297 St Columba in Boat

1298 St Columba on Iona

1299 St Augustine with King Ethelbert

1300 St Augustine with Model of Cathedral

(Des Claire Melinsky. Gravure Enschedé)

1997 (11 Mar). Religious Anniversaries. Multicoloured Two phosphor bands. Perf 14½.

1972	**1297**	26p. St Columba in Boat	40	40
		a. Imperf (pair)	£950	
1973	**1298**	37p. St Columba on Iona	60	60
1974	**1299**	43p. St Augustine with King Ethelbert	80	85
1975	**1300**	63p. St Augustine with Model of Cathedral	90	95
Set of 4			2·50	2·50
Set of 4 Gutter Pairs			5·00	
First Day Cover				3·00
Presentation Pack (PO Pack No. 275)			3·25	
PHQ Cards (set of 4) (186)			80	3·00

Nos. 1972/1973 commemorate the 1400th death anniversary of St Columba.

Nos. 1974/1975 the 1400th anniversary of the arrival of St Augustine of Canterbury in Kent.

Special First Day of Issue Postmarks

Philatelic Bureau, Edinburgh		3·00
Isle of Iona		3·00

For Nos. 1976/1977, Types **1301**/**1302**, see Decimal Machin Definitives section.

Nos. 1978/1979 are vacant.

1303 Dracula

1304 Frankenstein

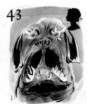

1305 Dr Jekyll and Mr Hyde

1306 The Hound of the Baskervilles

(Des I. Pollock. Gravure Walsall)

1997 (13 May). Europa. Tales and Legends. Horror Stories. Multicoloured Two phosphor bands. Perf 14×15.

1980	**1303**	26p. Dracula	40	40
1981	**1304**	31p. Frankenstein	55	60
1982	**1305**	37p. Dr Jekyll and Mr Hyde	70	75

1983	**1306**	43p. *The Hound of the Baskervilles*............	80	85
		Set of 4...	2·25	2·40
		Set of 4 Gutter Pairs...	4·50	
		First Day Cover..		2·75
		Presentation Pack (PO Pack No. 276).................	3·00	
		PHQ Cards (set of 4) (187).................................	80	2·75

Nos. 1980/1983 commemorate the birth bicentenary of Mary Shelley (creator of Frankenstein) with the 26p. and 31p. values incorporating the EUROPA emblem.

Each value has features printed in fluorescent ink which are visible under ultraviolet light.

Special First Day of Issue Postmarks

Philatelic Bureau, Edinburgh..	2·75
Whitby...	2·75

1307 Reginald Mitchell and Supermarine Spitfire MkIIA

1308 Roy Chadwick and Avro Lancaster MkI

1309 Ronald Bishop and de Havilland Mosquito B MkXVI

1310 George Carter and Gloster Meteor T Mk7

1311 Sir Sydney Camm and Hawker Hunter FGA Mk9

(Des Turner Duckworth, Gravure Harrison)

1997 (10 June). British Aircraft Designers. Multicoloured One phosphor band (20p.) or two phosphor bands (others). Perf 15×14.

1984	**1307**	20p. Reginald Mitchell and Supermarine Spitfire MkIIA............	40	40
1985	**1308**	26p. Roy Chadwick and Avro Lancaster MkI...	50	50
1986	**1309**	37p. Ronald Bishop and de Havilland Mosquito B MkXVI..........................	60	60
1987	**1310**	43p. George Carter and Gloster Meteor T Mk7...................................	80	80
1988	**1311**	63p. Sir Sydney Camm and Hawker Hunter FGA Mk9.............................	90	90
		Set of 5...	3·00	3·00
		Set of 5 Gutter Pairs...	6·00	
		First Day Cover..		3·25
		Presentation Pack (PO Pack No. 277).................	3·50	
		PHQ Cards (set of 5) (188).................................	1·00	3·25

See also No. 2868.

Special First Day of Issue Postmarks

Philatelic Bureau, Edinburgh..	3·50
Duxford, Cambridge...	3·50

1312 Carriage Horse and Coachman

1313 Lifeguards Horse and Trooper

1314 Blues and Royals Drum Horse and Drummer

1315 Duke of Edinburgh's Horse and Groom

(Des J.-L. Benard. Litho Walsall)

1997 (8 July). All the Queen's Horses. 50th Anniversary of the British Horse Society. Multicoloured One phosphor band (20p.) or two phosphor bands (others). Perf 14½.

1989	**1312**	20p. Carriage Horse and Coachman.......	40	40
1990	**1313**	26p. Lifeguards Horse and Trooper........	55	60
1991	**1314**	43p. Blues and Royals Drum Horse and Drummer......................................	70	75
1992	**1315**	63p. Duke of Edinburgh's Horse and Groom...	85	85
		Set of 4...	2·25	2·50
		Set of 4 Gutter Pairs...	4·50	
		First Day Cover..		2·75
		Presentation Pack (PO Pack No. 278).................	3·00	
		PHQ Cards (set of 4) (189).................................	50	2·75

Special First Day of Issue Postmarks

Philatelic Bureau, Edinburgh..	2·75
Windsor, Berks..	2·75

1315a Caernarfon Castle

1315b Edinburgh Castle

1315c Carrickfergus Castle

1315d Windsor Castle

CASTLE

Harrison plates (Nos. 1611/1614)

CASTLE

Enschedé plates (Nos. 1993/1996)

Differences between Harrison and Enschedé printings:

Harrison: 'C' has top serif and tail of letter points to right. 'A' has flat top. 'S' has top and bottom serifs.

Enschedé: 'C' has no top serif and tail of letter points upwards. 'A' has pointed top. 'S' has no serifs.

There are numerous other differences between the work of the two printers, but as the word 'CASTLE' is common to all values we have confined the comparison to that area of the stamps.

(Des from photos by Prince Andrew, Duke of York. Eng Inge Madle Recess (Queen's head by silk screen process) Enschedé)

1997 (29 July). Designs as Nos. 1611/1614 with Queen's head in silhouette as T **1044**, but re-engraved with differences in inscription as shown above. Perf 15×14 (with one elliptical hole in each vertical side).

1993	**1315a**	£1·50 Caernarfon Castle (maroon and gold†)..	12·00	6·00
		a. Gold (Queen's head) omitted........	—	£950

1994	**1315b**	£2 Edinburgh Castle (indigo and gold†)...........	14·00	2·25
		a. Gold (Queen's head) omitted.......	£550	
1995	**1315c**	£3 Carrickfergus Castle (violet and gold†)...........	30·00	3·50
		a. Gold (Queen's head) omitted.......	£2800	
1996	**1315d**	£5 Windsor Castle (deep brown and gold†)...........	35·00	10·00
		a. Gold (Queen's head) omitted.......	£4000	
Set of 4...........			80·00	18·00
Set of 4 Gutter Pairs (vert or horiz)...........			£175	
Presentation Pack (PO Pack No. 40)...........			£150	

† The Queen's head on these stamps is printed in optically variable ink which changes colour from gold to green when viewed from different angles.

No. 1996a occurs on R. 5/8 and 6/8 from some sheets.

There was no official Royal Mail first day cover service provided for Nos. 1993/1996.

See also Nos. 1410/1413 and 1611/1614.

1316 Haroldswick, Shetland

1317 Painswick, Gloucestershire

1318 Beddgelert, Gwynedd

1319 Ballyroney, County Down

(Des T. Millington. Gravure Enschedé)

1997 (12 Aug). Sub-Post Offices. Multicoloured One phosphor band (20p.) or two phosphor bands (others). Perf 14½.

1997	**1316**	20p. Haroldswick, Shetland...........	40	40
1998	**1317**	26p. Painswick, Gloucestershire...........	55	60
1999	**1318**	43p. Beddgelert, Gwynedd...........	70	75
2000	**1319**	63p. Ballyroney, County Down...........	85	85
Set of 4...........			2·25	2·40
Set of 4 Gutter Pairs...........			4·50	
First Day Cover...........				2·75
Presentation Pack (PO Pack No. 279)...........			3·00	
PHQ Cards (set of 4) (190)...........			80	2·75

Nos. 1997/2000 were issued on the occasion of the Centenary of the National Federation of Sub-Postmasters.

Special First Day of Issue Postmarks

Philatelic Bureau, Edinburgh...........	2·75
Wakefield...........	2·75

PRINTERS. Harrison and Sons Ltd became De La Rue Security Print on 8 September 1997. This was not reflected in the sheet imprints until mid-1998.

Enid Blyton's *Noddy*
1320 Noddy

Enid Blyton's *Famous Five*
1321 Famous Five

Enid Blyton's *Secret Seven*
1322 Secret Seven

Enid Blyton's *Faraway Tree*
1323 Faraway Tree

Enid Blyton's *Malory Towers*
1324 Malory Towers

(Des C. Birmingham. Gravure Enschedé)

1997 (9 Sept). Birth Centenary of Enid Blyton (children's author). Multicoloured One phosphor band (20p.) or two phosphor bands (others). Perf 14×14½.

2001	**1320**	20p. Noddy...........	30	30
2002	**1321**	26p. Famous Five...........	50	50
2003	**1322**	37p. Secret Seven...........	55	60
2004	**1323**	43p. Faraway Tree...........	65	70
2005	**1324**	63p. Malory Towers...........	75	80
Set of 5...........			2·50	2·75
Set of 5 Gutter Pairs...........			5·00	
First Day Cover...........				3·00
Presentation Pack (PO Pack No. 280)...........			3·00	
PHQ Cards (set of 5) (191)...........			1·00	3·00

Special First Day of Issue Postmarks

Philatelic Bureau, Edinburgh...........	3·25
Beaconsfield...........	3·25

1325 Children and Father Christmas pulling Cracker

1326 Father Christmas with Traditional Cracker

1327 Father Christmas riding Cracker

1328 Father Christmas on Snowball

1329 Father Christmas and Chimney

(Des J. Gorham and M. Thomas (1st), J. Gorham (others) Gravure Harrison)

1997 (27 Oct). Christmas. 150th Anniversary of the Christmas Cracker. Multicoloured One phosphor band (2nd) or two phosphor bands (others). Perf 15×14.

2006	**1325**	(2nd) Children and Father Christmas pulling Cracker	90	35
		a. Imperf (pair)	£1400	
2007	**1326**	(1st) Father Christmas with Traditional Cracker	1·20	55
2008	**1327**	31p. Father Christmas riding Cracker	50	60
		a. Imperf (pair)	£1500	
2009	**1328**	43p. Father Christmas on Snowball	50	70
2010	**1329**	63p. Father Christmas and Chimney	70	80
Set of 5			3·25	2·75
Set of 5 Gutter Pairs			6·50	
First Day Cover				3·00
Presentation Pack (PO Pack No. 282)			4·00	
PHQ Cards (set of 5) (192)			1·00	3·00

The 1st value was re-issued on 3 October 2000 in sheets of ten, each with a *se-tenant* label showing Christmas greetings (*sold for £2·95*) (No. LS3) or a personal photograph (*sold for £5·95*). These sheets were printed in gravure by Questa and were sold by the Philatelic Bureau and selected philatelic outlets.

Similar sheets were available from 9 October 2001 when the price for the personalised version was increased to £12·95 for two sheets. These could also be purchased, on an experimental basis, from photo-booths situated at six post offices.

From 1 October 2002 the size of the sheet was increased to 20 either with greetings labels (*sold for £5·95*) (No. LS10) or personal photographs (*sold for £14·95*). These stamps were printed by Questa in lithography and perforated 14½×14.

Special First Day of Issue Postmarks

Philatelic Bureau, Edinburgh		3·00
Bethlehem, Llandeilo		3·00

20 **ENDANGERED SPECIES**
Common dormouse
Muscardinus avellanarius
1332 Common Dormouse

26 **ENDANGERED SPECIES**
Lady's slipper orchid
Cypripedium calceolus
1333 Lady's Slipper Orchid

31 **ENDANGERED SPECIES**
Song thrush
Turdus philomelos
1334 Song Thrush

37 **ENDANGERED SPECIES**
Shining ram's-horn snail
Segmentina nitida
1335 Shining Ram's-horn Snail

1330 Wedding Photograph, 1947

1331 Queen Elizabeth II and Prince Philip, 1997

(Des D. Driver (20p., 43p.), Lord Snowdon (26p., 63p.) Gravure Harrison)

1997 (13 Nov). Royal Golden Wedding. One phosphor band (20p.) or two phosphor bands (others). Perf 15.

2011	**1330**	20p. Wedding Photograph, 1947. Gold, yellow-brown and grey-black	40	40
		a. Imperf (pair)	£3000	
		b. Face value omitted	£4750	
2012	**1331**	26p. Queen Elizabeth II and Prince Philip, 1997. Multicoloured	60	60
		a. Imperf (vert pair)	£2500	
2013	**1330**	43p. Wedding Photograph, 1947. Gold, bluish green and grey-black	1·10	1·10
2014	**1331**	63p. Queen Elizabeth II and Prince Philip, 1997. Multicoloured	1·50	1·50
Set of 4			3·25	3·25
Set of 4 Gutter Pairs			6·50	
First Day Cover				3·50
Presentation Pack (PO Pack No. 281)			3·75	
PHQ Cards (set of 4) (193)			80	3·50

For 26p. and (1st) Machin printed in gold, see Nos. 1672, Y1692, 2295, U2942, U2948/U2952, U2958, U2964/U2968, U3002 and U3015.

Special First Day of Issue Postmarks

Philatelic Bureau, Edinburgh		3·50
London, SW1		3·75

Year Pack

1997 (13 Nov). Comprises Nos. 1965/1975, 1980/1992 and 1997/2014.

CP2014a	Year Pack (Pack No. 283)	32·00

Post Office Yearbook

1997 (13 Nov). Comprises Nos. 1965/1975, 1980/1992 and 1997/2014 in hardback book with slip case

YB2014a	Yearbook	26·00

43 **ENDANGERED SPECIES**
Mole cricket
Gryllotalpa gryllotalpa
1336 Mole Cricket

63 **ENDANGERED SPECIES**
Devil's bolete
Boletus satanas
1337 Devil's Bolete

(Des R. Maude. Litho Questa)

1998 (20 Jan). Endangered Species. Multicoloured One side phosphor band (20p.) or two phosphor bands (others). Perf 14×14½.

2015	**1332**	20p. Common Dormouse	40	40
2016	**1333**	26p. Lady's Slipper Orchid	50	50
2017	**1334**	31p. Song Thrush	60	60
2018	**1335**	37p. Shining Ram's-horn Snail	70	70
2019	**1336**	43p. Mole Cricket	85	85
2020	**1337**	63p. Devil's Bolete	1·00	1·00
Set of 6			3·75	3·75
Set of 6 Gutter Pairs			7·50	
First Day Cover				4·00
Presentation Pack (PO Pack No. 284)			4·25	
PHQ Cards (set of 6) (194)			1·25	4·00

Special First Day of Issue Postmarks

Philatelic Bureau, Edinburgh		4·25
Selborne, Alton		4·25

1338 Diana, Princess of Wales (photo by Lord Snowdon)

1339 At British Lung Foundation Function, April 1997 (photo by John Stillwell)

1340 Wearing Tiara, 1991 (photo by Lord Snowdon)

1341 On Visit to Birmingham, October 1995 (photo by Tim Graham)

1342 In Evening Dress, 1987 (photo by Terence Donovan)

(Des B. Robinson. Gravure Harrison)

1998 (3 Feb). Diana, Princess of Wales Commemoration. Multicoloured Two phosphor bands. Perf 14×15.

2021	**1338**	26p. Diana, Princess of Wales.................	50	30
		a. Horiz strip of 5. Nos. 2021/2025.....	2·00	2·00
		ab. Imperf (horiz strip of 5. Nos. 2021/2025)........................	£12000	
		ac. Imperf (horiz strip of 4. Nos. 2021/2024)........................	—	
		ad. Imperf (horiz strip of 3. Nos. 2021/2023)........................	£3750	
2022	**1339**	26p. At British Lung Foundation Function, April 1997................	50	30
2023	**1340**	26p. Wearing Tiara, 1991................	50	30
2024	**1341**	26p. On Visit to Birmingham, October 1995................	50	30
2025	**1342**	26p. In Evening Dress, 1987................	50	30
Set of 5................			2·00	2·00
Gutter Strip of 10................			4·00	
First Day Cover................				3·00
Presentation Pack (unnumbered)................			8·00	
Presentation Pack (Welsh)................			60·00	

Nos. 2021/2025 were printed together, *se-tenant*, in horizontal strips of five throughout the sheet.

No. 2021ac shows No. 2025 perforated at right only.

In addition to the generally issued Presentation Pack a further pack with all text printed in English and Welsh was available.

Special First Day of Issue Postmarks

Philatelic Bureau, Edinburgh................	3·00
Kensington, London................	3·00

1343 Lion of England and Griffin of Edward III

1344 Falcon of Plantagenet and Bull of Clarence

1345 Lion of Mortimer and Yale of Beaufort

1346 Greyhound of Richmond and Dragon of Wales

1347 Unicorn of Scotland and Horse of Hanover

(Des J. Matthews. Recess and litho Harrison)

1998 (24 Feb). 650th Anniversary of the Order of the Garter. The Queen's Beasts. Multicoloured Two phosphor bands. Perf 15×14.

2026	**1343**	26p. Lion of England and Griffin of Edward III................	50	30
		a. Horiz strip of 5. Nos. 2026/2030.....	2·25	2·25
		ab. Missing green (on Nos. 2026, 2028/2029) (horiz strip of 5)...........	—	
		Eay. Horiz strip of 5. Phosphor omitted	25·00	
2027	**1344**	26p. Falcon of Plantagenet and Bull of Clarence................	50	30
2028	**1345**	26p. Lion of Mortimer and Yale of Beaufort................	50	30
2029	**1346**	26p. Greyhound of Richmond and Dragon of Wales................	50	30
		a. Silver (Queen's head and value omitted)................	—	
2030	**1347**	26p. Unicorn of Scotland and Horse of Hanover................	50	30
Set of 5................			2·25	2·25
Gutter Block of 10................			4·50	
First Day Cover................				2·75
Presentation Pack (PO Pack No. 285)................			2·50	
PHQ Cards (set of 5) (195)................			1·00	2·75

Nos. 2026/2030 were printed together, *se-tenant*, in horizontal strips of five throughout the sheet.

The phosphor bands on Nos. 2026/2030 are only half the height of the stamps and do not cover the silver parts of the designs.

Special First Day of Issue Postmarks

Philatelic Bureau, Edinburgh................	2·75
London SW1................	2·75

1348   **1348a**

1348b

(Des G. Knipe, adapted Dew Gibbons Design Group. Gravure Walsall)

1998 (10 Mar). As T **157** (Wilding Definitive of 1952–1954) but with face values in decimal currency as T **1348**. One side phosphor band (20p.) or two phosphor bands (others). Perf 14 (with one elliptical hole in each vertical side).

2031	**1348**	20p. light green (1 band at right)........	40	40
		a. Band at left................	40	40
		b. Booklet pane. Nos. 2031/2031a each×3 with margins all round....	2·50	
		c. Booklet pane. Nos. 2031/2031a and 2032/2033, all×2, and central label with margins all round........................	4·50	
2032	**1348a**	26p. red-brown................	50	50
		a. Booklet pane. No. 2032×9 with margins all round................	3·25	
		b. Booklet pane. Nos. 2032/2033, each×3 with margins all round....	4·25	
2033	**1348b**	37p. light purple................	1·10	1·10
Set of 3 (cheapest)................			1·90	1·90
First Day Cover (No. 2031c)................				4·75

Nos. 2031/2033 were only issued in the 1998 £7·49 Wilding Definitives stamp booklet No. DX20.

For further Wilding designs with decimal face values and on paper watermarked W **1565** see Nos. 2258/2259, **MS**2326, **MS**2367, 2378/2379, and 3329.

Special First Day of Issue Postmarks

Philatelic Bureau, Edinburgh................	4·75
London SW1................	4·75

1349 St John's Point Lighthouse, County Down

1350 Smalls Lighthouse, Pembrokeshire

1351 Needles Rock Lighthouse, Isle of Wight, *circa* 1900

1352 Bell Rock Lighthouse, Arbroath, mid-19th-century

1353 Original Eddystone Lighthouse, Plymouth, 1698

(Des D. Davis and J. Boon. Litho Questa)

1998 (24 Mar). Lighthouses. Multicoloured One side phosphor band (20p.) or two phosphor bands (others). Perf 14½×14.

2034	**1349**	20p. St John's Point Lighthouse.............	40	40
2035	**1350**	26p. Smalls Lighthouse...........................	50	50
2036	**1351**	37p. Needles Rock Lighthouse................	60	60
2037	**1352**	43p. Bell Rock Lighthouse......................	80	80
2038	**1353**	63p. Original Eddystone Lighthouse......	90	90
Set of 5...			3·00	3·00
Set of 5 Gutter Pairs.......................................			6·00	
First Day Cover..				3·25
Presentation Pack (PO Pack No. 286)....................			3·50	
PHQ Cards (set of 5) (196).................................			1·00	3·25

Nos. 2034/2038 commemorate the 300th anniversary of the first Eddystone Lighthouse and the final year of manned lighthouses.

Special First Day of Issue Postmarks

Philatelic Bureau, Edinburgh..	3·50
Plymouth..	3·50

For Nos. 2039/2040 see Decimal Machin Definitives section.

1354 Tommy Cooper

1355 Eric Morecambe

1356 Joyce Grenfell

1357 Les Dawson

1358 Peter Cook

(Des G. Scarfe. Litho Walsall)

1998 (23 Apr). Comedians. Multicoloured One side phosphor band (20p.) or two phosphor bands (others). Perf 14½×14.

2041	**1354**	20p. Tommy Cooper...............................	40	40
		a. Vermilion printed double..................		£850
		b. Vermilion and black both printed quadruple with rose-pink and new blue both printed double.......	†	£1300
		c. Vermilion and black both printed double..	†	£1100
2042	**1355**	26p. Eric Morecambe..............................	50	50
		a. Vermilion printed double..............	£400	
		b. Vermilion printed triple..................	£600	
		c. Black printed double, vermilion printed triple....................................	£1000	
		d. Black and vermilion printed triple..	£1000	
		e. Vermilion and black both printed quadruple..........................		
2043	**1356**	37p. Joyce Grenfell................................	60	60
2044	**1357**	43p. Les Dawson....................................	80	80
2045	**1358**	63p. Peter Cook.....................................	90	90
		a. Vermilion printed triple...................	†	—
Set of 5...			3·00	3·00
Set of 5 Gutter Pairs.......................................			6·00	
First Day Cover..				3·25
Presentation Pack (PO Pack No. 287)...................			3·50	
PHQ Cards (set of 5) (197).................................			1·00	3·25

Stamps as T **1356**, but with a face value of 30p., were prepared but not issued. Mint examples and a first day cover have been reported (*Price* £1800).

On No. 2045a the red can appear double and the black also shows slight doubling. It is only known on the first day cover.

Special First Day of Issue Postmarks

Philatelic Bureau, Edinburgh..	3·50
Morecambe..	3·50

1359 Hands forming Heart

1360 Adult and Child holding Hands

1361 Hands forming Cradle

1362 Hand taking Pulse

(Des V. Frost from photos by A. Wilson. Litho Questa)

1998 (23 June). 50th Anniversary of the National Health Service. Multicoloured One side phosphor band (20p.) or two phosphor bands (others). Perf 14×14½.

2046	**1359**	20p. Hands forming Heart......................	40	40
2047	**1360**	26p. Adult and Child holding Hands......	50	50

2048	**1361**	43p. Hands forming Cradle......................	80	80
2049	**1362**	63p. Hand taking Pulse...........................	90	90
		Set of 4...	2·25	2·25
		Set of 4 Gutter Pairs.................................	4·50	
		First Day Cover...		2·75
		Presentation Pack (PO Pack No. 288)...........	2·75	
		PHQ Cards (set of 4) (198)..........................	50	2·50

Special First Day of Issue Postmarks

Philatelic Bureau, Edinburgh..........................		2·75
Tredegar, Wales..		2·75

1363 *The Hobbit* (J. R. R. Tolkien)

1364 *The Lion, The Witch and the Wardrobe* (C. S. Lewis)

1365 *The Phoenix and the Carpet* (E. Nesbit)

1366 *The Borrowers* (Mary Norton)

1367 *Through the Looking Glass* (Lewis Carroll)

(Des P. Malone. Gravure D.L.R.)

1998 (21 July). Famous Children's Fantasy Novels. Multicoloured One centre phosphor band (20p.) or two phosphor bands (others). Perf 15×14.

2050	**1363**	20p. *The Hobbit*..	35	35
2051	**1364**	26p. *The Lion, The Witch and the Wardrobe*...................................	45	45
		a. Imperf (pair).....................................	£1100	
2052	**1365**	37p. *The Phoenix and the Carpet*..............	60	60
2053	**1366**	43p. *The Borrowers*..................................	80	80
2054	**1367**	63p. *Through the Looking Glass*.................	90	90
		Set of 5...	3·00	3·00
		Set of 5 Gutter Pairs.................................	6·00	
		First Day Cover...		3·25
		Presentation Pack (PO Pack No. 289)...........	3·25	
		PHQ Cards (set of 5) (199)..........................	1·00	3·25

Nos. 2050/2054 commemorate the birth centenary of C. S. Lewis and the death centenary of Lewis Carroll.

The PHQ card showing the T **1363** design is known incorrectly inscribed 'Tolkein'.

Special First Day of Issue Postmarks

Philatelic Bureau, Edinburgh..........................		3·50
Oxford...		3·50

1368 Woman in Yellow Feathered Costume

1369 Woman in Blue Costume and Headdress

1370 Group of Children in White and Gold Robes

1371 Child in Tree Costume

(Des T. Hazael. Gravure Walsall)

1998 (25 Aug). Europa. Festivals. Notting Hill Carnival. Multicoloured One centre phosphor band (20p.) or two phosphor bands (others). Perf 14×14½.

2055	**1368**	20p. Woman in Yellow Feathered Costume...	40	40
		a. Imperf (pair)....................................	£950	
2056	**1369**	26p. Woman in Blue Costume and Headdress...	60	60
2057	**1370**	43p. Group of Children in White and Gold Robes.....................................	75	75
2058	**1371**	63p. Child in Tree Costume.....................	1·00	1·00
		Set of 4...	2·50	2·50
		Set of 4 Gutter Pairs.................................	5·00	
		First Day Cover...		3·00
		Presentation Pack (PO Pack No. 290)...........	2·75	
		PHQ Cards (set of 4) (200)..........................	80	3·00

The 20p. and 26p. incorporate the EUROPA emblem.

Special First Day of Issue Postmarks

Philatelic Bureau, Edinburgh..........................		3·00
London W11...		3·00

1372 Sir Malcolm Campbell's *Bluebird*, 1925

1373 Sir Henry Segrave's *Sunbeam*, 1926

1374 John G. Parry Thomas's *Babs*, 1926

1375 John R. Cobb's *Railton Mobil Special*, 1947

1376 Donald Campbell's *Bluebird CN7*, 1964

(Des Roundel Design Group. Gravure Walsall (Nos. 2059a/2059ac) or De La Rue (others))

1998 (29 Sept–13 Oct). British Land Speed Record Holders. Multicoloured One phosphor band (20p.) or two phosphor bands (others). Perf 15×14.

2059	**1372**	20p. Sir Malcolm Campbell's *Bluebird*....	30	30
		a. Perf 14½×13½ (1 side band at right) (13.10.98)...............................	75	75
		ab. Band at left......................................	75	75
		ac. Booklet pane. Nos. 2059a and 2059ab, each×2, with margins all round..	3·25	

2060	**1373**	26p. Sir Henry Segrave's *Sunbeam*..........	40	40
		a. Rosine (face value) omitted............	£2000	
		b. '2' from face value omitted.............	£1100	
		c. '6' from face value omitted.............	£1100	
2061	**1374**	30p. John G. Parry Thomas's *Babs*..........	60	60
2062	**1375**	43p. John R. Cobb's *Railton Mobil*		
		Special..	80	80
2063	**1376**	63p. Donald Campbell's *Bluebird CN7*....	90	90
Set of 5...			2·75	2·75
Set of 5 Gutter Pairs...			5·50	
First Day Cover..				3·00
Presentation Pack (PO Pack No. 291).................			3·25	
PHQ Cards (set of 5) (201)..................................			1·00	3·00

Nos. 2059/2063 commemorate the 50th death anniversary of Sir Malcolm Campbell.

Nos. 2060a/2060c occur on the fourth vertical row of several sheets. Other examples show one or other of the figures partially omitted.

Nos. 2059/2059ac come from the £6·16 British Land Speed Record Holders stamp booklet, No. DX21, and were printed by Walsall.

There are minor differences of design between No. 2059 (sheet stamp printed by De La Rue) and Nos. 2059a/2059ab (booklet stamps printed by Walsall), which omit the date and copyright symbol.

Trials with different face values, and an alternative photograph of the *Railton Mobil Special* are known.

Each stamp also has in large yellow or silver numerals the record speed attained. (*Prices from £500 each*)

Special First Day of Issue Postmarks

Philatelic Bureau, Edinburgh...	3·00
Pendine..	3·00

The mis-spelling 'PHILALETIC' in the Bureau datestamp was later corrected; same price, either spelling.

1377 Angel with Hands raised in Blessing

1378 Angel praying

1379 Angel playing Flute

1380 Angel playing Lute

1381 Angel praying

(Des Irene von Treskow. Gravure De La Rue)

1998 (2 Nov). Christmas. Angels. Multicoloured One centre phosphor band (20p.) or two phosphor bands (others). Perf 15×14.

2064	**1377**	20p. Angel with Hands raised in		
		Blessing..	35	35
		a. Imperf (pair)................................	£400	
2065	**1378**	26p. Angel praying...............................	45	45
		a. Imperf (pair)................................	£1500	
2066	**1379**	30p. Angel playing Flute......................	60	60
		a. Imperf (pair)................................	£500	
2067	**1380**	43p. Angel playing Lute........................	80	80
		a. Imperf (pair)................................	£2000	
2068	**1381**	63p. Angel praying...............................	90	90
Set of 5...			2·75	2·75
Set of 5 Gutter Pairs...			5·50	
First Day Cover..				3·00
Presentation Pack (PO Pack No. 292).................			3·25	
PHQ Cards (set of 5) (202)..................................			60	3·00

Special First Day of Issue Postmarks

Philatelic Bureau, Edinburgh...	3·00
Bethlehem...	3·00

Year Pack

1998 (2 Nov). Comprises Nos. 2015/2030, 2034/2038 and 2041/2068.

CP2068a	Year Pack (Pack No. 293)......................	40·00

Post Office Yearbook

1998 (2 Nov). Comprises Nos. 2015/2030, 2034/2038 and 2041/2068 in hardback book with slip case

YB2068a	Yearbook...	35·00

MILLENNIUM SERIES: Consecutive 1999 designs are numbered downwards from 1999/1948 to 1999/1991. 2000 designs are numbered upwards from 2000/2001 to 2000/2048.

1382 Greenwich Meridian and Clock (John Harrison's chronometer)

1383 Industrial Worker and Blast Furnace (James Watt's discovery of steam power)

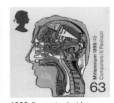

1384 Early Photos of Leaves (Henry Fox-Talbot's photographic experiments)

1385 Computer inside Human Head (Alan Turing's work on computers)

(Des D. Gentleman (20p.), P. Howson (26p.), Z. and Barbara Baran (43p.), E. Paolozzi (63p.), gravure, Questa (63p. No. 2072a), Enschedé (20p.) or De La Rue (others))

1999 (12 Jan–21 Sept). Millennium Series. The Inventors' Tale. Multicoloured One centre phosphor band (20p.) or two phosphor bands (others). P 14×14½.

2069	**1382**	20p. Greenwich Meridian and Clock......	40	40
		a. Imperf (horiz pair)...........................	£1500	
2070	**1383**	26p. Industrial Worker and Blast		
		Furnace...	60	60
2071	**1384**	43p. Early Photographs of Leaves...........	80	80
2072	**1385**	63p. Computer inside Human Head.......	1·00	1·00
		a. Perf 13½×14 (21.9.99)......................	1·75	1·75
		ab. Booklet pane. No. 2072a×4 with		
		margins all round............................	7·50	
Set of 4...			2·50	2·50
Set of 4 Gutter Pairs...			5·00	
First Day Cover (Philatelic Bureau) (Type J, see				
Introduction)...				4·25
First Day Cover (Greenwich, London SE)............				4·25
Presentation Pack (PO Pack No. 294).................			3·25	
PHQ Cards (set of 4) (203)..................................			80	2·75

No. 2072a comes from the £6·99 World Changers booklet, No. DX23.

1386 Airliner hugging Globe (International air travel)

1387 Woman on Bicycle (Development of the bicycle)

1388 Victorian Railway Station (Growth of public transport)

1389 Captain Cook and Maori (Captain James Cook's voyages)

1395 Dove and Norman Settler (medieval migration to Scotland)

1396 Pilgrim Fathers and Native American (17th-century migration to America)

(Des G. Hardie (20p.), Sara Fanelli (26p.), J. Lawrence (43p.), A. Klimowski (63p.). Gravure Enschedé (20p., 63p.) or De La Rue (26p.). Litho Enschedé (43p.))

1999 (2 Feb). Millennium Series. The Travellers' Tale. Multicoloured One centre phosphor band (20p.) or two phosphor bands (others). Perf 14×14½.

2073	**1386**	20p. Airliner hugging Globe	40	40
2074	**1387**	26p. Woman on Bicycle	60	60
2075	**1388**	43p. Victorian Railway Station	80	80
2076	**1389**	63p. Captain Cook and Maori	1·00	1·00
		Set of 4	2·50	2·50
		Set of 4 Gutter Pairs	5·00	
		First Day Cover (Philatelic Bureau) (Type J, see Introduction)		3·25
		First Day Cover (Coventry)		3·25
		Presentation Pack (PO Pack No. 295)	3·25	
		PHQ Cards (set of 4) (204)	80	3·25

For Nos. 2077/2079, T **1390**, see Decimal Machins Definitive section

1391 Vaccinating Child (pattern in cow markings) (Jenner's development of smallpox vaccine)

1392 Patient on Trolley (nursing care)

1397 Sailing Ship and Aspects of Settlement (19th-century migration to Australia)

1398 Hummingbird and Superimposed Stylised Face (20th-century migration to Great Britain)

(Des J. Byrne (20p.), W. McLean (26p.), J. Fisher (43p.), G. Powell (63p.). Litho (20p.) or gravure (others) Walsall))

1999 (6 Apr–12 May). Millennium Series. The Settlers' Tale. Multicoloured One centre phosphor band (20p.) or two phosphor bands (others). Perf 14×14½.

2084	**1395**	20p. Dove and Norman Settler	40	40
2085	**1396**	26p. Pilgrim Fathers and Native American	60	60
		a. Booklet pane. Nos. 2085 and 2089 with margins all round (12.5.99)	3·00	
2086	**1397**	43p. Sailing Ship and Aspects of Settlement	80	80
2087	**1398**	63p. Hummingbird and Superimposed Stylised Face	1·00	1·00
		Set of 4	2·50	2·50
		Set of 4 Gutter Pairs	5·00	
		First Day Cover (Philatelic Bureau) (Type J, see Introduction)		3·25
		First Day Cover (Plymouth)		3·25
		Presentation Pack (PO Pack No. 297)	3·25	
		PHQ Cards (set of 4) (206)	80	3·25

No. 2085a comes from the £2·60 booklet, No. HBA1.
Imperf pairs of Nos. 2085 and 2089 are known and believed to be of proof status (Price £750).
Imperf pairs of No. 2085 with silver and phosphor omitted are known and believed to be of proof status (Price £350).
Imperf pairs of No. 2086 are known with gold, chocolate and phosphor omitted and believed to be of proof status (Price £350).

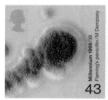

1393 Penicillin Mould (Fleming's discovery of penicillin)

1394 Sculpture of Test Tube Baby (development of in-vitro fertilisation)

(Des P. Brookes (20p.), Susan Macfarlane (26p.), M. Dempsey (43p.), A. Gormley (63p.). Gravure Questa)

1999 (2 Mar–21 Sept). Millennium Series. The Patients' Tale. Multicoloured One centre phosphor band (20p.) or two phosphor bands (others). Perf 13½×14.

2080	**1391**	20p. Vaccinating Child	40	40
		a. Booklet pane. No. 2080×4 with margins all round (21.9.99)	1·60	
2081	**1392**	26p. Patient on Trolley	60	60
		a. Imperf (pair)	£2500	
2082	**1393**	43p. Penicillin Mould	80	80
2083	**1394**	63p. Sculpture of Test-tube Baby	1·00	1·00
		Set of 4	2·50	2·50
		Set of 4 Gutter Pairs	5·00	
		First Day Cover (Philatelic Bureau) (Type J, see Introduction)		3·25
		First Day Cover (Oldham)		3·25
		Presentation Pack (PO Pack No. 296)	3·25	
		PHQ Cards (set of 4) (205)	80	3·25

No. 2080a comes from the £6·99 World Changers booklet, No. DX23.

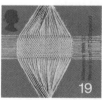

1399 Woven Threads (woollen industry)

1400 Salts Mill, Saltaire (worsted cloth industry)

1401 Hull on Slipway (shipbuilding)

1402 Lloyd's Building (City of London finance centre)

(Des P. Collingwood (19p.), D. Hockney (26p.), B. Sanderson (44p.), B. Neiland (64p.). Litho (19p.) or gravure (others) De La Rue)

1999 (4 May). Millennium Series. The Workers' Tale. Multicoloured One centre phosphor band (19p.) or two phosphor bands (others). Perf 14×14½.

2088	**1399**	19p. Woven Threads..................................	40	40
		a. Bronze (Queen's head) omitted......	£500	
		ay. Bronze and phosphor omitted.......	£500	
2089	**1400**	26p. Salts Mill, Saltaire............................	60	60
2090	**1401**	44p. Hull on Slipway..............................	80	80
2091	**1402**	64p. Lloyd's Building..............................	1·00	1·00
		Set of 4...	2·50	2·50
		Set of 4 Gutter Pairs..............................	5·00	

First Day Cover (Philatelic Bureau) (Type J, see Introduction).. 3·25
First Day Cover (Belfast)... 3·25
Presentation Pack (PO Pack No. 298)............. 3·25
PHQ Cards (set of 4) (207).......................... 80 3·25

For No. 2089, printed by Walsall in photogravure, see booklet pane No. 2085a.

1403 Freddie Mercury (lead singer of Queen) (Popular Music)

1404 Bobby Moore with World Cup, 1966 (Sport)

1405 Dalek from *Dr Who* (science-fiction series) (Television)

1406 Charlie Chaplin (film star) (Cinema)

(Des P. Blake (19p.), M. White (26p.), Lord Snowdon (44p.), R. Steadman (64p.). Gravure Enschedé)

1999 (1 June). Millennium Series. The Entertainers' Tale. Multicoloured One centre phosphor band (19p.) or two phosphor bands (others). Perf 14×14½.

2092	**1403**	19p. Freddie Mercury.............................	40	40
2093	**1404**	26p. Bobby Moore with World Cup........	60	60
2094	**1405**	44p. Dalek from *Dr Who*.......................	80	80
2095	**1406**	64p. Charlie Chaplin..............................	1·00	1·00
		Set of 4...	2·50	2·50
		Set of 4 Gutter Pairs..............................	5·00	

First Day Cover (Philatelic Bureau) (Type J, see Introduction).. 3·25
First Day Cover (Wembley).......................... 3·25
Presentation Pack (PO Pack No. 299)............. 3·25
PHQ Cards (set of 4) (208).......................... 80 3·25

1407   **1408**

Prince Edward and Miss Sophie Rhys-Jones (from photos by John Swannell)

(Adapted J. Gibbs. Gravure De La Rue)

1999 (15 June). Royal Wedding. Multicoloured Two phosphor bands. Perf 15×14.

2096	**1407**	26p. Prince Edward and Miss Sophie Rhys-Jones.......................................	40	40
		a. Imperf (pair)...................................	£900	
2097	**1408**	64p. Prince Edward and Miss Sophie Rhys-Jones.......................................	1·00	1·00
		Set of 2...	1·25	1·25
		Set of 2 Gutter Pairs..............................	2·50	

First Day Cover (Philatelic Bureau)....................................... 2·00
First Day Cover (Windsor)... 2·00
Presentation Pack (PO Pack No. M01)............. 2·00
PHQ Cards (set of 2) (PSM1)....................... 40 2·00

1409 Suffragette behind Prison Window (Equal Rights for Women)

1410 Water Tap (Right to Health)

1411 Generations of School Children (Right to Education)

1412 'MAGNA CARTA' (Human Rights)

(Des Natasha Kerr (19p.), M. Craig-Martin (26p.), A. Drummond (44p.), A. Kitching (64p.). Gravure De La Rue)

1999 (6 July). Millennium Series. The Citizens' Tale. Multicoloured One centre phosphor band (19p.) or two phosphor bands (others). Perf 14×14½.

2098	**1409**	19p. Suffragette behind Prison Window..	40	40
2099	**1410**	26p. Water Tap......................................	60	60
2100	**1411**	44p. Generations of School Children.....	80	80
2101	**1412**	64p. 'MAGNA CARTA'.............................	1·00	1·00
		Set of 4...	2·50	2·50
		Set of 4 Gutter Pairs..............................	5·00	

First Day Cover (Philatelic Bureau) (Type J, see Introduction).. 3·25
First Day Cover (Newtown, Powis)................. 3·25
Presentation Pack (PO Pack No. 300)............. 3·25
PHQ Cards (set of 4) (209).......................... 80 3·25

1413 Molecular Structures (DNA Decoding)

1414 Galapagos Finch and Fossilised Skeleton (Darwin's Theory of Evolution)

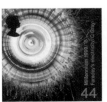
1415 Rotation of Polarised Light by Magnetism (Faraday's work on Electricity)

1416 Saturn (development of astronomical telescopes)

(Des M. Curtis (19p.), R. Harris Ching (26p.), C. Gray (44p.), from Hubble Space Telescope photograph (64p.). Gravure (19p., 64p.) or litho (26p., 44p.) Questa)

1999 (3 Aug–21 Sept). Millennium Series. The Scientists' Tale. Multicoloured One centre phosphor band (19p.) or two phosphor bands (others). Perf 13½×14 (19p., 64p.) or 14×14½ (26p., 44p.).

2102	**1413**	19p. Molecular Structures......................	40	40
2103	**1414**	26p. Galapagos Finch and Fossilised Skeleton................................	60	60
		a. Imperf (pair)................................	£575	
		b. Perf 14½×14 (21.9.99)....................	1·50	1·50
		ba. Booklet pane. No. 2103b×4 with margins all round..........................	6·50	
2104	**1415**	44p. Rotation of Polarised Light by Magnetism...........................	80	80
		a. Perf 14½×14 (21.9.99)....................	1·50	1·50
		ab. Booklet pane. No. 2104a×4 with margins all round...........................	6·50	
2105	**1416**	64p. Saturn.......................................	1·00	1·00
	Set of 4...		2·50	2·50
	Set of 4 Gutter Pairs.....................................		5·00	

First Day Cover (Philatelic Bureau) (Type J, see Introduction).. 3·25
First Day Cover (Cambridge)...................................... 3·25
Presentation Pack (PO Pack No. 301)...................... 3·25
PHQ Cards (set of 4) (210)............................ 80 3·25

Nos. 2103b and 2104a come from the £6·99 World Changers booklet, No. DX23.

1416a Solar Eclipse

1999 (11 Aug). Solar Eclipse. Sheet 89×121 mm. Multicoloured. Two phosphor bands. Perf 14×14½.

MS2106 Type **1416a** (sold at £2·56)......................	11·00	11·00
a. Imperf...................................	£4000	

First Day Cover (Philatelic Bureau)............................ 11·50
First Day Cover (Falmouth)... 11·50

1417 Upland Landscape (Strip Farming)

1418 Horse-drawn Rotary Seed Drill (Mechanical Farming)

1419 Man peeling Potato (Food Imports)

1420 Aerial View of Combine-harvester (Satellite Agriculture)

(Des D. Tress (19p.), C. Wormell (26p.), Tessa Traeger (44p.), R. Cooke (64p.). Gravure Walsall (No. 2108a) or De La Rue (others))

1999 (7–21 Sept). Millennium Series. The Farmers' Tale. Multicoloured One centre phosphor band (19p.) or two phosphor bands (others). Perf 14×14½.

2107	**1417**	19p. Upland Landscape...........................	40	40
2108	**1418**	26p. Horse-drawn Rotary Seed Drill.......	60	60
		a. Booklet pane. No. 2108×2 with margins all round (21.9.99).............	3·00	
2109	**1419**	44p. Man peeling Potato.........................	80	80
2110	**1420**	64p. Aerial View of Combine-harvester.	1·00	1·00
	Set of 4..		2·50	2·50
	Set of 4 Gutter Pairs...		5·00	

First Day Cover (Philatelic Bureau) (Type J, see Introduction).. 3·25
First Day Cover (Laxton, Newark)............................. 3·25
Presentation Pack (PO Pack No. 302)...................... 3·25
PHQ Cards (set of 4) (211)............................ 80 3·25

The 19p. includes the EUROPA emblem.
No. 2108a comes from the £2·60 booklet, No. HBA2.

1421 Robert the Bruce (Battle of Bannockburn, 1314)

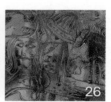

1422 Cavalier and Horse (English Civil War)

1423 War Graves Cemetery, The Somme (World Wars)

1424 Soldiers with Boy (Peacekeeping)

(Des A. Davidson (19p.), R. Kelly (26p.), D. McCullin (44p.), C. Corr (64p.). Litho (19p.) or gravure (others) Walsall)

1999 (5 Oct). Millennium Series. The Soldiers' Tale. Multicoloured. One centre phosphor band (19p.) or two phosphor bands (others). Perf 14×14½.

2111	**1421**	19p. Robert the Bruce............................	40	40
2112	**1422**	26p. Cavalier and Horse.........................	60	60
2113	**1423**	44p. War Graves Cemetery, The Somme..............................	80	80
2114	**1424**	64p. Soldiers with Boy............................	1·00	1·00
	Set of 4..		2·50	2·50
	Set of 4 Gutter Pairs...		5·00	

First Day Cover (Philatelic Bureau) (Type J, see Introduction).. 3·25
First Day Cover (London SW)..................................... 3·25
Presentation Pack (PO Pack No. 303*)..................... 3·25
PHQ Cards (set of 4) (212)............................ 80 3·25

* The presentation pack was numbered 302 in error.

1425 'Hark the herald angels sing' and Hymn book (John Wesley)

1426 King James I and Bible (Authorised Version of Bible)

1427 St Andrews Cathedral, Fife (Pilgrimage)

1428 Nativity (First Christmas)

(Des B. Neuenschwander (19p.), Clare Melinsky (26p.), Catherine Yass (44p.), C. Aitchison (64p.) Gravure De La Rue)

1999 (2 Nov). Millennium Series. The Christians' Tale. Multicoloured One centre phosphor band (19p.) or two phosphor bands (others). Perf 14×14½.

2115	**1425**	19p. 'Hark the herald angels sing' and Hymn book......................	40	40
		a. Imperf (pair)........................	£350	
2116	**1426**	26p. King James I and Bible..................	60	60
2117	**1427**	44p. St Andrews Cathedral, Fife.............	80	80
2118	**1428**	64p. Nativity.............................	1·00	1·00
Set of 4...			2·50	2·50
Set of 4 Gutter Pairs..................................			5·00	
First Day Cover (Philatelic Bureau) (Type J, see Introduction)..				3·25
First Day Cover (St Andrews, Fife)..................				3·25
Presentation Pack (PO Pack No. 304)...............			3·25	
PHQ Cards (set of 4) (213).........................			80	3·25

1429 'World of the Stage' (Allen Jones)

1430 'World of Music' (Bridget Riley)

1431 'World of Literature' (Lisa Milroy)

1432 'New Worlds' (Sir Howard Hodgkin)

(Gravure Walsall)

1999 (7 Dec). Millennium Series. The Artists' Tale. Multicoloured. One centre phosphor band (19p.) or two phosphor bands (others). Perf 14×14½.

2119	**1429**	19p. 'World of the Stage'..................	40	40
2120	**1430**	26p. 'World of Music'.....................	60	60
2121	**1431**	44p. 'World of Literature'.................	80	80
2122	**1432**	64p. 'New Worlds'........................	1·00	1·00
Set of 4...			2·50	2·50

Set of 4 Gutter Pairs..................................	5·00	
First Day Cover (Philatelic Bureau) (Type J, see Introduction)..		3·25
First Day Cover (Stratford-upon-Avon)...............		3·25
Presentation Pack (PO Pack No. 305)...............	3·25	
PHQ Cards (set of 4) (214).........................	80	3·25

Year Pack

1999 (7 Dec). Comprises Nos. 2069/2076, 2080/2105 and 2107/2122.

CP2122a	Year Pack (Pack No. 306).................	65·00

Post Office Yearbook

1999 (7 Dec). Comprises Nos. 2069/2076, 2080/2105 and 2107/2122 in hardback book with slip case

YB2122a	Yearbook..................................	50·00

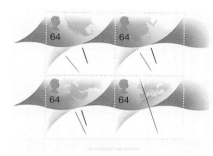

1433a Millennium Timekeeper

(Des D. Gentleman. Gravure De La Rue)

1999 (14 Dec). Millennium Series. Millennium Timekeeper. Sheet 120×89 mm. Multicoloured Two phosphor bands. Perf 14×14½.

MS2123	**1433a**	64p. Clock face and map of North America; 64p. Clock face and map of Asia; 64p. Clock face and map of Middle East; 64p. Clock face and map of Europe..................	11·00	11·00
First Day Cover (Philatelic Bureau).................				11·00
First Day Cover (Greenwich SE)....................				11·00
Presentation Pack (PO Pack No. M02).............			11·00	
PHQ Cards (set of 5) (PSM02).....................			1·00	11·00

No. **MS**2123 also exists overprinted 'EARLS COURT, LONDON 22-28 MAY 2000 THE STAMP SHOW 2000' from Exhibition Premium Passes, costing £10, available from 1 March 2000 (Price £17).

The five PHQ cards show the four individual stamps and the complete miniature sheet.

For No. 2124, T **1437**, see Decimal Machin Definitives section.

1438 Barn Owl (World Owl Trust, Muncaster)

1439 Night Sky (National Space Science Centre, Leicester)

1440 River Goyt and Textile Mills (Torrs Walkway, New Mills)

1441 Gannets (Seabird Centre, North Berwick)

(Litho (44p.), gravure (others) Walsall (No. 2126a/2126ab) or Questa (others))

2000 (18 Jan)–**02**. Millennium Projects (1st series). Above and Beyond. Multicoloured One centre phosphor band (19p.) or two phosphor bands (others). Perf 14×14½ (1st, 44p.) or 13½×14 (others).

2125	**1438**	19p. Barn Owl (World Owl Trust, Muncaster)...........................	40	40
		a. Imperf (pair)...............................	£300	
2126	**1439**	26p. Night Sky (National Space Science Centre, Leicester)...............	70	70
		aa. Imperf (pair)...........................	£300	
2126a		(1st) greenish yellow, magenta, pale new blue, black and silver (26.5.2000)............................	2·25	2·25
		ab. Booklet pane. Nos. 2126a and 2139 with margins all round..........	3·00	
		ac. Booklet pane. No. 2126a×4 with margins all round (24.9.02).............	9·00	
2127	**1440**	44p. River Goyt and Textile Mills (Torrs Walkway, New Mills)......................	1·00	1·00
2128	**1441**	64p. Gannets (Seabird Centre, North Berwick)...............................	1·25	1·25
		Set of 4 (ex No. 2126a)..........................	3·00	3·00
		Set of 4 Gutter Pairs................................	6·00	
		First Day Cover (Philatelic Bureau) (Type J, see Introduction) (Nos. 2125/2128).............		4·00
		First Day Cover (Muncaster, Ravenglass) (Nos. 2125/2128)....................................		4·00
		First Day Cover (Philatelic Bureau) (No. 2126ab)..............		4·00
		First Day Cover (Leicester) (No. 2126ab)..............		4·00
		Presentation Pack (PO Pack No. 307)..................	3·75	
		PHQ Cards (set of 4) (215).........................	80	3·50

No. 2126ab comes from the £2·70 Millennium booklet, No. HBA3.
No. 2162ac comes from the Across the Universe stamp booklet, No. DX29.

Imperforate pairs of No. 2125 with Queen's head in gold, Nos. 2126 and 2139 with inscriptions in an alternative typeface and No. 2128 with inscriptions in silver are all of proof status (*Prices from £200*).

929 Queen Victoria and Queen Elizabeth II

1446 Queen Victoria and Queen Elizabeth II

(Des J. Matthews. Gravure Walsall)

2000 (15 Feb)–**2017**. T **929** redrawn as T **1446** (No.2133a). Two phosphor bands. Perf 14 (No. 2133a) or perf 14½×14 (both with one elliptical hole in each vertical side).

2133	**929**	20p brownish black and cream (5.6.17).............................	1·10	1·10
2133a	**1446**	(1st) brownish black and cream.............	1·10	1·10
		al. Booklet pane. No. 2133a×6 with margins all round...................	8·50	
		First Day Cover (Philatelic Bureau) (No. 2133al).................		9·50
		First Day Cover (London SW5) (No. 2133al).................		9·50

No. 2133 comes from the £15·14 50th Anniversary of the Machin booklet, No. DY21.

No. 2133a was only issued in the £7·50 Special by Design booklet, No. DX24.

For Nos. 2133/2133a but printed Litho see Nos. 2955/2956.

See also Nos. 1478, **MS**1501 and **MS**3965.

1442 Millennium Beacon (Beacons across The Land)

1443 Garratt Steam Locomotive No. 143 pulling Train (Rheilffordd Eryri, Welsh Highland Railway)

1447 Beach Pebbles (Turning the Tide, Durham Coast)

1448 Frog's Legs and Water Lilies (National Pondlife Centre, Merseyside)

1444 Lightning (Dynamic Earth Centre, Edinburgh)

1445 Multicoloured Lights (Lighting Croydon's Skyline)

1449 Cliff Boardwalk (Parc Arfordirol, Llanelli Coast)

1450 Reflections in Water (Portsmouth Harbour Development)

(Gravure De La Rue)

2000 (1 Feb). Millennium Projects (2nd series). Fire and Light. Multicoloured One centre phosphor band (19p.) or two phosphor bands (others). Perf 14×14½.

2129	**1442**	19p. Millennium Beacon (Beacons across The Land).......................	40	40
2130	**1443**	26p. Garratt Steam Locomotive No. 143 pulling Train (Rheilffordd Eryri, Welsh Highland Railway).......	70	70
2131	**1444**	44p. Lightning (Dynamic Earth Centre, Edinburgh).............................	1·00	1·00
2132	**1445**	64p. Multicoloured Lights (Lighting Croydon's Skyline)...........................	1·25	1·25
		Set of 4..	3·00	3·00
		Set of 4 Gutter Pairs................................	6·00	
		First Day Cover (Philatelic Bureau) (Type J, see Introduction)....................................		3·50
		First Day Cover (Edinburgh 3°10'W)............		3·50
		Presentation Pack (PO Pack No. 308)..............	3·75	
		PHQ Cards (set of 4) (216).........................	1·25	3·50

(Litho (44p.), gravure (others) Walsall)

2000 (7 Mar). Millennium Projects (3rd series). Water and Coast. Multicoloured One centre phosphor band (19p.) or two phosphor bands (others). Perf 14×14½.

2134	**1447**	19p. Beach Pebbles (Turning the Tide, Durham Coast)................................	40	40
2135	**1448**	26p. Frog's Legs and Water Lilies (National Pondlife Centre, Merseyside).................................	70	70
2136	**1449**	44p. Cliff Boardwalk (Parc Arfordirol, Llanelli Coast).................................	1·00	1·00
2137	**1450**	64p. Reflections in Water (Portsmouth Harbour Development)...................	1·25	1·25
		a. Phosphor omitted...........................	£175	
		Set of 4..	3·00	3·00
		Set of 4 Gutter Pairs................................	6·00	
		First Day Cover (Philatelic Bureau) (Type J, see Introduction)....................................		4·00
		First Day Cover (Llanelli).........................		4·00
		Presentation Pack (PO Pack No. 309)..............	3·75	
		PHQ Cards (set of 4) (217).........................	1·25	4·50

1451 Reed Beds, River Braid (ECOS, Ballymena)

1452 South American Leafcutter Ants (Web of Life Exhibition, London Zoo)

1453 Solar Sensors (Earth Centre, Doncaster)

1454 Hydroponic Leaves (Project SUZY, Teesside)

(Gravure De La Rue)

2000 (4 Apr). Millennium Projects (4th series). Life and Earth. Multicoloured One centre phosphor band (2nd) or two phosphor bands (others). Perf 14×14½.

2138	**1451**	(2nd) Reed Beds, River Braid.....................	90	90
2139	**1452**	(1st) South American Leafcutter Ants....	1·00	1·00
		a. Imperf (pair)......................................		
2140	**1453**	44p. Solar Sensors...................................	1·00	1·00
2141	**1454**	64p. Hydroponic Leaves........................	1·25	1·25
Set of 4..			3·75	3·75
Set of 4 Gutter Pairs...			7·50	
First Day Cover (Philatelic Bureau) (Type J, see Introduction)...				4·00
First Day Cover (Doncaster)...				4·00
Presentation Pack (PO Pack No. 310)...........................			4·25	
PHQ Cards (set of 4) (218)..			1·25	4·50

For No. 2139 printed by Walsall in gravure, see booklet pane No. 2126ab. Types **1453**/**1454** with face values of 45p. and 65p. were prepared, but not issued.

1455 Pottery Glaze (Ceramica Museum, Stoke-on-Trent)

1456 Bankside Galleries (Tate Modern, London)

1457 Road Marking (Cycle Network Artworks)

1458 *People of Salford* (Lowry Centre, Salford)

(Gravure Enschedé)

2000 (2 May). Millennium Projects (5th series). Art and Craft. Multicoloured. One centre phosphor band (2nd) or two phosphor bands (others). Perf 14×14½.

2142	**1455**	(2nd) Pottery Glaze......................................	90	90
2143	**1456**	(1st) Bankside Galleries............................	1·00	1·00
2144	**1457**	45p. Road Marking...................................	1·00	1·00
2145	**1458**	65p. *People of Salford*.............................	1·25	1·25
Set of 4..			3·75	3·75
Set of 4 Gutter Pairs...			7·50	

First Day Cover (Philatelic Bureau) (Type J, see Introduction)...		4·00
First Day Cover (Salford)...		4·00
Presentation Pack (PO Pack No. 311)...........................	4·25	
PHQ Cards (set of 4) (219)..	1·25	4·00

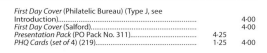

For Nos. **MS2146**/**MS**2147, Types **1459**/**1459a**, see Decimal Machin Definitives section.

1460 Children playing (Millennium Greens Project)

1461 Millennium Bridge, Gateshead

1462 Daisies (Mile End Park, London)

1463 African Hut and Thatched Cottage (On the Meridian Line Project)

(Gravure (2nd, 45p.) or litho (1st, 65p.) Walsall)

2000 (6 June). Millennium Projects (6th series). People and Places. Multicoloured One centre phosphor band (2nd) or two phosphor bands (others). Perf 14×14½.

2148	**1460**	(2nd) Children playing...............................	90	90
2149	**1461**	(1st) Millennium Bridge, Gateshead.......	1·00	1·00
2150	**1462**	45p. Daisies...	1·00	1·00
2151	**1463**	65p. African Hut and Thatched Cottage...	1·25	1·25
Set of 4..			3·75	3·75
Set of 4 Gutter Pairs...			7·50	
First Day Cover (Philatelic Bureau) (Type J, see Introduction)...				4·00
First Day Cover (Gateshead)..				4·00
Presentation Pack (PO Pack No. 312)...........................			4·25	
PHQ Cards (set of 4) (220)..			1·25	4·50

1464 Raising the Stone (Strangford Stone, Killyleagh)

1465 Horse's Hooves (Trans Pennine Trail, Derbyshire)

1466 Cyclist (Kingdom of Fife Cycleways, Scotland)

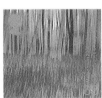

1467 Bluebell Wood (Groundwork's Changing Places Project)

(Gravure Walsall (Nos. 2153a, 2155a) or Enschedé (others))

2000 (4 July–18 Sept). Millennium Projects (7th series). Stone and Soil. Multicoloured One centre phosphor band (2nd) or two phosphor bands (others). Perf 14×14½

2152	**1464**	(2nd) Raising the Stone..............................	90	90
2153	**1465**	(1st) Horse's Hooves................................	1·00	1·00
		a. Booklet pane. Nos. 2153 and 2157 with margins all round (18.9.2000).................	2·40	
2154	**1466**	45p. Cyclist..	90	90
2155	**1467**	65p. Bluebell Wood................................	1·10	1·10
		a. Booklet pane. No. 2155×2 with margins all round (18.9.2000).........	2·25	
		Set of 4..	3·50	3·50
		Set of 4 Gutter Pairs................................	7·00	
		First Day Cover (Philatelic Bureau) (Type J, see Introduction)............................		4·00
		First Day Cover (Killyleagh)........................		4·00
		Presentation Pack (PO Pack No. 313)........	4·00	
		PHQ Cards (set of 4) (221).........................	1·25	4·25

No. 2153a comes from the £2·70 Millennium booklet, No. HBA4.
No. 2155a comes from the £7 Treasury of Trees booklet, No. DX26.

1468 Tree Roots (Yews for the Millennium Project)

1469 Sunflower (Eden Project, St Austell)

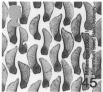
1470 Sycamore Seeds (Millennium Seed Bank, Wakehurst Place, West Sussex)

1471 Forest, Doire Dach (Forest for Scotland)

(Gravure Walsall (Nos. 2156a, 2158a, 2159a) or De La Rue (others))

2000 (1 Aug–18 Sept). Millennium Projects (8th series). Tree and Leaf. Multicoloured One centre phosphor band (2nd) or two phosphor bands (others). Perf 14×14½.

2156	**1468**	(2nd) Tree Roots.....................................	90	90
		a. Booklet pane. No. 2156×4 with margins all round (18.9.2000).........	4·00	
2157	**1469**	(1st) Sunflower.......................................	1·00	1·00
2158	**1470**	45p. Sycamore Seeds..............................	90	90
		a. Booklet pane. No. 2158×4 with margins all round (18.9.2000).........	3·75	
2159	**1471**	65p. Forest, Doire Dach...........................	1·10	1·10
		a. Booklet pane. No. 2159×2 with margins all round (18.9.2000).........	2·40	
		Set of 4..	3·50	3·50
		Set of 4 Gutter Pairs................................	7·00	
		First Day Cover (Philatelic Bureau) (Type J, see Introduction)............................		4·00
		First Day Cover (St Austell)........................		4·00
		Presentation Pack (PO Pack No. 314)........	4·00	
		PHQ Cards (set of 4) (222).........................	1·25	4·25

Nos. 2156a, 2158a and 2159a come from the £7 Treasury of Trees booklet, No. DX26.
For No. 2157 printed by Walsall in gravure, see booklet pane No. 2153a.

1472 Queen Elizabeth the Queen Mother

1472a Royal Family on Queen Mother's 100th Birthday

(Des J. Gibbs from photo by J. Swannell. Gravure Questa (Nos. 2160, **MS**2161a) or De La Rue (No. **MS**2161))

2000 (4 Aug). Queen Elizabeth the Queen Mother's 100th Birthday. Multicoloured Phosphorised paper plus two phosphor bands. Perf 14½.

2160	**1472**	27p. Queen Elizabeth the Queen Mother..	1·25	1·25
		a. Booklet pane. No. 2160×4 with margins all round............................	5·00	
MS2161		121×89mm. **1472a** 27p.×4, Royal Family on Queen Mother's 100th Birthday.................	5·00	5·00
		a. Booklet pane. As No. **MS**2161, but larger, 150×95 mm, and with additional silver frame.......................	5·00	5·25
		First Day Cover (Philatelic Bureau) (No. 2160a)..		5·25
		First Day Cover (London SW1) (No. 2160a)........		5·25
		First Day Cover (Philatelic Bureau) (No. **MS**2161)....		5·25
		First Day Cover (London SW1) (No. **MS**2161)........		5·25
		Presentation Pack (PO Pack No. M04) (No. **MS**2161).......	11·00	
		PHQ Cards (set of 5) (PSM04).........................	1·50	5·50

No. 2160 was only issued in the £7·03 The Life of the Century booklet, No. DX25 and as part of Nos. **MS**2161/**MS**2161a.
The complete miniature sheet is shown on one of the PHQ cards with the others depicting individual stamps.

1473 Head of *Gigantiops destructor* (Ant) (Wildscreen at Bristol)

1474 Gathering Water Lilies on Broads (Norfolk and Norwich Project)

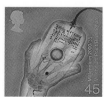
1475 X-ray of Hand holding Computer Mouse (Millennium Point, Birmingham)

1476 Tartan Wool Holder (Scottish Cultural Resources Access Network)

(Litho Walsall)

2000 (5 Sept). Millennium Projects (9th series). Mind and Matter. Multicoloured One centre phosphor band (2nd) or two phosphor bands (others). Perf 14×14½.

2162	**1473**	(2nd) Head of *Gigantiops destructor* (Ant).......................................	90	90
2163	**1474**	(1st) Gathering Water Lilies on Broads...	1·00	1·00
2164	**1475**	45p. X-ray of Hand holding Computer Mouse...	90	90
2165	**1476**	65p. Tartan Wool Holder.........................	1·10	1·10
		Set of 4..	3·50	3·50
		Set of 4 Gutter Pairs................................	7·00	

First Day Cover (Philatelic Bureau) (Type J, see
Introduction).. 4·00
First Day Cover (Norwich).. 4·00
Presentation Pack (PO Pack No. 315)............. 4·00
PHQ Cards (set of 4) (223)................. 1·25   4·25

1477 Acrobatic Performers
(Millennium Dome)

1478 Football Players
(Hampden Park, Glasgow)

1479 Bather (Bath Spa
Project)

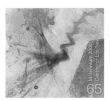

1480 Hen's Egg under
Magnification (Centre for
Life, Newcastle)

(Litho (2nd) or gravure (others) Questa)

2000 (3 Oct). Millennium Projects (10th series). Body and Bone.
Multicoloured One centre phosphor band (2nd) or two phosphor
bands (others). Perf 14×14½ (2nd) or 13½×14 (others).
2166 **1477** (2nd) Acrobatic Performers...................... 90   90
2167 **1478** (1st) Football Players............................. 1·00   1·00
2168 **1479** 45p. Bather... 90   90
2169 **1480** 65p. Hen's Egg under Magnification...... 1·10   1·10
Set of 4.. 3·50   3·50
Set of 4 Gutter Pairs.. 7·00
First Day Cover (Philatelic Bureau) (Type J, see
Introduction).. 4·00
First Day Cover (Glasgow)... 4·50
Presentation Pack (PO Pack No. 316)............. 4·00
PHQ Cards (set of 4) (224)................. 1·25   4·25

1481 Virgin and Child
Stained-glass Window, St
Edmundsbury Cathedral
(Suffolk Cathedral
Millennium Project)

1482 Floodlit Church
of St Peter and St Paul,
Overstowey (Church
Floodlighting Trust)

1483 12th-century Latin
Gradual (St Patrick Centre,
Downpatrick)

1484 Chapter House
Ceiling, York Minster (York
Millennium Mystery Plays)

(Gravure De La Rue)

2000 (7 Nov). Millennium Projects (11th series). Spirit and Faith.
Multicoloured One centre phosphor band (2nd) or two phosphor
bands (others). Perf 14×14½.
2170 **1481** (2nd) Virgin and Child Stained-glass
Window, St Edmundsbury
Cathedral.. 90   90
a. Imperf pair.. £400

2171 **1482** (1st) Floodlit Church of St Peter and St
Paul, Overstowey....................... 1·00   1·00
a. Imperf (pair).. £450
2172 **1483** 45p. 12th-century Latin Gradual............. 90   90
2173 **1484** 65p. Chapter House Ceiling, York
Minster...................................... 1·10   1·10
Set of 4.. 3·50   3·50
Set of 4 Gutter Pairs.. 7·00
First Day Cover (Philatelic Bureau) (Type J, see
Introduction).. 4·00
First Day Cover (Downpatrick)..................................... 4·00
Presentation Pack (PO Pack No. 317)............. 4·00
PHQ Cards (set of 4) (225)................. 1·25   4·25
No. 2173 has been reported with the gold omitted, leaving the Queen's
head in yellow. It is only known used.

Post Office Yearbook

2000 (7 Nov). Comprises Nos. 2125/2126, 2127/2132, 2134/2145,
2148/2159 and **MS**2161/2177 in hardback book with slip case
YB2173a   Yearbook................................... 48·00
The last two issues in the Millennium Projects Series were supplied for
insertion into the above at a later date.

1485 Church Bells (Ringing
in the Millennium)

1486 Eye (Year of the Artist)

1487 Top of Harp (Canolfan
Mileniwm, Cardiff)

1488 Silhouetted Figure
within Latticework (TS2K
Creative Enterprise Centres,
London)

(Gravure De La Rue)

2000 (5 Dec). Millennium Projects (12th series). Sound and Vision.
Multicoloured. One centre phosphor band (2nd) or two phosphor
bands (others). Perf 14×14½.
2174 **1485** (2nd) Church Bells.................................... 90   90
2175 **1486** (1st) Eye.. 1·00   1·00
2176 **1487** 45p. Top of Harp.................................. 90   90
2177 **1488** 65p. Silhouetted Figure within
Latticework.............................. 1·10   1·10
Set of 4.. 3·50   3·50
Set of 4 Gutter Pairs.. 7·00
First Day Cover (Philatelic Bureau) (Type J, see
Introduction).. 4·00
First Day Cover (Cardiff).. 4·00
Presentation Pack (PO Pack No. 318)............. 4·00
PHQ Cards (set of 4) (226)................. 1·25   4·25

Collectors Pack

2000 (Dec 5) Comprises Nos. 2125/216, 2127/2132, 2134/2145, 2148/2159
and **MS**2161/2177.
CP2177a   Collectors Pack (Pack No. 319)............ 65·00

1489 Flower (Nurture
Children)

1490 Tiger (Listen to
Children)

1491 Owl (Teach Children)

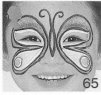

1492 Butterfly (Ensure Children's Freedom)

(Des Why Not Associates. Gravure De La Rue)

2001 (16 Jan). New Millennium. Rights of the Child. Face Paintings. Multicoloured One centre phosphor band (2nd) or two phosphor bands (others). Perf 14×14½.

2178	**1489**	(2nd) Flower (Nurture Children)...............	90	90
2179	**1490**	(1st) Tiger (Listen to Children).................	1·00	1·00
2180	**1491**	45p. Owl (Teach Children)......................	1·00	1·00
2181	**1492**	65p. Butterfly (Ensure Children's Freedom)..............................	1·25	1·25
Set of 4................................			3·75	3·75
Set of 4 Gutter Pairs.........................			7·50	
First Day Cover (Philatelic Bureau)....................				4·00
First Day Cover (Hope, Hope Valley)...................				4·00
Presentation Pack (PO Pack No. 319).............			4·25	
PHQ Cards (set of 4) (227).........................			1·25	4·25

1493 Love

1494 THANKS

1495 abc (New Baby)

1496 WELCOME

1497 Cheers

(Des Springpoint Design. Gravure Enschedé)

2001 (6–13 Feb). Greetings Stamps. Occasions. Multicoloured Two phosphor bands. Perf 14×14½.

2182	**1493**	(1st) Love................................	1·20	1·00
2183	**1494**	(1st) THANKS...........................	1·20	1·00
2184	**1495**	(1st) abc (New Baby).................	1·20	1·00
2185	**1496**	(1st) WELCOME.......................	1·20	1·00
2186	**1497**	(1st) Cheers............................	1·20	1·00
Set of 5..............................			5·50	4·50
Set of 5 Gutter Pairs..........................			11·00	
First Day Cover (Philatelic Bureau)................				4·75
First Day Cover (Merry Hill, Wolverhampton).......				4·75
Presentation Pack (PO Pack No. M05) (13.2.01)......			7·25	
PHQ Cards (set of 5) (PSM05).......................			1·50	5·00

The silver-grey backgrounds are printed in Iriodin ink which gives a shiny effect.

Further packs of Nos. 2182/2186 were sold from 3 July 2001. These comprised the listed stamps in blocks of ten (from sheets) with an insert describing the occasion (*Price £10 per pack*).

Nos. 2182/2186 were re-issued on 1 May 2001 in sheets of 20 printed by Questa in lithography instead of gravure, in connection with the 'customised' stamps scheme. Such sheets contained 20 examples of either Nos. 2182, 2184 or 2185, or ten each of Nos. 2183 and 2186.

Sheets with personal photographs printed on the labels were available from Royal Mail in Edinburgh at £12 each.

From 5 June 2001 a similar sheet (No. LS4) containing four of each design in horizontal strips, with postal symbols on the labels, was sold at £5·95.

1498 Dog and Owner on Bench

1499 Dog in Bath

1500 Boxer at Dog Show

1501 Cat in Handbag

1502 Cat on Gate

1503 Dog in Car

1504 Cat at Window

1505 Dog Behind Fence

1506 Cat watching Bird

1507 Cat in Washbasin

(Des johnson banks. Gravure Walsall)

2001 (13 Feb). Cats and Dogs. Multicoloured Self-adhesive. Two phosphor bands. Perf 15×14 die-cut.

2187	**1498**	(1st) Dog and Owner on Bench...............	1·20	1·00
		a. Sheetlet of 10. Nos. 2187/2196.......	11·00	9·00
		aa. Imperf (sheetlet)..............................	—	
		b. Booklet pane. Nos. 2187/2196 plus No. 2040×2....................	25·00	
		ba. Imperf (pane).................................		
2188	**1499**	(1st) Dog in Bath............................	1·20	1·00
2189	**1500**	(1st) Boxer at Dog Show...................	1·20	1·00
2190	**1501**	(1st) Cat in Handbag.......................	1·20	1·00
2191	**1502**	(1st) Cat on Gate...........................	1·20	1·00
2192	**1503**	(1st) Dog in Car.............................	1·20	1·00
2193	**1504**	(1st) Cat at Window........................	1·20	1·00
2194	**1505**	(1st) Dog Behind Fence....................	1·20	1·00
2195	**1506**	(1st) Cat watching Bird....................	1·20	1·00
2196	**1507**	(1st) Cat in Washbasin....................	1·20	1·00
Set of 10..................................			11·00	9·00
First Day Cover (Philatelic Bureau)................				9·75
First Day Cover (Petts Wood, Orpington)............				9·75
Presentation Pack (PO Pack No. 320)................			12·00	
PHQ Cards (set of 10) (228)........................			3·00	12·00

Nos. 2187/2196 were printed together in sheetlets of ten (5×2), with the surplus self-adhesive paper around each stamp retained. The pane has vertical roulettes between rows 2/3 and 4/5 with the design on the reverse of the backing paper similar to Booklet No. PM1.

1508 'RAIN'

1509 'FAIR'

1510 'STORMY'

1511 'VERY DRY'

1516 White Ensign

1517 Union Jack

1518 Jolly Roger flown by HMS Proteus (submarine)

1519 Flag of Chief of Defence Staff

1511a The Weather

(Des H. Brown and T. Meeuwissen. Gravure De La Rue)

2001 (13 Mar). The Weather. Multicoloured One side phosphor band (19p.) or two phosphor bands (others). Perf 14½.

2197	**1508**	19p. 'RAIN'..	70	70
2198	**1509**	27p. 'FAIR'..	80	80
2199	**1510**	45p. 'STORMY'...	95	95
2200	**1511**	65p. 'VERY DRY'...	1·10	1·10
Set of 4..			3·25	3·25
Set of 4 Gutter Pairs...			6·50	
First Day Cover (Philatelic Bureau).......................				3·50
First Day Cover (Fraserburgh)................................				3·50
Presentation Pack (PO Pack No. 321)....................			9·00	
MS2201 **1511a** 105×105 mm. Nos. 2197/2200................			9·25	9·25
First Day Cover (Philatelic Bureau).......................				10·00
First Day Cover (Fraserburgh)................................				10·00
PHQ Cards (set of 5) (229)....................................			1·50	14·00

Nos. 2197/2200 show the four quadrants of a barometer dial which are combined on the miniature sheet.

The reddish violet on both the 27p. and the miniature sheet is printed in thermochromic ink which changes from reddish violet to light blue when exposed to heat.

The PHQ cards depict the four values and the miniature sheet.

1519a Royal Navy Flags

(Des D. Davis. Gravure Questa)

2001 (10 Apr–22 Oct). Centenary of Royal Navy Submarine Service. Multicoloured One centre phosphor band (2nd) or two phosphor bands (others). Perf 15×14.

(a) Submarines. Ordinary gum.

2202	**1512**	(2nd) Vanguard Class Submarine, 1992...	90	90
		a. Perf 15½×15 (22.10.01)....................	2·00	2·00
		ab. Booklet pane. Nos. 2202a and 2204a, each×2, with margins all round..	7·00	
2203	**1513**	(1st) Swiftsure Class Submarine, 1973...	1·00	1·00
		a. Perf 15½×15 (22.10.01)....................	1·95	1·95
		b. Imperf (pair).....................................	£750	
		ab. Booklet pane. Nos. 2203a and 2205a, each×2, with margins all round..	8·00	
2204	**1514**	45p. Unity Class Submarine, 1939..........	90	90
		a. Perf 15½×15 (22.10.01)....................	2·00	2·00
2205	**1515**	65p. Holland Type Submarine, 1901......	1·10	1·10
		a. Perf 15½×15 (22.10.01)....................	2·00	2·00
Set of 4..			3·50	3·50
Set of 4 Gutter Pairs...			7·00	
First Day Cover (Philatelic Bureau).......................				3·75
First Day Cover (Portsmouth)................................				3·75
Presentation Pack (PO Pack No. 322)....................			16·00	
PHQ Cards (set of 4) (230)....................................			1·25	4·00

(b) Flags. Ordinary gum. Perf 14½.

MS2206 **1519a** 92×97 mm. (1st) White Ensign; (1st) Union Jack; (1st) Jolly Roger flown by HMS *Proteus* (submarine); (1st) Flag of Chief of Defence Staff (22.10.01)..		5·25	5·25
a. Booklet pane. As No. **MS**2206 but larger, 152×96 mm.		5·25	
First Day Cover (Tallents House)............................			4·75
First Day Cover (Rosyth, Dunfermline).................			5·25
Presentation Pack (PO Pack No. M06)..................		15·00	
PHQ Cards (set of 5) (PSM07)................................		1·50	6·00

1512 Vanguard Class Submarine, 1992

1513 Swiftsure Class Submarine, 1973

1514 Unity Class Submarine, 1939

1515 Holland Type Submarine, 1901

(c) Self-adhesive. Die-cut Perf 15½×14 (No. 2207) or 14½ (others).

2207	**1513**	(1st) Swiftsure Class Submarine, 1973 (17.4.01).............	30·00	30·00
		a. Booklet pane. No. 2207×2 plus No. 2040×4........................	70·00	
		ab. Booklet pane. Imperf......................	£3000	
2208	**1516**	(1st) White Ensign (22.10.01).............	7·00	7·00
		a. Booklet pane. Nos. 2208/2209 plus No. 2040×4..................	15·00	
		ab. Booklet pane. Imperf......................		
2209	**1518**	(1st) Jolly Roger flown by HMS *Proteus* (submarine) (22.10.01).............	7·00	7·00

Nos. 2202a/2205a were only issued in the £6·76 Unseen and Unheard booklet, No. DX27.

Nos. 2207/2209 only come from two different £1·62 self-adhesive booklets, Nos. PM2 and PM4.

T **1516** was re-issued on 21 June 2005 in sheets of 20, printed in lithography by Cartor and sold at £6·55, containing four vertical rows of five stamps alternated with half stamp-size printed labels showing signal flags (No. LS25). These sheets with personalised photographs were available at £14·95 from the Royal Mail.

It was subsequently issued, printed in lithography, perf 14½, in booklets Nos. DX35 and DX41 (see No. 2581).

T **1517** was re-issued on 27 July 2004 in sheets of 20, printed in lithography by Walsall and sold at £6·15 containing vertical strips of five stamps alternated with half stamp-size printed labels (No. LS20) These sheets with personalised photographs are available at £14·95 from the Royal Mail in Edinburgh.

It was subsequently issued, printed in lithography, perf 14½, in booklet No. DX41 (see No. 2805).

T **1518** was subsequently issued, printed in lithography, perf 14½, in booklet No. DX47 (see No. 2970).

The five PHQ cards depict the four designs and the complete miniature sheet, No. **MS**2206.

2211	**1521**	(1st) AEC Regent 1, Daimler COG5, Utility Guy Arab Mk II and AEC Regent III RT Type..............	1·20	1·00
2212	**1522**	(1st) AEC Regent III RT Type, Bristol KSW5G Open-top, AEC Routemaster and Bristol Lodekka FSF6G..................	1·20	1·00
		a. Grey omitted...............	—	
2213	**1523**	(1st) Bristol Lodekka FSF6G, Leyland Titan PD3/4, Leyland Atlantean PDR1/1 and Daimler Fleetline CRG6LX-33............	1·20	1·00
		a. Grey omitted...............	—	
2214	**1524**	(1st) Daimler Fleetline CRG6LX-33, MCW Metrobus DR102/43, Leyland Olympian ONLXB/1R and Dennis Trident............	1·20	1·00
		a. Grey omitted...............	—	
Set of 5..			5·50	4·50
Gutter Strip of 10...................................			11·00	
First Day Cover (Philatelic Bureau)........................				4·75
First Day Cover (Covent Garden, London WC2)........				4·75
Presentation Pack (PO Pack No. 323)........			9·00	
PHQ Cards (set of 6) (231)............			1·75	5·50
MS2215 120×105 mm. Nos. 2210/2214......			6·00	6·00
First Day Cover (Philatelic Bureau)........................				7·50
First Day Cover (Covent Garden, London WC2)........				7·50

Nos. 2210/2214 were printed together, *se-tenant*, in horizontal strips of five throughout the sheet. The illustrations of the first bus on No. 2210 and the last bus on No. 2214 continue onto the sheet margins.

In No. **MS**2215 the illustrations of the AEC Regent III RT Type and the Daimler Fleetline CRG6LX-33 appear twice.

The six PHQ cards show the six stamps and No. **MS**2215.

1520 Leyland X2 Open-top, London General B Type, Leyland Titan TD1 and AEC Regent 1

1521 AEC Regent 1, Daimler COG5, Utility Guy Arab Mk II and AEC Regent III RT Type

1522 AEC Regent III RT Type, Bristol KSW5G Open-top, AEC Routemaster and Bristol Lodekka FSF6G

1523 Bristol Lodekka FSF6G, Leyland Titan PD3/4, Leyland Atlantean PDR1/1 and Daimler Fleetline CRG6LX-33

1524 Daimler Fleetline CRG6LX-33, MCW Metrobus DR102/43, Leyland Olympian ONLXB/1R and Dennis Trident

(Des M. English. Litho Questa)

2001 (15 May). 150th Anniversary of First Double-decker Bus. Multicoloured 'All-over' phosphor. Perf 14½×14.

2210	**1520**	(1st) Leyland X2 Open-top, London General B Type, Leyland Titan TD1 and AEC Regent 1........	1·20	1·00
		a. Horiz strip of 5. Nos. 2210/2214.....	5·50	4·50
		ab. Imperf (horiz strip of 5)............	£3000	
		b. Grey omitted.................	—	

1525 Toque Hat by Pip Hackett

1526 Butterfly Hat by Dai Rees

1527 Top Hat by Stephen Jones

1528 Spiral Hat by Philip Treacy

(Des Rose Design from photos by N. Knight. Litho Enschedé)

2001 (19 June). Fashion Hats. Multicoloured 'All-over' phosphor. Perf 14½.

2216	**1525**	(1st) Toque Hat by Pip Hackett.............	1·20	1·00
2217	**1526**	(E) Butterfly Hat by Dai Rees.............	2·25	1·50
2218	**1527**	45p. Top Hat by Stephen Jones.............	90	90
2219	**1528**	65p. Spiral Hat by Philip Treacy.............	1·10	1·10
Set of 4..			4·75	4·00
Set of 4 Gutter Pairs...................................			9·50	
First Day Cover (Tallents House)........................				4·25
First Day Cover (Ascot)........................				4·25
Presentation Pack (PO Pack No. 324)........			5·25	
PHQ Cards (set of 4) (232)............			1·50	4·50

1529 Common Frog

1530 Great Diving Beetle

1531 Three-Spined Stickleback

1532 Southern Hawker Dragonfly

(Des J. Gibbs. Gravure De La Rue)

2001 (10 July). Europa. Pond Life. Multicoloured Two phosphor bands. Perf 15×14.

2220	**1529**	(1st) Common Frog....................................	1·00	1·00
2221	**1530**	(E) Great Diving Beetle..........................	1·75	1·50
2222	**1531**	45p. Three-Spined Stickleback...............	90	1·00
2223	**1532**	65p. Southern Hawker Dragonfly...........	1·10	1·20
Set of 4..			4·25	4·00
Set of 4 Gutter Pairs......................................			8·50	
First Day Cover (Tallents House)......................				4·75
First Day Cover (Oundle, Peterborough)...........				5·00
Presentation Pack (PO Pack No. 325)...............			5·00	
PHQ Cards (set of 4) (233)...............................			1·50	4·75

The 1st and E values incorporate the EUROPA emblem.

The bluish silver on all four values is in Iriodin ink and was used as a background for those parts of the design below the water line.

1533 Policeman

1534 Clown

1535 Mr Punch

1536 Judy

1537 Beadle

1538 Crocodile

(Des K. Bernstein from puppets by Bryan Clarkez)

2001 (4 Sept). Punch and Judy Show Puppets. Multicoloured Two phosphor bands. Perf 14×15.

(a) Gravure Walsall. Ordinary gum.

2224	**1533**	(1st) Policeman.............................	1·20	1·00
		a. Horiz strip of 6. Nos. 2224/2229.....	6·50	5·50
2225	**1534**	(1st) Clown..................................	1·20	1·00
2226	**1535**	(1st) Mr Punch.............................	1·20	1·00
2227	**1536**	(1st) Judy....................................	1·20	1·00
2228	**1537**	(1st) Beadle.................................	1·20	1·00
2229	**1538**	(1st) Crocodile.............................	1·20	1·00
Set of 6..			6·50	5·50

Gutter Block of 12..		13·00	
First Day Cover (Tallents House)................................			6·25
First Day Cover (Blackpool)..			6·50
Presentation Pack (PO Pack No. 326).........................		7·00	
PHQ Cards (set of 6) (234)..		1·75	6·25

(b) Gravure Questa. Self-adhesive. Die-cut Perf 14×15½.

2230	**1535**	(1st) Mr Punch.............................	7·00	7·00
		a. Booklet pane. Nos. 2230/2231 plus No. 2040×4..............	15·00	
2231	**1536**	(1st) Judy....................................	7·00	7·00

Nos. 2224/2229 were printed together, *se-tenant*, as horizontal strips of six in sheets of 60 (6×10).

Nos. 2230/2231 were only issued in £1·62 stamp booklet, No. PM3.

Imperforate strips of 6 with alternative background colours to Nos. 2224, 2228 and 2229 are of proof status (*Price £3000*).

1539 Carbon 60 Molecule (Chemistry)

1540 Globe (Economic Sciences)

1541 Embossed Dove (Peace)

1542 Crosses (Physiology or Medicine)

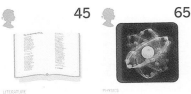

1543 Poem *The Addressing of Cats* by T. S. Eliot in Open Book (Literature)

1544 Hologram of Boron Molecule (Physics)

(Des P. Vermier. Eng Inge Madlé (1st). Printed Litho and silk-screen (2nd), litho and recess (1st), litho (45p.), litho and embossed (E), litho and hologram (65p.) Enschedé)

2001 (2 Oct). Centenary of Nobel Prizes. Multicoloured One side phosphor band (2nd) or phosphor frame (others). Perf 14½.

2232	**1539**	(2nd) Carbon 60 Molecule (Chemistry)...	90	90
2233	**1540**	(1st) Globe (Economic Sciences).............	1·20	1·00
2234	**1541**	(E) Embossed Dove (Peace).................	2·25	1·50
2235	**1542**	40p. Crosses (Physiology or Medicine)..	1·50	1·50
2236	**1543**	45p. Poem *The Addressing of Cats* by T. S. Eliot in Open Book (Literature)...	2·00	2·00
2237	**1544**	65p. Hologram of Boron Molecule (Physics)...	2·50	2·50
Set of 6..			8·75	8·50
Set of 6 Gutter Pairs......................................			17·00	
First Day Cover (Tallents House)......................				9·00
First Day Cover (Cambridge)...........................				9·00
Presentation Pack (PO Pack No. 327)...............			15·00	
PHQ Cards (set of 6) (235)...............................			1·75	9·75

The grey-black on No. 2232 is printed in thermochromic ink which temporarily changes to pale grey when exposed to heat.

The centre of No. 2235 is coated with a eucalyptus scent.

Trials, differing slightly from the issued stamps, are known for all values.

No. 2237 has been reported completely imperforate, its status is unknown.

1545 Robins with Snowman

1546 Robins on Bird Table

1547 Robins skating on Bird Bath

1548 Robins with Christmas Pudding

1549 Robins in Paper Chain Nest

(Des A. Robins and H. Brown. Gravure De La Rue)

2001 (6 Nov). Christmas. Robins. Self-adhesive. Multicoloured One centre phosphor band (2nd) or two phosphor bands (others). Die-cut perf 14½.

2238	**1545**	(2nd) Robins with Snowman.....................	90	90
		a. Booklet pane. No. 2238×24.............	22·00	
		b. Imperf (pair)...................................	£450	
2239	**1546**	(1st) Robins on Bird Table....................	1·20	1·00
		a. Booklet pane. No. 2239×12.............	16·00	
		b. Imperf (pair)...................................	—	
2240	**1547**	(E) Robins skating on Bird Bath...........	2·25	1·50
2241	**1548**	45p. Robins with Christmas Pudding.....	1·00	1·10
2242	**1549**	65p. Robins in Paper Chain Nest...........	1·10	1·25
		a. Imperf (pair) (die-cut perforations and roulettes omitted).....................	£600	
		ab. Imperf (pair) (die-cut perforations only omitted).....................................	£275	
		b. Imperf backing paper (pair) (roulettes omitted)............................	£125	
	Set of 5..		6·00	5·00
	First Day Cover (Tallents House)............................			5·50
	First Day Cover (Bethlehem, Llandeilo).................			5·50
	Presentation Pack (PO Pack No. 328)....................		6·25	
	PHQ Cards (set of 5) (236)...................................		1·50	5·50

Nos. 2238/2242 were each printed in sheets of 50 with the surplus backing paper around each stamp retained and separated by gauge 9 roulettes.

The 1st value was re-issued on 30 September 2003 in sheets of 20 (sold at £6·15) printed in lithography instead of gravure, each stamp accompanied by a stamp-size label showing a snowman (No. LS14). Sheets with personal photographs printed on the labels were available from Royal Mail, Edinburgh for £14·95 or photo-booths at selected post offices and Safeway stores for £15.

The 2nd and 1st values were re-issued together on 1 November 2005 in sheets of 20, printed in lithography by Cartor (sold at £5·60), containing ten 2nd class and ten 1st class stamps, each stamp accompanied by a label showing a snowman (No. LS27). Separate sheets of 20 2nd class and 20 1st class were available with personalised photographs at £9·95 (2nd) or £14·95 (1st) from Royal Mail.

No. 2238b shows both the die-cut perforations and the roulettes omitted.

Stamps from booklet panes Nos. 2238a and 2239a differ from those in sheets by omitting the roulettes in the backing paper between each stamp. Instead there are roulettes after the first and then every alternate horizontal row to assist with the folding of the booklets.

Trials of (2nd) and (1st) stamps in alternative designs are known.

Year Pack

2001 (6 Nov). Comprises Nos. 2178/2200, 2202/2206, 2210/2214, 2216/2229 and 2232/2242.

CP2242a	Year Pack (Pack No. 329)......................	70·00

Post Office Yearbook

2001 (6 Nov). Comprises Nos. 2178/2196, **MS**2201/2206, 2210/2214, 2216/2229 and 2232/2242 in hardback book with slip case

YB2242a	Yearbook..	48·00

1550 How the Whale got his Throat

1551 How the Camel got his Hump

1552 How the Rhinoceros got his Skin

1553 How the Leopard got his Spots

1554 The Elephant's Child

1555 The Sing-Song of Old Man Kangaroo

1556 The Beginning of the Armadillos

1557 The Crab that played with the Sea

1558 The Cat that walked by Himself

1559 The Butterfly that stamped

(Des I. Cohen. Gravure Walsall)

2002 (15 Jan). Centenary of Publication of Rudyard Kipling's Just So Stories. Self-adhesive. Multicoloured Two phosphor bands. Die-cut Perf 15×14.

2243	**1550**	(1st) How the Whale got his Throat.........	1·20	1·00
		a. Sheetlet of 10. Nos. 2243/2252.......	11·00	9·00
2244	**1551**	(1st) How the Camel got his Hump..........	1·20	1·00
2245	**1552**	(1st) How the Rhinoceros got his Skin......	1·20	1·00
2246	**1553**	(1st) How the Leopard got his Spots.........	1·20	1·00
2247	**1554**	(1st) The Elephant's Child........................	1·20	1·00
2248	**1555**	(1st) The Sing-Song of Old Man Kangaroo...	1·20	1·00
2249	**1556**	(1st) The Beginning of the Armadillos......	1·20	1·00
2250	**1557**	(1st) The Crab that played with the Sea...	1·20	1·00
2251	**1558**	(1st) The Cat that walked by Himself........	1·20	1·00
2252	**1559**	(1st) The Butterfly that stamped...............	1·20	1·00
	Set of 10..		11·00	9·00
	First Day Cover (Tallents House)............................			9·25
	First Day Cover (Burwash, Etchingham).................			9·25
	Presentation Pack (PO Pack No. 330)....................		12·00	
	PHQ Cards (set of 10) (237).................................		3·00	11·00

Nos. 2243/2252 were printed together in sheetlets of ten (5×2), with the surplus self-adhesive paper around each stamp retained.

No. 2243a was in the form of an unfolded booklet with vertical roulettes between columns 2/3 and 4/5 and the backing design being an illustrated booklet cover. However, since it was sold unfolded, we treat it as a sheetlet rather than a booklet.

1560 Queen Elizabeth II, 1952 (Dorothy Wilding)

1561 Queen Elizabeth II, 1968 (Cecil Beaton)

1562 Queen Elizabeth II, 1978 (Lord Snowdon)

1563 Queen Elizabeth II, 1984 (Yousuf Karsh)

1564 Queen Elizabeth II, 1996 (Tim Graham)　　**1565**

(Des Kate Stephens. Gravure De La Rue)

2002 (6 Feb). Golden Jubilee. Studio portraits of Queen Elizabeth II by photographers named. Multicoloured One centre phosphor band (2nd) or two phosphor bands (others). W **1565** (sideways). Perf 14½×14.

2253	**1560**	(2nd) Queen Elizabeth II, 1952 (Dorothy Wilding)	90	90
		a. Watermark upright	3·00	3·00
		b. Booklet pane. Nos. 2253a/2256a with margins all round	7·50	
2254	**1561**	(1st) Queen Elizabeth II, 1968 (Cecil Beaton)	1·20	1·00
		a. Watermark upright	1·40	1·40
		b. Booklet pane. Nos. 2254a/2257a with margins all round	8·00	
2255	**1562**	(E) Queen Elizabeth II, 1978 (Lord Snowdon)	2·25	1·50
		a. Watermark upright	2·00	1·40
2256	**1563**	45p. Queen Elizabeth II, 1984 (Yousef Karsh)	1·00	1·10
		a. Watermark upright	1·40	1·40
2257	**1564**	65p. Queen Elizabeth II, 1996 (Tim Graham)	1·10	1·25
		a. Watermark upright	3·00	3·00
Set of 5			5·75	5·00
Set of 5 Gutter Pairs			11·50	
First Day Cover (Tallents House)				5·25
First Day Cover (Windsor)				5·50
Presentation Pack (PO Pack No. 331)			7·00	
PHQ Cards (set of 5) (238)			1·50	5·75

The turquoise-green is used as an underlay for the black colour on all five values.

Nos. 2253a/2257a were only issued in the £7·29 A Glorious Accession booklet, No DX28.

Trials, including dates and with values in a different typeface, are known for all values.

1566

1566a

(Des M. Farrar-Bell (2nd), Enid Marx (1st). Gravure Enschedé)

2002 (6 Feb). As Types **154/155** (Wilding definitive of 1952–1954), but with service indicator as Types **1566/1566a**. One centre phosphor band (2nd) or two phosphor bands (1st). W **1565**. Uncoated paper. Perf 15×14 (with one elliptical hole in each vertical side).

2258	**1566**	(2nd) carmine-red	1·20	1·20
		a. Watermark diagonal	2·00	2·00
		b. Booklet pane. Nos. 2258×4, 2258a×4 and 2259×4 with centre blank label and margins all round. This is a pane of 12 stamps four of each type	8·00	
2259	**1566a**	(1st) green	1·25	1·25
Set of 2			2·12	2·20
First Day Cover (Tallents House) (No. 2258b)				8·00
First Day Cover (Windsor) (No. 2258b)				8·00

Nos. 2258/2259 were only issued in the £7·29 A Gracious Accession booklet, No. DX28.

No. 2258b contains a block of eight, four of each value, with a blank central label, plus an additional 2nd value shown to the left at such an angle so as to produce a diagonal watermark.

First day cover postmarks were as Nos. 2253/2257.

For other Wilding designs with decimal values see Nos. 2031/2033, **MS**2326, **MS**2367, 2378/2380 and 3329.

1567 Rabbits ('a new baby')

1568 'LOVE'

1569 Aircraft Skywriting 'hello'

1570 Bear pulling Potted Topiary Tree (Moving Home)

1571 Flowers ('best wishes')

(Des I. Bilbey (Nos. 2260, 2264), A. Kitching (No. 2261), Hoop Associates (No. 2262) and G. Percy (No. 2263))

2002 (5 Mar)–**2003**. Greetings Stamps. Occasions. Multicoloured Two phosphor bands.

(a) Litho Questa. Ordinary gum. Perf 15×14.

2260	**1567**	(1st) Rabbits 'a new baby'	1·20	1·10
2261	**1568**	(1st) 'LOVE'	1·20	1·10
2262	**1569**	(1st) Aircraft Skywriting 'hello'	1·20	1·10
2263	**1570**	(1st) Bear pulling Potted Topiary Tree (Moving Home)	1·20	1·10
2264	**1571**	(1st) 'best wishes'	1·20	1·10
Set of 5			5·50	5·00
Set of 5 Gutter Pairs			11·00	
First Day Cover (Tallents House)				5·25
First Day Cover (Merry Hill, Wolverhampton)				5·50
Presentation Pack (PO Pack No. M07)			5·75	
PHQ Cards (set of 5) (PSM08)			5·10	6·00

(b) Gravure Questa. Self-adhesive. Die-cut Perf 15×14.

2264a	**1569**	(1st) Aircraft Skywriting 'hello' (4.3.03)	3·00	3·00
		ab. Booklet pane. No. 2264a×2 plus No. 2295×4	7·50	

Nos. 2260/2264 were re-issued on 23 April 2002 in sheets of 20 with half stamp-size labels, with either the five designs *se-tenant* with greetings on the labels (No. LS7, *sold at* £5·95) or in sheets of one design with personal photographs on the labels (*sold at* £12·95). These stamps, printed by Questa in lithography, were perforated 14 instead of 15×14.

T **1569** was re-issued in sheets of 20 with half stamp-size *se-tenant* labels all printed in lithography as follows: on 30 January 2004 for Hong Kong Stamp Expo (No. LS17, Walsall), on 21 April 2005 for Pacific Explorer 2005 World Stamp Expo (No. LS24, Walsall, Perf 14), on 25 May 2006 for Washington 2006 International Stamp Exhibition (No. LS30, Cartor, Perf 14) on 14 November 2006 for Belgica 2006 International Stamp Exhibition (No. LS36, Cartor, Perf 14), on 5 August 2008 for Beijing 2008 Olympic Expo (No. LS48, Cartor, Perf 14), on 3 August 2009 for Thaipex 09 Stamp Exhibition (No. LS64, Cartor, Perf 14), on 21 October 2009 for Italia 2009 International Stamp Exhibition (No. LS66, Cartor, Perf 14) and on 4 December 2009 for MonacoPhil International Stamp Exhibition (No. LS69, Cartor, Perf 14).

No. 2264*a* was only issued in £1·62 stamp booklet, No. PM8, in which the surplus self-adhesive paper around each stamp was removed.

 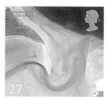

1572 Studland Bay, Dorset | **1573** Luskentyre, South Harris

1574 Cliffs, Dover, Kent | **1575** Padstow Harbour, Cornwall

1576 Broadstairs, Kent | **1577** St Abb's Head, Scottish Borders

 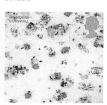

1578 Dunster Beach, Somerset | **1579** Newquay Beach, Cornwall

1580 Portrush, County Antrim | **1581** Sand-spit, Conwy

(Des R. Cooke. Litho Walsall)

2002 (19 Mar). British Coastlines. Multicoloured Two phosphor bands. Perf 14½.

2265	**1572**	27p. Studland Bay, Dorset........................	50	50
		a. Block of 10. Nos. 2265/2274............	4·50	4·50
		b. Silver omitted (block of 10).............	£3750	

2266	**1573**	27p. Luskentyre, South Harris.................	50	50
2267	**1574**	27p. Cliffs, Dover, Kent..........................	50	50
2268	**1575**	27p. Padstow Harbour, Cornwall............	50	50
2269	**1576**	27p. Broadstairs, Kent...........................	50	50
2270	**1577**	27p. St Abb's Head, Scottish Borders......	50	50
2271	**1578**	27p. Dunster Beach, Somerset...............	50	50
2272	**1579**	27p. Newquay Beach, Cornwall..............	50	50
2273	**1580**	27p. Portrush, County Antrim.................	50	50
2274	**1581**	27p. Sand-spit, Conwy...........................	50	50
Set of 10...			4·50	4·50
Gutter Block of 20..			9·00	
First Day Cover (Tallents House).........................				4·75
First Day Cover (Poolewe, Achnasheen)..............				5·00
Presentation Pack (PO Pack No. 332)...................			5·00	
PHQ Cards (set of 10) (239)................................			3·00	6·00

Nos. 2265/2274 were printed together, *se-tenant*, in blocks of ten (5×2) throughout the sheet.

1582 Slack Wire Act | **1583** Lion Tamer

1584 Trick Tri-cyclists | **1585** Krazy Kar

1586 Equestrienne

(Des R. Fuller. Gravure Questa)

2002 (10 Apr*). Europa. Circus. Multicoloured One centre phosphor band (2nd) or two phosphor bands (others). Perf 14½.

2275	**1582**	(2nd) Slack Wire Act................................	90	90
2276	**1583**	(1st) Lion Tamer.....................................	1·20	1·00
		a. Imperf (vert pair)............................	£1000	
2277	**1584**	(E) Trick Tri-cyclists...............................	2·25	1·50
		a. Imperf (pair)....................................	£1200	
2278	**1585**	45p. Krazy Kar.......................................	1·00	1·10
2279	**1586**	65p. Equestrienne.................................	1·10	1·25
Set of 5...			5·25	5·00
Set of 5 Gutter Pairs...			11·00	
First Day Cover (Tallents House).........................				5·25
First Day Cover (Clowne, Chesterfield)................				5·50
Presentation Pack (PO Pack No. 333)...................			5·75	
PHQ Cards (set of 5) (240)..................................			1·50	5·75

* Due to the funeral of the Queen Mother, the issue of Nos. 2275/2279 was delayed from 9 April, the date which appears on first day covers. The 1st and E values incorporate the EUROPA emblem.

1587 Queen Elizabeth the Queen Mother | **1587a** Queen Elizabeth

1587b Elizabeth,
Duchess of York

1587c Lady Elizabeth
Bowes-Lyon

(Des J. Gorham from photographs by N. Parkinson (1st), Dorothy Wilding (E), B. Park (45p.), Rita Martin (65p.). Gravure De La Rue)

2002 (25 Apr). Queen Elizabeth the Queen Mother Commemoration. Multicoloured Two phosphor bands. Perf 14×15.

2280	**1587**	(1st) Queen Elizabeth the Queen Mother........................	1·20	1·00
2281	**1587a**	(E) Queen Elizabeth..........................	2·25	1·50
2282	**1587b**	45p. Elizabeth, Duchess of York........	1·00	1·10
2283	**1587c**	65p. Lady Elizabeth Bowes-Lyon........	1·10	1·25
		Set of 4........................	4·75	4·25
		Set of 4 Gutter Pairs........................	9·50	
		First Day Cover (Tallents House)........................		4·50
		First Day Cover (London SW1)........................		4·75
		Presentation Pack (PO Pack No. M08)........................	5·00	

1588 Airbus A340-600 (2002)

1589 Concorde (1976)

1590 Trident (1964)

1591 VC10 (1964)

1592 Comet (1952)

(Des Roundel)

2002 (2 May). 50th Anniversary of Passenger Jet Aviation. Airliners. Multicoloured One centre phosphor band (2nd) or two phosphor bands (others). Perf 14½.

(a) Gravure De La Rue. Ordinary gum.

2284	**1588**	(2nd) Airbus A340-600 (2002)..................	90	90
2285	**1589**	(1st) Concorde (1976)........................	1·20	1·00
2286	**1590**	(E) Trident (1964)........................	2·25	1·50
2287	**1591**	45p. VC10 (1964)........................	1·20	1·20
2288	**1592**	65p. Comet (1952)........................	1·40	1·40
		Set of 5........................	6·25	6·00
		Set of 5 Gutter Pairs........................	12·50	
		First Day Cover (Tallents House)........................		6·50
		First Day Cover (Heathrow Airport, London)........................		7·00
		Presentation Pack (PO Pack No. 334)........................	7·00	
		MS2289 120×105 mm. Nos. 2284/2288....	7·00	7·00
		First Day Cover (Tallents House)........................		7·50
		First Day Cover (Heathrow Airport, London)........................		7·50
		PHQ Cards (set of 6) (241)........................	1·75	12·00

(b) Gravure Questa. Self-adhesive. Die-cut Perf 14½.

2290	**1589**	(1st) Concorde (1976)........................	3·00	3·00
		a. Booklet pane. No. 2040×4 and No. 2290×2........................	7·50	

No. 2290 was only issued in £1·62 stamp booklet, No. PM5.
The complete miniature sheet is shown on one of the PHQ cards with the others depicting individual stamps.
See also No. 2897.

1593 Crowned Lion with Shield of St George

1594 Top Left Quarter of English Flag, and Football

1595 Top Right Quarter of English Flag, and Football

1596 Bottom Left Quarter of English Flag, and Football

1597 Bottom Right Quarter of English Flag, and Football

(Des Sedley Place (No. 2291), H. Brown (No. **MS**2292). Gravure Walsall)

2002 (21 May). World Cup Football Championship, Japan and Korea. Multicoloured Two phosphor bands. Perf 14½×14.

(a) Ordinary gum.

2291	**1593**	(1st) Crowned Lion with Shield of St George..................	1·25	1·25
		Gutter Pair........................	2·50	

MS2292 145×74 mm. No. 2291; Type **1594** (1st) Top Left Quarter of English Flag, and Football; Type **1595** (1st) Top Right Quarter of English Flag, and Football; Type **1596** (1st) Bottom Left Quarter of English Flag, and Football; Type **1597** (1st) Bottom Right Quarter of English Flag, and Football. Perf 14½ (square) or 15×14 (horiz)........................

		5·00	5·00
First Day Cover (Tallents House) (No. **MS**2292)........			5·50
First Day Cover (Wembley) (No. **MS**2292)........			5·50
Presentation Pack (PO Pack No. 335) (No. **MS**2292)........	5·75		
PHQ Cards (set of 6) (242)........	1·75		7·50

(b) Self-adhesive. Die-cut Perf 15×14.

2293	**1594**	(1st) Top Left Quarter of English Flag, and Football........................	3·00	3·00
		a. Booklet pane. Nos. 2293/2294 plus No. 2040×4........................	7·50	
2294	**1595**	(1st) Top Right Quarter of English Flag, and Football........................	3·00	3·00

Stamps as T **1593** but with 'WORLD CUP 2002' inscription omitted were issued on 17 May 2007 in sheets of 20 with *se-tenant* labels showing scenes from Wembley Stadium, printed in lithography by Cartor (No. LS39).

Stamps as T **1597** also exist in sheets of 20 with *se-tenant* half stamp-sized labels, printed in lithography by Questa (No. LS8). Such sheets, with the labels showing match scenes or supporters, were available at £5·95 from philatelic outlets, or with personal photographs at £12·95 from Royal Mail in Edinburgh.

Nos. 2293/2294 were only issued in £1·62 stamp booklet, No. PM6.
The complete miniature sheet is shown on one of the PHQ cards with the others depicting individual stamps from No. **MS**2292 and No. 2291.

For Nos. 2295/2298 see Decimal Machin Definitives section.

1598 Swimming

1599 Running

1600 Cycling

1601 Long Jump

1602 Wheelchair Racing

(Des Madeleine Bennett. Gravure Enschedé)

2002 (16 July). 17th Commonwealth Games, Manchester. Multicoloured One side phosphor band (2nd) or two phosphor bands (others). Perf 14½.

2299	**1598**	(2nd) Swimming	90	90
2300	**1599**	(1st) Running	1·20	1·00
2301	**1600**	(E) Cycling	2·25	1·50
2302	**1601**	47p. Long Jump	1·10	1·25
2303	**1602**	68p. Wheelchair Racing	1·20	1·50
Set of 5			5·75	5·50
Set of 5 Gutter Pairs			11·50	
First Day Cover (Tallents House)				6·00
First Day Cover (Manchester)				6·00
Presentation Pack (PO Pack No. 336)			6·00	
PHQ Cards (set of 5) (243)			1·50	6·75

On Nos. 2300/2303 the phosphor bands appear at the right and the centre of each stamp.

1603 Tinkerbell

1604 Wendy, John and Michael Darling in front of Big Ben

1605 Crocodile and Alarm Clock

1606 Captain Hook

1607 Peter Pan

(Des Tutssels. Gravure De La Rue)

2002 (20 Aug). 150th Anniversary of Great Ormond Street Children's Hospital. *Peter Pan* by Sir James Barrie. Multicoloured One centre phosphor band (2nd) or two phosphor bands (others). Perf 15×14.

2304	**1603**	(2nd) Tinkerbell	90	90
2305	**1604**	(1st) Wendy, John and Michael Darling in front of Big Ben	1·20	1·00
2306	**1605**	(E) Crocodile and Alarm Clock	2·25	1·50
2307	**1606**	47p. Captain Hook	1·10	1·25
2308	**1607**	68p. Peter Pan	1·20	1·50
Set of 5			5·75	5·50
Set of 5 Gutter Pairs			11·50	
First Day Cover (Tallents House)				6·00
First Day Cover (Hook)				6·00
Presentation Pack (PO Pack No. 337)			6·00	
PHQ Cards (set of 5) (244)			1·50	6·75

1608 Millennium Bridge, 2001

1609 Tower Bridge, 1894

1610 Westminster Bridge, 1864

1611 Blackfriars Bridge, *circa* 1800 (William Marlow)

1612 London Bridge, *circa* 1670 (Wenceslaus Hollar)

(Des Sarah Davies and R. Maude)

2002 (10 Sept). Bridges of London. Multicoloured One centre phosphor band (2nd) or two phosphor bands (others).

(a) Litho Questa. Ordinary gum. Perf 15×14.

2309	**1608**	(2nd) Millennium Bridge, 2001	90	90
2310	**1609**	(1st) Tower Bridge, 1894	1·20	1·00
2311	**1610**	(E) Westminster Bridge, 1864	2·25	1·50
2312	**1611**	47p. Blackfriars Bridge, circa 1800	1·20	1·60
2313	**1612**	68p. London Bridge, circa 1670	1·40	1·75
Set of 5			6·25	6·00
Set of 5 Gutter Pairs			12·50	
First Day Cover (Tallents House)				6·25
First Day Cover (London SE1)				6·25
Presentation Pack (PO Pack No. 338)			30·00	
PHQ Cards (set of 5) (245)			1·50	7·00

(b) Gravure Questa. Self-adhesive. Die-cut Perf 15×14.

2314	**1609**	(1st) Tower Bridge, 1894	3·00	3·00
		a. Booklet pane. No. 2314×2, and No. 2295×4	7·50	

No. 2314 was only issued in £1·62 stamp booklets in which the surplus self-adhesive paper around each stamp was removed, No. PM7.

1613 Galaxies and Nebulae

(Des Rose Design. Gravure Questa)

2002 (24 Sept). Astronomy. Sheet 120×89 mm. Multicoloured Two phosphor bands. Perf 14½×14.

MS2315 **1613** Galaxies and Nebulae (1st) Planetary nebula in Aquila; (1st) Planetary nebula in Pegasus; (1st) Planetary nebula in Norma; (1st) Seyfert 2 galaxy in Circinus	4·80	4·80
a. Booklet pane. As No. **MS**2315, but larger, 150×95 mm	5·75	
First Day Cover (Tallents House)		5·00
First Day Cover (Star, Glenrothes)		5·00
Presentation Pack (PO Pack No. 339)	11·00	
PHQ Cards (set of 5) (246)	1·50	5·00

Booklet pane No. **MS**2315a comes from the £6·83 Across the Universe booklet No. DX29.

The five PHQ cards depict the four designs and the complete miniature sheet.

1614 Green Pillar Box, 1857

1615 Horizontal Aperture Box, 1874

1616 Air Mail Box, 1934

1617 Double Aperture Box, 1939

1618 Modern Style Box, 1980

(Des Silk Pearce. Eng C. Slania. Recess and litho Enschedé)

2002 (8 Oct). 150th Anniversary of the First Pillar Box. Multicoloured One centre phosphor band (2nd) or two phosphor bands (others). Perf 14×14½.

2316	**1614**	(2nd) Green Pillar Box, 1857	90	90
2317	**1615**	(1st) Horizontal Aperture Box, 1874	1·20	1·00
2318	**1616**	(E) Air Mail Box, 1934	2·25	1·50
2319	**1617**	47p. Double Aperture Box, 1939	1·20	1·10
2320	**1618**	68p. Modern Style Box, 1980	1·40	1·25
Set of 5			6·25	5·00
Set of 5 Gutter Pairs			12·50	
First Day Cover (Tallents House)				5·25
First Day Cover (Bishops Caundle, Sherborne)				5·25
Presentation Pack (PO Pack No. 340)			6·75	
PHQ Cards (set of 5) (247)			1·50	5·50

1619 Blue Spruce Star

1620 Holly

1621 Ivy

1622 Mistletoe

1623 Pine Cone

(Des Rose Design. Gravure De La Rue)

2002 (5 Nov). Christmas. Self-adhesive. Multicoloured One centre phosphor band (2nd) or two phosphor bands (others). Die-cut Perf 14½×14.

2321	**1619**	(2nd) Blue Spruce Star	90	90
		a. Booklet pane. No. 2321×24	22·00	
		b. Imperf (pair)	45·00	
2322	**1620**	(1st) Holly	1·20	1·00
		a. Booklet pane. No. 2322×12	16·00	
		b. Imperf (pair)	£125	
2323	**1621**	(E) Ivy	2·25	1·50
2324	**1622**	47p. Mistletoe	1·25	1·25
2325	**1623**	68p. Pine Cone	1·40	1·40
Set of 5			6·00	5·00
First Day Cover (Tallents House)				5·25
First Day Cover (Bethlehem, Llandeilo)				5·25
Presentation Pack (PO Pack No. 341)			6·00	
PHQ Cards (set of 5) (248)			1·50	5·75

Nos. 2321/2325 were each printed in sheets of 50, with the surplus backing paper retained around each stamp retained, separated by gauge 9 roulettes.

Nos. 2321b and 2322b show both the die-cut perforations and the roulettes omitted.

Year Pack

2002 (5 Nov). Comprises Nos. 2243/2257, 2260/2264, 2265/2288, **MS**2292, 2299/2313 and **MS**2315/2325.

CP2325a	Year Pack (Pack No. 342)	65·00

Post Office Yearbook

2002 (5 Nov). Comprises Nos. 2243/2257, 2260/2264, 2265/2288, 2291/2292, 2299/2313 and **MS**2315/2325 in hardback book with slip case

YB2325a	Yearbook	48·00

1623a Wilding Anniversary (1st issue)

(Des Rose Design. Gravure De La Rue)

2002 (5 Dec). 50th Anniversary of Wilding Definitives (1st issue). Sheet 124×70 mm, printed on pale cream. One centre phosphor band (2nd) or two phosphor bands (others). W **1565**. Perf 15×14 (with one elliptical hole in each vertical side).

MS2326 1623a 1p. orange-red; 2p. ultramarine; 5p. red-brown; (2nd) carmine-red; (1st) green; 33p. brown; 37p. magenta; 47p. bistre-brown; 50p. green and label showing National Emblems............	5·00	5·00	
a. Imperf...		£6000	
First Day Cover (Tallents House)..		5·25	
First Day Cover (Windsor)..		5·25	
Presentation Pack (PO Pack No. 59)......................................	25·00		
PHQ Cards (set of 5) (D21)....................................	1·50	5·00	

The five PHQ cards depict the 1st, 2nd, 33p., 37p. and 47p. stamps.
For further Wilding designs with decimal face values, see Nos. 2031/2033, 2258/2259, **MS2367** and 2378/2380.

1624 Barn Owl landing

1625 Barn Owl with folded Wings and Legs down

1626 Barn Owl with extended Wings and Legs down

1627 Barn Owl in Flight with Wings lowered

1628 Barn Owl in Flight with Wings raised

1629 Kestrel with Wings folded

1630 Kestrel with Wings fully extended upwards

1631 Kestrel with Wings horizontal

1632 Kestrel with wings partly extended downwards   **1633** Kestrel with wings fully extended downwards

(Des J. Gibbs from photographs by S. Dalton. Litho Walsall)

2003 (14 Jan). Birds of Prey. Multicoloured Phosphor background. Perf 14½.

2327	**1624**	(1st) Barn Owl landing.............................	1·20	1·00
		a. Block of 10. Nos. 2327/2336............	10·50	9·00
		ab. Brownish grey and phosphor omitted.................................	£1600	
2328	**1625**	(1st) Barn Owl with folded Wings and Legs down.............................	1·20	1·00
2329	**1626**	(1st) Barn Owl with extended Wings and Legs down.............................	1·20	1·00
2330	**1627**	(1st) Barn Owl in Flight with Wings lowered................................	1·20	1·00
2331	**1628**	(1st) Barn Owl in Flight with Wings raised.................................	1·20	1·00
2332	**1629**	(1st) Kestrel with Wings folded..............	1·20	1·00
2333	**1630**	(1st) Kestrel with Wings fully extended upwards.............................	1·20	1·00
2334	**1631**	(1st) Kestrel with Wings horizontal........	1·20	1·00
2335	**1632**	(1st) Kestrel with wings partly extended downwards.....................	1·20	1·00
2336	**1633**	(1st) Kestrel with wings fully extended downwards...............................	1·20	1·00
Set of 10..			10·50	9·00
Gutter Block of 20..			21·00	
First Day Cover (Tallents House)............................				9·25
First Day Cover (Hawkshead Ambleside)................				9·25
Presentation Pack (PO Pack No. 343).....................			11·00	
PHQ Cards (set of 10) (249).................................			3·00	11·00

Nos. 2327/2336 were printed together, se-tenant, in blocks of ten (5×2) throughout the sheet.
No. 2327ab shows the owl white on Nos. 2327/2331, and the face value with Queen's head omitted on Nos. 2332/2336.

1634 'Gold star, See me, Playtime'

1635 'IU, XXXX, S.W.A.L.K.'

1636 'Angel, Poppet, Little terror'

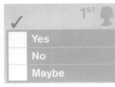

1637 'Yes, No, Maybe'

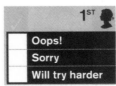

1638 'Oops!, Sorry, Will try harder'

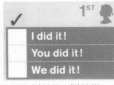

1639 'I did it!, You did it!, We did it!'

(Des UNA, Sara Wiegand and M. Exon. Litho Questa)

2003 (4 Feb). Greetings Stamps. Occasions. Multicoloured Two phosphor bands. Perf 14½×14.

2337	**1634**	(1st) 'Gold star, See me, Playtime'...............	1·20	1·00
		a. Block of 6. Nos. 2337/2342..............	6·25	5·50
		b. Imperf (block of 6).......................	£2000	
2338	**1635**	(1st) 'I ❤ U, XXXX, S.W.A.L.K.'..............	1·20	1·00
2339	**1636**	(1st) 'Angel, Poppet, Little terror'..........	1·20	1·00
2340	**1637**	(1st) 'Yes, No, Maybe'.........................	1·20	1·00
2341	**1638**	(1st) 'Oops!, Sorry, Will try harder'........	1·20	1·00
2342	**1639**	(1st) 'I did it!, You did it!, We did it!'......	1·20	1·00
		Set of 6....................................	6·25	5·50
		Gutter Block of 12.........................	12·50	
		First Day Cover (Tallents House)............		5·75
		First Day Cover (Merry Hill, Wolverhampton)...		5·75
		Presentation Pack (PO Pack No. M09).......	6·00	
		PHQ Cards (set of 6) (PSM09)...............	1·75	6·25

Nos. 2337/2342 were printed together, *se-tenant*, in blocks of six (3×2) throughout the sheet.

Nos. 2337/2342 were also issued in sheets of 20 (containing four of Nos. 2338 and 2340 and three each of the others) with *se-tenant* labels (No. LS12). Such sheets with the labels showing printed faces were available at £5·95 from philatelic outlets, or with personalised photographs at £14·95 from Royal Mail in Edinburgh.

1640 Completing the Genome Jigsaw

1641 Ape with Moustache and Scientist

1642 DNA Snakes and Ladders

1643 Animal Scientists

1644 Genome Crystal Ball

(Des Williams Murray Hamm and P. Brookes. Litho Enschedé)

2003 (25 Feb). 50th Anniversary of Discovery of DNA. Multicoloured One centre phosphor band (2nd) or two phosphor bands (others). Perf 14½.

2343	**1640**	(2nd) Completing the Genome Jigsaw.......	90	90
		a. Booklet pane. Nos. 2343/2344, each×2, with margins all round......	3·50	
2344	**1641**	(1st) Ape with Moustache and Scientist............................	1·20	1·00
2345	**1642**	(E) DNA Snakes and Ladders................	2·25	1·50
		a. Booklet pane. No. 2345×4 with margins all round..................	5·25	
2346	**1643**	47p. Animal Scientists.......................	1·10	1·40
2347	**1644**	68p. Genome Crystal Ball...................	1·25	1·60
		Set of 5....................................	6·00	5·75
		Set of 5 Gutter Pairs......................	12·00	
		First Day Cover (Tallents House)............		6·25
		First Day Cover (Cambridge).................		6·50
		Presentation Pack (PO Pack No. 344).......	6·00	
		PHQ Cards (set of 5) (250).................	1·50	6·25

Booklet panes Nos. 2343a and 2345a come from the £6·99 Microcosmos booklet, No. DX30.

1645 Strawberry   **1646** Potato

1647 Apple   **1648** Red Pepper

1649 Pear   **1650** Orange

1651 Tomato   **1652** Lemon

1653 Brussels Sprout   **1654** Aubergine

(Des johnson banks. Gravure Walsall)

2003 (25 Mar). Fruit and Vegetables. Self-adhesive. Multicoloured Two phosphor bands. Perf 14½×14 die-cut (without teeth around protruding tops or bottoms of the designs).

2348	**1645**	(1st) Strawberry.............................	1·20	1·00
		a. Sheetlet of 10. Nos. 2348/2357 and pane of decorative labels........	10·50	
		ab. Imperf (block of 10)...................	£1500	
2349	**1646**	(1st) Potato.................................	1·20	1·00
2350	**1647**	(1st) Apple..................................	1·20	1·00
2351	**1648**	(1st) Red Pepper............................	1·20	1·00
2352	**1649**	(1st) Pear...................................	1·20	1·00
2353	**1650**	(1st) Orange................................	1·20	1·00
2354	**1651**	(1st) Tomato................................	1·20	1·00
2355	**1652**	(1st) Lemon.................................	1·20	1·00
2356	**1653**	(1st) Brussels Sprout.......................	1·20	1·00
2357	**1654**	(1st) Aubergine.............................	1·20	1·00
		Set of 10...................................	10·50	9·00
		First Day Cover (Tallents House)............		9·25
		First Day Cover (Pear Tree, Derby)..........		9·25
		Presentation Pack (PO Pack No. 345).......	12·00	
		PHQ Cards (set of 10) (251)................	3·00	10·50

Nos. 2348/2357 were printed together in sheets of ten with the surplus self-adhesive paper around each stamp retained.

The stamp pane is accompanied by a similar-sized pane of self-adhesive labels showing ears, eyes, mouths, hats, etc which are intended for the adornment of fruit and vegetables depicted. This pane is separated from the stamps by a line of roulettes.

Nos. 2348/2357 were re-issued on 7 March 2006 in sheets of 20, containing two of each of the ten designs accompanied by se-tenant labels with speech bubbles and stickers showing eyes, hats, etc. in the sheet margin (No. LS29). These sheets were printed in lithography by Cartor and sold for £6·55.

No. 2355 was also available in sheets of 20 with personal photographs on the labels at £14·95 per sheet from Royal Mail Edinburgh.

For Nos. 2357a/2359 (Overseas Booklet Stamps), T **1655**, see Decimal Machin Definitives sections

1656 Amy Johnson (pilot) and Biplane

1657 Members of 1953 Everest Team

1658 Freya Stark (traveller and writer) and Desert

1659 Ernest Shackleton (Antarctic explorer) and Wreck of *Endurance*

1660 Francis Chichester (yachtsman) and *Gipsy Moth IV*

1661 Robert Falcon Scott (Antarctic explorer) and Norwegian Expedition at the Pole

(Des H. Brown)

2003 (29 Apr). Extreme Endeavours (British Explorers). Multicoloured One centre phosphor band (2nd) or two phosphor bands (others). Perf 15×14½.

(a) Gravure Questa. Ordinary gum.

2360	**1656**	(2nd) Amy Johnson	90	90
2361	**1657**	(1st) Members of 1953 Everest Team	1·20	1·00
2362	**1658**	(E) Freya Stark	2·25	1·50
2363	**1659**	42p. Ernest Shackleton	1·00	1·00
2364	**1660**	47p. Francis Chichester	1·10	1·25
2365	**1661**	68p. Robert Falcon Scott	1·25	1·40
Set of 6			6·75	6·25
Set of 6 Gutter Pairs			13·50	
First Day Cover (Tallents House)				7·00
First Day Cover (Plymouth)				7·00
Presentation Pack (PO Pack No. 346)			7·25	
PHQ Cards (set of 6) (252)			1·75	6·50

(b) Gravure De La Rue. Self-adhesive. Die-cut Perf 14½.

2366	**1657**	(1st) Members of 1953 Everest Team	3·00	3·00
		a. Booklet pane. No. 2366×2 plus No. 2295×4	7·50	

The phosphor bands on Nos. 2361/2365 are at the centre and right of each stamp.

No. 2366 was only issued in £1·62 stamp booklet, No. PM9, in which the surplus self-adhesive paper around each stamp was removed.

Gummed perforated trials with alternative face values and/or designs are known.

1661a Wilding Anniversary (2nd issue)

Des Rose Design. Gravure De La Rue)

2003 (20 May). 50th Anniversary of Wilding Definitives (2nd issue). Sheet 124×70 mm, printed on pale cream. One centre phosphor band (20p.) or two phosphor bands (others). W **1565**. Perf 15×14 (with one elliptical hole in each vertical side).

MS2367	**1661a**	4p. deep lilac; 8p. ultramarine; 10p. reddish purple; 20p. bright green; 28p. bronze-green; 34p. brown-purple; (E) chestnut; 42p. Prussian blue; 68p. grey-blue and label showing National Emblems	4·50	4·75
		a. Imperf	—	
First Day Cover (Tallents House)				5·50
First Day Cover (Windsor)				5·50
Presentation Pack (PO Pack No. 61)			9·00	

1662 Guardsmen in Coronation Procession

1663 East End Children reading Coronation Party Poster

1664 Queen Elizabeth II in Coronation Chair with Bishops of Durham and Bath and Wells

1665 Children in Plymouth working on Royal Montage

1666 Queen Elizabeth II in Coronation Robes (photograph by Cecil Beaton)

1667 Children's Race at East End Street Party

1668 Coronation Coach passing through Marble Arch

1669 Children in Fancy Dress

1670 Coronation Coach outside Buckingham Palace

1671 Children eating at London Street Party

(Des Kate Stephens. Gravure De La Rue (sheets) or Walsall (booklets))

2003 (2 June). 50th Anniversary of Coronation. W **1565**. Multicoloured Two phosphor bands. Perf 14½×14.

2368	**1662**	(1st) Guardsmen in Coronation Procession......................	1·20	1·00
		a. Block of 10. Nos. 2368/2377............	10·50	9·00
		b. Booklet pane. Nos. 2368, 2370, 2373 and 2375 with margins all round......................	4·25	
2369	**1663**	(1st) East End Children..........................	1·20	1·00
		b. Booklet pane. Nos. 2369, 2372, 2374 and 2377 with margins all round......................	4·25	
2370	**1664**	(1st) Queen Elizabeth II in Coronation Chair..................................	1·20	1·00
2371	**1665**	(1st) Children in Plymouth......................	1·20	1·00
2372	**1666**	(1st) Queen Elizabeth II in Coronation Robes..................................	1·20	1·00
2373	**1667**	(1st) Children's Race..............................	1·20	1·00
2374	**1668**	(1st) Coronation Coach passing through Marble Arch......................	1·20	1·00
2375	**1669**	(1st) Children in Fancy Dress.................	1·20	1·00
2376	**1670**	(1st) Coronation Coach outside Buckingham Palace..................	1·20	1·00
2377	**1671**	(1st) Children eating at London Street Party...................................	1·20	1·00
Set of 10................................			10·50	9·00
Gutter Block of 20................			21·00	
First Day Cover (Tallents House)............				9·50
First Day Cover (London SW1)................				9·50
Presentation Pack (PO Pack No. 347)................			11·00	
PHQ Cards (set of 10) (253)................			3·00	10·00

Nos. 2368/2377 were printed together, *se-tenant*, as blocks of ten (5×2) in sheets of 60 (2 panes of 30).

No. 2372 does not show a silhouette of the Queen's head in gold as do the other nine designs.

Booklet pane Nos. 2368b/2369b come from the £7·46 A perfect Coronation booklet, No. DX31.

1671a

1671b

1671c

(Gravure Walsall)

2003 (2 June). 50th Anniversary of Coronation. Booklet stamps. W **1565**. Two phosphor bands. Perf 15×14 (with one elliptical hole in each vertical side for Nos. 2378/2379).

2378	**1671a**	47p. bistre-brown..................	2·00	2·00
		a. Booklet pane. Nos. 2378/2379, each×2, and 2380 with margins all round........................	32·00	
2379	**1671b**	68p. grey-blue..........................	2·50	2·50
2380	**1671c**	£1 deep yellow-green....................	26·00	26·00
Set of 3................			30·00	30·00

Nos. 2378/2380 were only issued in the £7·46 A Perfect Coronation booklet, No. DX31.

Stamps as Nos. 2378/2379, but on pale cream, were also included in the Wilding miniature sheets, No. **MS**2326 or No. **MS**2367.

A £1 design as No. 2380, but on phosphorised paper, was previously included in the Stamp Show 2000 miniature sheet, No. **MS**2147.

1672 Prince William in September 2001 (Brendan Beirne)

1673 Prince William in September 2000 (Tim Graham)

1674 Prince William in September 2001 (Camera Press)

1675 Prince William in September 2001 (Tim Graham)

(Des Madeleine Bennett. Gravure Walsall)

2003 (17 June). 21st Birthday of Prince William of Wales. Multicoloured Phosphor backgrounds. Perf 14½.

2381	**1672**	28p. Prince William in September 2001	95	95
2382	**1673**	(E) Prince William in September 2000	2·25	1·50
2383	**1674**	47p. Prince William in September 2001	1·70	1·90
2384	**1675**	68p. Prince William in September 2001	2·10	2·25
Set of 4................			6·25	6·00
Set of 4 Gutter Pairs................			12·50	
First Day Cover (Tallents House)................				6·25
First Day Cover (Cardiff)................				6·25
Presentation Pack (PO Pack No. 348)................			8·00	
PHQ Cards (set of 4) (254)................			1·25	6·75

1676 Loch Assynt, Sutherland

1677 Ben More, Isle of Mull

1678 Rothiemurchus, Cairngorms

1679 Dalveen Pass, Lowther Hills

1680 Glenfinnan Viaduct, Lochaber

1681 Papa Little, Shetland Islands

(Des Phelan Barker. Gravure De La Rue)

2003 (15 July). A British Journey. Scotland. Multicoloured One centre phosphor band (2nd) or two phosphor bands (others). Perf 14½.

(a) Ordinary gum.

2385	**1676**	(2nd) Loch Assynt, Sutherland..................	90	90
2386	**1677**	(1st) Ben More, Isle of Mull......................	1·20	1·00
2387	**1678**	(E) Rothiemurchus, Cairngorms.............	2·25	1·50
2388	**1679**	42p. Dalveen Pass, Lowther Hills.............	1·00	1·00
2389	**1680**	47p. Glenfinnan Viaduct, Lochaber........	1·10	1·25
2390	**1681**	68p. Papa Little, Shetland Islands...........	1·25	1·40
Set of 6			7·00	6·25
Set of 6 Gutter Pairs			14·00	
First Day Cover (Tallents House)				6·75
First Day Cover (Baltasound, Unst, Shetland)				6·75
Presentation Pack (PO Pack No. 349)			7·00	
PHQ Cards (set of 6) (255)			1·75	6·75

(b) Self-adhesive. Die-cut Perf 14½.

2391	**1677**	(1st) Ben More, Isle of Mull................	3·00	3·00
		a. Booklet pane. No. 2391×2, and		
		No. 2295×4............................	7·50	

No. 2391 was only issued in £1·68 stamp booklet, No. PM10, in which the surplus self-adhesive paper around each stamp was removed.

Perforated trials of this set with alternative face values or designs are known.

1682 'The Station' (Andrew Davidson)

1683 'Black Swan' (Stanley Chew)

1684 'The Cross Keys' (George Mackenney)

1685 'The Mayflower' (Ralph Ellis)

1686 'The Barley Sheaf' (Joy Cooper)

(Des Elmwood. Gravure De La Rue)

2003 (12 Aug). Europa. British Pub Signs. Multicoloured Two phosphor bands. Perf 14×14½.

2392	**1682**	(1st) 'The Station'.......................................	1·20	1·00
		a. Booklet pane. No. 2392×4 with		
		margins all round (16.3.04).............	4·25	
2393	**1683**	(E) 'Black Swan'.......................................	2·25	1·50
2394	**1684**	42p. 'The Cross Keys'................................	1·00	1·00
2395	**1685**	47p. 'The Mayflower'...............................	1·25	1·25
2396	**1686**	68p. 'The Barley Sheaf'............................	1·40	1·40
Set of 5			6·25	5·50
Set of 5 Gutter Pairs			12·50	
First Day Cover (Tallents House)				5·75
First Day Cover (Cross Keys, Hereford)				5·75
Presentation Pack (PO Pack No. 350)			6·75	
PHQ Cards (set of 5) (256)			1·50	6·00

The 1st and E values include the EUROPA emblem.

No. 2392a comes from the £7·44 Letters by Night booklet, No. DX32.

1687 Meccano Constructor Biplane, *circa* 1931

1688 Wells-Brimtoy Clockwork Double-decker Omnibus, *circa* 1938

1689 Hornby M1 Clockwork Locomotive and Tender, *circa* 1948

1690 Dinky Toys Ford Zephyr, *circa* 1956

1691 Mettoy Friction Drive Space Ship *Eagle*, *circa* 1960

(Des Trickett and Webb)

2003 (18 Sept). Classic Transport Toys. Multicoloured Two phosphor bands.

(a) Gravure Enschedé. Ordinary gum. Perf 14½×14.

2397	**1687**	(1st) Meccano Constructor Biplane........	1·20	1·00
2398	**1688**	(E) Wells-Brimtoy Clockwork Double-decker Omnibus................................	2·25	1·50
2399	**1689**	42p. Hornby M1 Clockwork Locomotive and Tender..................	95	1·00
2400	**1690**	47p. Dinky Toys Ford Zephyr..................	1·25	1·25
2401	**1691**	68p. Mettoy Friction Drive Space Ship Eagle...................................	1·40	1·50
Set of 5			6·25	5·50
Set of 5 Gutter Pairs			12·50	
First Day Cover (Tallents House)				5·75
First Day Cover (Toye, Downpatrick)				5·75
Presentation Pack (PO Pack No. 351)			6·75	
PHQ Cards (set of 6) (257)			1·75	6·00
MS2402 115×105mm. Nos. 2397/2401			6·50	5·50
First Day Cover (Philatelic Bureau, Edinburgh)				6·75

(b) Gravure De La Rue. Self-adhesive. Die-cut Perf 14½×14.

2403	**1687**	(1st) Meccano Constructor Biplane........	3·00	3·00
		a. Booklet pane. No. 2403×2 and		
		No. 2295×4............................	7·50	

No. 2403 was only issued in £1·68 stamp booklet, No. PM11, in which the surplus self-adhesive paper around each stamp was removed.

The complete miniature sheet is shown on one of the PHQ cards with the others depicting individual stamps.

1692 Coffin of Denytenamun, Egyptian, *circa* 900BC

1693 Alexander the Great, Greek, *circa* 200BC

1694 Sutton Hoo Helmet, Anglo-Saxon, *circa* AD600

1695 Sculpture of Parvati, South Indian, *circa* AD1550

1696 Mask of Xiuhtecuhtli, Mixtec-Aztec, *circa* AD1500

1697 Hoa Hakananai'a, Easter Island, *circa* AD1000

(Des Rose Design. Gravure Walsall)

2003 (7 Oct). 250th Anniversary of the British Museum. Multicoloured One side phosphor band (2nd), two phosphor bands ((1st), (E), 47p.) or phosphor background at left and band at right (42p., 68p.). Perf 14×14½.

2404	**1692**	(2nd) Coffin of Denytenamun.....................	90	90
2405	**1693**	(1st) Alexander the Great.........................	1·20	1·00
2406	**1694**	(E) Sutton Hoo Helmet...........................	2·25	1·50
2407	**1695**	42p. Sculpture of Parvati.........................	90	1·00
2408	**1696**	47p. Mask of Xiuhtecuhtli........................	1·00	1·00
2409	**1697**	68p. Hoa Hakananai'a.............................	1·10	1·25
Set of 6..			6·25	6·00
Set of 6 Gutter Pairs..			12·50	
First Day Cover (Tallents House)..............................				6·50
First Day Cover (London WC1)...............................				6·50
Presentation Pack (PO Pack No. 352).......................			7·00	
PHQ Cards (*set of 6*) (258)...................................			1·75	6·00

1698 Ice Spiral

1699 Icicle Star

1700 Wall of Ice Blocks

1701 Ice Ball

1702 Ice Hole

1703 Snow Pyramids

(Des D. Davis. Gravure De La Rue)

2003 (4 Nov). Christmas. Ice Sculptures by Andy Goldsworthy. Self-adhesive. Multicoloured One side phosphor band (2nd), 'all-over' phosphor (1st) or two bands (others). Die-cut Perf 14½×14.

2410	**1698**	(2nd) Ice Spiral..	90	90
		a. Booklet pane. No. 2410×24.............	22·00	
2411	**1699**	(1st) Icicle Star...	1·20	1·00
		a. Booklet pane. No. 2411×12.............	16·00	
2412	**1700**	(E) Wall of Ice Blocks.............................	2·25	1·50
2413	**1701**	53p. Ice Ball..	1·25	1·25
2414	**1702**	68p. Ice Hole...	1·40	1·50
2415	**1703**	£1·12 Snow Pyramids..............................	1·50	1·60
Set of 6..			7·50	6·75
First Day Cover (Tallents House)..............................				7·50
First Day Cover (Bethlehem, Llandeilo)......................				7·50
Presentation Pack (PO Pack No. 353).......................			7·25	
PHQ Cards (*set of 6*) (259)....................................			1·75	7·00

Nos. 2410/2415 were each printed in sheets of 50 with the surplus backing paper around each stamp removed.

The 2nd and 1st class were also issued in separate sheets of 20 printed in lithography instead of gravure, each stamp accompanied by a half stamp-size *se-tenant* label showing either ice sculptures (2nd) or animals (1st) (Nos. LS15/LS16). Both sheets have the backing paper around each stamp retained.

The 2nd class sheet was sold for £4·20 and the 1st class for £6·15. These sheets were also available with personal photographs instead of labels at £9·95 (2nd) or £14·95 (1st) from Royal Mail, Edinburgh or £15 from photo-booths at selected post offices and Safeway stores.

Year Pack

2003 (4 Nov). Comprises Nos. 2327/2357, 2360/2365, 2368/2377, 2381/2390, 2392/2401 and 2404/2415.

CP2415*a*	Year Pack (Pack No. 354)......................	70·00

Post Office Yearbook

2003 (4 Nov). Comprises Nos. 2327/2357, 2360/2365, 2368/2377, 2381/2390, 2392/2401 and 2404/2415 in hardback book with slipcase

YB2415*a*	Yearbook..	55·00

1704 Rugby Scenes

(Des Why Not Associates. Litho Walsall)

2003 (19 Dec). England's Victory in Rugby World Cup Championship, Australia. Sheet 115×85 mm. Multicoloured Two phosphor bands. Perf 14.

MS2416 **1704** (1st) England flags and fans; (1st) England team standing in circle before match; 68p. World Cup trophy; 68p. Victorious England players after match.......................	9·00	9·00
First Day Cover (Tallents House)..............................		9·25
First Day Cover (Twickenham).................................		9·25
Presentation Pack (PO Pack No. M9B)......................	20·00	

1705 *Dolgoch*, Rheilffordd Talyllyn Railway, Gwynedd

1706 CR Class 439, Bo'ness and Kinneil Railway, West Lothian

1707 GCR Class 8K, Leicestershire

1708 GWR Manor Class *Bradley Manor*, Severn Valley Railway, Worcestershire

1709 SR West Country Class *Blackmoor Vale*, Bluebell Railway, East Sussex

1710 BR Standard Class, Keighley and Worth Valley Railway, Yorkshire

(Des Roundel. Litho De La Rue)

2004 (13 Jan–16 Mar). Classic Locomotives. Multicoloured One side phosphor band (20p.) or two phosphor bands (others). Perf 14½.

2417	**1705**	20p. *Dolgoch*, Rheilffordd Talyllyn Railway....................	65	65
2418	**1706**	28p. CR Class 439, Bo'ness and Kinneil Railway....................	75	75
		a. Booklet pane. Nos. 2418/2420 with margins all round (16.3.04)....	2·25	
2419	**1707**	(E) GCR Class 8K....................	2·25	1·50
2420	**1708**	42p. GWR Manor Class *Bradley Manor*, Severn Valley Railway....................	1·00	1·10
2421	**1709**	47p. SR West Country Class *Blackmoor Vale*, Bluebell Railway....................	1·10	1·25
		a. Imperf (pair)....................	£1200	
2422	**1710**	68p. BR Standard Class, Keighley and Worth Valley Railway....................	1·25	1·25
Set of 6....................			5·75	5·50
Set of 6 Gutter Pairs....................			12·50	
First Day Cover (Tallents House)....................				6·00
First Day Cover (York)....................				6·00
Presentation Pack (PO Pack No. 355)....................			10·00	
PHQ Cards (set of 7) (260)....................			2·00	6·25
MS2423 190×67 mm. Nos. 2417/2422....................			14·50	14·50
First Day (Tallents House)....................				15·00
First Day (York)....................				15·00

No. 2418a comes from the £7·44 Letters by Night booklet, No. DX32.
The seven PHQ cards depict the six individual stamps and the miniature sheet.

1711 Postman

1712 Face

1713 Duck

1714 Baby

1715 Aircraft

(Des S. Kambayashi. Litho De La Rue)

2004 (3 Feb). Occasions. Multicoloured Two phosphor bands. Perf 14½×14.

2424	**1711**	(1st) Postman....................	1·20	1·00
		a. Horiz strip of 5. Nos. 2424/2428.....	5·50	4·50
		ab. Imperf strip of 5....................		
2425	**1712**	(1st) Face....................	1·20	1·00
2426	**1713**	(1st) Duck....................	1·20	1·00
2427	**1714**	(1st) Baby....................	1·20	1·00
2428	**1715**	(1st) Aircraft....................	1·20	1·00
Set of 5....................			5·50	4·50
Gutter Block of 10....................			11·00	
First Day Cover (Tallents House)....................				5·00
First Day Cover (Merry Hill, Wolverhampton)....................				5·00
Presentation Pack (PO Pack No. M10)....................			5·75	
PHQ Cards (set of 5) (PSM10)....................			1·50	6·00

Nos. 2424/2428 were printed together, *se-tenant*, as horizontal strips of five in sheets of 25 (5×5).
Nos. 2424/2428 were also issued in sheets of 20 containing vertical strips of the five designs alternated with half stamp-size labels (No. LS18). These sheets with printed labels were available at £6·15 from philatelic outlets, or with personalised photographs at £14·95 from Royal Mail in Edinburgh.

1716 Map showing Middle Earth

1717 Forest of Lothlórien in Spring

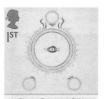

1718 Dust Jacket for The Fellowship of the Ring

1719 Rivendell

1720 The Hall at Bag End   **1721** Orthanc

1728 Slemish, Antrim
Mountains

1729 Banns Road, Mourne
Mountains

1722 Doors of Durin   **1723** Barad-dûr

1730 Glenelly Valley,
Sperrins

1731 Islandmore,
Strangford Lough

(Des Phelan Barker. Gravure Enschedé (sheets) or De La Rue (booklet))

2004 (16 Mar). A British Journey. Northern Ireland. Multicoloured One
side phosphor band (2nd) or two phosphor bands (others). Perf 14½.

(a) Ordinary gum.

2439	**1726**	(2nd) Ely Island, Lower Lough Erne..........	90	90
2440	**1727**	(1st) Giant's Causeway, Antrim Coast.....	1·20	1·00
2441	**1728**	(E) Slemish, Antrim Mountains.............	2·25	1·50
2442	**1729**	42p. Banns Road, Mourne Mountains....	85	85
2443	**1730**	47p. Glenelly Valley, Sperrins................	85	95
2444	**1731**	68p. Islandmore, Strangford Lough.......	1·00	1·10
Set of 6.............			6·25	5·50
Set of 6 Gutter Pairs.............			12·50	
First Day Cover (Tallents House).............				5·75
First Day Cover (Garrison, Enniskillen).............				5·75
Presentation Pack (PO Pack No. 357).............			6·75	
PHQ Cards (set of 6) (262).............			1·75	5·75

(b) Self-adhesive. Die-cut Perf 14½.

2445	**1727**	(1st) Giant's Causeway, Antrim Coast.....	3·25	3·25
		a. Booklet pane. No. 2445×2 and		
		No. 2295×4.............	6·75	
		ab. Imperf (pane).............	£950	

No. 2445 was only issued in £1·68 stamp booklet, No. PM12, in which the
surplus self-adhesive paper around each stamp was removed.

1724 Minas Tirith   **1725** Fangorn Forest

(Des HGV Design. Litho Walsall)

2004 (26 Feb). 50th Anniversary of Publication of *The Fellowship of the Ring*
and *The Two Towers* by J. R. R. Tolkien. Multicoloured Two phosphor
bands. Perf 14½.

2429	**1716**	(1st) Map showing Middle Earth.............	1·20	1·00
		a. Block of 10. Nos. 2429/2438.............	11·00	9·00
2430	**1717**	(1st) Forest of Lothlórien in Spring.........	1·20	1·00
2431	**1718**	(1st) Dust Jacket for *The Fellowship of*		
		the Ring.............	1·20	1·00
2432	**1719**	(1st) Rivendell.............	1·20	1·00
2433	**1720**	(1st) The Hall at Bag End.............	1·20	1·00
2434	**1721**	(1st) Orthanc.............	1·20	1·00
2435	**1722**	(1st) Doors of Durin.............	1·20	1·00
2436	**1723**	(1st) Barad-dûr.............	1·20	1·00
2437	**1724**	(1st) Minas Tirith.............	1·20	1·00
2438	**1725**	(1st) Fangorn Forest.............	1·20	1·00
Set of 10.............			11·00	9·00
Gutter Block of 20.............			22·00	
First Day Cover (Tallents House).............				9·25
First Day Cover (Oxford).............				9·25
Presentation Pack (PO Pack No. 356).............			11·50	
PHQ Cards (set of 10) (261).............			3·00	10·50

Nos. 2429/2438 were printed together, *se-tenant*, in blocks of ten (5×2)
throughout the sheet.

1732 *Lace 1* (trial
proof) 1968 (Sir Terry
Frost)

1733 *Coccinelle*
(Sonia Delaunay)

(Des Rose Design. Gravure Walsall)

2004 (6 Apr). Contemporary Paintings. Centenary of the Entente Cordiale.
Multicoloured Two phosphor bands. Perf 14×14½.

2446	**1732**	28p. *Lace 1* (trial proof) 1968................	80	80
2447	**1733**	57p. *Coccinelle*.............	1·25	1·25
Set of 2.............			1·75	1·75
Set of 2 Gutter Pairs.............			3·50	
Set of 2 Traffic Light Gutter Blocks of 4.............			10·00	
First Day Cover (Tallents House).............				1·90
First Day Cover (London SW1).............				1·90
First Day Cover (UK and French stamps).............				5·00
Presentation Pack (PO Pack No. 358).............			8·00	
Presentation Pack (UK and French stamps).............			8·00	
PHQ Cards (set of 2) (263).............			60	2·00

Stamps in similar designs were issued by France and these are included
in the joint Presentation Pack.

1726 Ely Island, Lower
Lough Erne

1727 Giant's Causeway,
Antrim Coast

1734 *RMS Queen Mary 2, 2004* (Edward D. Walker)

1735 *SS Canberra, 1961* (David Cobb)

1736 *RMS Queen Mary, 1936* (Charles Pears)

1737 *RMS Mauretania, 1907* (Thomas Henry)

1738 *SS City of New York, 1888* (Raphael Monleaon y Torres)

1739 *PS Great Western, 1838* (Joseph Walter)

1739a Ocean Liners

(Des J. Gibbs. Gravure De La Rue)

2004 (13 Apr). Ocean Liners. Multicoloured Two phosphor bands. Perf 14½×14.

(a) Ordinary gum.

2448	**1734**	(1st) RMS *Queen Mary 2*, 2004................	1·20	1·00
2449	**1735**	(E) SS *Canberra*, 1961............................	2·25	1·50
		a. Imperf (pair)......................................	£375	
2450	**1736**	42p. RMS *Queen Mary*, 1936....................	70	80
2451	**1737**	47p. RMS *Mauretania*, 1907....................	75	85
2452	**1738**	57p. SS *City of New York*, 1888..............	80	90
2453	**1739**	68p. PS *Great Western*, 1838..................	85	95
Set of 6..			5·75	5·00
Set of 6 Gutter Pairs..			11·50	
First Day Cover (Tallents House).........................				5·50
First Day Cover (Southampton)...........................				5·50
Presentation Pack (PO Pack No. 359)..................			6·00	
PHQ Cards (set of 7) (264).................................			2·00	5·25
MS2454 *1739a* 114×104mm. Nos. 2448/2453.			7·25	7·25
First Day Cover (Tallents House).........................				7·50
First Day Cover (Southampton)...........................				7·50

(b) Self-adhesive. Die-cut Perf 14½×14.

2455	**1734**	(1st) RMS *Queen Mary 2*, 2004................	3·00	3·00
		a. Booklet pane. No. 2455×2 and No. 2295×4..	7·50	

Nos. 2448/2455 commemorate the introduction to service of the *Queen Mary 2*.

No. 2455 was only issued in £1·68 stamp booklet, No. PM13, in which the surplus self-adhesive paper around each stamp was removed.

No. **MS**2454 is known to exist with a face value of '53' on No. 2452. It is known perforated and imperforate.

The complete miniature sheet is shown on one of the PHQ cards with the others depicting individual stamps.

See also No. 2614.

1740 *Dianthus Allwoodii,* Group

1741 Dahlia, Garden Princess

1742 Clematis, Arabella

1743 Miltonia, French Lake

1744 Lilium, Lemon Pixie

1745 Delphinium, Clifford Sky

(Des Rose Design. Gravure Enschedé)

2004 (25 May). Bicentenary of the Royal Horticultural Society (1st issue). Multicoloured One side phosphor band (2nd) or 'all-over' phosphor (others). Perf 14½.

2456	**1740**	(2nd) *Dianthus Allwoodii* Group...............	90	90
		a. Booklet pane. Nos. 2456, 2458/2459 and 2461 with margins all round............................	6·75	
2457	**1741**	(1st) Dahlia, Garden Princess..................	1·20	1·00
		a. Booklet pane. Nos. 2457 and 2460, each×2, with margins all round..	5·75	
2458	**1742**	(E) Clematis, Arabella.............................	2·25	1·50
2459	**1743**	42p. Miltonia, French Lake......................	80	85
2460	**1744**	47p. Lilium, Lemon Pixie........................	85	90
2461	**1745**	68p. Delphinium, Clifford Sky.................	90	1·00
Set of 6..			6·00	5·50
Set of 6 Gutter Pairs..			12·00	
First Day Cover (Tallents House).........................				5·75
First Day Cover (Wisley, Woking).......................				5·75
Presentation Pack (PO Pack No. 360).................			6·50	
PHQ Cards (set of 7) (265).................................			2·00	6·50
MS2462 115×105 mm. Nos. 2456/2461..........			6·50	6·50
First Day Cover (Tallents House).........................				7·25
First Day Cover (Wisley, Woking).......................				7·25

Booklet panes Nos. 2456a/2457a come from the £7·23 Glory of the Garden booklet, No. DX33.

The 1st class stamp was also issued in sheets of 20, printed in lithography by Walsall and sold at £6·15, containing vertical strips of five stamps alternated with printed labels giving information about dahlias (No. LS19). These sheets with personalised photographs were available at £14·95 from the Royal Mail in Edinburgh.

The complete miniature sheet is shown on one of the PHQ cards with the others depicting individual stamps.

1280 Gentiana acaulis (Georg Ehret)

1283 Tulipa (Ehret)

1287 Iris latifolia (Ehret)

(Litho Enschedé)

2004 (25 May). Bicentenary of the Royal Horticultural Society (2nd issue). Booklet stamps. Designs as Nos. 1955, 1958 and 1962 (1997 Greetings Stamps 19th-century Flower Paintings). Multicoloured Two phosphor bands. Perf 15×14 (with one elliptical hole in each vert side.)

2463	**1280**	(1st) Gentiana acaulis (Georg Ehret).......	2·75	2·75
		a. Booklet pane. Nos. 2463, 2464×2		
		and 2465 with margins all round...	7·00	
2464	**1283**	(1st) Tulipa (Ehret)............................	1·40	1·40
2465	**1287**	(1st) Iris latifolia (Ehret).....................	2·75	2·75
Set of 3..			6·50	6·50

On Nos. 2463/2465 the phosphor bands appear at the left and the centre of each stamp.

Nos. 2463/2465 were only issued in the £7·23 Glory of the Garden booklet, No. DX33.

1746 Barmouth Bridge

1747 Hyddgen, Plynlimon

1748 Brecon Beacons

1749 Pen-pych, Rhondda Valley

1750 Rhewl, Dee Valley

1751 Marloes Sands

(Des Phelan Barker. Gravure De La Rue)

2004 (15 June). A British Journey. Wales. Multicoloured One centre phosphor band (2nd), 'all-over' phosphor (1st) or two phosphor bands (others). Perf 14½.

(a) Ordinary gum.

2466	**1746**	(2nd) Barmouth Bridge..........................	90	90
		a. Imperf (pair)................................	£300	
2467	**1747**	(1st) Hyddgen, Plynlimon.......................	1·20	1·00
		a. Imperf (pair)................................	£300	
2468	**1748**	40p. Brecon Beacons.............................	70	70

2469	**1749**	43p. Pen-pych, Rhondda Valley..............	75	75
2470	**1750**	47p. Rhewl, Dee Valley..........................	80	85
		a. Imperf (pair)................................	£250	
2471	**1751**	68p. Marloes Sands.............................	90	95
		a. Imperf (pair)................................	£300	
Set of 6..			4·50	4·50
Set of 6 Gutter Pairs...			9·00	
First Day Cover (Tallents House)...........................				4·75
First Day Cover (Llanfair)....................................				4·75
Presentation Pack (PO Pack No. 361).................			4·75	
PHQ Cards (set of 6) (266)................................			1·75	5·25

(b) Self-adhesive. Die-cut Perf 14½.

2472	**1747**	(1st) Hyddgen, Plynlimon......................	3·00	3·00
		a. Booklet pane. No. 2472×2 and		
		No. 2295×4...................................	7·50	

The 1st and 40p. values include the EUROPA emblem.

Imperf pairs of Types **1748** and **1749** with alternative face values are of proof status. (Price £1000 per pair).

No. 2472 was only issued in £1·68 stamp booklet, No. PM14, in which the surplus self-adhesive paper around each stamp was removed.

1752 Sir Rowland Hill Award

1753 William Shipley (Founder of Royal Society of Arts)

1754 'RSA' as Typewriter Keys and Shorthand

1755 Chimney Sweep

1756 Gill Typeface

1757 'Zero Waste'

(Des D. Birdsall. Litho Walsall)

2004 (10 Aug). 250th Anniversary of the Royal Society of Arts. Multicoloured Two phosphor bands. Perf 14.

2473	**1752**	(1st) Sir Rowland Hill Award...................	1·20	1·00
2474	**1753**	40p. William Shipley..............................	75	75
2475	**1754**	43p. 'RSA' as Typewriter Keys and		
		Shorthand.....................................	80	80
2476	**1755**	47p. Chimney Sweep.............................	1·00	1·00
2477	**1756**	57p. Gill Typeface................................	1·25	1·25
2478	**1757**	68p. 'Zero Waste'.................................	1·50	1·50
Set of 6..			5·50	5·50
Set of 6 Gutter Pairs...			11·00	
First Day Cover (Tallents House)...........................				5·75
First Day Cover (London WC2).............................				5·75
Presentation Pack (PO Pack No. 362).................			6·00	
PHQ Cards (set of 6) (267)................................			1·75	6·50

1758 Pine Marten

1759 Roe Deer

1760 Badger

1761 Yellow-necked Mouse

1762 Wild Cat

1763 Red Squirrel

1764 Stoat

1765 Natterer's Bat

1766 Mole

1767 Fox

(Des Kate Stephens. Gravure Enschedé)

2004 (16 Sept). Woodland Animals. Multicoloured Two phosphor bands. Perf 14½.

2479	**1758**	(1st) Pine Marten..............................	1·20	1·00
		a. Block of 10. Nos. 2479/2488...........	10·50	9·00
2480	**1759**	(1st) Roe Deer.................................	1·20	1·00
2481	**1760**	(1st) Badger...................................	1·20	1·00
2482	**1761**	(1st) Yellow-necked Mouse................	1·20	1·00
2483	**1762**	(1st) Wild Cat.................................	1·20	1·00
2484	**1763**	(1st) Red Squirrel............................	1·20	1·00
2485	**1764**	(1st) Stoat....................................	1·20	1·00
2486	**1765**	(1st) Natterer's Bat.........................	1·20	1·00
2487	**1766**	(1st) Mole....................................	1·20	1·00
2488	**1767**	(1st) Fox......................................	1·20	1·00
Set of 10..			10·50	9·00
Gutter Block of 20.......................................			21·00	
Traffic Light Gutter Block of 20.......................			40·00	
First Day Cover (Tallents House)......................				9·25
First Day Cover (Woodland, Bishop Auckland)........				9·25
Presentation Pack (PO Pack No. 363).................			11·00	
PHQ Cards (set of 10) (268)...........................			3·00	10·00

Nos. 2479/2488 were printed together, *se-tenant*, in blocks of ten (5×2) throughout sheets of 30.

For the miniature sheet celebrating the opening of the new Scottish Parliament Building, Edinburgh, issued 5 October 2004, see Regionals Section.

1768 Private McNamara, 5th Dragoon Guards, Heavy Brigade charge, Battle of Balaklava

1769 Piper Muir, 42nd Regt of Foot, amphibious assault on Kerch

1770 Sergeant Major Edwards, Scots Fusilier Guards, gallant action, Battle of Inkerman

1771 Sergeant Powell, 1st Regt of Foot Guards, Battles of Alma and Inkerman

1772 Sergeant.Major Poole, Royal Sappers and Miners, defensive line, Battle of Inkerman

1773 Sergeant Glasgow, Royal Artillery, gun battery besieged Sevastopol

(Des Atelier Works. Litho Walsall)

2004 (12 Oct). 150th Anniversary of the Crimean War. One centre phosphor band (2nd) or two phosphor bands (others). Perf 14.

2489	**1768**	(2nd) Private McNamara..........................	90	90
		a. Greyish silver and phosphor omitted..	£700	
2490	**1769**	(1st) Piper Muir................................	1·20	1·00
2491	**1770**	40p. Sergeant Major Edwards.................	1·00	1·00
2492	**1771**	57p. Sergeant Powell..........................	1·10	1·10
		a. Imperf.	£375	
2493	**1772**	68p. Sergeant Major Poole....................	1·25	1·25
		a. Imperf.	£600	
2494	**1773**	£1·12 Sergeant Glasgow........................	1·60	1·60
Set of 6..			6·00	6·00
Set of 6 Gutter Pairs.....................................			12·00	
Set of 6 Traffic Light Gutter Pairs.....................			38·00	
First Day Cover (Tallents House).......................				6·25
First Day Cover (London SW3).........................				6·50
Presentation Pack (PO Pack No. 364).................			6·25	
PHQ Cards (set of 6) (269)............................			1·75	7·00

Nos. 2489/2494 show Crimean Heroes photographs taken in 1856.

1774 Father Christmas on Snowy Roof

1775 Celebrating the Sunrise

1776 On Roof in Gale

1777 With Umbrella in Rain

1778 On Edge of Roof with Torch

1779 Sheltering behind Chimney

(Des R. Briggs. Gravure De La Rue)

2004 (2 Nov). Christmas. Multicoloured One centre phosphor band (2nd) or two phosphor bands (others). Perf 14½×14.

(a) Self-adhesive.

2495	**1774**	(2nd) Father Christmas on Snowy Roof...	90	90
		a. Booklet pane. No. 2495×24..........	22·00	
2496	**1775**	(1st) Celebrating the Sunrise..............	1·20	1·00
		a. Booklet pane. No. 2496×12..........	16·00	
2497	**1776**	40p. On Roof in Gale..........................	80	80
2498	**1777**	57p. With Umbrella in Rain.................	1·00	1·00
2499	**1778**	68p. On Edge of Roof with Torch..........	1·10	1·10
2500	**1779**	£1·12 Sheltering behind Chimney..........	1·25	1·25
Set of 6..			5·50	5·50
First Day Cover (Tallents House)....................				5·75
First Day Cover (Bethlehem, Llandeilo)............				6·00
Presentation Pack (PO Pack No. 365)................			5·75	
PHQ Cards (set of 7) (270).............................			2·00	6·25

(b) Ordinary gum.

MS2501 115×105 mm. As Nos. 2495/2500........		6·00	6·00
First Day Cover (Tallents House)....................			6·25
First Day Cover (Bethlehem, Llandeilo)............			6·50

Nos. 2495/2500 were each printed in sheets of 50 with the surplus backing paper around each stamp removed.

The 2nd and 1st class were also issued together in sheets of 20, sold at £5·40, containing ten 2nd class and ten 1st class, each value arranged in vertical rows of five alternated with rows of half stamp-size labels showing Father Christmas (No. LS21).

Separate sheets of 20 2nd class and 20 1st class were available with personalised photographs at £9·95 (2nd class) or £14·95 (1st class) from Royal Mail, Edinburgh. These sheets were printed in lithography instead of photogravure and had the backing paper around the stamps retained.

Trials are known showing alternative face values.

The seven PHQ cards depict the six individual stamps and the miniature sheet.

Year Pack

2004 (2 Nov). Comprises Nos. 2417/22422, 2424/2444, 2446/2453, 2456/2461, 2466/2471 and 2473/2500.

CP2500*a*	Year Pack (Pack No. 366)......................	65·00

Post Office Yearbook

2004 (2 Nov). Comprises Nos. 2417/2422, 2424/2444, 2446/2453, 2456/2461, 2466/2471 and 2473/2500 in hardback book with slipcase

YB2500*a*	Yearbook..	60·00

1780 British Saddleback Pigs

1781 Khaki Campbell Ducks

1782 Clydesdale Mare and Foal

1783 Dairy Shorthorn Cattle

1784 Border Collie Dog

1785 Light Sussex Chicks

1786 Suffolk Sheep

1787 Bagot Goat

1788 Norfolk Black Turkeys

1789 Embden Geese

(Des C. Wormell. Gravure Enschedé)

2005 (11 Jan). Farm Animals. Multicoloured Two phosphor bands. Perf 14½.

2502	**1780**	(1st) British Saddleback Pigs..................	1·20	1·00
		a. Block of 10. Nos. 2502/2511..........	10·50	9·00
2503	**1781**	(1st) Khaki Campbell Ducks....................	1·20	1·00
2504	**1782**	(1st) Clydesdale Mare and Foal..............	1·20	1·00
2505	**1783**	(1st) Dairy Shorthorn Cattle..................	1·20	1·00
2506	**1784**	(1st) Border Collie Dog.........................	1·20	1·00
2507	**1785**	(1st) Light Sussex Chicks.......................	1·20	1·00
2508	**1786**	(1st) Suffolk Sheep...............................	1·20	1·00
2509	**1787**	(1st) Bagot Goat...................................	1·20	1·00
2510	**1788**	(1st) Norfolk Black Turkeys....................	1·20	1·00
2511	**1789**	(1st) Embden Geese.............................	1·20	1·00
Set of 10..			10·50	9·00
Gutter Block of 20...			21·00	
Traffic Light Gutter Block of 20........................			65·00	
First Day Cover (Tallents House)....................				9·25
First Day Cover (Paddock, Huddersfield)............				9·50
Presentation Pack (PO Pack No. 367)..............			11·00	
PHQ Cards (set of 10) (271)..........................			3·00	10·50

Nos. 2502/2511 were printed together, *se-tenant*, in blocks of ten (5×2) throughout sheets of 30.

Nos. 2502/2511 were also issued in sheets of 20, containing two of each of the ten designs, arranged in vertical strips of five alternated with printed labels showing black and white illustrations of farm scenes (No. LS22). These sheets were printed in lithography by Walsall and sold for £6·15.

They were also available with personal photographs on the labels at £14·95 per sheet from Royal Mail, Edinburgh.

1790 Old Harry Rocks, Studland Bay

1791 Wheal Coates, St Agnes

1792 Start Point, Start Bay

1793 Horton Down, Wiltshire

1794 Chiselcombe, Exmoor

1795 St James's Stone, Lundy

(Des J. Phelan and Lissa Barker. Gravure De La Rue)

2005 (8 Feb). A British Journey. South West England. Multicoloured One centre phosphor band (2nd) or two phosphor bands (others). Perf 14½.

2512	**1790**	(2nd) Old Harry Rocks, Studland Bay.......	90	90
2513	**1791**	(1st) Wheal Coates, St Agnes..................	1·20	1·00
2514	**1792**	40p. Start Point, Start Bay......................	75	75
2515	**1793**	43p. Horton Down, Wiltshire..................	85	85
2516	**1794**	57p. Chiselcombe, Exmoor......................	1·00	1·00
2517	**1795**	68p. St James's Stone, Lundy..................	1·25	1·25
	Set of 6...		5·25	5·25
	Set of 6 Gutter Pairs.......................................		10·50	
	First Day Cover (Tallents House).....................			5·50
	First Day Cover (The Lizard, Helston).............			5·75
	Presentation Pack (PO Pack No. 368).............		5·50	
	PHQ Cards (set of 6) (262).............................		1·75	5·75

Perforated examples of T **1794** are known with face value of 47p are known (*price* £1250).

1796 Mr Rochester

1797 Come to Me

1798 In the Comfort of her Bonnet

1799 La Ligne des Rats

1800 Refectory

1801 Inspection

(Des P. Willberg. Litho Walsall)

2005 (24 Feb). 150th Death Anniversary of Charlotte Brontë. Illustrations of scenes from *Jane Eyre* by Paula Rego. Multicoloured One centre phosphor band (2nd), or two phosphor bands (others). Perf 14×14½.

2518	**1796**	(2nd) Mr Rochester..........................	90	90
		a. Booklet pane. Nos. 2518/2519, both×2, with margins all round.....	3·50	
2519	**1797**	(1st) Come to Me...........................	1·20	1·00
2520	**1798**	40p. In the Comfort of her Bonnet........	1·00	1·00
		a. Booklet pane. Nos. 2520/2523 with margins all round..................	4·50	
2521	**1799**	57p. La Ligne des Rats.....................	1·25	1·25
2522	**1800**	68p. Refectory................................	1·40	1·40
2523	**1801**	£1·12 Inspection.............................	1·60	1·60
	Set of 6..		6·50	6·50
	Set of 6 Gutter Pairs....................................		13·00	
	Set of 6 Traffic Light Gutter Blocks of 4.........		48·00	
	First Day Cover (Tallents House)..................			6·75
	First Day Cover (Haworth, Keighley).............			7·00
	Presentation Pack (PO Pack No. 369)............		6·75	
	PHQ Cards (set of 7) (273).........................		2·00	7·00
MS2524	114×105 mm. Nos. 2518/2523......		6·50	6·50
	First Day Cover (Tallents House)..................			6·75
	First Day Cover (Haworth, Keighley).............			7·00

Booklet panes Nos. 2518a and 2520a come from the £7·43 The Brontë Sisters booklet, No. DX34.

The complete miniature sheet is shown on one of the PHQ cards with the others depicting individual stamps.

1802 Spinning Coin

1803 Rabbit out of Hat Trick

1804 Knotted Scarf Trick

1805 Card Trick

1806 Pyramid under Fez Trick

(Des G. Hardie and Tatham Design. Gravure Walsall)

2005 (15 Mar). Centenary of the Magic Circle. Multicoloured Two phosphor bands. Perf 14½×14.

2525	**1802**	(1st) Spinning Coin.........................	1·20	1·00
2526	**1803**	40p. Rabbit out of Hat Trick.............	1·00	1·00
2527	**1804**	47p. Knotted Scarf Trick..................	1·25	1·25
2528	**1805**	68p. Card Trick..............................	1·40	1·40
2529	**1806**	£1·12 Pyramid under Fez Trick............	5·50	5·50
	Set of 5..		5·75	5·75
	Set of 5 Gutter Pairs....................................		11·50	
	First Day Cover (Philatelic Bureau, Edinburgh)..........			6·00
	First Day Cover (London NW1).....................			6·00
	Presentation Pack (PO Pack No. 370)............		6·00	
	PHQ Cards (set of 5) (274).........................		1·50	6·00

Nos. 2525/2529 are each printed with instructions for the illusion or trick on the stamp.

No. 2525 can be rubbed with a coin to reveal the 'head' or 'tail' of a coin. The two versions, which appear identical before rubbing, are printed in alternate rows of the sheet, indicated by the letters H and T in the side margins of the sheet.

No. 2525 was also issued in sheets of 20, printed in lithography instead of gravure and sold at £6·15, containing vertical rows of five stamps alternated with half stamp-size printed labels illustrating magic tricks (No. LS23). These sheets were also available with personal photographs on the labels at £14·95 per sheet from Royal Mail, Edinburgh.

Nos. 2526 and 2528 each show optical illusions.

The bright mauve on No. 2527 and the bright mauve, new blue, and lilac on No. 2529 are printed in thermochromic inks which fade temporarily when exposed to heat, making the pyramid under the centre fez visible.

1806a First Castles Definitives

(Des Sedley Place. Recess and litho Enschedé)

2005 (22 Mar). 50th Anniversary of First Castles Definitives. Printed on pale
cream paper. 'All-over' phosphor. Perf 11×11½.

MS2530 127×73 mm. **1806a** First Castles Definitives
50p. brownish-black; 50p. black; £1 dull vermilion;

£1 royal blue..	4·50	4·50
First Day Cover (Tallents House).....................................		5·75
First Day Cover (Windsor)...		5·75
Presentation Pack (PO Pack No. 69)................................	5·75	
PHQ Cards (set of 5) (D28)..	1·50	5·75

The five PHQ cards depict the whole miniature sheet and the four
stamps it contains.
See also No. 3221.

1807 Royal Wedding

(Des Rose Design. Litho Enschedé)

2005 (9 Apr). Royal Wedding. Sheet 85×115 mm. Multicoloured 'All-over'
phosphor. Perf 13½×14.

MS2531 **1807** Royal Wedding 30p.×2 Prince Charles
and Mrs Camilla Parker Bowles laughing; 68p.×2
Prince Charles and Mrs Camilla Parker Bowles

smiling into camera..	4·50	4·50
First Day Cover (Tallents House).....................................		5·00
First Day Cover (Windsor)...		5·00
Presentation Pack (PO Pack No. M10)............................	8·00	

No. **MS**2531 was officially issued on 9 April. It was originally intended
for issue on 8 April, and many post offices put it on sale on that day. Royal
Mail first day covers were dated 8 April, but could be ordered with a 9 April
Windsor handstamp. Our prices cover either date.

1808 Hadrian's Wall,
England

1809 Uluru-Kata Tjuta
National Park, Australia

1810 Stonehenge, England

1811 Wet Tropics of
Queensland, Australia

1812 Blenheim Palace,
England

1813 Greater Blue
Mountains Area, Australia

1814 Heart of Neolithic
Orkney, Scotland

1815 Purnululu National
Park, Australia

(Des J. Godfrey. Litho Enschedé)

2005 (21 Apr). World Heritage Sites. Multicoloured One side phosphor
band (2nd) or two phosphor bands (others). Perf 14½.

2532	**1808**	2nd Hadrian's Wall, England...................	90	90
		a. Horiz pair. Nos. 2532/2533..............	1·75	1·75
2533	**1809**	2nd Uluru-Kata Tjuta National Park,		
		Australia..	90	90
2534	**1810**	1st Stonehenge, England......................	1·20	1·00
		a. Horiz pair. Nos. 2534/2535..............	2·40	2·40
2535	**1811**	1st Wet Tropics of Queensland,		
		Australia..	1·20	1·00
2536	**1812**	47p. Blenheim Palace, England.............	80	80
		a. Horiz pair. Nos. 2536/2537..............	1·60	1·60
2537	**1813**	47p. Greater Blue Mountains Area,		
		Australia..	80	80
2538	**1814**	68p. Heart of Neolithic Orkney,		
		Scotland..	1·00	1·00
		a. Horiz pair. Nos. 2538/2539..............	2·00	2·00
2539	**1815**	68p. Purnululu National Park, Australia.	1·00	1·00
Set of 8...			6·50	6·50
Set of 4 Gutter Strips of 4..			14·00	
Set of 4 Traffic Light Gutter Blocks of 8...........................			32·00	
First Day Cover (Tallents House)..				7·75
First Day Cover (Blenheim Palace, Woodstock)...................				7·75
First Day Covers (UK and Australian stamps) (2)................				12·50
Presentation Pack (PO Pack No. 371)................................			7·50	
Presentation Pack (UK and Australian stamps)...................			11·00	
PHQ Cards (set of 8) (275)..			2·50	7·50

The two designs of each value were printed together, *se-tenant*, in
horizontal pairs in sheets of 30 (6×5).
Stamps in these designs were also issued by Australia and these are
included in the joint Presentation Pack.

1816 Ensign of the Scots
Guards, 2002

1817 Queen taking the
salute as Colonel-in-Chief
of the Grenadier Guards,
1983

1818 Trumpeter of the Household Cavalry, 2004

1819 Welsh Guardsman, 1990s

1820 Queen riding side-saddle, 1972

1821 Queen and Duke of Edinburgh in carriage, 2004

(Des A. Altmann. Litho Walsall)

2005 (7 June). Trooping the Colour. Multicoloured One phosphor band (2nd), two phosphor bands (others). Perf 14½.

2540	**1816**	(2nd) Ensign of the Scots Guards, 2002...	90	90
2541	**1817**	(1st) Queen taking the salute as Colonel-in-Chief of the Grenadier Guards, 1983....................	1·20	1·00
2542	**1818**	42p. Trumpeter of the Household Cavalry, 2004....................	85	85
2543	**1819**	60p. Welsh Guardsman, 1990s..............	1·00	1·00
2544	**1820**	68p. Queen riding side-saddle, 1972.....	1·10	1·10
2545	**1821**	£1·12 Queen and Duke of Edinburgh in carriage, 2004....................	1·60	1·60
Set of 6........................			5·75	5·75
Set of 6 Gutter Pairs........................			11·50	
First Day Cover (Tallents House)........................				6·00
First Day Cover (London SW1)........................				6·00
Presentation Pack (PO Pack No. 372)........................			5·75	
PHQ Cards (set of 7) (276)........................			2·00	11·00
MS2546 115×105 mm. Nos. 2540/2545..			5·50	5·50
First Day Cover (Tallents House)........................				5·75
First Day Cover (London SW1)........................				5·75

The seven PHQ cards show the six stamps and No. **MS**2546.

1823 Norton F.1, Road Version of Race Winner (1991)

1824 BSA Rocket 3, Early Three Cylinder 'Superbike' (1969)

1825 Vincent Black Shadow, Fastest Standard Motorcycle (1949)

1826 Triumph Speed Twin, Two Cylinder Innovation (1938)

1827 Brough Superior, Bespoke Luxury Motorcycle (1930)

1828 Royal Enfield, Small Engined Motor Bicycle (1914)

(Des I. Chilvers and M. English. Litho Walsall)

2005 (19 July). Motorcycles. Multicoloured Two phosphor bands. Perf 14×14½.

2548	**1823**	(1st) Norton F.1........................	1·20	90
2549	**1824**	40p. BSA Rocket 3........................	60	60
2550	**1825**	42p. Vincent Black Shadow........................	65	65
2551	**1826**	47p. Triumph Speed Twin........................	80	80
2552	**1827**	60p. Brough Superior........................	1·00	1·00
2553	**1828**	68p. Royal Enfield........................	1·25	1·25
Set of 6........................			4·50	4·50
Set of 6 Gutter Pairs........................			9·50	
First Day Cover (Tallents House)........................				5·75
First Day Cover (Solihull)........................				5·75
Presentation Pack (PO Pack No. 373)........................			5·25	
PHQ Cards (set of 6) (277)........................			1·75	5·75

1822 End of the War

(Des J. Matthews. Gravure Enschedé)

2005 (5 July). 60th Anniversary of End of the Second World War. Sheet 115×105 mm containing design as T **1200** (1995 Peace and Freedom) but with service indicator and No. 1668×5. Two phosphor bands. Perf 15×14 (with one elliptical hole in each vert side) (No. 1668) or 14½×14 (other).

MS2547 **1822** End of the War (1st) gold×5; (1st) silver, blue and grey-black........................		6·25	5·25
First Day Cover (Tallents House)........................			5·50
First Day Cover (Peacehaven, Newhaven)........................			5·50

1829 London 2012 Host City

(Des CDT Design. Litho Walsall)

2005 (5 Aug). London's Successful Bid for Olympic Games, 2012. Sheet 115×105 mm containing designs as Types **1255/1259**, but with service indicator. Multicoloured Two phosphor bands. Perf 14½.

MS2554 **1829** London 2012 Host City (1st) Athlete celebrating×2; (1st) Javelin; (1st) Swimming; (1st) Athlete on starting blocks; (1st) Basketball..............		6·00	5·00
First Day Cover (Tallents House)........................			5·75
First Day Cover (London E15)........................			5·75
Presentation Pack (PO Pack No. M11)........................		6·25	

Stamps from No. **MS**2554 are all inscribed 'London 2012–Host City' and have imprint date 2005.

The design as T **1259** omits the Olympic rings.

1830 African Woman eating Rice

1831 Indian Woman drinking Tea

1832 Boy eating Sushi

1833 Woman eating Pasta

1834 Woman eating Chips

1835 Teenage Boy eating Apple

(Des Catell Ronca and Rose Design. Gravure Enschedé)

2005 (23 Aug). Europa. Gastronomy. Changing Tastes in Britain. Multicoloured. One side phosphor band (2nd) or two phosphor bands (others). Perf 14½.

2555	**1830**	(2nd) African Woman eating Rice............	90	90
2556	**1831**	(1st) Indian Woman drinking Tea............	1·20	1·00
2557	**1832**	42p. Boy eating Sushi............................	60	60
2558	**1833**	47p. Woman eating Pasta.......................	75	75
2559	**1834**	60p. Woman eating Chips.......................	90	90
2560	**1835**	68p. Teenage Boy eating Apple..............	1·10	1·25
Set of 6..			4·75	4·75
Set of 6 Gutter Pairs...			9·50	
First Day Cover (Tallents House)..........................				5·00
First Day Cover (Cookstown)...............................				5·00
Presentation Pack (PO Pack No. 374)...................			5·00	
PHQ Cards (set of 6) (278).................................			1·75	5·75

The 1st and 42p. values include the EUROPA emblem.

1836 Inspector Morse

1837 Emmerdale

1838 Rising Damp

1839 The Avengers

1840 The South Bank Show

1841 Who Wants to be a Millionaire

(Des Kate Stephens. Litho D.L.R.)

2005 (15 Sept). 50th Anniversary of Independent Television. Classic ITV Programmes. Multicoloured One side phosphor band (2nd) or two phosphor bands (others). Perf 14½×14.

2561	**1836**	(2nd) Inspector Morse............................	90	90
2562	**1837**	(1st) Emmerdale....................................	1·20	1·00
2563	**1838**	42p. Rising Damp...................................	60	60
2564	**1839**	47p. The Avengers.................................	75	75
2565	**1840**	60p. The South Bank Show......................	90	90
2566	**1841**	68p. Who Wants to be a Millionaire..........	1·10	1·10
Set of 6..			4·75	4·75
Set of 6 Gutter Pairs...			9·50	
First Day Cover (Tallents House)..........................				5·25
First Day Cover (London SE19)............................				5·25
Presentation Pack (PO Pack No. 375)...................			5·00	
PHQ Cards (set of 6) (279).................................			1·75	5·75

The 1st class stamps were also issued in sheets of 20 sold at £6·55, printed in lithography by Walsall, containing four vertical rows of five stamps alternated with half stamp-size labels (No. LS26). These sheets with personalised photographs were available at £14·95 from the Royal Mail.

1842 Gazania splendens (Charlotte Sowerby)

1842a Aircraft Skywriting 'hello'

1842b 'LOVE'

1842c Union Flag

1842d Teddy Bear

1842e European Robin in Mouth of Pillar Box

(Gravure Walsall)

2005 (4 Oct). Smilers Booklet stamps (1st series). Self-adhesive. Multicoloured Two phosphor bands. Die-cut Perf 15×14.

2567	**1842**	(1st) Gazania splendens.........................	1·20	1·25
		a. Booklet pane. Nos. 2567/2572..........	9·00	
2568	**1842a**	(1st) Aircraft Skywriting 'hello'..............	1·20	1·25
2569	**1842b**	(1st) 'LOVE'..	1·20	1·25
2570	**1842c**	(1st) Union Jack.....................................	1·20	1·25
2571	**1842d**	(1st) Teddy Bear....................................	1·20	1·25
2572	**1842e**	(1st) European Robin in Mouth of Pillar Box..	1·20	1·25
Set of 6..			9·00	9·00
First Day Cover (Tallents House) (Type K, see Introduction)..				9·25
First Day Cover (Windsor) (Type K).......................				9·25

Nos. 2567/2572 were only issued in stamp booklets, Nos. QA1 and QA2, in which the surplus backing paper around each stamp was removed.

Stamps in these designs in separate sheets printed in lithography by Cartor were available with personal photographs on the labels at £14·95 per sheet from Royal Mail, Edinburgh.

Nos. 2567/2572 were re-issued on 4 July 2006 in sheets of 20 with *se-tenant* greetings labels (No. LS32), printed by Cartor in lithography instead of gravure and sold at £6·95 per sheet.

Nos. 2568/2570 were re-issued on 15 January 2008 in sheets of 20 with circular *se-tenant* labels printed in lithography by Cartor and sold at £7·35 (No. LS45). These sheets were perforated with one elliptical hole on each vert side.

These three designs were available in separate sheets of ten (*sold at* £8·95) or 20 (*sold at* £14·95) with personal photographs on the labels from Royal Mail, Edinburgh).

No. 2572 was re-issued on 8 May 2010 with other greetings stamps in sheets of 20 with *se-tenant* greetings labels, printed in lithography by Cartor (No. LS73), and sold for £10 per sheet. These sheets were printed with one elliptical hole in each vertical side.

For stamp as No. 2569 with one elliptical hole in each vertical side see No. 2693.

For stamps as Nos. 2567/2568 and 2570 with one elliptical hole in each vertical side see Nos. 2819/2821.

1843 Cricket Scenes

(Des Why Not Associates. Litho Cartor)

2005 (6 Oct). England's Ashes Victory. Sheet 115×90 mm. Multicoloured Two phosphor bands. Perf 14½×14.

MS2573	**1843**	Cricket Scenes (1st) England team with Ashes trophy; (1st) Kevin Pietersen, Michael Vaughan and Andrew Flintoff on opening day of First Test, Lord's; 68p. Michael Vaughan, Third Test, Old Trafford; 68p. Second Test cricket, Edgbaston....	4·00	4·00
		First Day Cover (Tallents House).............................		5·00
		First Day Cover (London SE11)...............................		5·00
		Presentation Pack (PO Pack No. M12).................................	4·25	

1844 *Entrepreante* with dismasted British *Belle Isle*

1845 Nelson wounded on Deck of HMS *Victory*

1846 British Cutter *Entrepreante* attempting to rescue Crew of burning French *Achille*

1847 Cutter and HMS *Pickle* (schooner)

1848 British Fleet attacking in Two Columns

1849 Franco/Spanish Fleet putting to Sea from Cadiz

(Des D. Davis. Litho Cartor)

2005 (18 Oct). Bicentenary of the Battle of Trafalgar (1st issue). Scenes from *Panorama of the Battle of Trafalgar* by William Heath. Multicoloured Two phosphor bands. Perf 15×14½.

2574	**1844**	(1st) *Entrepreante* with dismasted British *Belle Isle*..................	1·20	1·00
		a. Horiz pair. Nos. 2574/2575.............	2·40	2·00
		b. Booklet pane. Nos. 2574, 2576 and 2578.............................	2·75	
2575	**1845**	(1st) Nelson wounded on Deck of HMS *Victory*......................	1·20	1·00
		b. Booklet pane. Nos. 2575, 2577 and 2579...........................	2·75	
2576	**1846**	42p. British Cutter *Entrepreante* attempting to rescue Crew of burning French *Achille*....................	70	80
		a. Horiz pair. Nos. 2576/2577............	1·60	1·60
2577	**1847**	42p. Cutter and HMS *Pickle* (schooner)..	70	80
2578	**1848**	68p. British Fleet attacking in Two Columns................................	1·00	1·10
		a. Horiz pair. Nos. 2578/2579............	2·00	2·00
2579	**1849**	68p. Franco/Spanish Fleet putting to Sea from Cadiz................................	1·00	1·10
Set of 6..			5·00	5·00
Set of 3 Gutter Strips of 4..........................			10·50	
First Day Cover (Tallents House).....................				5·50
First Day Cover (Portsmouth)........................				5·50
Presentation Pack (PO Pack No. 376)...............			5·75	
PHQ Cards (set of 7) (280)..........................			2·00	11·50
MS2580 190×68 mm. Nos. 2574/2579................			5·25	5·50
First Day Cover (Tallents House).....................				5·75
First Day Cover (Portsmouth)........................				5·75

Nos. 2574/2575, 2576/2577 and 2578/2579 were each printed together, *se-tenant*, in horizontal pairs throughout the sheets, each pair forming a composite design.

Booklet panes Nos. 2574b/2575b come from the £7·26 Battle of Trafalgar booklet, No. DX35.

The phosphor bands are at just left of centre and at right of each stamp.

The seven PHQ cards depict the six individual stamps and the miniature sheet.

1516 White Ensign

(Litho Cartor or De La Rue)

2005 (18 Oct). Bicentenary of the Battle of Trafalgar (2nd issue). Booklet stamp. Design as T **1516** (2001 White Ensign from Submarine Centenary). Multicoloured Two phosphor bands. Perf 14½.

2581	**1516**	(1st) White Ensign. Multicoloured..........	1·50	1·50
		a. Booklet pane. No. 2581×3 with margins all round...........................	7·00	

No. 2581 was issued in the £7·26 Bicentenary of the Battle of Trafalgar booklet, No. DX35, printed by Cartor, the £7·40 Ian Fleming's James Bond booklet, No. DX41, which was printed by De La Rue (see booklet pane No. 2805a) and the £7·93 Royal Navy Uniforms booklet, No. DX47.

1850 Black Madonna and Child from Haiti

1851 *Madonna and Child* (Marianne Stokes)

1852 The Virgin Mary with the Infant Christ

1853 *Choctaw Virgin Mother and Child* (Fr. John Giuliani)

1854 Madonna and the Infant Jesus (from India)

1855 *Come let us adore Him* (Dianne Tchumut)

(Des Irene von Treskow. Gravure De La Rue)

2005 (1 Nov). Christmas. Madonna and Child Paintings. Multicoloured One side phosphor band (2nd) or two phosphor bands (others). Perf 14½×14.

		(a) Self-adhesive.		
2582	**1850**	(2nd) Black Madonna and Child from Haiti...............	90	90
		a. Booklet pane. No. 2582×24.............	22·00	
2583	**1851**	(1st) *Madonna and Child*..........................	1·20	1·00
		a. Booklet pane. No. 2583×12.............	16·00	
2584	**1852**	42p. The Virgin Mary with the Infant Christ.................	90	90
2585	**1853**	60p. *Choctaw Virgin Mother and Child*....	1·00	1·00
2586	**1854**	68p. Madonna and the Infant Jesus.......	1·25	1·25
2587	**1855**	£1·12 *Come let us adore Him*................	1·40	1·40
Set of 6..			5·75	5·75
First Day Cover (Tallents House)........................				6·00
First Day Cover (Bethlehem, Llandeilo)..................				6·00
Presentation Pack (PO Pack No. 377)...................			6·00	
PHQ Cards (set of 7) (281)...............................			2·00	12·00

The seven PHQ cards depict the six individual stamps and the miniature sheet.

	(b) Ordinary gum.		
MS2588 115×102 mm. As Nos. 2582/2587......................	5·75	5·75
First Day Cover (Tallents House)........................		6·00
First Day Cover (Bethlehem, Llandeilo)..................		6·00

Year Pack

2005 (1 Nov). Comprises Nos. 2502/2523, 2525/2529, **MS**2531/2545, 2548/2553, 2555/2566, 2574/2579 and 2582/2587.
CP2587*a*   Year Pack (Pack No. 378)...................... 65·00

Post Office Yearbook

2005 (1 Nov). Comprises Nos. 2502/2523, 2525/2529, **MS**2531/2545, 2548/2553, 2555/2566, 2574/2579 and 2582/2587.
YB2587*a*   Yearbook.. 60·00

Miniature Sheet Collection

2005 (1 Nov). Comprises Nos. **MS**2524, **MS**2530/**MS**2531, **MS**2546/ **MS**2547, **MS**2554, **MS**2573, **MS**2580 and **MS**2588.
MS2588*a* Miniature Sheet Collection................................ 45·00

1858 *The Enormous Crocodile* (Roald Dahl)

1859 *More About Paddington* (Michael Bond)

1860 *Comic Adventures of Boots* (Satoshi Kitamura)

1861 *Alice's Adventures in Wonderland* (Lewis Carroll)

1862 *The Very Hungry Caterpillar* (Eric Carle)

1863 *Maisy's ABC* (Lucy Cousins)

(Des Rose Design. Litho D.L.R.)

2006 (10 Jan). Animal Tales. Multicoloured One side phosphor band (2nd) or two phosphor bands (others). Perf 14½.

2589	**1856**	(2nd) *The Tale of Mr Jeremy Fisher* (Beatrix Potter).................................	90	90
		a. Horiz pair. Nos. 2589/2590..............	1·75	1·75
2590	**1857**	(2nd) *Kipper* (Mick Inkpen)......................	90	90
2591	**1858**	(1st) *The Enormous Crocodile* (Roald Dahl)......................................	1·20	1·00
		a. Horiz pair. Nos. 2591/2592..............	2·40	2·40
2592	**1859**	(1st) *More About Paddington* (Michael Bond)......................................	1·20	1·00
2593	**1860**	42p. *Comic Adventures of Boots* (Satoshi Kitamura).........................	80	80
		a. Horiz pair. Nos. 2593/2594..............	1·60	1·60
2594	**1861**	42p. *Alice's Adventures in Wonderland* (Lewis Carroll).................................	80	80
2595	**1862**	68p. *The Very Hungry Caterpillar* (Eric Carle)....................................	1·00	1·00
		a. Horiz pair. Nos. 2595/2596..............	2·00	2·00
2596	**1863**	68p. *Maisy's ABC* (Lucy Cousins)..............	1·00	1·00
Set of 8..			7·00	6·75
Set of 4 Gutter Blocks of 4...............................			14·00	
Set of 4 Traffic Light Gutter Blocks of 8................			50·00	
First Day Cover (Tallents House)........................				7·75
First Day Cover (Mousehole, Penzance, Cornwall)............				7·75
First Day Cover (Nos. 2595/2596 UK and US stamps)........				4·00
Presentation Pack (PO Pack No. 379)...................			8·75	
PHQ Cards (set of 8) (282)...............................			2·50	7·75

Nos. 2589/2590, 2591/2592, 2593/2594 and 2595/2596 were printed together, *se-tenant*, in horizontal pairs in sheets of 60 (2 panes 6×5).

A design as No. 2592 but self-adhesive was issued in sheets of 20, printed in lithography by Cartor sold at £6·55, containing four vertical rows of five stamps alternated with printed labels (No. LS28). This sheet was also available with personal photographs on the labels at £14·95 from Royal Mail.

No. 2595 contains two die-cut holes.

1856 *The Tale of Mr Jeremy Fisher* (Beatrix Potter)

1857 *Kipper* (Mick Inkpen)

1864 Carding Mill Valley, Shropshire

1865 Beachy Head, Sussex

1866 St Paul's Cathedral, London

1867 Brancaster, Norfolk

1868 Derwent Edge, Peak District

1869 Robin Hood's Bay, Yorkshire

1870 Buttermere, Lake District

1871 Chipping Campden, Cotswolds

1872 St Boniface Down, Isle of Wight

1873 Chamberlain Square, Birmingham

(Des Phelan Barker Design Consultants. Gravure D.L.R.)

2006 (7 Feb). A British Journey. England. Multicoloured Two phosphor bands. Perf 14½.

2597	**1864**	(1st) Carding Mill Valley, Shropshire.......	1·20	1·00
		a. Block of 10. Nos. 2597/2606............	10·50	9·00
2598	**1865**	(1st) Beachy Head, Sussex......................	1·20	1·00
2599	**1866**	(1st) St Paul's Cathedral, London............	1·20	1·00
2600	**1867**	(1st) Brancaster, Norfolk........................	1·20	1·00
2601	**1868**	(1st) Derwent Edge, Peak District...........	1·20	1·00
2602	**1869**	(1st) Robin Hood's Bay, Yorkshire............	1·20	1·00
2603	**1870**	(1st) Buttermere, Lake District.................	1·20	1·00
2604	**1871**	(1st) Chipping Campden, Cotswolds......	1·20	1·00
2605	**1872**	(1st) St Boniface Down, Isle of Wight......	1·20	1·00
2606	**1873**	(1st) Chamberlain Square, Birmingham	1·20	1·00
Set of 10..			10·50	9·00
Gutter Block of 20...			21·00	
First Day Cover (Tallents House)..........................				9·50
First Day Cover (Tea Green, Luton).......................				9·75
Presentation Pack (PO Pack No. 380)..................			11·00	
PHQ Cards (set of 10) (283)................................			3·00	9·75

Nos. 2597/2606 were printed together, se-tenant, as blocks of ten (5×2) in sheets of 60 (2 panes of 30).

1874 Royal Albert Bridge

1875 Box Tunnel

1876 Paddington Station

1877 PSS *Great Eastern* (paddle-steamer)

1878 Clifton Suspension Bridge Design

1879 Maidenhead Bridge

(Des Hat-trick Design. Litho Enschedé)

2006 (23 Feb). Birth Bicentenary of Isambard Kingdom Brunel (engineer) (1st issue). Multicoloured Phosphor-coated paper (42p.) or two phosphor bands (others). Perf 14×13½.

2607	**1874**	(1st) Royal Albert Bridge.........................	1·20	1·00
		a. Booklet pane. Nos. 2607, 2609 and 2612...	2·50	
2608	**1875**	40p. Box Tunnel......................................	60	60
		a. Booklet pane. Nos. 2608 and 2610/2611..	2·50	
2609	**1876**	42p. Paddington Station........................	65	65
2610	**1877**	47p. PSS *Great Eastern*............................	80	80
		a. Booklet pane. No. 2610 and No. 2614×2...	7·00	
2611	**1878**	60p. Clifton Suspension Bridge..............	1·00	1·00
2612	**1879**	68p. Maidenhead Bridge........................	1·25	1·25
Set of 6..			4·75	4·75
Set of 6 Gutter Pairs...			9·50	
First Day Cover (Tallents House)..........................				5·25
First Day Cover (Bristol)......................................				5·25
Presentation Pack (PO Pack No. 381).................			5·75	
PHQ Cards (set of 7) (284).................................			2·00	11·00
MS2613 190×65 mm. Nos. 2607/2612............			5·00	5·00
		a. Imperforate...............................	—	
First Day Cover (Philatelic Bureau, Edinburgh)..................				5·50
First Day Cover (Bristol)......................................				5·50

The phosphor bands on Nos. 2607/2608 and 2610/2612 are at just left of centre and at right of each stamp.

Booklet panes Nos. 2607a/2608a and 2610a come from the £7·40 Isambard Kingdom Brunel booklet, No. DX36.

The complete miniature sheet is shown on one of the PHQ Cards with the others depicting individual stamps.

1739 PS *Great Western*, 1838 (Joseph Walter)

(Litho Enschedé)

2006 (23 Feb). Birth Bicentenary of Isambard Kingdom Brunel (2nd issue). Booklet stamp. Design as T **1739** (PSS *Great Western* from 2004 Ocean Liners). Multicoloured Two phosphor bands. Perf 14½×14.

2614	**1739**	68p. *PSS Great Western, 1838* (Joseph Walter)	2·50	2·50

No. 2614 was only issued in the £7·40 Isambard Kingdom Brunel booklet, No. DX36.

For the miniature sheet celebrating the opening of the New Welsh Assembly, Cardiff, issued 1 March 2006, see the Regional Section.

1887 At Heathrow Airport, 2001   **1888** As Young Princess Elizabeth with Duchess of York, 1931

1880 Sabre-tooth Cat   **1881** Giant Deer

1889 At State Banquet, Ottawa, 1951   **1890** Queen in 1960

1882 Woolly Rhino   **1883** Woolly Mammoth

1891 As Princess Elizabeth, 1940   **1892** With Duke of Edinburgh, 1951

1884 Cave Bear

(Des A. Davidson and H. Brown. Litho Enschedé)

2006 (21 Mar). Ice Age Animals. Black and silver. Two phosphor bands. Perf 14½.

2615	**1880**	(1st) Sabre-tooth Cat	1·20	1·00
2616	**1881**	42p. Giant Deer	90	90
2617	**1882**	47p. Woolly Rhino	1·00	1·00
2618	**1883**	68p. Woolly Mammoth	1·10	1·10
2619	**1884**	£1·12 Cave Bear	1·50	1·50
		Set of 5	5·00	5·00
		Set of 5 Gutter Pairs	10·00	
		First Day Cover (Tallents House)		5·50
		First Day Cover (Freezywater, Enfield)		5·50
		Presentation Pack (PO Pack No. 382)	5·50	
		PHQ Cards (set of 5) (285)	1·50	5·75

(Des Sedley Place. Gravure Enschedé)

2006 (18 Apr). 80th Birthday of Queen Elizabeth II. Black, turquoise-green and grey. One side phosphor band (No. 2620), one centre phosphor band (No. 2621) or two phosphor bands (others). Perf 14½.

2620	**1885**	(2nd) On *Britannia*, 1972	90	90
		a. Horiz pair. Nos. 2620/2621	1·75	1·75
2621	**1886**	(2nd) At Royal Windsor Horse Show, 1985	90	90
2622	**1887**	(1st) At Heathrow Airport, 2001	1·20	1·00
		a. Horiz pair. Nos. 2622/2623	2·40	2·00
2623	**1888**	(1st) As Young Princess Elizabeth with Duchess of York, 1931	1·20	1·00
2624	**1889**	44p. At State Banquet, Ottawa, 1951	75	75
		a. Horiz pair. Nos. 2624/2625	1·50	1·50
2625	**1890**	44p. Queen in 1960	75	75
2626	**1891**	72p. As Princess Elizabeth, 1940	1·00	1·00
		a. Horiz pair. Nos. 2626/2627	2·00	2·00
2627	**1892**	72p. With Duke of Edinburgh, 1951	1·00	1·00
		Set of 8	6·75	6·50
		Set of 4 Gutter Strips of 4	13·50	
		First Day Cover (Tallents House)		6·75
		First Day Cover (Windsor)		6·75
		Presentation Pack (PO Pack No. 383)	7·00	
		PHQ Cards (set of 8) (286)	2·50	7·50

Nos. 2620/2621, 2622/2623, 2624/2625 and 2626/2627 were each printed together, *se-tenant*, as horizontal pairs in sheets of 60 (2 panes 6×5).

1885 On *Britannia*, 1972   **1886** At Royal Windsor Horse Show, 1985

1893 England (1966)   **1894** Italy (1934, 1938, 1982)

44

1895 Argentina (1978, 1986)

50

1896 Germany (1954, 1974, 1990)

64

1897 France (1998)

72

1898 Brazil (1958, 1962, 1970, 1994, 2002)

(Des Madeleine Bennett. Litho Walsall)

2006 (6 June). World Cup Football Championship, Germany. World Cup Winners. Multicoloured Two phosphor bands. Perf 14½.

2628	**1893**	(1st) England	1·20	1·00
2629	**1894**	42p. Italy	80	80
2630	**1895**	44p. Argentina	85	85
2631	**1896**	50p. Germany	1·00	1·00
2632	**1897**	64p. France	1·25	1·25
2633	**1898**	72p. Brazil	1·40	1·40
Set of 6			5·50	5·50
Set of 6 Gutter Pairs			11·00	
First Day Cover (Tallents House)				5·75
First Day Cover (Balls Park, Hertford)				5·75
Presentation Pack (PO Pack No. 384)			6·00	
PHQ Cards (set of 6) (287)			1·75	6·50

The 1st class stamp was also issued in sheets of 20, sold for £6·95, printed in lithography by Cartor, containing four vertical rows of five stamps alternated with labels showing scenes from the 1966 World Cup final (No. LS31).

1st

1899 30 St Mary Axe, London

42

1900 Maggie's Centre, Dundee

44

1901 Selfridges, Birmingham

50

1902 Downland Gridshell, Chichester

64

1903 An Turas, Isle of Tiree

72

1904 The Deep, Hull

(Des Roundel. Gravure Walsall)

2006 (20 June). Modern Architecture. Multicoloured Two phosphor bands. Perf 14½.

2634	**1899**	(1st) 30 St Mary Axe, London	1·20	1·00
2635	**1900**	42p. Maggie's Centre, Dundee	65	65
2636	**1901**	44p. Selfridges, Birmingham	70	70
2637	**1902**	50p. Downland Gridshell, Chichester	85	85
2638	**1903**	64p. An Turas, Isle of Tiree	1·00	1·00
2639	**1904**	72p. The Deep, Hull	1·25	1·25
Set of 6			5·00	5·00
Set of 6 Gutter Pairs			10·00	
First Day Cover (Tallents House)				5·50
First Day Cover (London EC3)				5·50
Presentation Pack (PO Pack No. 385)			5·50	
PHQ Cards (set of 6) (288)			1·75	5·75

1st

1905 Sir Winston Churchill (Walter Sickert)

1st

1906 Sir Joshua Reynolds (self-portrait)

1st

1907 T. S. Eliot (Patrick Heron)

1st

1908 Emmeline Pankhurst (Georgina Agnes Brackenbury)

1st

1909 Virginia Woolf (photo by George Charles Beresford)

1st

1910 Bust of Sir Walter Scott (Sir Francis Leggatt Chantry)

1st

1911 Mary Seacole (Albert Charles Challen)

1st

1912 William Shakespeare

1st

1913 Dame Cicely Saunders

1st

1914 Charles Darwin (John Collier)

(Des P. Willberg. Gravure De La Rue)

2006 (18 July). 150th Anniversary of National Portrait Gallery, London. Multicoloured Two phosphor bands. Perf 14½.

2640	**1905**	(1st) Sir Winston Churchill	1·20	1·00
		a. Block of 10. Nos. 2640/2649	10·50	9·00
2641	**1906**	(1st) Sir Joshua Reynolds	1·20	1·00
2642	**1907**	(1st) T. S. Eliot	1·20	1·00
2643	**1908**	(1st) Emmeline Pankhurst	1·20	1·00
2644	**1909**	(1st) Virginia Woolf	1·20	1·00
2645	**1910**	(1st) Bust of Sir Walter Scott	1·20	1·00

2646	**1911**	(1st) *Mary Seacole*	1·20	1·00
2647	**1912**	(1st) *William Shakespeare*	1·20	1·00
2648	**1913**	(1st) *Dame Cicely Saunders*	1·20	1·00
2649	**1914**	(1st) *Charles Darwin*	1·20	1·00

Set of 10	10·50	9·00
Gutter Block of 20	21·00	
Traffic Light Gutter Block of 20	40·00	
First Day Cover (Tallents House)		9·50
First Day Cover (London WC2)		9·50
Presentation Pack (PO Pack No. 386)	11·00	
PHQ Cards (set of 10) (289)	3·00	10·00

Nos. 2640/2649 were printed together, *se-tenant*, as blocks of ten (5×2) in sheets of 60 (2 panes of 30).

For Nos. 2650/2657, **MS**2658, Types **1915**/**1917** see Decimal Machin Definitives section.

1918 Corporal Agansing Rai

1919 Boy Seaman Jack Cornwell

1920 Midshipman Charles Lucas

1921 Captain Noel Chavasse

1922 Captain Albert Ball

1923 Captain Charles Upham

(Des Atelier Works. Litho Enschedé)

2006 (21 Sept). 150th Anniversary of the Victoria Cross (1st issue). Multicoloured One side phosphor band. Perf 14½×14.

2659	**1918**	(1st) Corporal Agansing Rai	1·20	1·00
		a. Horiz pair. Nos. 2659/2660	2·40	2·00
		b. Booklet pane. Nos. 2659, 2661 and 2663	3·60	
		ba. Booklet pane. Bronze and phosphor omitted	£6500	
2660	**1919**	(1st) Boy Seaman Jack Cornwell	1·20	1·00
		b. Booklet pane. Nos. 2660, 2662 and 2664	3·60	
		ba. Booklet pane. Bronze and phosphor omitted	£6500	
2661	**1920**	64p. Midshipman Charles Lucas	90	90
		a. Horiz pair. Nos. 2661/2662	1·75	1·75
2662	**1921**	64p. Captain Noel Chavasse	90	90
2663	**1922**	72p. Captain Albert Ball	1·25	1·25
		a. Horiz pair. Nos. 2663/2664	2·40	2·40
2664	**1923**	72p. Captain Charles Upham	1·25	1·25

Set of 6	6·25	6·00
Set of 3 Gutter Strips of 4	12·20	
First Day Cover (Tallents House)		6·25
First Day Cover (Cuffley, Potters Bar, Herts)		6·25
Presentation Pack (PO Pack No. 387)	6·50	
PHQ Cards (set of 7) (290)	2·00	13·50
MS2665 190×67 mm. Nos. 2659/2664 and 2666	6·50	6·50
a. Imperforate	—	
First Day Cover (Tallents House)		6·50
First Day Cover (Cuffley, Potters Bar, Herts)		6·50

Nos. 2659/2660, 2661/2662 and 2663/2664 were each printed together, *se-tenant*, as horizontal pairs in sheets of 60 (2 panes 6×5).

Booklet panes Nos. 2659b/2660b come from the £7·44 Victoria Cross booklet No. DX37.

The seven PHQ Cards depict the six individual stamps and the miniature sheet.

959 Victoria Cross

(Litho Enschedé)

2006 (21 Sept). 150th Anniversary of the Victoria Cross (2nd issue). Booklet stamp. Design as No. 1517 (1990 Gallantry Awards). Multicoloured 'All-over' phosphor. Perf 14×14½.

2666	**959**	20p. Victoria Cross	1·50	1·50
		a. Booklet pane. Nos. 2666×4	6·50	6·50

No. 2666 was only issued in No. **MS**2665 and in the £7·44 Victoria Cross booklet, No. DX37. See also No. 1517.

1924 Sitar Player and Dancer

1925 1924 Reggae Bass Guitarist and African Drummer

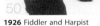

1926 Fiddler and Harpist

1927 Sax Player and Blues Guitarist

1928 Maraca Player and Salsa Dancers

(Des CDT Design. Litho Cartor)

2006 (3 Oct). Europa. Integration. Sounds of Britain. Multicoloured 'All-over' phosphor. Perf 14½.

2667	**1924**	(1st) Sitar Player and Dancer	1·20	1·00
2668	**1925**	42p. Reggae Bass Guitarist and African Drummer	1·00	1·00
2669	**1926**	50p. Fiddler and Harpist	1·10	1·10
2670	**1927**	72p. Sax Player and Blues Guitarist	1·25	1·25
2671	**1928**	£1·19 Maraca Player and Salsa Dancers	1·75	1·75

Set of 5	5·50	5·50
Set of 5 Gutter Pairs	11·00	
Set of 5 Traffic Light Gutter Blocks of 4	26·00	
First Day Cover (Tallents House)		6·00
First Day Cover (Rock, Kidderminster, Worcs)		6·00
Presentation Pack (PO Pack No. 388)	6·00	
PHQ Cards (set of 5) (291)	1·50	6·25

The 1st class and 50p. values include the EUROPA emblem.

1929 'New Baby' (Alison Carmichael)

1930 'Best Wishes' (Alan Kitching)

1931 'THANK YOU' (Alan Kitching)

1932 Balloons (Ivan Chermayeff)

1933 Firework (Kam Tang)

1934 Champagne, Flowers and Butterflies (Olaf Hajek)

(Des NB Studio. Gravure Walsall)

2006 (17 Oct). Smilers Booklet stamps (2nd series). Occasions. Self-adhesive. Multicoloured Two phosphor bands. Die-cut Perf 15×14.

2672	1929	(1st) 'New Baby'	1·20	1·00
		a. Booklet pane. Nos. 2672/2677	7·50	
2673	1930	(1st) 'Best Wishes'	1·20	1·00
2674	1931	(1st) 'THANK YOU'	1·20	1·00
2675	1932	(1st) Balloons	1·20	1·00
2676	1933	(1st) Firework	1·20	1·00
2677	1934	(1st) Champagne, Flowers and Butterflies	1·20	1·00
Set of 6			7·00	6·00
First Day Cover (Tallents House)				6·25
First Day Cover (Grinshill, Shrewsbury)				6·25
Presentation Pack (PO Pack No. M13)			10·00	
PHQ Cards (set of 6) (D29)			1·75	7·00

Nos. 2672/2677 were issued in £1·92 stamp booklet, No. QA3, in which the surplus backing paper around each stamp was removed.

Nos. 2672/2677 were also issued in sheets of 20 (No. LS33), containing four of Nos. 2672 and 2677 and three of each of the other designs, each stamp accompanied by a *se-tenant* greetings label. These sheets were printed by Cartor in lithography instead of gravure and sold at £6·95 each.

These designs were available in separate sheets with personal photographs printed on the labels from Royal Mail in Edinburgh at £14·95 each.

Stamps as No. 2672 but perforated with one elliptical hole on each vertical side were issued on 28 October 2008 in sheets of 20 with circular *se-tenant* Peter Rabbit labels (No. LS50). These sheets were printed by Cartor in lithography instead of gravure and sold for £7·95 each.

Similar sheets of ten stamps and ten *se-tenant* labels were sold in £7·95 packs.

No. 2674 was issued on 8 May 2010 with other greetings stamps in sheets of 20 with *se-tenant* greetings labels printed in lithography by Cartor (No. LS73), sold for £10 per sheet. These sheets were printed with one elliptical hole in each vertical side.

1935 Snowman

1936 Father Christmas

1937 Snowman

1938 Father Christmas

1939 Reindeer

1940 Christmas Tree

(Des T. Kiuchi, Rose Design and CDT Design. Gravure De La Rue)

2006 (7 Nov). Christmas. Multicoloured One centre phosphor band (No. 2678) or two phosphor bands (others). Perf 15×14.

(a) Self-adhesive.

2678	1935	(2nd) Snowman	90	90
		a. Booklet pane. No. 2678×12	13·50	
2679	1936	(1st) Father Christmas	1·20	1·00
		a. Booklet pane. No. 2679×12	16·00	
2680	1937	(2nd Large) Snowman	1·25	1·00
2681	1938	(1st Large) Father Christmas	1·70	1·25

2682	1939	72p. Reindeer	1·10	1·10
2683	1940	£1·19 Christmas Tree	1·50	1·50
Set of 6			6·75	6·00
First Day Cover (Tallents House)				7·00
First Day Cover (Bethlehem, Llandeilo)				7·00
Presentation Pack (PO Pack No. 389)			7·25	
PHQ Cards (set of 7) (292)			2·00	13·50

(b) Ordinary gum.

MS2684 115×102 mm. As Nos. 2678/2683	6·75	6·75
First Day Cover (Tallents House)		7·00
First Day Cover (Bethlehem, Llandeilo)		7·00

The 2nd and 1st class stamps were also issued together in sheets of 20 sold at £6, printed in lithography by Cartor, containing ten 1st class and ten 2nd class stamps, each value arranged in vertical rows of five alternating with rows of printed labels (No. LS34).

The phosphor bands have the date (2006) reversed out at the bottom (2nd) or bottom left (others).

Separate sheets of 20×1st or 20×2nd class were available with personalised photographs at £9·95 (2nd class) or £14·95 (1st class) and in 2010 the same designs with one elliptical hole on each vertical side were available from Royal Mail, Edinburgh. All these sheets had the backing paper around the stamps retained.

The seven PHQ Cards depict the six individual stamps and the miniature sheet.

1941 Lest We Forget

(Des Hat-trick Design. Gravure De La Rue)

2006 (9 Nov). Lest We Forget (1st issue). 90th Anniversary of the Battle of the Somme. Sheet 124×71 mm containing new stamp as No. 2883 and designs as Nos. EN17a, NI102, S120 and W109. Multicoloured Two phosphor bands. Perf 14½ (1st) or 15×14 (with one elliptical hole in each vertical side) (72p.).

MS2685 1941 Lest We Forget (1st) Poppies on barbed wire stems; 72p.×4 As Nos. EN17 (Type I), NI102, S120 and W109	5·50	5·50
First Day Cover (Tallents House)		6·00
First Day Cover (London SW1)		6·00
Presentation Pack (PO Pack No. 390)	7·25	

The 1st class stamp was also issued in sheets of 20 with *se-tenant* labels showing war memorials, printed in lithography by Cartor (No. LS35).

No. MS2685 (including the Northern Ireland stamp) is printed in gravure. See also Nos. MS2796 and MS2886.

Year Pack

2006 (9 Nov). Comprises Nos. 2589/2612, 2615/2649, 2659/2664, 2667/2671, 2678/2683 and MS2685.

CP2685a	Year Pack (Pack No. 391)	65·00

Post Office Yearbook

2006 (9 Nov). Comprises Nos. 2589/2612, 2615/2649, 2659/2664, 2667/2671, 2678/2683 and MS2685.

YB2685a	Yearbook	75·00

Miniature Sheet Collection

2006 (30 Nov). Comprises Nos. MS2613, MS2658, MS2665, MS2684/MS2685, MSS153 and MSW143.

MS2685a Miniature Sheet Collection	38·00

1942 *with the beatles*

1943 *Sgt Pepper's Lonely Hearts Club Band*

1944 *Help!*

1945 *Abbey Road*

1946 *Revolver*

1947 *Let It Be*

1948 Beatles Memorabilia

(Des johnson banks)

2007 (9 Jan). The Beatles. Album Covers. Multicoloured Two phosphor bands.

(a) Self-adhesive. Gravure Walsall. Die-cut irregular Perf 13½-14½.

2686	**1942**	(1st) *with the beatles*.......................	1·20	1·00
		a. Horiz pair. Nos. 2686/2687............	2·40	
2687	**1943**	(1st) *Sgt Pepper's Lonely Hearts Club Band*.......................	1·20	1·00
2688	**1944**	64p. *Help!*.......................	90	90
		a. Horiz pair. Nos. 2688/2689............	1·80	
2689	**1945**	64p. *Abbey Road*.......................	90	90
2690	**1946**	72p. *Revolver*.......................	1·25	1·25
		a. Horiz pair. Nos. 2690/2691............	2·50	
2691	**1947**	72p. *Let It Be*.......................	1·25	1·25
Set of 6.......................			6·25	6·00
First Day Cover (Tallents House).......................				6·25
First Day Cover (Liverpool).......................				6·50
Presentation Pack (PO Pack No. 392) (Nos. 2686/ **MS**2692).......................			10·00	
PHQ Cards (set of 11) (293).......................			3·25	15·50

(b) Ordinary gum. Litho Walsall. Perf 14.

MS2692 115×89 mm. **1948** Beatles Memorabilia (1st) Guitar; (1st) Yellow Submarine lunch box and keyrings; (1st) Record *Love Me Do*; (1st) Beatles tea tray and badges.

	3·75	3·75
First Day Cover (Tallents House).......................		6·25
First Day Cover (Liverpool).......................		6·50

Nos. 2686/2691 are all die-cut in the shape of a pile of records.

Nos. 2686/2687, 2688/2689 and 2690/2691 were each printed together in sheets of 60 (2 panes of 30), with the two designs alternating horizontally and the surplus backing paper around each stamp removed.

Nos. 2686/**MS**2692 commemorate the 50th anniversary of the first meeting of Paul McCartney and John Lennon.

The complete miniature sheet is on one of the 11 PHQ cards, with the others depicting individual stamps, including those from No. **MS**2692.

1842b

(Gravure Walsall)

2007 (16 Jan)–**2008**. Smilers Booklet stamp (3rd series). 'LOVE' design as No. 2569. Self-adhesive. Multicoloured. Two phosphor bands. Die-cut Perf 15×14 (with one elliptical hole in each vertical side).

2693	**1842b**	(1st) multicoloured.......................	5·50	5·50
		a. Booklet pane. No. 2655×5 and No. 2693.......................	18·00	
		b. Booklet pane. No. 2693×2 with two attached labels and No. 2295×4 (15.1.08).......................	16·00	

No. 2693 was issued in stamp booklets, Nos. SA1 and SA2, in which the surplus backing paper around each stamp was removed.

No. 2693 was re-issued on 8 May 2010 with other greetings stamps in sheets of 20 with *se-tenant* greetings labels printed in lithography by Cartor (No. LS73), sold for £10 per sheet.

Nos. 2694/2698 are left vacant.

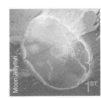

1949 Moon Jellyfish

1951 Beadlet Anemone

1950 Common Starfish

1952 Bass

1953 Thornback Ray

1954 Lesser Octopus

1955 Common Mussels

1956 Grey Seal

1957 Shore Crab

1958 Common Sun Star

(Des A. Ross. Litho Walsall)

2007 (1 Feb). Sea Life. Multicoloured Two phosphor bands. Perf 14½.

2699	1949	(1st) Moon Jellyfish..................................	1·20	1·00
		a. Block of 10. Nos. 2699/2708............	10·50	9·00
2700	1950	(1st) Common Starfish.............................	1·20	1·00
2701	1951	(1st) Beadlet Anemone...........................	1·20	1·00
2702	1952	(1st) Bass...	1·20	1·00
2703	1953	(1st) Thornback Ray................................	1·20	1·00
2704	1954	(1st) Lesser Octopus..............................	1·20	1·00
2705	1955	(1st) Common Mussels...........................	1·20	1·00
2706	1956	(1st) Grey Seal.......................................	1·20	1·00
2707	1957	(1st) Shore Crab.....................................	1·20	1·00
2708	1958	(1st) Common Sun Star...........................	1·20	1·00

Set of 10..	10·50	9·00
Gutter Block of 20...	21·00	
First Day Cover (Tallents House)...........................		9·25
First Day Cover (Seal Sands, Middlesbrough, Cleveland).		9·50
Presentation Pack (PO Pack No. 393).....................	11·00	
PHQ Cards (set of 10) (294).................................	3·00	10·50

Nos. 2699/2708 were printed together, *se-tenant*, as blocks of ten (5×2) in sheets of 60 (2 panes of 30).

1959 Saturn Nebula C55

1960 Eskimo Nebula C39

1961 Cat's Eye Nebula C6

1962 Helix Nebula C63

1963 Flaming Star Nebula C31

1964 The Spindle C53

(Des D. Davis. Gravure Walsall)

2007 (13 Feb). 50th Anniversary of *The Sky at Night* (TV programme). Nebulae. Self-adhesive. Multicoloured Two phosphor bands. Die-cut Perf 14½×14.

2709	1959	(1st) Saturn Nebula C55........................	1·20	1·00
		a. Horiz pair. Nos. 2709/2710..............	2·40	
2710	1960	(1st) Eskimo Nebula C39........................	1·20	1·00
2711	1961	50p. Cat's Eye Nebula C6.......................	1·00	1·00
		a. Horiz. pair. Nos. 2711/2712.............	2·00	
2712	1962	50p. Helix Nebula C63............................	1·00	1·00
2713	1963	72p. Flaming Star Nebula C31.................	1·25	1·25
		a. Horiz. pair. Nos. 2713/2714.............	2·40	
2714	1964	72p. The Spindle C53.............................	1·25	1·25

Set of 6..	6·00	5·75
First Day Cover (Tallents House)...........................		6·25
First Day Cover (Star, Glenrothes, Fife)................		6·25
Presentation Pack (PO Pack No. 394).....................	7·00	
PHQ Cards (set of 6) (295).................................	1·75	7·00

Nos. 2709/2710, 2711/2712 and 2713/2714 were each printed together in sheets of 60 (2 panes of 30), with the two designs alternating horizontally and the surplus backing paper around each stamp removed.

1965 Iron Bridge (Thomas Telford)

1966 Steam Locomotive and Railway Tracks

1967 Map of British Isles and Australia (telephone)

1968 Camera and Television (John Logie Baird)

1969 Globe as Web (email and internet)

1970 Couple with Suitcases on Moon (space travel)

(Des P. Willberg. Gravure De La Rue)

2007 (1 Mar). World of Invention (1st issue). Self-adhesive. Multicoloured Two phosphor bands. Die-cut Perf 14½×14.

2715	1965	(1st) Iron Bridge....................................	1·20	1·00
		a. Horiz pair. Nos. 2715/2716.............	2·40	
2716	1966	(1st) Steam Locomotive and Railway Tracks...	1·20	1·00
2717	1967	64p. Map of British Isles and Australia...	90	90
		a. Horiz pair. Nos. 2717/2718.............	1·75	
2718	1968	64p. Camera and Television.....................	90	90
2719	1969	72p. Globe as Web..................................	1·25	1·25
		a. Horiz pair. Nos. 2719/2720.............	2·50	
2720	1970	72p. Couple with Suitcases on Moon.......	1·25	1·25

Set of 6..	6·25	6·00
First Day Cover (Tallents House)...........................		6·25
First Day Cover (Pont Menai, Menai Bridge, Gwynedd).....		6·25
Presentation Pack (PO Pack No. 395).....................	6·50	
PHQ Cards (set of 7) (296).................................	2·00	7·25

Nos. 2715/2716, 2717/2718 and 2719/2720 were each printed together in sheets of 60 (2 panes of 30), with the two designs alternating horizontally and the surplus backing paper around each stamp removed.

The seven PHQ Cards depict the six individual stamps and No. **MS**2727.

(Gravure De La Rue)

2007 (1 Mar). World of Invention (2nd issue). Ordinary gum. Multicoloured Two phosphor bands. Perf 14½×14.

2721	1965	(1st) Iron Bridge....................................	1·20	1·00
		a. Booklet pane. Nos. 2721/2724........	7·00	
		b. Booklet pane. Nos. 2721/2722 and 2725/2726...........................	7·00	
2722	1966	(1st) Steam Locomotive and Railway Tracks...	1·20	1·00
2723	1967	64p. Map of British Isles and Australia...	2·50	2·50
2724	1968	64p. Camera and Television.....................	2·50	2·50
2725	1969	72p. Globe as Web..................................	2·50	2·50
2726	1970	72p. Couple with Suitcases on Moon.....	2·50	2·50

Set of 6..	11·00	11·00
MS2727 115×104 mm. Nos. 2721/2726.....................	12·00	12·00
First Day Cover (Tallents House)...........................		12·50
First Day Cover (Pont Menai, Menai Bridge, Gwynedd)....		12·50

Nos. 2721/2726 were only issued in the £7·49 World of Invention booklet, No. DX38 and in No. **MS**2727.

1971 William Wilberforce and Anti-slavery Poster

1972 Olaudah Equiano and Map of Slave Trade Routes

1973 Granville Sharp and Slave Ship

1974 Thomas Clarkson and Diagram of Slave Ship

1975 Hannah More and Title Page of *The Sorrows of Yamba*

1976 Ignatius Sancho and Trade/ Business Card

(Des Howard Brown. Litho Cartor)

2007 (22 Mar). Bicentenary of the Abolition of the Slave Trade. Multicoloured Two phosphor bands. Perf 14½.

2728	**1971**	(1st) William Wilberforce	1·00	1·00
		a. Horiz pair. Nos. 2728/2729	2·00	
		ab. Gold and phosphor omitted	£3000	
2729	**1972**	(1st) Olaudah Equiano	1·00	1·00
2730	**1973**	50p. Granville Sharp	80	80
		a. Horiz pair. Nos. 2730/2731	1·60	
2731	**1974**	50p. Thomas Clarkson	80	80
2732	**1975**	72p. Hannah More	90	90
		a. Horiz pair. Nos. 2732/2733	1·75	
2733	**1976**	72p. Ignatius Sancho	90	90
	Set of 6		5·00	5·00
	Set of 3 Gutter Strips of 4		11·00	
	Set of 3 Traffic Light Gutter Strips of 4		42·00	
	First Day Cover (Tallents House)			5·75
	First Day Cover (Hull)			5·75
	Presentation Pack (PO Pack No. 396)		6·00	
	PHQ Cards (set of 6) (297)		1·75	6·00

Nos. 2728/2729, 2730/2731 and 2732/2733 were each printed together, *se-tenant*, in horizontal pairs throughout the sheets.

For miniature sheet entitled Celebrating England, issued 23 April 2007, see Regionals Section

1977 Ice Cream Cone

1978 Sandcastle

1979 Carousel Horse

1980 Beach Huts

1981 Deckchairs

1982 Beach Donkeys

(Des Phelan Barker. Gravure De La Rue)

2007 (15 May). Beside the Seaside. Multicoloured Two phosphor bands. Perf 14½.

2734	**1977**	1st Ice Cream Cone	1·20	1·00
2735	**1978**	46p. Sandcastle	80	80
2736	**1979**	48p. Carousel Horse	90	90
2737	**1980**	54p. Beach Huts	1·00	1·00
2738	**1981**	69p. Deckchairs	1·10	1·10
2739	**1982**	78p. Beach Donkeys	1·25	1·25

Set of 6	5·50	5·50
Set of 6 Gutter Pairs	11·00	
First Day Cover (Tallents House)		5·75
First Day Cover (Blackpool)		5·75
Presentation Pack (PO Pack No. 397)	6·00	
PHQ Cards (set of 6) (298)	1·75	6·25

For T **1977**, but self-adhesive, see No. 2848

1983 Wembley Stadium

(Des Roundel. Gravure De La Rue)

2007 (17 May). New Wembley Stadium, London. Sheet 113×103 mm containing design as T **1593** but with 'WORLD CUP 2002' inscription omitted, and Nos. EN6b and EN18, each×2. Multicoloured One centre phosphor band (2nd) or two phosphor bands (others). Perf 14½×14 (1st) or 15×14 (with one elliptical hole in each vertical side) (2nd, 78p.).

MS2740	**1983**	Wembley Stadium (1st) As Type **1593**; (2nd) No. EN6b×2; 78p. No. EN18×2 and one central stamp-size label	4·75	4·75
		First Day Cover (Tallents House)		5·00
		First Day Cover (Wembley)		5·00

The design as T **1593** omits the 'WORLD CUP 2002' inscription at the left of the stamp. T **1593** (without 'WORLD CUP' inscription) was issued in sheets of 20 with *se-tenant* labels (No. LS39). These sheets were sold for £7·35.

1984 Arnold Machin

1985 1967 4d. Machin

1986 The Machin Definitives

(Des Jeffery Matthews and Together Design. Gravure and embossed De La Rue)

2007 (5 June). 40th Anniversary of the First Machin Definitives. 'All-over' phosphor (1st) or two phosphor bands (others). Perf 14½ (1st) or 15×14 (with one elliptical hole in each vertical side) (£1).

2741	**1984**	(1st) Arnold Machin	1·75	1·75
		a. Booklet pane. Nos. 2741/2742, each×2, with margins all round	7·50	
2742	**1985**	(1st) 1967 4d. Machin	1·75	1·75

MS2743 127×73mm **1986** The Machin Definitives Nos.

2741/2742, Y1743 and Y1744......................	4·75	4·75
a. Imperf..............................	£4500	
First Day Cover (Tallents House) (No. **MS**2743).................		5·00
First Day Cover (Windsor) (No. **MS**2743)........................		5·00
First Day Cover (Stoke-on-Trent) (No. **MS**2743)........		5·00
Presentation Pack (PO Pack No. 398) (No. **MS**2743)...	5·50	
PHQ Cards (set of 3) (299) (Nos. 2741/**MS**2743).............	1·00	7·50

Nos. 2741/2742 were only issued in the £7·66 The Machin, The Making of a Masterpiece booklet, No. DX39 and in No. **MS**2743.

Stamps as T **1984** but with phosphor frames were issued in sheets of 20 with *se-tenant* labels showing the 1967–1969 Machin definitives (No. LS40). These sheets were sold for £7·35.

1987 Stirling Moss in Vanwall 2.5L, 1957

1988 Graham Hill in BRM P57, 1962

1989 Jim Clark in Lotus 25 Climax, 1963

1990 Jackie Stewart in Tyrrell 006/2, 1973

1991 James Hunt in McLaren M23, 1976

1992 Nigel Mansell in Williams FW11, 1986

(Des True North. Litho Cartor)

2007 (3 July). Grand Prix. Racing Cars. Multicoloured Two phosphor bands. Perf 14½.

2744	**1987**	(1st) Stirling Moss in Vanwall 2.5L.........	1·20	1·00
2745	**1988**	(1st) Graham Hill in BRM P57...................	1·20	1·00
2746	**1989**	54p. Jim Clark in Lotus 25 Climax..........	90	90
2747	**1990**	54p. Jackie Stewart in Tyrrell 006/2........	90	90
2748	**1991**	78p. James Hunt in McLaren M23...........	1·25	1·25
2749	**1992**	78p. Nigel Mansell in Williams FW11.......	1·25	1·25
Set of 6..			5·75	5·50
Set of 6 Gutter Pairs..................................			11·00	
First Day Cover (Tallents House)............................				6·00
First Day Cover (Silverstone, Towcester, Northants)...........				6·00
Presentation Pack (PO Pack No. 399)........................			6·00	
PHQ Cards (set of 6) (300)...........................			1·75	6·25

Nos. 2744/2749 commemorate the 50th anniversary of Stirling Moss' victory in the British Grand Prix and the centenary of the opening of Brooklands race track.

1993 *Harry Potter and the Philosopher's Stone*

1994 *Harry Potter and the Chamber of Secrets*

1995 *Harry Potter and the Prisoner of Azkaban*

1996 *Harry Potter and the Goblet of Fire*

1997 *Harry Potter and the Order of the Phoenix*

1998 *Harry Potter and the Half-Blood Prince*

1999 *Harry Potter and the Deathly Hallows*

2000 Crests of Hogwarts School and its Four Houses

(True North. Litho Walsall)

2007 (17 July). Publication of Final Book in the Harry Potter Series. Multicoloured

(a) Book Covers. 'All-over' phosphor. Perf 14½.

2750	**1993**	(1st) Harry Potter and the Philosopher's Stone....................	1·20	1·00
		a. Horiz strip of 7. Nos. 2750/2756.....	7·25	6·25
2751	**1994**	(1st) Harry Potter and the Chamber of Secrets........................	1·20	1·00
2752	**1995**	(1st) Harry Potter and the Prisoner of Azkaban........................	1·20	1·00
2753	**1996**	(1st) Harry Potter and the Goblet of Fire...	1·20	1·00
2754	**1997**	(1st) Harry Potter and the Order of the Phoenix.........................	1·20	1·00
2755	**1998**	(1st) Harry Potter and the Half-Blood Prince..........................	1·20	1·00
2756	**1999**	(1st) Harry Potter and the Deathly Hallows........................	1·20	1·00
Set of 7...			7·25	6·25
Gutter Block of 14...................................			14·50	
Traffic Light Gutter Block of 14..........................			32·00	
First Day Cover (Tallents House)........................				6·50
First Day Cover (Broom, Alcester, Warwickshire)...............				6·50
Presentation Pack (Nos. 2750/2757) (PO Pack No. M16)...			12·00	
PHQ Cards (set of 13) (HP)............................			4·00	19·50

(b) Crests of Hogwarts School and its Four Houses. Multicoloured Two phosphor bands. Perf 15×14.

MS2757 123×70 mm. **2000** Crests of Hogwarts School and its Four Houses (1st) Gryffindor; (1st) Hufflepuff; (1st) Hogwarts; (1st) Ravenclaw; (1st) Slytherin................... 5·50 5·50
First Day Cover (Tallents House)....................... 5·75
First Day Cover (Broom, Alcester, Warwickshire)............... 5·75

Nos. 2750/2756 were printed together, *se-tenant*, as horizontal strips of seven stamps in sheets of 56 (2 panes 7×4).

Stamps as those within No. **MS**2757 but self-adhesive were issued in sheets of 20 containing the five designs *se-tenant* with labels depicting either magic spells (No. LS41), sold for £7·35 or personal photographs (*sold* for £14·95). The magic spells labels are printed in thermochromic ink which fades temporarily when exposed to heat, revealing the meaning of the spells.

The complete miniature sheet is shown on one of the 13 PHQ cards with the others depicting individual stamps including those from No. **MS**2757.

2001 Scout and Campfire

2002 Scouts Rock Climbing

2003 Scout Planting Tree

2004 Adult Volunteer Teaching Scout Archery

2005 Scouts Learning Gliding

2006 Scouts From Many Nations

(Des Gez Fry and The Work Room. Litho Enschedé)

2007 (26 July). Europa. Centenary of Scouting and 21st World Scout Jamboree, Chelmsford, Essex. Multicoloured Two phosphor bands. Perf 14½×14.

2758	**2001**	(1st) Scout and Campfire	1·20	1·00
2759	**2002**	46p. Scouts Rock climbing	80	80
2760	**2003**	48p. Scout planting Tree	85	85
2761	**2004**	54p. Adult Volunteer teaching Scout Archery	95	95
2762	**2005**	69p. Scouts learning gliding	1·10	1·10
2763	**2006**	78p. Scouts from Many Nations	1·25	1·25
Set of 6			5·50	5·50
Set of 6 *Gutter Pairs*			11·00	
First Day Cover (Tallents House)				6·00
First Day Cover (Brownsea Island, Poole, Dorset)				6·00
Presentation Pack (PO Pack No. 400)			6·00	
PHQ Cards (*set of* 6) (301)			1·75	6·25

The 1st class and 48p. values include the EUROPA emblem.

2007 White-tailed Eagle

2008 Bearded Tit

2009 Red Kite

2010 Cirl Bunting

2011 Marsh Harrier

2012 Avocet

2013 Bittern

2014 Dartford Warbler

2015 Corncrake

2016 Peregrine Falcon

(Des Kate Stephens. Litho Da La Rue)

2007 (4 Sept). Action for Species (1st series). Birds. Multicoloured Two phosphor bands. Perf 14½.

2764	**2007**	(1st) White-tailed Eagle	1·20	1·00
		a. Block of 10. Nos. 2764/2773	10·50	9·00
2765	**2008**	(1st) Bearded Tit	1·20	1·00
2766	**2009**	(1st) Red Kite	1·20	1·00
2767	**2010**	(1st) Cirl Bunting	1·20	1·00
2768	**2011**	(1st) Marsh Harrier	1·20	1·00
2769	**2012**	(1st) Avocet	1·20	1·00
2770	**2013**	(1st) Bittern	1·20	1·00
2771	**2014**	(1st) Dartford Warbler	1·20	1·00
2772	**2015**	(1st) Corncrake	1·20	1·00
2773	**2016**	(1st) Peregrine Falcon	1·20	1·00
Set of 10			10·50	9·00
Gutter Block of 20			21·00	
First Day Cover (Tallents House)				9·50
First Day Cover (Dartford)				9·50
Presentation Pack (PO Pack No. 401)			11·00	
PHQ Cards (*set of* 10) (302)			3·00	9·75

Nos. 2764/2773 were printed together, *se-tenant*, as blocks of ten (5×2) in sheets of 60 (2 panes of 30).

2017 NCO, Royal Military Police, 1999

2018 Tank Commander, 5th Royal Tank Regiment, 1944

2019 Observer, Royal Field Artillery, 1917

2020 Rifleman, 95th Rifles, 1813

2021 Grenadier, Royal Regiment of Foot of Ireland, 1704

2022 Trooper, Earl of Oxford's Horse, 1661

(Des Graham Turner and Atelier Works. Litho Enschedé)

2007 (20 Sept)–**2015**. Military Uniforms (1st series). British Army Uniforms. Multicoloured Two phosphor bands. Perf 14½.

2774	**2017**	(1st) NCO, Royal Military Police	1·20	1·00
		a. Horiz strip of 3. Nos. 2774/2776	3·60	3·00
		b. Booklet pane. Nos. 2774/2776 with margins all round (14.5.15)	3·60	
2775	**2018**	(1st) Tank Commander, 5th Royal Tank Regiment	1·00	1·00
2776	**2019**	(1st) Observer, Royal Field Artillery	1·00	1·00
		a. Booklet pane. No. 2776×4 with margins all round (14.5.15)	1·00	1·00

		b. Booklet pane No. 2776×4 with margins all round........................	4·00	
2777	**2020**	78p. Rifleman, 95th Rifles......................	1·25	1·25
		a. Horiz strip of 3. Nos. 2777/2779.....	3·75	3·75
		b. Booklet pane. Nos. 2777/2779 with margins all round...................	3·75	3·75
2778	**2021**	78p. Grenadier, Royal Regiment of Foot of Ireland...................................	1·25	1·25
2779	**2022**	78p. Trooper, Earl of Oxford's Horse.......	1·25	1·25
Set of 6...			7·00	6·50
Set of 2 Gutter blocks of 6...................................			14·00	
Set of 2 Traffic Light Gutter blocks of 6..................			30·00	
First Day Cover (Tallents House)............................				7·00
First Day Cover (Boot, Holmrook, Cumbria)...........				7·00
Presentation Pack (PO Pack No. 402)......................			7·25	
PHQ Cards (set of 6) (303).....................................			1·75	7·00

Nos. 2774/2776 and 2777/2779 were each printed together, *se-tenant*, in horizontal strips of three stamps in sheets of 60 (2 panes 6×5).

Booklet panes Nos. 2774b and 2777b come from the £7·66 British Army Uniforms booklet, No., DX40.

Booklet pane 2776b comes from the £13·96 Centenary of First World War (2nd issue) booklet, No DY13.

See also Nos. 2862/2867 and 2964/2969.

2023 Leaving St Paul's Cathedral after Thanksgiving Service, 2006

2024 Inspecting King's Troop Royal Horse Artillery, Regents Park, 1997

2025 At Garter Ceremony, Windsor, 1980

2026 At Royal Ascot, 1969

2027 At Premiere of *The Guns of Navarone*, 1961

2028 At Clydebank, 1947

2029 Photographs of the Royal Family

(Des Studio David Hillman)

2007 (16 Oct). Diamond Wedding of Queen Elizabeth II and Duke of Edinburgh. Blackish brown and black.

(a) Ordinary gum. Litho Cartor. 'All-over' phosphor. Perf 14½×14.

2780	**2023**	(1st) Leaving St Paul's Cathedral............	1·20	1·00
		a. Horiz pair. Nos. 2780/2781...............	2·40	2·00
2781	**2024**	(1st) Inspecting King's Troop Royal Horse Artillery..................................	1·20	1·00

2782	**2025**	54p. At Garter Ceremony......................	85	85
		a. Horiz pair. Nos. 2782/2783...............	1·75	1·75
2783	**2026**	54p. At Royal Ascot...........................	85	85
2784	**2027**	78p. At Premiere of *The Guns of Navarone*..	1·25	1·25
		a. Horiz pair. Nos. 2784/2785...............	2·50	2·50
2785	**2028**	78p. At Clydebank..............................	1·25	1·25
Set of 6...			5·75	5·50
Set of 3 Gutter blocks of 4....................................			11·50	
First Day Cover (Tallents House)............................				7·25
First Day Cover (Windsor, Berks)...........................				7·25
Presentation Pack (PO Pack No. 403) (Nos. 2780/ **MS**2786)..			11·50	
PHQ Cards (set of 11) (304)...................................			3·25	15·50

(b) Self-adhesive. Gravure Walsall. Multicoloured Two phosphor bands. Perf 14½.

MS2786 115×89 mm. **2029** Photographs of the Royal Family (1st) Royal family, Balmoral, 1972; (1st) Queen and Prince Philip, Buckingham Palace, 2007; 69p. Royal family, Windsor Castle, 1965; 78p. Princess Elizabeth, Prince Philip, Prince Charles and Princess Anne, Clarence House, 1951........... 4·25 4·25

First Day Cover (Tallents House)............................		5·75
First Day Cover (Windsor, Berks)...........................		5·75

Nos. 2780/2781, 2782/2783 and 2784/2785 were each printed together, *se-tenant*, in horizontal pairs throughout the sheets.

The complete miniature sheet is shown on one of the 11 PHQ cards with the others depicting individual stamps including those from No. **MS**2786.

2030 *Madonna and Child* (William Dyce), *circa* 1827

2031 *The Madonna of Humility* (Lippo di Dalmasio), *circa* 1390–1400)

(Des Peter Willberg. Gravure De La Rue)

2007 (6 Nov). Christmas (1st issue). Paintings of the Madonna and Child. Self-adhesive. Multicoloured One centre phosphor band (2nd) or two phosphor bands (1st). Die-cut Perf 15×14 (with one elliptical hole in each vertical side).

2787	**2030**	(2nd) Madonna and Child........................	90	90
2788	**2031**	(1st) *The Madonna of Humility*................	1·20	1·10
First Day Cover (Tallents House)............................				2·75
First Day Cover (Bethlehem, Llandeilo)...................				2·75

2032 Angel playing Trumpet ('PEACE')

2033 Angel playing Lute ('GOODWILL')

2034 Angel playing Trumpet ('PEACE')

2035 Angel playing Lute ('GOODWILL')

2036 Angel playing Flute ('JOY')

2037 Angel playing Tambourine ('GLORY')

(Des Marco Ventura and Rose Design. Gravure De La Rue)

2007 (6 Nov). Christmas (2nd issue). Angels. Multicoloured One centre phosphor band (No. 2789) or two phosphor bands (others). Perf 15×14.

(a) Self-adhesive.

2789	**2032**	(2nd) Angel playing Trumpet...................	90	90
		a. Booklet pane. No. 2789×12.............	13·50	
2790	**2033**	(1st) Angel playing Lute........................	1·20	1·00
		a. Booklet pane. No. 2790×12.............	16·00	
2791	**2034**	(2nd Large) Angel playing Trumpet........	1·25	1·25
2792	**2035**	(1st Large) Angel playing Lute...............	1·70	1·50
2793	**2036**	78p. Angel playing Flute......................	1·50	1·50
2794	**2037**	£1·24 Angel playing Tambourine............	2·25	2·25
Set of 6...			7·75	7·50

First Day Cover (Tallents House)...		7·75
First Day Cover (Bethlehem, Llandeilo)...............................		8·00
Presentation Pack (Nos. 2787/2794) (PO Pack No. 404).....	9·75	
PHQ Cards (set of 9) (305)..	2·75	17·50

(b) *Ordinary gum.*

MS2795 115×102 mm. As Nos. 2789/2794.........................	7·75	7·50
First Day Cover (Tallents House)...		7·75
First Day Cover (Bethlehem, Llandeilo)...............................		8·00

The phosphor bands on Nos. 2791/2792 are at the centre and right of each stamp.

The 2nd class, 1st class and 78p. stamps were also issued together in sheets of 20 sold at £8·30 containing 8×1st class, 8×2nd class and 4×78p., arranged in vertical strips of five stamps alternated with printed labels (No. LS42).

Separate sheets of 20×1st, 20×2nd or 10×78p. were available with personalised photographs from Royal Mail, Edinburgh. These were sold at £9·95 for 20×2nd or £14·95 for 20×1st or 10×78p.

All these sheets were printed in lithography by Cartor and had the backing paper around the stamps retained.

The PHQ cards depict Nos. 2787/2794 and **MS**2795.

2038 Lest We Forget

(Des Hat-trick design. Litho De La Rue)

2007 (8 Nov). Lest We Forget (2nd issue). 90th Anniversary of the Battle of Passchendaele. Sheet 124×70 mm containing new stamp as No. 2884 and designs as Nos. EN18, NI128, S121 and W110. Multicoloured Two phosphor bands. Perf 14½ (1st) or 15×14 (with one elliptical hole in each vertical side) (78p.).

MS2796 **2038** Lest We Forget (1st) Soldiers in poppy flower; 78p.×4 As Nos. EN18, NI128, S121 and W110..	6·00	6·00
First Day Cover (Tallents House)..		6·25
First Day Cover (London SW1)...		6·25
Presentation Pack (PO Pack No. 405)...................................	6·50	

No. **MS**2796 (including the England, Northern Ireland, Scotland and Wales stamps) is printed in lithography. A single example of the Soldiers in Poppy stamp from No. **MS**2796 is known with the silver (Queen's head and value) omitted.

The 1st class stamp was also issued in sheets of 20 with *se-tenant* labels showing soldiers and their letters home, printed in lithography by Cartor and sold at £7·35 (No. LS43).

Year Pack

2007 (8 Nov). Comprises Nos. 2686/2692, 2699/2720, 2728/2739, **MS**2743/2794 and **MS**2796.

CP2796*a*	Year Pack (Pack No. 406)......................	£120

Post Office Yearbook

2007 (8 Nov). Comprises Nos. 2686/2692, 2699/2720, 2728/2739, **MS**2743/2794 and **MS**2796.

YB2796*a*	Yearbook...	80·00

Miniature Sheet Collection

2007 (8 Nov). Comprises Nos. **MS**2692, **MS**2727, **MS**2740, **MS**2743, **MS**2757, **MS**2786 and **MS**2795/**MS**2796.

MS2796*a* Miniature Sheet Collection..................................	48·00

2039 *Casino Royale*

2040 *Dr No*

2041 *Goldfinger*

2042 *Diamonds are Forever*

2043 *For Your Eyes Only*

2044 *From Russia with Love*

(Des A2. Litho De La Rue)

2008 (8 Jan). Birth Centenary of Ian Fleming (author of James Bond books). Book Covers. Multicoloured Two phosphor bands. Perf 14½×14.

2797	**2039**	(1st) *Casino Royale*............................	1·20	1·00
		a. Booklet pane. Nos. 2797, 2799 and 2801 with margins all round...	3·00	
2798	**2040**	(1st) *Dr No*.......................................	1·20	1·00
		a. Booklet pane. Nos. 2798, 2800 and 2802 with margins all round...	3·00	
		aa. Phosphor omitted........................	£850	
2799	**2041**	54p. *Goldfinger*...............................	90	90
2800	**2042**	54p. *Diamonds are Forever*...............	90	90
2801	**2043**	78p. *For Your Eyes Only*..................	1·25	1·25
2802	**2044**	78p. *From Russia with Love*..............	1·25	1·25
Set of 6...			5·50	5·50
Set of 6 Gutter Pairs...			11·00	
First Day Cover (Tallents House)...............................				6·75
First Day Cover (London SE1)..................................				6·75
Presentation Pack (PO Pack No. 407).......................			6·50	
PHQ Cards (set of 7) (306)......................................			2·00	15·00
MS2803 189×68 mm. Nos. 2797/2802......................			9·25	9·25
First Day Cover (Tallents House)...............................				9·50
First Day Cover (London SE1)..................................				9·50

Booklet panes Nos. 2797a/2798a come from the £7·40 Ian Fleming's James Bond booklet, No. DX41.

The seven PHQ cards depict the individual stamps and No. **MS**2803.

No. 2804 is vacant.

1517 Union Jack

(Litho De La Rue)

2008 (8 Jan). Ian Fleming's James Bond. Booklet stamp. Design as T **1517** (2001 Union Jack from Submarine Centenary). Multicoloured Two phosphor bands. Perf 14½.

2805	**1517**	(1st) multicoloured.................................	2·00	2·00
		a. Booklet pane. Nos. 2581 and 2805, each×2, with margins all round..	7·00	

No. 2805 was issued in the £7·40 Ian Fleming's James Bond booklet, No. DX41. It had previously been issued in Post Office Label sheet No. LS20.

For White Ensign stamp from booklet No. DX41 see No. 2581.

2045 Assistance Dog carrying Letter (Retriever, Rowan)

2046 Mountain Rescue Dog (Cross-bred, Merrick)

2047 Police Dog (German Shepherd, Max)

2048 Customs Dog (Springer Spaniel, Max)

2049 Sheepdog (Border Collie, Bob)

2050 Guide Dog (Labrador, Warwick)

(Des Redpath Design. Litho Cartor)

2008 (5 Feb). Working Dogs. Multicoloured Two phosphor bands. Perf 14½.

2806	**2045**	(1st) Assistance Dog carrying Letter.......	1·20	1·00
2807	**2046**	46p. Mountain Rescue Dog....................	80	80
2808	**2047**	48p. Police Dog................................	80	80
2809	**2048**	54p. Customs Dog..............................	1·00	1·00
2810	**2049**	69p. Sheepdog..................................	1·10	1·10
2811	**2050**	78p. Guide Dog.................................	1·25	1·25
		Set of 6...	5·25	5·25
		Set of 6 Gutter Pairs............................	10·50	
		First Day Cover (Tallents House)...............		6·75
		First Day Cover (Hound Green, Basingstoke, Hants)..........		6·75
		Presentation Pack (PO Pack No. 408)...........	6·50	
		PHQ Cards (set of 6) (307).....................	1·75	6·25

The 1st class value includes the EUROPA emblem.

2051 Henry IV (1399–1413)

2052 Henry V (1413–1422)

2053 Henry VI (1422–1461 and 1470–1471)

2054 Edward IV (1461–1470 and 1471–1483)

2055 Edward V (1483)

2056 Richard III (1483–1485)

2057 The Age of Lancaster and York

(Des Atelier Works. Litho Cartor)

2008 (28 Feb). Kings and Queens (1st issue). Houses of Lancaster and York. Multicoloured Two phosphor bands. Perf 14½.

2812	**2051**	(1st) Henry IV............................	1·20	1·00
2813	**2052**	(1st) Henry V.............................	1·20	1·00
2814	**2053**	54p. Henry VI............................	90	1·00
2815	**2054**	54p. Edward IV..........................	90	1·00
2816	**2055**	69p. Edward V...........................	1·10	1·10
2817	**2056**	69p. Richard III.........................	1·10	1·10
		Set of 6..................................	5·25	5·25
		Set of 6 Gutter Pairs....................	10·50	
		Set of 6 Traffic Light Gutter Blocks of 4................	35·00	
		First Day Cover (Tallents House)........		6·75
		First Day Cover (Tewkesbury)............		6·75
		Presentation Pack (PO Pack No. 409) (Nos. 2812/		
		MS2818)................................	11·00	
		PHQ Cards (set of 11) (308).............	3·25	15·00

MS2818 123×70 mm. **2057** The Age of Lancaster and York (1st) Owain Glyn Dwr (Parliament), 1404; (1st) Henry V's triumph at Battle of Agincourt, 1415; 78p. Yorkist victory at Battle of Tewkesbury, 1471; 78p. William Caxton, first English printer, 1477......... 4·00 4·25

First Day Cover (Tallents House)................................ 5·00
First Day Cover (Tewkesbury)................................ 5·00

The complete miniature sheet is shown on one of the 11 PHQ cards with the others depicting individual stamps including those from No. **MS**2818.

1842 Gazania splendens (Charlotte Sowerby)

1842a Aircraft Skywriting 'hello'

1842c Union Flag

1932 Balloons (Ivan Chermayeff)

1933 Firework (Kam Tang)

1934 Champagne, Flowers and Butterflies (Olaf Hajek)

(Gravure Walsall)

2008 (28 Feb). Smilers Booklet stamps (4th series). Self-adhesive. Multicoloured Two phosphor bands. Die-cut Perf 15×14 (with one elliptical hole in each vertical side).

2819	**1842a**	(1st) Aircraft Skywriting 'hello'...........	5·50	5·50
		a. Booklet pane. Nos. 2819/2824.....	30·00	
2820	**1842**	(1st) Gazania splendens...................	5·50	5·50
2821	**1842c**	(1st) Union Jack...........................	5·50	5·50
2822	**1932**	(1st) Balloons.............................	5·50	5·50
2823	**1933**	(1st) Firework.............................	5·50	5·50
2824	**1934**	(1st) Champagne, Flowers and		
		Butterflies...........................	5·50	5·50
		Set of 6..................................	30·00	30·00

Nos. 2819/2824 were issued in £2·04 booklet, No. QA4, in which the surplus backing paper around each stamp was removed.

Similar sheets of ten stamps and ten se-tenant labels were only sold in packs for £7·95 each.

No. 2819 is also present on label sheets (Nos. LS92 and LS100) and No. 2823 on label sheet (No. LS91).

Nos. 2819, 2820 and 2822 were issued again on 30 April 2009 in separate sheets of 20, (Nos. LS60/LS63) with circular se-tenant labels showing Jeremy Fisher (No. 2819), Wild Cherry fairy (No. 2820), Little Miss Sunshine or Big Ears (No. 2822), sold for £8·50 per sheet.

Similar sheets of ten stamps and ten *se-tenant* labels were sold in £7·95 packs.

Nos. 2820 and 2822 were each issued on 28 October 2008 in separate sheets of 20, (Nos. LS51/LS53) with circular *se-tenant* labels showing the Almond Blossom fairy (No. 2820), Mr Men or Noddy (No. 2822). These sheets were printed in lithography by Cartor and originally sold for £9·95 per sheet.

Nos. 2821/2823 were issued on 8 May 2010 with other greetings stamps in sheets of 20 with *se-tenant* greetings labels, (No. LS73) sold for £10 per sheet.

No. 2821 was issued on 12 February 2011 in sheets of 20 with *se-tenant* labels for Indipex International Stamp Exhibition, (No. LS76) sold at £8·50 per sheet.

No. 2823 was issued in sheets of 20 with *se-tenant* labels on 20 January 2012 for Lunar New Year, Year of the Dragon (No. LS80), on 7 February 2013 for Year of the Snake (No. LS84), 10 December 2013 for Year of the Horse (No. LS89), on 19 November 2014 for Year of the Sheep (No. LS91), on 9 November 2015 for Year of the Monkey (No. LS98), on 15 November 2016 for Year of the Rooster (No. LS104), on 16 November 2017 for Year of the Dog (No. LS109), on 15 November 2018 for Year of the Pig (No. LS114), on 18 November 2019 for Year of the Rat (No. LS119), on 8 December 2020 for Year of the Ox (No. LS130), on 8 December 2021 for Year of the Tiger (No. LS137) and on 8 December 2022 for Year of the Rabbit (LS146).

All the above sheets were printed by Cartor (known from late 2013 onwards as International Security Printers) in lithography instead of photogravure.

For the miniature sheet entitled Celebrating Northern Ireland, issued 11 March 2008, see Regionals Section.

2058 Lifeboat, Barra

2059 Lifeboat approaching Dinghy, Appledore

2060 Helicopter Winchman, Portland

2061 Inshore lifeboat, St Ives

2062 Rescue Helicopter, Lee-on-Solent

2063 Launch of Lifeboat, Dinbych-y-Pysgod, Tenby

(Des Hat-trick Design. Litho Walsall)

2008 (13 Mar). Rescue at Sea. Multicoloured 'All-over' phosphor. Perf 14½×14*.

2825	**2058**	(1st) Lifeboat, Barra................................	1·20	1·00
2826	**2059**	46p. Lifeboat approaching Dinghy, Appledore..................................	80	80
2827	**2060**	48p. Helicopter Winchman, Portland.....	90	90
2828	**2061**	54p. Inshore lifeboat, St Ives..................	1·00	1·00
2829	**2062**	69p. Rescue Helicopter, Lee-on- Solent	1·10	1·10
2830	**2063**	78p. Launch of Lifeboat, Dinbych-y-Pysgod, Tenby...............................	1·25	1·25
Set of 6..............................			5·25	5·25
Set of 6 Gutter Pairs................			10·50	
First Day Cover (Tallents House)................				6·50
First Day Cover (Poole, Dorset)................				6·50
Presentation Pack (PO Pack No. 411)................			6·00	
PHQ Cards (set of 6) (309)................			1·50	6·25

* Nos. 2825/2830 have interrupted perforations along the top and bottom edges of the stamps, the gaps in the perforations forming the three dots and three dashes that spell out 'SOS' in morse code.

2064 *Lysandra bellargus* (Adonis Blue)

2065 *Coenagrion mercuriale* (Southern Damselfly)

2066 *Formica rufibarbis* (Red-barbed Ant)

2067 *Pareulype berberata* (Barberry Carpet Moth)

2068 *Lucanus cervus* (Stag Beetle)

2069 *Cryptocephalus coryli* (Hazel Pot Beetle)

2070 *Gryllus campestris* (Field Cricket)

2071 *Hesperia comma* (Silver-spotted Skipper)

2072 *Pseudepipona herrichii* (Purbeck Mason Wasp)

2073 *Gnorimus nobilis* (Noble Chafer)

(Des Andrew Ross. Litho De La Rue)

2008 (15 Apr). Action for Species (2nd series). Insects. Multicoloured Phosphor background. Perf 14½.

2831	**2064**	(1st) *Lysandra bellargus* (Adonis blue)....	1·20	1·00
		a. Block of 10. Nos. 2831/2840...........	10·50	9·00
2832	**2065**	(1st) *Coenagrion mercuriale* (southern damselfly)...........................	1·20	1·00
2833	**2066**	(1st) *Formica rufibarbis* (red-barbed ant)...........................	1·20	1·00
2834	**2067**	(1st) *Pareulype berberata* (barberry carpet moth)...........................	1·20	1·00
2835	**2068**	(1st) *Lucanus cervus* (stag beetle)...........	1·20	1·00
2836	**2069**	(1st) *Cryptocephalus coryli* (hazel pot beetle)...........................	1·20	1·00
2837	**2070**	(1st) *Gryllus campestris* (field cricket)......	1·20	1·00
2838	**2071**	(1st) *Hesperia comma* (silver-spotted skipper)...........................	1·20	1·00
2839	**2072**	(1st) *Pseudepipona herrichii* (Purbeck mason wasp)...........................	1·20	1·00
2840	**2073**	(1st) *Gnorimus nobilis* (noble chafer)......	1·20	1·00
Set of 10...........................			10·50	9·00

Gutter Block of 20		21·00	
First Day Cover (Tallents House)			9·25
First Day Cover (Crawley, W. Sussex)			9·50
Presentation Pack (PO Pack No. 412)		11·00	
PHQ Cards (set of 10) (310)		3·00	9·75

Nos. 2831/2840 were printed together, *se-tenant*, as blocks of ten (5×2) in sheets of 60 (2 panes of 30).

2074 Lichfield Cathedral

2075 Belfast Cathedral

2076 Gloucester Cathedral

2077 St David's Cathedral

2078 Westminster Cathedral

2079 St Magnus Cathedral, Kirkwall, Orkney

2080 St Paul's Cathedral

(Des Howard Brown. Litho Enschedé)

2008 (13 May). Cathedrals. Multicoloured 'All-over' phosphor. Perf 14½.

2841	**2074**	(1st) Lichfield Cathedral	1·20	1·00
2842	**2075**	48p. Belfast Cathedral	85	85
2843	**2076**	50p. Gloucester Cathedral	1·00	1·00
2844	**2077**	56p. St David's Cathedral	1·10	1·10
2845	**2078**	72p. Westminster Cathedral	1·25	1·25
2846	**2079**	81p. St Magnus Cathedral, Kirkwall, Orkney	1·40	1·40
Set of 6			6·00	6·00
Set of 6 Gutter Pairs			12·00	
Set of 6 Traffic Light Gutter Pairs			32·00	
First Day Cover (Tallents House)				6·75
First Day Cover (London EC4)				6·75
Presentation Pack (PO Pack No. 413) (Nos. 2841/ MS2847)			11·00	
PHQ Cards (set of 11) (311)			3·25	16·00

MS2847 115×89 mm. **2080** St Paul's Cathedral (1st) multicoloured; (1st) multicoloured; 81p. multicoloured; 81p. multicoloured. Perf 14½×14...... 4·00 | 4·00

First Day Cover (Tallents House)		4·50
First Day Cover (London EC4)		4·50

No. **MS**2847 commemorates the 300th anniversary of St Paul's Cathedral. The complete miniature sheet is shown on one of the 11 PHQ cards with the others depicting individual stamps including those from No. **MS**2847.

1977 Ice Cream Cone

(Gravure Walsall)

2008 (13 May). Beside the Seaside (2nd series). As T **1977** but self-adhesive. Multicoloured Two phosphor bands. Die-cut Perf 14½.

2848	**1977**	(1st) Ice Cream Cone. Multicoloured	3·00	3·00
		a. Booklet pane. No. 2848×2 and No. 2295×4	7·50	

No. 2848 was only issued in £2·16 booklet, No. PM15, in which the surplus self-adhesive paper was removed from around the 1st class gold stamps (No. 2295), but retained from around No. 2848.

2081 *Carry on Sergeant*

2082 *Dracula*

2083 *Carry on Cleo*

2084 *The Curse of Frankenstein*

2085 *Carry on Screaming*

2086 *The Mummy*

(Des Elmwood. Litho Walsall)

2008 (10 June). Posters for Carry On and Hammer Horror Films. Multicoloured Two phosphor bands. Perf 14.

2849	**2081**	(1st) *Carry on Sergeant*	1·20	1·00
2850	**2082**	48p. *Dracula*	80	80
2851	**2083**	50p. *Carry on Cleo*	90	90
2852	**2084**	56p. *The Curse of Frankenstein*	1·00	1·00
2853	**2085**	72p. *Carry on Screaming*	1·10	1·10
2854	**2086**	81p. *The Mummy*	1·25	1·25
Set of 6			5·50	5·50
Set of 6 Gutter Pairs			11·00	
First Day Cover (Tallents House)				6·25
First Day Cover (Bray, Maidenhead, Berks)				6·25
Presentation Pack (PO Pack No. 414)			6·25	
PHQ Cards (set of 6) (312)			1·50	7·00
PHQ Cards (brick wall background) and Stamps Set			7·00	

Nos. 2849/2854 commemorate the 50th anniversary of *Dracula* and the first Carry On film (*Carry on Sergeant*).

2087 Red Arrows, Dartmouth Regatta Airshow, 2006

2088 RAF Falcons Parachute Team, Biggin Hill, 2006

2089 Spectator watching Red Arrows, Farnborough, 2006

2090 Prototype Avro Vulcan Bombers and Avro 707s, Farnborough, 1953

2091 Parachutist Robert Wyndham on Wing of Avro 504, 1933

2092 Air Race rounding the Beacon, Hendon, c 1912

(Des Roundel. Gravure De La Rue)

2008 (17 July). Air Displays. Multicoloured Two phosphor bands. Perf 14½×14.

2855	**2087**	(1st) Red Arrows	1·20	1·00
2856	**2088**	48p. RAF Falcons Parachute Team	80	80
2857	**2089**	50p. Spectator watching Red Arrows	90	90
2858	**2090**	56p. Prototype Avro Vulcan Bombers and Avro 707s	1·00	1·00
2859	**2091**	72p. Parachutist Robert Wyndham on Wing of Avro 504	1·10	1·10
2860	**2092**	81p. Air Race rounding the Beacon	1·25	1·25
		Set of 6	5·50	5·50
		Set of 6 Gutter Pairs	11·00	
		First Day Cover (Tallents House)		6·25
		First Day Cover (Farnborough, Hants)		6·25
		Presentation Pack (PO Pack No. 415)	6·25	
		PHQ Cards (set of 6) (313)	1·75	6·25

The 1st class stamp was also issued in sheets of 20 with *se-tenant* labels, printed in lithography by Cartor, and sold for £7·75 per sheet (No. LS47). See also No. 2869.

2093 Landmarks of Beijing and London

(Des Why Not Associates. Litho Walsall)

2008 (22 Aug). Handover of Olympic Flag from Beijing to London. Sheet 115×76 mm. Multicoloured Phosphorised paper. Perf 14½.

MS2861	**2093**	Landmarks of Beijing and London		
		(1st) National Stadium, Beijing; (1st) London Eye; (1st) Tower of London; (1st) Corner Tower of the Forbidden City, Beijing	5·00	5·00
		a. UV varnish (Olympic Rings) omitted	£4000	
		First Day Cover (Tallents House)		5·25
		First Day Cover (London E15)		5·25
		Presentation Pack (PO Pack No. M17)	30·00	
		PHQ Cards (set of 5) (OGH)	60	5·00

The Olympic rings overprinted on No. **MS**2861 are in silk-screen varnish.
The five PHQ cards show the four individual stamps and the complete miniature sheet.

2094 Drum Major, RAF Central Band, 2007

2095 Helicopter Rescue Winchman, 1984

2096 Hawker Hunter Pilot, 1951

2097 Lancaster Air Gunner, 1944

2098 WAAF Plotter, 1940

2099 Pilot, 1918

(Des Graham Turner and Atelier Works. Litho Walsall)

2008 (18 Sept). Military Uniforms (2nd series). RAF Uniforms. Multicoloured Two phosphor bands. Perf 14.

2862	**2094**	(1st) Drum Major, RAF Central Band	1·20	1·00
		a. Horiz strip of 3. Nos. 2862/2864	3·50	3·00
		b. Booklet pane. Nos. 2862/2864 with margins all round	3·50	
2863	**2095**	(1st) Helicopter Rescue Winchman	1·20	1·00
2864	**2096**	(1st) Hawker Hunter Pilot	1·20	1·00
2865	**2097**	81p. Lancaster Air Gunner	1·40	1·40
		a. Horiz strip of 3. Nos. 2865/2867	4·25	4·25
		b. Booklet pane. Nos. 2865/2867 with margins all round	4·25	
2866	**2098**	81p. WAAF Plotter	1·40	1·40
2867	**2099**	81p. Pilot	1·40	1·40
		Set of 6	7·00	6·75
		Set of 2 Gutter Strips of 6	14·00	
		Set of 2 Traffic Light Gutter Blocks of 12	28·00	
		First Day Cover (Tallents House)		7·00
		First Day Cover (Hendon, London NW9)		7·00
		Presentation Pack (PO Pack No. 416)	7·00	
		PHQ Cards (set of 6) (314)	1·75	7·75

Nos. 2862/2864 and 2865/2867 were each printed together, *se-tenant*, as horizontal strips of three stamps in sheets of 60 (2 panes 6×5).

Booklet panes Nos. 2862b and 2865b come from the £7·15 Pilot to Plane, RAF Uniforms booklet No. DX42.

See also Nos. 2774/2779 and 2964/2969.

1307 Reginald Mitchell and Supermarine Spitfire MkIIA

2087 Red Arrows, Dartmouth Regatta Airshow, 2006

(Litho Walsall)

2008 (18 Sept). Pilot to Plane. RAF Uniforms. Booklet stamps. Designs as T **1307** (Spitfire from 1997 British Aircraft Designers) and T **2087** (Red Arrows from 2008 Air Displays). Multicoloured Two phosphor bands. Perf 14.

2868	**1307**	20p. Reginald Mitchell and Supermarine Spitfire MkIIA	1·25	1·25
		a. Booklet pane. Nos. 2868/2869, each×2, with margins all round	6·00	
2869	**2087**	(1st) Red Arrows	1·25	1·25

Nos. 2868/2869 were only issued in the £7·15 Pilot to Plane, RAF Uniforms booklet, No. DX42.

2100 Millicent Garrett Fawcett (suffragist)

2101 Elizabeth Garrett Anderson (physician, women's health)

2102 Marie Stopes (family planning pioneer)

2103 Eleanor Rathbone (family allowance campaigner)

2104 Claudia Jones (civil rights activist)

2105 Barbara Castle (politician, Equal Pay Act)

(Des Together Design. Gravure Walsall)

2008 (14 Oct). Women of Distinction. Multicoloured 'All-over' phosphor. Perf 14×14½.

2870	**2100**	(1st) Millicent Garrett Fawcett..................	1·20	1·00
2871	**2101**	48p. Elizabeth Garrett Anderson............	80	80
2872	**2102**	50p. Marie Stopes.................................	90	90
2873	**2103**	56p. Eleanor Rathbone..........................	1·00	1·00
2874	**2104**	72p. Claudia Jones.................................	1·10	1·10
2875	**2105**	81p. Barbara Castle................................	1·25	1·25
Set of 6..			5·25	5·25
Set of 6 Gutter Pairs...			10·50	
First Day Cover (Tallents House)...........................				6·25
First Day Cover (Aldeburgh, Suffolk)......................				6·25
Presentation Pack (PO Pack No. 417).....................			6·00	
PHQ Cards (set of 6) (315)...................................			1·75	6·25

SELF-ADHESIVE STAMPS. Collectors are reminded that from November 2008, self-adhesive stamps no longer incorporated a layer of water-soluble gum and will not 'soak-off'. It is advised that, from this point, all used self-adhesive stamps are collected with a neat margin of backing paper.

2106 Ugly Sisters from *Cinderella*

2107 Genie from *Aladdin*

2108 Ugly Sisters from *Cinderella*

2109 Captain Hook from *Peter Pan*

2110 Genie from *Aladdin*

2111 Wicked Queen from *Snow White*

(Des Steve Haskins. Gravure De La Rue)

2008 (4 Nov). Christmas. Multicoloured One centre band (No. 2876) or two phosphor bands (others). Perf 15×14.

(a) Self-adhesive.

2876	**2106**	(2nd) Ugly Sisters.................................	90	90
		a. Booklet pane. No. 2876×12............	13·50	
2877	**2107**	(1st) Genie..	1·20	1·00
		a. Booklet pane. No. 2877×12............	16·00	
2878	**2108**	(2nd Large) Ugly Sisters........................	1·25	1·25
2879	**2109**	50p. Captain Hook................................	1·00	1·00
2880	**2110**	(1st Large) Genie..................................	1·70	1·50
2881	**2111**	81p. Wicked Queen..............................	1·75	1·75
Set of 6..			6·25	6·25
First Day Cover (Tallents House)...........................				6·50
First Day Cover (Bethlehem, Llandeilo)..................				6·50
Presentation Pack (PO Pack No. 418).....................			7·00	
PHQ Cards (set of 7) (316)...................................			2·00	12·00

(b) Ordinary gum.

MS2882 114×102 mm. As Nos. 2876/2881........................	6·50	6·50
First Day Cover (Tallents House)...........................		6·75
First Day Cover (Bethlehem, Llandeilo)..................		7·00

The phosphor bands on Nos. 2878 and 2880 are at the centre and right of each stamp.

The 2nd class, 1st class and 81p. stamps were also issued together in sheets of 20, sold for £8·85, containing 8×1st class, 8×2nd class and 4×81p. stamps, arranged in vertical strips of five stamps alternated with printed labels (No. LS54).

Separate sheets of 10×1st, 20×1st, 20×2nd or 10×81p. stamps were available with personalised photographs from Royal Mail, Edinburgh. These were sold at £7·50 for ten×1st, £8·50 for 20×2nd or £13·50 for 20×1st or 10×81p.

Separate sheets of 10×1st, 20×1st, 20×2nd or 10×81p. stamps were available with personalised photographs.

All these sheets were printed in lithography by Cartor and had the backing paper around the stamps retained.

The seven PHQ cards depict the six stamps and No. **MS**2882.

2112 Seven Poppies on Barbed Wire Stems

2113 Soldiers in Poppy Flower

2114 Soldier's Face in Poppy Flower

2115 Lest We Forget

(Des Hat–trick design. Litho Cartor ISP (No. 2883b) or De La Rue (others))

2008 (6 Nov)–**2017**. Lest We Forget (3rd issue). 90th Anniversary of the Armistice. Multicoloured Two phosphor bands. Perf 14½ (1st) or 15×14 (with one elliptical hole in each vertical side) (81p.).

2883	**2112**	(1st) Seven Poppies on Barbed Wire		
		Stems...	1·20	1·00
		a. Horiz strip of 3. Nos. 2883/2885.....	3·50	4·50

		b. Booklet pane No. 2883, 2884×2		
		and 2885 se-tenant (31.7.17)...........	5·00	
2884	**2113**	(1st) Soldiers in Poppy Flower.................	1·20	1·00
2885	**2114**	(1st) Soldier's Face in Poppy Flower.......	1·20	1·00

Set of 3... 3·50 4·50
Gutter Strip of 6.. 7·00
Traffic Light Gutter Block of 12............................ 25·00
MS2886 124×70 mm. **2115** Lest We Forget No. 2885
and as Nos. EN19, NI129, S122 and W111................ 5·75 5·75
First Day Cover (Tallents House)............................. 6·75
First Day Cover (London SW1)................................. 6·75
Presentation Pack (PO Pack No. 419).................... 7·25
PHQ Cards (set of 6) (317)...................................... 1·80 9·50

No. 2883/2885 were printed together, se-tenant, in horizontal strips of three stamps in sheets of 30.

No. **MS**2886 (including the England, Northern Ireland, Scotland and Wales stamps) is printed in lithography.

The 1st class stamp, T **2114**, was also issued in sheets of 20 with se-tenant labels showing artefacts from the trenches, printed in lithography by Cartor and sold at £7·75 (No. LS55).

No. 2885 has the two phosphor bands shaped around each side of the poppy.

A Miniature Sheet Collection containing Nos. **MS**2685, **MS**2796, **MS**2886 and a replica embroidered postcard in a folder was sold for £26·95.

Booklet pane 2883b is from the £15·41 premium booklet Centenary of the First World War (4th issue) No. DY22.

The six PHQ cards depict Nos. **MS**2685, **MS**2796 and 2883/**MS**2886.

Year Pack

2008 (6 Nov). Comprises Nos. 2797/2802, 2806/**MS**2818, 2825/**MS**2847, 2849/2867, 2870/2881, **MS**2886 and **MS**NI152
CP2886a Year Pack (Pack No. 420)...................... 85·00

Post Office Yearbook

2008 (6 Nov). Comprises Nos. 2797/2802, 2806/**MS**2818, 2825/**MS**2847, 2849/2867, 2870/2881, **MS**2886 and **MS**NI152/**MS**NI153
YB2886a Yearbook... 85·00

Miniature Sheet Collection

2008 (6 Nov). Comprises Nos. **MS**2803, **MS**2818, **MS**2847, **MS**2861, **MS**2882, **MS**2886 and **MS**NI152/**MS**NI153
MS2886a Miniature Sheet Collection................................. 45·00

2116 Supermarine Spitfire (R. J. Mitchell)

2117 Mini Skirt (Mary Quant)

2118 Mini (Sir Alec Issigonis)

2119 Anglepoise Lamp (George Carwardine)

2120 Concorde (Aérospatiale-BAC)

2121 K2 Telephone Kiosk (Sir Giles Gilbert Scott)

2122 Polypropylene Chair (Robin Day)

2123 Penguin Books (Edward Young)

2124 London Underground Map (based on original design by Harry Beck)

2125 Routemaster Bus (design team led by AAM Durrant)

(Des HGV Design. Litho Cartor)

2009 (13 Jan). British Design Classics (1st series). Multicoloured Phosphor background. Perf 14½.

2887	**2116**	(1st) Supermarine Spitfire.......................	1·20	1·00
		a. Block of 10. Nos. 2887/2896............	10·50	9·00
		ab. Black printed treble.........................	—	
		b. Booklet pane. Nos. 2887, 2889		
		and 2896×2.............................	4·75	
2888	**2117**	(1st) Mini Skirt...................................	1·20	1·00
		a. Booklet pane. Nos. 2888, 2890,		
		2892 and 2893/2895............	6·00	
2889	**2118**	(1st) Mini..	1·20	1·00
2890	**2119**	(1st) Anglepoise Lamp...........................	1·20	1·00
2891	**2120**	(1st) Concorde.....................................	1·20	1·00
		a. Booklet pane. Nos. 2891 and		
		2897, each×2.........................	4·75	
2892	**2121**	(1st) K2 Telephone Kiosk........................	1·20	1·00
2893	**2122**	(1st) Polypropylene Chair.......................	1·20	1·00
2894	**2123**	(1st) Penguin Books...............................	1·20	1·00
2895	**2124**	(1st) London Underground Map...............	1·20	1·00
2896	**2125**	(1st) Routemaster Bus...........................	1·20	1·00

Set of 10... 10·50 9·00
Gutter Block of 20... 21·00
First Day Cover (Tallents House)........................... 9·00
First Day Cover (Longbridge, Birmingham)......... 9·00
Presentation Pack (PO Pack No. 421)................... 11·00
PHQ Cards (set of 10) (318).................................. 3·00 9·75

No. 2887 was also issued on 15 September 2010 in sheets of 20 with se-tenant labels, (No. LS74), sold at £8·50 per sheet.

Nos. 2887/2896 were printed together, se-tenant, in blocks of ten (2×5) throughout sheets of 30 stamps.

Booklet panes Nos. 2887b, 2888a and 2891a come from the £7·68 British Design Classics booklet, No. DX44.

No. 2889 was also issued in sheets of 20 with se-tenant labels, on 13 January 2009. (No. LS56), sold at £7·75 per sheet.

No. 2891 was also issued on 2 March 2009 in sheets of 20 with se-tenant labels, (No. LS57), and sold at £7·75 per sheet.

The above sheets were all printed in lithography by Cartor and perforated 14×14½.

For self-adhesive versions of these stamps see Nos. 2911/2915b.

1589 Concorde (1976)

(Litho Cartor)

2009 (13 Jan). British Design Classics (2nd series). Booklet stamp. Design as No. 2285 (Concorde from 2002 Passenger Jet Aviation). Multicoloured Two phosphor bands. Perf 14½.
2897 **1589** (1st) Concorde (1976). Multicoloured.... 4·50 4·50
No. 2897 was only issued in the £7·68 British Design Classics booklet, No. DX44.

For the miniature sheet entitled Robert Burns 250th Anniversary, issued on 22 January, see the Regional Section.

2126 Charles Darwin

2127 Marine Iguana

2128 Finches

2129 Atoll

2130 Bee Orchid

2131 Orangutan

2132 Fauna and Map of the Galapagos Islands

(Des Hat-trick design (Nos. 2898/2903) or Howard Brown (No. **MS**2904)

2009 (12 Feb). Birth Bicentenary of Charles Darwin (naturalist and evolutionary theorist) (1st issue). Multicoloured

(a) Self-adhesive. Gravure De La Rue. 'All-over' phosphor. Perf 14.

2898	**2126**	(1st) Charles Darwin................................	1·20	1·00
2899	**2127**	48p. Marine Iguana..............................	1·10	1·10
2900	**2128**	50p. Finches......................................	1·25	1·25
2901	**2129**	56p. Atoll..	1·40	1·40
2902	**2130**	72p. Bee Orchid.................................	1·75	1·75
2903	**2131**	81p. Orangutan.................................	2·00	2·00
Set of 6..			7·50	7·50
First Day Cover (Tallents House)...............................				8·25
First Day Cover (Shrewsbury)...................................				8·25
Presentation Pack (PO Pack No. 423) (Nos. 2898/				
MS2904)...			10·50	
PHQ Cards (set of 11) (320)......................................			3·25	16·50

(b) Ordinary gum. Litho De La Rue. Two phosphor bands. Perf 14.

MS2904 115×89 mm. **2132** Fauna and Map of the Galapagos Islands (1st) Flightless Cormorant; (1st) Giant Tortoise and Cactus Finch; 81p. Marine Iguana; 81p. Floreana Mockingbird............................	5·00 5·00
a. Booklet pane. No. **MS**2904 150×96 mm.	5·00
First Day Cover (Tallents House)...............................	6·00
First Day Cover (Shrewsbury)...................................	6·00

Nos. 2898/2903 have jigsaw perforations on the two vertical sides.

Booklet pane No. 2904a comes from the £7·75 Charles Darwin booklet No. DX45.

The complete miniature sheet is shown on one of the 11 PHQ cards with the others depicting individual stamps, including those from No. **MS**2904.

(Gravure De La Rue)

2009 (12 Feb). Birth Bicentenary of Charles Darwin (naturalist and evolutionary theorist) (2nd issue). Multicoloured Phosphorised paper. Perf 14.

2905	**2126**	(1st) Charles Darwin................................	6·00	6·00
		a. Booklet pane. Nos. 2905 and 2909/2910.........................	13·50	
2906	**2127**	48p. Marine Iguana..............................	6·00	6·00
		a. Booklet pane. Nos. 2906/2908........	13·50	
2907	**2128**	50p. Finches......................................	6·00	6·00
2908	**2129**	56p. Atoll..	6·00	6·00
2909	**2130**	72p. Bee Orchid.................................	6·00	6·00
2910	**2131**	81p. Orangutan.................................	6·00	6·00
Set of 6..			32·00	32·00

Nos. 2905/2910 were only issued in the £7·75 Charles Darwin booklet, No. DX45.

Nos, 2905/2910 have Jigsaw perforations on both vertical sides.

For Nos. U2911/U2954, U2975/U3037, U3045/U3052 U3055/U3059 and U3060/U3157 and Types **2132a/2132d** see Decimal Machin Definitives section.

(Gravure Walsall)

2009 (10 Mar)–**2010**. British Design Classics (3rd series). Booklet stamps. Designs as Nos. 2887/2889, 2891/2892 and 2896. Self-adhesive. Multicoloured. Phosphor background. Die-cut perf 14½.

2911	**2121**	(1st) K2 Telephone Kiosk......................	2·00	2·00
		a. Booklet pane. Nos. 2911/2912 and U2983×4.................	7·50	
2912	**2125**	(1st) Routemaster Bus..........................	2·00	2·00
2913	**2118**	(1st) Mini (21.4.09).............................	2·00	2·00
		a. Booklet pane. No. 2913×2 and U2983×4........................	7·50	
2914	**2120**	(1st) Concorde (18.8.09).......................	2·00	2·00
		a. Booklet pane. No. 2914×2 and U2983×4........................	7·50	
2915	**2117**	(1st) Mini Skirt (17.9.09).......................	2·00	2·00
		a. Booklet pane. No. 2915×2 and U2983×4........................	5·75	
2915b	**2116**	(1st) Supermarine Spitfire (15.9.10).......	2·00	2·00
		ba.Booklet pane. No. 2915b×2 and U3016×4.........................	7·50	
Set of 6..			10·00	10·00

Nos. 2911/2915b were only issued in booklets, Nos. PM16/PM17, PM19/PM20 and PM25, initially sold for £2·16 (No. PM16) or £2·34 (Nos. PM17, PM19/PM20) or £2·46 (No. PM25).

2133 Matthew Boulton and Factory (manufacturing)

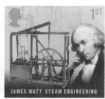

2134 James Watt and Boulton & Watt Condensing Engine (steam engineering)

2135 Richard Arkwright and Spinning Machine (textiles)

2136 Josiah Wedgwood and Black Basalt Teapot and Vase (ceramics)

2137 George Stephenson and Locomotion (railways)

2138 Henry Maudslay and Table Engine (machine making)

2139 James Brindley and Bridgewater Canal Aqueduct (canal engineering)

2140 John McAdam (road building)

(Des Webb and Webb. Litho Enschedé)

2009 (10 Mar). Pioneers of the Industrial Revolution. Multicoloured 'All-over' phosphor. Perf 14×14½.

2916	**2133**	(1st) Matthew Boulton	1·20	1·00
		a. Horiz pair. Nos. 2916/2917	2·40	2·00
2917	**2134**	(1st) James Watt	1·20	1·00
2918	**2135**	50p. Richard Arkwright	70	70
		a. Horiz pair. Nos. 2918/2919	1·40	1·40
2919	**2136**	50p. Josiah Wedgwood	70	70
2920	**2137**	56p. George Stephenson	85	85
		a. Horiz pair. Nos. 2920/2921	1·75	1·75
2921	**2138**	56p. Henry Maudslay	85	85
2922	**2139**	72p. James Brindley	1·00	1·00
		a. Horiz pair. Nos. 2922/2923	2·00	2·00
2923	**2140**	72p. John McAdam	1·00	1·00
Set of 8			6·75	6·50
Set of 4 Gutter Strips of 4			13·50	
First Day Cover (Tallents House)				7·50
First Day Cover (Steam Mills, Cinderford)				7·50
Presentation Pack (PO Pack No. 425)			7·25	
PHQ Cards (set of 8) (321)			2·40	8·00

Nos. 2916/2917, 2918/2919, 2920/2921 and 2922/2923 were each printed together, *se-tenant*, as horizontal pairs in sheets of 60 (2 panes 6×5).

2141 Henry VII (1485–1509)

2142 Henry VIII (1509–1547)

2143 Edward VI (1547–1553)

2144 Lady Jane Grey (1553)

2145 Mary I (1553–1558)

2146 Elizabeth I (1558–1603)

2147 The Age of the Tudors

(Des Atelier Works. Litho Cartor)

2009 (21 Apr). Kings and Queens (2nd issue). House of Tudor. Multicoloured Two phosphor bands. Perf 14.

2924	**2141**	(1st) Henry VII	1·20	1·00
2925	**2142**	(1st) Henry VIII	1·20	1·00
2926	**2143**	62p. Edward VI	90	90
2927	**2144**	62p. Lady Jane Grey	90	90
		a. Imperf (pair)	£3500	
2928	**2145**	81p. Mary I	1·25	1·25
2929	**2146**	81p. Elizabeth I	1·25	1·25
Set of 6			5·75	5·50
Set of 6 Gutter Pairs			11·50	
Set of 6 Traffic Light Gutter Blocks of 4			30·00	
First Day Cover (Tallents House)				7·50
First Day Cover (London SE10)				7·50
Presentation Pack (PO Pack No. 426) (Nos. 2924/MS2930)			7·25	
PHQ Cards (set of 11) (322)			3·25	16·00

MS2930 123×70 mm. **2147** The Age of the Tudors (1st) *Mary Rose* (galleon), 1510; (1st) Field of Cloth of Gold Royal Conference, 1520; 90p. Royal Exchange (centre of commerce), 1565; 90p. Francis Drake (circumnavigation), 1580 .... 4·25 4·25

First Day Cover (Tallents House)		5·00
First Day Cover (London SE10)		5·00

The complete miniature sheet is shown on one of the 11 PHQ cards with the others depicting individual stamps including those from No. **MS**2930.

The PHQ Card for the Royal Exchange design has the inscription for Sir Francis Drake and vice versa.

2148 *Allium sphaerocephalon* (Round-headed Leek)

2149 *Luronium natans* (Floating Water-plantain)

2150 *Cypripedium calceolus* (Lady's Slipper Orchid)

2151 *Polygala amarella* (Dwarf Milkwort)

2152 *Saxifraga hirculus* (Marsh Saxifrage)

2153 *Stachys germanica* (Downy Woundwort)

2154 *Euphorbia serrulata* (Upright Spurge)

2155 *Pyrus cordata* (Plymouth Pear)

2156 *Polygonum maritimum* (Sea Knotgrass)

2157 *Dianthus armeria* (Deptford Pink)

2158 Royal Botanic Gardens, Kew

(Des Studio Dempsey. Litho Cartor)

2009 (19 May). Action for Species (3rd series). Plants. Multicoloured

(a) Phosphor background. Perf 14½.

2931	**2148**	(1st) *Allium sphaerocephalon* (Round-headed Leek).....................	1·20	1·00
		a. Block of 10. Nos. 2931/2940...........	10·50	9·00
2932	**2149**	(1st) *Luronium natans* (Floating Water-plantain).....................	1·20	1·00
2933	**2150**	(1st) *Cypripedium calceolus* (Lady's Slipper Orchid).....................	1·20	1·00
2934	**2151**	(1st) *Polygala amarella* (Dwarf Milkwort).....................	1·20	1·00
2935	**2152**	(1st) *Saxifraga hirculus* (Marsh Saxifrage).....................	1·20	1·00
2936	**2153**	(1st) *Stachys germanica* (Downy Woundwort).....................	1·20	1·00
2937	**2154**	(1st) *Euphorbia serrulata* (Upright Spurge).....................	1·20	1·00
2938	**2155**	(1st) *Pyrus cordata* (Plymouth Pear)........	1·20	1·00
2939	**2156**	(1st) *Polygonum maritimum* (Sea Knotgrass).....................	1·20	1·00
2940	**2157**	(1st) *Dianthus armeria* (Deptford Pink)...	1·20	1·00
		Set of 10.....................	10·50	9·00
		Gutter Block of 10.....................	21·00	
		First Day Cover (Tallents House).....................		11·00
		First Day Cover (Kew, Richmond).....................		11·00
		Presentation Pack (PO Pack No. 427) (Nos. 2931/MS2941).....................	15·00	
		PHQ Cards (set of 15) (323).....................	4·50	13·50

(b) 250th Anniversary of Royal Botanic Gardens, Kew. Two phosphor bands. Perf 14×14½.

MS2941 **2158** 115×89 mm. (1st) Palm House, Kew Gardens; (1st) Millennium Seed Bank, Wakehurst Place; 90p. Pagoda, Kew Gardens; 90p. Sackler Crossing, Kew Gardens...................... 4·25 4·25

First Day Cover (Tallents House)..................... 5·00
First Day Cover (Kew, Richmond)..................... 5·00

Nos. 2931/2940 were printed together, *se-tenant*, as blocks of ten (5×2) in sheets of 60 (2 panes of 30).

The complete miniature sheet is shown on one of the 15 PHQ cards with the others depicting individual stamps including those from No. **MS**2941.

1287 *Iris latifolia* (Ehret)   **1283** *Tulipa* (Ehret)

(Gravure Walsall)

2009 (21 May). 50th Anniversary of NAFAS (National Association of Flower Arrangement Societies). Booklet stamps. Designs as Nos. 1958 and 1962 (1997 Greetings Stamps, 19th-century Flower Paintings). Self-adhesive. Multicoloured Two phosphor bands. Die-cut Perf 14 (with one elliptical hole in each vert side).

2942	**1287**	(1st) *Iris latifolia*.....................	4·25	4·25
		a. Booklet pane. Nos. 2942/2943 and U2983×4.....................	10·00	
2943	**1283**	(1st) *Tulipa*.....................	4·25	4·25

Nos. 2942/2943 were only issued in stamp booklet, No. PM18.

2159 Dragon   **2160** Unicorn

2161 Giant   **2162** Pixie

2163 Mermaid   **2164** Fairy

(Des Dave McKean and Morgan Radcliffe. Gravure De La Rue)

2009 (16 June). Mythical Creatures. Multicoloured 'All-over' phosphor. Perf 14½.

2944	**2159**	(1st) Dragon.....................	1·20	1·00
2945	**2160**	(1st) Unicorn.....................	1·20	1·00
2946	**2161**	62p. Giant.....................	1·00	1·00
2947	**2162**	62p. Pixie.....................	1·00	1·00
2948	**2163**	90p. Mermaid.....................	1·50	1·50
2949	**2164**	90p. Fairy.....................	1·50	1·50
		Set of 6.....................	6·50	6·25
		Set of 6 Gutter Pairs.....................	13·00	
		First Day Cover (Tallents House).....................		8·00
		First Day Cover (Dragonby, Scunthorpe).....................		8·00
		Presentation Pack (PO Pack No. 428).....................	7·00	
		PHQ Cards (set of 6) (324).....................	1·75	8·00

2165 George V Type B Wall Letter Box, 1933–1936

2166 Edward VII Ludlow Letter Box, 1901–1910

2167 Victorian Lamp Letter Box, 1896

2168 Elizabeth II Type A Wall Letter Box, 1962–1963

919 Royal Mail Coach

(Litho Cartor)

2009 (18 Aug). Treasures of the Archive (2nd series). Booklet stamps. Design as T **919** (1989 Lord Mayor's Show). Multicoloured 'All-over' phosphor. Perf 14.

2957	**919**	20p. Royal Mail Coach. Multicoloured....	1·50	1·50
		a. Booklet pane. No. 2957×4 with margins all round.............................	6·00	

No. 2957 was only issued in the £8·18 Treasures of the Archive booklet, No. DX46.

2169 Post Boxes

(Des Elmwood. Litho Cartor)

2009 (18 Aug). Post Boxes. Multicoloured 'All-over' phosphor. Perf 14.

2950	**2165**	(1st) George V Type B Wall Letter Box.....	1·20	1·00
		a. Booklet pane. Nos. 2950/2953 with margins all round....................	4·25	
2951	**2166**	56p. Edward VII Ludlow Letter Box........	1·10	1·10
2952	**2167**	81p. Victorian Lamp Letter Box..............	1·25	1·25
2953	**2168**	90p. Elizabeth II Type A Wall Letter Box.	1·25	1·25
Set of 4..			4·25	4·25
MS2954 145×74 mm **2169** Post Boxes Nos. 2950/2953..			4·25	4·25
First Day Cover (Tallents House)..				5·00
First Day Cover (Wakefield, West Yorkshire)........................				5·00
Presentation Pack (PO Pack No. 430)...................................			4·75	
PHQ Cards (set of 5) (326)..			1·50	9·25

Nos. 2950/2953 were only issued in the £8·18 Treasures of the Archive booklet, No. DX46 and in No. **MS**2954.

T **2165** was also issued in sheets of 20 with *se-tenant* labels showing post boxes (No. LS65), sold for £8·35 per sheet.

The five PHQ cards show the four individual stamps and the miniature sheet.

2170 Firefighting

2171 Chemical Fire

2172 Emergency Rescue

2173 Flood Rescue

929 Queen Victoria and Queen Elizabeth II

1446 Queen Victoria and Queen Elizabeth II

(Litho Cartor)

2009 (18 Aug). Treasures of the Archive (1st series). Booklet stamps. Designs as T **929** (1990 150th anniversary of the Penny Black) and T **1446** (with redrawn 1st face value). Printed in lithography. Two phosphor bands. Perf 14½×14 (with one elliptical hole in each vert side).

2955	**929**	20p. brownish-black and grey-brown....	80	80
		a. Booklet pane. Nos. 2955/2956, each×4 with central label and margins all round.............................	7·00	
2956	**1446**	(1st) brownish-black and grey-brown....	1·25	1·25

Nos. 2955/2956 were only issued in the £8·18 Treasures of the Archive booklet, No. DX46.

For Nos. 2955/2956 printed gravure see Nos. 2133/2133*a*.

Also see Nos. 1478, **MS**1501 and **MS**3695.

2174 Search and Rescue

2175 Fire Safety

(Des Rose Design. Gravure De La Rue)

2009 (1 Sept). Fire and Rescue Service. Multicoloured 'All-over' phosphor. Perf 14×14½.

2958	**2170**	(1st) Firefighting......................................	1·20	1·00
2959	**2171**	54p. Chemical Fire....................................	90	90
2960	**2172**	56p. Emergency Rescue............................	1·10	1·10
2961	**2173**	62p. Flood Rescue....................................	1·25	1·25
2962	**2174**	81p. Search and Rescue...........................	1·25	1·40
2963	**2175**	90p. Fire Safety.......................................	1·40	1·40
Set of 6..			6·25	6·25
Set of 6 Gutter Pairs..			12·50	
First Day Cover (Tallents House)..				7·50
First Day Cover (Hose, Melton Mowbray)............................				7·50
Presentation Pack (PO Pack No. 429)...................................			6·75	
PHQ Cards (set of 6) (325)..			1·75	7·50

2176 Flight Deck Officer, 2009

2177 Captain, 1941

2178 Second Officer WRNS, 1918

2179 Able Seaman, 1880

2180 Royal Marine, 1805

2181 Admiral, 1795

(Des Graham Turner and Atelier Works. Litho Cartor)

2009 (17 Sept). Military Uniforms (3rd series). Royal Navy Uniforms. Multicoloured Phosphor background. Perf 14.

2964	**2176**	(1st) Flight Deck Officer	1·20	1·00
		a. Horiz strip of 3. Nos. 2964/2966	3·50	3·00
		b. Booklet pane. Nos. 2964/2966 with margins all round	3·50	
2965	**2177**	(1st) Captain	1·20	1·00
2966	**2178**	(1st) Second Officer WRNS	1·20	1·00
2967	**2179**	90p. Able Seaman	1·40	1·40
		a. Horiz strip of 3. Nos. 2967/2969	4·00	4·00
		b. Booklet pane. Nos. 2967/2969 with margins all round	4·00	
2968	**2180**	90p. Royal Marine	1·40	1·40
2969	**2181**	90p. Admiral	1·40	1·40
Set of 6			7·00	6·50
Set of 2 Gutter Strips of 6			14·00	
Set of 2 Traffic Light Gutter Blocks of 12			30·00	
First Day Cover (Tallents House)				7·75
First Day Cover (Portsmouth)				7·75
Presentation Pack (PO Pack No. 431)			7·50	
PHQ Cards (set of 6) (327)			21·00	13·00

Nos. 2964/2966 and 2967/2969 were each printed together, *se-tenant*, as horizontal strips of three in sheets of 60 (2 panes 6×5).

Booklet panes Nos. 2964b and 2967b were from the £7·93 Royal Navy Uniforms booklet, No. DX47.

1518 Jolly Roger flown by HMS *Proteus* (submarine)

(Litho Cartor)

2009 (17 Sept). Royal Navy Uniforms. Booklet stamp. Design as T **1518** (Jolly Roger flag from 2001 Submarine Centenary). Multicoloured Two phosphor bands. Perf 14½.

2970	**1518**	(1st) Jolly Roger flown by HMS *Proteus* (submarine)	4·75	6·00
		a. Booklet pane. Nos. 2970 and 2581, each×2 with margins all round	7·00	

No. 2970 was only issued in the £7·93 Royal Navy Uniforms booklet, No. DX47.

2182 Fred Perry 1909–1995 (lawn tennis champion)

2183 Henry Purcell 1659–1695 (composer and musician)

2184 Sir Matt Busby 1909–1994 (footballer and football manager)

2185 William Gladstone 1809–1898 (statesman and Prime Minister)

2186 Mary Wollstonecraft 1759–1797 (pioneering feminist)

2187 Sir Arthur Conan Doyle 1859–1930 (writer and creator of Sherlock Holmes)

2188 Donald Campbell 1921–1967 (water speed record broken 1959)

2189 Judy Fryd 1909–2000 (campaigner and founder of MENCAP)

2190 Samuel Johnson 1709–1784 (lexicographer, critic and poet)

2191 Sir Martin Ryle 1918–1984 (radio survey of the Universe 1959)

(Des Together Design. Litho Cartor)

2009 (8 Oct). Eminent Britons. Multicoloured Phosphor background. Perf 14½.

2971	**2182**	(1st) Fred Perry	1·20	1·00
		a. Horiz strip of 5. Nos. 2971/2975	5·25	4·50
2972	**2183**	(1st) Henry Purcell	1·20	1·00
2973	**2184**	(1st) Sir Matt Busby	1·20	1·00
2974	**2185**	(1st) William Gladstone	1·20	1·00
2975	**2186**	(1st) Mary Wollstonecraft	1·20	1·00
2976	**2187**	(1st) Sir Arthur Conan Doyle	1·20	1·00
		a. Horiz strip of 5. Nos. 2976/2980	5·25	4·50
2977	**2188**	(1st) Donald Campbell	1·20	1·00
2978	**2189**	(1st) Judy Fryd	1·20	1·00
2979	**2190**	(1st) Samuel Johnson	1·20	1·00
2980	**2191**	(1st) Sir Martin Ryle	1·20	1·00
Set of 10			10·50	9·00

Set of 2 Gutter Strips of 10			21·00	
First Day Cover (Tallents House)				9·25
First Day Cover (Britannia, Bacup, Lancashire)				9·25
Presentation Pack (PO Pack No. 432)			11·00	
PHQ Cards (set of 10) (328)			3·00	9·75

Nos. 2971/2975 and 2976/2980 were each printed together, *se-tenant*, as horizontal strips of five stamps in sheets of 50 (2 panes 5×5).

No. 2980 includes the EUROPA emblem.

2192 Canoe Slalom

2193 Paralympic Games Archery

2194 Athletics, Track

2195 Diving

2196 Paralympic Games, Boccia

2197 Judo

2198 Paralympic Games, Dressage

2199 Badminton

2200 Weightlifting

2201 Basketball

(Des John Royle (No. 2981), George Hardie (No. 2982), Nathalie Guinamard (No. 2983), Julian Opie (No. 2984), David Doyle (No. 2985), Paul Slater (No. 2986), Andrew Davidson (No. 2987), David Holmes (No. 2988), Guy Billout (No. 2989), Huntley Muir (No. 2990) and Studio David Hillman (all). Litho Cartor)

2009 (22 Oct)–**2012**. Olympic and Paralympic Games, London (2012) (1st issue). Multicoloured 'All-over' phosphor. Perf 14½.

2981	**2192**	(1st) Canoe Slalom	1·20	1·00
		a. Horiz strip of 5. Nos. 2981/2985	5·25	4·50
2982	**2193**	(1st) Paralympic Games Archery	1·20	1·00
		b. Booklet pane. Nos. 2982 and 2987 with margins all round (27.7.12)	3·75	
2983	**2194**	(1st) Athletics, Track	1·20	1·00

		b. Booklet pane. Nos. 2983 and 3104 with margins all round (27.7.12)	3·75	
2984	**2195**	(1st) Diving	1·20	1·00
		b. Booklet pane. Nos. 2984 and 3196 with margins all round (27.7.12)	3·75	
2985	**2196**	(1st) Paralympic Games Boccia	1·20	1·00
2986	**2197**	(1st) Judo	1·20	1·00
		a. Horiz strip of 5. Nos. 2986/2990	5·25	4·50
2987	**2198**	(1st) Paralympic Games Dressage	1·20	1·00
2988	**2199**	(1st) Badminton	1·20	1·00
2989	**2200**	(1st) Weightlifting	1·20	1·00
2990	**2201**	(1st) Basketball	1·20	1·00
Set of 10			10·50	9·00
Set of 2 Gutter Strips of 10			21·00	
First Day Cover (Tallents House)				9·25
First Day Cover (Badminton, Glos)				9·25
Presentation Pack (PO Pack No. M18)			11·00	
PHQ Cards (set of 10) (OXPG1)			3·00	10·00

Nos. 2981/2985 and 2986/2990 were each printed together, *se-tenant*, as horizontal strips of five stamps in sheets of 50 (2 panes 5×5).

Booklet panes Nos. 2982b, 2983b and 2984b were from the £10.71 Olympic and Paralympic Games, London booklet, No. DY5.

See also Nos. 3020/3023.

2202 Angel playing Lute

2203 Madonna and Child

2204 Angel playing Lute

2205 Joseph

2206 Madonna and Child

2207 Wise Man

2208 Shepherd

(Des Andrew Ross. Gravure De La Rue)

2009 (3 Nov). Christmas. Stained-glass Windows. Multicoloured. One centre band (No. 2202) or two phosphor bands (others). Perf 14½×14 (with one elliptical hole in each vert side).

(a) Self-adhesive.

2991	**2202**	(2nd) Angel playing Lute	90	90
		a. Booklet pane. No. 2991×12	13·50	
2992	**2203**	(1st) Madonna and Child	1·20	1·00
		a. Booklet pane. No. 2992×12	16·00	
2993	**2204**	(2nd Large) Angel playing Lute	1·25	1·10
2994	**2205**	56p. Joseph	1·10	1·10
2995	**2206**	(1st Large) Madonna and Child	1·70	1·40
2996	**2207**	90p. Wise Man	1·75	1·75
2997	**2208**	£1·35 Shepherd	2·40	2·40
Set of 7			9·25	8·75
First Day Cover (Tallents House)				9·00
First Day Cover (Bethlehem, Llandeilo)				9·00
Presentation Pack (PO Pack No. 433)			9·50	
PHQ Cards (set of 8) (328)			2·40	17·50

(b) Ordinary gum.

MS2998	115×102 mm. As Nos. 2991/2997		9·25	8·75
First Day Cover (Tallents House)				9·00
First Day Cover (Bethlehem, Llandeilo)				9·00

The 2nd class, 1st class, 56p. and 90p. stamps were also issued together in sheets of 20 (No. LS67), sold for £9, containing 8×2nd class, 8×1st class, 2×56p. and 2×90p. stamps, each stamp accompanied by a *se-tenant* label.

Separate sheets of 20×2nd, 20×1st, 10×1st, 10×56p. and 10×90p. were available with personal photographs from Royal Mail, Edinburgh. These were sold at £7·50 for 10×1st, £9·50 for 20×2nd or 10×56p. or £13·50 for 20×1st or 10×90p.

All these sheets were printed in lithography by Cartor and had the backing paper around the stamps retained.

For the 2nd class stamp printed in lithography with ordinary gum see No. 3186a.

The eight PHQ cards show the seven stamps and No. **MS**2998.

For Nos. U3045/U3052 see Decimal Machin Definitives section.

Year Pack

2009 (3 Nov). Comprises Nos. 2887/2896, 2898/**MS**2904, 2916/**MS**2941, 2944/2949, **MS**2954, 2958/2969, 2971/2997, **MS**S157 and **MS**W147.
CP2998*a*   Year Pack (Pack No. 434) (*sold for*
£60)..   95·00

Post Office Yearbook

2009 (3 Nov). Comprises Nos. 2887/2896, 2898/**MS**2904, 2916/**MS**2941, 2944/2949, **MS**2954, 2958/2969, 2971/2997, **MS**S157 and **MS**W147.
YB2998*a*   Yearbook (*sold for* £65).........................   95·00

Miniature Sheet Collection

2009 (3 Nov). Comprises Nos. **MS**2904, **MS**2930, **MS**2941, **MS**2954, **MS**2998, **MS**S157 and **MS**W147.
MS2998*a* Miniature Sheet Collection (*sold for* £21·30).....   32·00

2209 *The Division Bell* (Pink Floyd)   **2210** *A Rush of Blood to the Head* (Coldplay)

2211 *Parklife* (Blur)   **2212** *Power Corruption and Lies* (New Order)

2213 *Let It Bleed* (Rolling Stones)   **2214** *London Calling* (The Clash)

2215 *Tubular Bells* (Mike Oldfield)   **2216** *Led Zeppelin IV* (Led Zeppelin)

2217 *Screamadelica* (Primal Scream)   **2218** *The Rise and Fall of Ziggy Stardust and the Spiders from Mars* (David Bowie)

(Des Studio Dempsey)

2010 (7 Jan). Classic Album Covers (1st issue). Multicoloured 'All-over' phosphor.

(*a*) *Self-adhesive. Gravure De La Rue. Die-cut Perf 14½ (interrupted).*
2999	**2209**	(1st) *The Division Bell* (Pink Floyd)...........	1·20	1·00
		a. Horiz strip of 5. Nos. 2999/3003.....	5·25	—
3000	**2210**	(1st) *A Rush of Blood to the Head* (Coldplay).............................	1·20	1·00
3001	**2211**	(1st) *Parklife* (Blur).................................	1·20	1·00
3002	**2212**	(1st) *Power Corruption and Lies* (New Order).......................................	1·20	1·00
3003	**2213**	(1st) *Let It Bleed* (Rolling Stones).............	1·20	1·00

3004	**2214**	(1st) *London Calling* (The Clash)..............	1·20	1·00
		a. Horiz strip of 5. Nos. 3004/3008.....	5·25	—
3005	**2215**	(1st) *Tubular Bells* (Mike Oldfield)............	1·20	1·00
3006	**2216**	(1st) *IV* (Led Zeppelin).............................	1·20	1·00
3007	**2217**	(1st) *Screamadelica* (Primal Scream).......	1·20	1·00
3008	**2218**	(1st) *The Rise and Fall of Ziggy Stardust and the Spiders from Mars* (David Bowie)..	1·20	1·00
Set of 10..			10·50	9·00
First Day Cover (Tallents House)........................				9·25
First Day Cover (Oldfield, Keighley)..................				9·25
Presentation Pack (PO Pack No. 435)................			11·00	
PHQ Cards (set of 10) (330).............................			4·00	12·00

Nos. 2999/3003 and 3004/3008 were each printed together, as horizontal strips of five stamps in sheets of 50 (2 panes of 25).

The right-hand edges of Nos. 2999/3008 are all cut around to show the vinyl disc protruding from the open edge of the album cover.

MS3019 2218*a* Album Covers

2010 (7 Jan). Classic Album Covers (2nd issue). Multicoloured 'All-over' phosphor. Litho Cartor. Perf 14½ (interrupted).
3009	**2213**	(1st) *Let It Bleed* (Rolling Stones).............	1·25	1·25
		a. Booklet pane. Nos. 3009/3014.......	7·75	
3010	**2216**	(1st) *Led Zeppelin IV* (Led Zeppelin).........	1·25	1·25
3011	**2218**	(1st) *The Rise and Fall of Ziggy Stardust and the Spiders from Mars* (David Bowie)..	1·25	1·25
3012	**2212**	(1st) *Power Corruption and Lies* (New Order).......................................	1·25	1·25
3013	**2217**	(1st) *Screamadelica* (Primal Scream).......	1·25	1·25
3014	**2209**	(1st) *The Division Bell* (Pink Floyd)...........	1·25	1·25
3015	**2215**	(1st) *Tubular Bells* (Mike Oldfield)............	1·25	1·25
		a. Booklet pane. Nos. 3015/3018.......	5·25	
3016	**2214**	(1st) *London Calling* (The Clash)..............	1·25	1·25
3017	**2211**	(1st) *Parklife* (Blur).................................	1·25	1·25
3018	**2210**	(1st) *A Rush of Blood to the Head* (Coldplay).............................	1·25	1·25
Set of 10..			13·00	13·00
MS3019 2218*a* 223×189 mm. Nos. 3009/3018....			25·00	25·00
First Day Cover (Tallents House)........................				25·00
First Day Cover (Oldfield, Keighley)..................				25·00

Nos. 3009/3018 were only issued in the £8·06 Classic Album Covers booklet, No. DX48 and in No. **MS**3019.

The right-hand edges of Nos. 3009/3018 and the miniature sheet No. **MS**3019 are all cut around in an imperforate section to show the vinyl disc protruding from the open edge of the album cover.

A miniature sheet containing No. 3014×10 *The Division Bell* (Pink Floyd) was issued on 6 March 2010 and sold for £4·75 per sheet.

2197 *Judo*   **2193** *Paralympic Games Archery*

2194 Athletics, Track   **2201** Basketball

(Gravure Walsall)

2010 (7 Jan–25 Feb). Olympic and Paralympic Games, London (2012) (2nd issue). Booklet stamps. Designs as Nos. 2982/2983, 2986 and 2990. Self-adhesive. Multicoloured 'All-over' phosphor. Die-cut Perf 14½.

3020	**2197**	(1st) Judo..........................	2·00	2·00
		a. Booklet pane. Nos. 3020/3021 and U2983×4................................	7·50	
3021	**2193**	(1st) Paralympic Games Archery.............	2·00	2·00
3022	**2194**	(1st) Athletics, Track (25.2.10).................	2·00	2·00
		a. Booklet pane. Nos. 3022/3023 and U3016×4................................	7·50	
3023	**2201**	(1st) Basketball (25.2.10)........................	2·00	2·00
Set of 4..			5·50	5·50

Nos. 3020/3021 and 3022/3023 were only issued in separate booklets, Nos. PM21/PM22, each sold for £2·34.

2219 Smilers

(Des Hat-trick Design. Litho Cartor)

2010 (26 Jan). Business and Consumer Smilers. Sheet 124×71 mm. Multicoloured Two phosphor bands. Perf 14½×14 (with one elliptical hole in each vertical side).

MS3024 **2219** Smilers (1st) Propellor driven aircraft (Andrew Davidson); (1st) Vintage sports roadster (Andrew Davidson); (1st) Recreation of crown seal (Neil Oliver); (1st) Birthday cake (Annabel Wright); (1st) Steam locomotive (Andrew Davidson); (1st) Ocean liner (Andrew Davidson); (1st) Six poppies on barbed wire stems; (1st) Birthday present (Annabel Wright); (Europe up to 20 grams) Bird carrying envelope (Lucy Davey); (Worldwide up to 20 grams) 'hello' in aeroplane vapour trail (Lucy Davey)............. 12·50   10·00

First Day Cover (Tallents House)...		10·50
Presentation Pack (PO Pack No. M19)................................	13·00	
PHQ Cards (set of 11) (D31)......................................	4·25	20·00

No. **MS**3024 was sold for £4·58.

Stamps in designs as within No. **MS**3024 but self-adhesive were available printed together, *se-tenant*, in sheets of 20 containing two of each design with greetings labels (No. LS70), sold for £9·70 per sheet.

The (1st) birthday cake, (1st) birthday present, Europe and Worldwide designs were also available in separate sheets with personal photographs.

A stamp as the crown seal design in No. **MS**3024 but self-adhesive was issued on 15 September 2011 in sheets of 20 with postmark labels for the 350th Anniversary of the Postmark, No. LS78 sold for £9·50.

The other 1st class designs were for the business customised service. Stamps as the (1st) birthday cake (×4), (1st) birthday present (×4), Europe bird carrying envelope (×2) and Worldwide 'hello' in aeroplane vapour trail (×2) designs but self-adhesive were issued together with Nos. 2572, 2674, 2693 and 2821/2823 on 8 May 2010 in sheets of 20 stamps with *se-tenant* greetings labels printed in lithography by Cartor, (No. LS73), and sold for £10 per sheet.

The 11 PHQ cards show the ten individual stamps and the complete miniature sheet.

2220 Girlguiding UK

(Des Together Design. Litho Cartor)

2010 (2 Feb). Centenary of Girlguiding. Sheet 190×67 mm. Multicoloured Phosphor background. Perf 14×14½.

MS3025 **2220** Girlguiding UK (1st) Rainbows; 56p. Brownies; 81p. Guides; 90p. Senior Section members... 4·25   4·50

First Day Cover (Tallents House)..		5·25
First Day Cover (Guide, Blackburn).....................................		5·25
Presentation Pack (PO Pack No. 436)................................	5·50	
PHQ Cards (set of 5) (331)..	2·00	9·00

The five PHQ cards show the four individual stamps and the complete miniature sheet.

2221 Sir Robert Boyle (chemistry)   **2222** Sir Isaac Newton (optics)

2223 Benjamin Franklin (electricity)   **2224** Edward Jenner (pioneer of smallpox vaccination)

2225 Charles Babbage (computing)   **2226** Alfred Russel Wallace (theory of evolution)

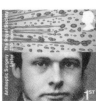

2227 Joseph Lister (antiseptic surgery)   **2228** Ernest Rutherford (atomic structure)

2229 Dorothy Hodgkin (crystallography)   **2230** Sir Nicholas Shackleton (earth sciences)

(Des Hat-trick Design. Litho Cartor)

2010 (25 Feb). 350th Anniversary of the Royal Society. Multicoloured 'All-over' phosphor. Perf 14½.

3026	**2221**	(1st) Sir Robert Boyle..............................	1·20	1·00
		a. Block of 10. Nos. 3026/3035............	10·50	9·00
		b. Booklet pane. Nos. 3026, 3030/3031 and 3035 with margins all round..........................	4·25	
3027	**2222**	(1st) Sir Isaac Newton............................	1·20	1·00
		a. Booklet pane. Nos. 3027/3028 and 3033×2 with margins all round.................................	4·25	
3028	**2223**	(1st) Benjamin Franklin..........................	1·20	1·00
3029	**2224**	(1st) Edward Jenner...............................	1·20	1·00
		a. Booklet pane. Nos. 3029×2, 3032 and 3034 with margins all round...	4·25	
3030	**2225**	(1st) Charles Babbage............................	1·20	1·00
3031	**2226**	(1st) Alfred Russel Wallace....................	1·20	1·00
3032	**2227**	(1st) Joseph Lister................................	1·20	1·00
3033	**2228**	(1st) Ernest Rutherford..........................	1·20	1·00
3034	**2229**	(1st) Dorothy Hodgkin...........................	1·20	1·00
3035	**2230**	(1st) Sir Nicholas Shackleton..................	1·20	1·00
Set of 10...			10·50	9·00
Gutter Block of 20......................................			21·00	
First Day Cover (Tallents House)...................				10·00
First Day Cover (London SW1)......................				10·00
Presentation Pack (PO Pack No. 437).............			11·00	
PHQ Cards (*set of 10*) (332)......................			4·00	11·50

Nos. 3026/3035 were printed together, *se-tenant*, as blocks of ten (5×2) in sheets of 60 (2 panes of 30).

Booklet panes Nos. 3026b, 3027a and 3029a come from the £7·72 350th Anniversary of The Royal Society booklet, No. DX49.

2239 Leonard (Jack Russell cross)   **2240** Tia (terrier cross)

(Des CDT Design. Litho Cartor)

2010 (11 Mar). 150th Anniversary of Battersea Dogs and Cats Home. Multicoloured. Phosphor background. Perf 14½.

3036	**2231**	(1st) Pixie (mastiff cross)......................	1·20	1·00
		a. Block of 10. Nos. 3036/3045............	10·50	9·00
3037	**2232**	(1st) Button..	1·20	1·00
3038	**2233**	(1st) Herbie (mongrel)...........................	1·20	1·00
3039	**2234**	(1st) Mr Tumnus..................................	1·20	1·00
3040	**2235**	(1st) Tafka (border collie)......................	1·20	1·00
3041	**2236**	(1st) Boris (bulldog cross)......................	1·20	1·00
3042	**2237**	(1st) Casey (lurcher).............................	1·20	1·00
3043	**2238**	(1st) Tigger...	1·20	1·00
3044	**2239**	(1st) Leonard (Jack Russell cross)............	1·20	1·00
3045	**2240**	(1st) Tia (terrier cross)..........................	1·20	1·00
Set of 10...			10·50	9·00
Gutter Block of 20......................................			21·00	
First Day Cover (Tallents House)...................				9·50
First Day Cover (London SW8)......................				9·50
Presentation Pack (PO Pack No. 438).............			11·00	
PHQ Cards (*set of 10*) (333)......................			4·00	11·50

Nos. 3036/3045 were printed together, *se-tenant*, as blocks of ten (5×2) in sheets of 60 (2 panes of 30).

2231 Pixie (mastiff cross)   **2232** Button

2233 Herbie (mongrel)   **2234** Mr Tumnus

2241 James I (1406–1437)   **2242** James II (1437–1460)   **2243** James III (1460–1488)

2235 Tafka (border collie)   **2236** Boris (bulldog cross)

2244 James IV (1488–1513)   **2245** James V (1513–1542)   **2246** Mary (1542–1567)

2237 Casey (lurcher)   **2238** Tigger

2247 James VI (1567–1625)

2248 The Age of the Stewarts

(Des Atelier Works. Litho Cartor)

2010 (23 Mar). Kings and Queens (3rd issue). House of Stewart. Multicoloured Two phosphor bands. Perf 14.

3046	**2241**	(1st) James I	1·20	1·00
3047	**2242**	(1st) James II	1·20	1·00
3048	**2243**	(1st) James III	1·20	1·00
3049	**2244**	62p. James IV	1·00	1·00
3050	**2245**	62p. James V	1·00	1·00
3051	**2246**	81p. Mary	1·25	1·25
3052	**2247**	81p. James VI	1·25	1·25
Set of 7			7·25	6·75
Set of 7 Gutter Pairs			14·50	
Set of 7 Traffic Light Gutter Blocks of 4			32·00	
First Day Cover (Tallents House)				8·00
First Day Cover (Linlithgow, West Lothian)				8·00
Presentation Pack (PO Pack No. 439) (Nos. 3046/ MS3053)			12·00	
PHQ Cards (set of 12) (334)			4·75	11·50

MS3053 123×70 mm. **2248** The Age of the Stewarts (1st) Foundation of the University of St Andrews, 1413; (1st) Foundation of the College of Surgeons, Edinburgh, 1505; 81p. Foundation of Court of Session, 1532; 81p. John Knox (Reformation, 1559).. 4·25   4·25

First Day Cover (Tallents House) ... 4·75
First Day Cover (Linlithgow, West Lothian) ... 4·75

The complete miniature sheet is shown on one of the 12 PHQ cards with the others depicting individual stamps including those from No. **MS**3053.

2249 Humpback Whale (*Megaptera novaeangliae*)

2250 Wildcat (*Felis silvestris*)

2251 Brown Long-eared Bat (*Plecotus auritus*)

2252 Polecat (*Mustela putorius*)

2253 Sperm Whale (*Physeter macrocephalus*)

2254 Water Vole (*Arvicola terrestris*)

2255 Greater Horseshoe Bat (*Rhinolophus ferrumequinum*)

2256 Otter (*Lutra lutra*)

2257 Dormouse (*Muscardinus avellanarius*)

2258 Hedgehog (*Erinaceus europaeus*)

(Des Jason Godfrey. Litho Cartor)

2010 (13 Apr). Action for Species (4th series). Mammals. Multicoloured 'All-over' phosphor. Perf 14½.

3054	**2249**	(1st) Humpback Whale	1·20	1·00
		a. Block of 10. Nos. 3054/3063	10·50	9·00
3055	**2250**	(1st) Wildcat	1·20	1·00
3056	**2251**	(1st) Brown Long-eared Bat	1·20	1·00
3057	**2252**	(1st) Polecat	1·20	1·00
3058	**2253**	(1st) Sperm Whale	1·20	1·00
3059	**2254**	(1st) Water Vole	1·20	1·00
3060	**2255**	(1st) Greater Horseshoe Bat	1·20	1·00
3061	**2256**	(1st) Otter	1·20	1·00
3062	**2257**	(1st) Dormouse	1·20	1·00
3063	**2258**	(1st) Hedgehog	1·20	1·00
Set of 10			10·50	9·00
Gutter Block of 20			21·00	
First Day Cover (Tallents House)				9·50
First Day Cover (Batts Corner, Farnham)				9·50
Presentation Pack (PO Pack No. 440)			11·00	
PHQ Cards (set of 10) (335)			4·00	11·00

Nos. 3054/3063 were printed together, *se-tenant*, as blocks of ten (5×2) in sheets of 60 (2 panes of 30).
See also Nos. 3095/3096.

No. 3064, T **2259** is vacant.

2260 King George V and Queen Elizabeth II (1st); Two portraits of King George V (£1)

(Des Sedley Place. Litho Cartor)

2010 (6 May). London 2010 Festival of Stamps and Centenary of Accession of King George V (1st issue). 'All-over' phosphor. Perf 14½×14.

MS3065 141×74 mm **2260** (1st) rosine; £1 blackish brown, grey-brown and silver		3·75	4·00
First Day Cover (Tallents House)			12·00
First Day Cover (Sandringham, Norfolk)			12·00

A miniature sheet as No. **MS**3065 but inscr 'BUSINESS DESIGN CENTRE, LONDON 8–15 MAY 2010' along the top right margin was only available at London 2010 Festival of Stamps (*Price* £9·75).

The eight PHQ cards depict the individual stamps from Nos. **MS**3065 and **MS**3072 and the complete miniature sheets.

2261 King George V and Queen Elizabeth II

2262 1924 British Empire Exhibition 1½d. Brown Stamp

2263 1924 British Empire Exhibition 1d. Scarlet Stamp

2264 Two Portraits of King George V

2265 1913 £1 Green Sea Horses Design Stamp

2266 1913 10s. Blue Sea Horses Design Stamp

2267 London 2022 Festival of Stamps

(Des Sedley Place. Litho Cartor (Nos. 3066 and 3069) or recess and litho Enschedé (others))

2010 (6–8 May). London 2010 Festival of Stamps and Centenary of Accession of King George V (2nd issue). (except Nos. 3066, 3069) 'All-over' phosphor. Perf 14½×14.

3066	**2261**	(1st) rosine (6.5.10).....................	1·25	1·25
		a. Booklet pane. Nos. 3066 and 3069, each×3 with margins all round (8.5.10)......................	9·50	
3067	**2262**	(1st) 1924 British Empire Exhibition 1½d. Brown Stamp (8.5.10)............	1·50	1·50
		a. Booklet pane. Nos. 3067/3068, each×2......................	6·00	
3068	**2263**	(1st) 1924 British Empire Exhibition 1d. Scarlet Stamp (8.5.10)......................	1·50	1·50
3069	**2264**	£1 blackish brown, grey-brown and silver (8.5.10)......................	2·50	2·50

3070	**2265**	£1 1913 £1 Green Sea Horses Design Stamp (8.5.10)......................	2·25	2·25
		a. Booklet pane. Nos. 3070/3071 with margins all round....................	4·50	
3071	**2266**	£1 1913 10s. Blue Sea Horses Design Stamp (8.5.10)......................	2·25	2·25
Set of 6........			11·00	11·00
Gutter Pair (No. 3066)............			2·50	
MS3072 **2267**		115×90 mm. Nos. 3067/3068 and 3070/3071 (8.5.10)............	4·50	4·75
First Day Cover (Tallents House) (No. **MS**3072)............				12·00
First Day Cover (London N1) (No. **MS**3072)............				12·00
Presentation Pack (PO Pack No. 441) (Nos. **MS**3065 and **MS**3072)............			8·50	
PHQ Cards (*set of 8*) (336)............			3·25	13·00

No. 3066 was also issued as a sheet stamp on 6 May 2010.

Nos. 3066/3071 come from the £11·15 1910–1936, King George V booklet, No. DX50.

Nos. 3066 and 3069 also come from No. **MS**3065, issued on 6 May 2010.

Nos. 3067/3068 and 3070/3071 also come from No. **MS**3072, issued on 8 May 2010.

For presentation pack and PHQ cards for No. **MS**3072 see under **MS**3065. The eight PHQ cards depict the individual stamps from Nos. **MS**3065 and **MS**3072 and the complete miniature sheets.

For No. **MS**3073, T **2268**, see Decimal Machin Definitives section.

2269 Winston Churchill

2270 Land Girl

2271 Home Guard

2272 Evacuees

2273 Air Raid Wardens

2274 Woman working in Factory

2275 Royal Broadcast by Princess Elizabeth and Princess Margaret

2276 Fire Service

(Des Why Not Associates. Litho Cartor)

2010 (13 May). Britain Alone (1st issue). Pale stone, pale bistre and black. 'All-over' phosphor. Perf 14½.

3074	**2269**	(1st) Winston Churchill............	1·20	1·00
		a. Booklet pane. Nos. 3074/3075 and 3079/3080 with margins all round............	4·50	
3075	**2270**	(1st) Land Girl............	1·20	1·00
3076	**2271**	60p. Home Guard............	90	90

		a. Booklet pane. Nos. 3076/3078 and 3081..........................	4·50	
3077	2272	60p. Evacuees.......................	90	90
3078	2273	67p. Air Raid Wardens.............	1·00	1·00
3079	2274	67p. Woman working in Factory.............	1·00	1·00
3080	2275	97p. Royal Broadcast by Princess Elizabeth and Princess Margaret....	1·40	1·40
3081	2276	97p. Fire Service.......................	1·40	1·40
		Set of 8..........................	7·75	7·50
		Set of 8 Gutter Pairs..................	15·50	
		First Day Cover (Tallents House)................		8·50
		First Day Cover (Dover, Kent)................		8·50
		Presentation Pack (PO Pack No. 442) (Nos. 3074/3081 and **MS**3086).............	13·00	
		PHQ Cards (set of 13) (337)................	5·25	11·00

Booklet panes Nos. 3074a and 3076a come from the £9·76 Britain Alone booklet, No. DX51.

The 13 PHQ cards depict Nos. 3074/3085 and the complete miniature sheet No. **MS**3086.

2277 Evacuation of British Soldiers from Dunkirk

2278 Vessels from Upper Thames Patrol in Operation Little Ships

2279 Rescued Soldiers on Board Royal Navy Destroyer, Dover

2280 Steamship and Other Boat loaded with Troops

2281 Evacuation of British Troops from Dunkirk, 1940

(Des Why Not Associates. Litho Cartor)

2010 (13 May). Britain Alone (2nd issue). Pale stone, pale bistre and black. 'All-over' phosphor. Perf 14½.

3082	2277	(1st) Evacuation of British Soldiers.........	1·40	1·40
		a. Booklet pane. Nos. 3082/3085 with margins all round................	5·00	
3083	2278	60p. Vessels from Upper Thames Patrol	1·40	1·40
3084	2279	88p. Rescued Soldiers.................	1·40	1·40
3085	2280	97p. Steamship and Other Boat loaded with Troops.......................	1·40	1·40
		Set of 4..........................	5·00	5·00
		MS3086 115×89 mm. **2281** Evacuation of British Troops from Dunkirk, 1940 Nos. 3082/3085.............	5·00	5·00
		First Day Cover (Tallents House) (No. **MS**3086)................		5·50
		First Day Cover (Dover, Kent) (No. **MS**3086)................		5·50

Nos. 3082/3085 were only issued in the £9·76 Britain Alone booklet, No. DX51, and in No. **MS**3086.

2282 James I (1603–1625)

2283 Charles I (1625–1649)

2284 Charles II (1660–1685)

2285 James II (1685–1688)

2286 William III (1689–1702)

2287 Mary II (1689–1694)

2288 Anne (1702–1714)

2289 The Age of the Stuarts

(Des Atelier Works. Litho Cartor)

2010 (15 June). Kings and Queens (4th issue). House of Stuart. Multicoloured Two phosphor bands. Perf 14.

3087	2282	(1st) James I................	1·20	1·00
3088	2283	(1st) Charles I................	1·20	1·00
3089	2284	60p. Charles II................	90	90
3090	2285	60p. James II................	90	90
3091	2286	67p. William III................	1·10	1·10
3092	2287	67p. Mary II................	1·10	1·10
3093	2288	88p. Anne................	1·40	1·40
		Set of 7..........................	6·75	6·50
		Set of 7 Gutter Pairs..................	13·50	
		Set of 7 Traffic Light Gutter Blocks of 4..........	30·00	
		First Day Cover (Tallents House)................		8·50
		First Day Cover (Royal Oak, Filey)................		8·50
		Presentation Pack (PO Pack No. 443) (Nos. 3087/3093 and **MS**3094).............	12·00	
		PHQ Cards (set of 12) (338)................	4·75	16·00
		MS3094 123×70 mm. **2289** The Age of the Stuarts (1st) William Harvey (discovery of blood circulation, 1628); 60p. Civil War Battle of Naseby, 1645; 88p. John Milton (*Paradise Lost*, 1667); 97p. Castle Howard (John Vanbrugh, 1712).............	4·75	4·75
		First Day Cover (Tallents House)................		5·00
		First Day Cover (Royal Oak, Filey)................		5·00

The complete miniature sheet is shown on one of the 12 PHQ cards with the others depicting individual stamps including those from No. **MS**3094.

2256 Otter (Lutra lutra)   **2258** Hedgehog
(Erinaceus europaeus)

(Gravure Walsall)

2010 (15 June). Mammals. Booklet stamps. Designs as Nos. 3061 and 3063.
Self-adhesive. Multicoloured Die-cut Perf 14½.

3095	**2256**	(1st) Otter...	3·00	3·00
		a. Booklet pane. Nos. 3095/3096		
		and No. U3016×4............................	11·00	
3096	**2258**	(1st) Hedgehog.................................	3·00	3·00

Nos. 3095/3096 were only issued in booklet, No. PM23.

2290 Paralympic Games,   **2291** Shooting
Rowing

2292 Modern Pentathlon   **2293** Taekwondo

2294 Cycling   **2295** Paralympic Games,
Table Tennis

2296 Hockey   **2297** Football

2298 Paralympic Games,   **2299** Boxing
Goalball

(Des Marion Hill (No. 3097), David Hillman (No. 3098), Katherine
Baxter (No. 3099), James Fryer (No. 3100), Matthew Dennis (No.
3101), Michael Craig Martin (No. 3102), Darren Hopes (No. 3103), Alex
Williamson (No. 3104), Tobatron (No. 3105), Stephen Ledwidge (No.
3106), Studio David Hillman (all). Litho Cartor)

2010 (27 July). Olympic and Paralympic Games, London (2012) (3rd issue).
Multicoloured 'All-over' phosphor. Perf 14½.

3097	**2290**	(1st) Paralympic Games, Rowing............	1·20	1·00
		a. Horiz strip of 5. Nos. 3097/3101.....	5·25	4·50
3098	**2291**	(1st) Shooting..................................	1·20	1·00
3099	**2292**	(1st) Modern Pentathlon....................	1·20	1·00
3100	**2293**	(1st) Taekwondo...............................	1·20	1·00
3101	**2294**	(1st) Cycling...................................	1·20	1·00
3102	**2295**	(1st) Paralympic Games, Table Tennis...	1·20	1·00
		a. Horiz strip of 5. Nos. 3102/3106.....	5·25	4·50
3103	**2296**	(1st) Hockey...................................	1·20	1·00
3104	**2297**	(1st) Football..................................	1·20	1·00
3105	**2298**	(1st) Paralympic Games, Goalball..........	1·20	1·00
3106	**2299**	(1st) Boxing....................................	1·20	1·00
Set of 10			10·50	9·00
Set of 2 Gutter Strips of 10			21·00	
First Day Cover (Tallents House).................................				9·25
First Day Cover (Rowington, Warwick)..........................				9·25
Presentation Pack (PO Pack No. 444).........................			11·00	
PHQ Cards (set of 10) (339).....................................			4·00	11·00

Nos. 3097/3101 and 3102/3106 were each printed together, *se-tenant*, in
horizontal strips of five stamps in sheets of 50 (2 panes 5×5).

(Gravure Walsall)

2010 (27 July–12 Oct). Olympic and Paralympic Games, London (2012)
(4th issue). Booklet stamps. Designs as Nos. 3097, 3101/3102 and
3104. Self-adhesive. Multicoloured 'All-over' phosphor. Die-cut perf
14½.

3107	**2290**	(1st) Paralympic Games, Rowing............	2·00	2·00
		a. Booklet pane. Nos. 3107/3108		
		and Nos. U3016×4............................	7·50	
3108	**2295**	(1st) Paralympic Games, Table Tennis.....	2·00	2·00
3108*a*	**2297**	(1st) Football (12.10.10).....................	2·00	2·00
		ab. Booklet pane. Nos. 3108*a*/3108*b*		
		and U2932×4.................................	7·50	
3108*b*	**2294**	(1st) Cycling (12.10.10).....................	2·00	2·00
Set of 4			7·50	7·50

Nos. 3107/3108 and 3108*a*/3108*b* were only issued in two separate
stamp booklets, Nos. PM24 and PM26, each originally sold for £2·46.

2300 LMS Coronation Class   **2301** BR Class 9F Locomotive
Locomotive, Euston Station,   *Evening Star*, Midsomer Norton,
1938   1962

2302 GWR King Class   **2303** LNER Class A1 Locomotive
Locomotive *King William IV*, near   *Royal Lancer*, 1929
Teignmouth, 1935

2304 SR King Arthur Class   **2305** LMS NCC Class WT No. 2,
Locomotive *Sir Mador de la*   Larne Harbour, *c* 1947
Porte, Bournemouth Central
Station, 1935–1939

(Des Delaney Design Consultants. Gravure De La Rue)

2010 (19 Aug). Great British Railways. Gold, bluish grey and black. 'All-over' phosphor. Perf 14.

3109	**2300**	(1st) LMS Coronation Class Locomotive..........................	1·20	1·00
3110	**2301**	(1st) BR Class 9F Locomotive *Evening Star*......	1·20	1·00
3111	**2302**	67p. GWR King Class Locomotive *King William IV*......	90	90
3112	**2303**	67p. LNER Class A1 Locomotive *Royal Lancer*......	90	90
3113	**2304**	97p. SR King Arthur Class Locomotive *Sir Mador de la Porte*......	1·25	1·25
3114	**2305**	97p. LMS NCC Class WT No. 2..................	1·25	1·25
		Set of 6..........................	6·00	5·75
		Set of 6 Gutter Pairs..........................	12·00	
		First Day Cover (Tallents House)..........................		7·00
		First Day Cover (Swindon)..........................		7·00
		Presentation Pack (PO Pack No. 445)..........................	7·00	
		PHQ Cards (*set of 6*) (340)..........................	2·50	7·50

2306 Heart-regulating Beta Blockers (Sir James Black, 1962)

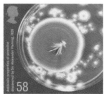

2307 Antibiotic Properties of Penicillin (Sir Alexander Fleming, 1928)

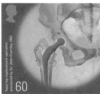

2308 Total Hip Replacement Operation (Sir John Charnley, 1962)

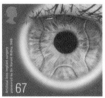

2309 Artificial Lens Implant Surgery (Sir Harold Ridley, 1949)

2310 Malaria Parasite transmitted by Mosquitoes (proved by Sir Ronald Ross, 1897)

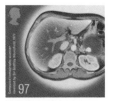

2311 Computed Tomography Scanner (Sir Godfrey Hounsfield, 1971)

(Des Howard Brown. Litho Cartor)

2010 (16 Sept). Medical Breakthroughs. Multicoloured 'All-over' phosphor. Perf 14×14½.

3115	**2306**	(1st) Heart-regulating Beta Blockers......	1·20	1·00
3116	**2307**	58p. Antibiotic Properties of Penicillin...	90	90
3117	**2308**	60p. Total Hip Replacement Operation.	1·00	1·00
3118	**2309**	67p. Artificial Lens Implant Surgery.......	1·10	1·10
3119	**2310**	88p. Malaria Parasite transmitted by Mosquitoes......	1·25	1·25
3120	**2311**	97p. Computed Tomography Scanner...	1·40	1·40
		Set of 6..........................	6·00	6·00
		Set of 6 Gutter Pairs..........................	12·00	
		First Day Cover (Tallents House)..........................		8·00
		First Day Cover (Paddington, London W2)..........................		8·00
		Presentation Pack (PO Pack No. 446)..........................	7·25	
		PHQ Cards (*set of 6*) (341)..........................	2·50	7·50

See also No. 3153.

2312 Winnie-the-Pooh and Christopher Robin (*Now we are Six*)

2313 Winnie-the-Pooh and Piglet (*The House at Pooh Corner*)

2314 Winnie-the-Pooh and Rabbit (*Winnie-the-Pooh*)

2315 Winnie-the-Pooh and Eeyore (*Winnie-the-Pooh*)

2316 Winnie-the-Pooh and Friends (*Winnie-the-Pooh*)

2317 Winnie-the-Pooh and Tigger (The House at Pooh Corner)

2318 Winnie-the-Pooh

(Des Magpie Studio. Litho Cartor)

2010 (12 Oct). Europa. Children's Books. Winnie-the-Pooh by A. A. Milne. Book Illustrations by E. H. Shepard. Yellow-brown, pale stone and black. 'All-over' phosphor. Perf 14×14½.

3121	**2312**	(1st) Winnie-the-Pooh and Christopher Robin......	1·20	1·00
3122	**2313**	58p. Winnie-the-Pooh and Piglet.........	90	90
3123	**2314**	60p. Winnie-the-Pooh and Rabbit.........	1·00	1·00
3124	**2315**	67p. Winnie-the-Pooh and Eeyore.........	1·10	1·10
3125	**2316**	88p. Winnie-the-Pooh and Friends........	1·25	1·25
3126	**2317**	97p. Winnie-the-Pooh and Tigger.........	1·40	1·40
		Set of 6..........................	6·00	6·00
		Set of 6 Gutter Pairs..........................	12·00	
		First Day Cover (Tallents House)..........................		8·00
		First Day Cover (Hartfield, East Sussex)..........................		8·00
		Presentation Pack (PO Pack No. 447) (Nos. 3121/3126 and **MS**3127)..........................	11·50	
		PHQ Cards (*set of 11*) (342)..........................	4·25	15·00

MS3127 115×89 mm. **2318** Winnie-the-Pooh (1st) Winnie-the-Pooh and Christopher Robin (from *Now we are six*); 60p. Christopher Robin reads to Winnie-the-Pooh (from *Winnie-the-Pooh*); 88p. Winnie-the-Pooh and Christopher Robin sailing in umbrella (from *Winnie-the-Pooh*); 97p. Christopher Robin (putting on wellingtons) and Pooh (from *Winnie-the-Pooh*). Perf 14½............................ 4·75 4·75
First Day Cover (Tallents House).................................... 6·25
First Day Cover (Hartfield, East Sussex)....................... 6·25

The 1st class value includes the EUROPA emblem.

Stamps from No. **MS**3127 show lines from poem *We Too* by A. A. Milne. 'Wherever I am, there's always Pooh' (1st); 'There's always Pooh and Me. Whatever I do, he wants to-day?' says Pooh: 'Well that's very odd 'cos I was too' (88p.); 'Let's go together,' says Pooh, says he. 'Let's go together,' says Pooh (97p.).

The 11 PHQ cards show the six stamps, the four individual stamps within No. **MS**3127 and the complete miniature sheet.

SELF-ADHESIVE STAMPS. Collectors are reminded that used self-adhesive stamps will no longer 'soak-off'. They should be collected with a neat margin of backing paper.

2319 Wallace and Gromit Carol singing

2320 Gromit posting Christmas Cards

2321 Wallace and Gromit Carol singing

2322 Wallace and Gromit decorating Christmas Tree

2323 Gromit posting Christmas Cards

2324 Gromit carrying Christmas Pudding

2325 Gromit wearing Oversized Sweater

2325a Wallace and Gromit

(Gravure De La Rue)

2010 (2 Nov). Christmas with Wallace and Gromit. Multicoloured One centre band (No. 3128) or two bands (others). Perf 14½×14 (with one elliptical hole in each vert side).

(a) Self-adhesive.

3128	**2319**	(2nd) Wallace and Gromit Carol singing..	90	90
		a. Booklet pane. No. 3128×12.............	13·50	
3129	**2320**	(1st) Gromit posting Christmas Cards....	1·20	1·00
		a. Booklet pane. No. 3129×12.............	16·00	
3130	**2321**	(2nd Large) Wallace and Gromit Carol singing................................	1·25	1·00
3131	**2322**	60p. Wallace and Gromit decorating Christmas Tree.................................	1·10	1·10
3132	**2323**	(1st Large) Gromit posting Christmas Cards..	1·70	1·40
3133	**2324**	97p. Gromit carrying Christmas Pudding..................................	1·40	1·40
3134	**2325**	£1·46 Gromit wearing Oversized Sweater................................	2·00	2·00
	Set of 7...		8·25	8·00

First Day Cover (Tallents House)................................ 9·50
First Day Cover (Bethlehem, Llandeilo)..................... 9·50
Presentation Pack (PO Pack No. 448)........ 10·00
PHQ Cards (set of 8) (343)..................... 3·25 16·50

(b) Ordinary gum.

MS3135 **2325a** 115×102 mm. Nos. 3128/3134............... 8·25 8·00
First Day Cover (Tallents House)................................ 9·50
First Day Cover (Bethlehem, Llandeilo)..................... 9·50

The 2nd class, 1st class, 60p and 97p stamps were also issued together in sheets of 20 (No. LS75), sold for £9·30, containing 8×2nd class, 8×1st class, 2×60p. and 2×97p. stamps, each stamp accompanied by a *se-tenant* label.

Separate sheets of 20×2nd, 20×1st, ten 1st, 10×60p. and 10×97p. were available with personal photographs on the labels from Royal Mail, Edinburgh. These were sold at £7·80 for 10×1st, £9·95 for 20×2nd or 10×60p., £13·95 for 20×1st and £14·50 for 10×97p.

All these sheets were printed in lithography by Cartor and had the backing paper around the stamps retained.

The eight PHQ cards show the seven individual stamps and the miniature sheet.

Year Pack

2010 (2 Nov). Comprises Nos. 2999/3008, **MS**3025/3063, **MS**3065, **MS**3072, 3074/3081, **MS**3086/**MS**3094, 3097/3106 and 3109/3134.
CP3135a Year Pack (Pack No. 449) (*sold for £80*).. £125

Post Office Yearbook

2010 (2 Nov). Comprises Nos. 2999/3008, **MS**3025/3063, **MS**3065, **MS**3072, 3074/3081, **MS**3086/**MS**3094, 3097/3106 and 3109/3134.
YB3135a Yearbook (*sold for £85*)........................ £110

Miniature Sheet Collection

2010 (2 Nov). Comprises Nos. **MS**3024, **MS**3025, **MS**3053, **MS**3065, **MS**3072, **MS**3086, **MS**3094, **MS**3127 and **MS**3135.
MS3135a Miniature Sheet Collection (*sold for £32*)......... 50·00

2326 Joe 90

2327 Captain Scarlet

2328 Thunderbird 2 (*Thunderbirds*)

2329 Stingray

2330 Fireball XL5

2331 Supercar

2332 Thunderbird 4; Thunderbird 3; Thunderbird 2; Thunderbird 1

(Des GBH)

2011 (11 Jan). F.A.B. The Genius of Gerry Anderson (producer of TV programmes). Multicoloured 'All-over' phosphor.

(a) Ordinary gum. Litho Cartor. Perf 14.

3136	**2326**	(1st) *Joe 90*............................	1·20	1·00
		a. Horiz strip of 3. Nos. 3136/3138.....	3·50	3·00
3137	**2327**	(1st) *Captain Scarlet*..................	1·20	1·00
3138	**2328**	(1st) Thunderbird 2 (*Thunderbirds*).........	1·20	1·00
3139	**2329**	97p. *Stingray*..........................	1·50	1·50
		a. Horiz strip of 3. Nos. 3139/3141.....	4·50	4·50
3140	**2330**	97p. *Fireball XL5*......................	1·50	1·50
3141	**2331**	97p. *Supercar*.........................	1·50	1·50

Set of 6... 7·25 6·75
Set of 2 Gutter Strips of 6.............................. 14·50
First Day Cover (Tallents House).......................... 7·75
First Day Cover (Slough).................................. 7·75
Presentation Pack (PO Pack No. 450) (Nos. 3136/3141 and **MS**3142)... 12·50
PHQ Cards (set of 11) (344)............................ 4·25 17·00

(b) Microlenticular Cartor and Outer Aspect Ltd, New Zealand. Perf 14.
MS3142 116×89 mm. **2332** 41p. Thunderbird 4; 60p. Thunderbird 3; 88p. Thunderbird 2; 97p.
Thunderbird 1.. 5·25 5·50
a. Error imperforate........................... —
First Day Cover (Tallents House).......................... 6·00
First Day Cover (Slough).................................. 6·00

(c) Self-adhesive. Gravure Walsall. Die-cut Perf 14.
3143 **2328** (1st) Thunderbird 2 (*Thunderbirds*)......... 2·00 2·00
a. Booklet pane. No. 3143×2 and U3016×4............................. 7·50

Nos. 3136/3138 and 3139/3141 were each printed together, *se-tenant*, as horizontal strips of three stamps in sheets of 60 (2 panes 6×5).

The stamps within No. **MS**3142 use microlenticular technology to show each vehicle's launch sequences when the miniature sheet is tilted. One example of No. **MS**3142a is known on a first day cover.

No. 3143 was only issued in booklet, No. PM27, sold for £2·46.

The complete miniature sheet is shown on one of the 11 PHQ cards with the others depicting individual stamps including those from No. **MS**3142.

2333 Classic Locomotives of England

(Des Delaney Design Consultants. Litho Cartor)

2011 (1 Feb). Classic Locomotives (1st series). England. Sheet 180×74 mm. Multicoloured 'All-over' phosphor. Perf 14.
MS3144 **2333** Classic Locomotives of England (1st) BR Dean Goods No. 2532; 60p. Peckett R2 *Thor*; 88p. Lancashire and Yorkshire Railway 1093 No. 1100; 97p. BR WD No. 90662.............................. 4·25 4·50
First Day Cover (Tallents House).......................... 5·00
First Day Cover (Liverpool)............................... 5·00
Presentation Pack (PO Pack No. 451)..................... 5·25
PHQ Cards (set of 5) (345)............................ 2·00 9·00

The five PHQ cards show the four individual stamps and the complete miniature sheet.

See also No. 3215.

2334 Oliver   **2335** Blood Brothers   **2336** We Will Rock You

2337 Spamalot   **2338** Rocky Horror Show   **2339** Me and My Girl

2340 Return to the Forbidden Planet   **2341** Billy Elliot

(Des Webb and Webb. Litho Cartor)

2011 (24 Feb). Musicals. Multicoloured 'All-over' phosphor. Perf 14.

3145	**2334**	(1st) *Oliver*................................	1·20	1·00
3146	**2335**	(1st) *Blood Brothers*...................	1·20	1·00
3147	**2336**	(1st) *We Will Rock You*................	1·20	1·00
3148	**2337**	(1st) *Spamalot*.........................	1·20	1·00
3149	**2338**	97p. *Rocky Horror Show*..............	1·30	1·30
3150	**2339**	97p. *Me and My Girl*..................	1·30	1·30
3151	**2340**	97p. *Return to the Forbidden Planet*........	1·30	1·30
3152	**2341**	97p. *Billy Elliot*......................	1·30	1·30

Set of 8... 8·75 8·25
Set of 8 Gutter Pairs.................................... 17·50
Set of 8 Traffic Light Gutter Pairs...................... 25·00
First Day Cover (Tallents House).......................... 9·25
First Day Cover (Dancers End, Tring)...................... 9·25
Presentation Pack (PO Pack No. 452)..................... 9·75
PHQ Cards (set of 8) (346)............................ 3·25 11·00

(Gravure Walsall)

2011 (24 Feb). 50th Anniversary of the British Heart Foundation. Booklet stamp. Design as No. 3115. Self-adhesive. Multicoloured 'All-over' phosphor. Die-cut Perf 14×14½.
3153 **2306** (1st) Heart-regulating Beta Blockers...... 2·00 2·00
a. Booklet pane. No. 3153×2 and U3016×4........................... 7·50

No. 3153 was only issued in booklet, No. PM28, sold for £2·46.

2342 Rincewind (Terry Pratchett's *Discworld*)   **2343** Nanny Ogg (Terry Pratchett's *Discworld*)

2344 Michael Gambon as Dumbledore (J. K. Rowling's Harry Potter)

2345 Ralph Fiennes as Lord Voldemort (J. K. Rowling's Harry Potter)

2346 Merlin (Arthurian Legend)

2347 Morgan Le Fay (Arthurian Legend)

2348 Aslan (C. S. Lewis's Narnia)

2349 Tilda Swinton as The White Witch (C. S. Lewis's Narnia)

(Des So Design Consultants. Gravure De La Rue)

2011 (8 Mar). Magical Realms. Multicoloured 'All-over' phosphor. Perf 14½.

3154	**2342**	(1st) Rincewind	1·20	1·00
		a. Vert pair. Nos. 3154/3155	2·40	2·00
3155	**2343**	(1st) Nanny Ogg	1·20	1·00
3156	**2344**	(1st) Michael Gambon as Dumbledore	1·20	1·00
		a. Vert pair. Nos. 3156/3157	2·40	2·00
3157	**2345**	(1st) Ralph Fiennes as Lord Voldemort	1·20	1·00
3158	**2346**	60p. Merlin	95	95
		a. Vert pair. Nos. 3158/3159	1·90	1·90
3159	**2347**	60p. Morgan Le Fay	95	95
3160	**2348**	97p. Aslan	1·25	1·25
		a. Vert pair. Nos. 3160/3161	2·50	2·50
3161	**2349**	97p. Tilda Swinton as The White Witch	1·25	1·25
Set of 8			8·00	
Set of 4 Gutter Strips of 4			16·00	
First Day Cover (Tallents House)				7·75
First Day Cover (Merlins Bridge, Haverfordwest)				7·75
Presentation Pack (PO Pack No. 453)			8·50	
Presentation Pack (Heroes and Villains containing Nos. 3156/3157, each×5) (2.12.11)			14·00	
PHQ Cards (set of 8) (347)			3·25	9·25

Nos. 3154/3155, 3156/3157, 3158/3159 and 3160/3161 were each printed together, *se-tenant*, as vertical pairs in sheets of 60 (2 panes 5×6).

For Nos. U3055/U3059 see Decimal Machin Definitives section

2350 African Elephant

2351 Mountain Gorilla

2352 Siberian Tiger

2353 Polar Bear

2354 Amur Leopard

2355 Iberian Lynx

 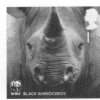

2356 Red Panda

2357 Black Rhinoceros

2358 African Wild Dog

2359 Golden Lion Tamarin

2360 Wildlife of the Amazon Rainforest

(Des Janice Nicholson and Rose Design (No. **MS**3172) or Rose Design Consultants (others). Litho Cartor)

2011 (22 Mar). 50th Anniversary of the WWF. Multicoloured 'All-over' phosphor. Perf 14 (Nos. **MS**3172/**MS**3172a) or 14½ (others).

3162	**2350**	(1st) African Elephant	1·20	1·00
		a. Horiz strip of 5. Nos. 3162/3166	5·25	4·50
		b. Booklet pane. Nos. 3162/3163 and 3170/3171 with margins all round	4·25	
3163	**2351**	(1st) Mountain Gorilla	1·20	1·00
3164	**2352**	(1st) Siberian Tiger	1·20	1·00
		b. Booklet pane. Nos. 3164/3169 with margins all round	6·50	
3165	**2353**	(1st) Polar Bear	1·20	1·00
3166	**2354**	(1st) Amur Leopard	1·20	1·00
3167	**2355**	(1st) Iberian Lynx	1·20	1·00
		a. Horiz strip of 5. Nos. 3167/3171	5·25	4·50
3168	**2356**	(1st) Red Panda	1·20	1·00

3169	**2357**	(1st) Black Rhinoceros..............................	1·20	1·00
3170	**2358**	(1st) African Wild Dog.............................	1·20	1·00
3171	**2359**	(1st) Golden Lion Tamarin......................	1·20	1·00

Set of 10.. 10·50 9·00
Set of 2 Gutter Strips of 10.. 21·00
First Day Cover (Tallents House)................................ 9·50
First Day Cover (Godalming, Surrey).......................... 9·50
Presentation Pack (PO Pack No. 454) (Nos. 3162/3171
and **MS**3172).. 16·00
PHQ Cards (set of 15) (348).......................... 6·00 21·00
MS3172 115×89 mm. **2360** Wildlife of the Amazon
Rainforest (1st) Spider monkey; 60p. Hyacinth
macaw; 88p. Poison dart frog; 97p. Jaguar............... 4·50 4·50
a. Booklet pane. No. **MS**3172 but
125×96 mm with line of roulettes at
left... 4·50 4·50
First Day Cover (Tallents House)................................ 5·25
First Day Cover (Godalming, Surrey).......................... 5·25

Nos. 3162/3166 and 3167/3171 were each printed together, *se-tenant*, as horizontal strips of five stamps in sheets of 50 (2 panes 5×5).

Booklet panes Nos. 3162b, 3164b and **MS**3172a come from the £9·05 50th Anniversary of the WWF booklet, No. DX52.

The 1st class value from No. **MS**3172 includes the EUROPA emblem.

The complete miniature sheet is shown on one of the 15 PHQ cards with the others depicting individual stamps including those from No. **MS**3172.

2361 David Tennant as Hamlet, 2008

2362 Antony Sher as Prospero, *The Tempest*, 2009

2363 Chuk Iwuji as Henry VI, 2006

2364 Paul Schofield as King Lear, 1962

2365 Sara Kestelman as Titania, *A Midsummer Night's Dream*, 1970

2366 Ian McKellen and Francesca Annis as Romeo and Juliet, 1976

2367 The Four Theatres of the Royal Shakespeare Company, Stratford-upon-Avon

(Des Hat-trick. Gravure (Nos. 3173/3178) or litho (No. **MS**3179) Walsall (Nos. 3173/3178) or Cartor (No. **MS**3179))

2011 (21 Apr). 50th Anniversary of the Royal Shakespeare Company. Black, brownish black and bright scarlet. 'All-over' phosphor. Perf 14½ (Nos. 3173/3178) or 14 (No. **MS**3179).

3173	**2361**	(1st) David Tennant as Hamlet................	1·20	1·00
3174	**2362**	66p. Antony Sher as Prospero, *The Tempest*..	1·00	1·00
3175	**2363**	68p. Chuk Iwuji as Henry VI....................	1·10	1·10
3176	**2364**	76p. Paul Schofield as King Lear.............	1·25	1·25
3177	**2365**	£1 Sara Kestelman as Titania, *A Midsummer Night's Dream*...............	1·50	1·50
3178	**2366**	£1·10 Ian McKellen and Francesca Annis as Romeo and Juliet...................	1·75	1·75

Set of 6.. 6·75 6·75
Set of 6 Gutter Pairs... 13·50
First Day Cover (Tallents House)................................ 8·00
First Day Cover (Stratford-upon-Avon)....................... 8·00
Presentation Pack (PO Pack No. 455) (Nos. 3173/3178
and **MS**3179).. 13·00
PHQ Cards (set of 11) (349)......................... 4·50 18·00
MS3179 115×89 mm. **2367** The Four Theatres of the
Royal Shakespeare Company, Stratford-upon-Avon
(1st) Janet Suzman as Ophelia, *Hamlet*, 1965,
Royal Shakespeare Theatre; 68p. Patrick Stewart
in *Antony and Cleopatra*, 2006, Swan Theatre; 76p.
Geoffrey Streatfield in *Henry V*, 2007, The Court-
yard Theatre; £1 Judy Dench as Lady Macbeth,
1976, The Other Place.. 4·25 4·25
First Day Cover (Tallents House)................................ 5·00
First Day Cover (Stratford-upon-Avon)....................... 5·00

The 11 PHQ cards show the six stamps, the four individual stamps within No. **MS**3179 and the complete miniature sheet.

2368 Prince William and Miss Catherine Middleton

(Litho Walsall)

2011 (21 Apr). Royal Wedding. Official Engagement Portraits by Mario Testino. Sheet 115×89 mm. Multicoloured 'All-over' phosphor. Perf 14½×14.

MS3180 **2368** Prince William and Miss Catherine
Middleton (1st)×2 Prince William and Miss
Catherine Middleton embracing; £1·10×2 Formal
portrait of Prince William and Miss Catherine
Middleton in Council Chamber, St James's Palace.... 5·50 5·50
First Day Cover (Tallents House)................................ 7·00
First Day Cover (London SW1).................................. 7·00
Presentation Pack (PO Pack No. M20)...................... 13·00
Commemorative Document...................................... 15·00

2369 Cray (fabric print by William Morris), 1884

2370 Cherries (detail from panel by Philip Webb), 1867

2371 Seaweed (wallpaper pattern by John Henry Dearle), 1901

2372 Peony (ceramic tile design by Kate Faulkner), 1877

2373 Acanthus (tile by William Morris and William de Morgan), 1876

2374 The Merchant's Daughter (detail of stained-glass window by Edward Burne-Jones), 1864

(Des Kate Stephens. Litho Cartor or Walsall (booklet stamps))

2011 (5 May). 150th Anniversary of Morris and Company (designers and manufacturers of textiles, wallpaper and furniture) (1st issue). Multicoloured 'All-over' phosphor. Perf 14×14½.

3181	**2369**	(1st) Cray....................................	1·20	1·00
		a. Booklet pane. Nos. 3181 and		
		3183/3185 with margins all round	5·25	
3182	**2370**	(1st) Cherries..............................	1·20	1·00
		a. Booklet pane. Nos. 3182 and		
		3186, each×2, with margins all		
		round....................................	5·25	
3183	**2371**	76p. Seaweed..............................	1·25	1·25
3184	**2372**	76p. Peony.................................	1·25	1·25
3185	**2373**	£1·10 Acanthus............................	1·75	1·75
3186	**2374**	£1·10 The Merchant's Daughter.........	1·75	1·75
Set of 6...			7·25	7·00
Set of 6 Gutter Pairs.................................			14·50	
First Day Cover (Tallents House).................				8·00
First Day Cover (Walthamstow)..................				8·00
Presentation Pack (PO Pack No. 456)............			7·75	
PHQ Cards (set of 6) (350)........................			2·50	8·25

Booklet panes Nos. 3181a and 3182a come from the £9·99 150th Anniversary of Morris and Company booklet, No. DY1.

2202 Angel playing Lute

2011 (5 May). 150th Anniversary of Morris and Company (2nd issue). Design as T **2202** (2009 Christmas. Stained-glass Windows). Multicoloured One centre band. Perf 14½×14 (with one elliptical hole in each vert side).

3186a	**2202**	(2nd) Angel playing Lute (William		
		Morris), Church of St James,		
		Staveley, Kendal, Cumbria..............	1·50	1·50
		ab. Booklet pane. No. 3186a×4 with		
		central label and margins all		
		round....................................	6·00	

No. 3186a was only issued in the £9·99 150th Anniversary of Morris and Company booklet, No. DY1.

2375 Thomas the Tank Engine

2376 James the Red Engine

2377 Percy the Small Engine

2378 Daisy (diesel railcar)

2379 Toby the Tram Engine

2380 Gordon the Big Engine

2381 Book Illustrations by John T. Kenny (76p.) or C. Reginald Dalby (others)

2382 "Goodbye, Bertie", called Thomas (from *Tank Engine Thomas Again*)

(Des Elmwood. Litho Cartor)

2011 (14 June). Thomas the Tank Engine. Multicoloured 'All-over' phosphor.

(a) Ordinary gum. Perf 14 (No. MS3193) or 14½×14 (others).

3187	**2375**	(1st) Thomas the Tank Engine..............	1·20	1·00
3188	**2376**	66p. James the Red Engine.................	1·00	1·00
3189	**2377**	68p. Percy the Small Engine...............	1·10	1·10
3190	**2378**	76p. Daisy (diesel railcar)..................	1·25	1·25
3191	**2379**	£1 Toby the Tram Engine....................	1·50	1·50

3192	**2380**	£1·10 Gordon the Big Engine..................	1·75	1·75
		Set of 6..	6·75	6·75
		Set of 6 Gutter Pairs.................................	13·50	
		First Day Cover (Tallents House)................		8·00
		First Day Cover (Box, Corsham, Wiltshire)............................		8·00
		Presentation Pack (PO Pack No. 457) (Nos. 3187/3192 and **MS**3193).........	13·00	
		PHQ Cards (set of 11) (351)......................	4·50	18·00

MS3193 115×89 mm. **2381** (1st) "Goodbye, Bertie", called Thomas (from *Tank Engine Thomas Again*); 68p. James was more dirty than hurt (from *Toby the Tram Engine*); 76p. "Yes, Sir", Percy shivered miserably (from *The Eight Famous Engines*); £1. They told Henry, "We shall leave you there for always" (from *The Three Railway Engines*)................... 4·25 | 4·25

		First Day Cover (Tallents House)................		5·00
		First Day Cover (Box, Corsham, Wiltshire)............................		5·00

(b) Self-adhesive. Die-cut perf 14 (Gravure Walsall).

3194	**2382**	(1st) "Goodbye, Bertie", called Thomas (from *Tank Engine Thomas Again*)...	2·00	2·00
		a. Booklet pane. Nos. 3194×2 and U3016×4......................	7·50	

Nos. 3187/3192 show scenes from TV series *Thomas and Friends*, and Nos. **MS**3193/3194 book illustrations from The Railway Series.

No. 3194 was only issued in stamp booklet, No. PM29, originally sold for £2·76.

The 11 PHQ cards show the six stamps, the four individual stamps within No. **MS**3193 and the complete miniature sheet.

2383 Paralympic Games, Sailing

2384 Athletics, Field

2385 Volleyball

2386 Wheelchair Rugby

2387 Wrestling

2388 Wheelchair Tennis

2389 Fencing

2390 Gymnastics

2391 Triathlon

2392 Handball

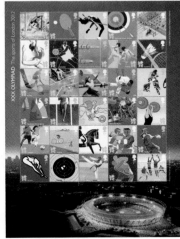

2392a

(Des Lara Harwood and Heart (No. 3195), Anthony Pike and The Art Market (No. 3196), Ben Dalling (No. 3197), Matthew Hollings and Illustration Ltd (No. 3198), Daniel Stolle and Anna Goodson Management (No. 3199), David McConochie and The Art Market (No. 3200), Lyndon Hayes and Dutch Uncle Agency (No. 3201), Kathy Wyatt (No. 3202), Adam Simpson and Heart (No. 3203), David Cutter and Folio (No. 3204). Litho Cartor)

2011 (27 July). Olympic and Paralympic Games, London (2012) (5th issue). Multicoloured 'All-over' phosphor. Perf 14½.

3195	**2383**	(1st) Paralympic Games, Sailing.............	1·20	1·00
		a. Horiz strip of 5. Nos. 3195/3199.....	5·25	4·50
3196	**2384**	(1st) Athletics, Field.................................	1·20	1·00
3197	**2385**	(1st) Volleyball..	1·20	1·00
3198	**2386**	(1st) Wheelchair Rugby...........................	1·20	1·00
3199	**2387**	(1st) Wrestling...	1·20	1·00
3200	**2388**	(1st) Wheelchair Tennis...........................	1·20	1·00
		a. Horiz strip of 5. Nos. 3200/3204.....	5·25	4·50
3201	**2389**	(1st) Fencing...	1·20	1·00
3202	**2390**	(1st) Gymnastics......................................	1·20	1·00
3203	**2391**	(1st) Triathlon..	1·20	1·00
3204	**2392**	(1st) Handball..	1·20	1·00
		Set of 10..	10·50	9·00
		Set of 2 Gutter Strips of 10.......................	21·00	
		First Day Cover (Tallents House)................		9·50
		First Day Cover (Rugby, Warks).................		9·50
		Presentation Pack (PO Pack No. 458)........	11·00	
		PHQ Cards (set of 10) (352)......................	4·00	12·00

MS3204*a* 210×300 mm. **2392a** Nos. 2981/2990, 3097/3106 and 3195/3204...................... 35·00 | 35·00

Nos. 3195/3199 and 3200/3204 were each printed together, *se-tenant*, in horizontal strips of five stamps in sheets of 50 (2 panes 5×5) and in No. **MS**3204*a*.

(Gravure Walsall)

2011 (27 July–15 Sept). Olympic and Paralympic Games (2012) (6th issue). Booklet stamps. Designs as Nos. 3195, 3198 and 3201/32022 . Self-adhesive. Multicoloured 'All-over' phosphor. Die-cut Perf 14½×14.

3205	**2386**	(1st) Wheelchair Rugby...........................	2·00	2·00
		a. Booklet pane. Nos. 3205/3206 and U3016×4......................	7·50	
3206	**2383**	(1st) Paralympic Games, Sailing.............	2·00	2·00
3206*a*	**2390**	(1st) Gymnastics (15.9.11)......................	2·00	2·00
		ab. Booklet pane. Nos. 3206*a*/3206*b* and U3016×4......................	7·50	
3206*b*	**2389**	(1st) Fencing (15.9.11)............................	2·00	2·00
		Set of 4..	7·50	7·50

Nos. 3205/3206 and 3206*a*/3206*b* were only issued in two separate stamp booklets, Nos. PM30 and PM32, each originally sold for £2·76.

2393 The Sovereign's Sceptre with Cross

2394 St Edward's Crown

2395 Rod and Sceptre with Doves

2396 Queen Mary's Crown

2397 The Sovereign's Orb

2398 Jewelled Sword of Offering

2399 Imperial State Crown

2400 Coronation Spoon

(Des Purpose. Litho Cartor)

2011 (23 Aug). Crown Jewels. Multicoloured Phosphor background. Perf 14×14½.

3207	**2393**	(1st) The Sovereign's Sceptre with Cross......	1·20	1·00
3208	**2394**	(1st) St Edward's Crown..........	1·20	1·00
3209	**2395**	68p. Rod and Sceptre with Doves..........	1·10	1·10
3210	**2396**	68p. Queen Mary's Crown..........	1·10	1·10
3211	**2397**	76p. The Sovereign's Orb..........	1·25	1·25
3212	**2398**	76p. Jewelled Sword of Offering..........	1·25	1·25
3213	**2399**	£1·10 Imperial State Crown..........	1·60	1·60
3214	**2400**	£1·10 Coronation Spoon..........	1·60	1·60
Set of 8..........			9·00	8·75
Set of 8 Gutter Pairs..........			18·00	
First Day Cover (Tallents House)..........				10·00
First Day Cover (London EC3)..........				10·00
Presentation Pack (PO Pack No. 459)..........			10·00	
PHQ Cards (set of 8) (353)..........			3·25	11·00

2401 BR Dean Goods No. 2532

(Gravure Walsall)

2011 (23 Aug). Classic Locomotives. Black and gold. Booklet stamp. Design as 1st class stamp within No. **MS**3144. Self-adhesive. Die-cut Perf 14.

3215	**2401**	(1st) BR Dean Goods No. 2532..........	2·00	2·00
		a. Booklet pane. No. 3215×2 and U3016×4..........	7·50	

No. 3215 was only issued in booklet, No. PM31, originally sold for £2·76. See also No. 3570.

2402 Pilot Gustav Hamel receiving Mailbag

2403 Gustav Hamel in Cockpit

2404 Pilot Clement Greswell and Blériot Monoplane

2405 Delivery of First Airmail to Postmaster General at Windsor

2406 First United Kingdom Aerial Post, 9 September 1911

(Des Robert Maude and Sarah Davies. Litho Cartor)

2011 (9 Sept). Centenary of First United Kingdom Aerial Post (1st issue). Multicoloured 'All-over' phosphor. Perf 14.

3216	**2402**	(1st) Pilot Gustav Hamel receiving Mailbag..........	1·75	1·75
		a. Booklet pane. Nos. 3216×2 and 3219, with margins all round..........	8·50	
3217	**2403**	68p. Pilot Gustav Hamel receiving Mailbag..........	1·75	1·75
		a. Booklet pane. Nos. 3217×2 and 3218..........	8·50	
3218	**2404**	£1 Pilot Clement Greswell and Blériot Monoplane..........	5·00	5·00
3219	**2405**	£1·10 Delivery of First Airmail to Postmaster General at Windsor......	5·00	5·00
Set of 4..........			13·50	13·50
MS3220 146×74 mm. **2406** First United Kingdom Aerial Post, 9 September 1911 Nos. 3216/3219..........			8·50	8·50
First Day Cover (Tallents House)..........				9·50
First Day Cover (Hendon, London NW4)..........				9·50
Presentation Pack (PO Pack No. 460)..........			9·50	
PHQ Cards (set of 5) (354)..........			2·00	21·00

Nos. 3216/3219 were only issued in £9·99 First United Kingdom Aerial Post stamp booklet, No. DY2, and in No. **MS**3220.

The five PHQ cards show the four individual stamps and the complete miniature sheet.

2407 Windsor Castle

(Recess Phil@poste of France and litho Cartor)

2011 (9 Sept). Centenary of First United Kingdom Aerial Post (2nd issue). Black and cream. Perf 11×11½.

3221	**2407**	50p. Windsor Castle..........	2·00	2·00
		a. Booklet pane. No. 3221×4, with margins all round..........	8·25	

No. 3221 was only issued in £9·97 First United Kingdom Aerial Post stamp booklet, No. DY2.

For No. **MS**3222, T **2408**, see Decimal Machin Definitives section

2409 George I
(1714–1727)

2410 George II
(1727–1760)

2411 George III
(1760–1820)

2412 George IV
(1820–1830)

2413 William IV
(1830–1837)

2414 Victoria
(1837–1901)

2415 The Age of the Hanoverians

(Des Atelier Works. Litho Cartor)

2011 (15 Sept). Kings and Queens (5th issue). House of Hanover.
Multicoloured Two phosphor bands. Perf 14.

3223	**2409**	(1st) George I	1·20	1·00
3224	**2410**	(1st) George II	1·20	1·00
3225	**2411**	76p. George III	1·25	1·25
3226	**2412**	76p. George IV	1·25	1·25
3227	**2413**	£1·10 William IV	1·75	1·75
3228	**2414**	£1·10 Victoria	1·75	1·75

Set of 6 .... 7·25 7·00
Set of 6 Gutter Pairs .... 14·50
Set of 6 Traffic Light Gutter Blocks of 4 .... 50·00
First Day Cover (Tallents House) .... 8·00
First Day Cover (London SW1) .... 8·00
Presentation Pack (PO Pack No. 461) (Nos. 3223/3228
and **MS**3229) .... 13·00
PHQ Cards (set of 11) (355) .... 4·50 18·00
MS3229 123×70 mm. **2415** The Age of the
Hanoverians (1st) Robert Walpole (first Prime
Minister, 1721; 68p. Ceiling by Robert Adam,
Kedleston Hall, 1763; 76p. Penny Black (uniform
postage), 1840; £1 Queen Victoria (Diamond
Jubilee), 1897 .... 4·25 4·25
First Day Cover (Tallents House) .... 5·00
First Day Cover (London SW1) .... 5·00

The photograph of Queen Victoria in No. **MS**2415 actually shows her at
the time of her Golden Jubilee in 1887.

The complete miniature sheet is shown on one of the 11 PHQ cards with
the others depicting individual stamps including those from No. **MS**3229.

2416 Angel of the North

2417 Blackpool Tower

2418 Carrick-a-Rede, Co.
Antrim

2419 Downing Street

2420 Edinburgh Castle

2421 Forth Railway Bridge

2422 Glastonbury Tor

2423 Harlech Castle

2424 Ironbridge

2425 Jodrell Bank

2426 Kursaal, Southend,
Essex

2427 Lindisfarne Priory

(Des Robert Maude and Sarah Davies. Litho Cartor)

2011 (13 Oct). UK A–Z (1st series). Multicoloured 'All-over' phosphor. Perf
14½.

3230	**2416**	(1st) *Angel of the North*	1·20	1·00
		a. Horiz strip of 6. Nos. 3230/3235	5·25	4·50
3231	**2417**	(1st) Blackpool Tower	1·20	1·00
3232	**2418**	(1st) Carrick-a-Rede, Co. Antrim	1·20	1·00
3233	**2419**	(1st) Downing Street	1·20	1·00
3234	**2420**	(1st) Edinburgh Castle	1·20	1·00
3235	**2421**	(1st) Forth Railway Bridge	1·20	1·00
3236	**2422**	(1st) Glastonbury Tor	1·20	1·00
		a. Horiz strip of 6. Nos. 3236/3241	5·25	4·50
3237	**2423**	(1st) Harlech Castle	1·20	1·00
3238	**2424**	(1st) Ironbridge	1·20	1·00
3239	**2425**	(1st) Jodrell Bank	1·20	1·00
3240	**2426**	(1st) Kursaal, Southend, Essex	1·20	1·00
3241	**2427**	(1st) Lindisfarne Priory	1·20	1·00

Set of 12 .... 10·50 9·00
Set of 2 Gutter Strips of 12 .... 21·00
Set of 2 Traffic Light Gutter Strips of 24 .... 48·00
First Day Covers (Tallents House) (2) .... 11·00
First Day Covers (Blackpool) (2) .... 11·00
Presentation Pack (PO Pack No. 462) .... 12·00
PHQ Cards (set of 12) (356) .... 4·75 13·00

Nos. 3230/3235 and 3236/3241 were each printed together, *se-tenant*,
as horizontal strips of six stamps in sheets of 60 (2 panes of 30) and were
also issued on 10 April 2012 in a sheet containing all 26 UK A–Z stamps.
See No. **MS**3308.

2428 Joseph visited by the Angel (Matthew 1:21)

2429 Madonna and Child (Matthew 1:23)

2430 Joseph visited by the Angel (Matthew 1:21)

2431 Madonna and Child (Matthew 1:23)

2432 Baby Jesus in the Manger (Luke 2:7)

2433 Shepherds visited by the Angel (Luke 2:10)

2434 Wise Men and Star (Matthew 2:10)

2434a *The King James Bible*

(Des Peter Malone/The Artworks and Together Design. Gravure De La Rue)

2011 (8 Nov). Christmas. 400th Anniversary of the *King James Bible*. Multicoloured One centre band (No. 3242) or two phosphor bands (others). Perf 14½×14 (with one elliptical hole in each vert side).

(a) Self-adhesive.

3242	**2428**	(2nd) Joseph visited by the Angel.............	90	90
		a. Booklet pane. Nos. 3242×12.............	13·50	
3243	**2429**	(1st) Madonna and Child........................	1·20	1·00
		a. Booklet pane. No. 3243×12.............	16·00	
3244	**2430**	(2nd Large) Joseph visited by the Angel........	1·25	1·10
3245	**2431**	(1st Large) Madonna and Child..............	1·70	1·40
3246	**2432**	68p. Baby Jesus in the Manger.................	1·25	1·25
3247	**2433**	£1·10 Shepherds visited by the Angel.....	1·90	1·90
3248	**2434**	£1·65 Wise Men and Star......................	2·50	2·50
Set of 7....................			9·25	9·00
First Day Cover (Tallents House)...................				11·00
First Day Cover (Bethlehem, Llandeilo)................				11·00
Presentation Pack (PO Pack No. 463)...................			10·00	
PHQ *Cards* (set of 8) (357)................			3·25	19·50

(b) Ordinary gum.

MS3249 **2434a** 116×102 mm. As Nos. 3242/3248..........		9·25	9·00
First Day Cover (Tallents House)...................			10·00
First Day Cover (Bethlehem, Llandeilo)................			10·00

The 2nd class, 1st class, 68p., and £1·10 stamps were also issued in sheets of 20 (No. LS79) printed in lithography and sold for £10·45, containing 8×2nd class, 8×1st class, 2×68p. and 2×£1·10 stamps, each stamp accompanied by a *se-tenant* label with a verse from the *King James Bible*.

Separate sheets of 20×2nd, 10×1st, 10×68p. and 10×£1·10 were available with personal photographs on the labels from Royal Mail, Edinburgh. These were sold at £8·30 for 10×1st, £10·95 for 20×2nd, £10·75 for 10×68p. or £15·80 for 10×£1·10.

The eight PHQ cards show the seven individual stamps and the miniature sheet.

Year Pack

2011 (8 Nov). Comprises Nos. 3136/3142, **MS**3144/3152, 3154/3193, 3195/3204, 3207/3214, **MS**3220 and 3223/3248.

CP3244a	Year Pack (Pack No. 464) (*sold for* £94).................	£130

Post Office Yearbook

2011 (8 Nov). Comprises Nos. 3136/3142, **MS**3144/3152, 3154/3193, 3195/3204, 3207/3214, **MS**3220 and 3223/3248.

YB3244a	Yearbook (*sold for* £99).................	£130

Miniature Sheet Collection

2011 (8 Nov). Comprises Nos. **MS**3142, **MS**3144, **MS**3172, **MS**3179/ **MS**3180, **MS**3193, **MS**3220, **MS**3229 and **MS**3249.

MS3244a Miniature Sheet Collection..................		45·00

2435 Paralympic Games Emblem

2436 Olympic Games Emblem

(Gravure Walsall (booklets) or De La Rue (others))

2012 (5 Jan). Olympic and Paralympic Games (7th issue). Self-adhesive. Two phosphor bands. Die-cut Perf 14½×14 (with one elliptical hole on each vert side).

3250	**2435**	(1st) Paralympic Games Emblem. Black and orange-red..............	1·25	1·25
		a. Booklet pane. Nos. 3250/3251, each×3..................	7·00	
3251	**2436**	(1st) Olympic Games Emblem. Black and orange-red..............	1·25	1·25
3252	**2435**	(Worldwide up to 20 g) Paralympic Games Emblem. Black, bright scarlet and greenish blue........	2·25	2·25
3253	**2436**	(Worldwide up to 20 g) Olympic Games Emblem. Black, bright scarlet and greenish blue..................	2·25	2·25
Set of 4....................			7·00	7·00
First Day Cover (Tallents House)...................				8·00
First Day Cover (Sennen, Penzance, Cornwall)...................				8·00
Presentation Pack (PO Pack No. D92)...................			9·00	
PHQ *Cards* (set of 4) (D32)...................			1·50	8·00

Nos. 3250/3251 were printed together in sheets of 50 (2 panes 5×5), with the two designs alternating horizontally and vertically. The upper pane had No. 3250 at top left and contained 13 of No. 3250 and 12 of No. 3251. The lower pane had No. 3251 at top left and contained 13 of No. 3251 and 12 of No. 3250.

Nos. 3250/3251 were also issued in stamp booklets, No. MB9/MB10, originally sold for £2·76.

Booklet pane 3250a exists in two versions which differ in the order of the stamps within the block of six.

Nos. 3252/3253 were printed together in sheets of 25 (5×5) with the two designs alternating horizontally and vertically. There were two versions of the sheets of 25, one having No. 3252 at top left and containing 13 of No. 3252 and 12 of No. 3253, and the other having No. 3253 at top left and containing 13 of No. 3253 and 12 of No. 3252.

Nos. 3250/3253 were also issued on 27 June 2012 in sheets of 20 containing Nos. 3250/3251, each×8, and Nos. 3252/3253, each×2, all with *se-tenant* labels showing Games venues (No. LS82). These sheets were printed in lithography by Cartor.

See also Nos. 3337/3340.

2437 *Charlie and the Chocolate Factory*

2438 *Fantastic Mr Fox*

2439 *James and the Giant Peach*

2440 *Matilda*

2441 *The Twits*

2442 *The Witches*

(Des Magpie Studio. Litho Cartor)

2012 (10 Jan). Roald Dahl's Children's Stories (1st issue). Book Illustrations by Quentin Blake. Multicoloured 'All-over' phosphor. Perf 14.

3254	**2437**	(1st) *Charlie and the Chocolate Factory...*	1·20	1·00
		a. Booklet pane. Nos. 3254 and 3256/3257 with margins all round	3·50	
3255	**2438**	66p. *Fantastic Mr Fox...*	1·00	1·00
		a. Booklet pane. Nos. 3255 and 3258/3259 with margins all round	4·50	
3256	**2439**	68p. *James and the Giant Peach...*	1·10	1·10
3257	**2440**	76p. *Matilda...*	1·25	1·25
3258	**2441**	£1 *The Twits...*	1·50	1·50
3259	**2442**	£1·10 *The Witches...*	1·75	1·75
Set of 6			6·75	6·75
Set of 6 Gutter Pairs			13·50	
Set of 6 Traffic Light Gutter Blocks of 4			30·00	
First Day Cover (Tallents House)				9·00
First Day Cover (Great Missenden, Bucks)				9·00
Presentation Pack (PO Pack No. 465) (Nos. 3254/3259 and **MS**3264)			16·00	
PHQ Cards (set of 11) (358)			4·25	25·00

Booklet panes Nos. 3254a and 3255a come from the £11.47 Roald Dahl, Master Storyteller premium booklets, No. DY3.

2443 The BFG Carrying Sophie in his Hand

2444 The BFG Wakes up the Giants

2445 Sophie Sitting on Buckingham Palace Window Sill

2446 The BFG and Sophie at Writing Desk

2447 Roald Dahl's The BFG

(Des Magpie Studio. Litho Cartor)

2012 (10 Jan). Roald Dahl's Children's Stories (2nd issue). Book Illustrations by Quentin Blake. Multicoloured 'All-over' phosphor. Perf 14×14½.

3260	**2443**	(1st) The BFG carrying Sophie in his Hand	2·40	2·40
		a. Booklet pane. Nos. 3260/3263	9·00	
3261	**2444**	68p. The BFG wakes up the Giants	2·40	2·40
3262	**2445**	76p. Sophie sitting on Buckingham Palace Window sill	2·40	2·40
3263	**2446**	£1 The BFG and Sophie at Writing Desk	2·40	2·40
Set of 4			9·00	9·00
MS3264 115×89 mm. **2447** Roald Dahl's The BFG Nos. 3260/3263			9·00	9·00
First Day Cover (Tallents House)				9·50
First Day Cover (Great Missenden, Bucks)				9·50

Nos. 3260/3263 were only issued in £11·47 Roald Dahl, Master Storyteller premium booklet, No. DY3, and in No. **MS**3264.

No. **MS**3264 commemorates the 30th anniversary of the publication of *The BFG*.

The complete miniature sheet is shown on one of the 11 PHQ cards with the others showing individual stamps including those from No. **MS**3264.

2448 Edward VII (1901–1910)

2449 George V (1910–1936)

2450 Edward VIII (1936)

2451 George VI (1936–1952)

2452 Elizabeth II (1952–)

2453 The Age of the Windsors

(Des Atelier Works. Litho Cartor)

2012 (2 Feb). Kings and Queens (6th issue). House of Windsor. Multicoloured Two phosphor bands. Perf 14.

3265	**2448**	(1st) Edward VII......	1·20	1·00
3266	**2449**	68p. George V......	1·00	1·00
3267	**2450**	76p. Edward VIII......	1·40	1·40
3268	**2451**	£1 George VI......	1·90	1·90
3269	**2452**	£1·10 Elizabeth II......	2·25	2·25

Set of 5......	6·75	6·75
Set of 5 Gutter Pairs......	13·50	
Set of 5 Traffic Light Gutter Blocks of 4......	25·00	
First Day Cover (Tallents House)......		7·50
First Day Cover (Windsor, Berkshire)......		7·50
Presentation Pack (PO Pack No. 466) (Nos. 3265/3269 and **MS**3270)......	11·50	
PHQ Cards (set of 10) (359)......	4·00	16·50

MS3270 123×70 mm. **2453** The Age of the Windsors (1st) Scott Expedition to South Pole, 1912; 68p. Queen Elizabeth the Queen Mother and King George VI in bomb damaged street, *circa* 1940; 76p. England's winning World Cup football team, 1966; £1 Channel Tunnel, 1996......

	4·25	4·25
First Day Cover (Tallents House)......		5·50
First Day Cover (Windsor, Berkshire)......		5·50

The complete miniature sheet is shown on one of the ten PHQ cards with the others depicting individual stamps including those from No. **MS**3270.

No. 3271 is vacant.

For Nos. U3271/U3278 see Decimal Machin Definitives section

2454 Diamond Jubilee

(Des Sedley Place. Gravure Walsall)

2012 (6 Feb). Diamond Jubilee. (2nd issue). Multicoloured Two phosphor bands. Perf 14½×14 (with one elliptical hole in each vertical side).
MS3272 146×74 mm. **2454** Diamond Jubilee (1st)×6 Portrait from photograph by Dorothy Wilding; 1960 £1 Banknote portrait by Robert Austin; 1971 £5 Banknote portrait by Harry Eccleston; 1953 Coinage portrait by Mary Gillick; 1971 decimal coin portrait by Arnold Machin; As No. U3279......

	7·25	7·25
First Day Cover (Tallents House)......		7·75
First Day Cover (London SW1)......		7·75
Presentation Pack (PO Pack No. 93)......	7·25	
PHQ Cards (set of 7) (D33)......	2·75	14·50
Commemorative Document......	12·00	

The 1st class slate-blue Machin stamp from No. **MS**3272 has an iridescent overprint reading 'DIAMOND JUBILEE' and the source code 'MMND'.

The seven PHQ cards show the six individual stamps and the complete miniature sheet.

2455 Coventry Cathedral, 1962 (Sir Basil Spence, architect)

2456 Frederick Delius (1862–1934, composer)

2457 Orange Tree, Embroidery (Mary 'May' Morris 1862–1938, designer and textile artist)

2458 Odette Hallowes (1912–1995, SOE agent in occupied France)

2459 Steam Engine, 1712 (Thomas Newcomen, inventor of atmospheric steam engine)

2460 Kathleen Ferrier (1912–1953, contralto)

2461 Interior of Palace of Westminster (Augustus Pugin 1812–1852, Gothic revival architect and designer)

2462 Montagu Rhodes James (1862–1936 scholar and author)

2463 Bombe Code Breaking Machine (Alan Turing 1912–1954, mathematician and World War II code breaker)

2464 Joan Mary Fry (1862–1955 relief worker and social reformer)

(Des Purpose. Litho Cartor)

2012 (23 Feb). Britons of Distinction. Multicoloured 'All-over' phosphor. Perf 14½.

3273	**2455**	(1st) Coventry Cathedral......	1·20	1·00
		a. Horiz strip of 5. Nos. 3273/3277....	5·25	4·50
3274	**2456**	(1st) Frederick Delius......	1·20	1·00
3275	**2457**	(1st) Orange Tree, Embroidery......	1·20	1·00
3276	**2458**	(1st) Odette Hallowes......	1·20	1·00
3277	**2459**	(1st) Steam Engine, 1712......	1·20	1·00

3278	**2460**	(1st) Kathleen Ferrier..............................	1·20	1·00
		a. Horiz strip of 5. Nos. 3278/3282.....	5·25	4·50
3279	**2461**	(1st) Interior of Palace of Westminster...	1·20	1·00
3280	**2462**	(1st) Montagu Rhodes James..................	1·20	1·00
3281	**2463**	(1st) Bombe Code Breaking Machine.....	1·20	1·00
3282	**2464**	(1st) Joan Mary Fry..............................	1·20	1·00
Set of 10..			10·50	9·00
Set of 2 Gutter Strips of 10............................			21·00	
First Day Cover (Tallents House)......................				9·25
First Day Cover (Coventry).............................				9·25
Presentation Pack (PO Pack No. 467)................			11·00	
PHQ Cards (*set of 10*) (360)..........................			4·00	11·50

Nos. 3273/3277 and 3278/3282 were each printed together, *se-tenant*, as horizontal strips of five stamps in sheets of 50 (2 panes 5×5).

No. 3281 also comes from booklet pane No. 3679b in £14·60 Inventive Britain booklet, No. DY12.

2465 Classic Locomotives of Scotland

(Des Delaney Design Consultants. Litho Cartor)

2012 (8 Mar). Classic Locomotives (2nd series). Scotland. Sheet 180×74 mm. Multicoloured 'All-over' phosphor. Perf 14.
MS3283 **2465** Classic Locomotives of Scotland (1st)
BR Class D34 Nos. 62471 *Glen Falloch* and 62496 *Glen Loy* at Ardlui, 9 May 1959; 68p. BR Class D40 No. 62276 *Andrew Bain* at Macduff, July 1950; £1 *Andrew Barclay* No. 807 *Bon Accord* propelling wagons along Miller Street, Aberdeen, June 1962; £1·10 BR Class 4P No. 54767 *Clan Mackinnon* pulling fish train, Kyle of Lochalsh, October 1948.....

.....	4·75	4·75
First Day Cover (Tallents House)......................		6·00
First Day Cover (Glasgow).............................		6·00
Presentation Pack (PO Pack No. 468)................	5·50	
PHQ Cards (*set of 5*) (361)..........................	2·00	9·00

The five PHQ cards show the four individual stamps and the complete miniature sheet.

2466 *The Dandy* and Desperate Dan

2467 *The Beano* and Dennis the Menace

2468 *Eagle* and Dan Dare

2469 *The Topper* and Beryl the Peril

2470 *Tiger* and Roy of the Rovers

2471 *Bunty* and the Four Marys

2472 *Buster* and Cartoon Character Buster

2473 *Valiant* and the Steel Claw

2474 *Twinkle* and Nurse Nancy

2475 *2000 AD* and Judge Dredd

(Des The Chase. Litho Cartor)

2012 (20 Mar). Comics. Multicoloured 'All-over' phosphor. Perf 14½.

3284	**2466**	(1st) *The Dandy* and Desperate Dan.......	1·20	1·00
		a. Horiz strip of 5. Nos. 3284/3288.....	5·25	4·50
3285	**2467**	(1st) *The Beano* and Dennis the Menace...........................	1·20	1·00
3286	**2468**	(1st) *Eagle* and Dan Dare..........................	1·20	1·00
3287	**2469**	(1st) *The Topper* and Beryl the Peril........	1·20	1·00
3288	**2470**	(1st) *Tiger* and Roy of the Rovers..............	1·20	1·00
3289	**2471**	(1st) *Bunty* and the Four Marys..............	1·20	1·00
		a. Horiz strip of 5. Nos. 3289/3293.....	5·25	4·50
3290	**2472**	(1st) *Buster* and Cartoon Character Buster..................	1·20	1·00
3291	**2473**	(1st) *Valiant* and the Steel Claw..............	1·20	1·00
3292	**2474**	(1st) *Twinkle* and Nurse Nancy................	1·20	1·00
3293	**2475**	(1st) *2000 AD* and Judge Dredd..............	1·20	1·00
Set of 10..			10·50	9·00
Set of 2 Gutter Strips of 5............................			21·00	
First Day Cover (Tallents House)......................				15·00
First Day Cover (Dundee).............................				15·00
Presentation Pack (PO Pack No. 469)................			11·00	
PHQ Cards (*set of 10*)..........................			4·00	11·50

2476 Manchester Town Hall

2477 Narrow Water Castle, Co. Down

2478 Old Bailey, London

2479 Portmeirion, Wales

2480 The Queen's College, Oxford

2481 Roman Baths, Bath

2482 Stirling Castle, Scotland

2483 Tyne Bridge, Newcastle

2484 Urquhart Castle, Scotland

2485 Victoria and Albert Museum, London

2486 White Cliffs of Dover

2487 Station X, Bletchley Park, Buckinghamshire

2488 York Minster

2489 London Zoo

2489a Composite sheet

(Des Robert Maude and Sarah Davies. Litho Cartor)

2012 (10 Apr). UK A–Z (2nd series). Multicoloured 'All-over' phosphor. Perf 14½.

3294	**2476**	(1st) Manchester Town Hall......................	1·20	1·00
		a. Horiz strip of 6. Nos. 3294/3299.....	6·50	5·50
3295	**2477**	(1st) Narrow Water Castle, Co. Down......	1·20	1·00
3296	**2478**	(1st) Old Bailey, London..........................	1·20	1·00
3297	**2479**	(1st) Portmeirion, Wales........................	1·20	1·00
3298	**2480**	(1st) The Queen's College, Oxford...........	1·20	1·00
3299	**2481**	(1st) Roman Baths, Bath..........................	1·20	1·00
3300	**2482**	(1st) Stirling Castle, Scotland..................	1·20	1·00
		a. Horiz strip of 6. Nos. 3300/3305.....	6·50	5·50
3301	**2483**	(1st) Tyne Bridge, Newcastle...................	1·20	1·00
3302	**2484**	(1st) Urquhart Castle, Scotland..............	1·20	1·00
3303	**2485**	(1st) Victoria and Albert Museum, London..	1·20	1·00

3304	**2486**	(1st) White Cliffs of Dover........................	1·20	1·00
3305	**2487**	(1st) Station X, Bletchley Park, Buckinghamshire.............................	1·20	1·00
3306	**2488**	(1st) York Minster....................................	1·20	1·00
		a. Horiz pair. Nos. 3306/3307..............	2·25	2·00
3307	**2489**	(1st) London Zoo.....................................	1·20	1·00

Set of 14.. 15·00 12·50
Set of 2 *Gutter Strips of* 12 *and* 1 *Gutter Strip of* 4.............. 30·00
Set of 2 *Traffic Light Gutter Strips of* 24 *and* 1 *Gutter Block of* 8.. 50·00
First Day Covers (Tallents House) (2).. 15·00
First Day Covers (Dover, Kent) (2)... 15·00
Presentation Pack (PO Pack No. 470).......................... 16·00
PHQ Cards (set of 14) (363).. 5·50 15·00
MS3308 297×210 mm. **2489a**. Nos. 3230/3241 and 3294/3307.. £100 £110

Nos. 3294/3299 and 3300/3305 were each printed together, *se-tenant*, as horizontal strips of six stamps in sheets of 60 (2 panes 6×5).

Nos. 3306/3307 were printed together, *se-tenant*, as horizontal pairs in sheets of 60 (2 panes 6×5).

No. 3303 includes the EUROPA emblem.

No. 3305 also comes from booklet pane No. 3679b in £14·60 Inventive Britain booklet No. DY12.

2490 Skirt Suit by Hardy Amies, late 1940s

2491 Outfit by Norman Hartnell, 1950s

2492 Jacket designed by John Pearce for Granny Takes a Trip Boutique, 1960s

2493 Print by Celia Birtwell for Outfit by Ossie Clark, late 1960s

2494 Suit designed for Ringo Starr by Tommy Nutter

2495 Outfit by Jean Muir, late 1970s/early 1980s

2496 'Royal' Dress by Zandra Rhodes, 1981

2497 Harlequin dress by Vivienne Westwood, 1993

2498 Suit by Paul Smith, 2003

2499 'Black Raven' by Alexander McQueen, 2009

(Des johnson banks. Litho Cartor)

2012 (15 May). Great British Fashion. Multicoloured Phosphor background. Perf 14½×14.

3309	**2490**	(1st) Skirt Suit by Hardy Amies...............	1·20	1·00
		a. Horiz strip of 5. Nos. 3309/3313.....	5·25	4·50
3310	**2491**	(1st) Outfit by Norman Hartnell.............	1·20	1·00
3311	**2492**	(1st) Jacket designed by John Pearce....	1·20	1·00
3312	**2493**	(1st) Print by Celia Birtwell for Outfit by Ossie Clark..................................	1·20	1·00
3313	**2494**	(1st) Suit designed...............................	1·20	1·00
3314	**2495**	(1st) Outfit by Jean Muir........................	1·20	1·00
		a. Horiz strip of 5. Nos. 3314/3318.....	5·25	4·50
3315	**2496**	(1st) 'Royal' Dress by Zandra Rhodes......	1·20	1·00
3316	**2497**	(1st) Harlequin dress by Vivienne Westwood..................................	1·20	1·00
3317	**2498**	(1st) Suit by Paul Smith...........................	1·20	1·00
3318	**2499**	(1st) 'Black Raven' by Alexander McQueen............................	1·20	1·00
Set of 10...			10·50	9·00
Set of 2 Gutter Strips of 10......................................			21·00	
Set of 2 Traffic Light Gutter Strips of 20...................			40·00	
First Day Cover (Tallents House)................................				11·00
First Day Cover (London W1).....................................				11·00
Presentation Pack (PO Pack No. 471)........................			11·00	
PHQ Cards (set of 10) (364).......................................			4·00	12·00

Nos. 3309/3313 and 3314/3318 were each printed together, *se-tenant*, as horizontal strips of five stamps in sheets of 50 (2 panes 5×5).

2500 Queen Elizabeth II at Golden Jubilee Thanksgiving Service, St Paul's Cathedral, London, 2002

2501 Queen Elizabeth II Trooping the Colour, 1967

2502 Queen Elizabeth II inspecting 2nd Battalion Royal Welsh, Tidworth, 1 March 2007

2503 First Christmas Television Broadcast, 1957

2504 Silver Jubilee Walkabout, 1977

2505 Queen Elizabeth II in Garter Ceremony Procession, 1997

2506 Queen Elizabeth II addressing the UN General Assembly, 1957

2507 Queen Elizabeth II at Commonwealth Games, Brisbane, Australia, 1982

(Des Kate Stephens. Photo De La Rue (3319A/3320A, 3323A/3326A), Enschedé (3321A/3322A), Litho Walsall (3319B/3326B) or Photo Walsall (3327B))

2012 (31 May)–**22**. Diamond Jubilee. Multicoloured. 'All-over' phosphor.

(a) Sheet stamps. Gravure. Ordinary gum. Perf 14×14½.

3319A	**2500**	(1st) Queen Elizabeth II at Golden Jubilee Service, St Paul's Cathedral, London, 2002............	1·20	1·00
3320A	**2501**	a. Horiz pair. Nos. 3319A/3320A.........	2·40	2·00
		(1st) Queen Elizabeth II Trooping the Colour, 1967..............................	1·20	1·00
3321A	**2502**	77p. Queen Elizabeth II inspecting 2nd Battalion Royal Welsh, Tidworth, 1 March 2007..............................	1·00	1·00
3322A	**2503**	a. Horiz pair. Nos. 3321A/3322A.........	2·00	2·00
		77p. First Christmas Television Broadcast, 1957..............................	1·00	1·00
3323A	**2504**	87p. Silver Jubilee Walkabout, 1977.......	1·25	1·25
3324A	**2505**	a. Horiz pair. Nos. 3323A/3324A.........	2·50	2·50
		87p. Queen Elizabeth II in Garter Ceremony Procession, 1997...........	1·25	1·25
3325A	**2506**	£1·28 Queen Elizabeth II addressing the UN General Assembly, 1957............	1·75	1·75
3326A	**2507**	a. Horiz pair. Nos. 3325A/3326A.........	2·50	3·50
		£1·28 Queen Elizabeth II at Commonwealth Games, Brisbane, Australia, 1982................................	1·75	1·75
Set of 8...			9·25	9·00
Set of 4 Gutter Strips of 4..			18·50	
First Day Cover (Tallents House).............................				11·00
Presentation Pack (PO Pack No. 72)........................			19·00	
PHQ Cards (Set of 8) (365).......................................			3·25	12·00

(b) Booklet stamps. Litho. Ordinary gum. Perf 14×14½.

3319B	**2500**	(1st) Queen Elizabeth II at Golden Jubilee Service, St Paul's Cathedral, London, 2002............	1·40	1·40
		b. Booklet pane. Nos. 3319B and 3323B/3325B with margins all round....................................	6·00	
		c. Booklet pane. Nos. 3319B/3320B and 3827/3828 with margins all round (4.2.22)................................	5·25	
3320B	**2501**	(1st) Queen Elizabeth II Trooping the Colour, 1967..............................	1·40	1·40
		b. Booklet pane. Nos. 3320B/3321B with margins all round....................	3·00	
3321B	**2502**	77p. Queen Elizabeth II inspecting 2nd Battalion Royal Welsh, Tidworth, 1 March 2007.........................	1·40	1·40
3322B	**2503**	77p. First Christmas Television Broadcast, 1957..............................	1·40	1·40
		b. Booklet pane. Nos. 3322B and 3326B with margins all round........	3·00	
3323B	**2504**	87p. Silver Jubilee Walkabout, 1977.......	1·40	1·40
3324B	**2505**	87p. Queen Elizabeth II in Garter Ceremony Procession, 1997...........	1·40	1·40
3325B	**2506**	£1·28 Queen Elizabeth II addressing the UN General Assembly, 1957............	1·75	1·75
3326B	**2507**	£1·28 Queen Elizabeth II at Commonwealth Games, Brisbane, Australia, 1982................................	1·75	1·75
Set of 8...			11·00	11·00

(c) Self-adhesive booklet stamp. Die-cut perf 14.

3327	**2500**	(1st) Queen Elizabeth II at Golden Jubilee Service, St Paul's Cathedral, London, 2002................	2·00	2·00
		a. Booklet pane. No. 3327×2 and No. U3274×4................................	7·50	

Nos. 3319A/3320A, 3321A/3322A, 3323A/3324A and 3325A/3326A were printed together, *se-tenant*, as horizontal pairs in sheets of 60 (2 panes 6×5).

Booklet pane Nos. 3319Bb and 3326Bb come from the £12·77 Diamond Jubilee booklet, No. DY4.

Booklet pane No. 3319Bc comes from the £19·50 Platinum Jubilee booklet, No. DY42.

No. 3327 was only issued in stamp booklet, No. PM33, originally sold for £3·60.

No. 3328 is vacant.

2507a Queen
Elizabeth II

(Des Sedley Place. Gravure Walsall)

2012 (31 May). Diamond Jubilee (4th issue). As T **2507a**. Two phosphor bands. Perf 14½×14 (with one elliptical hole in each vert side).
3329 **2507a** (1st) light brown.. 1·25 1·25
   A similar stamp was issued in No. **MS3272**.

> The stamp and pane, formerly listed as Nos. 3328/3328a have been renumbered as U3279/U3279l and will be found in the Machins section of this catalogue.

2508 Mr Bumble
(*Oliver Twist*)

2509 Mr Pickwick
(*The Pickwick Papers*)

2510 The Marchioness (*The Old Curiosity Shop*)

2511 Mrs Gamp
(*Martin Chuzzlewit*)

2512 Captain Cuttle
(*Dombey and Son*)

2513 Mr Micawber
(*David Copperfield*)

"No one who can read, ever looks at a book, even unopened on a shelf, like one who cannot."

2514 Scenes from *Nicholas Nickleby, Bleak House, Little Dorrit* and *A Tale of Two Cities*

(Des Howard Brown. Litho Cartor)

2012 (19 June). Birth Bicentenary of Charles Dickens. Illustrations from Character Sketches from Charles Dickens, *circa* 1890 by Joseph Clayton Clarke ('Kyd') (Nos. 3330/3335) or Book Illustrations by Hablot Knight Browne ('Phiz') (No. **MS3336**). Multicoloured One centre band (2nd) or 'all-over' phosphor (others). Perf 14 (Nos. 3330/3335) or 14×14½ (No. **MS3336**).
3330 **2508** (2nd) Mr Bumble (*Oliver Twist*)................... 90 90
3331 **2509** (1st) Mr Pickwick (*The Pickwick Papers*).. 1·20 1·00
3332 **2510** 77p. The Marchioness (*The Old Curiosity Shop*).................................. 1·00 1·00
3333 **2511** 87p. Mrs Gamp (*Martin Chuzzlewit*)........ 1·40 1·40
3334 **2512** £1·28 Captain Cuttle (*Dombey and Son*).. 2·00 2·00
3335 **2513** £1·90 Mr Micawber (*David Copperfield*)... 3·00 3·00
Set of 6.. 8·50 8·50
Set of 6 Gutter Pairs.. 17·00
Set of 6 Traffic Light Gutter Blocks of 4................... 38·00
First Day Cover (Tallents House)................................... 11·00
First Day Cover (Portsmouth).. 11·00
Presentation Pack (PO Pack No. 473) (Nos. 3330/3335 and **MS3336**).. 14·00
PHQ Cards (*set of 11*) (366)..................................... 4·50 17·00

MS3336 190×67 mm. **2514** Scenes from *Nicholas Nickleby, Bleak House, Little Dorrit* and *A Tale of Two Cities* (1st)×4 Nicholas Nickleby caning headmaster Wackford Squeers (*Nicholas Nickleby*); Mrs Bagnet is charmed with Mr Bucket (*Bleak House*); Amy Dorrit introduces Maggy to Arthur Clennam (*Little Dorrit*); Charles Darnay arrested by French revolutionaries (*A Tale of Two Cities*)......... 3·75 3·75
First Day Cover (Tallents House)................................ 4·50
First Day Cover (Portsmouth)..................................... 4·50
   The complete miniature sheet is shown on one of the 11 PHQ cards with the others depicting individual stamps including those from No. **MS3336**.

2435
Paralympic
Games Emblem

2436 Olympic
Games Emblem

(Litho Cartor)

2012 (27 July). Olympic and Paralympic Games (8th issue). Designs as Nos. 3250/3253. Multicoloured Two phosphor bands. Perf 14½×14 (with one elliptical hole in each vert side).
3337 **2436** (1st) Olympic Games Emblem. Black and orange-red.............. 4·00 4·00
      a. Booklet pane. Nos. 3337/3338, each×3, and 3339/3340 with central label and margins all round.............. 32·00
3338 **2435** (1st) Paralympic Games Emblem. Black and orange-red.............. 4·00 4·00
3339 **2436** (Worldwide up to 20 g) Olympic Games Emblem. Black, bright scarlet and greenish blue.................... 6·00 6·00
3340 **2435** (Worldwide up to 20 g) Paralympic Games Emblem. Black, bright scarlet and greenish blue........ 6·00 6·00
Set of 4.. 18·00 18·00
First Day Cover (Philatelic Bureau Edinburgh) (No. 3337a).. 20·00
First Day Cover (London E20) (No. 3337a).......................... 20·00
   Nos. 3339/3340 were for use on Worldwide Mail up to 20 grams.
   Nos. 3337/3340 were only issued in the £10·71 Olympic and Paralympic Games, London booklet, No. DY5.

2515 Sports and London Landmarks

(Des Hat-trick design. Litho Cartor)

2012 (27 July). Welcome to London, Olympic Games. Sheet 192×75 mm. Multicoloured 'All-over' phosphor. Perf 14½.
MS3341 **2515** Sports and London Landmarks (1st) Fencer and Tower Bridge; (1st) Athletes in race and Olympic Stadium; £1·28 Diver and Tate Modern; £1·28 Cyclist and London Eye...................................... 5·50 5·50
First Day Cover (Tallents House)................................ 10·00
First Day Cover (London E20)...................................... 10·00
Presentation Pack (PO Pack No. 474)............... 20·00
PHQ Cards (*set of 5*) (367).............................. 2·00 9·00
   The five PHQ Cards show the four individual stamps and the complete miniature sheet.

2516 Helen Glover and Heather Stanning (rowing, women's pairs)

2517 Bradley Wiggins (cycling, road, men's time trial)

2518 Tim Baillie and Etienne Stott (canoe slalom, men's canoe double (C2))

2519 Peter Wilson (shooting, shotgun men's double trap)

2520 Philip Hindes, Chris Hoy and Jason Kenny (cycling, track men's team sprint)

2521 Katherine Grainger and Anna Watkins (rowing, women's double sculls)

2522 Steven Burke, Ed Clancy, Peter Kennaugh and Geraint Thomas (cycling, track men's team pursuit)

2523 Victoria Pendleton (cycling, track women's keirin)

2524 Alex Gregory, Tom James, Pete Reed and Andrew Triggs Hodge (rowing, men's fours)

2525 Katherine Copeland and Sophie Hosking (rowing, lightweight women's double sculls)

2526 Dani King, Joanna Rowsell and Laura Trott (cycling, track women's team pursuit)

2527 Jessica Ennis (athletics, combined women's heptathlon)

2528 Greg Rutherford (athletics, field men's long jump)

2529 Mo Farah (athletics, track men's 10,000 m)

2530 Ben Ainslie (sailing, Finn men's heavyweight dinghy)

2531 Andy Murray (tennis, men's singles)

2532 Scott Brash, Peter Charles, Ben Maher and Nick Skelton (equestrian, jumping team)

2533 Jason Kenny (cycling, track men's sprint)

2534 Alistair Brownlee (men's triathlon)

2535 Carl Hester, Laura Bechtolsheimer and Charlotte Dujardin (equestrian, dressage team)

2536 Laura Trott (cycling, track women's omnium)

2537 Chris Hoy (cycling, track men's keirin)

2538 Charlotte Dujardin (equestrian, dressage individual)

2539 Nicola Adams (boxing, women's fly weight)

2540 Jade Jones (taekwondo, women's under 57 kg)

2541 Ed McKeever (canoe sprint, men's kayak single (K1) 200 m)

2542 Mo Farah (athletics, track men's 5000 m)

2543 Luke Campbell (boxing, men's bantam weight)

2544 Anthony Joshua (boxing, men's super heavy weight)

(Des True North and Royal Mail. Litho with digital overprint Walsall and six regional printers)

2012 (2 Aug–1 Sept). British Gold Medal Winners at London Olympic Games. Self-adhesive. Multicoloured Two phosphor panels. Die-cut perf 15×14½.

3342	**2516**	(1st) Helen Glover and Heather Stanning...............	1·25	1·25
		a. Sheetlet. No. 3342×6........	6·75	6·75
3343	**2517**	(1st) Bradley Wiggins (1.9.12).............	1·25	1·25
		a. Sheetlet. No. 3343×6........	6·75	6·75
3344	**2518**	(1st) Tim Baillie and Etienne Stott (3.8.12).............	1·25	1·25
		a. Sheetlet. No. 3344×6........	6·75	6·75
3345	**2519**	(1st) Peter Wilson (3.8.12).............	1·25	1·25
		a. Sheetlet. No. 3345×6........	6·75	6·75
3346	**2520**	(1st) Philip Hindes, Chris Hoy and Jason Kenny (3.8.12).............	1·25	1·25
		a. Sheetlet. No. 3346×6........	6·75	6·75
3347	**2521**	(1st) Katherine Grainger and Anna Watkins (4.8.12).............	1·25	1·25
		a. Sheetlet. No. 3347×6........	6·75	6·75
3348	**2522**	(1st) Steven Burke, Ed Clancy, Peter Kennaugh and Geraint Thomas (4.8.12).............	1·25	1·25
		a. Sheetlet. No. 3348×6........	6·75	6·75
		b. Phosphor omitted.............	35·00	
3349	**2523**	(1st) Victoria Pendleton (4.8.12)..........	1·25	1·25
		a. Sheetlet. No. 3349×6........	6·75	6·75
		b. Phosphor omitted.............	35·00	
3350	**2524**	(1st) Alex Gregory, Tom James, Pete Reed and Andrew Triggs Hodge (5.8.12).............	1·25	1·25
		a. Sheetlet. No. 3350×6........	6·75	6·75
		b. Phosphor omitted.............	35·00	
3351	**2525**	(1st) Katherine Copeland and Sophie Hosking (5.8.12).............	1·25	1·25
		a. Sheetlet. No. 3351×6........	6·75	6·75
		ab. Black ptg double.............		
		b. Phosphor omitted.............	35·00	
3352	**2526**	(1st) Dani King, Joanna Rowsell and Laura Trott (5.8.12).............	1·25	1·25
		a. Sheetlet. No. 3352×6........	6·75	6·75
		b. Phosphor omitted.............	35·00	
3353	**2527**	(1st) Jessica Ennis (5.8.12).............	1·25	1·25
		a. Sheetlet. No. 3353×6........	6·75	6·75
		b. Phosphor omitted.............	35·00	
3354	**2528**	(1st) Greg Rutherford (5.8.12)..........	1·25	1·25
		a. Sheetlet. No. 3354×6........	6·75	6·75
3355	**2529**	(1st) Mo Farah (5.8.12).............	1·25	1·25
		a. Sheetlet. No. 3355×6........	6·75	6·75
3356	**2530**	(1st) Ben Ainslie (6.8.12).............	1·25	1·25
		a. Sheetlet. No. 3356×6........	6·75	6·75
3357	**2531**	(1st) Andy Murray (6.8.12).............	1·25	1·25
		a. Sheetlet. No. 3357×6........	6·75	6·75
3358	**2532**	(1st) Scott Brash, Peter Charles, Ben Maher and Nick Skelton (7.8.12)......	1·25	1·25
		a. Sheetlet. No. 3358×6........	6·75	6·75
3359	**2533**	(1st) Jason Kenny (7.8.12).............	1·25	1·25
		a. Sheetlet. No. 3359×6........	6·75	6·75
3360	**2534**	(1st) Alistair Brownlee (8.8.12).............	1·25	1·25
		a. Sheetlet. No. 3360×6........	6·75	6·75
3361	**2535**	(1st) Carl Hester, Laura Bechtolsheimer and Charlotte Dujardin (8.8.12)......	1·25	1·25
		a. Sheetlet. No. 3361×6........	6·75	6·75
3362	**2536**	(1st) Laura Trott (8.8.12).............	1·25	1·25
		a. Sheetlet. No. 3362×6........	6·75	6·75
3363	**2537**	(1st) Chris Hoy (8.8.12).............	1·25	1·25
		a. Sheetlet. No. 3363×6........	6·75	6·75
3364	**2538**	(1st) Charlotte Dujardin (10.8.12)..........	1·25	1·25
		a. Sheetlet. No. 3364×6........	6·75	6·75
3365	**2539**	(1st) Nicola Adams (10.8.12)..........	1·25	1·25
		a. Sheetlet. No. 3365×6........	6·75	6·75
3366	**2540**	(1st) Jade Jones (10.8.12)..........	1·25	1·25
		a. Sheetlet. No. 3366×6........	6·75	6·75
3367	**2541**	(1st) Ed McKeever (12.8.12)..........	1·25	1·25
		a. Sheetlet. No. 3367×6........	6·75	6·75
		ab. Black printed double..........		
		ac. Types **2541** and **2542** printed together on the same stamps........		
3368	**2542**	(1st) Mo Farah (12.8.12)..........	1·25	1·25
		a. Sheetlet. No. 3368×6........	6·75	6·75
		ab. Black printed double..........		
3369	**2543**	(1st) Luke Campbell (12.8.12)..........	1·25	1·25
		a. Sheetlet. No. 3369×6........	6·75	6·75
3370	**2544**	(1st) Anthony Joshua (13.8.12)..........	1·25	1·25
		a. Sheetlet. No. 3370×6........	6·75	6·75
Set of 29 Single Stamps.............			35·00	35·00
3342a/3370a *Set of* 29 sheetlets.............			£175	£175
First Day Covers (Tallents House) or (London E20) (Sheetlets, Nos. 3342a/3370a) (29).............				£250
First Day Cover (Tallents House) (any single gold medal stamp).............				4·25
First Day Cover (London E20) (any single gold medal stamp).............				4·25

The self-adhesive base sheetlets for Nos. 3342/3370 were produced by Walsall with the image, name and event of the winning athletes digitally printed by regional printers in six different locations: Attleborough, Edinburgh, London, Preston, Solihull and Swindon.

Nos. 3368/3370 were not produced by the Preston printer due to machinery breakdown.

Post office sheets comprised four sheetlets of six stamps (3×2), the sheetlets being separated by roulettes. The four sheetlets had one of the following inscriptions on the left margin: emblem 'TEAM GB' and Olympic rings; 'The XXX Olympiad'; barcode; Sheet number, Issue date and Printer location.

Individual stamps had to be cut from the sheetlets using scissors.

Stamps for Royal Mail first day covers came from special coil printings on non-phosphor paper, so all stamps exist, phosphor omitted, used, from this source.

Nos. 3348b/3353b were subsequently released to the trade in unused coils.

2545 Paralympic Sports and London Landmarks (*Illustration reduced. Actual size 193×75 mm*)

(Des Pearce Marchbank. Litho Cartor)

2012 (29 Aug). Welcome to London, Paralympic Games. Sheet 193×75 mm. Multicoloured 'All-over' phosphor. Perf 14½.

MS3371 **2545** Paralympic Sports and London Landmarks (1st) Athlete wearing running blades and Olympic Stadium; (1st) Wheelchair basketball player and Palace of Westminster; £1·28 Powerlifter, Millennium Bridge and St Paul's Cathedral; £1·28 Cyclist and London Eye.............		5·50	5·50
First Day Cover (Tallents House).............			10·00
First Day Cover (London E20).............			10·00
Presentation Pack (PO Pack No. 475).............		9·00	
PHQ Cards (set of 5) (368).............		2·00	9·00

The five PHQ Cards show the four individual stamps and the complete miniature sheet.

2546 Sarah Storey (cycling, track women's C5 pursuit)

2547 Jonathan Fox (swimming, men's 100 m backstroke, S7)

2548 Mark Colbourne (cycling, track men's C1 pursuit)

2549 Hannah Cockroft (athletics, track women's 100 m, T34)

2550 Neil Fachie and Barney Storey (cycling, men's B 1 km time trial)

2551 Richard Whitehead (athletics, track men's 200 m, T42)

2552 Natasha Baker (equestrian, individual championship test, grade II)

2553 Sarah Storey (cycling : track women's C4-5 500 m time trial)

2554 Ellie Simmonds (swimming, women's 400 m freestyle, S6)

2555 Pamela Relph, Naomi Riches, James Roe, David Smith and Lily van den Broecke (rowing, mixed coxed four, LTAmix4+)

2556 Aled Davies (athletics, field men's discus, F42)

2557 Anthony Kappes and Craig MacLean (cycling, track men's B sprint)

2558 Jessica-Jane Applegate (swimming, women's 200 m freestyle, S14)

2559 Sophie Christiansen (equestrian, individual championship test, grade 1a)

2560 David Weir (athletics, track men's 5000 m, T54)

2561 *Natasha Baker (equestrian, individual freestyle test, grade II)*

2562 *Ellie Simmonds (swimming, women's 200 m individual medley, SM6)*

2563 *Mickey Bushell (athletics, track men's 100 m, T53)*

2564 Danielle Brown (archery, women's individual compound, open)

2565 Heather Frederiksen (swimming, women's 100 m backstroke, S8)

2566 Sophie Christiansen (equestrian, individual freestyle test, grade 1a)

2567 David Weir (athletics, track men's 1500 m, T54)

2568 Sarah Storey (cycling, road women's C5 time trial)

2569 Ollie Hynd (swimming, men's 200 m individual medley, SM8)

2570 Sophie Christiansen, Deb Criddle, Lee Pearson and Sophie Wells (equestrian team, open)

2571 Helena Lucas (sailing, single-person keelboat, 2·4mR)

2572 Sarah Storey (cycling, road women's C4-5 road race)

2573 Josef Craig (swimming, men's 400 m freestyle, S7)

2574 Hannah Cockroft (athletics, track women's 200 m, T34)

2575 David Weir (athletics, track men's 800 m, T54)

2576 Jonnie Peacock (athletics, track men's 100 m, T44)

2577 Josie Pearson (athletics, field women's discus, F51/52/53)

2578 David Stone (cycling, road mixed T1-2 road race)

2579 David Weir (athletics, road men's marathon, T54)

(Des True North and Royal Mail. Litho with digital overprint Walsall and six regional printers)

2012 (31 Aug–10 Sept). British Gold Medal Winners at London Paralympic Games. Self-adhesive. Multicoloured Two phosphor panels. Die-cut Perf 15×14½.

3372	2546	(1st) Sarah Storey.....................	1·25	1·25
		a. Sheetlet. No. 3372×2..........	2·50	2·50
3373	2547	(1st) Jonathan Fox (1.9.12).....................	1·25	1·25
		a. Sheetlet. No. 3373×2..........	2·50	2·50
3374	2548	(1st) Mark Colbourne (3.9.12)........	1·25	1·25
		a. Sheetlet. No. 3374×2..........	2·50	2·50
3375	2549	(1st) Hannah Cockroft (3.9.12).......	1·25	1·25
		a. Sheetlet. No. 3375×2..........	2·50	2·50
3376	2550	(1st) Neil Fachie and Barney Storey (3.9.12)......................	1·25	1·25
		a. Sheetlet. No. 3376×2..........	2·50	2·50
3377	2551	(1st) Richard Whitehead (3.9.12)............	1·25	1·25
		a. Sheetlet. No. 3377×2..........	2·50	2·50
3378	2552	(1st) Natasha Baker (3.9.12)........	1·25	1·25
		a. Sheetlet. No. 3378×2..........	2·50	2·50
3379	2553	(1st) Sarah Storey (3.9.12)........	1·25	1·25
		a. Sheetlet. No. 3379×2..........	2·50	2·50
3380	2554	(1st) Ellie Simmonds (3.9.12).......	1·25	1·25
		a. Sheetlet. No. 3380×2..........	2·50	2·50
3381	2555	(1st) Pamela Relph, Naomi Riches, James Roe, David Smith and Lily van den Broecke (4.9.12)........	1·25	1·25
		a. Sheetlet. No. 3381×2..........	2·50	2·50
3382	2556	(1st) Aled Davies (4.9.12).......	1·25	1·25
		a. Sheetlet. No. 3382×2..........	2·50	2·50
3383	2557	(1st) Anthony Kappes and Craig MacLean (4.9.12).......	1·25	1·25
		a. Sheetlet. No. 3383×2..........	2·50	2·50
3384	2558	(1st) Jessica-Jane Applegate (4.9.12)......	1·25	1·25
		a. Sheetlet. No. 3384×2..........	2·50	2·50
3385	2559	(1st) Sophie Christiansen (4.9.12)...........	1·25	1·25
		a. Sheetlet. No. 3385×2..........	2·50	2·50
3386	2560	(1st) David Weir (4.9.12)........	1·25	1·25
		a. Sheetlet. No. 3386×2..........	2·50	2·50
3387	2561	(1st) Natasha Baker (4.9.12)........	1·25	1·25
		a. Sheetlet. No. 3387×2..........	2·50	2·50
3388	2562	(1st) Ellie Simmonds (4.9.12).......	1·25	1·25
		a. Sheetlet. No. 3388×2..........	2·50	2·50
3389	2563	(1st) Mickey Bushell (5.9.12)..........	1·25	1·25
		a. Sheetlet. No. 3389×2..........	2·50	2·50
3390	2564	(1st) Danielle Brown (5.9.12).......	1·25	1·25
		a. Sheetlet. No. 3390×2..........	2·50	2·50
3391	2565	(1st) Heather Frederiksen (5.9.12)...........	1·25	1·25
		a. Sheetlet. No. 3391×2..........	2·50	2·50
3392	2566	(1st) Sophie Christiansen (5.9.12)...........	1·25	1·25
		a. Sheetlet. No. 3392×2..........	2·50	2·50
3393	2567	(1st) David Weir (7.9.12)........	1·25	1·25
		a. Sheetlet. No. 3393×2..........	2·50	2·50
3394	2568	(1st) Sarah Storey (7.9.12)........	1·25	1·25
		a. Sheetlet. No. 3394×2..........	2·50	2·50
3395	2569	(1st) Ollie Hynd (7.9.12)........	1·25	1·25
		a. Sheetlet. No. 3395×2..........	2·50	2·50
3396	2570	(1st) Sophie Christiansen, Deb Criddle, Lee Pearson and Sophie Wells (7.9.12)........	1·25	1·25
		a. Sheetlet. No. 3396×2..........	2·50	2·50
3397	2571	(1st) Helena Lucas (8.9.12)........	1·25	1·25
		a. Sheetlet. No. 3397×2..........	2·50	2·50
3398	2572	(1st) Sarah Storey (8.9.12)........	1·25	1·25
		a. Sheetlet. No. 3398×2..........	2·50	2·50
3399	2573	(1st) Josef Craig (8.9.12)........	1·25	1·25
		a. Sheetlet. No. 3399×2..........	2·50	2·50
3400	2574	(1st) Hannah Cockroft (8.9.12).......	1·25	1·25
		a. Sheetlet. No. 3400×2..........	2·50	2·50
3401	2575	(1st) David Weir (10.9.12)........	1·25	1·25
		a. Sheetlet. No. 3401×2..........	2·50	2·50

3402	2576	(1st) Jonnie Peacock (10.9.12).................	1·25	1·25
		a. Sheetlet. No. 3402×2..........	2·50	2·50
3403	2577	(1st) Josie Pearson (10.9.12)........	1·25	1·25
		a. Sheetlet. No. 3403×2..........	2·50	2·50
3404	2578	(1st) David Stone (10.9.12)........	1·25	1·25
		a. Sheetlet. No. 3404×2..........	2·50	2·50
3405	2579	(1st) David Weir (10.9.12)........	1·25	1·25
		a. Sheetlet. No. 3405×2..........	2·50	2·50

Set of 34.. 40·00 40·00
3372a/3405a *Set of 34 sheetlets*.................. 78·00 78·00
First Day Covers (Tallents House) (Sheetlets Nos.
3372a/3405a) (34).. £125
First Day Covers (London E20) (Sheetlets Nos.
3372a/3405a) (34).. £125
First Day Covers (Tallents House) (any single gold
medal stamp).. 4·25
First Day Covers (London E20) (any single gold medal
stamp)... 4·25

The self-adhesive base sheetlets for Nos. 3372/3405 were produced by Walsall with the image, name and event of the winning athletes digitally printed by regional printers in six different locations: Attleborough, Edinburgh, London, Preston, Solihull and Swindon.

These sheetlets of 16 stamps were divided by roulettes into eight panes of two stamps (1×2). The left margins were inscribed as follows (reading downwards): emblem and 'ParalympicsGB'; 'London 2012 Paralympic Games'; barcode; Sheet number, Issue date and Printer location.

Nos. 3372, 3373 and 3405 were each printed in separate sheetlets of 16 stamps.

Nos. 3374/3377, 3381/3384, 3385/3388, 3389/3392, 3393/3396, 3397/3400 and 3401/3404 were printed in sheetlets of 16 containing four stamps of each design.

The sheetlets of 16 containing Nos. 3378/3380 contained four each of Nos. 3378/3379 and eight of No. 3380.

2580 Scenes from Olympic and Paralympic Games

Des The Chase. Litho Walsall)

2012 (27 Sept). Memories of London 2012 Olympic and Paralympic Games. Sheet 192×75 mm. Multicoloured 'All-over' phosphor. Perf 14½.
MS3406 **2580** Scenes from Olympic and Paralympic Games (1st) Procession of athletes, Paralympic Games; (1st) Games makers and Olympic Stadium; £1·28 Opening ceremony of Paralympic Games; £1·28 Olympic Games closing ceremony and handover to Rio.. 9·00 9·00
First Day Cover (Tallents House).. 13·00
First Day Cover (London E20).. 13·00
Presentation Pack (PO Pack No. 476)................... 17·50
PHQ Cards (set of 5) (369)............................. 2·00 16·50

The five PHQ Cards show the four individual stamps and the complete miniature sheet.

2581 BR Class D34 Nos. 62471 *Glen Falloch* and 62496 *Glen Loy* at Ardlui, 9 May 1959

(Gravure Walsall)

2012 (27 Sept). Classic Locomotives of Scotland. Booklet stamp. Design as 1st class stamp within No. **MS**3283. Self-adhesive. Multicoloured 'All-over' phosphor. Die-cut perf 14.
3407 **2581** (1st) BR Class D34 Nos. 62471 *Glen Falloch* and 62496 *Glen Loy*............. 2·00 2·00
a. Booklet pane. No. 3407×2 and U3274×4... 7·50

No. 3407 was only issued in booklet, No. PM34, originally sold for £3·60.

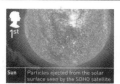

2582 Sun and Particles ejected from Solar Surface seen from SOHO Observatory

2583 Venus with Clouds in Southern Hemisphere seen from *Venus Express*

2584 Ice in Martian Impact Crater seen from *Mars Express*

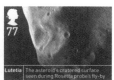

2585 Surface of Asteroid Lutetia seen from *Rosetta* Probe

2586 Saturn and its Rings seen from *Cassini* Satellite

2587 Titan (Saturn's largest moon) seen from *Huygens* Probe

(Des Osborne Ross Design. Litho Cartor)

2012 (16 Oct). Space Science. Multicoloured 'All-over' phosphor. Perf 14.

3408	**2582**	(1st) Sun	1·20	1·00
3409	**2583**	(1st) Venus	1·20	1·00
3410	**2584**	77p. Ice in Martian Impact Crater	1·25	1·25
3411	**2585**	77p. Surface of Asteroid Lutetia	1·25	1·25
3412	**2586**	£1·28 Saturn and its Rings	2·00	2·00
3413	**2587**	£1·28 Titan (Saturn's largest moon)	2·00	2·00

Set of 6			8·00	7·50
Set of 6 Gutter Pairs			16·00	
First Day Cover (Tallents House)				9·75
First Day Cover (Star, Gaerwen Gwynnedd)				9·75
Presentation Pack (PO Pack No. 477)			8·75	
PHQ Cards (set of 6) (370)			2·40	9·00

2588 Six Poppies on Barbed Wire Stems

(Des Hat-trick Design. Gravure Walsall)

2012 (23 Oct). Lest We Forget (4th issue). Self-adhesive. Multicoloured Two phosphor bands. Die-cut perf 14½×14 (with one elliptical hole in each vert side).

3414	**2588**	(1st) Six Poppies on Barbed Wire Stems	1·25	1·25

For T **2588** with ordinary gum, see No. 3717.

2589 Reindeer with Decorated Antlers

2590 Santa with Robin

2591 Reindeer with Decorated Antlers

2592 Snowman and Penguin

2593 Santa with Robin

2594 Robin with Star Decoration in Beak

2595 Cat and Mouse decorating Christmas Tree

(Des Axel Scheffler and Webb and Webb Design. Gravure Walsall (Nos. 3415a, 3416a) or De La Rue (others))

2012 (6 Nov). Christmas. Illustrations by Axel Scheffler. Multicoloured One centre band (No. 3415) or two phosphor bands (others).

(a) Self-adhesive. Die-cut perf 14½×14 (with elliptcal hole on each vert side).

3415	**2589**	(2nd) Reindeer with Decorated Antlers	90	90
		a. Booklet pane. No. 3415×12	13·50	
3416	**2590**	(1st) Santa with Robin	1·20	1·00
		a. Booklet pane. No. 3416×12	16·00	
3417	**2591**	(2nd Large) Reindeer with Decorated Antlers	1·25	1·10
3418	**2592**	87p. Snowman and Penguin	1·40	1·40
3419	**2593**	(1st Large) Santa with Robin	1·70	1·40
3420	**2594**	£1·28 Robin with Star Decoration in Beak	2·00	2·00
3421	**2595**	£1·90 Cat and Mouse decorating Christmas Tree	3·00	3·00

Set of 7			10·00	9·75
First Day Cover (Tallents House)				12·50
First Day Cover (Bethlehem, Llandeilo)				12·50
Presentation Pack (PO Pack No. 478)			11·00	
PHQ Cards (set of 8) (371)			3·25	21·00

(b) Ordinary gum. Perf 14½×14.

MS3422	115×102 mm. As Nos. 3415/3421		10·00	9·75
First Day Cover (Tallents House)				10·00
First Day Cover (Bethlehem, Llandeilo)				10·00

The 2nd class, 1st class, 87p. and £1·28 stamps were also issued in sheets of 20 (No. LS83) containing 8×2nd class, 8×1st class, 2×87p. and 2×£1·28 stamps, each with a *se-tenant* label. These sheets were printed in lithography and sold for £13·10 each.

Separate sheets of 20×2nd, 20×1st, 10×1st, 10×87p. and 10×£1·28 were available with personal photographs on the labels from Royal Mail, Edinburgh. These were sold at £13·99 for 20×2nd, £18·25 for 20×1st, £9·99 for 10×1st, £13·55 for 10×87p. and £18·50 for 10×£1·28.

The 1st class stamp printed in lithography, from either Post Office label sheets or Personalised Smilers sheets is known with the black printing double.

The eight PHQ cards depict the seven individual stamps and the miniature sheet.

Year Pack

2012 (6 Nov). Comprises Nos. 3254/3259, **MS**3264/**MS**3270, **MS**3272/3307, 3309/3318, 3319A/3326A, 3330/3336, **MS**3341, **MS**3371, **MS**3406, 3408/3413 and 3415/3421

CP3422a	Year Pack (Pack No. 479) *(sold for £80)*	£125

Post Office Yearbook

2012 (6 Nov). Comprises Nos. 3254/3259, **MS**3264/**MS**3270, **MS**3272/3307, 3309/3318, 3319A/3326A, 3330/3336, **MS**3341, **MS**3371, **MS**3406, 3408/3413 and 3415/3421

YB3422a	Yearbook *(sold for £90)*	£140

Miniature Sheet Collection

2012 (6 Nov). Comprises Nos. **MS**3264, **MS**3270, **MS**3272, **MS**3283, **MS**3336, **MS**3341, **MS**3371, **MS**3406 and **MS**3422

MS3422a	Miniature Sheet Collection *(sold for £35)*	55·00

2596 Steam Locomotive on Metropolitan Railway, 1863

2597 Navvies excavating 'Deep Cut' Tube Tunnel, 1898

2598 Commuters in Carriage, 1911

2599 Boston Manor Art Deco Station, 1934

2600 Train on 'Deep Cut' Line, 1938

2601 Canary Wharf Station, 1999

2602 Classic London Underground Posters

(Des NB Studios (No. **MS**3429) or Hat-trick Design (others). Litho Cartor (Nos. 3423/3429) or gravure Walsall (No. 3430))

2013 (9 Jan). 150th Anniversary of the London Underground. Multicoloured One centre band (2nd) or 'all-over' phosphor (others).

(a) Ordinary gum. Perf 14½.

3423	**2596**	(2nd) Steam Locomotive on Metropolitan Railway......................	90	90
3424	**2597**	(2nd) Navvies excavating Deep Cut Tube Tunnel.............................	90	90
3425	**2598**	(1st) Commuters in Carriage..................	1·20	1·00
3426	**2599**	(1st) Boston Manor Art Deco Station.....	1·20	1·00
3427	**2600**	£1·28 Train on Deep Cut Line......................	2·00	2·00
3428	**2601**	£1·28 Canary Wharf Station......................	2·00	2·00
Set of 6...			7·25	7·00
Set of 6 Gutter Pairs..			14·50	
First Day Cover (Tallents House).............................				8·75
First Day Cover (London W2)................................				8·75
Presentation Pack (PO Pack No. 480) (Nos. 3423/3428 and **MS**3429)..			15·00	
PHQ Cards (set of 6) (372).................................			4·50	18·00

MS3429 184×74 mm. **2602** Classic London Underground Posters (1st) Golders Green, 1908, By Underground to fresh air (Maxwell Armfield), 1915 and Summer Sales (Mary Koop), 1925; 77p. For the Zoo (Charles Paine), 1921, Power (Edward McKnight-Kauffer), 1931 and The Seen (James Fitton), 1948; 87p. A train every 90 seconds (Abram Games), 1937, Thanks to the Underground (Zero (Hans Schleger), 1935 and Cut travelling time, Victoria Line (Tom Eckersley), 1969; £1·28 The London Transport Collection (Tom Eckersley), 1975, London Zoo (Abram Games), 1976 and The Tate Gallery by Tube (David Booth), 1987..................

	5·00	5·25
First Day Cover (Tallents House)...........................		6·50
First Day Cover (London W2)...............................		6·50

(b) Self-adhesive. Die-cut perf 14½. Die-cut perf 14½.

3430	**2599**	(1st) Boston Manor Art Deco Station, 1934..	2·00	2·00
		a. Booklet pane. Nos. 3430×2 and U3022×4...	7·50	

No. 3430 was issued in stamp booklet, No. PM35, originally sold for £3·60.

The complete miniature sheet is shown on one of the 11 PHQ cards with the others depicting individual stamps, including those from No. **MS**3429.

2603 Elinor and Marianne Dashwood *(Sense and Sensibility)*

2604 Elizabeth Bennet and Portrait of Mr Darcy *(Pride and Prejudice)*

2605 Fanny Price *(Mansfield Park)*

2606 Emma Woodhouse and Mr Knightley *(Emma)*

2607 Catherine Morland *(Northanger Abbey)*

2608 Anne Elliot and Captain Wentworth *(Persuasion)*

(Des Angela Barrett and Webb and Webb. Litho Cartor)

2013 (21 Feb). Bicentenary of the Publication of Jane Austen's *Pride and Prejudice*. Multicoloured 'All-over' phosphor. Perf 14.

3431	**2603**	(1st) Elinor and Marianne Dashwood.....	1·20	1·00
3432	**2604**	(1st) Elizabeth Bennet and Portrait of Mr Darcy...	1·20	1·00
3433	**2605**	77p. Fanny Price.....................................	1·25	1·25
3434	**2606**	77p. Emma Woodhouse and Mr Knightley..	1·25	1·25
3435	**2607**	£1·28 Catherine Morland.......................	2·00	2·00
3436	**2608**	£1·28 Anne Elliot and Captain Wentworth..	2·00	2·00
Set of 6...			7·75	7·50
Set of 6 Gutter Pairs..			15·50	
Set of 6 Traffic Light Gutter Pairs............................			32·00	
First Day Cover (Tallents House).............................				10·00
First Day Cover (Steventon, Basingstoke)................				10·00
Presentation Pack (PO Pack No. 481).......................			9·00	
PHQ Cards (set of 6) (373).................................			2·50	9·25

2609 The 11th Doctor (Matt Smith, 2010–2014)

2610 The Tenth Doctor (David Tennant, 2005–2010)

2611 The Ninth Doctor (Christopher Eccleston, 2005)

2612 The Eighth Doctor (Paul McGann, 1996)

2613 The Seventh Doctor (Sylvester McCoy, 1987–1989)

2614 The Sixth Doctor (Colin Baker, 1984–1986)

2615 The Fifth Doctor (Peter Davison, 1982–1984)

2616 The Fourth Doctor (Tom Baker, 1974–1981)

2617 The Third Doctor (Jon Pertwee, 1970–1974)

2618 The Second Doctor (Patrick Troughton, 1966–1969)

2619 The First Doctor (William Hartnell, 1963–1966)

2620 Tardis

3442	**2614**	(1st) Colin Baker	1·20	1·00
3443	**2615**	(1st) Peter Davison	1·20	1·00
3444	**2616**	(1st) Tom Baker	1·20	1·00
		a. Horiz strip of 4. Nos. 3444/3447	4·25	4·00
		b. Booklet pane. Nos. 3444/3447	4·25	
3445	**2617**	(1st) Jon Pertwee	1·20	1·00
3446	**2618**	(1st) Patrick Troughton	1·20	1·00
3447	**2619**	(1st) William Hartnell	1·20	1·00
Set of 11			12·00	10·00
Set of 1 Gutter Strip of 3 and 2 Gutter Strips of 8			24·00	
First Day Covers (Tallents House) (2)				12·00
First Day Covers (Cardiff) (2)				12·00
Presentation Pack (PO Pack No. 482) (Nos. 3437/3447 and **MS**3451)			18·00	
PHQ Cards (set of 17)			6·75	18·50

(b) *Self-adhesive. One centre band (2nd) or two bands. Die-cut perf 14½ (2nd) or 14½×14 (with one elliptical hole in each vert side) (1st).*

3448	**2609**	(1st) Matt Smith	4·50	4·50
		a. Booklet pane. No. 3448, 3449×4 and 3450	14·00	
3449	**2620**	(1st) Tardis	1·25	1·25
3450	**2619**	(1st) William Hartnell	4·50	4·50
MS3451		115×89 mm. **2621** *Dr Who* 1963–2013 (2nd) Dalek; (2nd) The Ood; (2nd) Weeping Angel; (2nd) Cyberman; (1st) TARDIS	5·00	4·75
		a. Booklet pane. As No. **MS**3451 but 119×96 mm, with line of roulettes at left	8·00	
First Day Cover (Tallents House)				5·00
First Day Cover (Cardiff)				5·00

Nos. 3437/3439 were printed together, *se-tenant*, as horizontal strips of three stamps in sheets of 48 (2 panes 6×4).

Nos. 3440/3443 and 3444/3447 were each printed together, *se-tenant*, as horizontal strips of four stamps in sheets of 48 (2 panes 4×6).

Nos. 3448/3450 were issued in stamp booklet, No. PM36, sold for £3·60. Booklet panes Nos. 3437b, 3440b and 3444b come from the £13.77 50th Anniversary of Doctor Who booklet, No. DY6.

The 1st class TARDIS stamp from booklet pane No. **MS**3451a differs from the same design in the miniature sheet by being perforated 15 all round.

The design area of No. 3449 measures 17½×21½ mm, slightly larger than the same TARDIS design (T **2620**) from the miniature sheet and premium booklet pane (Nos. **MS**3451/**MS**3451a) which measures 17×21mm. (All are 20×24 mm measured perf to edge.)

The 1st class TARDIS stamp was also issued in sheets of 20, each stamp accompanied by a *se-tenant* label (No. LS85). These sheets were printed in lithography.

The complete miniature sheet is shown on one of the 17 PHQ cards with the others depicting individual stamps including those from the miniature sheet.

(Des GBH. Litho Cartor)

2013 (26 Mar). 50th Anniversary of *Doctor Who* (TV programme) (2nd issue). As No. 3449 but ordinary gum. Multicoloured Two phosphor bands. Perf 14½×14 with one elliptical hole in each vertical side

3452	**2620**	(1st) Tardis	1·25	1·25

No. 3452 only comes from pane No. U3072I in the £13·37 *Dr Who* premium booklet, No. DY6.

2621 *Dr Who* 1963–2013

(Des GBH. Litho Cartor (Nos. 3437/3447 and **MS**3451a) or gravure Walsall (Nos. 3448/3450) or Enschedé (No. **MS**3451))

2013 (26 Mar). 50th Anniversary of *Doctor Who* (TV programme) (1st issue). Multicoloured 'All-over' phosphor.

(a) *Ordinary gum. 'All-over' phosphor. Perf 14.*

3437	**2609**	(1st) Matt Smith	1·20	1·00
		a. Horiz strip of 3. Nos. 3437/3439	3·50	3·00
		b. Booklet pane. Nos. 3437/3439	3·50	
3438	**2610**	(1st) David Tennant	1·20	1·00
3439	**2611**	(1st) Christopher Eccleston	1·20	1·00
3440	**2612**	(1st) Paul McGann	1·20	1·00
		a. Horiz strip of 4. Nos. 3440/3443	4·25	4·00
		b. Booklet pane. Nos. 3440/3443	4·25	
3441	**2613**	(1st) Sylvester McCoy	1·20	1·00

2622 Norman Parkinson (1913–1990, portrait and fashion photographer)

2623 Vivien Leigh (1913–1967, actress)

2624 Peter Cushing (1913–1994, actor)

2625 David Lloyd George (1863–1945, Prime Minister 1916–1922)

2626 Elizabeth David
(1913–1992, cookery writer)

2627 John Archer
(1863–1932, politician and
civil rights campaigner)

2628 Benjamin Britten
(1913–1976, composer and
pianist)

2629 Mary Leakey
(1913–1996, archaeologist
and anthropologist)

2630 Bill Shankly
(1913–1981, football player
and manager)

2631 Richard Dimbleby
(1913–1965, journalist and
broadcaster)

(Des Together Design. Litho Cartor)

2013 (16 Apr). Great Britons. Multicoloured 'All-over' phosphor. Perf 14½.

3453	2622	(1st) Norman Parkinson	1·20	1·00
		a. Horiz strip of 5. Nos. 3453/3457	5·25	4·50
3454	2623	(1st) Vivien Leigh	1·20	1·00
3455	2624	(1st) Peter Cushing	1·20	1·00
3456	2625	(1st) David Lloyd George	1·20	1·00
3457	2626	(1st) Elizabeth David	1·20	1·00
3458	2627	(1st) John Archer	1·20	1·00
		a. Horiz strip of 5. Nos. 3458/3462	5·25	4·50
3459	2628	(1st) Benjamin Britten	1·20	1·00
3460	2629	(1st) Mary Leakey	1·20	1·00
3461	2630	(1st) Bill Shankly	1·20	1·00
3462	2631	(1st) Richard Dimbleby	1·20	1·00
Set of 10			10·50	9·00
Set of 2 Gutter Strips of 10			21·00	
First Day Cover (Tallents House)				11·00
First Day Cover (Great Ness, Shrewsbury)				11·00
Presentation Pack (PO Pack No. 483)			11·00	
PHQ Cards (set of 10) (375)			4·00	12·00

Nos. 3453/3457 and 3458/3462 were each printed together, *se-tenant*,
as horizontal strips of five stamps in sheets of 50 (2 panes 5×5).

2632 Jimmy Greaves
(England)

2633 John Charles
(Wales)

2634 Gordon Banks
(England)

2635 George Best
(Northern Ireland)

2636 John Barnes
(England)

2637 Kevin Keegan
(England)

2638 Denis Law
(Scotland)

2639 Bobby Moore
(England)

2640 Bryan Robson
(England)

2641 Dave Mackay
(Scotland)

2642 Bobby Charlton
(England)

(Des Andrew Kinsman and True North. Litho Cartor (Nos. 3463/3474)
or gravure Walsall (Nos. 3475/3476))

2013 (9 May)–**2014**. Football Heroes (1st issue). Multicoloured 'All-over'
phosphor.

(a) Ordinary gum. Perf 14½.

3463	2632	(1st) Jimmy Greaves	1·20	1·00
		a. Horiz strip of 5. Nos. 3463/3467	5·50	4·50
3464	2633	(1st) John Charles	1·20	1·00
3465	2634	(1st) Gordon Banks	1·20	1·00
3466	2635	(1st) George Best	1·20	1·00
3467	2636	(1st) John Barnes	1·20	1·00
3468	2637	(1st) Kevin Keegan	1·20	1·00
		a. Horiz strip of 6. Nos. 3468/3473	6·50	5·50
3469	2638	(1st) Denis Law	1·20	1·00
3470	2639	(1st) Bobby Moore	1·20	1·00
3471	2640	(1st) Bryan Robson	1·20	1·00
3472	2641	(1st) Dave Mackay	1·20	1·00
3473	2642	(1st) Bobby Charlton	1·20	1·00
Set of 11			12·00	10·00
Set of 1 Gutter Strip of 12 and 1 Gutter Strip of 10			24·00	
First Day Cover (Tallents House)				11·00
First Day Cover (Wembley, Middlesex)				11·00
Presentation Pack (PO Pack 484)			13·00	
PHQ Cards (set of 12) (376)			4·75	11·00
MS3474 192×74 mm. Nos. 3463/3473			12·00	10·00
First Day Cover				12·00

		(b) Self-adhesive. Die-cut perf 14½.		
3475	**2635**	(1st) George Best........................	4·50	4·50
		a. Booklet pane. Nos. 3475/3476		
		and U3022×4...................	11·00	
3476	**2639**	(1st) Bobby Moore.....................	4·50	4·50
3477	**2633**	(1st) John Charles (20.2.14)............	4·50	4·50
		a. Booklet pane. Nos. 3477/3478		
		and U3022×4...................	11·00	
3478	**2641**	(1st) Dave Mackay (20.2.14)...........	4·50	4·50
Set of 4........................			16·00	16·00

Nos. 3463/3489 commemorate the 150th anniversary of the Football Association and the 140th Anniversary of the Scottish Football Association.

Nos. 3463/3467 were printed together, *se-tenant*, as horizontal strips of five stamps in sheets of 30 (5×6).

Nos. 3468/3473 were printed together, *se-tenant*, as horizontal strips of six stamps in sheets of 30 (6×5).

Nos. 3475/3476 and 3477/3478 were issued in separate booklets, Nos. PM37 and PM41, both sold for £3·60.

The 12 PHQ cards depict the 11 individual stamps and the complete miniature sheet.

(Litho Cartor)

2013 (9 May). Football Heroes (2nd issue). Self-adhesive. Multicoloured 'All-over'. phosphor. Die-cut perf 14½×14.

3479	**2632**	(1st) Jimmy Greaves....................	1·60	1·60
		a. Booklet pane. Nos. 3479/3483......	7·25	7·25
3480	**2633**	(1st) John Charles.....................	1·60	1·60
3481	**2637**	(1st) Kevin Keegan.....................	1·60	1·60
3482	**2638**	(1st) Denis Law........................	1·60	1·60
3483	**2639**	(1st) Bobby Moore.....................	1·60	1·60
3484	**2634**	(1st) Gordon Banks....................	1·60	1·60
		a. Booklet pane. Nos. 3484/3489......	8·75	8·75
3485	**2635**	(1st) George Best.....................	1·60	1·60
3486	**2636**	(1st) John Barnes.....................	1·60	1·60
3487	**2640**	(1st) Bryan Robson...................	1·60	1·60
3488	**2641**	(1st) Dave Mackay....................	1·60	1·60
3489	**2642**	(1st) Bobby Charlton.................	1·60	1·60
Set of 11........................			16·00	16·00

Nos. 3479/3489 were issued in £11·11 Football Heroes premium booklet, No. DY7.

No. 3490 is vacant.

2646 Preliminary Oil Sketch for The Coronation of Queen Elizabeth II (Terence Cuneo), 1953

2647 Queen Elizabeth II in Garter Robes (Nicky Philipps), 2012

2648 Portrait by Andrew Festing, 1999

2649 Portrait by Pietro Annigoni, 1955

2650 Portrait by Sergei Pavlenko, 2000

2651 Her Majesty Queen Elizabeth II (Richard Stone), 1992

(Gravure Walsall)

2013 (30 May). 60th Anniversary of the Coronation. Six Decades of Royal Portraits. Multicoloured. Phosphor band at left (2nd) or 'all-over' phosphor (others). Perf 14.

3491	**2646**	(2nd) Preliminary Oil Sketch for The Coronation of Queen Elizabeth II (Terence Cuneo), 1953............	90	90
3492	**2647**	(1st) Queen Elizabeth II in Garter Robes (Nicky Philipps), 2012..........	1·20	1·00
3493	**2648**	78p. Portrait by Andrew Festing, 1999...	1·10	1·10
3494	**2649**	88p. Portrait by Pietro Annigoni, 1955...	1·50	1·50
3495	**2650**	£1·28 Portrait by Sergei Pavlenko, 2000..	2·10	2·10
3496	**2651**	£1·88 Her Majesty Queen Elizabeth II (Richard Stone), 1992...............	3·00	3·00
Set of 6........................			8·50	8·50
Set of 6 Gutter Pairs........................			17·00	

Set of 6 Traffic Light Gutter Blocks of 4...............		36·00	
First Day Cover (Tallents House)...............			11·00
First Day Cover (London SW1)...............			11·00
Presentation Pack (PO Pack No. 485)............		10·00	
PHQ Cards (set of 6) (377)...............		12·50	10·50
Commemorative Document (Nos. 3491/3492) (2.6.13).....		12·50	

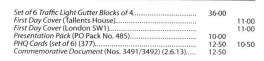

2652 UTA Class W No. 103 *Thomas Somerset* with Belfast Express, Downhill, near Castlerock, *c* 1950

2653 Classic Locomotives of Northern Ireland

(Des Delaney Design Consultants. Gravure Walsall (No. 3497) or litho Cartor (No. **MS**3498))

2013 (18 June). Classic Locomotives (3rd series). Northern Ireland. Black, grey and gold. 'All-over' phosphor.

(a) Self-adhesive. Die-cut perf 14.

3497	**2652**	(1st) UTA Class W No. 103 *Thomas Somerset* with Belfast Express.........	2·00	2·00
		a. Booklet pane. No. 3497×2 and U3022×4.........................	7·50	

(b) Ordinary gum. Sheet 180×74 mm. Perf 14

MS3498 Classic Locomotives of Northern Ireland. As T **2652**; 78p. UTA SG3 No. 35; 88p. Peckett No. 2; £1·28 CDRJC Class 5 No. 4................		5·00	5·25
First Day Cover (Tallents House)...............			6·50
First Day Cover (Belfast)...............			6·50
Presentation Pack (PO Pack No. 486)............		6·25	
PHQ Cards (set of 5) (378)...............		2·00	6·50

No. 3497 was issued in booklet, No. PM38, sold for £3·60.

The five PHQ cards show the four individual stamps and the complete miniature sheet.

2654 Comma (*Polygonia c-album*)

2655 Orange-tip (*Anthocharis cardamines*)

2656 Small Copper (*Lycaena phlaeas*)

2657 Chalkhill Blue (*Polyommatus coridon*)

2658 Swallowtail (Papilio machaon)

2659 Purple Emperor (Apatura iris)

2660 Marsh Fritillary (Euphydryas aurinia)

2661 Brimstone (Gonepteryx rhamni)

2662 Red Admiral (Vanessa atalanta)

2663 Marbled White (Melanargia galathea)

(Des Richard Lewington and Marc & Anna. Litho Cartor (Nos. 3499/3508) or gravure (Nos. 3509/3510) Walsall)

2013 (11 July). Butterflies. Multicoloured 'All-over' phosphor.

(a) Ordinary paper. Perf 14×14½.

3499	**2654**	(1st) Comma..	1·20	1·00
		a. Horiz strip of 5. Nos. 3499/3503.....	5·25	4·50
3500	**2655**	(1st) Orange-tip......................................	1·20	1·00
3501	**2656**	(1st) Small Copper.................................	1·20	1·00
3502	**2657**	(1st) Chalkhill Blue................................	1·20	1·00
3503	**2658**	(1st) Swallowtail....................................	1·20	1·00
3504	**2659**	(1st) Purple Emperor.............................	1·20	1·00
		a. Horiz strip of 5. Nos. 3504/3508.....	5·25	4·50
3505	**2660**	(1st) Marsh Fritillary.............................	1·20	1·00
3506	**2661**	(1st) Brimstone.......................................	1·20	1·00
3507	**2662**	(1st) Red Admiral...................................	1·20	1·00
3508	**2663**	(1st) Marbled White...............................	1·20	1·00
Set of 10..			10·50	9·00
Set of 2 Gutter Strips of 10..........................			21·00	
First Day Cover (Tallents House).................				12·00
First Day Cover (Lulworth Camp, Wareham, Dorset).........				12·00
Presentation Pack (PO Pack No. 487).........			11·00	
PHQ Cards (set of 10) (379)..........................			4·00	11·00

(b) Self-adhesive. Die-cut perf 14×14½.

3509	**2657**	(1st) Chalkhill Blue................................	2·00	2·00
		a. Booklet pane. Nos. 3509/3510 and U3022×4....................................	7·50	
3510	**2654**	(1st) Comma..	2·00	2·00

Nos. 3499/3503 and 3504/3508 were each printed together, se-tenant, as horizontal strips of five stamps in sheets of 50 (2 panes 5×5).

Nos. 3509/3510 were issued in stamp booklet, No. PM39, sold for £3·60.

2664 Andy Murray's Wimbledon Victory

(Litho Walsall)

2013 (8 Aug). Andy Murray, Men's Singles Champion, Wimbledon. Sheet 192×75 mm. Multicoloured 'All-over' phosphor. Perf 14½.

MS3511	**2664**	Andy Murray's Wimbledon Victory (1st) Andy Murray kissing Wimbledon Trophy; (1st) Andy Murray serving; £1·28 In action; £1·28 Holding Trophy................	5·25	5·50
First Day Cover (Tallents House)..........................				7·00
First Day Cover (Wimbledon, SW19).....................				7·00
Presentation Pack (PO Pack No. M21)...................			6·50	

2665 Jaguar E-Type, 1961

2666 Rolls-Royce Silver Shadow, 1965

2667 Aston Martin DB5, 1963

2668 MG MGB, 1962

2669 Morgan Plus 8, 1968

2670 Lotus Esprit, 1976

2671 The Workhorses

(Des Why Not Associates (Nos. 3512/3517) or Robert Maude and Sarah Davies (No. **MS**3518). Litho Cartor)

2013 (13 Aug). British Auto Legends. Multicoloured 'All-over' phosphor. Perf 13½ (Nos. 3512/3517) or 14 (No. MS3518).

3512	**2665**	(1st) Jaguar E-Type, 1961........................	1·20	1·00
		a. Horiz strip of 3. Nos. 3512/3514.....	3·25	2·75
3513	**2666**	(1st) Rolls-Royce Silver Shadow, 1965....	1·20	1·00
3514	**2667**	(1st) Aston Martin DB5, 1963..................	1·20	1·00
3515	**2668**	£1·28 MG MGB, 1962................................	1·60	1·60
		a. Horiz strip of 3. Nos. 3515/3517.....	4·25	4·25
3516	**2669**	£1·28 Morgan Plus 8, 1968......................	1·60	1·60
3517	**2670**	£1·28 Lotus Esprit, 1976..........................	1·60	1·60
Set of 6..			7·50	7·00
Set of 2 Gutter Strips of 6............................			15·00	
First Day Cover (Tallents House)..................				9·00

First Day Cover (Alwalton, Peterborough)............................. 9·00
Presentation Pack (PO Pack No. 488) (Nos. 3512/3517
and **MS**3518).. 13·50
PHQ Cards (set of 11) (380).. 4·50   17·00
MS3518 180×74 mm. **2671** The Workhorses (1st)×4
    Morris Minor Royal Mail van (1953–1971); Austin
    FX4 (1958–1997) London taxi; Ford Anglia 105E
    (1959–1967) police car; Coastguard Land Rover
    Defender 110 (from 1990) (all 40×30 mm)............... 4·50   4·00
First Day Cover (Tallents House)..................................... 4·50
First Day Cover (Alwalton, Peterborough)........................ 4·50

Nos. 3512/3514 and 3515/3517 were each printed together, *se-tenant*, as horizontal strips of three stamps in sheets of 60 (2 panes 6×5).

The 1st value from No. **MS**3518 is inscr EUROPA.

The complete miniature sheet is shown on one of the 11 PHQ cards with the others depicting individual stamps including those from the miniature sheet.

2672 East Indiaman *Atlas*, 1813

2673 Royal Mail Ship *Britannia*, 1840

2674 Tea Clipper *Cutty Sark*, 1870

2675 Cargo Liner *Clan Matheson*, 1919

2676 Royal Mail Ship *Queen Elizabeth*, 1940

2677 Bulk Carrier *Lord Hinton*, 1986

(Des Silk Pearce. Litho Enschedé (booklet panes) or Cartor (others))

2013 (19 Sept). Merchant Navy (1st issue). Multicoloured 'All-over' phosphor. Perf 14.
3519 **2672** (1st) East Indiaman *Atlas*, 1813............... 1·20   1·00
            a. Booklet pane. Nos. 3519/3521
                with margins all round.................... 4·00
3520 **2673** (1st) Royal Mail Ship *Britannia*, 1840...... 1·20   1·00
3521 **2674** (1st) Tea Clipper *Cutty Sark*, 1870........... 1·20   1·00
3522 **2675** £1·28 Cargo Liner *Clan Matheson*, 1919... 1·60   1·60
            a. Booklet pane. Nos. 3522/3524
                with margins all round.................... 5·00
3523 **2676** £1·28 Royal Mail Ship *Queen Elizabeth*,
                1940... 1·60   1·60
3524 **2677** £1·28 Bulk Carrier *Lord Hinton*, 1986........ 1·60   1·60
Set of 6.. 7·50   7·00
Set of 6 Gutter Pairs... 15·00
First Day Cover (Tallents House)..................................... 9·00
First Day Cover (Clydebank)... 9·00
Presentation Pack (PO Pack No. 489) (Nos. 3519/3524
and **MS**3529).. 14·50
PHQ Cards (set of 11) (381).. 4·50   17·00

Nos. 3519a and 3522a were only issued in the £11·19 Merchant Navy booklet, No DY8.

The complete miniature sheet is shown on one of the 11 PHQ cards with the others depicting individual stamps including those from No. **MS**3529.

2678 Destroyer HMS *Vanoc* escorting Atlantic Convoy

2679 Merchant Ship passing the Naval Control Base in the Thames Estuary

2680 Sailors clearing Ice from the Decks of HMS *King George V* in Arctic Waters

2681 Naval Convoy of 24 Merchant Ships in the North Sea

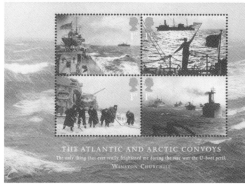

2682 Second World War Atlantic and Arctic Convoys

(Des Silk Pearce. Litho Enschedé)

2013 (19 Sept). Merchant Navy. Multicoloured 'All-over' phosphor. Perf 14.
3525 **2678** (1st) Destroyer HMS *Vanoc* escorting
                Atlantic Convoy................................ 2·25   2·25
            a. Booklet pane. Nos. 3525/3528......... 8·00
3526 **2679** (1st) Merchant Ship passing the Naval
                Control Base in the Thames
                Estuary... 2·25   2·25
3527 **2680** (1st) Sailors clearing Ice from the
                Decks of HMS *King George V* in
                Arctic Waters.................................. 2·25   2·25
3528 **2681** (1st) Naval Convoy of 24 Merchant
                Ships in the North Sea..................... 2·25   2·25
Set of 4.. 8·00   8·00
MS3529 115×89 mm. **2682** Second World War Atlantic
    and Arctic Convoys. Nos. 3525/3528........................ 6·00   6·00
First Day Cover (Tallents House)..................................... 6·75
First Day Cover (Clydebank)... 6·75

Nos. 3525/3528 were only issued in the £11·19 Merchant Navy premium booklet, No. DY8, and in No. **MS**3529.

2683 Royal Mail Van

2673 Royal Mail Ship *Britannia*, 1840

(Gravure Walsall)

2013 (19 Sept). Royal Mail Transport By Land and Sea. Multicoloured Die-cut perf 14.
3530 **2683** (1st) Royal Mail Van................................. 5·50   5·50
            a. Booklet pane Nos. 3530/3531 and
                No. U3022×4................................... 14·00
3531 **2673** (1st) Royal Mail Ship *Britannia*, 1840...... 5·50   5·50

The design of No. 3530 is as the Royal Mail van stamp within No. **MS**3518.

Nos. 3530/3531 were only issued in booklet, No. PM40, originally sold for £3·60.

No. 3530 includes the EUROPA emblem.

2684 Polacanthus

2685 Ichthyosaurus

2686 Iguanodon

2687 Ornithocheirus

2688 Baryonyx

2689 Dimorphodon

2690 Hypsilophodon

2691 Cetiosaurus

2692 Megalosaurus

2693 Plesiosaurus

(Des John Sibbick (illustrator) and Why Not Associates. Gravure Walsall)

2013 (10 Oct). Dinosaurs. Multicoloured 'All-over' phosphor. Die-cut perf 13½×14 (with no teeth around protruding parts at top or foot of the designs).

3532	**2684**	(1st) Polacanthus..........................	1·20	1·00
		a. Horiz strip of 5. Nos. 3532/3536.....	5·25	
3533	**2685**	(1st) Ichthyosaurus.......................	1·20	1·00
3534	**2686**	(1st) Iguanodon...........................	1·20	1·00
3535	**2687**	(1st) Ornithocheirus......................	1·20	1·00
3536	**2688**	(1st) Baryonyx............................	1·20	1·00
3537	**2689**	(1st) Dimorphodon.........................	1·20	1·00
		a. Horiz strip of 5. Nos. 3537/3541.....	5·25	
3538	**2690**	(1st) Hypsilophodon.......................	1·20	1·00
3539	**2691**	(1st) Cetiosaurus.........................	1·20	1·00
3540	**2692**	(1st) Megalosaurus........................	1·20	1·00
3541	**2693**	(1st) Plesiosaurus........................	1·20	1·00
Set of 10..			10·50	9·00
First Day Cover (Tallents House)......................				11·00
First Day Cover (Lyme Regis, Dorset)..................				11·00
Presentation Pack (PO Pack 490)......................			11·00	
PHQ Cards (set of 10) (382)..........................			4·00	11·00

Nos. 3532/3536 and 3537/3541 were each printed together as horizontal strips of five stamps in sheets of 50 (2 panes 5×5).

2694 Madonna and Child   **2695** Virgin and Child with the Young St John the Baptist   **2696** Madonna and Child

2697 St Roch Praying to the Virgin for an End to the Plague   **2698** Virgin and Child with the Young St John the Baptist   **2699** La Vierge au Lys

2700 Theotokos, Mother of God

MS3549 (Illustration reduced. Actual size 146×74 mm).

(Des Robert Maude and Sarah Davies. Gravure Walsall (Nos. 3542a, 3543a) or De La Rue (others))

2013 (5 Nov). Christmas. Madonna and Child Paintings. Multicoloured One centre band (No. 3542) or two bands (others).

(a) Self-adhesive. Die-cut perf 14½×15.

3542	**2694**	(2nd) Madonna and Child........................	90	90
		a. Booklet pane. No. 3542×12............	13·50	
3543	**2695**	(1st) Virgin and Child with the Young St John the Baptist (detail)...................	1·20	1·00
		a. Booklet pane. No. 3543×12............	16·00	
3544	**2696**	(2nd Large) Madonna and Child.............	1·25	1·10
3545	**2697**	88p. St Roch Praying to the Virgin for an End to the Plague (detail)................	1·40	1·40
3546	**2698**	(1st Large) Virgin and Child with the Young St John the Baptist (detail)....	1·70	1·40
3547	**2699**	£1·28 La Vierge au Lys..................	2·00	2·00
3548	**2700**	£1·88 Theotokos, Mother of God..............	3·00	3·00
Set of 7...			9·75	9·50
First Day Cover (Tallents House).....................				12·50
First Day Cover (Bethlehem, Llandeilo)...............				12·50
Presentation Pack (PO Pack No. 491).................			11·50	
PHQ Cards (set of 8) (383)..........................			3·25	19·00

(b) Ordinary gum. Perf 14½×15.

MS3549	146×74 mm. **2700a** As Nos. 3542/3548.............		9·75	9·50
First Day Cover				12·50

The 2nd class, 1st class, 88p., £1·28 and £1·88 stamps were also issued in sheets of 20 containing 8×2nd class, 8×1st class, 2×88p., 1×£1·28 and 1×£1·88 stamps, each stamp accompanied by a *se-tenant* label. These sheets were printed in lithography and sold for £13·62 each (No. LS88).

Separate sheets of 20×2nd, 10×1st, 10×88p. and 10×£1·28 were available with personal photographs on the labels from Royal Mail, Edinburgh. These were sold at £14·50 for 20×2nd, £10·20 for 10×1st, £14·45 for 10×88p. and £18·50 for 10×£1·28.

The eight PHQ cards show the seven individual stamps and the complete miniature sheet.

2701 Angels (Rosie Hargreaves)

2702 Santa (Molly Robson)

(Gravure Walsall)

2013 (5 Nov). Children's Christmas. Self-adhesive. Multicoloured One phosphor band at right (2nd) or two phosphor bands (1st). Die-cut perf 14½.

3550	2701	(2nd) Angels	1·00	1·00
3551	2702	(1st) Santa	1·25	1·25
First Day Cover (Tallents House)				4·25
First Day Cover (Bethlehem, Llandeilo)				4·25
Presentation Pack (PO Pack No. M22)			4·25	

Year Pack

2013 (5 Nov). Comprises Nos. 3423/3429, 3431/3447, MS3451, 3453/3473, 3491/3496, MS3498/3508, MS3511/3524, MS3529 and 3532/3548

| CP3551a | Year Pack (Pack No. 492) (sold for £85) | £130 |

Post Office Yearbook

2013 (5 Nov). Comprises Nos. 3423/3429, 3431/3447, MS3451, 3453/3473, 3491/3496, MS3498/3508, MS3511/3524, MS3529, 3532/3548 and 3550/3551

| YB3551a | Yearbook (sold for £90) | £135 |

Miniature Sheet Collection

2013 (5 Nov). Comprises Nos. MS3429, MS3451, MS3474, MS3498, MS3511, MS3518, MS3529 and MS3549

| MS3551a | Miniature Sheet Collection (sold for £33) | 45·00 |

2703 Andy Pandy

2704 Ivor the Engine

2705 Dougal (The Magic Roundabout)

2706 Windy Miller (Camberwick Green)

2707 Mr Benn

2708 Great Uncle Bulgaria (The Wombles)

2709 Bagpuss

2710 Paddington Bear

2711 Postman Pat

2712 Bob the Builder

2713 Peppa Pig

2714 Shaun the Sheep

(Des Interabang. Gravure Walsall)

2014 (7 Jan). Classic Children's TV. Self-adhesive. Multicoloured 'All-over' phosphor. Die-cut perf 15.

3552	2703	(1st) Andy Pandy	1·20	1·00
		a. Horiz strip of 6. Nos. 3552/3557	6·50	
3553	2704	(1st) Ivor the Engine	1·20	1·00
3554	2705	(1st) Dougal (The Magic Roundabout)	1·20	1·00
3555	2706	(1st) Windy Miller (Camberwick Green)	1·20	1·00
3556	2707	(1st) Mr Benn	1·20	1·00
3557	2708	(1st) Great Uncle Bulgaria (The Wombles)	1·00	1·00
3558	2709	(1st) Bagpuss	1·20	1·00
		a. Horiz strip of 6. Nos. 3558/3563	6·50	
3559	2710	(1st) Paddington Bear	1·20	1·00
3560	2711	(1st) Postman Pat	1·20	1·00
3561	2712	(1st) Bob the Builder	1·20	1·00
3562	2713	(1st) Peppa Pig	1·20	1·00
3563	2714	(1st) Shaun the Sheep	1·20	1·00
Set of 12			13·00	11·00
Set of 2 Gutter Strips of 12			26·00	
First Day Cover (Tallents House)				13·50
First Day Cover (Wimbledon, London SW19)				13·50
Presentation Pack (PO Pack No. 493)			14·00	
PHQ Cards (set of 12) (384)			4·75	12·50

Nos. 3552/3557 and 3558/3563 were each printed together, se-tenant, in horizontal strips of six stamps in sheets of 60 (6×10).

2715 Riding for the Disabled Association

2716 The King's Troop Ceremonial Horses

2717 Dray Horses

2718 Royal Mews Carriage Horses

2719 Police Horses

2720 Forestry Horse

(Des Michael Denny and Harold Batten. Litho Cartor)

2014 (4 Feb). Working Horses. Multicoloured 'All-over' phosphor. Perf 14.

3564	2715	(1st) Riding for the Disabled Association	1·20	1·00
3565	2716	(1st) The King's Troop Ceremonial Horses	1·20	1·00
3566	2717	88p. Dray Horses	1·40	1·40
3567	2718	88p. Royal Mews Carriage Horses	1·40	1·40
3568	2719	£1·28 Police Horses	2·10	2·10
3569	2720	£1·28 Forestry Horse	2·10	2·10
Set of 6			8·25	8·00
Set of 6 Gutter Pairs			16·50	

First Day Cover (Tallents House)...............................				10·00
First Day Cover (Horseheath, Cambridge).....................				10·00
Presentation Pack (PO Pack No. 494).....................			9·50	
PHQ Cards (set of 6) (385).................................			2·50	9·50

2721 BR Dean Goods No. 2532

2722 BR D34 Nos. 62471 and 62496

2723 UTA Class W No. 103 *Thomas Somerset*

2724 LMS No. 7720

2725 Peckett R2 *Thor*

2726 BR D40 No. 62276

2727 UTA SG3 No. 35

2728 Hunslet No. 589 *Blanche*

2729 Classic Locomotives of Wales

(Des Delaney Design Consultants. Litho Enschedé (booklet))

2014 (20 Feb). Classic Locomotives (4th and 5th series). Wales (No. **MS**3578) and United Kingdom. Multicoloured 'All-over' phosphor. Perf 14.

3570	**2721**	(1st) BR Dean Goods No. 2532................	2·75	2·75
		a. Booklet pane. Nos. 3570 and 3574, each×2 with margins all round.............................	7·50	
3571	**2722**	(1st) BR D34 Nos. 62471 and 62496.......	2·75	2·75
		a. Booklet pane. Nos. 3571 and 3575, each×2 with margins all round.............................	7·50	
3572	**2723**	(1st) UTA Class W No. 103......................	2·75	2·75
		a. Booklet pane. Nos. 3572 and 3576, each×2 with margins all round.............................	7·50	

3573	**2724**	(1st) LMS No. 7720..............................	2·75	2·75
		a. Booklet pane. Nos. 3573 and 3577, each×2 with margins all round.............................	7·50	
3574	**2725**	60p. Peckett R2 *Thor*...........................	2·75	2·75
3575	**2726**	68p. BR D40 No. 62276........................	2·75	2·75
3576	**2727**	78p. UTA SG3 No. 35............................	2·75	2·75
3577	**2728**	78p. Hunslet No. 589 *Blanche*..................	2·75	2·75
		Set of 8...	15·00	15·00

MS3578 180×74 mm. **2729** Classic Locomotives of Wales No. 3573; No. 3577; 88p. W&LLR No. 822 *The Earl*; £1·28 BR 5600 No. 5652..................................

		5·00	5·25
First Day Cover (Tallents House)...........................			6·50
First Day Cover (Porthmadog)...............................			6·50
Presentation Pack (PO Pack No. 495).....................		6·00	
PHQ Cards (set of 5) (386).................................		2·00	10·00

Nos. 3570/3577 were issued in the £13·97 Classic Locomotives booklet, No. DY9, or in No. **MS**3578 (Nos. 3573 and 3577).

For the self-adhesive version of No. 3573, see No. 3634

The five PHQ cards show the four individual stamps and the complete miniature sheet.

2730 Roy Plomley (1914–1985, broadcaster and writer)

2731 Barbara Ward (1914–1981, economist and broadcaster)

2732 Joe Mercer (1914–1990, football player and manager)

2733 Kenneth More (1914–1982, stage and screen actor)

2734 Dylan Thomas (1914–1953, poet and writer)

2735 Sir Alec Guinness (1914–2000, stage and screen actor)

2736 Noorunissa Inayat Khan (1914–1944, SOE agent in occupied France)

2737 Max Perutz (1914–2002, molecular biologist and Nobel laureate)

2738 Joan Littlewood (1914–2002, theatre director and writer)

2739 Abram Games (1914–1996, graphic designer)

(Des Purpose. Litho Cartor)

2014 (25 Mar). Remarkable Lives. Multicoloured 'All-over' phosphor. Perf 14½.

3579	**2730**	(1st) Roy Plomley..................................	1·20	1·00
		a. Horiz strip of 5. Nos. 3579/3583.....	5·25	4·50
3580	**2731**	(1st) Barbara Ward..............................	1·20	1·00
3581	**2732**	(1st) Joe Mercer..................................	1·20	1·00
3582	**2733**	(1st) Kenneth More..............................	1·20	1·00
3583	**2734**	(1st) Dylan Thomas..............................	1·20	1·00
3584	**2735**	(1st) Sir Alec Guinness.........................	1·20	1·00
		a. Horiz strip of 5. Nos. 3584/3588.....	5·25	4·50
3585	**2736**	(1st) Noorunissa Inayat Khan..................	1·20	1·00
3586	**2737**	(1st) Max Perutz..................................	1·20	1·00
3587	**2738**	(1st) Joan Littlewood...........................	1·20	1·00
3588	**2739**	(1st) Abram Games..............................	1·20	1·00
Set of 10..			10·50	9·00
Set of 2 Gutter Strips of 10..................................			21·00	
First Day Cover (Tallents House)............................				11·00
First Day Cover (Swansea)...................................				11·00
Presentation Pack (PO Pack No. 496).....................			11·00	
PHQ Cards (set of 10) (387)..................................			4·00	11·00

Nos. 3579/3583 and 3584/3588 were each printed together, *se-tenant*, as horizontal strips of five stamps in sheets of 50 (2 panes 5×5).

2740 Buckingham Palace, 2014

2741 Buckingham Palace, *circa* 1862

2742 Buckingham Palace, 1846

2743 Buckingham House, 1819

2744 Buckingham House, 1714

2745 Buckingham House, *circa* 1700

2746 The Grand Staircase   **2747** The Throne Room

(Des Howard Brown (sheet stamps). Litho ISP Cartor (No. 3589/3594) or Enschedé (booklet panes Nos. 3589b/3594b) or gravure ISP Walsall (Nos. 3595/3596))

2014 (15 Apr). Buckingham Palace, London (1st issue). Multicoloured 'All-over phosphor'.

		(a) Ordinary gum. Perf 14½.		
3589	**2740**	(1st) Buckingham Palace, 2014..............	1·20	1·00
		a. Horiz strip of 3. Nos. 3589/3591.....	3·25	2·75
		b. Perf 14×13½.....................................	1·25	1·25
		ba. Booklet pane. Nos. 3589b and 3590b, each×2 with margins all round......	5·00	
3590	**2741**	(1st) Buckingham Palace, *circa* 1862......	1·20	1·00
		b. Perf 14×13½.....................................	1·25	1·25
3591	**2742**	(1st) Buckingham Palace, 1846..............	1·20	1·00
		b. Perf 14×13½.....................................	1·25	1·25
		ba. Booklet pane. Nos. 3591b/3594b with margins all round...................	5·00	
3592	**2743**	(1st) Buckingham House, 1819..............	1·20	1·00
		a. Horiz strip of 3. Nos. 3592/3594.....	3·25	2·75
		b. Perf 14×13½.....................................	1·25	1·25
3593	**2744**	(1st) Buckingham House, 1714..............	1·20	1·00
		b. Perf 14×13½.....................................	1·25	1·25
3594	**2745**	(1st) Buckingham House, *circa* 1700......	1·20	1·00
		b. Perf 14×13½.....................................	1·25	1·25
Set of 6 (Nos. 3589/3594)...................................			6·50	5·50
Set of 6 (Nos. 3589b/3594b)...............................			7·50	7·50
Set of 2 Gutter Strips of 6...................................			13·00	
First Day Cover (Tallents House)............................				6·75
First Day Cover (London SW1)..............................				6·75
Presentation Pack (PO Pack No. 497) (Nos. 3589/3594 and **MS**3601)..			11·50	
PHQ Cards (set of 11) (388).................................			4·50	13·00
		(b) Self-adhesive. Die-cut perf 14.		
3595	**2746**	(1st) The Grand Staircase......................	2·25	2·25
		a. Booklet pane. Nos. 3595/3596 and U3022×4....................................	7·50	
3596	**2747**	(1st) The Throne Room..........................	2·25	2·25

Nos. 3589/3591 and 3592/3594 were each printed together, *se-tenant*, as horizontal strips of three stamps in sheets of 36 (2 panes 3×6).

Nos. 3589ba and 3591ba come from the £11·39 Buckingham Palace, London booklet, No. DY10.

Nos. 3595/3596 were issued in stamp booklet, No. PM42, originally sold for £3·72.

The complete miniature sheet is shown on one of the 11 PHQ cards with the others depicting individual stamps including those from No. **MS**3601.

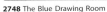

2748 The Blue Drawing Room   **2749** The Green Drawing Room

2750 Buckingham Palace

(Des Robert Maude and Sarah Davies (No. **MS**3601). Litho Enschedé)

2014 (15 Apr). Buckingham Palace, London (2nd issue). Multicoloured 'All-over' phosphor. Perf 14.

3597	**2747**	(1st) The Throne Room.............................	1·20	1·00
		a. Booklet pane. Nos. 3597/3600 with margins all round and roulettes at left..................................	4·25	
3598	**2746**	(1st) The Grand Staircase........................	1·20	1·00
3599	**2748**	(1st) The Blue Drawing Room...................	1·20	1·00
3600	**2749**	(1st) The Green Drawing Room..............	1·20	1·00
		Set of 4..	4·25	3·50
MS3601 146×74 mm. **2750** Buckingham Palace Nos.				
		3597/3600..	4·25	3·50
		a. Imperf...	—	—
		First Day Cover (Tallents House)..............................		4·50
		First Day Cover (London SW1)..................................		4·50

Nos. 3597/3600 were only issued in the £11·39 premium booklet, No. DY10 and No. **MS**3601.

2751 *A Matter of Life and Death* (1946)

2752 *Lawrence of Arabia* (1962)

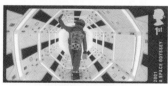

2753 *2001 A Space Odyssey* (1968)

2754 *Chariots of Fire* (1981)

2755 *Secrets and Lies* (1996)

2756 *Bend It Like Beckham* (2002)

2757 Films by GPO Film Unit

(Des johnson banks (Nos. 3602/3607) or Magpie Studio (No. **MS**3608). Litho ISP Cartor (Nos. 3602/3607) or Enschedé (No. **MS**3608))

2014 (13 May). Great British Films. Multicoloured 'All-over' phosphor. Perf 14½ (Nos. 3602/3607) or 14 (No. **MS**3608).

3602	**2751**	(1st) *A Matter of Life and Death*..............	1·20	1·00
		a. Horiz strip of 3. Nos. 3602/3604.....	3·25	2·75
3603	**2752**	(1st) *Lawrence of Arabia*...........................	1·20	1·00
3604	**2753**	(1st) *2001 A Space Odyssey*......................	1·20	1·00
3605	**2754**	£1·28 *Chariots of Fire*...............................	1·60	1·60
		a. Horiz strip of 3. Nos. 3605/3607.....	4·25	4·25
3606	**2755**	£1·28 *Secrets and Lies*..............................	1·60	1·60
3607	**2756**	£1·28 *Bend It Like Beckham*......................	1·60	1·60
		Set of 6..	7·50	7·00
		Set of 2 Gutter Strips of 6...........................	15·00	
		First Day Cover (Tallents House).........................		10·00
		First Day Cover (Blackheath London SE3)............		10·00
		Presentation Pack (PO Pack No. 498) (Nos. 3602/3607 and **MS**3608)..	15·00	
		PHQ Cards (set of 11) (389).........................	4·50	18·00

MS3608 115×89 mm. **2757** Films by GPO Film Unit (1st)×4 *Night Mail* (1936) directed by Harry Watt and Basil Wright; *Love on the Wing* (1938) directed by Norman McLaren; *A Colour Box* (1935) directed by Len Lye; *Spare Time* (1939) directed by Humphrey Jennings.. 5·00 4·75
First Day Cover (Tallents House)................................... 5·00
First Day Cover (Blackheath London SE3)..................... 5·00

Nos. 3602/3604 and 3605/3607 were each printed together, *se-tenant*, as horizontal strips of three stamps in sheets of 36 (2 panes 3×6).

The complete miniature sheet is shown on one of the 11 PHQ cards with the others depicting individual stamps including those from No. **MS**3608.

2758 Herring

2759 Red Gurnard

2760 Dab

2761 Pouting

2762 Cornish Sardine

2763 Common Skate

2764 Spiny Dogfish

2765 Wolffish

2766 Sturgeon

2767 Conger Eel

(Des Kate Stephens. Litho ISP Cartor)

2014 (5 June). Sustainable Fish (Nos. 3609/3613) and Threatened Fish (Nos. 3614/3618). Multicoloured 'All-over' phosphor. Perf 14×14½.

3609	**2758**	(1st) Herring	1·20	1·00
		a. Horiz strip of 5. Nos. 3609/3613	5·25	4·50
3610	**2759**	(1st) Red Gurnard	1·20	1·00
3611	**2760**	(1st) Dab	1·00	1·00
3612	**2761**	(1st) Pouting	1·20	1·00
3613	**2762**	(1st) Cornish Sardine	1·20	1·00
3614	**2763**	(1st) Common Skate	1·20	1·00
		a. Horiz strip of 5. Nos. 3614/3618	5·25	4·50
3615	**2764**	(1st) Spiny Dogfish	1·20	1·00
3616	**2765**	(1st) Wolffish	1·20	1·00
3617	**2766**	(1st) Sturgeon	1·20	1·00
3618	**2767**	(1st) Conger Eel	1·20	1·00
Set of 10			10·50	9·00
Set of 2 Gutter Strips of 10			21·00	
First Day Cover (Tallents House)				11·50
First Day Cover (Fishguard)				11·50
Presentation Pack (PO Pack No. 499)			11·00	
PHQ Cards (set of 10) (390)			4·00	11·00

Nos. 3609/3613 and 3614/3618 were each printed together, *se-tenant*, as horizontal strips of five in sheets of 50 (2 panes 5×5).

2768 Judo

2769 Swimming

2770 Marathon

2771 Squash

2772 Netball

2773 Para-athlete Cycling

(Des Nanette Hoogslag (illustration) and Howard Brown. Litho ISP Cartor (Nos. 3619/3624) or gravure ISP Walsall (No. 3625))

2014 (17 July). Commonwealth Games, Glasgow. Multicoloured One phosphor band (No. 3619) or two bands (others).

(a) Ordinary gum. Perf 14×14½.

3619	**2768**	(2nd) Judo	90	90
3620	**2769**	(1st) Swimming	1·00	1·00
3621	**2770**	97p. Marathon	1·40	1·40
3622	**2771**	£1·28 Squash	1·75	1·75
3623	**2772**	£1·47 Netball	2·50	2·50
3624	**2773**	£2·15 Para-athlete Cycling	3·50	3·50
Set of 6			10·00	10·00
Set of 6 Gutter Pairs			20·00	
First Day Cover (Tallents House)				11·50
First Day Cover (Glasgow)				11·50
Presentation Pack (PO Pack No. 500)			10·50	
PHQ Cards (set of 6) (391)			2·50	11·50

(b) Self-adhesive. Die-cut perf 14×14½.

3625	**2769**	(1st) Swimming	2·00	2·00
		a. Booklet pane. Nos. 3625×2 and U3022×4	7·50	

The phosphor band on No. 3619 is at centre right of the stamps. No. 3625 was issued in stamp booklet, No. PM43, originally sold for £3·72.

2774 *Poppy* (Fiona Strickland)

2775 Lines from *For the Fallen* (Laurence Binyon)

2776 Private William Cecil Tickle

2777 *A Star Shell* (C. R. W. Nevinson)

2778 *The Response* (sculpture by William Goscombe John)

2779 Princess Mary's Gift Box Fund

(Des Hat-trick Design. Litho ISP Cartor (Nos. 3626/3631) or Enschedé (booklet panes Nos. 3626b, 3629b))

2014 (28 July)–**2018**. Centenary of the First World War (1st issue). Multicoloured 'All-over' phosphor (Nos. 3627, 3629) or two bands (others). Perf 14½.

3626	**2774**	(1st) *Poppy*	1·20	1·00
		a. 'All-over' phosphor	1·25	1·50
		b. Booklet pane. Nos. 3626a, 3627, 3628a with margins all round	3·75	

3627	2775	(1st) Lines from *For the Fallen*..................	1·20	1·00
		b. Booklet pane. Nos. 3627, 3712, 3839 and 3984 with margins all round (13.9.18)..............................	4·75	
3628	2776	(1st) Private William Cecil Tickle...............	1·20	1·00
		a. 'All-over' phosphor........................	1·25	1·50
3629	2777	£1·47 *A Star Shell*...............................	2·50	2·50
		b. Booklet pane. Nos. 3629, 3630a, 3631a with margins all round........	9·00	
3630	2778	£1·47 *The Response*.............................	2·50	2·50
		a. 'All-over' phosphor........................	3·25	3·50
3631	2779	£1·47 Princess Mary's Gift Box Fund.........	2·50	2·50
		a. 'All-over' phosphor........................	3·25	3·50
		Set of 6..	10·00	9·25
		Set of 6 Gutter Pairs..............................	20·00	
		First Day Cover (Tallents House)...............		11·50
		First Day Cover (Newcastle upon Tyne).......		11·50
		Presentation Pack (PO Pack No. 501).........	11·50	
		PHQ Cards (set of 6) (392)......................	2·50	10·50

Nos. 3626a/3626b, 3628a, 3629b, 3630a and 3631a only come from £11·30 premium booklet, No. DY11.

No. 3627b comes from the £15.65 Centenary of the First World War (5th issue) booklet, No. DY26.

(Gravure ISP Walsall)

2014 (18 Aug). Sustainable Fish and Threatened Fish (2nd issue). Designs as Nos. 3613/3614. Self-adhesive. Multicoloured Die-cut perf 14×14½.

3632	2763	(1st) Common Skate..............................	2·00	2·00
		a. Booklet pane. Nos. 3632/3633 and U3022×4..............................	11·00	
3633	2762	(1st) Cornish Sardine............................	2·00	2·00

Nos. 3632/3633 were issued in stamp booklet, No. PM44, originally sold for £3·72.

2724 LMS No. 7720

(Gravure ISP Walsall)

2014 (18 Sept). Classic Locomotives of Wales. Booklet stamp as T **2724**. 'All-over' phosphor. Self-adhesive. Multicoloured Die-cut perf 14.

3634	2724	(1st) LMS No. 7720................................	2·00	2·00
		a. Booklet pane. No. 3634×2 and U3022×4..	7·50	

No. 3634 was only issued in booklet, No. PM45, originally sold for £3·72.

2780 Eastbourne Bandstand

2781 Tinside Lido, Plymouth

2782 Bangor Pier

2783 Southwold Lighthouse

2784 Blackpool Pleasure Beach

2785 Bexhill-on-Sea Shelter

2786 British Piers

(Des Why Not Associates. Litho ISP Cartor (Nos. 3635/3640) or Enschedé (No. **MS**3641))

2014 (18 Sept). Seaside Architecture. Multicoloured Two bands (Nos. 3635/3640) or 'All-over' phosphor (No. **MS**3641). Perf 14.

3635	2780	(1st) Eastbourne Bandstand...................	1·20	1·00
3636	2781	(1st) Tinside Lido, Plymouth..................	1·20	1·00
3637	2782	97p. Bangor Pier.................................	1·40	1·40
3638	2783	97p. Southwold Lighthouse....................	1·40	1·40
3639	2784	£1·28 Blackpool Pleasure Beach..............	2·10	2·10
3640	2785	£1·28 Bexhill-on-Sea Shelter..................	2·10	2·10
		Set of 6..	8·50	8·00
		Set of 6 Gutter Pairs..............................	17·00	
		First Day Cover (Tallents House)...............		10·00
		First Day Cover (Eastbourne)...................		10·00
		Presentation Pack (PO Pack No. 502) (Nos. 3635/3640 and **M**S3641)..	16·00	
		PHQ Cards (set of 11) (393)......................	4·50	19·00
		MS3641 125×89 mm. **2786** British Piers (1st) Llandudno Pier; (1st) Worthing Pier; £1·28 Dunoon Pier; £1·28 Brighton Pier..............................	5·50	5·50
		First Day Cover (Tallents House)...............		7·00

No. 3635 includes the EUROPA emblem.

The complete miniature sheet is shown on one of the 11 PHQ cards with the others depicting individual stamps including those from the miniature sheet.

2787 Margaret Thatcher

2788 Harold Wilson

2789 Clement Attlee

2790 Winston Churchill

2791 William Gladstone

2792 Robert Peel

2793 Charles Grey

2794 William Pitt the Younger

(Des Together. Litho ISP Cartor)

2014 (14 Oct). Prime Ministers. Multicoloured. 'All-over' phosphor. Perf 14½.

3642	**2787**	(1st) Margaret Thatcher............................	1·20	1·00
		a. Horiz strip of 4. Nos. 3642/3645.....	4·25	3·75
3643	**2788**	(1st) Harold Wilson..............................	1·20	1·00
3644	**2789**	(1st) Clement Attlee............................	1·20	1·00
3645	**2790**	(1st) Winston Churchill.......................	1·20	1·00
3646	**2791**	97p. William Gladstone.......................	1·60	1·60
		a. Horiz strip of 4. Nos. 3646/3649.....	5·75	5·75
3647	**2792**	97p. Robert Peel.................................	1·60	1·60
3648	**2793**	97p. Charles Grey...............................	1·60	1·60
3649	**2794**	97p. William Pitt the Younger............	1·60	1·60
Set of 8..			10·00	9·50
Set of 2 Gutter strips of 4...			20·00	
First Day Cover (Tallents House).......................................				11·00
First Day Cover (London SW1)..				11·00
Presentation Pack (PO Pack No. 503)................................			11·00	
PHQ Cards (set of 8) (394)...			3·25	11·50

Nos. 3642/3645 and 3646/3649 were each printed together, *se-tenant*, as horizontal strips of four stamps in sheets of 48 (2 panes 4×6).

SELF-ADHESIVE STAMPS. Collectors are reminded that used self-adhesive stamps will no longer 'soak-off'. They should be collected with a neat margin of backing paper.

2795 Collecting the Christmas Tree

2796 Posting Christmas Cards

2797 Collecting the Christmas Tree

2798 Posting Christmas Cards

2799 Building a Snowman

2800 Carol Singing

2801 Ice Skating

(Des True North. Gravure Walsall (Nos. 3650a, 3651a) or De La Rue (others))

2014 (4 Nov). Christmas. Illustrations by Andrew Bannecker. Multicoloured One centre band (No. 3650) or two bands (others)

(a) Self-adhesive. Die-cut perf 14½×15.

3650	**2795**	(2nd) Collecting the Christmas Tree.........	90	90
		a. Booklet pane. No. 3650×12.............	13·50	
3651	**2796**	(1st) Posting Christmas Cards..................	1·20	1·00
		a. Booklet pane. No. 3651×12.............	16·00	
3652	**2797**	(2nd Large) Collecting the Christmas Tree....................................	1·25	1·10
3653	**2798**	(1st Large) Posting Christmas Cards......	1·70	1·40
3654	**2799**	£1·28 Building a Snowman.......................	2·00	2·00
3655	**2800**	£1·47 Carol Singing...............................	2·50	2·50
3656	**2801**	£2·15 Ice Skating..................................	3·25	3·25
Set of 7..			11·50	11·00

First Day Cover (Tallents House)...		14·00
First Day Cover (Bethlehem, Llandeilo).................................		14·00
Presentation Pack (PO Pack No. 504)................................	13·00	
PHQ Cards (set of 8) (395)...	3·25	20·00

(b) Ordinary gum. Perf 14½×15.

MS3657 156×74 mm. Nos. 3650/3656..............................	11·50	11·00
First Day Cover (Tallents House)...		14·00
First Day Cover (Bethlehem, Llandeilo).................................		14·00

The 2nd class, 1st class, £1·28 and £1·47 stamps were also issued in sheets of 20 containing 8×2nd class, 8×1st class, 2×£1·28 and 2×£1·47 stamps, each stamp accompanied by a *se-tenant* label. These sheets were printed in lithography and sold for £15·20 per sheet (No. LS90).

Separate sheets of 20×2nd, 20×1st, 10×1st, 10×£1·28 and 10×£1·47 were available with personal photographs on the labels from Royal Mail, Edinburgh. These were sold at £14·50 for 20×2nd, £18·65 for 20×1st, £10·20 for 10×1st, £18·50 for 10×£1·28 and £21·85 for 10×£1·47.

The eight PHQ cards show the seven individual stamps and the complete miniature sheet.

Year Pack

2014 (4 Nov). Comprises Nos. 3552/3569, **MS**3578/3594, **MS**3601/3624, 3626/3631, 3635/3656.

CP3657*a*	Year Pack (Pack No. 505) (*sold for £86*)............	£130

Post Office Yearbook

2014 (4 Nov). Comprises Nos. 3552/3569, **MS**3578/3594, **MS**3601/3624, 3626/3631, 3635/3656.

YB3657*a*	Yearbook (*sold for £106*)......................	£160

Miniature Sheet Collection

2014 (4 Nov). Comprises Nos. **MS**3578, **MS**3601, **MS**3608, **MS**3641 and **MS**3657.

MS3657*a* Miniature Sheet Collection (*sold for £23*)..........	30·00

2802 The White Rabbit

2803 Down the Rabbit Hole

2804 Drink Me

2805 The White Rabbit's House

2806 The Cheshire Cat

2807 A Mad Tea Party

2808 The Queen of Hearts

2809 The Game of Croquet

2810 Alice's Evidence   **2811** A Pack of Cards

(Grahame Baker-Smith (illustration) and Godfrey Design. Litho ISP Cartor (Nos. 3658/3667) or gravure ISP Walsall (Nos. 3668/3669))

2015 (6 Jan). Alice in Wonderland. Multicoloured One phosphor band at right (2nd) or two phosphor bands (others).

(a) Ordinary gum. Perf 14½.

3658	**2802**	(2nd) The White Rabbit...........................	90	90
		a. Vert pair. Nos. 3658/3659........	1·75	1·75
3659	**2803**	(2nd) Down the Rabbit Hole................	90	90
3660	**2804**	(1st) Drink Me..	1·20	1·00
		a. Vert pair. Nos. 3660/3661........	2·40	2·00
3661	**2805**	(1st) The White Rabbit's House...........	1·20	1·00
3662	**2806**	81p. The Cheshire Cat............................	1·50	1·50
		a. Vert pair. Nos. 3662/3663........	3·00	3·00
3663	**2807**	81p. A Mad Tea Party.............................	1·50	1·50
3664	**2808**	£1·28 The Queen of Hearts..................	2·50	2·50
		a. Vert pair. Nos. 3664/3665........	5·00	5·00
3665	**2809**	£1·28 The Game of Croquet................	2·50	2·50
3666	**2810**	£1·47 Alice's Evidence...........................	3·25	3·25
		a. Vert pair. Nos. 3666/3667........	6·50	6·50
3667	**2811**	£1·47 A Pack of Cards............................	3·25	3·25
Set of 10...			16·75	16·50
Set of 5 Gutter Strips of 4...............................			35·00	
First Day Cover (Tallents House).......................				17·50
First Day Cover (Oxford).....................................				17·50
Presentation Pack (PO Pack No. 506).............			25·00	
PHQ Cards (Set of 10) (396).............................			5·00	18·00

(b) Self-adhesive. Die-cut perf 14½.

3668	**2804**	(1st) Drink Me..	5·00	5·00
		a. Booklet pane. Nos. 3668/3669		
		and U3022×4...............................	12·00	
3669	**2805**	(1st) The White Rabbit's House...........	5·00	5·00

Nos. 3658/3659, 3660/3661, 3662/3663, 3664/3665 and 3666/3667 were each printed together, *se-tenant*, as vertical pairs in sheets of 60 (2 panes 5×6).

Nos. 3658/3667 commemorate the 150th anniversary of the Publication of *Alice's Adventures in Wonderland* by Lewis Carroll.

Nos. 3668/3669 were only issued in stamp booklet, No. PM46, originally sold for £3·72

2812 Happy Birthday (NB Studio)   **2813** Well Done (Webb & Webb Design Ltd)   **2814** Wedding (Caroline Gardner Ltd)

2815 Love (Rebecca Sutherland)   **2816** Mum (The Chase)   **2817** New Baby (NB Studio)

2818 Grandparent (NB Studio)   **2819** Dad (Webb & Webb Design Ltd)

(Des Jenny Bowers and NB Studio. Gravure ISP Walsall (Nos. 3670/3677) or litho ISP Cartor (No. **MS**3678))

2015 (20 Jan). Smilers (5th series). Multicoloured Two phosphor bands.

(a) Self-adhesive booklet stamps. Die-cut perf 14½×14 (with one elliptical hole in each vert side).

3670	**2812**	(1st) Happy Birthday...............................	1·90	1·90
		a. Booklet pane. Nos. 3670×2, 3671,		
		3672/3673 each×2, 3674, 3675×2		
		and 3676/3677..............................	18·00	
3671	**2813**	(1st) Well Done..	2·75	2·75
3672	**2814**	(1st) Wedding..	1·90	1·90
3673	**2815**	(1st) Love..	1·90	1·90
3674	**2816**	(1st) Mum..	2·75	2·75
3675	**2817**	(1st) New Baby...	1·90	1·90
3676	**2818**	(1st) Grandparent...................................	2·75	2·75
3677	**2819**	(1st) Dad..	2·75	2·75
Set of 8..			15·00	15·00

(b) Ordinary gum. Perf 14½×14 (with one elliptical hole in each vert side).

MS3678 134×70 mm. As Nos. 3670/3677		10·00	10·00
First Day Cover (Tallents House)........................			10·00
First Day Cover (Greetwell, Lincoln).................			10·00
Presentation Pack (PO Pack No. M23).............		12·00	
PHQ Cards (set of 9) (D34)................................		6·75	25·00

Nos. 3670/3677 were issued in booklets of 12, No. QB1, originally sold for £7·44.

Nos. 3670/3677 were also issued in sheets of 20 with *se-tenant* greetings labels (No. LS93), printed by Cartor in lithography and originally sold at £12·90 per sheet.

Sheets of 20 stamps of the same design were available with personal photographs on the labels from Royal mail, Edinburgh.

The complete miniature sheet is shown on one of the nine PHQ cards with the others depicting individual stamps.

2820 Colossus, World's First Electronic Digital Computer   **2821** World Wide Web, Revolutionary Global Communications System

2822 Cats Eyes, Light-reflecting Road Safety Innovation   **2823** Fibre Optics, Pioneering Rapid-data-transfer Technology

2824 Stainless Steel, Non-corrosive, Versatile, 100% Recyclable Alloy   **2825** Carbon Fibre, High-strength, Lightweight, Composite Material

2826 DNA Sequencing, Revolution in Understanding the Genome

2827 i-LIMB, Bionic Hand with Individually Powered Digits

(Des GBH. Litho ISP Cartor)

2015 (19 Feb). Inventive Britain. Multicoloured Two phosphor bands. Perf 14½.

3679	**2820**	(1st) Colossus..............................	1·20	1·00
		a. Horiz pair. Nos. 3679/3680..............	2·40	2·00
		b. Booklet pane. Nos. 3305, 3281×2 and 3679 with margins all round...	4·00	
		c. Booklet pane. Nos. 3679/3680, 3683 and 3686..................	5·50	
3680	**2821**	(1st) World Wide Web............................	1·20	1·00
3681	**2822**	81p. Cats eyes....................................	1·10	1·10
		a. Horiz pair. Nos. 3681/3682..............	2·25	2·25
		b. Booklet pane. Nos. 3681/3682 and 3684/3685 with margins all round..	6·00	
3682	**2823**	81p. Fibre Optics.................................	1·10	1·10
3683	**2824**	£1·28 Stainless Steel............................	1·75	1·75
		a. Horiz pair. Nos. 3683/3684..............	3·75	3·75
3684	**2825**	£1·28 Carbon Fibre...............................	1·75	1·75
3685	**2826**	£1·47 DNA Sequencing...........................	2·25	2·25
		a. Horiz pair. Nos. 3685/3686..............	4·50	4·50
3686	**2827**	£1·47 i-LIMB......................................	2·25	2·25
Set of 8..			11·50	11·25
Set of 4 Gutter Blocks of 4............................			23·00	
First Day Cover (Tallents House).....................				15·50
First Day Cover (Harlow)................................				15·50
Presentation Pack (PO Pack No. 507)...............			13·50	
PHQ Cards (set of 8) (397).............................			4·00	17·00

Nos. 3679/3680, 3681/3682, 3683/3684 and 3685/3686 were each printed together, *se-tenant*, as horizontal pairs in sheets of 60 (2 panes 6×5).

Booklet panes Nos. 3679b/3679c and 3681b come from the £14·60 Inventive Britain booklet, No. DY12.

2828 Tarr Steps, River Barle

2829 Row Bridge, Mosedale Beck

2830 Pulteney Bridge, River Avon

2831 Craigellachie Bridge, River Spey

2832 Menai Suspension Bridge, Menai Strait

2833 High Level Bridge, River Tyne

2834 Royal Border Bridge, River Tweed

2835 Tees Transporter Bridge, River Tees

2836 Humber Bridge, River Humber

2837 Peace Bridge, River Foyle

(Des GBH. Litho ISP Cartor)

2015 (5 Mar). Bridges. Multicoloured Two phosphor bands. Perf 14½×14.

3687	**2828**	(1st) Tarr Steps, River Barle......................	1·20	1·00
		a. Horiz strip of 5. Nos. 3687/3691.........	5·25	4·50
3688	**2829**	(1st) Row Bridge, Mosedale Beck............	1·20	1·00
3689	**2830**	(1st) Pulteney Bridge, River Avon............	1·20	1·00
3690	**2831**	(1st) Craigellachie Bridge, River Spey.....	1·20	1·00
3691	**2832**	(1st) Menai Suspension Bridge, Menai Strait.......................................	1·20	1·00
3692	**2833**	(1st) High Level Bridge, River Tyne...........	1·20	1·00
		a. Horiz strip of 5. Nos. 3692/3696.........	5·25	4·50
3693	**2834**	(1st) Royal Border Bridge, River Tweed..	1·20	1·00
3694	**2835**	(1st) Tees Transporter Bridge, River Tees......................................	1·20	1·00
3695	**2836**	(1st) Humber Bridge, River Humber.......	1·20	1·00
3696	**2837**	(1st) Peace Bridge, River Foyle...............	1·20	1·00
Set of 10..			10·50	9·00
Set of 2 Gutter Strips of 10............................			21·00	
Set of 2 Traffic Light Gutter Strips of 10...............			26·00	
First Day Cover (Tallents House).....................				11·50
First Day Cover (Bridge, Canterbury)................				11·50
Presentation Pack (PO Pack No. 508)...............			11·50	
PHQ Cards (set of 10) (398).............................			5·00	12·50

Nos. 3687/3691 and 3692/3696 were each printed together, *se-tenant*, as horizontal strips of five stamps in sheets of 50 (2 panes 5×5).

2838 Spike Milligan

2839 The Two Ronnies

2840 Billy Connolly

2841 Morecambe and Wise

2842 Norman Wisdom

2843 Lenny Henry

2844 Peter Cook and Dudley Moore

2845 Monty Python

2846 French and Saunders

2847 Victoria Wood

(Des The Chase. Litho ISP Cartor (Nos. 3697/3706) or gravure ISP Walsall (Nos. 3707/3708))

2015 (1 Apr). Comedy Greats. Multicoloured Two phosphor bands.

(a) Ordinary gum. Perf 14.

3697	**2838**	(1st) Spike Milligan................................	1·20	1·00
		a. Horiz strip of 5. Nos. 3697/3701.....	5·25	4·50
3698	**2839**	(1st) The Two Ronnies...........................	1·20	1·00
3699	**2840**	(1st) Billy Connolly................................	1·20	1·00
3700	**2841**	(1st) Morecambe and Wise....................	1·20	1·00
3701	**2842**	(1st) Norman Wisdom............................	1·20	1·00
3702	**2843**	(1st) Lenny Henry.................................	1·20	1·00
		a. Horiz strip of 5. Nos. 3702/3706.....	5·25	4·50
3703	**2844**	(1st) Peter Cook and Dudley Moore.......	1·20	1·00
3704	**2845**	(1st) Monty Python...............................	1·20	1·00
3705	**2846**	(1st) French and Saunders....................	1·20	1·00
3706	**2847**	(1st) Victoria Wood..............................	1·20	1·00
Set of 10..			10·50	9·00
Set of 2 Gutter Strips of 10...............................			21·00	
First Day Cover (Tallents House)...........................				11·50
First Day Cover (Laughterton, Lincoln).................				11·50
Presentation Pack (PO Pack No. 509)...................			11·50	
PHQ Cards (set of 10) (399)................................			5·00	12·50

(b) Self-adhesive. Die-cut perf 14.

3707	**2842**	(1st) Norman Wisdom............................	5·50	5·50
		a. Booklet pane. Nos. 3707/3708		
		and U3022×4............................	15·00	
3708	**2841**	(1st) Morecambe and Wise....................	5·50	5·50

Nos. 3697/3701 and 3702/3706 were each printed together, *se-tenant*, as horizontal strips of five stamps in sheets of 50 (2 panes 5×5).

Nos. 3707/3708 were issued in stamp booklet, No. PM47, sold for £3·72.

2848 Penny Black

2849 Penny Black and 1840 2d. blue

(Des Sedley Place. Gravure ISP Walsall (No. 3709) or litho ISP Cartor (No. **MS**3710))

2015 (6 May). 175th Anniversary of the Penny Black. Multicoloured Two phosphor bands.

(a) Self-adhesive booklet stamps. Die-cut perf 14½×14 (with one elliptical hole in each vert side).

3709	**2848**	(1st) Penny Black.................................	2·00	2·00

(b) Ordinary gum. Perf 14½×14 (with one elliptical hole in each vert side).

MS3710 156×74 mm. **2849** (1st) Penny Black×2; (1st)		
1840 2d. blue×2..	3·50	3·75
First Day Cover (Tallents House)...........................		4·75

First Day Cover (Bath).. | | 4·75
Presentation Pack (PO Pack No. 510)................... | 4·25 |
PHQ Cards (set of 3) (400)................................. | 1·50 | 4·00

No. 3709 was issued in booklets of six, Nos. MB13 and MB21. Stamps from booklet No. MB13 have a pinkish hue, whilst those from the booklet No. MB21 have a beige hue to the non-black areas of the stamps.

Designs as No. 3709 and (1st) Twopenny Blue as within No. **MS**3710 were also issued in sheets of 20 (No. LS94) containing ten 1st class Penny Black and ten 1st class Twopenny Blue, each stamp accompanied by a se-tenant label. These sheets were printed in lithography by ISP Cartor and originally sold for £12·90.

Sheets of ten or 20 1st Penny Black were available with personal photographs on the labels from Royal Mail Edinburgh, sold for £10·20 (ten) or £18·65 (20).

Miniature sheets as No. **MS**3710 with a special inscription were available only at Europhilex 2015 (*Price* £30).

The three PHQ cards show the two individual stamps and the complete miniature sheet.

See also Nos. 3806/3809, 4331 and **MS**4355.

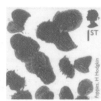

2850 Poppies (Howard Hodgkin)

2851 All the Hills and Vales Along (Charles Hamilton Sorley)

2852 Rifleman Kulbir Thapa

2853 The Kensingtons at Laventie (Eric Kennington)

2854 A British Soldier visits his Comrade's Grave

2855 London Irish Rifles' Football from Loos

(Des Hat-trick design. Litho ISP Cartor)

2015 (14 May). Centenary of the First World War (2nd issue). Multicoloured. Two phosphor bands. Perf 14½.

3711	**2850**	(1st) *Poppies*......................................	1·20	1·00
		a. Booklet pane. Nos. 3711/3713		
		with margins all round....................	3·50	
3712	**2851**	(1st) *All the Hills and Vales Along*.............	1·20	1·00
3713	**2852**	(1st) *Rifleman Kulbir Thapa*....................	1·20	1·00
3714	**2853**	£1·52 *The Kensingtons at Laventie*............	2·40	2·40
		a. Booklet pane. Nos. 3714/3716		
		with margins all round....................	7·50	
3715	**2854**	£1·52 *A British Soldier visits his*		
		Comrade's Grave on the Cliffs........	2·40	2·40
3716	**2855**	£1·52 London Irish Rifles' Football from		
		Loos.......................................	2·40	2·40
Set of 6..			9·50	9·00
Set of 6 Gutter Pairs...			19·00	
First Day Cover (Tallents House)...........................				12·00
First Day Cover (Winchester)...............................				12·00
Presentation Pack (PO Pack No. 511)...................			11·00	
PHQ Cards (set of 6) (401)................................			3·00	11·50

Nos. 3711a and 3714a were issued in the £13·96 Centenary of the First World War (2nd issue) booklet, No DY13.

2588 Six Poppies on Barbed Wire Fence

(Des Hat-trick Design. Litho ISP Cartor)

2015 (14 May)–**2017**. Centenary of the First World War. Premium Booklet stamp. As No. 3414 but ordinary gum. Multicoloured Two phosphor bands. Perf 14½×14 (with one elliptical hole in each vertical side).

3717	**2588**	(1st) Six Poppies on Barbed Wire Stems	1·50	1·50
		a. Booklet pane. Nos. 3717×4, EN51, NI95, S158a and W148 with central label and margins all round (21·6.16)..................................	21·00	
		b. Booklet pane. No. 3717×8 with central label and margins all round (31.7.17)................................	12·00	

First Day Cover (Tallents House) (No. 3717a)......................		23·00
First Day Cover (Lyness, Stromness) (No. 3717a)................		23·00
First Day Cover (Tallents House) (No. 3717b)......................		13·00
First Day Cover (Blaenannerch, Aberteifi, Cardigan) (No. 3717b)...		13·00

No. 3717 comes from pane No. U3070n in the £13·96 Centenary of the First World War (2nd issue) booklet, No. DY13, pane No. 3717a from the £16·49 Centenary of the First World War (3rd issue) booklet, No. DY18, pane No. 3717b from the £15·41 Centenary of the First World War (4th issue) booklet, No. DY22.

2856 Magna Carta 1215

2857 Simon de Montfort's Parliament, 1265

2858 Bill of Rights, 1689

2859 American Bill of Rights, 1791

2860 Universal Declaration of Human Rights, 1948

2861 Charter of the Commonwealth, 2013

(Des Howard Brown. Litho ISP Cartor)

2015 (2 June). 800th Anniversary of the *Magna Carta*. Multicoloured Two phosphor bands. Perf 14½.

3718	**2856**	(1st) Magna Carta................................	1·20	1·00
3719	**2857**	(1st) Simon de Montfort's Parliament....	1·20	1·00
3720	**2858**	£1·33 Bill of Rights...............................	1·60	1·60
3721	**2859**	£1·33 American Bill of Rights..................	1·60	1·60
3722	**2860**	£1·52 Universal Declaration of Human Rights...	3·00	3·00
3723	**2861**	£1·52 Charter of the Commonwealth......	3·00	3·00
Set of 6...			10·00	10·00
Set of 6 Gutter pairs...			20·00	
First Day Cover (Tallents House)..				12·00
First Day Cover (London NW1)...				12·00
Presentation Pack (PO Pack No. 512)................................			13·00	
PHQ Cards (set of 6) (402)...			3·00	12·50

2862 The Defence of Hougoumont

2863 The Scots Greys during the Charge of the Union Brigade

2864 The French Cavalry's Assault on Allied Defensive Squares

2865 The Defence of La Haye Sainte by the King's German Legion

2866 The Capture of Plancenoit by the Prussians

2867 The French Imperial Guard's Final Assault

(Des Silk Pearce. Litho ISP Cartor)

2015 (18 June). Bicentenary of the Battle of Waterloo (1st issue). Multicoloured Two phosphor bands. Perf 14½.

3724	**2862**	(1st) The Defence of Hougoumont.......	1·20	1·00
		a. Booklet pane. Nos. 3724 and 3729 with margins all round..................	4·00	
3725	**2863**	(1st) The Scots Greys during the charge of the Union Brigade.........	1·20	1·00
		a. Booklet pane. Nos. 3725/3728 with margins all round..................	6·25	
3726	**2864**	£1 The French Cavalry's assault on Allied defensive Squares................	1·40	1·40
3727	**2865**	£1 The Defence of La Haye Sainte by the King's German Legion.............	1·40	1·40
3728	**2866**	£1·52 The Capture of Plancenoit by the Prussians................................	2·50	2·50
3729	**2867**	£1·52 The French Imperial Guard's Final Assault........................	2·50	2·50
Set of 6........................			9·00	8·75
Set of 6 Gutter Pairs........................			18·00	
First Day Cover (Tallents House)........................				11·50
First Day Cover (Waterloo, Liverpool)........................				11·50
Presentation Pack (PO Pack No. 513) (Nos. 3724/3729 and **MS**3734)........................			17·00	
PHQ Cards (set of 11) (403)........................			5·50	22·00

Nos. 3724a and 3725a were only issued in the £14·47 Bicentenary of the Battle of Waterloo booklet, No. DY14.

The 11 PHQ cards depict the individual stamps, including those from No. **MS**3734, and the complete miniature sheet.

2868 15th Infantry Regiment, IV Corps, Prussian Army

2869 Light Infantry, King's German Legion, Anglo-Allied Army

2870 92nd Gordon Highlanders, Anglo-Allied Army

2871 Grenadiers, Imperial Guard, French Army

2872 Soldiers and Battle of Waterloo Map

(Des Chris Collingwood (illustrations) and Webb and Webb Design Ltd. Litho ISP Cartor)

2015 (18 June). Bicentenary of the Battle of Waterloo (2nd issue). Multicoloured Two phosphor bands. Perf 14.

3730	**2868**	(1st) 15th Infantry Regiment, IV Corps...	1·50	1·50
		a. Booklet pane. Nos. 3730/3733 with margins all round and roulettes at left................	6·00	
3731	**2869**	(1st) Light Infantry, King's German Legion........................	1·50	1·50
3732	**2870**	£1·33 92nd Gordon Highlanders.............	1·75	1·75
3733	**2871**	£1·33 Grenadiers, Imperial Guard............	1·75	1·75
Set of 4........................			6·00	6·00
MS3734 156×74 mm. **2872** Soldiers and Battle of Waterloo Map Nos. 3730/3733....................			6·00	6·00
First Day Cover (Tallents House)........................				7·50
First Day Cover (Waterloo, Liverpool)........................				7·50

Nos. 3730/3733 come from £14·47 Bicentenary of the Battle of Waterloo booklet, No. DY14, and No. **MS**3734.

2873 Battle of Britain

(Des Supple Studio (stamps) and The Team (miniature sheet). Litho ISP Cartor)

2015 (16 July). 75th Anniversary of the Battle of Britain. Multicoloured 'All-over' phosphor. Perf 14½×14.

MS3735 190×74 mm. **2873** (1st) Pilots scramble to their Hurricanes; (1st) Supermarine Spitfires of 610 Squadron, Biggin Hill, on patrol; (1st) Armourer Fred Roberts replaces ammunition boxes on Supermarine Spitfire; £1·33 Spotters of the Auxiliary Territorial Service looking for enemy aircraft; £1·33 Operations Room at Bentley Priory; £1·33 Pilots of 32 Squadron await orders, RAF Hawkinge, Kent..	8·25	8·25
First Day Cover (Tallents House)........................		11·00
First Day Cover (London NW9)........................		11·00
Presentation Pack (PO Pack No. 514)........................	10·00	
PHQ Cards (set of 7) (404)........................	3·50	13·50

The seven PHQ cards show the six individual stamps and the complete miniature sheet.

See also Nos. 4071/4073.

2874 Scabious Bee (Andrena hattorfiana) on Field Scabious (Knautia arvensis)

2875 Great Yellow Bumblebee (Bombus distinguendus) on Bird's-foot Trefoil (Lotus corniculatus)

2876 Northern Colletes Bee (*Colletes floralis*) on Wild Carrot (*Daucus carota*)

2877 Bilberry Bumblebee (*Bombus monticola*) on Bilberry (*Vaccinium myrtillus*)

2878 Large Mason Bee (*Osmia xanthomelana*) on Horseshoe Vetch (*Hippocrepis comosa*)

2879 Potter Flower Bee (*Anthophora retusa*) on Ground Ivy (*Glechoma hederacea*)

2880 The Honey Bee

(Des Richard Lewington (illustration) and Anna Ekelund (Nos. 3736/371) or Andy English (illustration) and Interabang (No. **MS**3742). Litho ISP Cartor (Nos. 3736/3742) or gravure ISP Walsall (No. 3743))

2015 (18 Aug). Bees. Multicoloured

(a) Ordinary gum. One centre band (No. 3736), two phosphor bands (Nos. 3737/3741) or phosphor background (No. MS3742). Perf 14×14½.

3736	**2874**	(2nd) Scabious Bee on Field Scabious.....	90	90
3737	**2875**	(1st) Great Yellow Bumblebee on Bird's-foot Trefoil............................	1·20	1·20
3738	**2876**	£1 Northern Colletes Bee on Wild Carrot..	1·50	1·50
3739	**2877**	£1·33 Bilberry Bumblebee on Bilberry.....	1·75	1·75
3740	**2878**	£1·52 Large Mason Bee on Horseshoe Vetch..	2·25	2·25
3741	**2879**	£2·25 Potter Flower Bee on Ground Ivy...	3·75	3·75
Set of 6..			10·00	10·00
Set of 6 Gutter Pairs..			20·00	
First Day Cover (Tallents House)...........................				13·50
First Day Cover (St Bees)......................................				13·50
Presentation Pack (PO Pack No. 515) (Nos. 3736/3741 and **MS**3743)..			19·00	
PHQ Cards (set of 7) (405)....................................			3·50	18·00
MS3742 191×74 mm. **2880** (1st) Waggle dance; (1st) Pollination; £1·33 Making honey; £1·33 Tending young..			5·50	5·75
First Day Cover (Tallents House)...........................				6·00
First Day Cover (St Bees)......................................				6·00

(b) Self-adhesive. Two phosphor bands. Die-cut perf 14×14½.

3743	**2875**	(1st) Great Yellow Bumblebee (*Bombus distinguendus*) on Bird's-foot Trefoil (*Lotus corniculatus*)...............	2·00	2·00
		a. Booklet pane. Nos. 3743×2 and U3022×4...............................	7·50	

No. 3743 was issued in stamp booklet, No. PM48, originally sold for £3·78.

The seven PHQ cards depict the six individual stamps and the complete miniature sheet.

Nos. 3744/3746 are vacant.

2881 'Long to Reign Over Us'

(Des Sedley Place. Eng C Matthews. Recess and gravure FNMT (Spain))

2015 (9 Sept) Long to Reign Over Us (2nd issue). Multicoloured Two phosphor bands. Perf 14½×14 (with one elliptical hole in each vertical side) (Machin) or 14 (others).

MS3747 194×75 mm. **2881** Long to Reign Over Us (1st) William Wyon's City Medal depicting Queen Victoria; (1st) Portrait of Queen Elizabeth II from photograph by Dorothy Wilding; As No. U3747 (but printed gravure); £1·52 Badge of the House of Windsor depicting Round Tower of Windsor Castle; £1·52 Device from The Queen's Personal Flag...........	8·00	8·00
First Day Cover (Tallents House)...........................		10·00
First Day Cover (Windsor).....................................		10·00
Presentation Pack (PO Pack No. 516)...................	3·00	
PHQ Cards (set of 6) (406)....................................	3·00	12·00

Stamps from No. **MS**3747 all have an iridescent overprint reading LONG TO REIGN OVER US.

The 1st class bright lilac stamp from No. **MS**3747 has a source code 'REIGM' and year code 'O15R' within this iridescent overprint.

The PHQ cards depict the five individual stamps and the complete miniature sheet.

2882 Tackle   **2883** Scrum

2884 Try   **2885** Conversion

2886 Pass   **2887** Drop Goal

2888 Ruck   **2889** Line-Out

(Des Hat-trick design and Geoff Appleton (illustrations). Litho ISP Cartor (Nos. 3748/3755) or gravure ISP Walsall (Nos. 3756/3757))

2015 (18 Sept). Rugby World Cup. Multicoloured One centre band (Nos. 3748/3749) or two bands (others).

(a) Ordinary gum. Perf 14.

3748	**2882**	(2nd) Tackle..	90	90
		a. Horiz pair. Nos. 3748/3749..............	1·75	1·75
3749	**2883**	(2nd) Scrum..	90	90
3750	**2884**	(1st) Try..	1·20	1·00
		a. Horiz pair. Nos. 3750/3751..............	2·40	2·00

3751	**2885**	(1st) Conversion	1·20	1·00
3752	**2886**	£1 Pass	1·50	1·50
		a. Horiz pair. Nos. 3752/3753	3·00	3·00
3753	**2887**	£1 Drop Goal	1·50	1·50
3754	**2888**	£1·52 Ruck	2·00	2·00
		a. Horiz pair. Nos. 3754/3755	4·00	4·00
3755	**2889**	£1·52 Line-Out	2·00	2·00

Set of 8.. 10·00 9·75
Set of 4 Gutter Blocks of 4....................... 20·00
First Day Cover (Tallents House)............................. 12·50
First Day Cover (Rugby)................................. 12·50
Presentation Pack (PO Pack No. 517)......... 12·50
PHQ Cards (set of 8) (407)......................... 4·00 13·00

(b) Self-adhesive. Die-cut perf 14.

3756	**2884**	(1st) Try	4·00	4·00
		a. Booklet pane. Nos. 3756/3757 and U3746×4	12·00	
3757	**2885**	(1st) Conversion	4·00	4·00

Nos. 3748/3749, 3750/3751, 3752/3753 and 3754/3755 were each printed together, *se-tenant*, as horizontal pairs in sheets of 60 (2 panes 6×5).

Nos. 3756/3757 were issued in stamp booklet, No. PM49, originally sold for £3·78.

2890 Darth Vader

2891 Yoda

2892 Obi-Wan Kenobi

2893 Stormtrooper

2894 Han Solo

2895 Rey

2896 Princess Leia

2897 The Emperor

2898 Luke Skywalker

2899 Boba Fett

2900 Finn

2901 Kylo Ren

2902 Star Wars

(Des Malcolm Tween (illustrations) and Interabang (Nos. 3758/3769) or GBH (No. **MS**3770). Litho ISP Cartor)

2015 (20 Oct)–**2017**. *Star Wars* (1st issue). Multicoloured Two phosphor bands and fluorescent emblems (Nos. 3758/3769) or 'All-over' phosphor (No. **MS**3770).

(a) Ordinary gum. Perf 14½.

3758	**2890**	(1st) Darth Vader	1·20	1·00
		a. Horiz strip of 6. Nos. 3758/3763	6·50	5·50
		b. Booklet pane. Nos. 3758, 3760, 3763 and 3767/3769 with margins all round (17.12.15)	6·50	
3759	**2891**	(1st) Yoda	1·20	1·00
		b. Booklet pane. Nos. 3759, 3761/3762 and 3764/3766 with margins all round (17.12.15)	6·50	
		c. Booklet pane. Nos. 3759, 3763, 4007 and 4009 with margins all round (14.12.17)	4·25	
3760	**2892**	(1st) Obi-Wan Kenobi	1·20	1·00
3761	**2893**	(1st) Stormtrooper	1·20	1·00
3762	**2894**	(1st) Han Solo	1·20	1·00
		b. Booklet pane. Nos. 3762, 3764 and 4012/4013 with margins all round (14.12.17)	4·25	
3763	**2895**	(1st) Rey	1·20	1·00
3764	**2896**	(1st) Princess Leia	1·20	1·00
		a. Horiz strip of 6. Nos. 3764/3769	6·50	5·50
3765	**2897**	(1st) The Emperor	1·20	1·00
3766	**2898**	(1st) Luke Skywalker	1·20	1·00
3767	**2899**	(1st) Boba Fett	1·20	1·00
3768	**2900**	(1st) Finn	1·20	1·00
3769	**2901**	(1st) Kylo Ren	1·20	1·00

Set of 12.. 13·00 11·00
Set of 2 Gutter Strips of 12....................... 26·00
First Day Cover (Tallents House)....................... 14·00
First Day Cover (Elstree, Borehamwood)............... 14·00
Presentation Pack (PO Pack No. 518) (Nos. 3758/3769 and **MS**3770).......................... 21·00
PHQ Cards (set of 19) (408)....................... 9·50 28·00

(b) Self-adhesive.

MS3770 204×75 mm. **2902** (1st) X-wing Starfighter (60×21 mm, perf 14½×14); (1st) TIE fighters (35×36 mm, perf 14); (1st) X-wing Starfighters (60×21 mm, perf 14½×14); (1st) AT-AT Walkers (41×30 mm, Perf 14); (1st) TIE fighters (27×37 mm, perf 14); (1st) *Millennium Falcon* (60×30 mm, perf 14½)............................... 7·00 6·50
First Day Cover (Tallents House)....................... 7·00
First Day Cover (Elstree, Borehamwood)............... 7·00

Nos. 3758/3763 and 3764/3769 were each printed together, *se-tenant*, as horizontal strips of six stamps in sheets of 60 (2 panes 6×5).

Nos. 3758/3769 all show fluorescent emblems under UV light. Nos. 3758, 3761 and 3765 show the symbol of the Galactic Empire, Nos. 3759/3760 show the Jedi Order symbol, Nos. 3762, 3764 and 3766 show the Rebel Alliance symbol, Nos. 3763 and 3768/3769 show the logo for the new film *Star Wars The Force Awakens* and No. 3767 shows the Mandalorian Crest.

Booklet pane Nos. 3758b and 3759b come from the £16·99 The Making of Star Wars - The British Story booklet, No. DY15.

Booklet pane Nos. 3759c and 3762b come from the £15·99 Star Wars: The Making of Droids, Aliens and Creatures booklet, No. DY23.

Nos. 3758/3769 were re-issued on 12 October 2017 with Nos. 4007/4014 in a sheet entitled *Star Wars*, The Ultimate Collectors' Sheet (No. **MS**4014a).

Designs as Nos. 3758/3759 and 3761/3762 but self-adhesive were issued in sheets of ten with *se-tenant* labels showing film stills (No. LS96), each sheet containing Nos. 3758/3759, each×3, and Nos. 3761/3762, each×2. These sheets were originally sold for £6·80 each.

The four designs were also available from Royal Mail, Edinburgh in separate sheets of ten with personal photographs on the labels, originally sold for £10·20 per sheet.

The 19 PHQ cards depict the individual stamps including those from No. **MS**3770 and the complete miniature sheet.

2903 The Journey to Bethlehem   **2904** The Nativity   **2905** The Journey to Bethlehem

2906 The Nativity   **2907** The Animals of the Nativity   **2908** The Shepherds

2909 The Three Wise Men   **2910** The Annunciation

(Des David Holmes (illustrations) and Studio David Hillman. Gravure ISP Walsall (Nos. 3771a, 3772a) or De La Rue (others))

2015 (3 Nov). Christmas. Multicoloured One centre band (No. 3771) or two bands (others).

(a) Self-adhesive. Die-cut perf 14½×15..

3771	**2903**	(2nd) The Journey to Bethlehem............	90	90
		a. Booklet pane. No. 3771×12............	13·50	
3772	**2904**	(1st) The Nativity................................	1·20	1·00
		a. Booklet pane. No. 3772×12............	16·00	
3773	**2905**	(2nd Large) The Journey to Bethlehem..	1·25	1·10
3774	**2906**	(1st Large) The Nativity......................	1·70	1·40
3775	**2907**	£1·00 The Animals of the Nativity............	1·75	1·75
3776	**2908**	£1·33 The Shepherds.................................	2·10	2·10
3777	**2909**	£1·52 The Three Wise Men......................	2·50	2·50
3778	**2910**	£2·25 The Annunciation........................	3·50	3·50
Set of 8..			13·25	12·75
First Day Cover (Tallents House)............................				16·75
First Day Cover (Bethlehem, Llandeilo).................				16·75
Presentation Pack (PO Pack No. 519)...................			15·00	
PHQ Cards (set of 9) (409)..................................			4·50	26·00

(b) Ordinary gum. Perf 14½×15..

MS3779 190×74 mm. As Nos. 3771/3778........	13·25	12·75
First Day Cover (Tallents House)............................		16·75
First Day Cover (Bethlehem, Llandeilo).................		16·75

The 2nd class, 1st class, £1, £1·33, £1·52 and £2·25 stamps were also issued in sheets of 20 (No. LS97), containing 8×2nd class, 8×1st class, 1×£1, 1×£1·33, 1×£1·52 and 1×£2·25 stamps, each stamp accompanied by a *se-tenant* label with a verse from the *King James Bible*. These sheets were printed in lithography by ISP Cartor and originally sold for £15·96.

The design of the 1st class stamps in the Post office Label Sheet is enlarged compared with those from counter sheets and booklets, resulting in a much diminished grey foreground at lower left.

The nine PHQ cards show the eight individual stamps and the complete miniature sheet.

Year Pack

2015 (3 Nov). Comprises Nos. 3658/3667, **MS**3678/3706, **MS**3710/3716, 3718/3729. **MS**3734, **MS**3735/**MS**3742, **MS**3747/3755 and 3758/3778

CP3779a	Year Pack (Pack No. 520) (*sold for £117*)...	£170

Post Office Yearbook

2015 (3 Nov). Comprises Nos. 3658/3667, **MS**3678/3706, **MS**3710/3729, **MS**3734, **MS**3735/**MS**3742, **MS**3747/3755 and 3758/3778

YB3779a	Yearbook (*sold for £137*)......................	£190

Miniature Sheet Collection

2015 (3 Nov). Comprises Nos. **MS**3678, **MS**3710, **MS**3734, **MS**3735, **MS**3742, **MS**3747, **MS**3770 and **MS**3779

MS3779a	Miniature Sheet Collection (*sold for £41*)...........	55·00

2911 X-wing Starfighter

2912 AT-AT Walkers   **2913** TIE Fighters

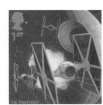

2914 TIE Fighters

2915 X-wing Starfighters

2916 *Millennium Falcon*

(Des GBH. Litho ISP Cartor)

2015 (17 Dec). *Star Wars* (2nd issue). Self-adhesive. Multicoloured 'Allover' phosphor. Die-cut perf 14½×14 (Nos. 3780, 3784), 14 (Nos. 3781/3783) or 14½ (No. 3785).

3780	**2911**	(1st) X-wing Starfighter.........................	1·25	1·25
		a. Booklet pane. Nos. 3780/3782........	3·50	
3781	**2912**	(1st) AT-AT Walkers............................	1·25	1·25
3782	**2913**	(1st) TIE fighters..................................	1·25	1·25
3783	**2914**	(1st) TIE fighters..................................	1·25	1·25
		a. Booklet pane. Nos. 3783/3785........	3·50	
3784	**2915**	(1st) X-wing Starfighters......................	1·25	1·25
3785	**2916**	(1st) *Millennium Falcon*......................	1·25	1·25
Set of 6...			6·75	6·75

Nos. 3780/3785 were only issued in £16·99 *Star Wars* premium booklet, No. DY15, or No. **MS**3770.

2917 Union Flag

(Litho ISP Cartor)

2015 (17 Dec). *Star Wars* (3rd issue). As No. 2570 but ordinary gum. Multicoloured Two phosphor bands. Perf 14½×14 (with one elliptical hole in each vert side).

3786	**2917**	(1st) Union Flag..........................	1·50	1·50

No. 3786 comes from booklet pane No. U3150l from £16·99 *Star Wars* booklet, No. DY15 and booklet pane No. U3071q from £16·99 James Bond booklet, No. DY33.

2918 Entering the Antarctic Ice, December 1914

2919 *Endurance* Frozen in Pack Ice, January 1915

2920 Striving to Free *Endurance*, February 1915

2921 Trapped in a Pressure Crack, October 1915

2922 Patience Camp, December 1915–April 1916

2923 Safe Arrival at Elephant Island, April 1916

2924 Setting out for South Georgia, April 1916

2925 Rescue of *Endurance* Crew, August 1916

(Des Robert Maude and Sarah Davies. Litho ISP Cartor)

2016 (7 Jan). Shackleton and the *Endurance* Expedition. Multicoloured. Two phosphor bands. Perf 14×14½.

3787	**2918**	(1st) Entering the Antarctic Ice..............	1·20	1·00
		a. Horiz pair. Nos. 3787/3788..............	2·40	2·00
3788	**2919**	(1st) *Endurance* Frozen in Pack Ice.........	1·20	1·00
3789	**2920**	£1 Striving to Free *Endurance*..............	1·50	1·50
		a. Horiz pair. Nos. 3789/3790..............	3·00	3·00
3790	**2921**	£1 Trapped in a Pressure Crack............	1·50	1·50
3791	**2922**	£1·33 Patience Camp............................	1·75	1·75
		a. Horiz pair. Nos. 3791/3792..............	3·75	3·75
3792	**2923**	£1·33 Safe Arrival at Elephant Island.......	1·75	1·75
3793	**2924**	£1·52 Setting out for South Georgia........	2·25	2·25
		a. Horiz pair. Nos. 3793/3794..............	4·50	4·50
3794	**2925**	£1·52 Rescue of *Endurance* Crew..............	2·25	2·25
Set of 8...			12·25	12·00
Set of 4 Gutter blocks of 4..................................			24·50	
First Day Cover (Tallents House)............................				16·00
First Day Cover (Plymouth)...................................				16·00
Presentation Pack (PO Pack No. 521).................			15·00	
PHQ Cards (set of 8) (410).................................			4·00	15·00

Nos. 3787/3788, 3789/3790, 3791/3792 and 3793/3794 were each printed together, *se-tenant*, as horizontal pairs in sheets of 60 (2 panes 6×5).

2926 Sir Brian Tuke, Master of the Posts

2927 *Mail Packet off Eastbourne* (Captain Victor Howes)

2928 Penfold Pillar Box

2929 River Post

2930 Mail Coach

2931 Medway Mail Centre

(Des Atelier Works (No. 3795/3800) or Purpose (No. **MS**3801). Litho ISP Cartor)

2016 (17–18 Feb). Royal Mail 500 (1st issue). Multicoloured. Two phosphor bands. Perf 14½×14 (Nos.3795/3800) or 14 (No. **MS**3801)

3795	**2926**	(1st) Sir Brian Tuke......................	1·20	1·00
		a. Booklet pane. Nos. 3795 and 3797/3798 with margins all round (18.2.16)......................	6·00	
3796	**2927**	(1st) *Mail Packet off Eastbourne*..............	1·20	1·00
		a. Booklet pane. Nos. 3796 and 3799/3800 with margins all round (18.2.16)......................	6·00	
3797	**2928**	(1st) Penfold Pillar Box............................	1·20	1·00
3798	**2929**	£1·52 River Post......................................	2·50	2·50
3799	**2930**	£1·52 Mail Coach....................................	2·50	2·50
3800	**2931**	£1·52 Medway Mail Centre......................	2·50	2·50
Set of 6...			10·00	9·50
Set of 6 Gutter Pairs...			20·00	
Set of 6 Traffic light Gutter pairs (two stamps only in each pair)..			21·00	
First Day Cover (Tallents House)............................				12·00
First Day Cover (London WC1).............................				12·00
Presentation Pack (PO Pack No. 522) (Nos. 3795/3800 and **MS**3801)..			18·00	
PHQ Cards (set of 11) (411).................................			5·50	24·00

2932 Classic GPO Posters

MS3801 125×89 mm. **2932** Classic GPO Posters (1st) 'QUICKEST WAY BY AIR MAIL' (Edward McKnight Kauffer, 1935); (1st) 'ADDRESS your letters PLAINLY' (Hans Schleger, 1942); £1·33 'pack your parcels carefully' (Hans Unger, 1950); £1·33 'STAMPS IN BOOKS SAVE TIME' (Harry Stevens, 1960)................... 7·00   7·25
First Day Cover (Tallents House)... 7·50
First Day Cover (London WC1)... 7·50

Nos. 3795/**MS**3801 commemorate 500 years of a regular, organised postal service.

Nos. 3795a and 3796a come from £16·36 500 Years of Royal mail premium booklet No. DY16.

No. **MS**3801 additionally inscribed 'Spring Stampex, 17-20 February 2016' was only available at that exhibition (*Price* £22).

The complete miniature sheet is shown on one of the 11 PHQ cards with the others depicting individual stamps including those from the miniature sheet.

2933 'QUICKEST WAY BY AIR MAIL' (Edward McKnight Kauffer, 1935)

2934 'ADDRESS your letters PLAINLY' (Hans Schleger, 1942)

2935 'STAMPS IN BOOKS SAVE TIME' (Harry Stevens, 1960)

2936 'pack your parcels carefully' (Hans Unger, 1950)

(Litho ISP Cartor)

2016 (17–18 Feb). Royal Mail 500 (2nd issue). Multicoloured Perf 14.
3802	**2933**	(1st) 'QUICKEST WAY BY AIR MAIL'..........	1·75	1·75
		a. Booklet pane. Nos. 3802/3805 with margins all round and roulettes at left (18.2.16).................	6·25	
3803	**2934**	(1st) 'ADDRESS your letters PLAINLY'.......	1·75	1·75
3804	**2935**	£1·33 'STAMPS IN BOOKS SAVE TIME'.......	1·75	1·75
3805	**2936**	£1·33 'pack your parcels carefully'...........	1·75	1·75
Set of 4..			6·25	6·25

Nos. 3802/3805 come from No. **MS**3801 and £16·36 500 years of Royal Mail premium booklet, No. DY16.

2937 Penny Red

(Gravure ISP Walsall)

2016 (18 Feb). 175th Anniversary of the Penny Red. Self-adhesive. Multicoloured Two phosphor bands. Die-cut perf 14½×14 (with one elliptical hole in each vert side).
3806	**2937**	(1st) Penny Red...	1·50	1·50

No. 3806 comes from booklets of six, No. MB16 and MB21.

No. 3806 was also issued in sheets of 20 with attached labels showing the Rainbow Trials from which the Penny Red evolved (No. LS99). These sheets were printed in lithography by ISP Cartor and originally sold for £13·10 each.

Sheets of ten or 20 of these Penny Red stamps were available from Royal Mail with personal photographs on the labels for £10·20 (ten) or £18·65 (20).

2848 Penny Black

2938 Two Pence Blue

(Des Atelier Works. Litho ISP Cartor)

2016 (18 Feb). Royal Mail 500 (3rd issue). Multicoloured Two phosphor bands. 14½×14 (with one elliptical hole in each vert side).
3807	**2848**	(1st) Penny Black.......................................	1·75	1·75
		a. Booklet pane. No. 3807×2 and Nos. 3808/3809 each×3 with central label and margins all round..................................	14·00	
3808	**2937**	(1st) Penny Red.......................................	1·50	1·50
3809	**2938**	(1st) 2d. Blue...	1·50	1·50
First Day Cover (Tallents House) (No. 3807a).....................				15·00
First Day Cover (London W1) (No. 3807a)...........................				15·00

Nos. 3807/3809 come from £16·36 500 Years of Royal Mail premium booklet, No. DY16 and £17·20 Queen Victoria premium booklet, No. DY30.

2939 Nicholas Winton (1909–2015)

2940 Sue Ryder (1924–2000)

2941 John Boyd Orr (1880–1971)

2942 Eglantyne Jebb (1876–1928)

2943 Joseph Rowntree (1836–1925)

2944 Josephine Butler (1828–1906)

(Des Hat-trick Design. Litho ISP Cartor)

2016 (15 Mar). British Humanitarians. Multicoloured Two phosphor bands. Perf 14½.
3810	**2939**	(1st) Nicholas Winton..............................	1·20	1·00
		a. Horiz strip of 3. Nos. 3810/3812.....	3·50	3·00
3811	**2940**	(1st) Sue Ryder.......................................	1·20	1·00
3812	**2941**	(1st) John Boyd Orr................................	1·20	1·00
3813	**2942**	£1·33 Eglantyne Jebb..............................	2·00	2·00
		a. Horiz strip of 3. Nos. 3813/3815.....	6·00	6·00
3814	**2943**	£1·33 Joseph Rowntree...........................	2·00	2·00
3815	**2944**	£1·33 Josephine Butler...........................	2·00	2·00
Set of 6..			8·75	8·25
Set of 2 Gutter Strips of 6..			17·50	
First Day Cover (Tallents House).................................				11·00
First Day Cover (Winton, Northallerton)......................				11·00
Presentation Pack (PO Pack No. 523)..........................			10·00	
PHQ Cards (set of 6) (412)...			3·00	11·00

Nos. 3810/3812 and 3813/3815 were each printed together, *se-tenant*, as horizontal strips of three stamps in sheets of 60 (2 panes 6×5).

2945 'to thine own self be true' (*Hamlet*)

COWARDS DIE MANY TIMES BEFORE THEIR DEATHS · THE **VALIANT** NEVER TASTE OF DEATH BUT ONCE·

JULIUS CAESAR   SHAKESPEARE

2946 'cowards die many times before their deaths. The valiant never taste of death but once.' (*Julius Caesar*)

Love is a smoke made with the fume of sighs

ROMEO AND JULIET   SHAKESPEARE

2947 'Love is a smoke made with the fume of sighs' (*Romeo and Juliet*)

THE FOOL DOTH THINK HE IS WISE, BUT THE WISE MAN KNOWS HIMSELF TO BE A FOOL.

AS YOU LIKE IT   SHAKESPEARE

2948 'The fool doth think he is wise, but the wise man knows himself to be a fool.' (*As You Like It*)

THERE WAS A STAR DANCED, and under that — WAS I — BORN.

MUCH ADO ABOUT NOTHING   SHAKESPEARE

2949 'There was a star danced, and under that was I born.' (*Much Ado About Nothing*)

BUT IF THE WHILE I THINK ON THEE, DEAR FRIEND, ALL LOSSES ARE RESTORED AND SORROWS END.

SONNET 30   SHAKESPEARE

2950 'But if the while I think on thee, dear friend, all losses are restored and sorrows end.' (*Sonnet 30*)

LOVE comforteth like sunshine after rain

VENUS AND ADONIS   SHAKESPEARE

2951 'LOVE comforteth like sunshine after rain' (*Venus and Adonis*)

WE ARE SUCH STUFF AS DREAMS ARE MADE ON; AND OUR LITTLE LIFE IS ROUNDED WITH A SLEEP.

THE TEMPEST   SHAKESPEARE

2952 'We are such stuff as dreams are made on; and our little life is rounded with a sleep.' (*The Tempest*)

Life's but a walking shadow, a poor player That struts and frets his hour upon the stage

MACBETH   SHAKESPEARE

2953 'Life's but a walking shadow, a poor player That struts and frets his hour upon the stage' (*Macbeth*)

RICHARD II   SHAKESPEARE

2954 'I wasted time, and now doth time waste me' (*Richard II*)

(Des The Chase. Litho ISP Cartor)

2016 (5 Apr). 400th Death Anniversary of William Shakespeare. Multicoloured Two phosphor bands. Perf 14½.

3816	**2945**	(1st) 'to thine own self be true'...............	1·20	1·00
		a. Horiz strip of 5. Nos. 3816/3820.....	5·25	4·50
3817	**2946**	(1st) 'cowards die many times before their deaths. The valiant never taste of death but once.'.................	1·20	1·00
3818	**2947**	(1st) 'Love is a smoke made with the fume of sighs'.................	1·20	1·00
3819	**2948**	(1st) 'The fool doth think he is wise, but the wise man knows himself to be a fool.'.................	1·20	1·00
3820	**2949**	(1st) 'There was a star danced, and under that was I born.'...................	1·20	1·00
3821	**2950**	(1st) 'But if the while I think on thee, dear friend, all losses are restored and sorrows end.'............................	1·20	1·00
		a. Horiz strip of 5. Nos. 3821/3825.....	5·25	4·50
3822	**2951**	(1st) 'LOVE comforteth like sunshine after rain'.................	1·20	1·00
3823	**2952**	(1st) 'We are such stuff as dreams are made on; and our little life is rounded with a sleep.'.................	1·20	1·00
3824	**2953**	(1st) 'Life's but a walking shadow, a poor player That struts and frets his hour upon the stage.'.................	1·20	1·00
3825	**2954**	(1st) 'I wasted time, and now doth time waste me' (*Richard II*).............	1·20	1·00
Set of 10..................			10·50	9·00
Set of 2 Gutter Strips of 10..................			21·00	
First Day Cover (Tallents House)................				12·00
First Day Cover (Stratford-upon-Avon)................				12·00
Presentation Pack (PO Pack No. 524)................			11·50	
PHQ Cards (set of 10) (413)................			5·00	12·00

Nos. 3816/3820 and 3821/3825 were each printed together, *se-tenant*, as horizontal strips of five stamps in sheets of 50 (2 panes 5×5).

2955 Princess Elizabeth and her Father the Duke of York (later King George VI), *circa* 1930

2956 Queen Elizabeth II at State Opening of Parliament, 2012

2957 Queen Elizabeth II with Prince Charles and Princess Anne, 1952

2958 Queen Elizabeth II on Visit to New Zealand, 1977

2959 Queen Elizabeth II and Duke of Edinburgh, 1957

2960 Queen Elizabeth II with Nelson Mandela, 1996

2961 Prince Charles, Queen Elizabeth II, Prince George and Prince William

2962 Prince Charles **2963** Queen Elizabeth II

2964 Prince George **2965** Prince William

(Des Kate Stephens (Nos. 3826/3831). Litho ISP Cartor (Nos. 3826/ **MS**3832) or Gravure ISP Walsall (Nos. 3833/3836))

2016 (21 Apr–9 June). 90th Birthday of Queen Elizabeth II. Multicoloured Two phosphor bands (Nos. 3826/3831) or 'all-over' phosphor (Nos. **MS**3832/**MS**3832b, 3833/38336).

*(a) Ordinary gum. Perf 14×14½ (Nos. 3826/3831) or 14 (No. **MS**3832).*

3826	**2955**	(1st) Princess Elizabeth and her Father the Duke of York	1·20	1·00
		a. Horiz strip of 3. Nos. 3826/3828	3·50	3·00
		b. Booklet pane. Nos. 3826/3828 and 3831 with margins all round	5·75	
3827	**2956**	(1st) Queen Elizabeth II at State Opening of Parliament	1·20	1·00
3828	**2957**	(1st) Queen Elizabeth II with Prince Charles and Princess Anne	1·20	1·00
3829	**2958**	£1·52 Queen Elizabeth II on Visit to New Zealand	2·25	2·25
		a. Horiz strip of 3. Nos. 3829/38231	6·75	6·75
		b. Booklet pane. Nos. 3829/3830 with margins all round	4·25	
3830	**2959**	£1·52 Queen Elizabeth II and Duke of Edinburgh	2·25	2·25
3831	**2960**	£1·52 Queen Elizabeth II with Nelson Mandela	2·25	2·25
Set of 6			9·25	8·75
Set of 2 Gutter Strips of 6			18·50	
First Day Cover (Tallents House)				11·50
First Day Cover (Windsor)				11·50
Presentation Pack (PO Pack No. 525) (Nos. 3826/3831 and **MS**3832)			14·50	
PHQ Cards (set of 11) (414)			5·50	19·00
MS3832 189×75 mm. **2961** (1st×4) Prince Charles, Queen Elizabeth II, Prince George and Prince William			4·50	4·25
		b. Booklet pane. No. **MS**3832 but 150×95 mm with roulettes at left	5·00	
First Day Cover (Tallents House)				4·75
First Day Cover (Windsor)				4·75

(b) Self-adhesive. Die-cut perf 14.

3833	**2962**	(1st) Prince Charles	5·75	5·75
		a. Booklet pane. Nos. 3833/3834 and U3746×4	15·00	
3834	**2963**	(1st) Queen Elizabeth II	5·75	5·75
3835	**2964**	(1st) Prince George (9.6.16)	5·75	5·75
		a. Booklet pane. Nos. 3835/3836 and U3746×4	7·50	
3836	**2965**	(1st) Prince William (9.6.16)	2·00	2·00
Set of 4			14·00	14·00

Nos. 3826/3828 and 3829/3831 were each printed together, *se-tenant*, as horizontal strips of three stamps in sheets of 60 (2 panes 6×5)

Booklet pane Nos. 3826b, 3829b and **MS**3832b come from the £15·11 90th Birthday of Queen Elizabeth II booklet, DY17.

Nos. 3833/3836 were issued in stamp booklets, Nos. PM50/PM51, originally sold for £3·84 each.

Miniature sheets as No. **MS**3832 are also available with a special inscription 'Stampex 60 Years'.

2966 Animail

(Des Osborne Ross. Litho ISP Cartor)

2016 (17 May). Animail. Sheet 203×74 mm. Multicoloured 'All-over' phosphor. Die-cut and die-cut perf 14.

MS3837 **2966** Animail (1st) Woodpecker; (1st) Snake; £1·05 Chimpanzee; £1·05 Bat; £1·33 Orangutan; £1·33 Koala		8·50	8·75
First Day Cover (Tallents House)			11·00
First Day Cover (Playing Place, Truro)			11·00
Presentation Pack (PO Pack No. 526)		10·00	
PHQ Cards (set of 7) (415)		3·50	15·00

The seven PHQ cards show the six individual stamps and the complete miniature sheet.

2967 *Battlefield Poppy* (Giles Revell)

2968 'Your battle wounds are scars upon my heart' (poem *To My Brother*, Vera Brittain)

2969 Munitions Worker Lottie Meade

2970 *Travoys Arriving with Wounded at a Dressing-Station at Smol, Macedonia, September 1916* (Stanley Spencer)

2971 Thiepval Memorial, Somme, France

2972 Captain A. C. Green's Battle of Jutland Commemorative Medal

(Des Hat-trick design. Litho ISP Cartor)

2016 (21 June). Centenary of the First World War (3rd issue). Multicoloured
Two phosphor bands. Perf 14½.

3838	**2967**	(1st) *Battlefield Poppy*...............................	1·20	1·00
		a. Booklet pane. Nos. 3838/3840		
		with margins all round...................	3·50	
3839	**2968**	(1st) 'Your battle wounds are scars		
		upon my heart'.............................	1·20	1·00
3840	**2969**	(1st) Munitions Worker Lottie Meade.....	1·20	1·00
3841	**2970**	£1·52 *Travoys Arriving with Wounded*		
		at a Dressing-Station at Smol,		
		Macedonia, September 1916.........	2·50	2·50
		a. Booklet pane. Nos. 3841/3843,		
		with margins all round...................	7·50	
3842	**2971**	£1·52 Thiepval Memorial, Somme,		
		France............................	2·50	2·50
3843	**2972**	£1·52 Captain A. C. Green's Battle of		
		Jutland Commemorative Medal.....	2·50	2·50
Set of 6..			10·00	9·50
Set of 6 Gutter Pairs......................................			20·00	
First Day Cover (Tallents House).......................				12·00
First Day Cover (Lyness, Stromness).................				12·00
Presentation Pack (PO Pack No. 527) (Nos. 3838/3843				
and **MS**3848)..			18·00	
PHQ Cards (set of 11) (416).............................			5·50	26·00

Booklet pane Nos. 3838a and 3841a come from the £16·49 Centenary
of the First World War (3rd issue) booklet, No. DY18.

2973 The Post Office Rifles

2974 Writing a Letter from the Western Front

2975 Delivering the Mail on the Home Front

2976 Home Depot at Regent's Park, London

2977 The Post Office at War, 1914–1918

(Des Hat-trick design. Litho ISP Cartor)

2016 (21 June). Centenary of the First World War (3rd issue). Multicoloured
Two phosphor bands Perf 14.

3844	**2973**	(1st) The Post Office Rifles........................	1·60	1·60
		a. Booklet pane. Nos. 3844/3847		
		with margins all round...................	7·25	
3845	**2974**	(1st) Writing a Letter from the Western		
		Front..	1·60	1·60
3846	**2975**	£1·33 Delivering the Mail on the Home		
		Front..	2·50	2·50
3847	**2976**	£1·33 Home Depot at Regent's Park,		
		London...	2·50	2·50
Set of 4..			7·25	7·25
MS3848 156×74 mm. **2977** The Post Office at War,				
1914–1918 Nos. 3844/3847............................			7·25	7·25
First Day Cover (Tallents House).......................				8·25
First Day Cover (Lyness, Stromness).................				8·25

Nos. 3844/3847 were issued in the £16·49 Centenary of the First Wold
War (3rd issue) booklet, No. DY18, and in No. **MS**3848.

2978 *The Piper at the Gates of Dawn* (1967)

2979 *Atom Heart Mother* (1970)

2980 *The Dark Side of the Moon* (1973)

2981 *Animals* (1977)

2982 *Wish You Were Here* (1975)

2983 *The Endless River* (2014)

2984 Pink Floyd on Stage

(Gravure ISP Walsall (Nos. 3849/3854) or litho ISP Cartor (No. **MS**3855))

2016 (7 July). Pink Floyd. Multicoloured

(a) Album Covers. Self-adhesive. Two phosphor bands. Die-cut perf 14½.

3849	**2978**	(1st) *The Piper at the Gates of Dawn*		
		(1967)..	1·20	1·00
3850	**2979**	(1st) *Atom Heart Mother* (1970)..........	1·20	1·00
3851	**2980**	(1st) *The Dark Side of the Moon* (1973)....	1·20	1·00
3852	**2981**	£1·52 *Animals* (1977)............................	2·50	2·50
3853	**2982**	£1·52 *Wish You Were Here* (1975)..............	2·50	2·50
3854	**2983**	£1·52 *The Endless River* (2014)...................	2·50	2·50
Set of 6..			10·00	9·50
First Day Cover (Tallents House).......................				12·00
First Day Cover (Grantchester, Cambridge).........				12·00
Presentation Pack (PO Pack No. 528) (Nos. 3849/3854				
and **MS**3855)..			18·00	
PHQ Cards (set of 11) (417).............................			5·50	24·00

(b) Pink Floyd on Stage. Ordinary gum. Phosphor frame. Perf 14½.

MS3855 202×74 mm. **2984** Pink Floyd on Stage (1st)		
UFO Club, 1966; (1st) The Dark Side of the Moon		
Tour, 1973; £1·52 The Wall Tour, 1981; £1·52 The		
Division Bell Tour, 1994.............................	6·25	6·25
First Day Cover (Tallents House).......................		8·00
First Day Cover (Grantchester, Cambridge).........		8·00

The right-hand edges of Nos. 3849/3854 are all cut around to show the
vinyl disc protruding from the open edge of the album cover.

A *Dark Side of the Moon* maxi sheet containing No. 3851×10 was sold
at £12·95, a premium from the open edge of face value.

The 11 PHQ cards depicts the individual stamps including those from
No. **MS**3855 and the complete miniature sheet.

2985 Peter Rabbit　　**2986** Mrs Tiggy-Winkle

2987 Squirrel Nutkin　　**2988** Jemima Puddle-Duck

2989 Tom Kitten　　**2990** Benjamin Bunny

(Des Charlie Smith Design. Litho ISP Cartor (Nos. 3856/3861) or gravure ISP Walsall (Nos. 3862/3863))

2016 (28 July). 150th Birth Anniversary of Beatrix Potter (writer, illustrator and conservationist) (1st issue). Multicoloured Two phosphor bands.

(a) Ordinary gum. Perf 14½×14.

3856	**2985**	(1st) Peter Rabbit.................................		1·20	1·00
		a. Horiz pair. Nos. 3856/3857..............		2·40	2·00
		b. Booklet pane. Nos. 3856, 3858 and 3861 with margins all round...		5·00	
3857	**2986**	(1st) Mrs Tiggy-Winkle.........................		1·20	1·00
		b. Booklet pane. Nos. 3857 and 3859/3860 with margins all round		5·00	
3858	**2987**	£1·33 Squirrel Nutkin............................		2·00	2·00
		a. Horiz pair. Nos. 3858/3859..............		4·00	4·00
3859	**2988**	£1·33 Jemima Puddle-Duck....................		2·00	2·00
3860	**2989**	£1·52 Tom Kitten..................................		2·25	2·25
		a. Horiz pair. Nos. 3860/3861..............		4·50	4·50
3861	**2990**	£1·52 Benjamin Bunny..........................		2·25	2·25
Set of 6............				9·75	9·50
Set of 3 *Gutter Pairs* (two stamps only in each pair).......				19·50	
Set of 3 *Traffic Light Gutter Pairs* (two stamps only in each pair)...............				21·00	
First Day Cover (Tallents House)............................					12·00
First Day Cover (Near Sawrey, Ambleside).................					12·00
Presentation Pack (PO Pack No. 529) (Nos. 3856/3856 and **MS**3868)...............				18·50	
PHQ Cards (set of 11) (418)...............				5·50	24·00

(b) Self-adhesive. Die-cut perf 14½×14.

3862	**2985**	(1st) Peter Rabbit.................................		4·00	4·00
		a. Booklet pane. Nos. 3862/3863 and U3746×4....................		11·00	
3863	**2986**	(1st) Mrs Tiggy-Winkle.........................		4·00	4·00

Nos. 3856/3857, 3858/3859 and 3860/3861 were printed together, *se-tenant*, as horizontal pairs in sheets of 60 (2 panes 6×5).

Nos. 3862/3863 were issued in stamp booklet, No. PM52, originally sold for £3·84.

The 11 PHQ cards depict the ten individual stamps including those from No. **MS**3868 and the complete miniature sheet.

2991 Now run along, and don't get into mischief.　　**2992** And then, feeling rather sick, he went to look for some parsley.

2993 But Peter, who was very naughty, ran straight away to Mr McGregor's garden, and squeezed under the gate!　　**2994** He slipped underneath the gate, and was safe at last.

2995 Illustrations from *The Tale of Peter Rabbit*

(Des Magpie Studio (No. **MS**3868). Litho ISP Cartor)

2016 (28 July). 150th Birth Anniversary of Beatrix Potter (writer, illustrator and conservationist) (2nd issue). Multicoloured Two phosphor bands. Perf 14½.

3864	**2991**	(1st) Now run along, and don't get into mischief................		2·25	2·25
		a. Booklet pane. Nos. 3864/3867 with margins all round and roulettes at left...........		8·00	
3865	**2992**	(1st) And then, feeling rather sick, he went to look for some parsley........		2·25	2·25
3866	**2993**	£1·33 But Peter, who was very naughty, ran straight away to Mr McGregor's garden, and squeezed under the gate!...............		2·25	2·25
3867	**2994**	£1·33 He slipped underneath the gate, and was safe at last........		2·25	2·25
Set of 4.........				8·25	8·25
MS3868 125×89 mm. **2995** Nos. 3864/3867 (*The Tale of Peter Rabbit*)...........				5·50	5·75
First Day Cover (Tallents House)...........					7·50
First Day Cover (Near Sawrey, Ambleside).............					7·50

Nos. 3864/3867 were issued in £15·37 The Tale of Beatrix Potter booklet, DY19, and in No. **MS**3868.

2996 Blenheim Palace　　**2997** Longleat

2998 Compton Verney

2999 Highclere Castle

3000 Alnwick Castle

3001 Berrington Hall

3002 Stowe

3003 Croome Park

(Des Robert Maude and Sarah Davies. Litho ISP Cartor (Nos. 3869/3876) or gravure ISP Walsall (Nos. 3877/3878))

2016 (16 Aug). Landscape Gardens (300th Birth Anniversary of Capability Brown). Multicoloured One centre band (2nd) or two phosphor bands (others).

(a) Ordinary gum. Perf 14.

3869	2996	(2nd) Blenheim Palace.....................	90	90
		a. Horiz pair. Nos. 3869/3870.............	1·80	1·80
3870	2997	(2nd) Longleat............................	90	90
3871	2998	(1st) Compton Verney....................	1·20	1·00
		a. Horiz pair. Nos. 3871/3872.............	2·40	2·00
3872	2999	(1st) Highclere Castle...................	1·20	1·00
3873	3000	£1·05 Alnwick Castle...................	1·50	1·50
		a. Horiz pair. Nos. 3873/3874.............	3·00	3·00
3874	3001	£1·05 Berrington Hall..................	1·50	1·50
3875	3002	£1·33 Stowe.............................	2·00	2·00
		a. Horiz pair. Nos. 3875/3876.............	4·00	4·00
3876	3003	£1·33 Croome Park.....................	2·00	2·00
Set of 8			10·00	10·00
Set of 4 Gutter Blocks of 4			20·00	
First Day Cover (Tallents House)				13·00
First Day Cover (Kirkharle, Newcastle)				13·00
Presentation Pack (PO Pack No. 530)			13·00	
PHQ Cards (set of 8) (419)			4·00	12·00

(b) Self-adhesive. Die-cut perf 14.

3877	2998	(1st) Compton Verney....................	3·50	3·50
		a. Booklet pane. Nos. 3877/3878 and U3746x4..	10·00	
3878	2999	(1st) Highclere Castle...................	3·50	3·50

Nos. 3869/3870, 3871/3872, 3873/3874 and 3875/3876 were each printed together, *se-tenant*, as horizontal pairs in sheets of 60 (2 panes 6×5).

Nos. 3877/3878 were issued in stamp booklet, No. PM53, originally sold for £3·84.

3004 Fire Breaks Out in Bakery on Pudding Lane, Sunday 2nd September 1666

3005 The Fire Spreads Rapidly, Sunday 2nd September 1666

3006 Houses are Pulled, Monday 3rd September 1666

3007 As the Fire reaches St Paul's Citizens witness the Cathedral's Destruction, Tuesday 4th September 1666

3008 The Fire Dies Out, Wednesday 5th September 1666

3009 Christopher Wren develops Plans for the Regeneration of the City, Tuesday 11th September 1666

(Des John Higgins (artwork) and The Chase. Litho ISP Cartor)

2016 (2 Sept). 350th Anniversary of the Great Fire of London. Multicoloured Two phosphor bands. Perf 14½.

3879	3004	(1st) Fire Breaks Out in Bakery on Pudding Lane..................	1·20	1·00
		a. Horiz pair. Nos. 3879/3880.............	2·40	2·00
3880	3005	(1st) The Fire Spreads Rapidly.................	1·20	1·00
3881	3006	£1·05 Houses are Pulled Down to Create Breaks.....................	1·60	1·60
		a. Horiz pair. Nos. 3881/3882.............	3·25	3·25
3882	3007	£1·05 As the Fire reaches St Paul's Citizens witness the Cathedral's Destruction............	1·60	1·60
3883	3008	£1·52 The Fire Dies Out............	2·25	2·35
		a. Horiz pair. Nos. 3883/3884.............	4·50	4·50
3884	3009	£1·52 Christopher Wren develops Plans for the Regeneration of the City.....	2·25	2·35
Set of 6			9·25	9·25
Set of 3 Gutter Blocks of 4			18·50	
First Day Cover (Tallents House)				12·00
First Day Cover (London EC3)				12·00
Presentation Pack (PO Pack No. 531)			11·00	
PHQ Cards (set of 6) (420)			3·00	11·00

Nos. 3879/3880, 3881/3882 and 3883/3884 were each printed together, *se-tenant*, as horizontal pairs in sheets of 60 (2 panes 6×5).

3010 *Murder on the Orient Express*

3011 *And Then There Were None*

3012 *The Mysterious Affair at Styles*

3013 *The Murder of Roger Ackroyd*

3014 *The Body in the Library*

3015 *A Murder is Announced*

(Des Studio Sutherland. Litho ISP Cartor)

2016 (15 Sept). 40th Death Anniversary of Agatha Christie (writer). Multicoloured Two phosphor bands. Perf 14½.

3885	**3010**	(1st) *Murder on the Orient Express*............	1·20	1·00
		a. Vert pair. Nos. 3885/3886................	2·40	2·00
3886	**3011**	(1st) *And Then There Were None*...............	1·20	1·00
3887	**3012**	£1·33 *The Mysterious Affair at Styles*.........	2·00	2·00
		a. Vert pair. Nos. 3887/3888................	4·00	4·00
3888	**3013**	£1·33 *The Murder of Roger Ackroyd*............	2·00	2·00
3889	**3014**	£1·52 *The Body in the Library*....................	2·25	2·25
		a. Vert pair. Nos. 3889/3890................	4·50	4·50
3890	**3015**	£1·52 *A Murder is Announced*....................	2·25	2·25
		Set of 6..	9·75	9·50
		Set of 3 Gutter Pairs (two stamps in each gutter pair).......	10·25	
		First Day Cover (Tallents House)................................		13·00
		First Day Cover (Torquay)..		13·00
		Presentation Pack (PO Pack No. 532)........................	12·00	
		PHQ Cards (set of 6) (421)......................................	3·00	11·00

Nos. 3885/3886, 3887/3888 and 3889/3890 were each printed together, *se-tenant*, as vertical pairs in sheets of 48 (2 panes 4×6).

They all feature hidden secrets in the form of microtext, uv ink or thermochronic ink.

3016 *Mr Happy*

3017 *Little Miss Naughty*

3018 *Mr Bump*

3019 *Little Miss Sunshine*

3020 *Mr Tickle*

3021 *Mr Grumpy*

3022 *Little Miss Princess*

3023 *Mr Strong*

3024 *Little Miss Christmas*

3025 *Mr Messy*

(Des Supple Studio. Litho ISP Cartor (Nos. 3891/3900) or gravure ISP Walsall (Nos. 3901/3902))

2016 (20 Oct). Mr Men and Little Miss (children's books by Roger Hargreaves). Multicoloured Two phosphor bands.

(a) Ordinary gum. Perf 14½.

3891	**3016**	(1st) *Mr Happy*..	1·20	1·00
		a. Horiz strip of 5. Nos. 3891/3895......	5·25	4·50
3892	**3017**	(1st) *Little Miss Naughty*............................	1·20	1·00
3893	**3018**	(1st) *Mr Bump*...	1·20	1·00
3894	**3019**	(1st) *Mr Sunshine*.......................................	1·20	1·00
3895	**3020**	(1st) *Mr Tickle*..	1·20	1·00
3896	**3021**	(1st) *Mr Grumpy*...	1·20	1·00
		a. Horiz strip of 5. Nos. 3896/3900......	5·25	4·50
3897	**3022**	(1st) *Little Miss Princess*..........................	1·20	1·00
3898	**3023**	(1st) *Mr Strong*..	1·20	1·00
3899	**3024**	(1st) *Little Miss Christmas*.......................	1·20	1·00
3900	**3025**	(1st) *Mr Messy*...	1·20	1·00
		Set of 10..	10·50	9·00
		Set of 2 Gutter Strips of 10..................................	21·00	
		First Day Cover (Tallents House).............................		11·50
		First Day Cover (Cleckheaton)................................		11·50
		Presentation Pack (PO Pack No. 533)......................	12·00	
		PHQ Cards (set of 10) (422)..................................	5·00	12·50

(b) Self-adhesive. Die-cut perf 14½.

3901	**3016**	(1st) *Mr Happy*..	1·50	1·50
		a. Booklet pane. Nos. 3901/3902 and U3027×4...................................	7·50	
3902	**3020**	(1st) *Mr Tickle*..	1·50	1·50

Nos. 3891/3895 and 3896/3900 were each printed together, *se-tenant*, as horizontal strips of five stamps in sheets of 50 stamps (2 panes 5×5).

Nos. 3901/3902 were issued in stamp booklet, No. PM54, originally sold for £3·84.

Designs as Nos. 3891/3900 but self-adhesive were issued in sheets of ten with *se-tenant* labels, (No. LS101), originally sold for £6·90.

Designs as Nos. 3891, 3893/3894, 3896/3897 and 3900 were also available in sheets of ten with personal photographs on the labels, originally sold for £10·20.

SELF-ADHESIVE STAMPS. Collectors are reminded that used self-adhesive stamps will no longer 'soak-off'. They should be collected with a neat margin of backing paper.

3026 Snowman   **3027** Robin   **3028** Snowman

3029 Robin   **3030** Christmas Tree

3031 Lantern   **3032** Stocking   **3033** Christmas Pudding

3033a Christmas

(Des Helen Musselwhite (illustrations) and The Chase. Gravure ISP Walsall (Nos. 3903a, 3904a) or De La Rue (others))

2016 (8 Nov). Christmas. Multicoloured One centre band (No. 3903) or two bands (others).

(a) Self-adhesive. Die-cut perf 14½×15..

3903	**3026**	(2nd) Snowman	90	90
		a. Booklet pane. No. 3903×12	13·50	
3904	**3027**	(1st) Robin	1·00	1·00
		a. Booklet pane. No. 3904×12	16·00	
3905	**3028**	(2nd Large) Snowman	1·25	1·10
3906	**3029**	(1st Large) Robin	1·70	1·40
3907	**3030**	£1·05 Christmas Tree	1·75	1·75
3908	**3031**	£1·33 Lantern	2·00	2·00
3909	**3032**	£1·52 Stocking	2·50	2·50
3910	**3033**	£2·25 Christmas Pudding	3·50	3·50
Set of 8			13·25	13·00
First Day Cover (Tallents House)				16·50
First Day Cover (Bethlehem, Llandeilo)				16·50
Presentation Pack (PO Pack No. 534)			16·50	
PHQ Cards (set of 9) (423)			4·50	28·00

(b) Ordinary gum. Perf 14½×15.

MS3911 189×74 mm. **3033a** As Nos. 3903/3910	13·25	13·00
First Day Cover (Tallents House)		16·50
First Day Cover (Bethlehem, Llandeilo)		16·50

The 2nd class, 1st class, £1·05, £1·33, £1·52 and £2·25 values were also issued in sheets of 20, (No. LS102), containing 8×2nd class, 8×1st class, 1×£1·05, 1×£1·33, 1×£1·52 and 1×£2·25 stamps, each stamp accompanied by a *se-tenant* label showing paper cut out work by Helen Musselwhite forming a snowy landscape. These sheets were sold for £16·21.

Separate sheets of 20×2nd, 10×1st, 10×£1·05, 10×£1·33 and 10×£1·52 were available with personal photographs on the labels. These were sold at £14·60 for 20×2nd, £18·65 for 20×1st, £10·20 for 10×1st, £14·45 for 10×£1·05, £18·50 for 10×£1·33 and £21·85 for 10×£1·52.

The 2nd class and 1st class values were also issued in sheets of 20, Celebrating 50 Years of Christmas Stamps, each stamp accompanied by a greetings label.

The 2nd class and 1st class values were also issued in sheets of 20, (No. LS103), Celebrating 50 Years of Christmas Stamps containing 10×2nd class and 10×1st class stamps, each stamp accompanied by a greetings label. These sheets were sold at £12·40.

The nine PHQ cards show the eight individual stamps and the complete miniature sheet.

Year Pack

2016 (8 Nov). Comprises Nos. 3787/**MS**3801, 3810/**MS**3832, **MS**3837/3843, **MS**3848/3861, **MS**3868/3876, 3879/3900 and 3903/3910

CP3911*a*	Year Pack (Pack No. 535) (*sold for £120*)	£175

Post Office Yearbook

2016 (8 Nov). Comprises Nos. 3787/**MS**3801, 3810/**MS**3832, **MS**3837/3843, **MS**3848/3861, **MS**3868/3876, 3879/3900 and 3903/3910

YB3911*a*	Yearbook (*sold for £140*)	£200

Miniature Sheet Collection

2016 (8 Nov). Comprises Nos. **MS**3801, **MS**3832, **MS**3837, **MS**3848, **MS**3855, **MS**3868 and **MS**3911

MS3911*a* Miniature Sheet Collection (*sold for £36*)	50·00

3034 Battersea Shield, London, 350–50 BC   **3035** Skara Brae Village, Orkney Islands, 3100–2500 BC

3036 Star Carr Headdress, Yorkshire, 9000 BC   **3037** Maiden Castle Hill Fort, Dorset, 400 BC

3038 Avebury Stone Circles, Wiltshire, 2500 BC   **3039** Drumbest Horns, County Antrim, 800 BC

3040 Grime's Graves Flint Mines, Norfolk, 2500 BC   **3041** Mold Cape, Flintshire, 1900–1600 BC

(Des Rebecca Strickson (illustrations) and True North. Litho ISP Cartor)

2017 (17 Jan). Ancient Britain. Multicoloured Two phosphor bands. Perf 14.

3912	**3034**	(1st) Battersea Shield	1·20	2·00
		a. Horiz pair. Nos. 3912/3913	2·40	2·00
3913	**3035**	(1st) Skara Brae Village	1·20	1·00
3914	**3036**	£1·05 Star Carr Headdress	1·75	1·75
		a. Horiz pair. Nos. 3914/3915	3·50	3·50
3915	**3037**	£1·05 Maiden Castle Hill Fort	1·75	1·75
3916	**3038**	£1·33 Avebury Stone Circles	2·00	2·00
		a. Horiz pair. Nos. 3916/3917	4·00	4·00
3917	**3039**	£1·33 Drumbest Horns	2·00	2·00
3918	**3040**	£1·52 Grime's Graves Flint Mines	2·25	2·25
		a. Horiz pair. Nos. 3918/3919	4·50	4·50
3919	**3041**	£1·52 Mold Cape	2·25	2·25
Set of 8			13·00	13·00
Set of 4 Gutter Blocks of 4			26·00	
First Day Cover (Tallents House)				17·00
First Day Cover (Avebury, Marlborough)				17·00

Presentation Pack (PO Pack No. 536)...................................... 15·50
PHQ Cards (set of 8) (424).. 4·00   15·00

Nos. 3912/3913, 3914/3915, 3916/3917 and 3918/3919 were each printed together, *se-tenant*, as horizontal pairs in sheets of 60 (2 panes 6×5).

> For No. U3920, T **3041a**, See Decimal Machin section.

3042 The Long Walk

3043 The Round Tower

3044 The Norman Gate

3045 St George's Hall

3046 The Queen's Ballroom

3047 The Waterloo Chamber

(Des Up. Litho ISP Cartor (Nos. 3920/3925) or gravure ISP Walsall (Nos. 3926/3927))

2017 (15 Feb). Windsor Castle (1st issue). Multicoloured Two phosphor bands.

(a) Ordinary gum. Perf 14½.

3920	**3042**	(1st) The Long Walk................................	1·20	1·00
		a. Horiz strip of 3. Nos. 3920/3922.....	3·50	3·00
		b. Booklet pane. Nos. 3920 and 3923 with margins all round....................	4·00	

3921	**3043**	(1st) The Round Tower..............................	1·20	1·00
		b. Booklet pane. Nos. 3921/3922 and 3924/3925 with margins all round..................	5·50	
3922	**3044**	(1st) The Norman Gate.............................	1·00	1·00
3923	**3045**	£1·52 St George's Hall..............................	2·00	2·00
		a. Horiz strip of 3. Nos. 3923/3925.....	6·00	6·00
3924	**3046**	£1·52 The Queen's Ballroom......................	2·00	2·00
3925	**3047**	£1·52 The Waterloo Chamber....................	2·00	2·00
Set of 6..			8·75	8·25
Set of 2 Gutter Strips of 3........................			17·00	
First Day Cover (Tallents House)...................				11·00
First Day Cover (Windsor)...........................				11·00
Presentation Pack (PO Pack No. 537) (Nos. 3920/3925 and **MS**3932)...........			18·00	
PHQ Cards (set of 11) (425).........................			5·50	23·00

(b) Self-adhesive. Die-cut perf 14½.

3926	**3048**	(1st) Sir Reginald Bray Roof Boss............	2·00	2·00
		a. Booklet pane. Nos. 3926/3927 and U3027×4................................	7·50	
3927	**3049**	(1st) Fan-vaulted Roof............................	2·00	2·00

Nos. 3920/3922 and 3923/3925 were each printed together, *se-tenant*, as horizontal strips of three stamps in sheets of 60 (2 panes 6×5).

Booklet pane No. 3920b and No. 3921b come from the £14.58 Windsor Castle booklet, No. DY20.

Nos. 3926/3927 were issued in stamp booklet, No. PM55, originally sold for £3·84.

The 11 PHQ cards show the individual stamps including those from No. **MS**3932 and the complete miniature sheet.

3048 St George's Chapel Nave: Sir Reginald Bray Roof Bass

3049 St George's Chapel Nave: Fan-vaulted Roof

3050 St George's Chapel Quire, Garter Banners

3051 St George's Chapel Quire, St George's Cross Roof Boss

3052 St George's Chapel

(Des Up. Litho ISP Cartor)

2017 (15 Feb). Windsor Castle (2nd issue). Multicoloured Two phosphor bands. Perf 14½.

3928	**3048**	(1st) Sir Reginald Bray Roof Boss............	1·60	1·60
		a. Booklet pane. Nos. 3928/3931 with margins all round and roulettes at left...............................	7·25	
3929	**3049**	(1st) Fan-vaulted Roof............................	1·60	1·60

3930	**3050**	£1·33 Garter Banners......................	2·50	2·50
3931	**3051**	£1·33 St George's Cross Roof Boss...........	2·50	2·50
Set of 4..			7·25	7·25
MS3932 125×89 mm. **3052** Nos. 3928/3931.....................			7·25	7·25
First Day Cover (Tallents House).................................				8·00
First Day Cover (Windsor)...				8·00

Nos. 3928/3931 come from No. **MS**3932 and £14·58 Windsor Castle booklet, No. DY20.

No. **MS**3932 additionally inscribed 'Spring Stampex 2017' was available only at the exhibition (*Price* £50).

3053 *Hunky Dory*

3054 *Aladdin Sane*

3055 *Heroes*

3056 *Let's Dance*

3057 *Earthling*

3058 *Blackstar*

3059 David Bowie Live

(Gravure ISP Walsall (Nos. 3933/3938) or litho ISP Cartor (No. **MS**3939))

2017 (14 Mar). David Bowie (1947–2016, singer, songwriter and actor) Commemoration. Multicoloured Two phosphor bands.

(a) Self-adhesive. Die-cut perf 14½.

3933	**3053**	(1st) *Hunky Dory*.......................	1·20	1·00
3934	**3054**	(1st) *Aladdin Sane*......................	1·20	1·00
		a. Booklet pane. Nos. 3934/3935 and U3027×4.................................	7·50	
3935	**3055**	(1st) *Heroes*...............................	1·20	1·00
3936	**3056**	£1·52 *Let's Dance*.......................	2·25	2·25
3937	**3057**	£1·52 *Earthling*..........................	2·25	2·25
3938	**3058**	£1·52 *Blackstar*..........................	2·25	2·25
Set of 6..			9·25	8·75
First Day Cover (Tallents House).................................				11·50
First Day Cover (London SW9)...................................				11·50
Presentation Pack (PO Pack No. 538) (Nos. 3933/3938 and **MS**3939)...............................			17·00	
PHQ Cards (set of 11) (426).....................................			5·50	24·00

(b) Ordinary gum. Perf 14½.

MS3939 126×89 mm. **3059** David Bowie Live (1st) The Ziggy Stardust Tour, 1973; (1st) The Serious Moonlight Tour, 1983; £1·52 The Isolar II Tour, 1978; £1·52 A Reality Tour, 2004............................	6·25	6·25
First Day Cover (Tallents House).................................		8·25
First Day Cover (London SW9)...................................		8·25

Nos. 3933/3938 were printed in separate sheets of 50 (2 panes 5×5).

Nos. 3934/3935 were also issued in booklet, No. PM56, originally sold for £3·84.

The right-hand edges of Nos. 3933/3938 are all cut around to show the vinyl disc protruding from the open edge of the album cover.

Four Fan sheets, printed on ordinary gummed paper, were available from Royal Mail at premium prices. The Album Fan Sheet contains the complete set, Types **3053/3058**, and was originally sold for £12·95. *The Hunky Dory* (T **3053**×5), *Aladdin Sane* (T **3054**×5) and *Heroes* (T **3055**×5) were originally sold for £7·50 each.

The 11 PHQ cards show the individual stamps including those from No. **MS**3939 and the complete miniature sheet all printed on ordinary gummed paper, were available from Royal Mail at premium prices.

3060 Frankel

3061 Red Rum

3062 Shergar

3063 Kauto Star

3064 Desert Orchid

3065 Brigadier Gerard

3066 Arkle

3067 Estimate

(Des Michael Heslop (illustrations) and Together Design. Litho ISP Cartor)

2017 (6 Apr). Racehorse Legends. Multicoloured Two phosphor bands. Perf 14.

3940	**3060**	(1st) Frankel...............................	1·20	1·00
3941	**3061**	(1st) Red Rum.............................	1·20	1·00
3942	**3062**	£1·17 Shergar.............................	1·75	1·75
3943	**3063**	£1·17 Kauto Star.........................	1·75	1·75
3944	**3064**	£1·40 Desert Orchid.....................	2·25	2·25
3945	**3065**	£1·40 Brigadier Gerard.................	2·25	2·25
3946	**3066**	£1·57 Arkle.................................	2·50	2·50
3947	**3067**	£1·57 Estimate............................	2·50	2·50
Set of 8..			13·75	13·50
Set of 8 Gutter Pairs..			27·50	
First Day Cover (Tallents House).................................				17·00
First Day Cover (Newmarket)....................................				17·00
Presentation Pack (PO Pack No. 539)............................			16·00	
PHQ Cards (set of 8) (427).....................................			4·00	17·00

3068 Great Tit (*Parus major*)

3069 Wren (*Troglodytes troglodytes*)

3070 Willow Warbler (*Phylloscopus trochilus*)

3071 Goldcrest (*Regulus regulus*)

3072 Skylark (*Alauda arvensis*)

3073 Blackcap (*Sylvia atricapilla*)

3074 Song Thrush (*Turdus philomelos*)

3075 Nightingale (*Luscinia megarhynchos*)

3076 Cuckoo (*Cuculus canorus*)

3077 Yellowhammer (*Emberiza citrinella*)

(Des Federico Gemma (illustrations) and Osborne Ross. Litho ISP Cartor)

2017 (4 May). Songbirds. Multicoloured Two phosphor bands. Perf 14½.

3948	**3068**	(1st) Great Tit	1·20	1·00
		a. Horiz strip of 5. Nos. 3948/3952	5·25	4·50
3949	**3069**	(1st) Wren	1·20	1·00
3950	**3070**	(1st) Willow Warbler	1·20	1·00
3951	**3071**	(1st) Goldcrest	1·20	1·00
3952	**3072**	(1st) Skylark	1·20	1·00
3953	**3073**	(1st) Blackcap	1·20	1·00
		a. Horiz strip of 5. Nos. 3953/3957	5·25	4·50
3954	**3074**	(1st) Song Thrush	1·20	1·00
3955	**3075**	(1st) Nightingale	1·20	1·00
3956	**3076**	(1st) Cuckoo	1·20	1·00
3957	**3077**	(1st) Yellowhammer	1·20	1·00
Set of 10			10·50	9·00
Set of 2 Gutter Strips of 10			21·00	
First Day Cover (Tallents House)				12·00
First Day Cover (Warbleton, Heathfield)				12·00
Presentation Pack (PO Pack No. 540)			12·00	
PHQ Cards (set of 10) (428)			5·00	12·50

Nos. 3948/3952 and 3953/3957 were each printed together, *se-tenant*, as horizontal strips of five in sheets of 50 (2 panes 5×5).

3078 Preliminary sketch by Arnold Machin based on the Penny Black, January 1966

3079 Preparatory work by Arnold Machin using photograph of his coin mould, February 1966

3080 Essay with coinage head surrounded by Country symbols, April/May 1966

3081 Essay of Coinage head cropped and simplified, with only the denomination, October 1966

3082 Photo by John Hedgecoe with Queen Elizabeth II wearing the diadem, August 1966

3083 Essay of the first plaster cast of the Diadem Head, without corsage, October 1966

3084 The Machin definitive 50 Years of a design icon

3085 The Machin definitive Golden Anniversary celebration

3086 £1 gold foil Machin

3079 Preparatory work by Arnold Machin using photograph of his coin mould, February 1966

2017 (5 June). 50th Anniversary of the Machin Definitive. Multicoloured Two phosphor bands. Perf 14×15

3958	**3078**	(1st) Preliminary sketch based on the Penny Black	1·25	1·25
		a. Booklet pane. Nos. 3958/3960 with margins all round	3·75	
3959	**3079**	(1st) Preparatory work using photograph of his coin mould	1·25	1·25

3960	**3080**	(1st) Essay with coinage head surrounded by Country symbols, April/May 1966..............	1·25	1·25
3961	**3081**	(1st) Essay of coinage head, with only the denomination..............	1·25	1·25
		a. Booklet pane. Nos. 3961/3963 with margins all round..................	3·75	
3962	**3082**	(1st) Photograph by John Hedgecoe.....	1·25	1·25
3963	**3083**	(1st) Essay of the first plaster cast of the Diadem Head.............................	1·25	1·25
Set of 6...			6·75	6·75
MS3964 202×74 mm. **3084** 6×(1st) Types **3078/3083**...			11·00	11·00
First Day Cover (Tallents House) (No. **MS**3964)..................				12·00
First Day Cover (High Wycombe) (No. **MS**3964).................				12·00
PHQ Cards (Set of 11) (429)..			5·50	21·00

Nos. 3958/3963 were issued in the £15·14 50th Anniversary of the Machin Definitive booklet, DY21, and in No. **MS**3964.

The 5p, 20p and £1 stamps in No. **MS**3965 do not have an elliptical hole in each vertical side.

On No. **MS**3965 only the £1 gold foil stamp is embossed.

Please note that Nos. **MS**3965 and U3966/U3966l are listed in the Machin section of this catalogue.

For the 20p. stamp as T **929** from the 50th Anniversary of the Machin booklet section see No. 2133, pane No. 1668sl.

3087 Nutley Windmill, East Sussex

3088 New Abbey Corn Mill, Dumfries and Galloway

3089 Ballycopeland Windmill, County Down

3090 Cheddleton Flint Mill, Staffordshire

3091 Woodchurch Windmill, Kent

3092 Felin Cochwillan Mill, Gwynedd

(Des Atelier Works. Litho ISP Cartor)

2017 (20 June). Windmills and Watermills. Multicoloured Two phosphor bands. Perf 14½×14

3967	**3087**	(1st) Nutley Windmill, East Sussex..........	1·20	1·00
		a. Vert pair. Nos. 3967/3968................	2·40	2·00
3968	**3088**	(1st) New Abbey Corn Mill, Dumfries and Galloway....................................	1·20	1·00
3969	**3089**	£1·40 Ballycopeland Windmill, County Down......................................	2·25	2·25
		a. Vert pair. Nos. 3969/3970................	4·50	4·50
3970	**3090**	£1·40 Cheddleton Flint Mill, Staffordshire................................	2·25	2·25
3971	**3091**	£1·57 Woodchurch Windmill, Kent..........	2·50	2·50
		a. Vert pair. Nos. 3971/72................	5·00	5·00
3972	**3092**	£1·57 Felin Cochwillan Mill, Gwynedd.....	2·50	2·50
Set of 6..			10·75	10·50
Set of 3 Gutter Blocks of 4...........................			21·50	
First Day Cover (Tallents House)........................				12·00
First Day Cover (Old Mill, Callington)......................				12·00

Presentation Pack (PO Pack No. 542).....................................	12·00	
PHQ Cards (set of 6) (430).......................................	3·00	12·00

Nos. 3967/3968, 3969/3970 and 3971/3972 were each printed together, *se-tenant*, as vertical pairs in sheets of 60 (2 panes 5×6).

3093 Aquatics Centre, Queen Elizabeth Olympic Park, London

3094 Library of Birmingham

3095 SEC Armadillo (formerly Clyde Auditorium), Glasgow

3096 Scottish Parliament, Edinburgh

3097 Giant's Causeway Visitor Centre, Co. Antrim

3098 National Assembly for Wales, Cardiff

3099 Eden Project, St Austell

3100 Everyman Theatre, Liverpool

3101 IWM (Imperial War Museum) North, Manchester

3102 Switch House, Tate Modern, London

(Des GBH. Litho ISP Cartor)

2017 (13 July). Landmark Buildings. Multicoloured Two phosphor bands. Perf 14½

3973	**3093**	(1st) Aquatics Centre, Queen Elizabeth Olympic Park, London.....................	1·20	1·00
		a. Horiz strip of 5. Nos. 3973/3977.....	5·25	5·00
3974	**3094**	(1st) Library of Birmingham.....................	1·20	1·00
3975	**3095**	(1st) SEC Armadillo (formerly Clyde Auditorium), Glasgow......................	1·20	1·00
3976	**3096**	(1st) Scottish Parliament, Edinburgh......	1·20	1·00
3977	**3097**	(1st) Giant's Causeway Visitor Centre, Co. Antrim...	1·20	1·00

3978	**3098**	(1st) National Assembly for Wales, Cardiff..	1·20	1·00
		a. Horiz strip of 5. Nos. 3978/3982.....	5·25	5·00
3979	**3099**	(1st) Eden Project, St Austell...................	1·20	1·00
3980	**3100**	(1st) Everyman Theatre, Liverpool...........	1·20	1·00
3981	**3101**	(1st) IWM (Imperial War Museum) North, Manchester.........................	1·20	1·00
3982	**3102**	(1st) Switch House, Tate Modern, London..	1·20	1·00

Set of 10.. 10·50 9·00
Set of 2 Gutter Strips of 5....................................... 21·00
First Day Cover (Tallents House).............................. 10·50
First Day Cover (St Austell)..................................... 10·50
Presentation Pack (PO Pack No. 543)...................... 12·00
PHQ Cards (set of 10) (431).................................. 5·00 10·00

Nos. 3973/3977 and 3978/3982 were each printed together, *se-tenant*, as horizontal strips of five stamps in sheets of 50 (2 panes 5×5).

3103 *Shattered Poppy* (John Ross)

3104 *Dead Man's Dump* (Isaac Rosenberg)

3105 Nurses Elsie Knocker and Mairi Chisholm

3106 *Dry Docked for Sealing and Painting* (Edward Wadsworth)

3107 Tyne Cot Cemetery, Zonnebeke, Ypres Salient Battlefields, Belgium

3108 Private Lemuel Thomas Rees's Life-saving Bible

(Des Hat-trick design. Litho ISP Cartor)

2017 (31 July). Centenary of the First World War (4th issue). Multicoloured Two phosphor bands. Perf 14½

3983	**3103**	(1st) *Shattered Poppy* (John Ross)...........	1·20	1·00
		a. Booklet pane. Nos. 3983/3985 with margins all round....................	4·00	
3984	**3104**	(1st) *Dead Man's Dump*...........................	1·20	1·00
3985	**3105**	(1st) Nurses Elsie Knocker and Mairi Chisholm.....................................	1·20	1·00
3986	**3106**	£1·57 *Dry Docked for Sealing and Painting*...............................	2·50	2·50
		a. Booklet pane. Nos. 3986/3988 with margins all round....................	7·50	
3987	**3107**	£1·57 Tyne Cot Cemetery, Belgium..........	2·50	2·50
3988	**3108**	£1·57 Private Lemuel Thomas Rees's Life-saving Bible.............................	2·50	2·50

Set of 6.. 10·00 9·50
Set of 6 Gutter Pairs.. 20·00
First Day Cover (Tallents House).............................. 11·00
First Day Cover (Blaenannerch, Aberteifi-Cardigan)........ 11·00
Presentation Pack (PO Pack No. 544)...................... 11·50
PHQ Cards (set of 6) (432)................................... 3·00 11·00

Booklet pane Nos. 3983a and 3786a were only issued in £15·41 Centenary of the First World War (4th issue) booklet, No DY22.

3109 The Merrythought Bear

3110 Sindy Weekender Doll

3111 Spirograph

3112 Stickle Bricks Super Set House

3113 Herald Trojan Warriors

3114 Spacehopper

3115 Fuzzy-Felt Farm Set

3116 Meccano Ferris Wheel

3117 Action Man Red Devil Parachutist

3118 Hornby Dublo Electric Train and TPO Mail Van

(Des Interabang. Litho ISP Cartor)

2017 (22 Aug). Classic Toys. Multicoloured Two phosphor bands. Perf 14½

3989	**3109**	(1st) The Merrythought Bear....................	1·20	1·00
		a. Horiz strip of 5. Nos. 3989/3993.....	5·25	5·00
3990	**3110**	(1st) Sindy Weekender Doll......................	1·20	1·00
3991	**3111**	(1st) Spirograph......................................	1·20	1·00
3992	**3112**	(1st) Stickle Bricks Super Set House........	1·20	1·00
3993	**3113**	(1st) Herald Trojan Warriors....................	1·20	1·00
3994	**3114**	(1st) Spacehopper....................................	1·20	1·00
		a. Horiz strip of 5. Nos. 3994/3998.....	5·25	5·00
3995	**3115**	(1st) Fuzzy-Felt Farm Set.......................	1·20	1·00
3996	**3116**	(1st) Meccano Ferris Wheel.....................	1·20	1·00
3997	**3117**	(1st) Action Man Red Devil Parachutist...	1·20	1·00
3998	**3118**	(1st) Hornby Dublo Electric Train and TPO Mail Van..................................	1·20	1·00

Set of 10.. 10·50 9·00
Set of 2 Gutter Strips of 5....................................... 21·00
First Day Cover (Tallents House).............................. 10·50
First Day Cover (Toys Hill, Edenbridge).................... 10·50
Presentation Pack (PO Pack No. 545)...................... 12·00
PHQ Cards (set of 10) (433).................................. 5·00 10·00

Nos. 3989/3993 and 3994/3998 were each printed together, *se-tenant*, as horizontal strips of five stamps in sheets of 50 (2 panes 5×5).

3119 *The Story of Nelson, The Story of the First Queen Elizabeth* and *Florence Nightingale* (Adventures from History)

3120 *The Gingerbread Boy, Cinderella* and *The Elves and the Shoemaker* (Well-loved Tales)

3121 *We have fun, Look at this* and *Things we do* (Key Words Reading Scheme)

3122 *Piggly Plays Truant, Tootles the Taxi and Other Rhymes* and *Smoke and Fluff* (Early Tales and Rhymes)

3123 *Things to Make, How it works: The Telephone* and *Tricks and Magic* (Hobbies and How it Works)

3124 *The Nurse, The Postman* and *The Fireman* (People at Work)

3125 *British Wild Flowers, Wild Life in Britain* and *Garden Flowers* (Nature and Conservation)

3126 *The Story of Ships, The Story of the Motor Car* and *The Story of Metals* (Achievements)

(Des True North. Litho ISP Cartor)

3127 Maz Kanata

3128 Chewbacca

3129 Supreme Leader Snoke

3130 Porg

3131 BB-8

3132 R2-D2

3133 C-3PO

3134 K-2SO

2017 (14 Sept). Ladybird Books. Multicoloured One centre band (Nos. 3999/4000) or two bands (others). Perf 14

3999	**3119**	(2nd) Adventures from History	90	90
		a. Horiz pair. Nos. 3999/4000	1·75	1·75
4000	**3120**	(2nd) Well-loved Tales	90	90
4001	**3121**	(1st) Key Words Reading Scheme	1·20	1·00
		a. Horiz pair. Nos. 4001/4002	2·40	2·00
4002	**3122**	(1st) Early Tales and Rhymes	1·20	1·00
4003	**3123**	£1·40 Hobbies and How it Works	2·25	2·25
		a. Horiz pair. Nos. 4003/4004	4·50	4·50
4004	**3124**	£1·40 People at Work	2·25	2·25
4005	**3125**	£1·57 Nature and Conservation	2·50	2·50
		a. Horiz pair. Nos. 4005/4006	5·00	5·00
4006	**3126**	£1·57 Achievements	2·50	2·50
		Set of 8	12·25	12·00
		Set of 4 Gutter Blocks of 4	24·50	
		First Day Cover (Tallents House)		13·50
		First Day Cover (Loughborough)		13·50
		Presentation Pack (PO Pack No. 546)	14·00	
		PHQ Cards (Set of 8) (434)	4·00	12·50

Nos. 3999/4000, 4001/4002, 4003/4004 and 4005/4006 were each printed together, *se-tenant*, as horizontal pairs in sheets of 60 (2 panes 6×5).

3134a Star Wars composite sheet

(Des Malcolm Tween (illustrations) and Interabang. Litho ISP Cartor (Nos. 4007/4014) or gravure Walsall (Nos. 4015/4018))

2017 (12 Oct–14 Dec). *Star Wars* (4th issue). Aliens and Droids. Multicoloured Two phosphor bands

(a) Ordinary gum. Perf 14½.

4007	**3127**	(1st) Maz Kanata......................................	1·20	1·00
		a. Horiz strip of 4. Nos. 4007/4010.....	4·25	4·00
4008	**3128**	(1st) Chewbacca....................................	1·20	1·00
		a. Booklet pane. Nos. 4008, 4010/4011 and 4014 with margins all round (14.12.17)..........	4·25	
4009	**3129**	(1st) Supreme Leader Snoke...................	1·20	1·00
4010	**3130**	(1st) Porg...	1·20	1·00
4011	**3131**	(1st) BB-8...	1·20	1·00
		a. Horiz strip of 4. Nos. 4011/4014.....	4·25	4·00
4012	**3132**	(1st) R2-D2..	1·20	1·00
4013	**3133**	(1st) C-3PO..	1·20	1·00
4014	**3134**	(1st) K-2SO..	1·20	1·00
Set of 8...			8·50	7·25
Set of 2 Gutter Strips of 4...........................			17·00	
First Day Cover (Tallents House)................................				9·00
First Day Cover (Wookey, Wells).................................				9·00
Presentation Pack (PO Pack No. 547).......................			10·00	
PHQ Cards (Set of 8) (435).......................................			4·00	9·00
MS4014a 297×212 mm. **3134a** Nos. 3758/3769 and 4007/4014..............................			30·00	45·00

(b) Self-adhesive. Die-cut perf 14½.

4015	**3127**	(1st) Maz Kanata......................................	1·75	1·75
		a. Booklet pane. Nos. 4015/4016 and U3027×4..........................	7·50	
4016	**3128**	(1st) Chewbacca....................................	1·75	1·75
4017	**3131**	(1st) BB-8...	1·75	1·75
		a. Booklet pane. Nos. 4017/4018 and U3027×4..........................	7·50	
4018	**3132**	(1st) R2-D2..	1·75	1·75

Nos. 4007/4010 and 4011/4014 were each printed together, *se-tenant*, as horizontal strips of four stamps in sheets of 48 (2 panes 4×6).

Nos. 4011/4014 (Droid stamps) are enhanced by UV ink features.

Booklet pane No. 4008a comes from the £14·32 *Star Wars*: The Making of the Droids, Aliens and Creatures booklet, No DY23.

Nos. 4015/4016 and 4017/4018 were each issued in stamp booklets with 1st bright scarlet stamp×4 stamps, Nos. PM57/PM58, originally sold for £3·90 each.

Designs as Nos. 4007/4014 but self-adhesive were issued in sheets of ten with *se-tenant* labels (No. LS106). These sheets originally sold for £7·20.

3135 *Virgin and Child* (attributed to Gerard David)

3136 *The Madonna and Child* (William Dyce)

3137 *Virgin and Child* (attributed to Gerard David)

3138 *The Madonna and Child* (William Dyce)

3139 *Virgin Mary with Child* (attributed to Quinten Massys)

3140 *The Small Cowper Madonna* (Raphael)

3141 *The Sleep of the Infant Jesus* (Giovanni Battista Sassoferrato)

3142 *St Luke painting the Virgin* (detail) (Eduard Jakob von Steinle)

3142a Madonna and Child

(Gravure De La Rue or ISP Walsall (Nos. 4019a/4019b, 4020a/4020b), Litho by ISP Cartor (No. **MS**4027))

2017 (7 Nov). Christmas. Madonna and Child. Multicoloured One centre phosphor band (No. 4019) or two bands

(a) Self-adhesive. Die-cut perf 14½×15.

4019	**3135**	(2nd) *Virgin and Child* (attributed to Gerard David)..................................	90	90
		a. Booklet pane. Nos. 4019 and 4028, each×6...........................	13·50	
		b. Booklet pane. Nos. 4019×12...........	13·50	
4020	**3136**	(1st) *The Madonna and Child* (William Dyce).................................	1·20	1·00
		a. Booklet pane. Nos. 4020 and 4029, each×6...........................	16·00	
		b. Booklet pane. Nos. 4020×12...........	16·00	
4021	**3137**	(2nd Large) *Virgin and Child* (attributed to Gerard David)............	1·25	1·10
4022	**3138**	(1st Large) *The Madonna and Child* (William Dyce)..............................	1·70	1·40
4023	**3139**	£1·17 *Virgin Mary with Child* (attributed to Quinten Massys).......................	1·80	1·80
4024	**3140**	£1·40 *The Small Cowper Madonna* (Raphael).......................................	2·25	2·25
4025	**3141**	£1·57 *The Sleep of the Infant Jesus* (Giovanni Battista Sassoferrato).....	2·50	2·50
4026	**3142**	£2·27 *St Luke painting the Virgin* (detail) (Eduard Jakob von Steinle).............	3·50	3·50
Set of 8...			13·50	13·00
First Day Cover (Tallents House) (Nos. 4019/4026 and 4028/4031).......................................				18·00
First Day Cover (Bethlehem, Llandeilo) (Nos. 4019/4026 and 4028/4031)..				18·00
Presentation Pack (PO Pack No. 548) (Nos. 4019/4026 and 4028/4031)..			19·00	
PHQ Cards (set of 13) (436).......................................			6·50	30·00

(b) Ordinary gum. Perf 14½×15.

MS4027..		13·50	13·00
First Day Cover (Tallents House)................................			17·00
First Day Cover (Bethlehem, Llandeilo).....................			17·00

Nos. 4019 and 4028, 4020 and 4029, 4021 and 4030 and 4022 and 4031 were printed together in sheets of 50 (5×10), the upper 25 stamps being Nos. 4019, 4020, 4021 or 4022 and the lower 25 stamps Nos. 4028, 4029, 4030 or 4031. Nos. 4023/4026 were printed individually in sheets of 50 (5×10).

Nos. 4019/4020 were reprinted for Christmas 2018 by ISP Walsall in composite sheets with the 2018 1st and 2nd class Christmas stamps.

The presentation pack (No. 548) contains Nos. 4019/4026 and 4028/4031.

The 2nd class (No. 4019), 1st class (No. 4020), £1·17, £1·40, £1·57 and £2·27 values were also issued in sheets of 20 containing 8×2nd class, 8×1st class, 1×£1·17, 1×£1·40, 1×£1·57 and 1×£2·27 values, each stamp accompanied by a *se-tenant* label (No. LS107).

The 13 PHQ cards show the 12 individual stamps and No. **MS**4027.

3143 Snow Family (Arwen Wilson)

3144 Santa Claus on his sleigh on a starry night (Ted Lewis-Clark)

3145 Snow Family (Arwen Wilson)

3146 Santa Claus on his sleigh on a starry night (Ted Lewis-Clark)

(Gravure De La Rue)

2017 (7 Nov). Children's Christmas. Multicoloured One centre phosphor band (No. 4028) or two bands. Self-adhesive. Die-cut perf 14½×15

4028	**3143**	(2nd) Snow Family (Arwen Wilson)..........	90	90
4029	**3144**	(1st) Santa Claus on his sleigh on a starry night (Ted Lewis-Clark)........	1·20	1·00
4030	**3145**	(2nd Large) Snow Family (Arwen Wilson)...............	1·25	1·10
4031	**3146**	(1st Large) Santa Claus on his sleigh on a starry night (Ted Lewis-Clark)...............	1·70	1·40
Set of 4................			4·00	4·00

An example of No. 4029 has been reported used in West Yorkshire in late September 2017.

The 2nd class (No. 4028) and 1st class (No. 4029) values were also issued in sheets of 20 containing 10×2nd class and 10×1st class, each stamp accompanied by a *se-tenant* label (No. LS108).

3147 Platinum Anniversary

(Des Mytton Williams. Litho ISP. Cartor)

2017 (20 Nov). Royal Platinum Wedding Anniversary of Queen Elizabeth II and Duke of Edinburgh. Multicoloured Two phosphor bands. Perf 14

MS4032 200×67 mm. **3147** (1st) Engagement of Princess Elizabeth and Lieutenant Philip Mountbatten; (1st) Princess Elizabeth and Duke of Edinburgh after their wedding at Westminster Abbey; (1st) Princess Elizabeth and Duke of Edinburgh looking at wedding photographs during their honeymoon; £1·57 Engagement photograph; £1·57 Princess Elizabeth and Duke of Edinburgh on their wedding day; £1·57 Princess Elizabeth and Duke of Edinburgh on honeymoon at Broadlands...

	10·00	10·00
First Day Cover (Tallents House)...............		12·00
First Day Cover (London SW1)...............		12·00
Presentation Pack (PO Pack No. 549)...............	12·00	
PHQ Cards (set of 7) (437)...............	3·50	18·00
Souvenir Pack...............	15·00	

A Limited Edition Pack of 5000 was available at £14·99.

Collectors Pack

2017 (20 Nov). Comprises Nos. 3912/3925, **MS**3932/3957, **MS**3964/ **MS**3965, 3967/4014, 4019/4029 and **MS**4032

CP4032a	Collectors Pack (Pack No. 550) (*sold for £119*)...............	£180

Post Office Yearbook

2017 (20 Nov). Comprises Nos. 3912/3925, **MS**3932/3957, **MS**3964/ **MS**3965, 3967/4014, 4019/4031 and **MS**4032

YB4032a	Yearbook (*sold for £139*)...............	£210

Miniature Sheet Collection

2017 (20 Nov). Comprises Nos. **MS**3932, **MS**3939, **MS**3964/**MS**3965, **MS**4027 and **MS**4032

MS4032a	Miniature Sheet Collection (*sold for £35*)..........	55·00

3148 Sansa Stark (Sophie Tucker)

3149 Jon Snow (Kit Harington)

3150 Eddard Stark (Sean Bean)

3151 Olenna Tyrell (Dianna Rigg)

3152 Tywin Lannister (Charles Dance)

3153 Tyrion Lannister (Peter Dinklage)

3154 Cersei Lannister (Lena Headey)

3155 Arya Stark (Maisie Williams)

3156 Jaime Lannister (Nicolaj Coster-Waldau)

3157 Daenerys Targaryen (Emilia Clarke)

3158 *Game of Thrones* non-human characters

3159 The Iron Throne

(Des GBH, Litho ISP Cartor (Nos. 4033/4042) or gravure Walsall (No. 4044))

2018 (23 Jan). *Game of Thrones* (1st issue). Multicoloured Two phosphor bands.

		(a) Ordinary gum. Perf 14.		
4033	**3148**	(1st) Sansa Stark (Sophie Tucker)............	1·20	1·00
		a. Horiz strip of 5. Nos. 4033/4037....	5·25	4·50
		b. Booklet pane Nos. 4033/4035, 4038/4040...............	6·00	
4034	**3149**	(1st) Jon Snow (Kit Harington)...............	1·20	1·00
4035	**3150**	(1st) Eddard Stark (Sean Bean)...............	1·20	1·00
4036	**3151**	(1st) Olenna Tyrell (Dianna Rigg)............	1·20	1·00
		b. Booklet pane Nos. 4036/4037, 4041/4042...............	6·00	
4037	**3152**	(1st) Tywin Lannister (Charles Dance)....	1·20	1·00
4038	**3153**	(1st) Tyrion Lannister (Peter Dinklage)...	1·20	1·00
		a. Horiz strip of 5. Nos. 4038/4042....	5·25	4·50
4039	**3154**	(1st) Cersei Lannister (Lena Headey)......	1·20	1·00
4040	**3155**	(1st) Arya Stark (Maisie Williams)............	1·20	1·00
4041	**3156**	(1st) Jaime Lannister (Nicolaj Coster-Waldau)...............	1·20	1·00
4042	**3157**	(1st) Daenerys Targaryen (Emilia Clarke)...............	1·20	1·00
Set of 10...............			10·50	9·00
Set of 2 Gutter Strips of 10...............			21·00	
First Day Cover (Tallents House)...............				10·50
First Day Cover (Belfast)...............				10·50
Presentation Pack (PO Pack No. 551)...............			12·00	
PHQ Cards (set of 16) (438)...............			8·00	23·00

(b) Self-adhesive. Die-cut perf 14½×14 (with one elliptical hole on each vert side) (Iron throne) or 14½ (others).

MS4043 202×75 mm. **3158** (1st) The Night King and
White Walkers; (1st) Giants, (1st) The Iron Throne
(18×22 mm); 1st Direwolves; (1st) Dragons.............. 7·50   7·50
First Day Cover (Tallents House)..   8·50
First Day Cover (Belfast)...   8·50

(c) Self-adhesive booklet stamp. Die-cut perf 14½×14 with one elliptical hole in each vert side.

4044 **3159** (1st) The Iron Throne................................. 1·50 1·50
            a. Booklet pane. Nos. 4044×6............. 9·00

Nos. 4033/4037 and 4038/4042 were each printed together, *se-tenant*, as horizontal strips of five stamps in sheets of 60 (2 panes 5×6).

Booklet pane Nos. 4033b and 4036b come from the £13·95 *Game of Thrones* booklet, No DY24.

No. 4044 was issued in stamp booklet No. MB20, sold for £3.90

Designs as Nos. 4033/4042 but self-adhesive were issued in sheets of ten with *se-tenant* labels (No. LS110), originally sold for £7·50.

The presentation pack (No. 549) contains Nos. 4033/4042 and **MS**4043.

The 16 PHQ cards show the 15 individual stamps and No. **MS**4043.

3160 The Night King and White Walkers

3161 Giants

3162 Direwolves

3163 Dragons

(Des GBH, Litho ISP Cartor)

2018 (23 Jan) *Game of Thrones* (2nd issue). Multicoloured Two phosphor bands. P.14
4045 **3160** (1st) The Night King and White Walkers 1·50 1·50
            a. Booklet pane Nos. 4045/4048........ 6·00
4046 **3161** (1st) Giants.. 1·50 1·50
4047 **3162** (1st) Direwolves................................ 1·50 1·50
4048 **3163** (1st) Dragons.................................... 1·50 1·50
Set of 4... 5·50 5·50

Nos. 4045/4048 were issued in £13·95 *Game of Thrones* booklet, No. DY24.

Self-adhesive stamps as Nos. 4045/4048 were additionally available from No. **MS**4043.

(Des GBH, litho ISP Cartor)

2018 (23 Jan) *Game of Thrones* (3rd issue). Multicoloured Two phosphor bands. Perf 14½×14 (with one elliptical hole in each vert side)
4049 **3159** (1st) The Iron Throne................................. 1·50 1·50

No. 4049 was issued in the Machin booklet pane from the £13·95 *Game of Thrones* booklet, No DY24.

3164 The Lone Suffragette in Whitehall, *circa* 1908

3165 The Great Pilgrimage of Suffragists, 1913

3166 Suffragette Leaders at Earl's Court, 1908

3167 Women's Freedom League poster parade, *circa* 1907

3168 Welsh Suffragettes, Coronation Procession, 1911

3169 Leigh and New Released from Prison, 1908

3170 Sophia Duleep Singh sells *The Suffragette*, 1913

3171 Suffragette Prisoners' Pageant, 1911

(Des Supple Studio, Litho ISP)

2018 (15 Feb) Votes for Women. Multicoloured One phosphor band (Nos. 4050/4051) or two bands. Perf 14½×14.
4050 **3164** (2nd) The Lone Suffragette in Whitehall. 90 90
            a. Horiz pair. Nos. 4050/4051............. 1·75 1·75
4051 **3165** (2nd) The Great Pilgrimage of
                    Suffragists................................... 90 90
4052 **3166** (1st) Suffragette Leaders at Earl's Court 1·20 1·00
            a. Horiz pair. Nos. 4052/4053............. 2·40 2·00
4053 **3167** (1st) Women's Freedom League poster
                    parade...................................... 1·20 1·00
4054 **3168** £1·40 Welsh Suffragettes, Coronation
                    Procession................................. 2·25 2·25
            a. Horiz pair. Nos. 4054/4055............. 4·50 4·50
4055 **3169** £1·40 Leigh and New Released from
                    Prison....................................... 2·25 2·25
4056 **3170** £1·57 Sophia Duleep Singh sells *The
                    Suffragette*................................. 2·50 2·50
            a. Horiz pair. Nos. 4056/4057............. 5·00 5·00
4057 **3171** £1·57 Suffragette Prisoners' Pageant....... 2·50 2·50
Set of 8.. 12·25 12·00
Set of 4 Gutter Blocks of 4.. 24·50
First Day Cover (Tallents House).....................................   14·00
First Day Cover (London SW1).......................................   14·00
Presentation Pack (PO Pack No. 552)............... 15·00
PHQ Cards (set of 8)....................................... 4·00 13·00

Nos. 4050/4051, 4052/4053, 4054/4055 and 4056/4057 were each printed together, *se-tenant*, as horizontal pairs in sheets of 60 (2 panes 6×5).

3172 Lightning F6

3173 Hawker Hurricane Mk.I

3174 Vulcan B2

3175 Typhoon FGR4

3176 Sopwith Camel F.1

3177 Nimrod MR2

3178 Royal Air Force Red Arrows

(Des Royal Mail Group Ltd with illustrations by Michael Turner, Litho ISP Cartor (Nos. 4058/4063, **MS**4064) or gravure ISP Walsall (Nos. 4065/4066))

2018 (20 Mar) RAF Centenary (1st issue). Multicoloured Two phosphor bands.

(a) Ordinary gum. Perf 14½×14.

4058	**3172**	(1st) Lightning F6.................................	1·50	1·40
		a. Horiz pair. Nos. 4058/4059..............	3·00	3·00
		b. Booklet Pane Nos. 4058×2, 4061×2,	6·00	
4059	**3173**	(1st) Hurricane Mk.I..............................	1·50	1·40
		b. Booklet pane Nos. 4059/4060, 4062/4063,	8·00	
4060	**3174**	£1·40 Vulcan B2....................................	3·25	3·25
		a. Horiz pair. Nos. 4060/4061..............	6·50	6·50
4061	**3175**	£1·40 Typhoon FGR4.............................	3·25	3·25
4062	**3176**	£1·57 Sopwith Camel F.1.......................	3·75	3·75
		a. Horiz pair. Nos. 4062/4063..............	7·50	7·50
4063	**3177**	£1·57 Nimrod MR2.................................	3·75	3·75
Set of 6..			15·00	15·00
Set of 3 Gutter Blocks of 4...........................			30·00	
First Day Cover (Tallents House)...................				16·00
First Day Cover (Cranwell, Sleaford)...........				16·00
Presentation Pack (PO Pack No. 553) (Nos. 4058/4063 and **MS**4064)................................			25·00	
PHQ Cards (set of 11) (440)........................			10·00	32·00
MS4064 192×74 mm. **3178** Nos. 4067/4070.			9·50	9·50
First Day Cover (Tallents House)...................				10·50
First Day Cover (Cranwell, Sleaford)...........				10·50

(b) Self-adhesive. Die-cut perf 14½.

4065	**3172**	(1st) Lightning F6.................................	1·75	1·75
		a. Booklet pane. Nos. 4065/4066 and U3027×4..................	7·50	
4066	**3173**	(1st) Hurricane Mk.I..............................	1·75	1·75

Nos. 4058/4059, 4060/4061 and 4062/4063 were each printed together, *se-tenant*, as horizontal pairs in sheets of 60 (2 panes 6×5).

Booklet pane Nos 4058b and 4059b come from the £18·69 RAF Centenary booklet, No. DY25.

Nos. 4065/4066 were issued in stamp booklet, No. PM59, originally sold for £3·90.

The 11 PHQ cards show the individual stamps including those from No. **MS**4064 and the complete miniature sheet.

3179 Red Arrows, Flypast

3180 Red Arrows, Swan

3181 Red Arrows, Syncro pair

3182 Red Arrows, Python

(Des Turner Duckworth, Litho ISP Cartor)

2018 (20 Mar) RAF Centenary (2nd issue). Red Arrows. Multicoloured Two phosphor bands. Perf 14½×14.

4067	**3179**	(1st) Red Arrows, Flypast........................	1·50	1·50
		a. Booklet pane Nos. 4067/4070........	7·00	
4068	**3180**	(1st) Red Arrows, Swan..........................	1·50	1·50
4069	**3181**	£1·40 Red Arrows, Syncro pair................	3·25	3·25
4070	**3182**	£1·40 Red Arrows, Python.......................	3·25	3·25
Set of 4...			7·00	7·00

Nos. 4067/4070 come from No. **MS**4064 and the £18·69 RAF Centenary booklet, No. DY25.

3183 Pilots scramble to their Hurricanes

3184 Supermarine Spitfires of 610 Squadron, Biggin Hill, on patrol

3185 Armourer Fred Roberts replaces ammunition boxes on Supermarine Spitfire

(Des Supple Studio (stamps) and Royal Mail Group, Supple Studio. Litho ISP Cartor)

2018 (20 Mar) RAF Centenary (3rd issue). Battle of Britain. Multicoloured Two phosphor bands. Perf 14½×14.

4071	**3183**	(1st) Pilots scramble...........................	1·50	1·50
		a. Booklet pane Nos. 4071, 4072×2, 4073................................	5·00	
4072	**3184**	(1st) Spitfires.....................................	1·50	1·50
4073	**3185**	(1st) Armourer replaces ammunition boxes..........	1·50	1·50
Set of 3...			4·00	4·00

Nos. 4071/4073 come from the £18·69 RAF Centenary booklet, No. DY25. The images on these three stamps were previously used in No. **MS**3735 issued on 16 July 2015 to commemorate the 75th Anniversary of the Battle of Britain; those stamps were 'all-over' phosphor.

3186 Osprey (*Pandion haliaetus*)

3187 Large Blue Butterfly (*Maculinea arion*)

3188 Eurasian Beaver (*Castor fiber*)

3189 Pool Frog (*Pelophylax lessonae*)

3190 Stinking Hawk's-beard (*Crepis foetida*)

3191 Sand Lizard (*Lacerta agilis*)

(Des Tanya Lock (illustration) and Godfrey Design. Litho ISP Cartor)

2018 (17 Apr). Reintroduced Species. Multicoloured Two phosphor bands. Perf 14½.

4074	**3186**	(1st) Osprey (*Pandion haliaetus*).............	1·20	1·00
		a. Horiz pair. Nos. 4074/4075.............	2·40	2·00
4075	**3187**	(1st) Large Blue Butterfly (*Maculinea arion*)................................	1·20	1·00
4076	**3188**	£1·45 Eurasian Beaver (*Castor fiber*).........	2·25	2·25
		a. Horiz pair. Nos. 4076/4077.............	4·50	4·50
4077	**3189**	£1·45 Pool Frog (*Pelophylax lessonae*)......	2·25	2·25
4078	**3190**	£1·55 Stinking Hawk's-beard (*Crepis foetida*)............................	2·50	2·50
		a. Horiz pair. Nos. 4078/4079.............	5·00	5·00
4079	**3191**	£1·55 Sand Lizard (*Lacerta agilis*).............	2·50	2·50
	Set of 6..		10·75	10·50
	Set of 3 Gutter Blocks of 4.............................		21·50	
	First Day Cover (Tallents House)........................			13·50
	First Day Cover (Frogpool, Truro)......................			13·50
	Presentation Pack (PO Pack No. 554).................		13·50	
	PHQ Cards (set of 6) (441)............................		4·00	12·00

Nos. 4074/4075, 4076/4077 and 4078/4079 were each printed together, *se-tenant*, as horizontal pairs in sheets of 60 (2 panes 6×5).

(Gravure ISP Walsall)

2018 (11 May). Centenary of the RAF (Royal Air Force) (4th issue). Multicoloured. Self-adhesive. Two phosphor bands. Die-cut perf 14

4080	**3179**	(1st) Red Arrows, Flypast......................	3·25	3·25
		a. Booklet pane. Nos. 4080/4081 and U3027×4..............................	12·50	
4081	**3180**	(1st) Red Arrows, Swan.........................	3·25	3·25

Nos. 4080/4081 were issued in stamp booklet, No. PM60, originally sold for £4·02.

3192 Barn Owl (*Tyto alba*)

3193 Little Owl (*Athene noctua*)

3194 Tawny Owl (*Strix aluco*)

3195 Short-eared Owl (*Asio flammeus*)

3196 Long-eared Owl (*Asio otus*)

3197 Two Young Barn Owls (*Tyto alba*)

3198 Little Owl Chicks (*Athene noctua*)

3199 Tawny Owl Chick (*Strix aluco*)

3200 Short-eared Owl Chick (*Asio flammeus*)

3201 Long-eared Owl Chick (*Asio otus*)

(Des Atelier Works. Litho ISP Cartor)

2018 (11 May). Owls. Multicoloured Two phosphor bands. Perf 14½×14.

4082	**3192**	(1st) Barn Owl (*Tyto alba*)......................	1·20	1·00
		a. Horiz strip of 5. Nos. 4082/4086.....	5·25	4·50
4083	**3193**	(1st) Little Owl (*Athene noctua*)...............	1·20	1·00
4084	**3194**	(1st) Tawny Owl (*Strix aluco*)..................	1·20	1·00
4085	**3195**	(1st) Short-eared Owl (*Asio flammeus*)...	1·20	1·00
4086	**3196**	(1st) Long-eared Owl (*Asio otus*)............	1·20	1·00
4087	**3197**	(1st) Two Young Barn Owls (*Tyto alba*)...	1·20	1·00
		a. Horiz strip of 5. Nos. 4087/4091.....	5·25	4·50
4088	**3198**	(1st) Little Owl Chicks (*Athene noctua*)...	1·20	1·00
4089	**3199**	(1st) Tawny Owl Chick (*Strix aluco*)........	1·20	1·00
4090	**3200**	(1st) Short-eared Owl Chick (*Asio flammeus*)................................	1·20	1·00
4091	**3201**	(1st) Long-eared Owl Chick (*Asio otus*)..	1·20	1·00
	Set of 10..		10·50	9·00
	Set of 2 Gutter Strips of 10............................		21·00	
	Set of 2 Traffic Light Gutter Strips of 20.............		40·00	
	First Day Cover (Tallents House)........................			12·50
	First Day Cover (Hooton, Ellesmere Port).............			12·50
	Presentation Pack (PO Pack No. 555).................		12·50	
	PHQ Cards (set of 10) (442)...........................		6·75	11·00

Nos. 4082/406 and 4087/4091 were each printed together, *se-tenant*, as horizontal strips of five stamps in sheets of 50 (2 panes 5×5).

3202 Royal Wedding

(Des The Chase. Litho ISP Cartor)

2018 (19 May). Royal Wedding. Multicoloured. 'All-over' phosphor. Perf 14½×14.

MS4092 116×89 mm. **3202** (1st) Prince Harry and Ms Meghan Markle×2; £1·55 Prince Harry and Ms Meghan Markle (black and white photograph)×2.... 7·00 7·00
First Day Cover (Tallents House)................................ 8·50
First Day Cover (Windsor)... 8·50
Presentation Pack (PO Pack No. M24)............... 7·50

A souvenir pack containing Nos. **MS**3932 and **MS**4092 with silver foil cachet postmarks and imagery from the Royal Wedding was available from Royal Mail from 29 June 2018 for £24·99.

3203 *Summer Exhibition* (Grayson Perry)

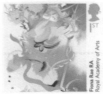

3204 *Queen of the Sky* (Fiona Rae)

3205 *St. Kilda. The Great Sea Stacs* (Norman Ackroyd)

3206 *Inverleith Allotments and Edinburgh Castle* (Barbara Rae)

3207 *Queuing at the RA* (Yinka Shonibare)

3208 *Saying Goodbye* (Tracey Emin)

(Litho ISP Cartor)

2018 (5 June). 250th Anniversary of the Royal Academy of Arts, London. Multicoloured. Two phosphor bands. Perf 14×14½.

4093	**3203**	(1st) *Summer Exhibition* (Grayson Perry).....................	1·20	1·00
		a. Vert pair. Nos. 4093/4094................	2·40	2·00
4094	**3204**	(1st) *Queen of the Sky* (Fiona Rae)...........	1·20	1·00
4095	**3205**	£1·25 *St Kilda. The Great Sea Stacs* (Norman Ackroyd)..................	1·90	1·90
		a. Vert pair. Nos. 4095/4096................	3·75	3·75
4096	**3206**	£1·25 *Inverleith Allotments and Edinburgh Castle* (Barbara Rae).......	1·90	1·90
4097	**3207**	£1·55 *Queuing at the RA* (Yinka Shonibare).....................	2·40	2·40
		a. Vert pair. Nos. 4097/4098................	4·75	4·75
4098	**3208**	£1·55 *Saying Goodbye* (Tracey Emin)........	2·40	2·40
Set of 6..			9·75	9·50
Set of 3 *Gutter Pairs* (only 2 stamps in each gutter pair)...			11·50	
First Day Cover (Tallents House)...............................				13·00
First Day Cover (London W1)..................................				13·00
Presentation Pack (PO Pack No. 556).......................			11·50	
PHQ Cards (set of 6) (443)......................................			4·00	11·50

Nos. 4093/4094, 4095/4096 and 4097/4098 were each printed together, *se-tenant*, as vertical pairs in sheets of 60 (2 panes 5×6).

3209 Sergeant Wilson (John Le Mesurier) 'Do you think that's wise, sir?'

3210 Private Pike (Ian Lavender) 'I'll tell Mum!'

3211 Captain Mainwaring (Arthur Lowe) 'You stupid boy!'

3212 Lance Corporal Jones (Clive Dunn) 'Don't panic! Don't panic!'

3213 Private Walker (James Beck) 'It won't cost you much...'

3214 Private Frazer (John Laurie) 'We're doomed. Doomed!'

3215 Private Godfrey (Arnold Ridley) 'Do you think I might be excused?'

3216 Chief Warden Hodges (Bill Pertwee) 'Put that light out!'

(Des Up Design. Litho ISP Cartor (Nos. 4099/4106) or gravure ISP Walsall (Nos. 4107/4108))

2018 (26 June). 50th Anniversary of *Dad's Army* (BBC television sitcom 1968–1977). Multicoloured. One centre band (2nd) or two phosphor bands (others).

(a) Ordinary gum. Perf 14½×14.

4099	**3209**	(2nd) Sergeant Wilson (John Le Mesurier) 'Do you think that's wise, sir?'.................................	90	90
		a. Horiz pair. Nos. 4099/4100..............	1·75	1·75
4100	**3210**	(2nd) Private Pike (Ian Lavender) 'I'll tell Mum!'..................................	90	90
4101	**3211**	(1st) Captain Mainwaring (Arthur Lowe) 'You stupid boy!'.......................	1·20	1·00
		a. Horiz pair. Nos. 4101/4102..............	2·40	2·00
4102	**3212**	(1st) Lance Corporal Jones (Clive Dunn) 'Don't panic! Don't panic!'....	1·20	1·00
4103	**3213**	£1·45 Private Walker (James Beck) 'It won't cost you much...'..............	2·25	2·25
		a. Horiz pair. Nos. 4103/4104..............	4·50	4·50
4104	**3214**	£1·45 Private Frazer (John Laurie) 'We're doomed. Doomed!'........................	2·25	2·25
4105	**3215**	£1·55 Private Godfrey (Arnold Ridley) 'Do you think I might be excused?'...............................	2·40	2·40
		a. Horiz pair. Nos. 4105/4106..............	4·75	4·75
4106	**3216**	£1·55 Chief Warden Hodges (Bill Pertwee) 'Put that light out!'...........	2·40	2·40
Set of 8..			12·25	12·00
Set of 4 Gutter Blocks of 4.....................................			24·50	
First Day Cover (Tallents House)...............................				16·00
First Day Cover (Thetford)......................................				16·00
Presentation Pack (PO Pack No. 557).......................			14·00	
PHQ Cards (set of 8) (444)......................................			5·50	14·00

(b) Self-adhesive. Die-cut perf 14½×14.

4107	**3211**	(1st) Captain Mainwaring (Arthur Lowe) 'You stupid boy!'....................	1·75	1·75
		a. Booklet pane. Nos. 4107/4108 and U3027×4...................................	13·00	
4108	**3212**	(1st) Lance Corporal Jones (Clive Dunn) 'Don't panic! Don't panic!'....	1·75	1·75

Nos. 4099/4100, 4101/4102, 4103/4104 and 4105/4106 were each printed, *se-tenant*, as horizontal pairs in sheets of 60 (2 pairs 6×5).

Nos. 4107/4108 were issued in stamp booklet, No. PM61, originally sold for £4·02.

Stamps as Nos. 4101/4102 but self-adhesive and perforated 14×14½ were issued in sheets of ten (No. LS111) containing five stamps of each design with labels showing stills from the television series. These sheets were printed in lithography by ISP Cartor and originally sold for £7·50 each.

3217 South Front

3218 West Front

3219 East Front

3220 Pond Gardens

3221 Maze

3222 Great Fountain Garden

3223 Hampton Court Palace

3224 Great Hall   **3225** King's Great Bedchamber

(Des Osborne Ross. Litho ISP Cartor (Nos. 4109/**MS**4115) or gravure ISP Walsall (Nos. 4116/4117))

2018 (31 July). Hampton Court Palace. Multicoloured Two phosphor bands.

(a) Ordinary gum. Perf 14½.

4109	**3217**	(1st) South Front..............................	1·20	1·00
		a. Horiz strip of 3. Nos. 4109/4111.....	3·50	3·00
4110	**3218**	(1st) West Front..............................	1·20	1·00
4111	**3219**	(1st) East Front..............................	1·20	1·00
4112	**3220**	£1·55 Pond Gardens.............................	2·40	2·40
		a. Horiz strip of 3. Nos. 4112/4114.....	7·25	7·25
4113	**3221**	£1·55 Maze.............................	2·40	2·40
4114	**3222**	£1·55 Great Fountain Garden....................	2·40	2·40
		Set of 6..............................	9·50	9·00
		Set of 2 Gutter Strips of 6..........	19·00	
		First Day Cover (Tallents House)..........		12·50
		First Day Cover (East Molesey)..........		12·50
		Presentation Pack (PO Pack No. 558) (Nos. 4104/4114 and **MS**4115)............	17·50	
		PHQ Cards (set of 11) (445)..........	7·50	22·00

MS4115 156×74 mm. **3223** (1st) Great Hall; (1st) King's Great Bedchamber; £1·45 Chapel Royal; £1·45 King's Staircase............ 6·50   6·50

First Day Cover (Tallents House)........................... 8·25

First Day Cover (East Molesey)........................... 8·25

(b) Self-adhesive. Die-cut perf 14.

4116	**3224**	(1st) Great Hall..............................	1·75	1·75
		a. Booklet pane. Nos. 4116/4117 and U3027×4...................................	25·00	
4117	**3225**	(1st) King's Great Bedchamber..............	1·75	1·75

Nos. 4109/4111 and 4112/4114 were each printed together, *se-tenant*, as horizontal strips of three stamps in sheets of 60 (2 panes 6×5).

Nos. 4116/4117 were issued in stamp booklet, No. PM62, originally sold for £4·02.

The 11 PHQ cards show the individual stamps including those from No. **MS**4115 and the complete miniature sheet.

3226 Joseph Banks, Red-tailed Tropicbird and Red Passion Flower   **3227** Chief Mourner of Tahiti and a Scene with a Canoe

Captain James Cook

3228 Captain James Cook and *Triumph of the Navigators*

The *Endeavour* voyage

3229 Drawings of the Observations of a Transit of Venus

The *Endeavour* voyage

3230 Scarlet Clianthus and Portrait of a Maori Chief

Sydney Parkinson - natural history artist

3231 Blue-Black Grassquit and Self-portrait of Sydney Parkinson

3232 The *Endeavour* Voyage

(Des Howard Brown (Nos. 4118/4123) or Webb & Webb Design Ltd (No. **MS**4124). Litho ISP Cartor)

2018 (16 Aug). Captain Cook and the *Endeavour* Voyage (1768–1771). Multicoloured One centre band (2nd) or two phosphor bands (others). Perf 14×14½ (Nos. 4118/4123) or 14 (No. **MS**4124).

4118	**3226**	(2nd) Joseph Banks, Red-tailed Tropicbird and Red Passion Flower	90	90
		a. Horiz pair. Nos. 4118/4119	1·75	1·75
4119	**3227**	(2nd) Chief Mourner of Tahiti and a Scene with a Canoe	90	90
4120	**3228**	(1st) Captain James Cook and *Triumph of the Navigators*	1·20	1·00
		a. Horiz pair. Nos. 4120/4121	2·40	2·00
4121	**3229**	(1st) Drawings of the Observations of a Transit of Venus	1·20	1·00
4122	**3230**	£1·45 Scarlet Clianthus and Portrait of a Maori Chief	2·25	2·25
		a. Horiz pair. Nos. 4122/4123	4·50	4·50
4123	**3231**	£1·45 Blue-Black Grassquit and Self-portrait of Sydney Parkinson	2·25	2·25
Set of 6			7·75	7·50
Set of 3 Gutter Blocks of 4			15·50	
First Day Cover (Tallents House)				10·50
First Day Cover (Plymouth)				10·50
Presentation Pack (PO Pack No.559) (Nos. 4118/4123 and **MS**4124)				15·00
PHQ Cards (set of 11) (446)			7·50	20·00

MS4124 125×89 mm. **3232** (1st) Chart of the discoveries made by Captain James Cook (Lieutenant Roberts) ('Charting a new course: New Zealand and Australia'); (1st) Boathouse and canoes on Raiatea, Society Islands (after Sydney Parkinson); £1·45 Arched rock with Maori clifftop fort, New Zealand ('Mapping New Zealand: a Maori clifftop fort'); £1·45 Repairing the *Endeavour* on the Endeavour River, Australia (after Sydney Parkinson)..... 6·50 6·50

First Day Cover (Tallents House)... 8·25
First Day Cover (Plymouth)... 8·25

Nos. 4118/4119, 4120/4121 and 4122/4123 were each printed together, *se-tenant*, as horizontal pairs in sheets of 60 (2 panes 6×5).

Nos. 4118/**MS**4124 commemorate the 250th Anniversary of the Departure of the *Endeavour*.

The 11 PHQ cards show the ten individual stamps including those from No. **MS**4124 and the complete miniature sheet.

3233 Laurence Olivier in *The Dance of Death*

3234 Glenda Jackson in *King Lear*

3235 Albert Finney in *Hamlet*

3236 Maggie Smith in *Hedda Gabler*

3237 John Gielgud and Ralph Richardson in *No Man's Land*

3238 Sharon Benson in *Carmen Jones*

3239 Judi Dench and John Stride in *Romeo and Juliet*

3240 Richard Burton in *Henry V*

(Des Hat-trick Design and Kelvyn Laurence Smith (typography). Litho ISP Cartor)

2018 (30 Aug). Bicentenary of The Old Vic, London. Multicoloured. Two phosphor bands. Perf 14½×14

4125	**3233**	(1st) Laurence Olivier in *The Dance of Death*	1·20	1·00
		a. Horiz pair. Nos. 4125/4126	2·40	2·00
4126	**3234**	(1st) Glenda Jackson in *King Lear*	1·20	1·00
4127	**3235**	£1·25 Albert Finney in *Hamlet*	1·90	1·90
		a. Horiz pair. Nos. 4127/4128	3·75	3·75
4128	**3236**	£1·25 Maggie Smith in *Hedda Gabler*	1·90	1·90
4129	**3237**	£1·45 John Gielgud and Ralph Richardson in *No Man's Land*	2·25	2·25
		a. Horiz pair. Nos. 4129/4130	4·50	4·50

4130	**3238**	£1·45 Sharon Benson in *Carmen Jones*.....	2·25	2·25
4131	**3239**	£1·55 Judi Dench and John Stride in		
		Romeo and Juliet............................	2·40	2·40
		a. Horiz pair. Nos. 4131/4132.............	4·75	4·75
4132	**3240**	£1·55 Richard Burton in *Henry V*	2·40	2·40

Set of 8.. 13·75 13·50
Set of 4 *Gutter Pairs* (only 2 stamps in each gutter pair)... 14·50
Set of 4 *Traffic Light Gutter Blocks* (4 stamps per block).... 29·00
First Day Cover (Tallents House)................................. 18·50
First Day Cover (London SE1)....................................... 18·50
Presentation Pack (PO Pack No. 560)................................ 16·00
PHQ Cards (set of 8) (447)................................. 5·50 15·00

Nos. 4125/416, 4127/4128, 4129/4130 and 4131/4132 were each printed together, *se-tenant*, as horizontal pairs in sheets of 60 (2 panes 6×5).

3241 *100 Poppies* (Zafer and Barbara Baran)

3242 *Anthem for Doomed Youth* (poem by Wilfred Owen) (woodblock print by Andrew Davidson)

3243 Second Lieutenant Walter Tull (1888–1918)

3244 *We Are Making a New World* (Paul Nash)

3245 The Grave of the Unknown Warrior, Westminster Abbey, London

3246 Lieutenant Francis Hopgood's Goggles

(Des Hat-trick Design. Litho ISP Cartor (Nos. 4133/41338, **MS**4138*a*) or gravure ISP Walsall (Nos. 4139/4140))

2018 (13 Sept). Centenary of the First World War (5th issue). Multicoloured.

(a) Ordinary gum. Two phosphor bands. Perf 14½.

4133	**3241**	(1st) *100 Poppies* (Zafer and Barbara Baran).......................	1·20	1·00
		a. Booklet pane. Nos. 4133/4135 with margins all round...................	3·50	
4134	**3242**	(1st) *Anthem for Doomed Youth* (poem by Wilfred Owen) (woodblock print by Andrew Davidson).............	1·20	1·00
4135	**3243**	(1st) Second Lieutenant Walter Tull (1888–1918)...................	1·20	1·00
4136	**3244**	£1·55 *We Are Making a New World* (Paul Nash)......................	2·40	2·40
		a. Booklet pane. Nos. 4136/4138 with margins all round....................	7·00	
4137	**3245**	£1·55 The Grave of the Unknown Warrior, Westminster Abbey, London..........................	2·40	2·40
4138	**3246**	£1·55 Lieutenant Francis Hopgood's Goggles.........................	2·40	2·40

Set of 6... 9·50 9·00
Set of 6 Gutter Pairs... 19·00
First Day Cover (Tallents House)................................... 12·50
First Day Cover (London SW1)....................................... 12·50
Presentation Pack (PO Pack No. 561)............................... 12·00
PHQ Cards (set of 6) (448).................................. 4·00 11·00
MS4138*a* 296×210 mm. **3246**a. Nos. 3626/3631, 3711/3716, 3838/3843, 3983/398 and 4133/4138.... 50·00 65·00

(b) Self-adhesive. Die-cut perf 14½.

4139	**2774**	(1st) *Poppy* (Fiona Strickland)...................	1·75	1·75
		a. Booklet pane. Nos. 4139/4140 and U3027×4..................	7·50	
4140	**3241**	(1st) *100 Poppies* (Zafer and Barbara Baran)......................	1·75	1·75

Booklet panes Nos. 4133a and 4136a come from the £15·65 Centenary of the First World War (5th issue) booklet, No. DY26.

Nos. 4139/4140 were issued in stamp booklet, No. PM63, originally sold for £4·02.

No. **MS**4138*a* was a special composite sheet sold for £32·94.

No. 4139 was as T **2774**, the poppy stamp issued in 2014 for the first Centenary of the First World War series, but self-adhesive and printed in gravure.

A souvenir pack containing the poppy stamps Nos. 3626, 3711, 3838, 3983 and 4133 each affixed to a poem print was sold by Royal Mail for £24·99.

3247 Hermione Granger (Emma Watson)

3248 *Hogwarts Express*

3249 Harry Potter (Daniel Radcliffe)

3250 *Flying Ford Anglia*

3251 Ron Weasley (Rupert Grint)

3252 *Hagrid's Motorbike*

3246a The Great War composite sheet

3253 Ginny Weasley (Bonnie Wright)

3254 Triwizard Cup

3255 Neville Longbottom (Matthew Lewis)

3256 *Knight Bus*

3257 Hogwarts Professors and The Marauders Map

(Des True North with digital image enhancement by Smoke & Mirrors (Nos. 4141/4150, 4152/4153) or The Chase (No. **MS**4151). Litho ISP Cartor (Nos. 4141/4150, **MS**4151) or gravure ISP Walsall (Nos. 4152/4153))

2018 (16 Oct–4 Dec). Harry Potter (1st issue) Multicolour. 'All-over' phosphor (No. **MS**4151 stamps only) or two phosphor bands (others).

(a) Ordinary gum. Perf 14×14½.

4141	3247	(1st) Hermione Granger (Emma Watson)...............................	1·20	1·00
		a. Horiz strip of 5. Nos. 4141/4145..	5·25	5·00
		b. Booklet pane. Nos. 4141, 4143, 4145, 4147 and 4149 with margins all round (4.12.18)............	5·25	
4142	3248	(1st) *Hogwarts Express*.............................	1·20	1·00
		b. Booklet pane. Nos. 4142, 4144, 4146, 4148 and 4150 with margins all round (4.12.18)............	5·25	
4143	3249	(1st) Harry Potter (Daniel Radcliffe)........	1·20	1·00
4144	3250	(1st) Flying Ford Anglia...........................	1·20	1·00
4145	3251	(1st) Ron Weasley (Rupert Grint).............	1·20	1·00
4146	3252	(1st) Hagrid's Motorbike..........................	1·20	1·00
		a. Horiz strip of 5. Nos. 4146/4150.....	5·25	5·00
4147	3253	(1st) Ginny Weasley (Bonnie Wright)......	1·20	1·00
4148	3254	(1st) Triwizard Cup..................................	1·20	1·00
4149	3255	(1st) Neville Longbottom (Matthew Lewis)..	1·20	1·00
4150	3256	(1st) *Knight Bus*....................................	1·20	1·00
		Set of 10..	10·50	9·00
		Set of 2 Gutter Strips of 10................................	21·00	
		First Day Cover (Tallents House).............................		13·00
		First Day Cover (Muggleswick, Consett)...................		13·00
		Presentation Pack (PO Pack No. 562) (Nos. 4141/4150 and **MS**4151)...	19·00	
		PHQ Cards (set of 16) (449)...................................	11·00	23·00

(b) Self-adhesive. Die-cut perf 14.

MS4151	202×74 mm. **3257** (1st) Pomona Sprout (Miriam Margolyes); (1st) Horace Slughorn (Jim Broadbent); (1st) Sybill Trelawney (Emma Thompson); (1st) Remus Lupin (David Thewlis); (1st) Severus Snape (Alan Rickman)........................		6·25	6·25
	b. No. **MS**4151 with margins all round (4.12.18)...................................		5·00	5·00
	First Day Cover (Tallents House)...............................			8·50
	First Day Cover (Muggleswick, Consett)...................			8·50

(c) Self-adhesive. Die-cut perf 14×14½.

4152	3247	(1st) Hermione Granger (Emma Watson)...	1·75	1·75
		a. Booklet pane. Nos. 4152/4153 and U3027×4...............................	7·50	
4153	3249	(1st) Harry Potter (Daniel Radcliffe)........	1·75	1·75

Nos. 4141/4145 and 4146/4150 were each printed together, *se-tenant*, as horizontal strips of five stamps in sheets of 50 (2 panes 5×5).

Booklet panes Nos. 4141b and 4142b come from the £15·50 Harry Potter booklet, No. DY27.

Nos. 4152/4153 were issued in stamp booklets, Nos. PM64/PM64a, originally sold for £4·02.

When placed under a UV light parts of the designs of Nos. 4141/4150 and 4152/4153 light up green, and No. **MS**4151 reveals additional inscriptions.

A collectors sheet (No. LS112) containing stamps as Nos. 4141/4150 but self-adhesive with labels showing Harry Potter film stills was sold for £7·70, a £1 premium over face value.

A Souvenir Stamp Art Folder containing pages of enlarged images of Nos. 4141/4150 with the stamps attached, cancelled with a special cachet postmark, and also a poster of the miniature sheet, were sold by Royal Mail for £24·99.

The 16 PHQ cards show the individual stamps including those from No. **MS**4151 and the complete miniature sheet.

3258 Man and Girl posting Letters in Wall-mounted Post Box

3259 Postal Worker emptying Post Box

3260 Man and Girl posting Letters in Wall-mounted Post Box

3261 Postal Worker emptying Post Box

3262 Man and Boy approaching Rural Pillar Box

3263 Man approaching Post Box

3264 Woman with Dog posting Letter

3265 Pillar Box near Church

(Des Andrew Davidson. Gravure ISP Walsall (No. 4154/4161) or litho ISP Cartor (No. **MS**4162))

2018 (1 Nov). Christmas. Post Boxes. Multicoloured One centre band (No. 4154) or two bands (others).

(a) Self-adhesive. Die-cut perf 14½×15.

4154	3258	(2nd) Man and Girl posting Letters in Wall mounted Post box.................	90	90
		a. Booklet pane. No. 4154×12............	17·00	
4155	3259	(1st) Postal Worker emptying Post box..	1·20	1·00
		a. Booklet pane. No. 4155×12............	20·00	
4156	3260	(2nd Large) Man and Girl posting Letters in Wall-mounted Post box..	1·25	1·10
4157	3261	(1st Large) Postal Worker emptying Post box..	1·70	1·40
4158	3262	£1·25 Man and Boy approaching Rural Pillar Box................................	1·90	1·90
4159	3263	£1·45 Man approaching Post Box............	2·25	2·25
4160	3264	£1·55 Woman with Dog posting Letter...	2·40	2·40
4161	3265	£2·25 Pillar Box near Church..................	3·50	3·50
		Set of 8..	13·50	13·00
		First Day Cover (Tallents House).............................		18·00
		First Day Cover (Bethlehem, Llandeilo)...................		18·00
		Presentation Pack (PO Pack No. 563).....................	15·00	
		PHQ Cards (set of 9) (450)...................................	6·00	25·00

(b) Ordinary gum. Perf 14½×15.

MS4162	190×74 mm. As Nos. 4154/4161.........	13·50	13·00
	First Day Cover (Tallents House)...............................		18·00
	First Day Cover (Bethlehem, Llandeilo)...................		18·00

Nos. 4154 and 4155 also occur together with Nos. 4019 and 4120 respectively as *se-tenant* pairs across the middle of counter sheets, due to the top and bottom halves of each sheet comprising the different stamps. Note that the original printings of Nos. 4019/4020 were by De La Rue, the 2018 reprints were by ISP (Walsall).

The 2nd class, 1st class, £1·25, £1·45, £1·55 and £2·25 values were also issued in sheets of 20 (No. LS113) containing 8×2nd class, 8×1st class, 1×£1·25, 1×£1·45, 1×£1·55 and 1×£2·25 values, each stamp accompanied by a *se-tenant* label. These sheets were printed in lithography by ISP Cartor and were originally sold for £17·50.

The nine PHQ cards show the individual stamps and the complete miniature sheet.

3266 70th Birthday of Prince of Wales

(Des Royal Mail Group Ltd/Davies Maude. Litho ISP Cartor)

2018 (14 Nov). 70th Birthday of the Prince of Wales. Multicolour. 'All-over' phosphor. Self-adhesive. Die-cut perf 14½×15

MS4163 203×74 mm. **3266** (1st) Prince Charles; (1st) Prince Charles with Camilla, Duchess of Cornwall; (1st) Prince Charles with Prince William and Prince Harry; £1·55 Prince Charles, Prince William and Prince Harry at Cirencester Park Polo Club; £1·55 Prince Charles at Castle of Mey; £1·55 Prince Charles with schoolchildren at Llancaiach Fawr

Manor..	10·50	10·50
First Day Cover (Tallents House)..................		13·00
First Day Cover (London SW1)....................		13·00
Presentation Pack (PO Pack No. 564)...........	12·00	
PHQ Cards (set of 7) (451).......................	4·75	12·00

Collectors Pack

2018 (14 Nov). Comprises Nos. 4033/**MS4043**, 4050/**MS4064**, 4074/4079, 4082/4106, 4109/**MS4115**, 4118/4138, 4141/**MS4151**, 4154/4161 and **MS4163**

CP4163a	Collectors Pack (Pack No. 565) (sold for £133).................	£200

Post Office Yearbook

2018 (14 Nov). Comprises Nos. 4033/**MS4043**, 4050/**MS4064**, 4074/4079, 4082/4106, 4109/**MS4115**, 4118/38, 4141/**MS4151**, 4154/4061 and **MS4163**

YB4163a	Yearbook (sold for £153)......................	£225

Miniature Sheet Collection

2018 (14 Nov). Comprises Nos. **MS4043**, **MS4064**, **MS4092**, **MS4115**, **MS4124**, **MS4151**, **MS4162** and **MS4163**

MS4163a Miniature Sheet Collection (sold for £42).........	65·00	

(The Chase. Litho ISP Cartor)

2018 (4 Dec). Harry Potter (2nd issue). Multicoloured. Self-adhesive. 'All-over' phosphor (stamps only). Die-cut perf 14.

4164	**3267**	(1st) Pomona Sprout (Miriam Margolyes).................		1·40	1·40
		a. Booklet pane. Nos. 4164/4166........		4·00	
4165	**3268**	(1st) Horace Slughorn (Jim Broadbent).		1·40	1·40
4166	**3269**	(1st) Sybill Trelawney (Emma Thompson)...........		1·40	1·40
4167	**3270**	(1st) Remus Lupin (David Thewlis).........		1·40	1·40
		a. Booklet pane. Nos. 4167/4168.......		2·75	
4168	**3271**	(1st) Severus Snape (Alan Rickman).......		1·40	1·40
Set of 5				6·25	6·25

Nos. 4164/4168 were issued in No. **MS4151** and in booklet panes 4164a and 4167a from the £15·50 Harry Potter booklet DY27.

Booklet panes Nos. 4164a and 4167a are as No. **MS4151** but in two panes with Marauder's Map margins.

When placed under UV light, Nos. 4164a and 4167a reveal additional inscriptions.

3272 Stamp Classics

(Des Hat-trick design. Litho ISP)

2019 (15 Jan). Stamp Classics Multicoloured. Phosphor frame. Perf 14×13½.

MS4169 203×74 mm. **3272** (1st) Queen Victoria 1891 £1 green; (1st) King Edward VII 1910 2d. Tyrian plum; (1st) King George V 1913 Sea horse 2s.6d. brown; £1·55 King Edward VIII 1936 1½d. red-brown; £1·55 King George VI (and Queen Victoria) 1940 Penny Black Centenary ½d. green; £1·55 Queen Elizabeth II 1953 Coronation 2½d.

carmine-red..	13·50	13·50
First Day Cover (Tallents House).....................		16·00
First Day Cover (London WC1)....................		16·00
Presentation Pack (PO Pack No. 566).............	14·50	
PHQ Cards (set of 7) (451).......................	4·75	22·00

No. **MS4169** commemorates the 150th Anniversary of the Royal Philatelic Society and the 50th Anniversary of Queen Elizabeth II opening the National Postal Museum, London.

No. **MS4169** additionally inscribed 'Stampex International The British National Stamp Exhibition' 13–16 February 2019' was only available at that exhibition (Price £15)

3267 Pomona Sprout (Miriam Margolyes)

3268 Horace Slughorn (Jim Broadbent)

3269 Sybill Trelawney (Emma Thompson)

3273 The Skull Sectioned

3274 A Sprig of Guelder-rose

3270 Remus Lupin (David Thewlis)

3271 Severus Snape (Alan Rickman)

3275 Studies of Cats

3276 Star-of-Bethlehem and Other Plants

3277 The Anatomy of the Shoulder and Foot

3278 The Head of Leda

3279 The Head of a Bearded Man

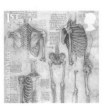

3280 The Skeleton

3281 The Head of St Philip

3282 A Woman in a Landscape

3283 A Design for an Equestrian Monument

3284 The Fall of Light on a Face

(Des Kate Stephens. Litho ISP Cartor)

2019 (13 Feb). 500th Death Anniversary of Leonardo da Vinci (1452–1519, artist) Multicoloured. Two phosphor bands. Perf 14½.

4170	**3273**	(1st) The Skull Sectioned..........................	1·20	1·00
		a. Horiz strip of 6. Nos. 4170/4175......	6·50	5·50
		b. Booklet pane. Nos. 4170, 4174, 4177 and 4181 with margins all round..	5·25	
4171	**3274**	(1st) A Sprig of Guelder-rose..................	1·20	1·00
		b. Booklet pane. Nos. 4171/4173 and 4180 with margins all round...	5·25	
4172	**3275**	(1st) Studies of Cats................................	1·20	1·00
4173	**3276**	(1st) A Star-of-Bethlehem and Other Plants..	1·20	1·00
4174	**3277**	(1st) The Anatomy of the Shoulder and Foot..	1·20	1·00
4175	**3278**	(1st) The Head of Leda.............................	1·20	1·00
		b. Booklet pane. Nos. 4175/4176 and 4178/4179 with margins all round..	5·25	
4176	**3279**	(1st) The Head of a Bearded Man............	1·20	1·00
		a. Horiz strip of 6. Nos. 4176/4181......	6·50	5·50
4177	**3280**	(1st) The Skeleton....................................	1·20	1·00
4178	**3281**	(1st) The Head of St Philip.......................	1·20	1·00
4179	**3282**	(1st) A Woman in a Landscape................	1·20	1·00
4180	**3283**	(1st) A Design for an Equestrian Monument..	1·20	1·00
4181	**3284**	(1st) The Fall of Light on a Face...............	1·20	1·00
		Set of 12..	13·00	11·00
		Set of 2 Gutter Strips of 12.........................	26·00	
		First Day Cover (Tallents House)................		14·00
		First Day Cover (Windsor)...........................		14·00
		Presentation Pack (PO Pack No. 567).........	17·00	
		PHQ Cards (set of 12) (453)......................	7·00	12·00

Nos. 4170/4175 and 4176/4181 were each printed together, *se-tenant*, as horizontal strips of six stamps in sheets of 60 (2 panes 6×5).

Booklet panes Nos. 4170b, 4171b and 4175b are from the £13·10 Leonardo da Vinci booklet, No. DY28.

3285 Spider-Man

3286 Captain Marvel

3287 Hulk

3288 Doctor Strange

3289 Captain Britain

3290 Peggy Carter

3291 Iron Man

3292 Union Jack

3293 Black Panther

3294 Thor

3295 Marvel Heroes UK

(Des Alan Davis (illustrations) and Interabang. Litho ISP Cartor (Nos. 4182/4191) or gravure ISP Walsall (Nos. 4193/4194))

2019 (14 Mar). Marvel (1st issue) Multicoloured. Two phosphor bands.

(a) Ordinary gum. Perf 14½.

4182	**3285**	(1st) Spider-Man......................................	1·20	1·00
		a. Horiz strip of 5. Nos. 4182/4186.....	5·25	4·50
		b. Booklet pane. Nos. 4182/4184 and 4186/4188 with margins all round..	5·25	
4183	**3286**	(1st) Captain Marvel.................................	1·20	1·00
4184	**3287**	(1st) Hulk...	1·20	1·00

4185	**3288**	(1st) Doctor Strange..................................	1·20	1·00
		b. Booklet pane. Nos. 4185 and		
		4189/4191 with margins all round	5·25	
4186	**3289**	(1st) Captain Britain...............................	1·20	1·00
4187	**3290**	(1st) Peggy Carter..................................	1·20	1·00
		a. Horiz strip of 5. Nos. 4187/4191.....	5·25	4·50
4188	**3291**	(1st) Iron Man..	1·20	1·00
4189	**3292**	(1st) Union Jack......................................	1·20	1·00
4190	**3293**	(1st) Black Panther.................................	1·20	1·00
4191	**3294**	(1st) Thor..	1·20	1·00
Set of 10..			10·50	9·00
Set of 2 Gutter Strips of 10............................			21·00	
First Day Cover (Tallents House)......................				17·00
First Day Cover (Shield Row, Stanley)..............				17·00
Presentation Pack (PO Pack No. 568) (Nos. 4182/4191				
and **MS**4192)..			20·00	
PHQ Cards (set of 16) (454)...........................			9·00	24·00

(b) Self-adhesive.
MS4192 203×74 mm. **3295** (1st) Thanos (Perf 14); (1st)
Thor, Doctor Strange and Iron Man ('He's strong.')
(Perf 14½×14); (1st) Hulk, Iron Man, Black Panther
and Spider-Man ('but we're stronger...') (Perf 14);
£1·25 Captain Britain, Spider-Man, Iron Man, Hulk,
Thor and Black Panther ('...together!') (Perf 14);
£1·45 Captain Britain ('Fury, a portal is opening.')

(Perf 14½×14)..	7·25	7·25
First Day Cover (Tallents House)......................		10·00
First Day Cover (Shield Row, Stanley)..............		10·00

(c) Self-adhesive booklet stamps. Die-cut perf 14½.

4193	**3285**	(1st) Spider-Man....................................	3·50	3·50
		a. Booklet pane. Nos. 4193/4194		
		and U3027×4....................................	10·00	
4194	**3287**	(1st) Hulk...	3·50	3·50

Nos. 4182/4186 and 4187/4191 were each printed together, *se-tenant*, as horizontal strips of five stamps in sheets of 50 (2 panes 5×5).

Booklet panes No. 4182b and 4185b come from the £17·45 MArvel booklet, No. DY29.

Nos. 4193/4194 were issued in stamp booklet, No. PM65, originally sold for £4·02.

Nos. 4182/4194 commemorate the 80th Anniversary of Marvel Comics.

A collector's sheet (No. LS115) containing stamps as Nos. 4182/4191 but self-adhesive was sold for £7·70, a £1 premium above face value.

The 16 PHQ cards show the 15 individual stamps, including those from No. **MS**4192, and the complete sheet.

3296 'Thanos'

3297 Thor, Doctor Strange and Iron Man ('He's strong.')

3298 Hulk, Iron Man, Black Panther and Spider-Man ('but we're stronger...')

3299 Captain Britain, Spider-Man, Iron Man, Hulk, Thor and Black Panther ('...together!')

3300 Captain Britain ('Fury, a portal is opening.')

(Des Alan Davis (illustrations) and Interabang. Litho ISP Cartor)

2019 (14 Mar). Marvel (2nd issue) Multicoloured. Self-adhesive. Two phosphor bands. Die-cut perf 14½×14 (Nos. 4196, 4199) or 14 (others).

4195	**3296**	(1st) Thanos..	1·25	1·25
		a. Booklet pane. Nos. 4195 and 4199	4·00	
4196	**3297**	(1st) Thor, Doctor Strange and Iron		
		Man ('He's strong.')..........................	1·25	1·25
		a. Booklet pane. Nos. 4196/4198......	5·00	
4197	**3298**	(1st) Hulk, Iron Man, Black Panther		
		and Spider-Man ('but we're		
		stronger...')...................................	1·25	1·25
4198	**3299**	£1·25 Captain Britain, Spider-Man,		
		Iron Man, Hulk, Thor and Black		
		Panther ('...together!')....................	2·50	2·50
4199	**3300**	£1·45 Captain Britain ('Fury, a portal is		
		opening.').....................................	2·75	2·75
Set of 5..			8·00	8·00

Nos. 4195/4199 were issued in No. **MS**4192 and in booklet panes 4195a and 4196a from the £17·45 Marvel booklet, No. DY29.

Booklet panes Nos. 4195a and 4196a are as No. **MS**4192 but in two panes with enlarged margins.

3301 White-tailed Eagle   **3302** Merlin

3303 Hobby   **3304** Buzzard

3305 Golden Eagle   **3306** Kestrel

3307 Goshawk   **3308** Sparrowhawk

3309 Red Kite   **3310** Peregrine Falcon

(Des GBH. Litho ISP Cartor (Nos. 4200/4209) or gravure ISP Walsall (Nos. 4210/4211)

2019 (4 Apr). Birds of Prey. Multicoloured. Phosphor background.

(a) Ordinary gum. Perf 14×14½.

4200	**3301**	(1st) White-tailed Eagle (*Haliaeetus albicilla*)...............	1·20	1·00
		a. Horiz strip of 5. Nos. 4200/4204.......	5·25	4·50
4201	**3302**	(1st) Merlin (*Falco columbarius*)................	1·20	1·00
4202	**3303**	(1st) Hobby (*Falco subbuteo*)....................	1·20	1·00
4203	**3304**	(1st) Buzzard (*Buteo buteo*)......................	1·20	1·00
4204	**3305**	(1st) Golden Eagle (*Aquila chrysaetos*)...	1·20	1·00
4205	**3306**	(1st) Kestrel (*Falco tinnunculus*)...............	1·20	1·00
		a. Horiz strip of 5. Nos. 4205/4209........	5·25	4·50
4206	**3307**	(1st) Goshawk (*Accipiter gentilis*).............	1·20	1·00
4207	**3308**	(1st) Sparrowhawk (*Accipiter nisus*).........	1·20	1·00
4208	**3309**	(1st) Red Kite (*Milvus milvus*)...................	1·20	1·00
4209	**3310**	(1st) Peregrine Falcon (*Falco peregrinus*)...................	1·20	1·00
Set of 10...			10·50	9·00
Set of 2 Gutter Strips of 10...................			21·00	
First Day Cover (Tallents House).............				13·00
First Day Cover (Eagle, Lincoln).............				13·00
Presentation Pack (PO Pack No. 569)....			13·00	
PHQ Cards (set of 10) (455)......................			6·00	12·00

(b) Self-adhesive. Die-cut perf 14×14½.

4210	**3304**	(1st) Buzzard (*Buteo buteo*)....................	15·00	15·00
		a. Booklet pane. Nos. 4210/4211 and U3027×4...........................	50·00	
4211	**3303**	(1st) Hobby (*Falco subbuteo*)..................	15·00	15·00

Nos. 4200/4204 and 4205/4209 were each printed together, *se-tenant*, as horizontal strips of five stamps in sheets of 50 (2 panes 5×5).

Nos. 4210/4211 were issued in stamp booklet, No. PM66, originally sold for £4·02.

3311 Raspberry Pi Microcomputer

3312 The Falkirk Wheel Rotating Boat Lift

Raspberry Pi microcomputer helps to teach programming

The Falkirk Wheel rotating boat lift connects Scottish waterways

3313 Three-way Catalytic Converter

3314 Crossrail

Three-way catalytic converter reduces pollutants in car exhaust

Crossrail created 26 miles (42km) of new rail tunnels under London

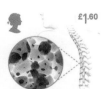

3315 Superconducting Magnet in MRI Scanner

3316 Synthetic Bone-graft

Superconducting magnet allows high-quality imaging in MRI

Synthetic bone-graft material encourages new bone growth

HARRIER JUMP JET 50TH ANNIVERSARY

3317 Harrier GR3

(Des Martin Woodward and Common Curiosity (Nos. 4212/4217) or Turner Duckworth (No. **MS**4218). Litho ISP Cartor)

2019 (2 May). British Engineering. Multicoloured. Two phosphor bands. Perf 14½×14 (Nos. 4212/4217) or 14 (No. **MS**4218).

4212	**3311**	(1st) Raspberry Pi Microcomputer........	1·20	1·00
		a. Horiz pair. Nos. 4212/4213.............	2·40	2·00
4213	**3312**	(1st) The Falkirk Wheel........................	1·20	1·00
4214	**3313**	£1·55 Three-way catalytic converter.......	2·40	2·40
		a. Horiz pair. Nos. 4214/4215..............	4·75	4·75
4215	**3314**	£1·55 Crossrail...................................	2·40	2·40
4216	**3315**	£1·60 Superconducting Magnet..............	2·50	2·50
		a. Horiz pair. Nos. 4216/4217..............	5·00	5·00
4217	**3316**	£1·60 Synthetic Bone-graft material........	2·50	2·50
Set of 6..			10·75	10·50
Set of 3 Gutter Pairs (only 2 stamps in each Gutter Pair)....			11·50	
Set of 3 Traffic Light Gutter Blocks of 4................			23·00	
First Day Cover (Tallents House).................				14·50
First Day Cover (London SW1)...................				14·50
Presentation Pack (PO Pack No. 570) (Nos. 4212/4217 and **MS**4218)...................			20·00	
PHQ Cards (set of 11) (456)......................			6·50	20·00

MS4218 203×75 mm. **3317** (1st) Harrier GR3 Short Take-off; (1st) Harrier GR3 Transition to Landing; £1·55 Harrier GR3 Conventional Flight; £1·55 Harrier GR3 Vertical Landing......................... 6·75 6·75

First Day Cover (Tallents House).................		8·50
First Day Cover (London SW1)...................		8·50

Nos. 4212/4213, 4214/4215 and 4216/4217 were each printed together, *se-tenant*, as horizontal pairs in sheets of 60 (2 panes 6×5).

The 11 PHQ cards show the ten individual stamps, including those from No. **MS**4218, and the complete sheet.

1890 Queen Victoria in her later years

3318 Queen Victoria (Heinrich von Angeli), 1890

1878 Queen Victoria and Benjamin Disraeli

3319 Queen Victoria and Benjamin Disraeli, 1878

1876 Queen Victoria with servant John Brown

3320 Queen Victoria with servant John Brown, 1876

Queen Victoria wearing her Robes of State

3321 Queen Victoria wearing her Robes of State, 1859

3322 Marriage of Queen Victoria and Prince Albert, 1840

1830 Princess Victoria aged 11

3323 Princess Victoria aged 11, 1830

THE LEGACY OF PRINCE ALBERT

3324 The Legacy of Prince Albert

(Des Webb & Webb Design. Litho ISP Cartor)

2019 (24 May). Birth Bicentenary of Queen Victoria (1st issue). Multicoloured. Two phosphor bands. Perf 14×14½ (Nos. 4219/4224) or 14 (No. **MS**4225).

4219	**3318**	(1st) Queen Victoria (Heinrich von Angeli), 1890	1·20	1·00
		a. Horiz pair. Nos. 4219/4220	2·40	2·00
		b. Booklet pane. Nos. 4219/4221 with margins all round	4·25	
4220	**3319**	(1st) Queen Victoria and Benjamin Disraeli, 1878	1·20	1·00
4221	**3320**	£1·35 Queen Victoria with Servant John Brown, 1876	2·00	2·00
		a. Horiz pair. Nos. 4221/4222	4·00	4·00
4222	**3321**	£1·35 Queen Victoria wearing her Robes of State, 1859	2·00	2·00
		b. Booklet pane. Nos. 4222/4224 with margins all round	7·00	
4223	**3322**	£1·60 Marriage of Queen Victoria and Prince Albert, 1840	2·50	2·50
		a. Horiz pair. Nos. 4223/4224	5·00	5·00
4224	**3323**	£1·60 Princess Victoria aged 11, 1830	2·50	2·50

Set of 6	10·50	10·00
Set of 3 Gutter Pairs	21·00	
First Day Cover (Tallents House)		13·50
First Day Cover (East Cowes)		13·50
Presentation Pack (PO Pack No. 571)	20·00	
PHQ Cards (set of 11) (457)	6·50	22·00

MS4225 156×74 mm. **3324** (1st) Model Lodge, Kennington; (1st) Balmoral Castle, Scotland; £1·55 The New Crystal Palace, Sydenham; £1·55 Royal Albert Hall, London ... 18·00 / 18·00

First Day Cover (Tallents House)		20·00
First Day Cover (East Cowes)		20·00

Nos. 4219/4220, 4221/4222 and 4223/4224 were each printed together, *se-tenant*, as horizontal pairs in sheets of 60 (2 panes 6×5).

Booklet panes No. 4219b and 4222b come from the £17.20 Queen Victoria booklet, No. DY30.

The 11 PHQ cards show the individual stamps including those from No. **MS**4225 and the complete miniature sheet.

3325 Model Lodge, Kennington

3326 Balmoral Castle, Scotland

3327 The New Crystal Palace, Sydenham

3328 Royal Albert Hall, London

(Des Webb & Webb Design. Litho ISP Cartor)

2019 (24 May). Birth Bicentenary of Queen Victoria (2nd issue). Multicoloured. Two phosphor bands. Perf 14

4226	**3325**	(1st) Model Lodge, Kennington	3·00	3·00
		a. Booklet pane. Nos. 4226/4229 with margins all round and roulettes at left	28·00	
4227	**3326**	(1st) Balmoral Castle, Scotland	3·00	3·00
4228	**3327**	£1·55 The New Crystal Palace, Sydenham	6·00	6·00
4229	**3328**	£1·55 Royal Albert Hall, London	6·00	6·00
Set of 4			18·00	18·00

Nos. 4226/4229 come from No. **MS**4225 and the £17·20 Queen Victoria booklet, No. DY30.

3329 British soldiers are briefed before embarkation

3330 HMS *Warspite* shelling in support of beach landings

3331 Paratroopers synchronising watches

3332 Soldiers wade ashore on Juno Beach

3333 An American light bomber provides air support

3334 British troops take cover as they advance inland

3335 The Normandy Landings

3336 Gold Beach   **3337** Sword Beach

(Des Baxter and Bailey. Litho ISP Cartor (Nos. 4230/**MS**4236) or gravure ISP Walsall (Nos. 4237/4238)

2019 (6 June). 75th Anniversary of D-Day. Multicoloured. Two phosphor bands.

(a) Ordinary gum. Perf 14½.

4230	**3329**	(1st) No. 4 Commando, 1st Special Service Brigade briefed by Commanding Officer Lieutenant-Colonel R. Dawson before Embarkation..................	1·20	1·00
		a. Vert pair. Nos. 4230/4231..............	2·40	2·00
4231	**3330**	(1st) HMS *Warspite* shelling German Gun Batteries...............	1·20	1·00
4232	**3331**	£1·35 Paratroopers...............	2·00	2·00
		a. Vert pair. Nos. 4232/4233..............	4·00	4·00
4233	**3332**	£1·35 Commandos wade ashore on Juno Beach.............	2·00	2·00
4234	**3333**	£1·60 American A-20 Havoc Light Bomber.................	2·50	2·50
		a. Vert pair. Nos. 4234/4235..............	5·00	5·00
4235	**3334**	£1·60 Troops take cover from enemy shell.................	2·50	2·50
Set of 6.............			10·25	10·00
Set of 3 Gutter Pairs (only 2 stamps in each gutter pair)...			11·50	
First Day Cover (Tallents House)................				13·00
First Day Cover (Southwick, Fareham)...............				13·00
Presentation Pack (PO Pack No. 572) (Nos. 4230/4235 and **MS**4236)................			18·00	
PHQ Cards (set of 12) (458)...............			7·00	22·00
MS4236 203×75 mm. **3335** (1st)×5 US 4th Infantry Division, Utah Beach; US troops going ashore at Omaha Beach; British 50th Division landing on Gold Beach; Canadian 3rd Division landing at Juno Beach; British 3rd Division landing at Sword Beach..			6·25	6·25
First Day Cover (Tallents House)................				7·50
First Day Cover (Southwick, Fareham)................				7·50

(b) Self-adhesive. Die-cut perf 14½.

4237	**3336**	(1st) British 50th Division landing on Gold Beach...............	3·25	3·25
		a. Booklet pane. Nos. 4237/4238 and U3027×4.........	10·00	
4238	**3337**	(1st) British 3rd Division landing at Sword Beach.............	3·25	3·25

Nos. 4230/4231, 4232/4233 and 4234/4235 were each printed together, *se-tenant*, as vertical pairs in sheets of 60 (5×6).

Nos. 4237/4238 were issued in stamp booklet, No. PM67, originally sold for £4·20.

The 12 PHQ cards show each of the individual stamps including those from No. **MS**4236 and the complete miniature sheet.

No. **MS**4236 additionally inscribed 'Stampex International The British National Stamp Exhibition' 11-14 September 2019 was only available at that exhibition (*Price £7*)

3338 Burning the Clocks, Brighton

3339 'Obby 'Oss, Padstow

3340 World Gurning Championships, Egremont

3341 Up Helly Aa, Lerwick

3342 Halloween, Londonderry

3343 Cheese Rolling, Cooper's Hill

3344 Horn Dance, Abbots Bromley

3345 Bog Snorkelling, Llanwrtyd Wells

(Des Jonny Hannah (illustrations) and NB Studio. Litho ISP Cartor)

2019 (19 July). Curious Customs. Multicoloured. One centre bank (2nd) or two bands (others). Perf 14×14½.

4239	**3338**	(2nd) Burning the Clocks, Brighton.........	90	90
		a. Horiz pair. Nos. 4239/4240..............	1·75	1·75
4240	**3339**	(2nd) 'Obby 'Oss, Padstow, Cornwall......	90	90
4241	**3340**	(1st) World Gurning Championships, Egremont, Cumbria.............	1·20	1·00
		a. Horiz pair. Nos. 4241/4242..............	2·40	2·00
4242	**3341**	(1st) Up Helly Aa, Lerwick, Shetland......	1·20	1·00
4243	**3342**	£1·55 Halloween, Londonderry..........	2·40	2·40
		a. Horiz pair. Nos. 4243/4244..............	4·75	4·75
4244	**3343**	£1·55 Cheese Rolling, Cooper's Hill, Brockworth, Gloucestershire..........	2·40	2·40
4245	**3344**	£1·60 Horn Dance, Abbots Bromley, Staffordshire..................	2·50	2·50
		a. Horiz pair. Nos. 4245/4246..............	5·00	5·00
4246	**3345**	£1·60 Bog Snorkelling, Llanwrtyd Wells, Wales..................	2·50	2·50
Set of 8.............			12·75	12·50
Set of 4 Gutter Pairs.............			25·50	
First Day Cover (Tallents House)................				14·00
First Day Cover (Maypole, Monmouth)................				14·00
Presentation Pack (PO Pack No. 573)................			15·00	
PHQ Cards (set of 8) (459).............			5·00	13·00

Nos. 4239/4240, 4241/4242, 4243/4244 and 4245/4246 were each printed together, *se-tenant*, as horizontal pairs in sheets of 60 (2 panes 6×5).

3346 Glen Affric

3347 The National Arboretum, Westonbirt

3348 Sherwood Forest

3349 *Coed y Brenin*

3350 *Glenariff Forest*

3351 *Kielder Forest*

(Des Up. Litho ISP Cartor)

2019 (13 Aug). Forests. Multicoloured. Two phosphor bands. Perf 14½.

4247	**3346**	(1st) Glen Affric...	1·20	1·00
		a. Vert pair. Nos. 4247/4248................	2·40	2·00
4248	**3347**	(1st) The National Arboretum,		
		Westonbirt, Gloucestershire..........	1·20	1·00
4249	**3348**	£1·55 Sherwood Forest,		
		Nottinghamshire............................	2·40	2·40
		a. Vert pair. Nos. 4249/4250................	4·75	4·75
4250	**3349**	£1·55 Coed y Brenin, Gwynedd, Wales.....	2·40	2·40
4251	**3350**	£1·60 Glenariff Forest, County Antrim,.....	2·50	2·50
		a. Vert pair. Nos. 4251/4252................	5·00	5·00
4252	**3351**	£1·60 Kielder Forest...................................	2·50	2·50
Set of 6..			10·75	10·50
Set of 3 Gutter Pairs (only 2 stamps in each gutter pair)...			12·00	
First Day Cover (Tallents House)......................................				13·50
First Day Cover (Westonbirt, Tetbury)...............................				13·50
Presentation Pack (PO Pack No. 574)...............................			13·00	
PHQ Cards (set of 6) (460)...			4·00	12·50

Nos. 4247/4248, 4249/4250 and 4251/4252 were each printed together, *se-tenant*, as vertical pairs in sheets of 60 (2 panes 5×6).

Nos. 4247/4252 commemorate the Centenary of the Forestry Commission.

3352 *Honky Château*

3353 *Goodbye Yellow Brick Road*

3354 *Caribou*

3355 *Captain Fantastic and The Brown Dirt Cowboy*

3356 *Sleeping with The Past*

3357 *The One*

3358 *Made in England*

3359 *Songs from The West Coast*

3360 Elton John Live

(Des Royal Mail Group Ltd from original design by Studio Dempsey. Litho ISP Cartor (Nos. 4253/**MS**4261) or gravure ISP Walsall (Nos. 4262/4263).

2019 (3 Sept). Elton John. Multicoloured. Two phosphor bands.

(a) Ordinary gum. Perf 14.

4253	**3352**	(1st) Honky Château	1·20	1·00
		a. Horiz strip of 4. Nos. 4253/4256.....	4·25	3·75
4254	**3353**	(1st) Goodbye Yellow Brick Road	1·20	1·00
4255	**3354**	(1st) Caribou	1·20	1·00
4256	**3355**	(1st) Captain Fantastic and The Brown		
		Dirt Cowboy..	1·20	1·00
4257	**3356**	£1·55 Sleeping with The Past......................	2·40	2·40
		a. Horiz strip of 4. Nos. 4257/4260.....	9·25	9·25
4258	**3357**	£1·55 The One..	2·40	2·40
4259	**3358**	£1·55 Made in England.............................	2·40	2·40
4260	**3359**	£1·55 Songs from The West Coast..............	2·40	2·40
Set of 8..			13·00	12·50
Set of 2 Gutter Strips of 8...			26·00	
First Day Cover (Tallents House)......................................				15·50
First Day Cover (Pinner)..				15·50
Presentation Pack (PO Pack No. 575) (Nos. 4253/4260				
and **MS**4261)..			24·00	
Goodbye Yellow Brick Road Character Pack (containing				
No. 4254×10)..			13·00	
Captain Fantastic and The Brown Dirt Cowboy Character				
Pack (containing No. 4256×10)......................................			13·00	
PHQ Cards (set of 13) (461)...			7·50	25·00
MS4261 156×74 mm. **3360** Elton John Live (1st)				
Madison Square Garden, 2018; (1st) Dodger				
Stadium, 1975; £1·55 Hammersmith Odeon, 1973;				
£1·55 Buckingham Palace, 2012................................			6·75	6·75
First day cover..				8·50

(b) Self-adhesive. Die-cut perf 14.

4262	**3353**	(1st) Goodbye Yellow Brick Road	5·00	5·00
		a. Booklet pane. Nos. 4262/4263		
		and U3027×4.................................	13·00	
4263	**3355**	(1st) Captain Fantastic and The Brown		
		Dirt Cowboy..................................	5·00	5·00

Nos. 4253/4256 and 4257/4260 were each printed together, *se-tenant*, as horizontal strips of four stamps in sheets of 48 (2 panes 4×6).

Nos. 4262/4263 were issued in stamp booklet, No. PM68, originally sold for £4·20.

A *Goodbye Yellow Brick Road* fan sheet containing No. 4254×4 was sold for £7·50.

A *Captain Fantastic and The Brown Dirt Cowboy* fan sheet containing No. 4256×4 was sold for £7·50.

A Album Collection fan sheet containing Nos. 4253/4260 was sold for £10·20.

The 13 PHQ cards show the individual stamps, including those from No. **MS**4261, and the complete miniature sheet.

3361 *Mary Rose*, 1511

3362 HMS *Queen Elizabeth*, 2014

3363 HMS *Victory*, 1765

3364 HMS *Dreadnought*, 1906

3365 HMS *Warrior*, 1860

3366 *Sovereign of the Seas*, 1637

3367 HMS *King George V*, 1939

3368 HMS *Beagle*, 1820

(Des Hat-trick design. Litho ISP Cartor (Nos. 4264/4271) or gravure ISP Walsall (Nos. 4272/4273)

2019 (19 Sept). Royal Navy Ships. Multicoloured. Two phosphor bands.

(a) Ordinary gum. Perf 14.

4264	**3361**	(1st) *Mary Rose*, 1511 (Geoff Hunt).........	1·20	1·00
		a. Horiz pair. Nos. 4264/4265..............	2·40	2·00
4265	**3362**	(1st) HMS *Queen Elizabeth*, 2014 (Robert G. Lloyd)..............................	1·20	1·00
4266	**3363**	£1·35 *Victory*, 1765 (Monamy Swaine)..............................	2·00	2·00
		a. Horiz pair. Nos. 4266/4267..............	4·00	4·00
4267	**3364**	£1·35 HMS *Dreadnought*, 1906 (H. J. Morgan)...............................	2·00	2·00
4268	**3365**	£1·55 HMS *Warrior*, 1860 (Thomas Goldsworth Dutton)......................	2·40	2·40
		a. Horiz pair. Nos. 4268/4269..............	4·75	4·75
4269	**3366**	£1·55 *Sovereign of the Seas*, 1637 (Paul Garnett)...............................	2·40	2·40
4270	**3367**	£1·60 HMS *King George V*, 1939 (Robert G. Lloyd)...............................	2·50	2·50
		a. Horiz pair. Nos. 4270/4271..............	5·00	5·00
4271	**3368**	£1·60 HMS *Beagle*, 1820 (John Chancellor)...............................	2·50	2·50
Set of 8...			14·25	14·00
Set of 4 Gutter Blocks of 4.......................................			28·50	
First Day Cover (Tallents House).............................				17·00
First Day Cover (Portsmouth)..................................				17·00
Presentation Pack (PO Pack No. 576).......................			17·00	
PHQ Cards (set of 8) (462)......................................			5·00	16·00

(b) Self-adhesive. Die-cut perf 14.

4272	**3361**	(1st) *Mary Rose*, 1511 (Geoff Hunt).........	15·00	15·00
		a. Booklet pane. Nos. 4272/4273 and U3027×4....................................	35·00	
4273	**3362**	(1st) HMS *Queen Elizabeth*, 2014 (Robert G. Lloyd)...........................	15·00	15·00

Nos. 4264/4265, 4266/4267, 4268/4269 and 4270/4271 were each printed together, *se-tenant*, as horizontal pairs in sheets of 60 (2 panes 6×5).

Nos. 4272/4273 were issued in stamp booklet, No. PM69, originally sold for £4·20.

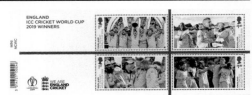

3369 Men's Cricket World Cup Winners

3370 Women's Cricket World Cup Winners

(Litho ISP Cartor)

2019 (26 Sept). ICC Cricket World Cup Winners. Multicoloured. All over phosphor. Perf 14½.

MS4274 203×74 mm. **3369** (1st) England Captain Eoin Morgan lifting Cricket World Cup Trophy; (1st) Eoin Morgan (with trophy) and England team; £1·60 England players celebrating; £1·60 England players congratulating Ben Stokes.............................	6·75	6·75
MS4275 203×74 mm. **3370** (1st) England team after their victory ('CHAMPIONS'); (1st) England players congratulating Anya Shrubsole; £1·60 England Captain Heather Knight and teammates celebrating; £1·60 England team celebrating on balcony at Lord's Cricket Ground (2017)....................	6·75	6·75
First Day Cover (Tallents House) (2)......................		16·00
First Day Covers (London NW8) (2).......................		16·00
Presentation Pack (PO Pack No. M25)...............................	16·00	

3371 'Scrambled snake!'

3372 'Gruffalo crumble!'

3373 'All was quiet in the deep dark wood.'

3374 'A mouse took a stroll'

3375 'Roasted fox!'

3376 'Owl ice cream?'

3378 Angel and Shepherd

3379 Mary and Baby Jesus   **3380** Angel and Shepherd

3381 Mary and Baby Jesus   **3382** Joseph

3383 Baby Jesus in Manger   **3384** Shepherds and Star   **3385** Three Wise Men

(Des Hari & Deepti (illustrations) and Charlie Smith Design. Gravure ISP Walsall (No. 4283/4290) or litho ISP Cartor (No. **MS**4291))

2019 (5 Nov). Christmas. Nativity. Multicoloured. One central band (No. 4283) or two (others).

(a) Self-adhesive. Gravure. Die-cut perf 14½×15..

4283	**3378**	(2nd) Angel and Shepherd..........................	90	90
		a. Booklet pane. No. 4283×12..............	17·00	
4284	**3379**	(1st) Mary and Baby Jesus.......................	1·20	1·00
		a. Booklet pane. No. 4284×12..............	16·00	
4285	**3380**	(2nd Large) Angel and Shepherd............	1·25	1·25
4286	**3381**	(1st Large) Mary and Baby Jesus...........	1·70	1·60
4287	**3382**	£1·35 Joseph..	2·00	2·00
4288	**3383**	£1·55 Baby Jesus in Manger.....................	2·40	2·40
4289	**3384**	£1·60 Shepherds and Star........................	2·50	2·50
4290	**3385**	£2·30 Three Wise Men..............................	3·50	3·50
Set of 8...			13·75	13·50
First Day Cover (Tallents House)....................................				17·00
First Day Cover (Bethlehem, Llandeilo)..........................				17·00
Presentation Pack (PO Pack No. 578)............................			17·00	
PHQ Cards (set of 9) (464)..			6·00	28·00

(b) Ordinary gum. Litho. Perf 14½×15..

MS4291 179×74 mm. Nos. 4283/4290..............................		13·75	13·50
First Day Cover (Tallents House)....................................			17·00
First Day Cover (Bethlehem, Llandeilo)..........................			17·00

The 2nd class, 1st class, £1·35, £1·55, £1·60 and £2·30 values were also issued in sheets of 20 (No. LS118) containing 8×2nd class, 8×1st class, 1×£1·35, 1×£1·55, 1×£1·60 and 1×£2·30 values, each stamp accompanied by a *se-tenant* label. These sheets were printed in lithography and originally sold for £18·40.

The nine PHQ cards show the individual stamps and the complete miniature sheet.

3377 *The Gruffalo*

(Des Rose Design. Litho ISP Cartor)

2019 (10 Oct). *The Gruffalo* (by Julia Donaldson, Illustrated by Axel Scheffler). Multicoloured. Two phosphor bands. Perf 14 (No. 4276/4281) or 14½ (No. **MS**4282)

4276	**3371**	(1st) 'Scrambled snake!'............................	1·20	1·00
		a. Horiz strip of 3. Nos. 4276/4278.....	3·50	3·00
4277	**3372**	(1st) 'Gruffalo crumble!'...........................	1·20	1·00
4278	**3373**	(1st) 'All was quiet in the deep dark		
		wood.'..	1·20	1·00
4279	**3374**	£1·60 'A mouse took a stroll'.....................	2·50	2·50
		a. Horiz strip of 3. Nos. 4279/4281.....	7·50	7·50
4280	**3375**	£1·60 'Roasted fox!'..................................	2·50	2·50
4281	**3376**	£1·60 'Owl ice cream?'..............................	2·50	2·50
Set of 6...			10·00	9·50
Set of 2 Gutter Strips of 6..			11·50	
First Day Cover (Tallents House)....................................				12·50
First Day Cover (Mousehole, Penzance)..........................				12·50
Presentation Pack (PO Pack No. 577) (Nos. 4276/4278				
and **MS**4282)...			19·00	
PHQ Cards (set of 11) (463)..			7·50	22·00
MS4282 126×89 mm. **3377** (1st) Owl; (1st) Mouse;				
£1·55 Snake; £1·55 Fox..			6·75	6·75
First Day Cover (Tallents House)....................................				8·50
First Day Cover (Mousehole, Penzance)..........................				8·50

Nos. 4276/4278 and 4279/4281 were each printed together, *se-tenant*, as horizontal strips of three stamps in sheets of 60 (2 panes 6×5).

Stamps as within No. **MS**4282 but self-adhesive were issued in sheets of ten (No. LS117) sold for £11·50, containing three of each of the two 1st class designs and two of each of the two £1·55 designs, with attached labels.

The 11 PHQ cards show the individual stamps, including those from No. **MS**4282, and the complete miniature sheet.

3386 Count Dooku   **3387** Lando Calrissian

3388 Sith Trooper

3389 Jannah

3390 Grand Moff Tarkin

3391 Darth Maul

3392 Zorii

3393 Wicket W. Warrick

3394 Poe Dameron

3395 Queen Amidala

3395a *Star Wars* Composite Sheet

3396 *Star Wars* Vehicles

(Des Malcolm Tween (illustrations) and Interabang. Litho ISP Cartor (Nos. 4292/**MS**4303) or gravure ISP Walsall (Nos. 4304/4305)

2019 (26 Nov). *Star Wars.* (5th issue). Multicoloured. 'All-over' phosphor (No. **MS**4303 stamp only) or two phosphor bands (others).

(a) Ordinary gum. Perf 14½.

4292	**3386**	(1st) Count Dooku (Christopher Lee).....	1·20	1·00
		a. Horiz strip of 5. Nos. 4292/4296.....	5·25	5·00
		b. Booklet pane. Nos. 4292, 4294/4296, 4299 and 4300 with margins all round............................	6·50	
4293	**3387**	(1st) Lando Calrissian (Billy Dee Williams)...	1·20	1·00
		b. Booklet pane. Nos. 4293, 4297/4298 and 4301 with margins all round............................	4·25	
4294	**3388**	(1st) Sith Trooper..	1·20	1·00
4295	**3389**	(1st) Jannah (Naomi Ackie)......................	1·20	1·00
4296	**3390**	(1st) Grand Moff Tarkin (Peter Cushing)	1·20	1·00
4297	**3391**	(1st) Darth Maul (Ray Park)......................	1·20	1·00
		a. Horiz strip of 5. Nos. 4297/4301.....	5·25	5·00
4298	**3392**	(1st) Zorii (Kerri Russell)...........................	1·20	1·00
4299	**3393**	(1st) Wicket W. Warrick (Warwick Davis)...	1·20	1·00
4300	**3394**	(1st) Poe Dameron (Oscar Isaac).............	1·20	1·00
4301	**3395**	(1st) Queen Amidala (Natalie Portman)	1·20	1·00
		Set of 10...	9·00	9·00
		Set of 2 Gutter Strips of 10..............................	21·00	
		First Day Cover (Tallents House).....................		12·00
		First Day Cover (Maulden, Bedford)...............		12·00
		Presentation Pack (PO Pack No. 579) (Nos. 4292/4301 and **MS**4303)...	20·00	
		PHQ Cards (set of 16)...	11·50	20·00

MS4302 210×297 mm. **3395a** Nos. 3758/3769, 4007/4014 and 4292/4301...................... 35·00 50·00

(b) Self-adhesive.

MS4303 192×74 mm. **3396** (1st) Poe's X-wing fighter (41×30 mm) (Perf 14); (1st) Jedi starfighter (27×37 mm) (Perf 14); (1st) Slave 1 (27×37 mm) (Perf 14); (1st) TIE silencer (41×30 mm) (Perf 14); (1st) Podracers (60×21 mm) (Perf 14½×14); (1st) Speeder bikes (60×21 mm) (Perf 14½×14)................. 7·00 7·00

First Day Cover (Tallents House).....................		8·75
First Day Cover (Maulden, Bedford)...............		8·75

(c) Self-adhesive. Die-cut perf 14½.

4304	**3394**	(1st) Poe Dameron (Oscar Isaac).............	1·75	1·75
		a. Booklet pane. Nos. 4304/4305 and U3027×4..............................	12·00	
4305	**3388**	(1st) Sith Trooper..	1·75	1·75

Nos. 4292/4296 and 4297/4301 were each printed together, *se-tenant*, as horizontal strips of five stamps in sheets of 50 (2 panes 5×5).

Booklet panes Nos. 4292b and 4393b come from the £17·65 *Star Wars: The Making of the Vehicles* booklet, No. DY31.

Nos. 4304/4305 were issued in stamp booklet, No. PM70, originally sold for £4·20.

A collectors sheet (No. LS120) containing stamps as Nos. 4292/4301 but self-adhesive with labels showing film scenes was sold for £8·10, a £1·10 premium over face value.

The three *Star Wars* presentation packs from 2015, 2017 and 2019, containing Nos. 3758/3769 and **MS**3770 (PO Pack No. 518), Nos. 4007/4014 (PO Pack No. 547) and Nos. 4292/4301 and **MS**4303 (PO Pack No. 579) were issued in a trilogy by Royal Mail for £29·99.

3397 Poe's X-wing Fighter

3398 Jedi Starfighter

3399 Podracers

3400 Slave 1   **3401** TIE Silencer

3402 Speeder Bikes

2019 (26 Nov). *Star Wars* (6th issue). Multicoloured. 'All-over' phosphor (stamps only). Self-adhesive. Die-cut perf 14 (Nos. 4306/4307, 4309/4310) or 14½×14 (Nos. 4308, 4311).

4306	**3397**	(1st) Poe's X-wing Fighter........................	1·30	1·30
		a. Booklet pane. Nos. 4306/4308........	3·50	
4307	**3398**	(1st) Jedi Starfighter................................	1·30	1·30
4308	**3399**	(1st) Podracers.......................................	1·30	1·30
4309	**3400**	(1st) Slave 1..	1·30	1·30
		a. Booklet pane. Nos. 4309/4311........	3·50	
4310	**3401**	(1st) TIE Silencer.....................................	1·30	1·30
4311	**3402**	(1st) Speeder Bikes.................................	1·30	1·30
Set of 6...			7·00	7·00

Nos. 4306/4311 were issued in No. **MS**4303 and in booklet panes 4306a and 4309a from the £17·65 *Star Wars* The Making of the Vehicles booklet, No. DY31.

Collectors Pack

2019 (26 Nov). Comprises Nos. **MS**4169/**MS**4192, 4200/4209, 4212/ **MS**4225, 4230/**MS**4236, 4239/**MS**4261, **MS**4274/4290, 4292/**MS**4301 and **MS**4303

CP4311a	Collectors Pack (Pack No. 580) (*sold for £156*)...	£250

Post Office Yearbook

2019 (26 Nov). Comprises Nos. **MS**4169/**MS**4192, 4200/4209, 4212/ **MS**4225, 4230/**MS**4236, 4239/**MS**4261, 4264/4271, **MS**4274/4290, 4294/4301 and **MS**4303

YB4311a	Yearbook (*sold for £176*).......................	£275

Miniature Sheet Collection

2019 (26 Nov). Comprises Nos. **MS**4169, **MS**4192, **MS**4218, **MS**4225/ **MS**4236, **MS**4261, **MS**4274/**MS**4275, **MS**4282, **MS**4291 and **MS**4303.

MS4311a Miniature Sheet Collection (*sold for £58*)..........	70·00

3403 *Elite*, 1984

3404 *Worms*, 1995

3405 *Sensible Soccer*, 1992

3406 *Lemmings*, 1991

3407 *Wipeout*, 1995

3408 *Micro Machines*, 1991

3409 *Dizzy*, 1987

3410 *Populous*, 1989

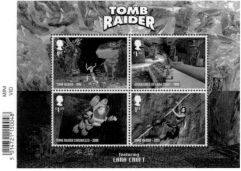

3411 *Tomb Raider*

3412 *Tomb Raider*, 1996   **3413** *Tomb Raider*, 2013

(Des Supple Studio and Bitmap Books. Litho ISP Cartor (Nos. 4312/**MS**4320) or gravure Walsall (Nos. 4321/4322))

2020 (21 Jan). Video Games. Multicoloured.

(a) Ordinary gum. Band at right (No. 4312), centre band (No. 4313) or two bands (others). Perf 14.

4312	**3403**	(2nd) *Elite*, 1984...........................	90	90
		a. Vert pair. Nos. 4312/4313...............	1·75	1·75
4313	**3404**	(2nd) *Worms*, 1995...........................	90	90
4314	**3405**	(1st) *Sensible Soccer*, 1992....................	1·20	1·00
		a. Vert pair. Nos. 4314/4315...............	2·40	2·00
4315	**3406**	(1st) *Lemmings*, 1991.......................	1·20	1·00
4316	**3407**	£1·55 *Wipeout*, 1995.......................	2·40	2·40
		a. Vert pair. Nos. 4316/4317...............	4·75	4·75
4317	**3408**	£1·55 *Micro Machines*, 1991................	2·40	2·40
4318	**3409**	£1·60 *Dizzy*, 1987..........................	2·50	2·50
		a. Vert pair. Nos. 4318/4319...............	5·00	5·00
4319	**3410**	£1·60 *Populous*, 1989......................	2·50	2·50
Set of 8..			12·75	12·50
Set of 4 Gutter Blocks of 4.........................			25·50	
First Day Cover (Tallents House)...................				17·00
First Day Cover (Sheffield).........................				17·00
Presentation Pack (PO Pack No. 581) (Nos. 4312/4319 and **MS**4320)......................................			20·00	
PHQ Cards (set of 13)...............................			8·75	25·00

MS4320 126×90 mm. **3411** (1st) *Tomb Raider*, 1996; (1st) *Tomb Raider*, 2013; £1·55 *Adventures of Lara Croft*, 1998; £1·55 *Tomb Raider Chronicles*, 2000........ 6·75 6·75

First Day Cover (Tallents House)...................	9·25
First Day Cover (Sheffield).........................	9·25

(b) Self-adhesive. Two phosphor bands. Die-cut perf 14.

4321	**3412**	(1st) *Tomb Raider*, 1996...................	5·25	5·25
		a. Booklet pane. Nos. 4321/4322 and U3027×4.............................	15·00	
4322	**3413**	(1st) *Tomb Raider*, 2013...................	5·25	5·25

Nos. 4312/4313, 4314/4315, 4316/4317 and 4318/4319 were printed together, *se-tenant*, as vertical pairs in sheets of 60 (2 panes 5×6).

Nos. 4312/4322 have hidden features in UV ink.

Nos. 4321/4322 were issued in stamp booklet, No. PM71, originally sold for £4·20.

Stamps as within No. **MS**4320 but self-adhesive were issued in sheets of ten (No. LS121) containing three of each of the 1st class designs and two of each of the £1·55 designs, with *se-tenant* labels. These sheets were printed in lithography and originally sold for £11·40.

A Gamer Collectors Pack with eight postcards, each with stamp affixed, and certificate of authenticity all packed inside silver case, was originally sold for £14·95. It was a limited edition of 2,500 units.

The 13 PHQ cards show the 12 individual stamps, including those from No. **MS**4320, and the complete miniature sheet.

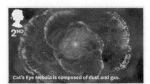

3414 Cat's Eye Nebula

3415 Enceladus

3416 Pulsars

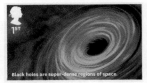

3417 Black Holes

3418 Jupiter's Auroras

3419 Gravitational Lensing

3420 Comet 67P

3421 Cygnus A Galaxy

(Des True North. Litho ISP Cartor)

2020 (11 Feb). Visions of the Universe. Multicoloured. One centre band (2nd) or two bands (others). Perf 14.

4323	**3414**	(2nd) Cat's Eye Nebula...................	90	90
		a. Horiz pair. Nos. 4323/4324..........	1·75	1·75
		b. Booklet pane. Nos. 4323, 4325, 4327 and 4329 with margins all round..	7·00	
4324	**3415**	(2nd) Enceladus (Saturn's moon)...........	90	90
		b. Booklet pane. Nos. 4324, 4326, 4328 and 4330 with margins all round..	7·00	
4325	**3416**	(1st) Pulsars................................	1·25	1·25
		a. Horiz pair. Nos. 4325/4326...........	2·50	2·50
4326	**3417**	(1st) Black holes...........................	1·25	1·25
4327	**3418**	£1·55 Jupiter's auroras.....................	2·40	2·40
		a. Horiz pair. Nos. 4327/4328...........	4·75	4·75
4328	**3419**	£1·55 Gravitational lensing................	2·40	2·40
4329	**3420**	£1·60 Comet 67P...........................	2·50	2·50
		a. Horiz pair. Nos. 4329/4330...........	5·00	5·00
4330	**3421**	£1·60 Cygnus A.............................	2·50	2·50
Set of 8..			12·50	12·50
Set of 4 Gutter Pairs................................			25·00	
First Day Cover (Tallents House)...................				17·00
First Day Cover (London W1)......................				17·00
Presentation Pack (PO Pack No. 582).............			15·00	
PHQ Cards (set of 8)................................			5·50	15·00

Nos. 4323/4324, 4325/4326, 4327/4328 and 4329/4330 were each printed together, *se-tenant*, as horizontal pairs in sheets of 60 (2 panes 6×5).

Booklet panes Nos. 4323b and 4324b come from the £16·55 Visions of the Universe booklet, No. DY32.

(Des Sedley Place. Gravure ISP Walsall)

2020 (10 Mar). London 2020 International Stamp Exhibition. Multicoloured. Self-adhesive. Two phosphor bands. Die-cut perf 14½×14 (with one elliptical hole in each vert side).

4331	**2938**	(1st) Two Pence Blue..............................	1·25	1·25
		a. Booklet pane. Nos. 3709, 3806		
		and 4331, each×2...........................	10·00	

Booklet pane 4331a comes from booklet No. MB21, originally sold for £4·20.

3422 James Bond in *Casino Royale*

3423 James Bond in *Goldeneye*

3424 James Bond in *The Living Daylights*

3425 James Bond in *Live and Let Die*

3426 James Bond in *On Her Majesty's Secret Service*

3427 James Bond in *Goldfinger*

3428 Q Branch

3429 Bell-Textron Jet Pack, *Thunderball*

3430 Aston Martin DB5, *Skyfall*

(Des Interabang. Litho ISP Cartor (Nos. 4332/4337)or gravure ISP Walsall (Nos. 4339/4340))

2020 (17 Mar). James Bond. Multicoloured. (a) Ordinary gum. Two phosphor bands or 'all-over' phosphor (No. **MS**4338). Perf 14½ (No. 4332/4337) or 14×14½ (£1·55) or 14 (1st) (No. **MS**4338)

4332	**3422**	(1st) James Bond (Daniel Craig) in		
		Casino Royale...................................	1·25	1·25
		a. Horiz strip of 3. Nos. 4332/4334.....	3·75	3·75
		b. Booklet pane. Nos. 4332/4335		
		with margins all round....................	6·25	
4333	**3423**	(1st) James Bond (Pierce Brosnan) in		
		Goldeneye..	1·25	1·25
4334	**3424**	(1st) James Bond (Timothy Dalton) in		
		The Living Daylights........................	1·25	1·25
4335	**3425**	£1·60 James Bond (Roger Moore) in *Live*		
		and Let Die....................................	2·50	2·50
		a. Horiz strip of 3. Nos. 4335/4337.....	7·50	
4336	**3426**	£1·60 James Bond (George Lazenby) in		
		On Her Majesty's Secret Service.......	2·50	2·50
		b. Booklet pane. Nos. 4336/4337		
		with margins all round....................	5·00	
4337	**3427**	£1·60 James Bond (Sean Connery) in		
		Goldfinger..	2·50	2·50
Set of 6..			10·50	10·50
Set of 2 Gutter Strips of 6..			21·00	
First Day Cover (Tallents House)................................				13·50
First Day Cover (Spy Post, Wellington).......................				13·50
Presentation Pack (PO Pack No. 583)........................			19·00	
PHQ Cards (set of 11)...			7·50	22·00

MS4338 202×74 mm. **3428** Bell-Textron Jet Pack, *Thunderball*; (1st) Aston Martin DB5, *Skyfall*; £1·55 Lotus Esprit Submarine, *The Spy Who Loved Me*; £1·55 Little Nellie, *You Only Live Twice*......................

			6·75	6·75
First Day Cover (Tallents House)................................				9·25
First Day Cover (Spy Post, Wellington).......................				9·25

(b) Self-adhesive. 'All-over' phosphor. Die-cut perf 14.

4339	**3429**	(1st) Bell-Textron Jet Pack, *Thunderball*..	5·25	5·25
		a. Booklet pane. Nos. 4339/4340		
		and U3027×4...................................	15·00	
4340	**3430**	(1st) Aston Martin DB5, *Skyfall*..............	5·25	5·25

Nos. 4332/4334 and 4335/4337 were each printed together, *se-tenant*, as horizontal strips of three in sheets of 36 (2 panes 3×6).

Stamps from No. **MS**4338 have '007' perforations at top right, top left, bottom right or bottom left.

Nos. 4339/4340 were issued in stamp booklet, No. PM72, originally sold for £4·20.

Booklet panes Nos. 4332b and 4336b come from the £16·99 James Bond prestige booklet, No. DY33.

A collector's sheet (No. LS122) with stamps as Nos 4332/4337 but perforated 14 with attached labels showing film scenes was originally sold for £12·60. It contained Nos. 4332×2, 4333/4336 and 4337×3.

A *No Time to Die* collector's sheet (No. LS128) containing ten self-adhesive stamps as T **3430** perforated 14×14½ with attached labels showing film scenes was issued on 3 November 2020 and sold for £8·80.

The 11 PHQ cards show the ten individual stamps, including those from No. **MS**4338, and the complete miniature sheet.

3431 Little Nellie, *You Only Live Twice*

3432 Lotus Esprit Submarine, *The Spy Who Loved Me*

(Litho ISP Cartor)

2020 (17 Mar). James Bond (2nd issue). Multicoloured. 'All-over' phosphor. Perf 14 (1st) or 14×14½ (£1·55), all with '007' perforations at top right, top left, bottom right or bottom left.

4341	**3429**	(1st) Bell-Textron Jet Pack, *Thunderball*..	1·25	1·25
		a. Booklet pane. Nos. 4341/4344 with margins all round....................	7·25	
4342	**3430**	(1st) Aston Martin DB5, *Skyfall*.................	1·25	1·25
4343	**3431**	£1·55 Little Nellie, *You Only Live Twice*......	2·40	2·40
4344	**3432**	£1·55 Lotus Esprit Submarine, *The Spy Who Loved Me*..................................	2·40	2·40
Set of 4......			7·25	7·25

Nos. 4341/4344 were issued in No. **MS**4338 and in booklet pane No. 4341a from £16·99 James Bond booklet, No. DY33.

3433 *The Progress of Rhyme* (John Clare)

3434 *Frost at Midnight* (Samuel Taylor Coleridge)

3435 *Auguries of Innocence* (William Blake)

3436 *The Lady of the Lake* (Walter Scott)

3437 *To a Skylark* (Percy Bysshe Shelley)

3438 *The Rainbow* (William Wordsworth)

3439 *Ode to the Snowdrop* (Mary Robinson)

3440 *The Fate of Adelaide* (Letitia Elizabeth Landon)

3441 *Ode to a Grecian Urn* (John Keats)

3442 *She Walks in Beauty* (Lord Byron)

(Des The Chase. Litho ISP Cartor)

2020 (7 Apr). Romantic Poets. Black and orange-brown. Two phosphor bands. Perf 14.

4345	**3433**	(1st) *The Progress of Rhyme* (John Clare)...............................	1·25	1·25
		a. Horiz strip of 5. Nos. 4345/4349.....	6·25	6·25
4346	**3434**	(1st) *Frost at Midnight* (Samuel Taylor Coleridge)...........................	1·25	1·25
4347	**3435**	(1st) *Auguries of Innocence* (William Blake)...................................	1·25	1·25
4348	**3436**	(1st) *The Lady of the Lake* (Walter Scott).	1·25	1·25
4349	**3437**	(1st) *To a Skylark* (Percy Bysshe Shelley)	1·25	1·25
4350	**3438**	(1st) *The Rainbow* (William Wordsworth)..................................	1·25	1·25
		a. Horiz strip of 5. Nos. 4350/4354.....	6·25	6·25
4351	**3439**	(1st) *Ode to the Snowdrop* (Mary Robinson)................................	1·25	1·25
4352	**3440**	(1st) *The Fate of Adelaide* (Letitia Elizabeth Landon)....................	1·25	1·25
4353	**3441**	(1st) *Ode on a Grecian Urn* (John Keats).	1·25	1·25
4354	**3442**	(1st) *She Walks in Beauty* (Lord Byron)....	1·25	1·25
Set of 10............			11·50	11·50
Set of 2 Gutter Strips of 10............			23·00	
First Day Cover (Tallents House)............				13·50
First Day Cover (Grasmere, Ambleside)............				13·50
Presentation Packs (PO Pack No. 584)............			13·50	
PHQ Cards (set of 10) (469)............			5·75	13·00

Nos. 4345/4349 and 4350/4354 were printed together, *se-tenant*, as horizontal strips of five in sheets of 50 (2 panes 5×5).

3442a

(Litho ISP Cartor)

2020 (6 May). 180th Anniversary of the Penny Black. As T **2848** but ordinary gum. Litho. Perf 14½×14 (with one elliptical hole in each vert side).

MS4355 122×141 mm. **3442a** (1st) Penny Black×25........ 40·00 40·00

No. **MS**4355 was issued in sheets of 25 stamps and originally sold for £19.

3443 Servicemen returning home

3444 Nurses Celebrating

3445 Crowd Celebrating

3446 Evacuees Returning

3447 Marching Troops

3448 Demobilised Servicemen

3449 Liberated Prisoners

3450 Navy Personnel Celebrating

3451 Memorials

(Des Hat-trick design (photo colourisation (Nos. 4356/4363) Royston Leonard). Litho ISP Cartor)

2020 (8 May). 75th Anniversary of the End of the Second World War (1st issue). Multicoloured. One centre band (2nd) or two phosphor bands (others). Perf 14 (Nos. 4356/4363) or 14½ (No. **MS**4364).

4356	**3443**	(2nd) Serviceman Returning Home.........	90	90
		a. Vert pair. Nos. 4356/4357................	1·75	1·75
		b. Booklet pane. Nos. 4356/4359 with margins all round....................	4·25	
4357	**3444**	(2nd) VE Day, Liverpool, 1945.....................	90	90
4358	**3445**	(1st) Crowds celebrating VE Day, Piccadilly, London, 1945..................	1·25	1·25
		a. Vert pair. Nos. 4358/4359................	2·50	2·50
4359	**3446**	(1st) Evacuee children returning home, London, 1945............................	1·25	1·25
4360	**3447**	£1·42 Troops march along Oxford Street, London, 1945.....................	2·00	2·00
		a. Vert pair. Nos. 4360/4361...............	4·00	4·00
		b. Booklet pane. Nos. 4360/4363 with margins all round....................	8·50	
4361	**3448**	£1·42 Soldiers and sailors leaving demobilisation centre with boxes of civilian clothes............................	2·00	2·00
4362	**3449**	£1·63 Liberated Allied prisoners of war, Aomori Camp, near Yokohama, Japan....................................	2·25	2·25
		a. Vert pair. Nos. 4362/4363................	4·50	4·50
4363	**3450**	£1·63 Navy personnel in VE Day celebrations, Glasgow, 1945...........	2·25	2·25

Set of 8... 11·50 11·50
Set of 4 Gutter Strips of 4.. 23·00
First Day Cover (Tallents House).. 14·00
First Day Cover (London SW1).. 14·00
Presentation Pack (PO Pack No. 585) (Nos. 4356/4363 and **MS**4364)... 20·00
PHQ Cards (set of 13) (470).. 7·75 20·00

MS4364 202×74 mm. **3451** (1st) Hall of Names, Holocaust History Museum, Yad Vashem, Jerusalem; (1st) Plymouth Naval Memorial; £1·63 Rangoon Memorial, Myanmar (all 60×30 mm)............................. 6·75 6·75
First Day Cover (Tallents House).. 9·00
First Day Cover (London SW1).. 9·00

Nos. 4356/4357, 4358/4359, 4360/4361 and 4362/4363 were printed together, *se-tenant*, as vertical pairs in sheets of 60 (2 panes 5×6).

Booklet panes Nos. 4365b and 4360b come from the £19·80 75th Anniversary of the End of the Second World War booklet, No. DY34.

The 13 PHQ cards show the ten individual stamps, including those from No. **MS**4364 and the complete miniature sheet.

3452 Hall of Names, Holocaust History Museum, Yad Vashem, Jerusalem

3453 Runnymede Memorial

3454 Plymouth Naval Memorial

3455 Rangoon Memorial, Myanmar

(Des Hat-trick design. Litho ISP Cartor)

2020 (8 May). 75th Anniversary of the End of the Second World War (2nd issue). Multicoloured. Two phosphor bands. Perf 14½.

4365	**3452**	(1st) Hall of Names, Holocaust History Museum, Yad Vashem, Jerusalem..	1·75	1·75
		a. Booklet pane. Nos. 4365/4368 with margins all round....................	9·50	
4366	**3453**	(1st) Runnymede Memorial..............	1·75	1·75
4367	**3454**	£1·63 Plymouth Naval Memorial..............	3·00	3·00
4368	**3455**	£1·63 Rangoon Memorial, Myanmar........	3·00	3·00

Set of 4... 9·50 9·50

Nos. 4365/4368 were issued in No. **MS**4364 and in booklet pane No. 4365a from the £19·80 75th Anniversary of the End of the Second World War booklet, No. DY34.

3456 'That woman's tongue...' (Edna Sharples and Elsie Tanner)

3457 'Woman, Stanley, Woman' (Stan and Hilda Ogden)

3458 'Vera my little swamp duck' (Jack and Vera Duckworth)

3459 'Ken! do something!' (Deirdre and Ken Barlow)

3460 'I can't abide to see...' (Rita Sullivan and Norris Cole)

3461 'Be nice if everyday...' (Hayley and Roy Cropper)

3462 'I love you...' (Dev and Sunita Alahan)

3463 'I always thought...' (Tracy Barlow and Steve McDonald)

3464 *Rovers Return* Barmaids

(Des The Chase. ISP Cartor (Nos. 4369/4376) or gravure ISP Walsall (Nos. 4378/4379))

2020 (28 May). *Coronation Street*. Multicoloured. One centre band (2nd) or two phosphor bands (others)

(a) Ordinary gum. Perf 14.

4369	**3456**	(2nd) 'That woman's tongue... (Ena Sharples and Elsie Tanner)..............	90	90
		a. Horiz pair. Nos. 4369/4370..............	1·75	1·75
4370	**3457**	(2nd) 'Woman, Stanley, woman.' Stan and Hilda Ogden...........................	90	90
4371	**3458**	(1st) 'Vera, my little swamp duck.' (Jack and Vera Duckworth)......................	1·25	1·25
		a. Horiz pair. Nos. 4371/4372..............	2·50	2·50
4372	**3459**	(1st) 'Ken! Do something!' (Deirdre and Ken Barlow).....................................	1·25	1·25
4373	**3460**	£1·42 'I can't abide to see people gossiping.' (Rita Sullivan and Norris Cole)...........................	2·00	2·00
		a. Horiz pair. Nos. 4373/4374..............	4·00	4·00
4374	**3461**	£1·42 'Be nice if every day...'(Hayley and Roy Cropper)...........................	2·00	2·00
4375	**3462**	£1·63 'I love you...' (Dev and Sunita Alahan)..	2·25	2·25
		a. Horiz pair. Nos. 4375/4376..............	4·50	4·50
4376	**3463**	£1·63 'I always thought...' (Tracy Barlow and Steve McDonald)......................	2·25	2·25
Set of 8..			11·50	11·50
Set of 8 Gutter Pairs.......................................			23·00	
First Day Cover (Tallents House).....................				14·00
First Day Cover (Salford).................................				14·00
Presentation Pack (PO Pack No. 586) (Nos. 4369/4376 and **MS**4377)................................			20·00	
PHQ Card (set of 13) (471).............................			7·50	22·00
MS4377 156×74 mm. **3464** (1st) Bet Lynch; (1st) Raquel Watts; £1·42 Liz McDonald; £1·42 Gemma Winter (all 27×36 mm)................................			6·50	6·50
First Day Cover (Tallents House).....................				9·00
First Day Cover (Salford).................................				9·00

(b) Self-adhesive. Die-cut perf 14.

4378	**3458**	(1st) 'Vera, my little swamp duck.' (Vera and Jack Duckworth)......................	1·75	1·75
		a. Booklet pane. Nos. 4378/4379 and U3027×4..................................	7·50	
4379	**3457**	(1st) 'Ken! Do something!' (Deirdre and Ken Barlow).....................................	1·75	1·75

Nos. 4369/4370, 4371/4372, 4373/4374 and 4375/4376 were printed together, *se-tenant*, as horizontal pairs in sheets of 60 (2 panes 6×5).

Nos. 4378/4379 were issued in stamp booklet, No. PM73, originally sold for £4·56.

Stamps as Nos. 4371/4372 but self-adhesive and perf 14×14½ were issued in collector's sheets containing five of each design, (No. LS123), sold for £8·80.

The 13 PHQ cards show the 12 individual stamps, including those from No. **MS**4377, and the complete miniature sheet.

3465 Dover Lighthouse

3466 Bignor Mosaic

3467 Amphitheatre at Isca Fortress, Caerleon

3468 Ribchester Helmet

3469 Bridgeness Distance Slab at Eastern end of Antonine Wall

3470 Copper-alloy Figurine of Warrior God, Cambridgeshire

3471 Gorgon's Head from Temple to Sulis Minerva, Bath

3472 Hadrian's Wall

(Des Up. Litho ISP Cartor)

2020 (18 June). *Roman Britain*. Multicoloured. One centre band (2nd) or two bands (others). Perf 14½×14.

4380	**3465**	(2nd) Dover Lighthouse.............................	90	90
		a. Horiz pair. Nos. 4380/4381..............	1·75	1·75
4381	**3466**	(2nd) Bignor Mosaic................................	90	90
4382	**3467**	(1st) Amphitheatre, Caerleon..................	1·25	1·25
		a. Horiz pair. Nos. 4382/4383..............	2·50	2·50
4383	**3468**	(1st) Ribchester Helmet...........................	1·25	1·25
4384	**3469**	£1·63 Bridgeness distance slab, Antonine Wall..............................	2·25	2·25
		a. Horiz pair. Nos. 4384/4385..............	4·50	4·50
4385	**3470**	£1·63 Copper-alloy figurine of Warrior God, Cambridgeshire...............	2·25	2·25
4386	**3471**	£1·68 Gorgon's head, Bath......................	2·40	2·40
		a. Horiz pair. Nos. 4386/4387..............	4·75	4·75
4387	**3472**	£1·68 Hadrian's Wall...............................	2·40	2·40
Set of 8..			12·00	12·00
Set of 4 Gutter Pairs (only 2 stamps in each gutter pair)...			14·00	
Set of 4 Traffic Light Gutter Blocks (4 stamps in each gutter block)...			28·00	
First Day Cover (Tallents House).....................				14·50
First Day Cover (Colchester)...........................				14·50
Presentation Pack (PO Pack No. 587).............			14·00	
PHQ Cards (set of 8) (472).............................			4·75	13·00

Nos. 4380/4381, 4382/4383, 4384/4385 and 4386/4387 were each printed together, *se-tenant*, as horizontal pairs in sheets of 60 (2 panes 6×5).

3473 *Queen II*, 1974

3474 *Sheer Heart Attack*, 1974

3475 *A Night At The Opera*, 1975

3476 *News of the World*, 1977

3477 *The Game*, 1980

3478 *Greatest Hits*, 1981

3479 *The Works*, 1984

3480 *Innuendo*, 1991

3481 Queen Live

(Litho ISP Cartor (Nos. 4388/4395) or gravure ISP Walsall (Nos. 4397/4398))

2020 (9 July). Queen (rock band) (1st issue). Multicoloured. Two phosphor bands.

(a) Ordinary gum. Perf 14 (Nos. 4388/4395), 14½×14 (Queen machin size stamp from No. **MS***4396) or 14½ (other stamps from No.* **MS***4396).*

4388	**3473**	(1st) *Queen II*, 1974..................................	1·25	1·25
		a. Horiz strip of 4. Nos. 4388/4391.....	5·00	5·00
		b. Booklet pane. Nos. 4388/4391		
		with margins all round...................	5·00	
4389	**3474**	(1st) *Sheer Heart Attack*, 1974.............	1·25	1·25
4390	**3475**	(1st) *A Night At The Opera*, 1975.............	1·25	1·25
4391	**3476**	(1st) *News of the World*, 1977...................	1·25	1·25
4392	**3477**	£1·63 *The Game*, 1980...............................	2·25	2·25
		a. Horiz strip of 4. Nos. 4392/4395.....	9·00	9·00
		b. Booklet pane. Nos. 4392/4395		
		with margins all round...................	9·00	
4393	**3478**	£1·63 *Greatest Hits*, 1981........................	2·25	2·25
4394	**3479**	£1·63 *The Works*, 1984...............................	2·25	2·25
4395	**3480**	£1·63 *Innuendo*, 1991...............................	2·25	2·25
Set of 8..			12·50	12·50
Set of 2 Gutter Strips of 8........................			25·00	
First Day Cover (Tallents House).......................				15·00
First Day Cover (Knebworth)..............................				15·00
Presentation Pack (PO Pack No. 588) (Nos. 4388/4395				
and **MS**4396)...			22·00	
PHQ Cards (set of 15) (473).......................			8·25	23·00

MS4396 202×74 mm. **3481** (1st) Freddie Mercury, Magic Tour, Wembley Stadium, 1986; (1st) Roger Taylor, Hyde Park Concert, 1976; (1st) Queen, Primrose Hill, London, 1974; £1·63 John Deacon, A Night at the Opera Tour, Hammersmith Odeon, 1975; £1·63 Brian May, Magic Tour, Nepstadion, Budapest, 1986.... 7·75 7·75

First Day Cover (Tallents House)..............................		10·00
First Day Cover (Knebworth)....................................		10·00

(b) Self-adhesive. Die-cut perf 14.

4397	**3473**	(1st) *Queen II*, 1974...........................	1·75	1·75
		a. Booklet pane. Nos. 4397/4398		
		and U3027×4................................	15·00	
4398	**3475**	(1st) *A Night At The Opera*, 1975.............	1·75	1·75

Nos. 4388/4395 were printed together, *se-tenant*, as horizontal strips of four stamps in sheets of 24 (2 panes 4×6).

Booklet panes Nos. 4388b and 4392b come from the £19·10 Queen booklet, No. DY35.

Nos. 4397/4398 were issued in stamp booklet, No. PM74, originally sold for £4·56.

Stamps as Nos. 4388×2, 4389, 4390×2 and 4391/4395 but self-adhesive and perf 13 with one elliptical hole in each vert side were issued with labels in a Queen Album Cover collector's sheet, (No. LS124), originally sold for £13·15.

An Album Cover Collection fan sheet containing Nos. 4388/4395 was originally sold for £10·20.

A *Night at the Opera* fan sheet containing No. 4390×4 was originally sold for £7·50.

The 15 PHQ cards show the 14 individual stamps including those from No. **MS**4396 and the complete miniature sheet.

3482 Freddie Mercury, Magic Tour, Wembley Stadium, 1986

3483 Roger Taylor, Hyde Park Concert, 1976

3484 John Deacon, A Night at the Opera Tour, Hammersmith Odeon, 1975

3485 Brian May, Magic Tour, Nepstadion, Budapest, 1986

(Litho ISP Cartor)

2020 (9 July). Queen (rock band) (2nd issue). Multicoloured. Two phosphor bands. Perf 14½.

4399	**3482**	(1st) Freddie Mercury..............................	1·75	1·75
		a. Booklet pane. Nos. 4399/4402		
		with margins all round...................	9·50	
4400	**3483**	(1st) Roger Taylor.................................	1·75	1·75
4401	**3484**	£1·63 John Deacon.................................	3·00	3·00
4402	**3485**	£1·63 Brian May...................................	3·00	3·00
Set of 4..			9·50	9·50

Nos. 4399/4402 were issued in No. **MS**4396 and booklet pane No. 4399a from the £19·10 Queen booklet, No. DY35.

3486 Queen, Primrose Hill, London, 1974

(Litho ISP Cartor)

2020 (9 July). Queen (rock band) (3rd issue). Multicoloured. Two phosphor bands. Perf 14½×14 (with one elliptical hole in each vert side).

4403	**3486**	(1st) Queen, 1974..................................	1·75	1·75

No. 4403 was issued in No. **MS**4396 and the machin booklet pane No. U3070r from the £19·10 Queen premium booklet, No. DY35.

A stamp as No. 4403 but self-adhesive was issued in a Queen Live Collector's Sheet containing ten stamps with labels, (No. LS125), originally sold for £8·80 and in booklets of six, No. MB22, originally sold for £5·10. See also No. 4502.

3487 Palace of Westminster from Old Palace Yard

3488 Palace of Westminster from River Thames

3489 Elizabeth Tower

3490 Commons Chamber

3491 Central Lobby

3492 Lords Chamber

3493 Palace of Westminster

(Des Steers McGillan Eves. Litho ISP Cartor)

2020 (30 July). Palace of Westminster. Multicoloured. Two phosphor bands. Perf 14½.

4404	**3487**	(1st) Palace of Westminster from Old Palace Yard	1·25	1·25
		a. Horiz strip of 3. Nos. 4404/4406	3·75	3·75
4405	**3488**	(1st) Palace of Westminster from River Thames	1·25	1·25
4406	**3489**	(1st) Elizabeth Tower	1·25	1·25
4407	**3490**	£1·68 Commons Chamber	2·40	2·40
		a. Horiz strip of 3. Nos. 4407/4409	7·00	7·00
4408	**3491**	£1·68 Central Lobby	2·40	2·40
4409	**3492**	£1·68 Lords Chamber	2·40	2·40
	Set of 6		9·75	9·75
	Set of 2 Gutter Strips of 6		20·00	
	First Day Cover (Tallents House)			12·00
	First Day Cover (London SW1)			12·00
	Presentation Pack (PO Pack No. 589) (Nos. 4404/4409, **MS**4410)		18·00	
	PHQ Cards (set of 11) (474)		6·50	20·00

MS4410 203×74 mm. **3493** (1st) Norman Porch; (1st) Chapel of St Mary Undercroft; £1·63 St Stephen's Hall; £1·63 Royal Gallery........ 6·75 6·75

First Day Cover (Tallents House) .... 9·00
First Day Cover (London SW1) .... 9·00

Nos. 4404/4406 and 4407/4409 were each printed together, *se-tenant*, as horizontal strips of three in sheets of 36 (2 panes 3×6).

The 11 PHQ cards show the ten individual stamps, including those from No. **MS**4410, and the complete miniature sheet.

3494 *The Reichenbach Fall*

3495 *A Study in Pink*

3496 *The Great Game*

3497 *The Empty Hearse*

3498 *A Scandal in Belgravia*

3499 *The Final Problem*

3500 Sherlock Holmes Mysteries by Sir Arthur Conan Doyle

3501 *The Red-*
Headed League

3502 *The Adventure*
of the Speckled band

(Des So Design Consultants (Nos. 4411/4416) or Karolis Strautniekas (illustrations) and NB Studio (No. **MS**4417). Litho ISP Cartor (Nos. 4411/ **MS**4417) or gravure (Nos. 4418/4419))

2020 (18 Aug). Sherlock. Multicoloured. Two phosphor bands.

*(a) Ordinary gum. Perf 14½ (Nos. 4411/4416) or 14 (No. **MS**4417).*

4411	**3494**	(1st) *The Reichenbach Fall*......................	1·25	1·25
		a. Vert pair. Nos. 4411/4412................	2·50	2·50
4412	**3495**	(1st) *A Study in Pink*...............................	1·25	1·25
4413	**3496**	£1·42 *The Great Game*...........................	2·00	2·00
		a. Vert pair. Nos. 4413/4414................	4·00	4·00
4414	**3497**	£1·42 *The Empty Hearse*.......................	2·00	2·00
4415	**3498**	£1·68 *A Scandal in Belgravia*................	2·40	2·40
		a. Vert pair. Nos. 4415/4416................	4·75	4·75
4416	**3499**	£1·68 *The Final Problem*.......................	2·40	2·40
Set of 6...			10·00	10·00
Set of 3 Gutter Pairs (only 2 stamps in each gutter pair)...			12·00	
First Day Cover (Tallents House)...............................				12·00
First Day Cover (London NW1).................................				12·00
Presentation Pack (PO Pack No. 590) (Nos. 4411/4416				
and **MS**4417)..			19·00	
PHQ Cards (set of 11) (475).....................................			6·50	19·00

MS4417 126×89 mm. **3500** (1st) *The Adventure of*
the Speckled Band; (1st) *The Red-Headed League*;
£1·68 *The Adventure of the Second Stain*; £1·68 *The*
Adventure of the Dancing Men...................................... 6·75 6·75

First Day Cover (Tallents House)...............................		9·00
First Day Cover (London NW1).................................		9·00

(b) Self-adhesive. Die-cut perf 14.

4418	**3501**	(1st) *The Red-Headed League*..................	2·50	2·50
		a. Booklet pane. Nos. 4418/4419		
		and U3027×4..................................	10·00	
4419	**3502**	(1st) *The Adventure of the Speckled*		
		Band...	2·50	2·50

Nos. 4411/4412, 4413/4414 and 4415/4416 were each printed together, *se-tenant*, as vertical pairs in sheets of 36 (2 panes 3×6).

Nos. 4411/4416 show scenes from the *Sherlock* television series, and show additional inscriptions when UV light is shone over the stamps.

Stamps as Nos. 4411/4416 but self-adhesive and perf 14 were issued in collector's sheets, (No. LS126), with labels containing Nos. 4411×4, 4412×2 and one each of Nos. 4413/4416, originally sold for £11·95.

Nos. 4411 and 4413 have the two phosphor bands at left and right of the stamps as usual.

Nos. 4412 and 4414 have the two phosphor bands at left and centre of the stamp.

No. 4415 has the two phosphor bands at left and just right of centre.

No. 4416 has the two phosphor bands at left and centre right.

Nos. 4418/4419 were issued in stamp booklet, No. PM75, originally sold for £4·56.

The 11 PHQ cards show the ten individual stamps, including those from No. **MS**4417, and the complete miniature sheet.

3503 Then with a terrifying
roar (*Rupert's Rainy*
Adventure)

3504 The bath is rocked
from side to side (*Rupert's*
Rainy Adventure)

3505 Then Algy looks a
trifle glum (*Rupert and the*
Mare's Nest)

3506 The large bird says
(*Rupert and the Mare's Nest*)

3507 'There's something
puzzling all of you,' Says
Rupert (*Rupert and the Lost*
Cuckoo)

3508 'My cuckoo's back
again' (*Rupert and the Lost*
Cuckoo)

3509 Though Rupert
searches all around
(*Rupert's Christmas Tree*)

3510 The tree is such
a lovely sight (*Rupert's*
Christmas Tree)

(Des Rose (from illustrations by Alfred Bestall). Litho ISP Cartor)

2020 (3 Sept). Rupert Bear. Multicoloured. Centre band (2nd) or two bands (others). Perf 14½×14

4420	**3503**	(2nd) Then with a terrifying roar...		
		(*Rupert's Rainy Adventure*)..............	90	90
		a. Horiz pair. Nos. 4420/4421.............	1·75	1·75
4421	**3504**	(2nd) The bath is rocked... (*Rupert's*		
		Rainy Adventure)............................	90	90
4422	**3505**	(1st) Then Algy looks a trifle glum...		
		(*Rupert and the Mare's Nest*)............	1·25	1·25
		a. Horiz pair. Nos. 4422/4423.............	2·50	2·50
4423	**3506**	(1st) The large bird says... (*Rupert and*		
		the Mare's Nest).............................	1·25	1·25
4424	**3507**	£1·45 'There's something puzzling...'		
		(*Rupert and the Lost Cuckoo*)............	2·00	2·00
		a. Horiz pair. Nos. 4424/4425.............	4·00	4·00
4425	**3508**	£1·45 'My cuckoo's back again...' (*Rupert*		
		and the Lost Cuckoo).......................	2·00	2·00

4426	**3509**	£1·70 Though Rupert searches...		
		(*Rupert's Christmas Tree*).................	2·40	2·40
		a. Horiz pair. Nos. 4426/4427........	4·75	4·75
4427	**3510**	£1·70 The tree is such a lovely sight...		
		(*Rupert's Christmas Tree*).................	2·40	2·40

Set of 8..	11·50	11·50
Set of 4 Gutter Pairs (only 2 stamps in each gutter pair)...	13·00	
Set of 4 Traffic Light Blocks of 4........................	30·00	
First Day Cover (Tallents House)...........................		14·00
First Day Cover (Canterbury)...............................		14·00
Presentation Pack (PO Pack No. 591).....................	14·00	
PHQ Cards (set of 8) (476)................................	7·50	13·00

Nos. 4420/4421, 4422/4423, 4424/4425 and 4426/4427 were each printed together, *se-tenant*, as horizontal pairs in sheets of 60 (2 panes 6×5).

3511 Common Carder Bee (*Bombus pascuorum*)

3512 Painted Lady Butterfly (*Vanessa cardui*)

3513 Longhorn Beetle (*Rutpela maculata*)

3514 Elephant Hawk-moth (*Deilephila elpenor*)

3515 Marmalade Hoverfly (*Episyrphus balteatus*)

3516 Ruby-tailed Wasp (*Chrysis ignita* agg)

(Des Richard Lewington. Litho ISP Cartor)

2020 (1 Oct). Brilliant Bugs. Multicoloured. Two phosphor bands. Perf 14×14½.

4428	**3511**	(1st) Common Carder Bee (*Bombus pascuorum*)........................	1·25	1·25
		a. Vert pair. Nos. 4428/4429........	2·50	2·50
4429	**3512**	(1st) Painted Lady Butterfly (*Vanessa cardui*)........................	1·25	1·25
4430	**3513**	£1·45 Longhorn Beetle (*Rutpela maculata*)........................	2·00	2·00
		a. Vert pair. Nos. 4430/4431........	4·00	4·00
4431	**3514**	£1·45 Elephant Hawk-moth (*Deilephila elpenor*)........................	2·00	2·00
4432	**3515**	£1·70 Marmalade Hoverfly (*Episyrphus balteatus*)........................	2·40	2·40
		a. Vert pair. Nos. 4432/4433........	4·75	4·75
4433	**3516**	£1·70 Ruby-tailed Wasp (*Chrysis ignita* agg)........................	2·40	2·40

Set of 6..	10·00	10·00
Set of 3 Gutter Pairs (only 2 stamps in each gutter pair)...	12·00	
First Day Cover (Tallents House)...........................		12·50
First Day Cover (Bugford Dartmouth).....................		12·50
Presentation Pack (PO Pack No. 592).....................	12·00	
PHQ Cards (set of 8) (477)................................	3·50	12·00

Nos. 4428/4429, 4430/4431 and 4432/4433 were each printed together, *se-tenant*, as vertical pairs in sheets of 60 (2 panes 5×6).

3517 Adoration of the Magi (detail), St Andrew's Church, East Lexham

3518 Virgin and Child, St Andrew's Church, Coln Rogers

3519 Adoration of the Magi, St Andrew's Church, Lexham

3520 Virgin and Child, St Andrew's Church, Coln Rogers

3521 Virgin and Child, Church of St James, Hollowell

3522 Virgin and Child, All Saints' Church, Otley

3523 The Holy Family (detail), St Columba's Church, Topcliffe

3524 Virgin and Child, Christ Church, Coalville

(Des Up. Gravure ISP Walsall (Nos. 4434/4441) or litho ISP Cartor (No. **MS**4442))

2020 (3 Nov). Christmas. Stained-glass Windows. Multicoloured. One centre band (No. 4434) or two bands (others).

(a) Self-adhesive. Die-cut perf 14½×15..

4434	**3517**	(2nd) Adoration of the Magi (detail), St Andrew's Church, East Lexham......	90	90
		a. Booklet pane. No. 4434×12.......	12·50	
4435	**3518**	(1st) Virgin and Child, St Andrew's Church, Coln Rogers......................	1·00	1·00
		a. Booklet pane. No. 4435×12.......	15·00	
4436	**3519**	(2nd Large) Adoration of the Magi, St Andrew's Church, Lexham..............	1·25	1·25
4437	**3520**	(1st Large) Virgin and Child, St Andrew's Church, Coln Rogers...........	1·60	1·60
4438	**3521**	£1·45 Virgin and Child, Church of St James, Hollowell......................	2·00	2·00
4439	**3522**	£1·70 Virgin and Child, All Saints' Church, Otley......................	2·40	2·40
4440	**3523**	£2·50 The Holy Family (detail), St Columba's Church, Topcliffe...........	3·50	3·50
4441	**3524**	£2·55 Virgin and Child, Christ Church, Coalville............................	3·50	3·50

Set of 8..	14·50	14·50
First Day Cover (Tallents House)...........................		17·00
First Day Cover (Bethlehem Llandeilo)...................		17·00
Presentation Pack (PO Pack No. 593).....................	17·00	
PHQ Cards (set of 9) (478)................................	5·25	20·00

(b) Ordinary gum. Perf 14½×15..

MS4442 189×74 mm. As Nos. 4434/4441........................	16·00	16·00
First Day Cover (Tallents House)...........................		17·00
First Day Cover (Bethlehem Llandeilo)...................		17·00

The 2nd class, 1st class, £1·45, £1·70, £2·50 and £2·55 values were also issued in sheets of 20, (No. LS127), containing 8×2nd class, 8×1st class, 1×£1·45, 1×£1·70, 1×£2·50 and 1×£2·55 values, each stamp accompanied by a *se-tenant* label.

The nine PHQ cards show the individual stamps and the complete miniature sheet.

3525 Captain James T. Kirk (William Shatner), *The Original Series*

3526 Captain Jean-Luc Picard (Patrick Stewart), *The Next Generation*

3527 Captain Benjamin Sisko (Avery Brooks), *Deep Space Nine*

3528 Captain Kathryn Janeway (Kate Mulgrew), *Voyager*

3529 Captain Jonathan Archer (Scott Bakula), *Enterprise*

3530 Captain Gabriel Lorca (Jason Isaacs), *Discovery*

3531 Spock (Leonard Nimoy), *The Original Series*

3532 Deanna Troi (Marina Sirtis), *The Next Generation*

3533 Julian Bashir (Alexander Siddig), *Deep Space Nine*

3534 Malcolm Reed (Dominic Keating), *Enterprise*

3535 Michael Burnham (Sonequa Martin-Greene), *Discovery*

3536 Ash Tyler/Voq (Shazad Latif), *Discovery*

3537 *Star Trek. The Movies*

(Des Freya Betts (illustrations Nos. 4443/4454) and Interabang. Litho ISP Cartor (Nos. 4443/**MS**4455) or gravure ISP Walsall Nos. 4456/4457))

2020 (13 Nov). *Star Trek* (1st issue). Multicoloured. Two phosphor bands.

(a) Ordinary gum. Perf 14½.

4443	3525	(1st) Captain James T. Kirk......................	1·25	1·25
		a. Horiz strip of 6. Nos. 4443/4448.....	7·50	7·50
		b. Booklet pane. Nos. 4443/4448 with margins all round..................	7·50	
4444	3526	(1st) Captain Jean-Luc Picard.................	1·25	1·25
4445	3527	(1st) Captain Benjamin Sisko..................	1·25	1·25
4446	3528	(1st) Captain Kathryn Janeway...............	1·25	1·25
4447	3529	(1st) Captain Jonathan Archer................	1·25	1·25
4448	3530	(1st) Captain Gabriel Lorca....................	1·25	1·25
4449	3531	(1st) Spock..	1·25	1·25
		a. Horiz strip of 6. Nos. 4449/4454.....	7·50	7·50
		b. Booklet pane. Nos. 4449/4454 with margins all round..................	7·50	
4450	3532	(1st) Deanna Troi.................................	1·25	1·25
4451	3533	(1st) Julian Bashir................................	1·25	1·25
4452	3534	(1st) Malcolm Reed...............................	1·25	1·25
4453	3535	(1st) Michael Burnham..........................	1·25	1·25
4454	3536	(1st) Ash Tyler/Voq..............................	1·25	1·25
Set of 12..			13·50	13·50
Set of 2 Gutter Strips of 12.....................................			27·00	
First Day Cover (Tallents House)...............................				15·00
First Day Cover (Beambridge Craven Arms)...............				15·00
Presentation Pack (PO Pack No. 594) (Nos. 4443/4454 and **MS**4455)..			22·00	
PHQ Cards (set of 19) (479).....................................			11·00	22·00

(b) Self-adhesive.

MS4455 146×74 mm. **3537** (1st) Montgomery Scott (Simon Pegg), new Movie Series (60×21 mm) (Perf 14½); (1st) Praetor Shinzon (Tom Hardy), Next Generation Movie, *Nemesis* (60×21 mm) (Perf 14½); (1st) Tolian Soran (Malcolm McDowell), Original Movie Series, *Generations* (27×37 mm) (Perf 14); (1st) Klingon Chancellor Gorkon (David Warner), Original Movie Series (27×37 mm) (Perf 14); (1st) Dr Carol Marcus (Alice Eve), new Movie Series, *Star Trek Into Darkness* (27×37 mm) (Perf 14); (1st) Krall (Idris Elba), new Movie Series (27×37 mm) (Perf 14) ... 7·50 · 7·50

First Day Cover (Tallents House)............................... 8·50
First Day Cover (Beambridge, Craven Arms)............... 8·50

(c) Self-adhesive. Die-cut perf 14½.

4456	3525	(1st) Captain James T. Kirk......................	1·75	1·75
		a. Booklet pane. Nos. 4456/4457 and U3027×4................................	7·50	
4457	3526	(1st) Captain Jean-Luc Picard.................	1·75	1·75

Nos. 4443/4448 and 4449/4454 were printed together, *se-tenant*, as horizontal strips of five stamps in sheets of 60 (2 panes 6×5).

Booklet panes Nos. 4443b and 4449b come from the £18·25 Star Trek booklet, No. DY36.

Nos. 4456/4457 were issued in stamp booklet, No. PM76, originally sold for £4·56.

A collector's sheet containing stamps as Nos. 4443/4454 but self-adhesive, (No. LS129), was originally sold for £8·70.

The 19 PHQ cards show the 18 individual stamps, including those from No. **MS**4455, and the complete miniature sheet.

3538 Montgomery Scott (Simon Pegg), New Movie Series

3539 Praetor Shinzon (Tom Hardy), Next Generation Movie. *Nemesis*

3540 Tolian Soran (Malcolm McDowell), Original Movie Series. *Generations*

3541 Klingon Chancellor Gorkon (David Warner), Original Movie Series. *The Undiscovered Country*

3542 Dr Carol Marcus (Alice Eve), New Movie Series. *Star Trek Into Darkness*

3543 Krall (Idris Elba), *Star Trek Beyond*

(Des Interabang. Litho ISP Cartor)

2020 (13 Nov). *Star Trek* (2nd issue). Multicoloured. Self-adhesive. Two phosphor bands. Perf 14½ (Nos. 4458/4459) or 14 (Nos. 4460/4463).

4458	**3538**	(1st) Montgomery Scott............................	1·50	1·50
		a. Booklet pane. Nos. 4458/4463........	8·00	
4459	**3539**	(1st) Praetor Shinzon................................	1·50	1·50
4460	**3540**	(1st) Tolian Soran.....................................	1·50	1·50
4461	**3541**	(1st) Klingon Chancellor Gorkon.............	1·50	1·50
4462	**3542**	(1st) Dr Carol Marcus...............................	1·50	1·50
4463	**3543**	(1st) Krall..	1·50	1·50
Set of 6..			8·00	8·00

Nos. 4458/4463 were issued in No. **MS**4455 and in booklet pane No. 4458a from the £18·35 *Star Trek* booklet, No. DY36.

Collectors Pack

2020 (13 Nov). Comprises Nos. 4312/**MS**4320, 4323/4330, 4332/**MS**4338, 4345/4354, 4356/**MS**4364, 4369/**MS**4377, 4380/**MS**4396, 4404/**MS**4417, 4420/4441 and 4433/**MS**4455

CP4463a	Collectors Pack (*sold for* £186) (Pack No. 595)...	£285

Post Office Yearbook

2020 (13 Nov). Comprises Nos. 4312/**MS**4320, 4323/4330, 4332/**MS**4338, 4345/4354, 4356/**MS**4364, 4369/**MS**4377, 4380/**MS**4396, 4404/**MS**4417, 4420/4441 and 4433/**MS**4455

YB4463a	Yearbook (*sold for* £186)......................	£285

Miniature Sheet Collection

2020 (13 Nov). Comprises Nos. **MS**4320, **MS**4338, **MS**4364, **MS**4377, **MS**4396, **MS**4410, **MS**4417, **MS**4442, **MS**4455 and **MS**S180

MS4463a	Miniature Sheet Collection (*sold for* £57)..........	85·00

3544 Dartmoor

3545 New Forest

3546 Lake District

3547 Loch Lomond and The Trossachs

3548 Snowdonia

3549 North York Moors

3550 South Downs

3551 Peak District

3552 Pembrokeshire Coast

3553 Broads

(Des Studio Mean. Litho ISP Cartor (Nos. 4464/4473) or gravure ISP Walsall (Nos. 4474/4475))

2021 (14 Jan). National Parks. Multicoloured. Two phosphor bands.

(a) Ordinary gum. Perf 14×14½.

4464	**3544**	(1st) Dartmoor...	1·25	1·25
		a. Horiz strip of 5. Nos. 4464/4468.....	6·25	6·25
4465	**3545**	(1st) New Forest.......................................	1·25	1·25
4466	**3546**	(1st) Lake District....................................	1·25	1·25
4467	**3547**	(1st) Loch Lomond and The Trossachs...	1·25	1·25
4468	**3548**	(1st) Snowdonia......................................	1·25	1·25
4469	**3549**	(1st) North York Moors............................	1·25	1·25
		a. Horiz strip of 5. Nos. 4469/4473.....	6·25	6·25
4470	**3550**	(1st) South Downs....................................	1·25	1·25
4471	**3551**	(1st) Peak District....................................	1·25	1·25
4472	**3552**	(1st) Pembrokeshire Coast......................	1·25	1·25
4473	**3553**	(1st) Broads..	1·25	1·25
Set of 10...			11·50	11·50
Set of 2 Gutter Strips of 10....................................			23·00	
First Day Cover (Tallents House).............................				14·00
First Day Cover (Bakewell).....................................				14·00
Presentation Pack (PO Pack No. 596).....................			13·50	
PHQ Cards (set of 10) (480).....................................			5·75	13·00

(b) Self-adhesive. Die-cut perf 14×14½.

4474	**3551**	(1st) Peak District....................................	1·75	1·75
		a. Booklet pane. Nos. 4474/4475 and U3027×4...................................	7·50	
4475	**3548**	(1st) Snowdonia......................................	1·75	1·75

Nos. 4464/4468 and 4469/4473 were each printed together, *se-tenant*, as horizontal strips of five stamps in sheets of 50 (2 panes 5×5).

Nos. 4474/4475 were issued in stamp booklet, No. PM77, originally sold for £4·56.

3554 United Kingdom. A Celebration

(Des Hat-trick design. Litho ISP Cartor)

2021 (26 Jan). United Kingdom, A Celebration. Multicoloured. 'All-over' phosphor. Perf 15×14½

MS4476 203×74 mm. **3554** (1st) Wheelchair athlete, cricket ball, football and racing car (Great Sport); (1st) Glass façade of office building, microphone stand silhouette, book pages and television studio (Great Creativity); £1·70 Hands making heart-shape, London Marathon, 2011, nurse reassuring patient and rainbow (Great Community); £1·70 3D illustration of binary code, London skyline, carbon fibre material and DNA (Great Industry and Innovation).. 7·25   7·25
First Day Cover (Tallents House)...   9·50
First Day Cover (London EC1)..   9·50
Presentation Pack (PO Pack No. M26)................................ 9·50
PHQ Cards (set of 5) (481)... 3·00   8·00

3555 'I Knew you was cheating...' (Del Boy and Boycie)

3556 'Don't worry he's house trained...' (Marlene, Del Boy and Rodney)

3557 'Play it nice and cool...' (Del Boy and Trigger)

3558 'Now brace yourself...' (Rodney and Del Boy)

3559 'Our coach has just blown up!' (Rodney and Denzel)

3560 'What have you been doing...' (Rodney and Cassandra)

3561 'It's a baby, Raquel...' (Del Boy and Raquel)

3562 'That's just over...' (Del Boy and Rodney)

3563 Del Boy, Rodney, Uncle Albert and Grandad

3564 Del Boy

3565 Rodney

(Des Interabang. Litho ISP Cartor (Nos. 4477/**MS**4485) or gravure Walsall (Nos. 4486/4487))

2021 (16 Feb). *Only Fools and Horses* (TV sitcom, 1981–2003) (1st issue). Multicoloured. Two phosphor bands.
(a) Ordinary gum. Perf 14.

4477	**3555**	(1st) 'I knew you was cheating...', (Del Boy and Boycie).................................	1·25	1·25
		a. Vert pair. Nos. 4477/4478...............	2·50	2·50
		b. Booklet pane. Nos. 4477/4480 with margins all round.....................	5·00	
4478	**3556**	(1st) 'Don't worry he's house trained...' (Marlene, Del Boy and Rodney)......	1·25	1·25
4479	**3557**	(1st) 'Play it nice and cool...' (Del Boy and Trigger)................................	1·25	1·25
		a. Vert pair. Nos. 4479/4480...............	2·50	2·50
4480	**3558**	(1st) 'Now brace yourself...' (Rodney and Del Boy).....................................	1·25	1·25

4481	3559	£1·70 'Our coach has just blown up!' (Rodney and Denzel)............	2·40	2·40
		a. Vert pair. Nos. 4481/4482................	4·75	4·75
		b. Booklet pane. Nos. 4481/4484 with margins all round....................	9·50	
4482	3560	£1·70 'What have you been doing...' (Rodney and Cassandra).................	2·40	2·40
4483	3561	£1·70 'It's a baby, Raquel...' (Del Boy and Raquel).......................................	2·40	2·40
		a. Vert pair. Nos. 4483/4484................	4·75	4·75
4484	3562	£1·70 'That's just over...' (Del Boy and Rodney)......................................	2·40	2·40

Set of 8...			13·00	13·00
Set of 4 Gutter Pairs (only 2 stamps in each pair)................			15·00	
First Day Cover (Tallents House)...............................				15·00
First Day Cover (London SE15)................................				15·00
Presentation Pack (PO Pack No. 597) (Nos. 4477/4484 and **MS**4485)..			23·00	
PHQ Cards (set of 13) (482)...................................			7·50	22·00

MS4485 203×74 mm. **3563** (1st) Del Boy (David Jason); (1st) Rodney (Nicholas Lyndhurst); £1·70 Uncle Albert (Buster Merryfield); £1·70 Grandad (Lennard Pearce)... 7·25 / 7·25

| *First Day Cover* (Tallents House)............................... | | | | 9·50 |
| *First Day Cover* (London SE15)................................ | | | | 9·50 |

(b) Self-adhesive. Die-cut perf 14.

4486	3564	(1st) Del Boy....................................	1·75	1·75
		a. Booklet pane. Nos. 4486/4487 and U3027×4..........................	7·25	
4487	3565	(1st) Rodney......................................	1·75	1·75

Nos. 4477/4478, 4479/4480, 4481/4482 and 4483/4484 were each printed together, *se-tenant*, as vertical pairs in sheets of 60 (2 panes 5×6). Booklet panes Nos. 4477b and 4481b come from the £21·70 *Only Fools and Horses* booklet, No. DY37.

Nos. 4486/4487 were issued in stamp booklet, No. PM78, originally sold for £5·10.

A fan souvenir folder containing excerpts from writer John Sullivan's personal *Only Fools and Horses* scripts along with first day covers for Nos. 4477/4484 and **MS**4485 was sold by Royal Mail for £19·99.

Self-adhesive designs as Types **3564/3565** perforated 14×14½ were issued in sheets of ten, (No. LS131), containing five stamps of each design with labels. These sheets were printed in Lithography by ISP Cartor and originally sold for £9·60.

The 13 PHQ cards show the 12 individual stamps, including those from No. **MS**4485, and the complete miniature sheet.

3566 Uncle Albert   **3567** Grandad

(Des Interabang. Litho ISP Cartor)

2021 (16 Feb). *Only Fools and Horses* (2nd issue). Multicoloured. Two phosphor bands. Perf 14.

4488	3564	(1st) Del Boy (David Jason)......................	1·50	1·50
		a. Booklet pane. Nos. 4488/4491 with margins all round...............	7·50	
4489	3565	(1st) Rodney (Nicholas Lyndhurst)..........	1·50	1·50
4490	3566	£1·70 Uncle Albert (Buster Merryfield)....	2·75	2·75
4491	3567	£1·70 Grandad (Lennard Pearce)...............	2·75	2·75
Set of 4........			7·50	7·50

Nos. 4488/4491 were issued in No. **MS**4485 and in booklet pane 4488a from £21·70 *Only Fools and Horses* booklet, No. DY37.

3568 Merlin and the Baby Arthur   **3569** Arthur Draws the Sword from the Stone

3570 Arthur takes Excalibur   **3571** Arthur Marries Guinevere

3572 Sir Gawain and the Green Knight   **3573** Knights of the Round Table

3574 Sir Lancelot Defeats the Dragon   **3575** Sir Galahad and the Holy Grail

3576 Arthur Battles Mordred   **3577** The Death of King Arthur

(Des Jaime Jones Stamp Design. Litho ISP Cartor)

2021 (16 Mar). The Legend of King Arthur. Multicoloured. Two phosphor bands. Perf 14½.

4492	3568	(1st) Merlin and the Baby Arthur............	1·25	1·25
		a. Horiz strip of 5. Nos. 4492/4496.....	6·25	6·25
4493	3569	(1st) Arthur draws the Sword from the Stone.....................................	1·25	1·25
4494	3570	(1st) Arthur takes Excalibur.....................	1·25	1·25
4495	3571	(1st) Arthur marries Guinevere..............	1·25	1·25
4496	3572	(1st) Sir Gawain and the Green Knight....	1·25	1·25
4497	3573	£1·70 Knights of the Round Table............	2·40	2·40
		a. Horiz strip of 5. Nos. 4497/4501.....	12·00	12·00
4498	3574	£1·70 Sir Lancelot defeats the Dragon.....	2·40	2·40
4499	3575	£1·70 Sir Galahad and the Holy Grail........	2·40	2·40
4500	3576	£1·70 Arthur battles Mordred...................	2·40	2·40
4501	3577	£1·70 The Death of King Arthur................	2·40	2·40
Set of 10................			16·00	16·00
Set of 2 Gutter Strips of 10....................			32·00	
First Day Cover (Tallents House)...............................				18·00
First Day Cover (Winchester)...................................				18·00
Presentation Pack (PO Pack No. 598).......................			18·00	
PHQ Cards (set of 10) (483)...................................			5·75	16·00

Nos. 4492/4496 and 4497/4501 were each printed together, *se-tenant*, as horizontal strips of five in sheets of 50 (2 panes 5×5).

3486 Queen, 1974

(Gravure ISP Walsall)

2021 (29 Mar). Queen (Rock Band) (4th issue). As T **3486** but self-adhesive. Two phosphor bands. Die-cut perf 14½×14 (with one elliptical hole in each vert side).

4502	**3486**	(1st) Queen, 1974..................................	1·50	1·50
		a. Booklet pane. No. 4502×6..............	8·00	

No. 4502 was issued in booklets of six, No. MB22, originally sold for £5·10.

3579 *Frankenstein* (Mary Shelley)

3580 *The Time Machine* (H. G. Wells)

3581 *Brave New World* (Aldous Huxley)

3582 *The Day of the Triffids* (John Wyndham)

3583 *Childhood's End* (Arthur C. Clarke)

3584 *Shikasta* (Doris Lessing)

(Des Webb & Webb Design Ltd (illustrations Sabina Šinko (No. 4503), Francisco Rodriguez (No. 4504), Thomas Danthony (No. 4505), Mick Brownfield (No. 4506), Matt Murphy (No. 4507), Sarah Jones (No. 4508). Litho ISP Cantor)

2021 (15 Apr). Classic Science Fiction. Multicoloured. Two phosphor bands. Perf 14½.

4503	**3579**	(1st) *Frankenstein* (Mary Shelley)............	1·25	1·25
		a. Horiz pair. Nos. 4503/4504..............	2·50	2·50
4504	**3580**	(1st) *The Time Machine* (H. G. Wells)........	1·25	1·25
4505	**3581**	£1·70 *Brave New World* (Aldous Huxley)...	2·50	2·50
		a. Horiz pair. Nos. 4505/4506..............	5·00	5·00
4506	**3582**	£1·70 *The Day of the Triffids* (John Wyndham)...	2·50	2·50
4507	**3583**	£2·55 *Childhood's End* (Arthur C. Clarke)..	3·50	3·50
		a. Horiz pair. Nos. 4507/4508..............	7·00	7·00
4508	**3584**	£2·55 *Shikasta* (Doris Lessing)..................	3·50	3·50
Set of 6..			13·00	13·00
Set of 3 Gutter Pairs...			26·00	
First Day Cover (Tallents House).........................				16·00
First Day Cover (London NW1)............................				16·00
Presentation Pack (PO Pack No. 599)..................			15·00	
PHQ Cards (set of 6) (484)................................			3·75	14·50

Nos. 4503/4504, 4505/4506 and 4507/4508 were printed together, *se-tenant*, as horizontal pairs in sheets of 60 (2 panes 6×5).

3585 Battle of Bosworth, 1485

3586 Battle of Tewkesbury, 1471

3587 Battle of Barnet, 1471

3588 Battle of Edgecote Moor, 1469

3589 Battle of Towton, 1461

3590 Battle of Wakefield, 1460

3591 Battle of Northampton, 1460

3592 First Battle of St Albans, 1455

(Des Graham Turner. Litho ISP Cartor)

2021 (4 May). Wars of the Roses. Multicoloured. One centre band (2nd) or two phosphor bands (others). Perf 14.

4509	**3585**	(2nd) Battle of Bosworth, 1485................	90	90
		a. Horiz pair. Nos. 4509/4510..............	1·75	1·75
4510	**3586**	(2nd) Battle of Tewkesbury, 1471............	90	90
4511	**3587**	(1st) Battle of Barnet, 1471......................	1·25	1·25
		a. Horiz pair. Nos. 4511/4512..............	2·50	2·50

4512	**3588**	(1st) Battle of Edgecote Moor, 1469.......	1·25	1·25
4513	**3589**	£1·70 Battle of Towton, 1461...................	2·50	2·50
		a. Horiz pair. Nos. 4513/4514..............	5·00	5·00
4514	**3590**	£1·70 Battle of Wakefield, 1460..............	2·50	2·50
4515	**3591**	£2·55 Battle of Northampton, 1460........	3·50	3·50
		a. Horiz pair. Nos. 4515/4516..............	7·00	7·00
4516	**3592**	£2·55 First Battle of St Albans, 1455........	3·50	3·50
Set of 8			14·50	14·50
Set of 4 Gutter Pairs			29·00	
First Day Cover (Tallents House)				17·00
First Day Cover (Tewkesbury)				17·00
Presentation Pack (PO Pack No. 600)			15·00	
PHQ Pack (set of 8) (485)			5·00	9·75

Nos. 4509/4510, 4511/4512, 4513/4514 and 4515/4516 were each printed together, *se-tenant*, as horizontal pairs in sheets of 60 (2 panes 6×5).

3593 *McCartney*   **3594** *RAM*

 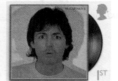

3595 *Venus and Mars*   **3596** *McCartney II*

3597 *Tug of War*   **3598** *Flaming Pie*

3599 *Egypt Station*   **3600** *McCartney III*

3601 Paul McCartney in the Studio

(Des Baxter & Bailey. Litho ISP Cartor (Nos. 4517/4224) or gravure ISP Walsall (Nos. 4226/4227))

2021 (28 May). Paul McCartney (1st issue). Multicoloured. Two phosphor bands.

(a) Ordinary gum. Perf 14 (Nos. 4517/4524, 4526/4527) or 14½ (No. MS4525).

4517	**3593**	(1st) *McCartney*..............................	1·25	1·25
		a. Horiz strip of 4. Nos. 4517/4520.....	5·00	5·00
		b. Booklet pane. Nos. 4517/4520 with margins all round....................	5·50	
4518	**3594**	(1st) *RAM*..	1·25	1·25
4519	**3595**	(1st) *Venus and Mars*......................	1·25	1·25
4520	**3596**	(1st) *McCartney II*..........................	1·25	1·25
4521	**3597**	£1·70 *Tug of War*............................	2·50	2·50
		a. Horiz strip of 4. Nos. 4521/4524.....	10·00	10·00
		b. Booklet pane. Nos. 4521/4524 with margins all round....................	10·00	
4522	**3598**	£1·70 *Flaming Pie*..........................	2·50	2·50
4523	**3599**	£1·70 *Egypt Station*........................	2·50	2·50
4524	**3600**	£1·70 *McCartney III*.......................	2·50	2·50
Set of 8			13·50	13·50
Set of 2 Gutter Strips of 8			27·00	
First Day Cover (Tallents House)				16·00
First Day Cover (Liverpool)				16·00
Presentation Pack (PO Pack No. 601) (Nos. 4517/4524 and MS4525)			23·00	
PHQ Cards (set of 13) (486)			8·25	24·00
Souvenir Folder (containing Nos. 4517/4524 and MS4525 plus prints of the stamps at record cover size)..			38·00	
MS4525 126×89 mm. **3601** (1st) *McCartney*, 1970; (1st) *RAM*, 1971; £1·70 *McCartney II*, 1980; £1·70 *Flaming Pie*, 1997			7·50	7·50
First Day Cover (Tallents House)				10·00
First Day Cover (Liverpool)				10·00

(b) Self-adhesive. Die-cut perf 14.

4526	**3593**	(1st) *McCartney*..............................	1·75	1·75
		a. Booklet pane. Nos. 4526/4527 and U3027×4..................................	7·50	
4527	**3596**	(1st) *McCartney II*..........................	1·75	1·75

Nos. 4517/4520 and 4521/4524 were each printed together, *se-tenant*, as horizontal strips of four stamps in sheets of 48 (2 panes 4×6).

Booklet panes Nos. 4517b and 4521b come from the £20·25 Paul McCartney booklet, No. DY38.

Nos. 4626/4627 were issued in stamp booklet, No. PM79, originally sold for £5·10.

A Paul McCartney Album Covers Collector's Sheet containing Nos. 4517/4518×2 and 4519/4524 with labels was originally sold for £13.

An Album cover collection fan sheet containing Nos. 4517/4524 was originally sold for £10·90.

A *RAM* fan sheet containing No. 4518×4 was originally sold for £7·50.

A *McCartney III* album fan sheet containing No. 4524×4 was originally sold for £7·50.

The 13 PHQ Cards show the 12 individual stamps, including those from No. **MS**4525 and the complete miniature sheet.

3602 *McCartney*, 1970   **3603** *RAM*, 1971

3604 *McCartney II*, 1980   **3605** *Flaming Pie*, 1997

2021 (28 May). Paul McCartney (2nd issue). Multicoloured. Two phosphor bands. Perf 14½.

4528	**3602**	(1st) *McCartney*, 1970....................	1·50	1·50
		a. Booklet pane. Nos. 4528/4531 with margins all round....................	8·50	
4529	**3603**	(1st) *RAM*, 1971............................	1·50	1·50
4530	**3604**	£1·70 *McCartney II*, 1980................	2·75	2·75
4531	**3605**	£1·70 *Flaming Pie*, 1997.................	2·75	2·75
Set of 4			8·50	8·50

Nos. 4528/4531 were issued in No. **MS**4525 and in booklet pane 4528a from the £20·25 Paul McCartney booklet, No. DY38.

3606 Prince Philip, Duke of Edinburgh

(Des Kate Stephens. Litho ISP Cartor)

2021 (24 June). Prince Philip, Duke of Edinburgh (1921–2021) Commemoration. Multicoloured. Phosphor band at left (2nd) or 'all-over' phosphor (others). Perf 14½×14.

MS4532 200×67 mm. **3606** (2nd) Prince Philip, Duke of Edinburgh, *circa* 1952; (1st) Prince Philip at passing out parade of Prince Andrew, Dartmouth Naval College, 1980; £1·70 Prince Philip at Royal Windsor Horse Show; £2·55 Prince Philip, *circa* 1992		8·25	8·25
First Day Cover (Tallents House)			11·00
First Day Cover (Windsor)			11·00
Presentation Pack (PO Pack No. 602)		10·50	
PHQ Cards (set of 5) (487)		3·25	9·75

3607 Dennis's First Comic Strip, 1951

3608 Dennis Adopts Gnasher, 1968

3609 Dennis's Front Cover Debut, 1974

3610 Dennis Adopts Rasher the Pig, 1979

3611 Dennis Meets his Sister Bea, 1998

3612 Dennis Reveals Dad was Dennis, 2015

(Des The Chase. Gravure ISP Walsall (Nos. 4540/4541) or litho ISP Cartor (others))

2021 (1 July). Dennis and Gnasher. Multicoloured. Two phosphor bands.

(a) Ordinary gum. Perf 14.

4533	**3607**	(1st) Dennis's First Comic Strip, 1951	1·25	1·25
		a. Horiz strip of 3. Nos. 4533/4535	3·75	3·75
4534	**3608**	(1st) Dennis adopts Gnasher, 1968	1·25	1·25
4535	**3609**	(1st) Dennis's Front Cover Debut, 1974	1·25	1·25
4536	**3610**	£1·70 Dennis adopts Rasher the Pig, 1979	2·50	2·50
		a. Horiz strip of 3. Nos. 4536/4538	7·50	7·50
4537	**3611**	£1·70 Dennis meets his Sister Bea, 1998	2·50	2·50
4538	**3612**	£1·70 Dennis reveals Dad was Dennis, 2015	2·50	2·50
Set of 6			10·00	10·00
Set of 2 Gutter Strips of 6			20·00	
First Day Cover (Tallents House)				12·50
First Day Cover (Dundee)				12·50
Presentation Pack (PO Pack No. 603) (Nos. 4533/4538 and **MS**4539)			20·00	
PHQ Cards (set of 11) (488)			7·00	20·00

3613 Happy Birthday Dennis

(b) Self-adhesive. Die-cut perf 14 (Minnie the Minx) or 14½ (others).

MS4539 203×74 mm. **3613** (1st) Dennis; (1st) Gnasher; £1·70 Minnie the Minx (26×31 mm); £1·70 Dennis, his baby sister Bea and parents	7·25	7·25
First Day Cover (Tallents House)		9·75
First Day Cover (Dundee)		9·75

3614 Dennis   **3615** Gnasher

(c) Self-adhesive booklet stamps. Die-cut perf 14½.

4540	**3614**	(1st) Dennis	1·75	1·75
		a. Booklet pane. Nos. 4540/4541 and U3027×4	7·50	
4541	**3615**	(1st) Gnasher	1·75	1·75

Nos. 4533/4535 and 4536/4538 were each printed together, *se-tenant*, as horizontal strips of three in sheets of 60 (2 panes 6×5).

Nos. 4540/4541 were issued in stamp booklet, No. PM80, originally sold for £5·10.

A Collector's Sheet containing 1st self-adhesive Dennis and Gnasher stamps×10 as Types **3614**/**3615** each×5 was originally sold for £9·70.

The 11 PHQ cards show the ten individual stamps, including those from No. **MS**4539, and the complete miniature sheet.

3616 Northern Gannet **3617** Common Cuttlefish

3618 Grey Seal

3619 Bottlenose Dolphin

3620 Spiny Spider Crab

3621 Long-snouted Seahorse

3622 Orca

3623 Fried-egg Anemone

3624 Cuckoo Wrasse

3625 Cold-water Coral Reef

3626 Marine Food Chain

(Des Steers McGillan Eves (Nos. 4542/4551) or Maite Franchi (No. **MS**4552). Litho ISP Cartor (Nos. 4542/4551) or gravure ISP Walsall (Nos. 4553/4554))

2021 (22 July). Wild Coasts. Multicoloured. Two phosphor bands.

*(a) Ordinary gum. Perf 14½ (Nos. 4542/4551) or 14 (No. **MS**4552).*

4542	**3616**	(1st) Northern Gannet	1·25	1·25
		a. Horiz strip of 5. Nos. 4542/4546	6·25	6·25
4543	**3617**	(1st) Common Cuttlefish	1·25	1·25
4544	**3618**	(1st) Grey Seal	1·25	1·25
4545	**3619**	(1st) Bottlenose Dolphin	1·25	1·25
4546	**3620**	(1st) Spiny Spider Crab	1·25	1·25
4547	**3621**	(1st) Long-snouted Seahorse	1·25	1·25
		a. Horiz strip of 5. Nos. 4547/4551	6·25	6·25
4548	**3622**	(1st) Orca	1·25	1·25
4549	**3623**	(1st) Fried-egg Anemone	1·25	1·25
4550	**3624**	(1st) Cuckoo Wrasse	1·25	1·25
4551	**3625**	(1st) Cold-water Coral Reef	1·25	1·25
Set of 10			11·00	11·00
Set of 2 Gutter Strips of 10			22·00	
First Day Cover (Tallents House)				13·00
First Day Cover (Achnasheen)				13·00
Presentation Pack (PO Pack No. 604) (Nos. 4542/4551				
and **MS**4552)			21·00	
PHQ Cards (set of 15) (489)			9·50	21·00

MS4552 202×74 mm. **3626** (1st) Phytoplankton; (1st) Zooplankton; £1·70 Atlantic Herring; £1·70

Harbour Porpoise	7·25	7·25
First Day Cover (Tallents House)		9·25
First Day Cover (Achnasheen)		9·25

(b) Self-adhesive. Die-cut perf 14½×14.

4553	**3622**	(1st) Orca	1·75	1·75
		a. Booklet pane. Nos. 4553/4554		
		and U3027×4	7·50	
4554	**3618**	(1st) Grey Seal	1·75	1·75

Nos. 4542/4546 and 4547/4551 were each printed together, *se-tenant*, as horizontal strips of five in sheets of 50 (2 panes 5×5).

Nos. 4553/4554 were issued in stamp booklets, No. PM81, originally sold for £5·10.

A Collector's Sheet containing designs as Nos. 4542/4551 but self-adhesive was originally sold for £9·70.

The 15 PHQ cards show the 14 individual stamps, including those from No. **MS**4552, and the complete miniature sheet.

3627 Bessemer Process, Henry Bessemer, 1856

3628 Watt's Rotative Steam Engine, James Watt, 1780s

3629 Penydarren Locomotive, Richard Trevithick, 1804

3630 Spinning Jenny, James Hargreaves, *circa* 1764

3631 Lombe's Silk Mill, Lombe Brothers, 1721

3632 Portland Cement, Joseph Aspdin, 1824

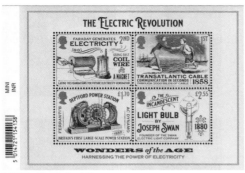

3633 The Electric Revolution

(Des Common Curiosity. Litho ISP Cartor)

2021 (12 Aug). Industrial Revolutions (1st issue). Multicoloured. One centre band (2nd) or two bands (others). Perf 14½ (Nos. 4555/4560) or 14 (No. **MS**4561).

4555	**3627**	(2nd) Bessemer process, Henry Bessemer, 1856......................	90	90
		a. Vert pair. Nos. 4555/4556...............	1·75	1·75
		b. Booklet pane. Nos. 4555/4558 with margins all round....................	4·25	
4556	**3628**	(2nd) Watt's rotative steam engine, James Watt, 1780s...................	90	90
4557	**3629**	(1st) Penydarren locomotive, Richard Trevithick, 1804..................	1·25	1·25
		a. Vert pair. Nos. 4557/4558...............	2·50	2·50
		b. Booklet pane. Nos. 4557/4560 with margins all round....................	7·50	
4558	**3630**	(1st) Spinning Jenny, James Hargreaves, circa 1764..................	1·25	1·25
4559	**3631**	£1·70 Lombe's Silk Mill, Lombe Brothers, 1721..........................	2·50	2·50
		a. Vert pair. Nos. 4559/4560...............	5·00	5·00
4560	**3632**	£1·70 Portland Cement, Joseph Aspdin, 1824..........................	2·50	2·50
Set of 6..			8·25	8·25
Set of 3 Gutter Strips of 4...			17·00	
First Day Cover (Tallents House)...................................				11·00
First Day Cover (Derby)...				11·00
Presentation Pack (PO Pack No. 605) (Nos. 4555/4560 and **MS**4561)...			19·00	
PHQ Cards (set of 11) (490)..			7·00	19·00

MS4561 126×89 mm. **3633** (2nd) Michael Faraday generates electricity, 1831; (1st) First transatlantic cable, communication, 1858; £1·70 Deptford Power Station, 1889; £2·55 The incandescent light bulb by Joseph Swan, 1880.......

	8·25	8·25
First Day Cover (Tallents House)...................		10·50
First Day Cover (Derby)...............................		10·50

Nos. 4555/4556, 4557/4558 and 4559/4560 were each printed together, *se-tenant*, as vertical pairs in sheets of 60 (2 panes 5×6).

Booklet panes Nos. 4555b and 4557b come from the £18·03 Industrial Revolution booklet, No. DY39.

The 11 PHQ cards show the ten individual stamps, including those from No. **MS**4561, and the complete miniature sheet.

3634 Michael Faraday Generates Electricity using just Coil Wire and a Magnet, 1831

3635 First Transatlantic Cable, Communication in Seconds Through 2000 Miles of Cable, 1858

3636 AC Dynamo, Sebastian de Ferranti's Deptford Power Station, Britain's First Large-scale Power Station, 1889

3637 The Incandescent Light Bulb by Joseph Swan, Founder of the Swan Electric Light Company, 1880

(Des Common Curiosity. Litho ISP Cartor)

2021 (12 Aug). Industrial Revolutions (2nd issue). Multicoloured. One centre band (2nd) or two bands (others). Perf 14.

4562	**3634**	(2nd) Michael Faraday generates electricity, 1831........................	1·25	1·25
		a. Booklet pane. Nos. 4562/4565 with margins all round....................	10·00	
4563	**3635**	(1st) First transatlantic cable communication, 1858.....................	1·75	1·75
4564	**3636**	£1·70 Deptford Power Station, 1889........	3·00	3·00
4565	**3637**	£2·55 The incandescent light bulb by Joseph Swan, 1880........................	4·00	4·00
Set of 4..			10·00	10·00

Nos. 4562/4565 were issued in £18·03 premium booklet, No. DY39.

3638 Mk IV Tank

3639 Matilda Mk II (A12 Infantry Tank)

3640 Churchill AVRE (Armoured Vehicles Royal Engineers) Tank

3641 Centurion Mk 9 Tank

3642 Scorpion Tank

3643 Chieftain Mk 5 Tank

3644 Challenger 2 Tank

3645 Ajax (turreted, reconnaissance and strike vehicle)

3646 British Army Vehicles

(Des Mike Graham. Litho ISP Cartor)

2021 (2 Sept). British Army Vehicles. Multicoloured. Two phosphor bands. Perf 14.

4566	**3638**	(1st) Mk IV Tank	1·25	1·25
		a. Horiz strip of 4. Nos. 4566/4569	5·00	5·00
4567	**3639**	(1st) Matilda Mk II	1·25	1·25
4568	**3640**	(1st) Churchill AVRE Tank	1·25	1·25
4569	**3641**	(1st) Centurion Mk 9 Tank	1·25	1·25
4570	**3642**	£1·70 Scorpion Tank	2·50	2·50
		a. Horiz strip of 4. Nos. 4570/4573	10·00	10·00
4571	**3643**	£1·70 Chieftain Mk 5 Tank	2·50	2·50
4572	**3644**	£1·70 Challenger 2 Tank	2·50	2·50
4573	**3645**	£1·70 Ajax	2·50	2·50
Set of 8			13·50	13·50
Set of 8 Gutter Pairs			27·00	
First Day Cover (Tallents House)				16·00
First Day Cover (Bovington, Wareham)				16·00
Presentation Pack (PO Pack No. 606) (Nos. 4566/4573 and **MS**4574)			23·00	
PHQ Cards (set of 13) (491)			8·25	23·00

MS4574 125×89 mm. **3646** (1st) Coyote Tactical Support Vehicle; (1st) Army Wildcat Mk 1 Reconnaissance Helicopter; £1·70 Trojan Armoured Vehicle Royal Engineers; £1·70 Foxhound Light Protected Patrol Vehicle....... 7·25 7·25

First Day Cover (Tallents House)		9·75
First Day Cover (Bovington, Wareham)		9·75

the 13 PHQ cards show the 12 individual stamps, including those from No. **MS**4574, and the complete miniature sheet.

3647 Batman

3648 Batwoman

3649 Robin

3650 Batgirl

3651 Alfred

3652 Nightwing

3653 The Joker

3654 Harley Quinn

3655 The Penguin

3656 Poison Ivy

3657 Catwoman

3658 The Riddler

3659 Justice League

3660 Wonder Woman

(Des Interabang, illustration Jim Cheung, colourist Laura Martin. Litho ISP Cartor (Nos. 4575/**MS**4587) or gravure Walsall (Nos. 4588/4589)

2021 (17 Sept). DC Collection (1st issue). Multicoloured. Two phosphor bands.

(a) Ordinary gum. Perf 14½.

4575	**3647**	(1st) Batman......................................	1·25	1·25
		a. Horiz strip of 6. Nos. 4575/4580.....	7·50	7·50
		b. Booklet pane. Nos. 4575/4580 with margins all round...................	7·25	
4576	**3648**	(1st) Batwoman....................................	1·25	1·25
4577	**3649**	(1st) Robin..	1·25	1·25
4578	**3650**	(1st) Batgirl..	1·25	1·25
4579	**3651**	(1st) Alfred...	1·25	1·25
4580	**3652**	(1st) Nightwing...................................	1·25	1·25
4581	**3653**	(1st) The Joker....................................	1·25	1·25
		a. Horiz strip of 6. Nos. 4581/4586.....	7·50	7·50
		b. Booklet pane. Nos. 4581/4586 with margins all round...................	7·25	
4582	**3654**	(1st) Harley Quinn...............................	1·25	1·25
4583	**3655**	(1st) The Penguin................................	1·25	1·25
4584	**3656**	(1st) Poison Ivy...................................	1·25	1·25
4585	**3657**	(1st) Catwoman..................................	1·25	1·25
4586	**3658**	(1st) The Riddler.................................	1·25	1·25
Set of 12..			15·00	15·00
Set of 2 Gutter Strips of 12...............................			30·00	
First Day Cover (Tallents House)..........................				17·00
First Day Cover (Gotham, Nottingham)................				17·00
Presentation Pack (PO Pack No. 607) (Nos. 4575/4586 and **MS**4587)...			24·00	
PHQ Cards (set of 19) (492).................................			12·00	24·00

(b) Self-adhesive.

MS4587 202×74 mm. **3659** (1st) Batman (50×30 mm) (perf 14); (1st) Wonder Woman (35×36 mm) (perf 14); (1st) Superman (60×23 mm) (perf 14½×14); (1st) Green Lantern and The Flash (50×30 mm) (perf 14); (1st) Cyborg and Aquaman (35×36 mm) (perf 14); (1st) Supergirl and Shazam! (27×36 mm) (perf 14)..			7·50	7·50
First Day Cover (Tallents House)..........................				10·00
First Day Cover (Gotham, Nottingham)................				10·00

(c) Self-adhesive booklet stamps. Die-cut perf 14½×14.

4588	**3647**	(1st) Batman......................................	1·75	1·75
		a. Booklet pane. Nos. 4588/4589 and U3027×4..................................	7·50	
4589	**3649**	(1st) Robin..	1·75	1·75
4590	**3660**	(1st) Wonder Woman..........................	1·75	1·75
		a. Booklet pane. No. 4590×2 and U3027×4..................................	7·50	
Set of 3..			5·00	5·00

Nos. 4575/4580 and 4581/4586 were each printed together, *se-tenant*, as horizontal strips of six in sheets of 60 (2 panes 6×5).

Booklet panes Nos. 4757b and 4581b come from the £21·20 DC Collection booklet, No. DY40.

Nos. 4588/4589 were issued in stamp booklet, No. PM82, originally sold for £5·10.

A Batman Collector's Sheet containing designs as Nos. 4575/4586 but self-adhesive was originally sold for £11·40.

No. 4590 was issued in stamp booklet, No. PM83, originally sold for £5·10.

The 19 PHQ cards show the 18 individual stamps, including those from No. **MS**4587, and the complete miniature sheet.

3661 Batman

3662 Green Lantern and The Flash

3663 Superman

3664 Cyborg and Aquaman   **3665** Supergirl and Shazam!

(Des Interabang illustration Jim Cheung colourist Laura Martin. Litho ISP Cartor)

2021 (17 Sept). DC Collection (2nd issue). Multicoloured. Self-adhesive. Two phosphor bands. Perf 14½×14 (No. 4594) or 14 (others).

4591	**3661**	(1st) Batman......................................	1·50	1·50
		a. Booklet pane. Nos. 4591/4592........	3·00	
4592	**3662**	(1st) Green Lantern and The Flash..........	1·50	1·50
4593	**3660**	(1st) Wonder Woman..........................	1·50	1·50
		a. Booklet pane. Nos. 4593/4596........	6·00	
4594	**3663**	(1st) Superman...................................	1·50	1·50
4595	**3664**	(1st) Cyborg and Aquaman..................	1·50	1·50
4596	**3665**	(1st) Supergirl and Shazam!................	1·50	1·50
Set of 6..			9·00	9·00

Nos. 4591/4596 were issued in booklet panes Nos. 4591a and 4593a from the £21·20 DC Collection booklet No. DY40.

Booklet panes Nos. 4591a and 4593a contain stamps in the same designs as No. **MS**4587 but are in two panes with pale blue margins.

3666 Women's Rugby World Cup Final, 2014   **3667** Five Nations Championship, 1970

3668 Women's Six Nations Championship, 2015   **3669** Five Nations Championship, 1984

3670 Women's Home Nations Championship, 1998   **3671** Five Nations Championship, 1994

3672 Women's Six Nations Championship, 2009   **3673** Rugby World Cup Final, 2003

(Des True North. Litho ISP Cartor)

2021 (19 Oct). Rugby Union. Multicoloured. One phosphor band, slightly right of centre (2nd) or two bands (others). Perf 14×14½.

4597	**3666**	(2nd) Women's Rugby World Cup Final, 2014..................	90	90
		a. Horiz pair. Nos. 4597/4598.	1·75	1·75
4598	**3667**	(2nd) Five Nations Championship, 1970.	90	90
4599	**3668**	(1st) Women's Six Nations Championship, 2015................	1·25	1·25
		a. Horiz pair. Nos. 4599/4600.	2·50	2·50
4600	**3669**	(1st) Five Nations Championship, 1984.	1·25	1·25
4601	**3670**	£1·70 Women's Home Nations Championship, 1998...............	2·50	2·50
		a. Horiz pair. Nos. 4601/4602.	3·00	3·00
4602	**3671**	£1·70 Five Nations Championship, 1994.	2·50	2·50
4603	**3672**	£2·55 Women's Six Nations Championship, 2009...............	3·50	3·50
		a. Horiz pair. Nos. 4603/4604.	7·00	7·00
4604	**3673**	£2·55 Rugby World Cup Final, 2003.	3·50	3·50
Set of 8			13·00	13·00
Set of 4 Gutter Strips of 4			26·00	
First Day Cover (Tallents House)				16·00
First Day Cover (Twickenham)				16·00
Presentation Pack (PO Pack No. 608)			15·00	
PHQ Cards (set of 8) (493)			5·00	14·50

Nos. 4597/4598, 4599/4600, 4601/4602 and 4603/4604 were each printed together, *se-tenant*, as horizontal pairs in sheets of 60 (2 panes 6×5).

3674 Angels   **3675** Angels

3676 Mary and Baby Jesus   **3677** Mary and Baby Jesus

3678 Joseph and Mary on Road to Bethlehem   **3679** Shepherds see Angels

3680 Wise Men Following Star of Bethlehem   **3681** Mary and Baby Jesus Visited by the Shepherds

(Des Supple Studio. Gravure ISP Walsall (Nos. 4605/4612) or litho (No. **MS**4613))

2021 (2 Nov). Christmas. Nativity Illustrations by Jorge Cocco. Multicoloured. One centre phosphor band (Nos. 4605/4606) or two bands (others). Self-adhesive. Die-cut perf 14½×15 (Nos. 4606, 4608) or 15×14½ (others).

(a) Gravure.

4605	**3674**	(2nd) Angels.................	90	90
4606	**3675**	(2nd) Angels.................	90	90
		a. Booklet pane. No. 4606×12.	12·50	
4607	**3676**	(1st) Mary and Baby Jesus........	1·00	1·00
4608	**3677**	(1st) Mary and Baby Jesus........	1·00	1·00
		a. Booklet pane. No. 4608×12.	17·50	

4609	**3678**	(2nd Large) Joseph and Mary on road to Bethlehem..............	1·10	1·10
4610	**3679**	(1st Large) Shepherds see Angels....	1·40	1·40
4611	**3680**	£1·70 Wise Men following Star of Bethlehem...............	2·75	2·75
4612	**3681**	£2·55 Mary and baby Jesus visited by the Shepherds..............	4·00	4·00
Set of 8			12·00	12·00
First Day Cover (Tallents House)				14·50
First Day Cover (Bethlehem, Llandeilo)				14·50
Presentation Pack (PO Pack No. 609)			14·00	
PHQ Cards (set of 9) (494)			5·50	13·00

(b) Litho.

MS4613 189×74 mm. As Nos. 4605/4612.		13·00	13·00
First Day Cover (Tallents House)			14·50
First Day Cover (Bethlehem, Llandeilo)			14·50

The 2nd class and 1st class stamps with barcodes, Nos. 4605 and 4607, were each issued in counter sheets of 50.

The 2nd class with no barcode, No. 4606, was issued in booklets of 12 originally sold for £7·92.

The 1st class with no barcode, No. 4608, was issued in booklets of 12 originally sold for £10·20.

The 2nd class with no barcode, 1st class with no barcode, £1·70 and £2·55 values were also issued in sheets of 20 containing 8×2nd class, 8×1st class, 2×£1·70 and 2×£2·55 values. These sheets were printed in lithography instead of gravure.

The nine PHQ cards show the individual stamps and the complete miniature sheet.

Collectors Pack

2021 (2 Nov). Comprises Nos. 4464/4473, **MS**4476/**MS**4485, 4492/4501, 4503/**MS**4525, **MS**4532/**MS**4539, 4542/**MS**4552, 4555/**MS**4561, 4566/**MS**4587 and 4597/4612

CP4613*a*	Collectors Pack (Pack No. 610) (*sold for £180*)	£275

Post Office Yearbook

2021 (2 Nov). Comprises Nos. 4464/4473, **MS**4476/**MS**4485, 4492/4501, 4503/**MS**4525, **MS**4532/**MS**4539, 4543/**MS**4552, 4555/**MS**4561, 4566/**MS**4587 and 4597/4612

YB4613*a*	Yearbook (*sold for £199*)	£300

Miniature Sheet Collection

2021 (2 Nov). Comprises Nos. **MS**4476, **MS**4485, **MS**4525, **MS**4532, **MS**4539, **MS**4552, **MS**4561, **MS**4574, **MS**4587 and **MS**4613

MS4613*a* Miniature Sheet Collection (*sold for £59*)	90·00	

3682 London, July 1969

3683 East Rutherford, New Jersey, USA, August 2019

3684 Rotterdam, Netherlands, August 1995

3685 Tokyo, Japan, March 1995

3686 New York, July 1972

3687 Oslo, Norway, May 2014

3688 Hertfordshire, August 1976

3689 Dusseldorf, Germany, October 2017

3690 Rolling Stones and Tour Posters

(Des Baxter & Bailey. Litho ISP Cartor)

2022 (20 Jan). The Rolling Stones (1st issue). Multicoloured. Two phosphor bands. Perf 14 (No. 4614/4621) or 14½ (No. **MS**4622).

4614	**3682**	(1st) London, July 1969...........................	1·25	1·25
		a. Horiz strip of 4. Nos. 4614/4617.....	5·00	5·00
		b. Booklet pane. Nos. 4614/4615 and 4618/4619 with margins all round..	7·25	
4615	**3683**	(1st) East Rutherford, New Jersey, USA, August 2019.....................................	1·25	1·25
4616	**3684**	(1st) Rotterdam, Netherlands, August 1995..	1·25	1·25
		b. Booklet pane. Nos. 4616/4617 and 4620/4621 with margins all round..	7·25	
4617	**3685**	(1st) Tokyo, Japan, March 1995...............	1·25	1·25
4618	**3686**	£1·70 New York, July 1972........................	2·50	2·50
		a. Horiz strip of 4. Nos. 4618/4621.....	10·00	10·00
4619	**3687**	£1·70 Oslo, Norway, May 2014.................	2·50	2·50

4620	**3688**	£1·70 Hertfordshire, August 1976............	2·50	2·50
4621	**3689**	£1·70 Dusseldorf, Germany, October 2017..	2·50	2·50
		Set of 8..	13·50	13·50
		Set of 2 Gutter Strips of 8...........................	27·00	
		First Day Cover (Tallents House)...................		16·00
		First Day Cover (Dartford).............................		16·00
		Presentation Pack (PO Pack No. 611) (Nos. 4614/4621 and **MS**4622)................	23·00	
		PHQ Cards (set of 13) (495).........................	8·25	24·00
		Souvenir Folder (Nos. 4617/4621 and **MS**4622) (originally sold for £24·99).........................	35·00	

MS4622 202×74 mm. **3690** (1st) The Rolling Stones; (1st) The Rolling Stones; £1·70 Posters for Tour of Europe, 1974 and Tour of the Americas, 1975; £1·70 Posters for UK Tour, 1971 and American Tour, 1981.

....	7·25	7·25
First Day Cover (Tallents House)...................		9·50
First Day Cover (Dartford).............................		9·50

Nos. 4614/4617 and 4618/4621 were each printed together, *se-tenant*, as horizontal strips of four in sheets of 60 (2 panes 4×6).

Booklet panes Nos. 4614b and 4616b come from the Rolling Stones £20·85 booklet, No. DY41.

A Hyde Park fan sheet containing No. 4614×3 was originally sold for £7.

A Voodoo Lounge fan sheet containing No. 4617×3 was originally sold for £7.

The 13 PHQ cards show the 12 individual stamps, including those from No. **MS**4622, and the complete miniature sheet.

3691 The Rolling Stones

3692 The Rolling Stones

3693 Posters for Tour of Europe, 1974 and Tour of the Americas, 1975

3694 Posters for UK Tour, 1971 and American Tour, 1981

(Des Baxter & Bailey. Litho ISP Cartor)

2022 (20 Jan). The Rolling Stones (2nd issue). Multicoloured. Two phosphor bands. Perf 14½.

4623	**3691**	(1st) The Rolling Stones...........................	1·50	1·50
		a. Booklet pane. Nos. 4623/4626 with margins all round.....................	9·00	9·00
4624	**3692**	(1st) The Rolling Stones...........................	1·50	1·50
4625	**3693**	£1·70 Posters for Tour of Europe, 1974 and Tour of the Americas, 1975......	3·00	3·00
4626	**3694**	£1·70 Posters for UK Tour, 1971 and American Tour, 1981.......................	3·00	3·00
		Set of 4..	9·00	9·00

Nos. 4623/4626 come from No. **MS**4622 and the £20·85 premium booklet, No. DY41.

3695 Queen Elizabeth II at Headquarters of MI5, London, February 2020

3696 Queen Elizabeth II and Duke of Edinburgh, Washington, USA, October 1957

3697 Queen Elizabeth II on Walkabout in Worcester, April 1980

3698 Trooping the Colour, London, June 1978

3699 Leaving Provincial Museum of Alberta, Edmonton, Canada, May 2005

3700 During Silver Jubilee celebrations, Camberwell, June 1977

3701 At Victoria Park, St Vincent, February 1966

3702 Order of the Garter Ceremony, Windsor, June 1999

(Des Kate Stephens. Litho ISP Walsall)

2022 (4 Feb). Platinum Jubilee. Multicoloured. Two phosphor bands. Perf 14½.

4627	**3695**	(1st) Queen Elizabeth II at headquarters of MI5, London, February 2020...................................	1·25	1·25
		a. Horiz strip of 4. Nos. 4627/4630.....	5·00	5·00
		b. Booklet pane. Nos. 4627, 4630/4631 and 4634 with margins all round............................	7·25	
4628	**3696**	(1st) Queen Elizabeth II and Duke of Edinburgh, Washington, USA, October 1957.................................	1·25	1·25
		b. Booklet pane. Nos. 4628/4629 and 4632/4633 with margins all round...	7·25	
4629	**3697**	(1st) Queen Elizabeth II on walkabout in Worcester, April 1980..................	1·25	1·25
4630	**3698**	(1st) Trooping the Colour, London, June 1978................................	1·25	1·25
4631	**3699**	£1·70 Leaving Provincial Museum of Alberta, Edmonton, Canada, May 2005..	2·50	2·50
		a. Horiz strip of 4. Nos. 4631/4634.....	10·00	10·00

4632	**3700**	£1·70 During Silver Jubilee celebrations, Camberwell, June 1977...................	2·50	2·50
4633	**3701**	£1·70 At Victoria Park, St Vincent, February 1966..............................	2·50	2·50
4634	**3702**	£1·70 Order of the Garter ceremony, Windsor, June 1999........................	2·50	2·50
Set of 8..			13·50	13·50
Set of 2 Gutter Strips of 8..			27·00	
First Day Cover (Tallents House)..................................				15·00
First Day Cover (London SW1).....................................				15·00
Presentation Pack (PO Pack No. 612)......................			15·00	
PHQ Cards (set of 8) (496)..			5·00	14·00

Nos. 4627/4630 and 4631/4634 were each printed together, *se-tenant*, as horizontal strips of four in sheets of 48 (2 panes 4×6).

Booklet panes Nos. 4627b and 4628b come from the £19·50 Platinum Jubilee booklet, No. DY42.

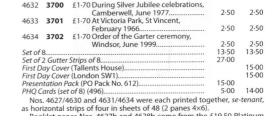

3703 The Stamp Designs of David Gentleman

(Des Hat-trick design. Litho ISP)

2022 (18 Feb). The Stamp Designs of David Gentleman. Multicoloured. One centre band (2nd) or two bands (others). Perf 14½.

MS4635 202×74 mm. **3703** (2nd) 1962 3d. National Productivity Year; (2nd) 1969 9d. British Ships; (1st) 1973 9p. British Trees; (1st) 1976 8½p. Social Reformers; £1·70 1966 6d. 900th Anniversary of the Battle of Hastings; £1·70 4d. 1965 25th Anniversary of the Battle of Britain...........................	9·25	9·25
First Day Cover (Tallents House)..		10·50
First Day Cover (London NW1)...		10·50
Presentation Pack (PO Pack No. 613)...................................	9·50	
PHQ Cards (set of 7) (497)..	4·50	9·50

No. **MS**4236 additionally inscribed 'London 2022 19 to 26 February' was only available at that exhibition (*Price* £11).

3704 Arsenal Players Charlie George and Frank McLintock Parading FA Cup, 1971

3705 Crowds on Pitch at Wembley Stadium During 1923 Cup Final

3706 West Bromwich Albion Supporters at 1968 Cup Final

3707 Keith Houchen Equalises for Coventry City Against Tottenham Hotspur, 1987 Final

3708 Lincoln City Reach Quarter Finals, 2017 (FA Cup Upsets)

3709 King George VI and Queen Elizabeth Present FA Cup to Sunderland Captain Raich Carter, 1937

3710 The FA Cup

(Des The Chase. Litho ISP Cartor)

2022 (8 Mar). The FA Cup. Multicoloured. Two phosphor bands. Perf 14½ (Nos. 4636/4641) or 14 (No. **MS**4642).

4636	**3704**	(1st) Arsenal Players Charlie George and Frank McLintock parading FA Cup, 1971......	1·25	1·25
		a. Vert pair. Nos. 4636/4637.............	2·50	2·50
4637	**3705**	(1st) Crowds on pitch at Wembley Stadium during 1923 Cup Final......	1·25	1·25
4638	**3706**	£1·70 West Bromwich Albion Supporters at 1968 Cup Final........	2·50	2·50
		a. Vert pair. Nos. 4638/4639.........	5·00	5·00
4639	**3707**	£1·70 Keith Houchen equalises for Coventry City, 1987 Final...........	2·50	2·50
4640	**3708**	£2·55 Lincoln City reach Quarter Finals, 2017 (FA Cup Upsets)............	3·50	3·50
		a. Vert pair. Nos. 4640/4641..........	7·00	7·00
4641	**3709**	£2·55 King George VI and Queen Elizabeth present FA Cup, 1937......	3·50	3·50
Set of 6..........			13·00	13·00
Set of 3 Gutter Pairs (only 2 stamps in each pair).............			15·00	
First Day Cover (Tallents House).........................				15·00
First Day Cover (Wembley).................................				15·00
Presentation Pack (PO Pack No. 614) (Nos. 4636/4641 and **MS**4642)........................			22·00	
PHQ Cards (set of 11) (498)...........................			6·00	22·00

MS4642 202×74 mm. **3710** (1st) Supporter's memorabilia; (1st) Winners' medal and trophy; £1·70 Official match-day items; £1·70 Cup Final souvenirs........................

	7·25	7·25
First Day Cover (Tallents House)...........................		9·00
First Day Cover (Wembley).................................		9·00

Nos. 4636/4637, 4638/4639 and 4640/4641 were each printed together, se-tenant, in vertical pairs in sheets of 36 (2 panes 3×6).

The 11 PHQ cards show the ten individual stamps including those from No. **MS**4642 and the complete miniature sheet.

3711 NHS Workers (Jessica Roberts)

3712 Captain Sir Tom Moore (Shachow Ali)

3713 NHS Hospital Cleaners (Raphael Valle Martin)

3714 NHS/My Mum (Alfie Craddock)

3715 Lab Technician (Logan Pearson)

3716 Delivery Driver (Isabella Grover)

3717 The NHS (Connie Stuart)

3718 Doctors, Nurses (Ishan Bains)

(Des Children's Competition/Royal Mail Design Team. Litho Cartor)

2022 (23 Mar). Heroes of the Covid Pandemic. Winning Entries from Schoolchildren's Stamp Design Competition. Multicoloured. Two phosphor bands. Perf 14×14½.

4643	**3711**	(1st) NHS Workers (Jessica Roberts).......	1·25	1·25
		a. Horiz strip of 4. Nos. 4643/4646.....	5·00	5·00
4644	**3712**	(1st) Captain Sir Tom Moore (Shachow Ali)......................................	1·25	1·25
4645	**3713**	(1st) NHS Hospital Cleaners (Raphael Valle Martin)............................	1·25	1·25
4646	**3714**	(1st) NHS/My Mum (Alfie Craddock)......	1·25	1·25
4647	**3715**	(1st) Lab Technician (Logan Pearson).....	1·25	1·25
		a. Horiz strip of 4. Nos. 4647/4650.....	5·00	5·00
4648	**3716**	(1st) Delivery Driver (Isabella Grover)....	1·25	1·25
4649	**3717**	(1st) The NHS (Connie Stuart).................	1·25	1·25
4650	**3718**	(1st) Doctors, Nurses (Ishan Bains).........	1·25	1·25
Set of 8...........			9·00	9·00
Set of 2 Gutter Strips of 8.............			18·00	
First Day Cover (Tallents House)...........................				11·00
First Day Cover (London EC1)...............................				11·00
Presentation Pack (PO Pack No. 615).................................			10·00	
PHQ Cards (set of 8) (499)..............................			5·00	10·00

Nos. 4243/4246 and 4247/4250 were printed together, se-tenant, as horizontal strips of four in sheets of 48 (2 panes 4×6).

3722 Nightjar (Caprimulgus europaeus)

3723 Pied Flycatcher (Ficedula hypoleuca)

3724 Swift (*Apus apus*)

3725 Yellow Wagtail (*Motacilla flava*)

3726 Arctic Skua (*Stercorarius parasiticus*)

3727 Stone-curlew (*Burhinus oedicnemus*)

3728 Arctic Tern (*Sterna paradisaea*)

3729 Swallow (*Hirundo rustica*)

3730 Turtle Dove (*Streptopelia turtur*)

3731 Montagu's Harrier (*Circus pygargus*)

(Des Killian Mullarney (illustration) and Hat-trick design. Litho Cartor)

2022 (7 Apr). Migratory Birds. Multicoloured. Two phosphor bands. Perf 14.

4651	**3722**	(1st) Nightjar (*Caprimulgus europaeus*)..	1·25	1·25
		a. Horiz strip of 5. Nos. 4651/4655.....	6·25	6·25
4652	**3723**	(1st) Pied Flycatcher (*Ficedula hypoleuca*)............................	1·25	1·25
4653	**3724**	(1st) Swift (*Apus apus*)............................	1·25	1·25
4654	**3725**	(1st) Yellow Wagtail (*Motacilla flava*)......	1·25	1·25
4655	**3726**	(1st) Arctic Skua (*Stercorarius parasiticus*)........................	1·25	1·25
4656	**3727**	(1st) Stone-curlew (*Burhinus oedicnemus*)........................	1·25	1·25
		a. Horiz strip of 5. Nos. 4656/4660.....	6·25	6·25
4657	**3728**	(1st) Arctic Tern (*Sterna paradisaea*).......	1·25	1·25
4658	**3729**	(1st) Swallow (*Hirundo rustica*)................	1·25	1·25
4659	**3730**	(1st) Turtle Dove (*Streptopelia turtur*).....	1·25	1·25
4660	**3731**	(1st) Montagu's Harrier (*Circus pygargus*)............................	1·25	1·25
	Set of 10...		12·50	12·50
	Set of 2 Gutter Strips of 10........................		24·00	
	First Day Cover (Tallents House)..................			15·00
	First Day Cover (Swallownest, Sheffield).........			15·00
	Presentation Pack (PO Pack No. 616)............		14·00	
	PHQ Cards (set of 10) (500).......................		6·25	14·00

Nos. 4651/4655 and 4656/4660 were each printed together, *se-tenant*, as horizontal strips of five in sheets of 50 (2 panes 5×5).

3732 Air Raid Precautions (Protecting Civilians)

3733 Queen Alexandra's Imperial Military Nursing Service (Nursing on the front line)

3734 Auxiliary Territorial Service (Repairing Army Vehicles)

3735 Women's Royal Naval Service (Arming the Fleet)

3736 Factory Worker (Powering the War Effort)

3737 Codebreakers (Deciphering Enemy Messages)

3738 Women's Voluntary Services (Supplying Military Production)

3739 Auxiliary Territorial Service (Lighting the Way to Victory)

3740 Women's Auxiliary Air Force (Maintaining RAF Aircraft)

3741 Women's Land Army (Meeting Britain's Demand)

3742 Spitfire Women, Ferry Pilots of the Air Transport Auxiliary

(Des Supple Studio. Litho ISP Cartor)

2022 (5 May). Unsung Heroes. Women of World War II (1st issue). Multicoloured. Two phosphor bands. Perf 14½ (Nos. 4661/4670) or 14 (No. **MS**4671).

4661	**3732**	(1st) Air Raid Precautions (Protecting Civilians)...............................	1·25	1·25
		a. Horiz strip of 5. Nos. 4661/4665.....	6·25	6·25
		b. Booklet pane. Nos. 4661/4663 and 4666/4668 with margins all round....................................	9·75	
4662	**3733**	(1st) Queen Alexandra's Imperial Military Nursing Service (Nursing on the front line)............................	1·25	1·25
4663	**3734**	(1st) Auxiliary Territorial Service (Repairing Army Vehicles)...............	1·25	1·25
4664	**3735**	(1st) Women's Royal Naval Service (Arming the Fleet)..........................	1·25	1·25
		b. Booklet pane. Nos. 4664/4665 and 4669/4670 with margins all round....................................	6·50	
4665	**3736**	(1st) Factory Worker (Powering the War Effort)...............................	1·25	1·25
4666	**3737**	(1st) Codebreakers (Deciphering Enemy Messages)......................	1·25	1·25
		a. Horiz strip of 5. Nos. 4666/4670.....	6·25	6·25
4667	**3738**	(1st) Women's Voluntary Services (Supplying Military Production).....	1·25	1·25
4668	**3739**	(1st) Auxiliary Territorial Service (Lighting the Way to Victory).........	1·25	1·25
4669	**3740**	(1st) Women's Auxiliary Air Force (Maintaining RAF Aircraft)...............	1·25	1·25
4670	**3741**	(1st) Women's Land Army (Meeting Britain's Demand)............................	1·25	1·25
Set of 10........................			12·50	12·50
Set of 2 Gutter Strips of 10..........................			24·00	
First Day Cover (Tallents House).....................				15·00
First Day Cover (London SW1).........................				15·00
Presentation Pack (PO Pack No. 617)................			14·00	
PHQ Cards (set of 15) (501)............................			8·75	15·00
MS4671 202×74 mm. **3742** (1st) Pilots meet in their Ferry Pool briefing room; (1st) Pilot climbing into the cockpit of a Supermarine Spitfire; £1·85 Pilot completing her post-flight paperwork in a Lockheed Hudson; £1·85 Pilots of the No. 5 Ferry Pool disembarking from an Avro Anson....................			7·50	7·50
First Day Cover (Tallents House).....................				9·50
First Day Cover (London SW1).........................				9·50

The 15 PHQ cards show the 14 individual stamps including those from No. **MS**4671 and the complete miniature sheet.

Booklet panes Nos. 4661b and 4664b come from the £20·75 Unsung Heroes: Women of World War II booklet, No. DY43.

3743 Pilots meet in their Ferry Pool Briefing Room

3744 Pilot climbing into the Cockpit of a Supermarine Spitfire

3745 Pilot completing her Post-Flight Paperwork in a Lockheed Hudson

3746 Pilots of the No. 5 Ferry Pool disembarking from an Avro Anson

(Des Supple Studio. Litho ISP Cartor)

2022 (5 May). Unsung Heroes. Women of World War II (2nd issue). Two phosphor bands. Perf 14.

4672	**3743**	(1st) Pilots meet in their Ferry Pool Briefing Room....................	1·50	1·50
		a. Booklet pane. Nos. 4672/4675 with margins all round.............	9·50	
4673	**3744**	(1st) Pilot climbing into the Cockpit of a Supermarine Spitfire....................	1·50	1·50

4674	**3745**	£1·85 Pilot completing her Post-Flight Paperwork in a Lockheed Hudson	2·75	2·75
4675	**3746**	£1·85 Pilots of the No. 5 Ferry Pool disembarking from an Avro Anson.................................	2·75	2·75
Set of 4........................			8·50	8·50

Nos. 4672/4675 were issued in No. **MS**4671 and booklet pane No. 4672a from the £20·75 Unsung Heroes. Women of World War II booklet, No. DY43.

3747 Siamese Cat Grooming

3748 Tabby Cat Stalking

3749 Ginger Cat Playing

3750 British Shorthair Cat Sleeping

3751 Maine Coon Cat Staring

3752 Black and White Cat on Alert

3753 Bengal Cat being Curious

3754 Tabby and White Cat Stretching

(Des Studio Up. Litho ISP Cartor)

2022 (9 June). Cats. Multicoloured. One centre phosphor band (2nd) or two phosphor bands (others). Perf 14.

4676	**3747**	(2nd) Siamese cat grooming...................	90	90
		a. Vert pair. Nos. 4676/4677...............	1·75	1·75
4677	**3748**	(2nd) Tabby cat stalking........................	90	90
4678	**3749**	(1st) Ginger cat playing........................	1·25	1·25
		a. Vert pair. Nos. 4678/4679...............	2·50	2·50
4679	**3750**	(1st) British Shorthair cat sleeping.........	1·25	1·25
4680	**3751**	£1·85 Maine Coon cat staring....................	2·50	2·50
		a. Vert pair. Nos. 4680/4681...............	5·00	5·00
4681	**3752**	£1·85 Black and white cat on alert...........		
4682	**3753**	£2·55 Bengal cat being curious................	3·50	3·50
		a. Vert pair. Nos. 4682/4683...............	7·00	7·00
4683	**3754**	£2·55 Tabby and white cat stretching......	3·50	3·50
Set of 8........................			14·50	14·50
Set of 4 Gutter Pairs.....................................			29·00	
First Day Cover (Tallents House).....................				17·00
First Day Cover (Purfleet)...............................				17·00
Presentation Pack (PO Pack No. 618)................			17·00	
PHQ Cards (set of 8) (502)............................			4·75	16·00

Nos. 4676/4677, 4678/4679, 4680/4681 and 4682/4683 were each printed together, se-tenant, as vertical pairs in sheets of 30 (2 panes 5×6).

A collector's sheet containing stamps as Nos. 4676/4677, 4678/4679, each×2 and Nos. 4680/4683 but self-adhesive with labels was originally sold for £15·20.

3743 Pilots meet in their Ferry Pool Briefing Room

3755 Couple Kissing

3756 Marchers in Rally and 'LOVE' Slogan

3757 Three Couples and Pink, White and Blue Transgender Pride Flag

3758 Rally with Marcher Carrying Intersex Progress Pride Flag

3759 Marchers with 'GAY PRIDE' and 'LESBIANS UNITE' Banners

3760 Rally with Motorcyclist and 'GLAD TO BE GAY' Placard

3761 Couple Kissing, 'Gay Liberation' and Rainbow Flag

3762 Drag Queen, Marchers Carrying Rainbow Placard and 'LOVE ALWAYS WINS' Slogan on Flag

(Des Sofie Birkin (illustration) and NB Studio. Litho ISP Cartor)

2022 (1 July). Pride. Multicoloured. Two phosphor bands. Perf 14.

4684	**3755**	(1st) Couple kissing..........................	1·25	1·25
		a. Horiz pair. Nos. 4684/4685.............	2·50	2·50
4685	**3756**	(1st) Marchers in rally and 'LOVE' slogan....................................	1·25	1·25
4686	**3757**	(1st) Three couples and pink, white and blue Transgender Pride flag....	1·25	1·25
		a. Horiz pair. Nos. 4686/4687.............	2·50	2·50
4687	**3758**	(1st) Rally with marcher carrying Intersex Progress Pride flag............	1·25	1·25
4688	**3759**	£1·85 Marchers with 'GAY PRIDE' and 'LESBIANS UNITE' banners..............	2·50	2·50
		a. Horiz pair. Nos. 4688/4689.............	5·00	5·00
4689	**3760**	£1·85 Rally with motorcyclist and 'GLAD TO BE GAY' placard.........................	2·50	2·50
4690	**3761**	£1·85 Couple kissing, 'Gay Liberation' and rainbow flag............................	2·50	2·50
		a. Horiz pair. Nos. 4690/4691.............	5·00	5·00
4691	**3762**	£1·85 Drag queen, marchers carrying rainbow placard and 'LOVE ALWAYS WINS' slogan on flag.........	2·50	2·50
Set of 8...			13·50	13·50
Set of 4 Gutter Pairs...			27·00	
First Day Cover (Tallents House)...............................				16·00
First Day Cover (London WC2)...................................				16·00
Presentation Pack (PO Pack No. 619)......................			16·00	
PHQ Cards (set of 8) (503)...................................			4·75	15·00

Nos. 4684/4685, 4686/4687, 4688/4689 and 4690/4691 were each printed together, *se-tenant*, as horizontal pairs in sheets of 60 (2 panes 6×5).

A collector's sheet containing stamps as Nos. 4684/4691 but self-adhesive with labels was originally sold for £12·40.

3763 Diving

3764 Boxing

3765 Para Table Tennis

3766 Para Powerlifting

3767 Artistic Gymnastics

3768 Mountain Biking

3769 Athletics   **3770** Wheelchair Basketball

(Des Charis Tsevis (illustration) and Interbang. Litho ISP Cartor)

2022 (28 July). Commonwealth Games, Birmingham. Multicoloured. Two
   phosphor bands. Perf 14½.

4692	**3763**	(1st) Diving..................................	1·25	1·25
		a. Horiz strip of 4. Nos. 4692/4695.....	5·00	5·00
4693	**3764**	(1st) Boxing.................................	1·25	1·25
4694	**3765**	(1st) Para table tennis..............	1·25	1·25
4695	**3766**	(1st) Para powerlifting..............	1·25	1·25
4696	**3767**	£1·85 Artistic gymnastics............	2·50	2·50
		a. Horiz strip of 4. Nos. 4696/4699..	10·00	10·00
4697	**3768**	£1·85 Mountain biking................	2·50	2·50
4698	**3769**	£1·85 Athletics...........................	2·50	2·50
4699	**3770**	£1·85 Wheelchair basketball..........	2·50	2·50
Set of 8..			13·50	13·50
Set of 2 Gutter Strips of 8....................			27·00	
First Day Cover (Tallents House)...............				16·00
First Day Cover (Birmingham)..................				16·00
Presentation Pack (PO Pack No. 620)........			16·00	
PHQ Cards (set of 8) (504).....................			4·75	15·00

Nos. 4692/4695 and 4696/4699 were each printed together, *se-tenant*,
as horizontal strips of four in sheets of 48 (2 panes 4×6).

3771 Optimus Prime

3772 Megatron

3773 Bumblebee

3774 Starscream

3775 Grimlock

3776 Shockwave

3777 Arcee

3778 Soundwave

3779 The Dinobots

(Des The Chase. Illustrations Andrew Wildman (pencils), Stephen
Baskerville (inks) and John-Paul Bove (colours). Litho Cartor)

2022 (1 Sept). Transformers (1st issue). Multicoloured. One centre band
   (2nd) or two bands (others).

(a) Ordinary gum. Perf 14.

4700	**3771**	(1st) Optimus Prime....................	1·25	1·25
		a. Horiz pair. Nos. 4700/4701..............	2·50	2·50
		b. Booklet pane. Nos. 4700/4703		
		with margins all round..................	5·50	
4701	**3772**	(1st) Megatron.............................	1·25	1·25
4702	**3773**	(1st) Bumblebee...........................	1·25	1·25
		a. Horiz pair. Nos. 4702/4703..............	2·50	2·50
4703	**3774**	(1st) Starscream..........................	1·25	1·25
4704	**3775**	£1·85 Grimlock.............................	2·50	2·50
		a. Horiz pair. Nos. 4704/4705..............	5·00	5·00
		b. Booklet pane. Nos. 4704/4707		
		with margins all round..................	11·00	
4705	**3776**	£1·85 Shockwave..........................	2·50	2·50
4706	**3777**	£1·85 Arcee.................................	2·50	2·50
		a. Horiz pair. Nos. 4706/4707..............	5·00	5·00
4707	**3778**	£1·85 Soundwave..........................	2·50	2·50
Set of 8..			13·50	13·50
Set of 4 Gutter Pairs...........................			27·00	
First Day Cover (Tallents House)...............				16·00
First Day Cover (Arkholme)....................				16·00
Presentation Pack (PO Pack No. 621)........			23·00	
PHQ Cards (set of 14) (505)...................			8·25	16·00

(b) Self-adhesive. Die-cut perf 14.

MS4708 210×68 mm. **3779** (2nd) Swoop (27×36 mm);
   (1st) Slug (35×35 mm); (1st) Sludge (27×36 mm);
   (1st) Grimlock (35×35 mm); £1·85 Snarl (35×35
   mm)... 7·50   7·50
First Day Cover (Tallents House)........................... 10·00
First Day Cover (Arkholme)................................. 10·00

Nos. 4700/4701, 4702/4703, 4704/4705 and 4706/4707 were each
printed together, *se-tenant*, as horizontal pairs in sheets of 60 (2 panes
6×5).

A collector's sheet containing stamps as Nos. 4700/4707 but self-
adhesive with labels was originally sold for £12·40.

An Optimus Prime fan sheet containing No. 4700×3 was originally
sold for £7.

A Bumblebee fan sheet containing No. 4702×3 was originally sold for £7.

The 14 PHQ cards show the 13 individual stamps including those from
No. **MS**4708 and the complete miniature sheet.

Booklet panes Nos. 4700b and 4704b come from the £21·25 Transformers
booklet, No. DY44.

3780 Swoop

3781 Slug

3782 Sludge

3783 Grimlock

3784 Snarl

(Des The Chase. Illustrations Andrew Wildman (pencils), Stephen Baskerville (inks) and John-Paul Bove (colours). Litho Cartor)

2022 (1 Sept). Transformers (2nd issue). Multicoloured. Self-adhesive. One centre band (2nd) or two bands (others). Die-cut perf 14.

4709	**3780**	(2nd) Swoop...................................	1·00	1·00
		a. Booklet pane. Nos. 4709/4710........	2·50	
4710	**3781**	(1st) Slug......................................	1·50	1·50
4711	**3782**	(1st) Sludge..................................	1·50	1·50
		a. Booklet pane. Nos. 4711/4713........	5·75	
4712	**3783**	(1st) Grimlock...............................	1·50	1·50
4713	**3784**	£1·85 Snarl....................................	2·75	2·75
Set of 5........			8·25	8·25

Nos. 4709/4713 come from booklet panes Nos. 4709a and 4711a from the £21·25 Transformers booklet, No. DY44, and also No. **MS**4722.

3785 Aviation Operations

3786 Cold-weather Operations

3787 Mountain Operations

3788 Arid-Climate Operations

3789 Commando Training

3790 Band Service

3791 Amphibious Operations

3792 Maritime Security Operations

3793 Royal Marines Uniforms

(Des Osborne Ross. Litho International Security Printers)

2022 (29 Sept). Royal Marines. Multicoloured. Two phosphor bands. Perf 14½×14.

4714	**3785**	(1st) Aviation Operations.........................	1·25	1·25
		a. Horiz strip of 4. Nos. 4714/4717.....	5·00	5·00
4715	**3786**	(1st) Cold-weather Operations...............	1·25	1·25
4716	**3787**	(1st) Mountain Operations.....................	1·25	1·25
4717	**3788**	(1st) Arid-Climate Operations................	1·25	1·25
4718	**3789**	£1·85 Commando Training......................	2·50	2·50
		a. Horiz strip of 4. Nos. 4718/4721.....	10·00	10·00
4719	**3790**	£1·85 Band Service................................	2·50	2·50
4720	**3791**	£1·85 Amphibious Operations................	2·50	2·50
4721	**3792**	£1·85 Maritime Security Operations........	2·50	2·50
Set of 8........			13·50	13·50
Set of 2 Gutter Strips of 8........			27·00	
First Day Cover (Tallents House)........				16·00
First Day Cover (Lympstone, Exmouth).............				16·00
Presentation Pack (PO Pack No. 622)........			23·00	
PHQ Cards (set of 13) (506)........			7·50	16·00
First Day Cover (Lympstone, Exmouth)........				9·50

MS4722 115×89 mm. **3793** (1st) Sea Soldier, Duke of York and Albany's Maritime Regiment of Foot, 1664; (1st) Grenadier, Chatham Division, His Majesty's Marine Forces, 1775; £1·85 Sergeant, 4th Battalion, Royal Marines, 1918; £1·85 Officer, 48th Royal Marine Commando, 1944...........

	7·50	7·50
First Day Cover (Tallents House)........		9·50

Nos. 4714/4717 and 4718/4721 were each printed together, *se-tenant*, as horizontal strips four in sheets of 24 (2 panes 4×6).

Types **3794/3798** are vacant.
The 13 PHQ cards show the 12 individual stamps including those from No. **MS**4722 and the complete miniature sheet.

3799 Rocky and Ginger (*Chicken Run*)

3800 Feathers McGraw (*The Wrong Trousers*)

3801 *Wallace and Gromit*

3802 Frank the Tortoise (*Creature Comforts*)

3803 Timmy (*Shaun the Sheep, Timmy Time*)

3804 Morph and Chas (*The Amazing Adventures af Morph & more*)

3805 Robin (*Robin Robin*, 2021)

3806 Shaun and Blitzer (*Shaun the Sheep*)

3807 Wallace and Gromit Cracking Moments

(Des Studio Up (Nos. 4723/4730) or Aardman Animations and Studio Up (No. **MS**4731). Litho Cartor)

2022 (19 Oct). Aardman Classics. Multicoloured. Self-adhesive. One centre phosphor band (2nd) or 'all-over' phosphor (others). Die-cut perf 13½×14 (Nos. 4723/4730) or 14 (No. **MS**4731).

4723	**3799**	(2nd) Rocky and Ginger (*Chicken Run*).....	90	90
4724	**3800**	(2nd) Feathers McGraw (*The Wrong Trousers*)........................	90	90
4725	**3801**	(1st) *Wallace and Gromit*........................	1·25	1·25
4726	**3802**	(1st) Frank the Tortoise (*Creature Comforts*).............................	1·25	1·25
4727	**3803**	£1·85 Timmy (*Shaun the Sheep, Timmy Time*)........................	2·50	2·50
4728	**3804**	£1·85 Morph and Chas (*The Amazing Adventures of Morph & more*)............	2·50	2·50
4729	**3805**	£2·55 Robin (*Robin Robin*, 2021)	3·50	3·50
4730	**3806**	£2·55 Shaun and Bitzer (*Shaun the Sheep*)	3·50	3·50
Set of 8............................			14·50	14·50
First Day Cover (Tallents House)...............				17·00
First Day Cover (Bristol).......................				17·00
Presentation Pack (PO Pack 623).............			24·00	
PHQ Cards (set of 13) (507)...................			7·50	17·00

MS4731 192×74 mm. **3807** (1st) *A Close Shave* (vert); (1st) *A Matter of Loaf and Death*; £1·85 *The Wrong Trousers*; £1·85 *A Grand Day Out*...................... 7·50 7·50
First Day Cover (Tallents House)........................ 9·50
First Day Cover (Bristol)........................ 9·50

Nos. 4723/4724, 4725/4726, 4727/4728 and 4729/4730 were each printed together as horizontal pairs in sheets of 60 (2 panes 6×5).

The 13 PHQ cards show the 12 individual stamps including those from No. **MS**4731 and the complete miniature sheet.

3808 The Annunciation

3809 Holy Family

3810 Journey to Bethlehem

3811 Angel

3812 Angel and Shepherds

3813 Magi

(Des Baxter & Bailey. Gravure Cartor)

2022 (3 Nov). Christmas. Nativity Illustrations by Katie Ponder. Multicoloured. Self-adhesive. One centre phosphor band (No. 4732) or two bands (others). Die-cut perf 15×14½.

4732	**3808**	(2nd) The Annunciation......................	90	90
		a. Booklet pane. No. 4732×8..............	8·25	
4733	**3809**	(1st) Holy Family......................	1·00	1·00
		a. Booklet pane. No. 4733×8..............	12·00	
4734	**3810**	(2nd Large) Journey to Bethlehem........	1·10	1·10
4735	**3811**	(1st Large) Angel..........................	1·40	1·40
4736	**3812**	£1·85 Angel and Shepherds.................	2·50	2·50
4737	**3813**	£2·55 Magi..........................	3·50	3·50
Set of 6..................................			14·00	14·00
First Day Cover (Tallents House).................				16·00
First Day Cover (Bethlehem, Llandeilo).................				16·00
Presentation Pack (PO Pack No. 624)..............			16·00	
PHQ Cards (set of 7) (508).....................			4·25	15·00
MS4738 179×74 mm. Nos. 4732/4737............			15·00	15·00
First Day Cover (Tallents House).................				17·00
First Day Cover (Bethlehem, Llandeilo).................				15·00

Nos. 4732/4737 were each issued in counter sheets of 50.

The 2nd class No. 4732 was issued in booklets of 8 originally sold for £5·44.

The 1st class No. 4733 was issued in booklets of 8 originally sold for £7·60.

The 2nd class, 1st class, £1·85 and £2·55 values were also issued in sheets of 20 containing eight 2nd class, eight 1st class, and two each of the £1·70 and £2·55 values. These sheets were printed in lithography instead of gravure.

The seven PHQ cards show the individual stamps and the complete miniature sheet.

3814 Queen Elizabeth II, 1952 (Dorothy Wilding)

3815 Queen Elizabeth II, 1968 (Cecil Beaton)

3816 Queen Elizabeth II, 1984 (Yousef Karsh)

3817 Queen Elizabeth II, 1996 (Tim Graham)

(Des Kate Stephens. Litho Cartor)

2022 (10 Nov). Queen Elizabeth II (1926–2022) Commemoration. Agate, grey and black. One phosphor band at right (2nd) or 'all-over' phosphor (others). Perf 14½×14.

4739	**3814**	(2nd) Queen Elizabeth II, 1952.................	90	90
4740	**3815**	(1st) Queen Elizabeth II, 1968.................	1·25	1·25
4741	**3816**	£1·85 Queen Elizabeth II, 1984.................	2·50	2·50
4742	**3817**	£2·55 Queen Elizabeth II, 1996.................	3·50	3·50
Set of 4..........................			7·25	7·25
Set of 4 Gutter Pairs.........................			14·50	
First Day Cover (Tallents House).................				9·50
First Day Cover (Windsor).....................				9·50
Presentation Pack (PO Pack No. M27)..............			9·50	
PHQ Cards (set of 4) (D35).....................			2·25	9·50

3818 Head of the King

3819 Inlaid Fan

3820 Gold Mask

3821 Falcon Pendant

3822 Lion Couch (detail)

3823 Throne (detail)

3824 Boat Model

3825 Guardian Statue

3826 Discovering Tutankhamen's Tomb

(Des Andy Altmann. Litho Cartor)

2022 (24 Nov). Tutankhamun (1st issue). Multicoloured. One phosphor band at left (2nd) or two phosphor bands (others). Perf 14×14½ (Nos. 4743/4750) or 14 (No. **MS**4751).

4743	**3818**	(2nd) Head of the King.............................	90	90
		a. Horiz pair. Nos. 4743/4744..............	1·75	1·75
		b. Booklet pane. Nos. 4743/4744 and 4749/4750 with margins all round..	11·00	
4744	**3819**	(2nd) Inlaid fan...	90	90
4745	**3820**	(1st) Gold mask..	1·25	1·25
		a. Horiz pair. Nos. 4745/4746..............	2·50	2·50
		b. Booklet pane. Nos. 4745/4748 and 4747/4748 with margins all round..	9·00	
4746	**3821**	(1st) Falcon pendant................................	1·25	1·25
4747	**3822**	£1·85 Lion couch (detail)........................	2·50	2·50
		a. Horiz pair. Nos. 4747/4748..............	5·00	5·00
4748	**3823**	£1·85 Throne (detail)...............................	2·50	2·50
4749	**3824**	£2·55 Boat model......................................	3·50	3·50
		a. Horiz pair. Nos. 4749/4750..............	7·00	7·00
4750	**3825**	£2·55 Guardian statue.............................	3·50	3·50
		Set of 8..	13·00	13·00
		Set of 4 Gutter Strips of 4.......................	26·00	
		First Day Cover (Tallents House)...............................		15·00
		First Day Cover (Oxford)...		15·00

Presentation Pack (PO Pack No. 625).....................................	23·00	
PHQ Cards (set of 13) (509)...	7·50	15·00

MS4751 146×74 mm. **3826** (1st) Objects in the antechamber; (1st) Head of the outermost coffin; £1·85 Examining the innermost coffin; £1·85 Moving small shrine to laboratory...................... 7·50 7·50
First Day Cover (Tallents House)... 9·50
First Day Cover (Oxford)... 9·50

Nos. 4743/4744, 4745/4746, 4747/4748 and 4749/4750 were printed together, se-tenant, as horizontal pairs in sheets of 60 (2 panes 6×5).

The 13 PHQ cards show the 12 individual stamps including those from No. **MS**4751 and the complete miniature sheet.

Booklet panes Nos. 4743b and 4745b come from the £21·55 Tutankhamun booklet, No. DY45.

Nos. 4752/4755 come from No. **MS**4651 and the £21·55 Tutankhamun booklet, No. DY45.

Collectors Pack

2022 (24 Nov). Comprises Nos. 4614/**MS**4622, 4627/**MS**4671, 4676/**MS**4708, 4714/4737 and 4739/**MS**4751
CP4751a   Collectors Pack (Pack No. 626) (sold for £204)................................. £300

Post Office Yearbook

2022 (24 Nov). Comprises Nos. 4614/**MS**4622, 4627/**MS**4671, 4676/**MS**4708, 4714/4737 and 4739/**MS**4751
YB4751a   Yearbook (sold for £224)...................... £325

Miniature Sheet Collection

2022 (24 Nov). Comprises Nos. **MS**4622, **MS**4635, **MS**4642, **MS**4671, **MS**4708, **MS**4722, **MS**4731, **MS**4738 and **MS**4751
MS4751a Miniature Sheet Collection (sold for £55).......... 85·00

3827 Objects in the Antechamber

3828 Head of the Outermost Coffin

3829 Examining the Innermost Coffin

3830 Moving Small Shrine to Laboratory

(Litho Cartor)

2022 (24 Nov). Tutankhamun (2nd issue). Two phosphor bands. Perf 14.

4752	**3827**	(1st) Objects in the antechamber............	1·25	1·25
		a. Booklet pane. Nos. 4752/4755 with margins all round....................	7·50	
4753	**3828**	(1st) Head of the outermost coffin.........	1·25	1·25
4754	**3829**	£1·85 Examining the innermost coffin.....	2·50	2·50
4755	**3830**	£1·85 Moving small shrine to laboratory	2·50	2·50
		Set of 4..	7·50	7·50

Nos. 4752/4755 come from the £21·55 Tutankhamun booklet, No. DY45, and also No. **MS**4751.

3831 Steve Harris, Vancouver, June 2010

3832 Bruce Dickinson, Hammersmith Odeon, London, May 1983

3833 Dave Murray, Adrian Smith and Steve Harris, Pamplona, Spain, September 1988

3834 Nicko McBrain, Quito, Ecuador, March 2009

3835 Dave Murray, Bruce Dickinson and Janick Gers, Rio de Janeiro, January 2001

3836 Adrian Smith and Steve Harris, Helsinki, May 2018

3837 Iron Maiden, Twickenham Stadium, London, July 2008

3838 Bruce Dickinson sword fights with Mascot Eddie, Birmingham, August 2018

3839 Eddie the Iron Maiden Mascot

(Litho ISP Cartor)

2023 (12 Jan). Iron Maiden. Multicoloured. Two phosphor bands. Perf 14 (Nos. 4756/4763) or 14×14½ (No. **MS**4764).

4756	**3831**	(1st) Steve Harris, Vancouver, June 2010....................	1·25	1·25
		a. Horiz strip of 4. Nos. 4756/4759.....	5·00	5·00
4757	**3832**	(1st) Bruce Dickinson, Hammersmith Odeon, London, May 1983..............	1·25	1·25
4758	**3833**	(1st) Dave Murray, Adrian Smith and Steve Harris, Pamplona, Spain, September 1988.............................	1·25	1·25
4759	**3834**	(1st) Nicko McBrain, Quito, Ecuador, March 2009....................	1·25	1·25
4760	**3835**	£1·85 Dave Murray, Bruce Dickinson and Janick Gers, Rio de Janeiro, January 2001..........................	3·00	3·00
		a. Horiz strip of 4. Nos. 4760/4763.....	12·00	12·00
4761	**3836**	£1·85 Adrian Smith and Steve Harris, Helsinki, May 2018.........................	3·00	3·00
4762	**3837**	£1·85 Iron Maiden, Twickenham Stadium, London, July 2008...........	3·00	3·00
4763	**3838**	£1·85 Bruce Dickinson sword fighting with Mascot Eddie, Birmingham, August 2018....................................	3·00	3·00

Set of 8..	17·00	17·00
Set of 2 Gutter Strips of 8...........................	34·00	
First Day Cover (Tallents House)...		19·00
First Day Cover (London E11)..		19·00
Presentation Pack (Nos. 4756/4763 and **MS**4764) (PO. Pack No. 626)...	30·00	
PHQ Cards (set of 13).....................................	9·00	30·00
MS4764 191×74 mm. **3839** (1st) The Trooper Eddie; (1st) Aces High Eddie; £1·85 Iron Maiden Eddie, 1980; £1·85 Senjutsu Eddie..........................	3·00	3·00
First Day Cover (Tallents House)...		11·00
First Day Cover (London E11)..		11·00

Nos. 4756/4759 and 4760/4763 were each printed together, *se-tenant*, as horizontal strips of four in sheets of 48 (2 panes 4×6).

An Iron Maiden Eddie fan sheet containing (1st) The Trooper Eddie; £1·85 Iron Maiden Eddie, 1980; and £1·85 Senjutsu Eddie was originally sold for £7.50. Iron Maiden 'Eddie' and an Iron Maiden 'Live Performances' Collector sheets each containing Nos. 4756/4763 were sold for £12.40 each.

The 13 PHQ cards show the 12 individual stamps, including those from No. **MS**4622, and the complete miniature sheet.

3840 Professor X

3841 Kitty Pryde

3842 Angel

3843 Colossus

3844 Jubilee

3845 Cyclops

3846 Wolverine

3847 Jean Grey

3848 Iceman

3849 Storm

3850 Beast

3851 Rogue

3852 Enemies of the X-Men

(Des Mike McKone (illustration 4765/4776), Lee Garbutt (illustration **MS**4777) Chris Soto (colourist) and Interabang. Litho Cartor)

2023 (16 Feb). X-Men (1st issue). Multicoloured. One band at right (2nd) or two bands (others).

(a) Ordinary gum. P 14½.

4765	**3840**	(2nd) Professor X...	90	90
		a. Horiz strip of 6. Nos. 4765/4770.....	5·50	5·50
		b. Booklet pane. Nos. 4765, 4767, 4770, 4772 and 4774/4775 with margins all round............................	6·50	
4766	**3841**	(2nd) Kitty Pryde..	90	90
		b. Booklet pane. Nos. 4766, 4768/4769, 4771, 4773 and 4776 with margins all round....................	6·50	
4767	**3842**	(2nd) Angel..	90	90
4768	**3843**	(2nd) Colossus..	90	90
4769	**3844**	(2nd) Jubilee..	90	90
4770	**3845**	(2nd) Cyclops...	90	90
4771	**3846**	(1st) Wolverine..	1·25	1·25
		a. Horiz strip of 6. Nos. 4771/4776.....	7·50	7·50
4772	**3847**	(1st) Jean Grey..	1·25	1·25
4773	**3848**	(1st) Iceman..	1·25	1·25
4774	**3849**	(1st) Storm..	1·25	1·25
4775	**3850**	(1st) Beast..	1·25	1·25
4776	**3851**	(1st) Rogue...	1·25	1·25
Set of 12..			13·00	13·00
Set of 2 Gutter Strips of 12................................			26·00	26·00
First Day Cover (Tallents House)...........................				15·00
First Day Cover (Muir of Ord)..............................				15·00
Presentation Pack (Nos. 4765/4776 and **MS**4777) (PO Pack No. 627)...			15·00	
PHQ Cards (set of 18)..			10·00	15·00

(b) Self-adhesive.

MS4777 192×74 mm. **3852** (1st) Juggernaut (p 14½); (1st) Mystique (27×37 mm) (p 14); (1st) Emma Frost (27×37 mm) (p 14); (1st) Sabretooth (p 14½); £1·85 Magneto (p 14½)................ 10·00 10·00
First Day Cover (Tallents House)........................... 12·00
First Day Cover (Muir of Ord).............................. 12·00

Nos. 4765/4770 and 4771/4776 were each printed together, *se-tenant*, as horizontal strips of six in sheets of 60 (2 panes 6×5).

The 18 PHQ cards show the 17 individual stamps, including those from No. **MS**4777, and the complete miniature sheet.

3853 Juggernaut   **3854** Mystique

3855 Emma Frost   **3856** Sabretooth

3857 Magneto

(Litho Cartor)

2023 (16 Feb). X-Men (2nd issue). Multicoloured. Self-adhesive. Two phosphor bands. Perf 14½ (Nos. 4778, 4781/4782) or 14 (Nos. 4779/4780).

4778	**3853**	(1st) Juggernaut.....................................	1·60	1·60
		a. Booklet pane. Nos. 4778/4779 and 4782.................................	6·50	
4779	**3854**	(1st) Mystique...	1·60	1·60
4780	**3855**	(1st) Emma Frost.....................................	1·60	1·60
		a. Booklet pane. Nos. 4780/4781.......	3·25	3·25
4781	**3856**	(1st) Sabretooth......................................	1·60	1·60
4782	**3857**	£1·85 Magneto...	3·00	3·00
Set of 5..			9·75	9·75

Nos. 4778/4782 come from **MS**4777 and booklet panes 4778a and 4780a from the £19·95 X-Men booklet, No. DY46.

A Jean Grey fan sheet containing No. 4772x4 and a Wolverine fan sheet containing No. 4771x4 were sold for £7·00 each. A Collector sheet containing No. 4767/4776 plus 12 labels was sold for £10·99.

A 2nd Class stamp pack containing Nos. 4765/4770 each x2 were sold for £8·46. A 1st Class stamp pack containing Nos. 4771/4776 each x2 were sold for £11·70.

3858 No. 60103, Pickering Station, North Yorkshire Moors Railway, 2016

3859 The 'Christmas Dalesman' Steam Special, Yorkshire Dales National Park, 2019

3860 The 'Cathedrals Express' crossing Ribblehead Viaduct, Yorkshire Dales National Park, 2019

3861 Steaming through Blyth, Northumberland, 2016

3862 In Blizzard, Heap Bridge, East Lancashire Railway, 2016

3863 The 'Cathedrals Express' crossing Royal Border Bridge, Berwick-upon-Tweed, 2016

3864 At Victoria Station, London, 2002

3865 Shildon, County Durham, 2019

3866 *Flying Scotsman* Posters and Advertisement

(Des Steers McGillan Eves. Litho Cartor)

2023 (9 Mar). Centenary of the *Flying Scotsman* (steam locomotive) (1st issue). Multicoloured. Two phosphor bands. Perf 14.

4783	3858	(1st) No. 60103, Pickering Station, North Yorkshire Moors Railway, 2016	1·60	1·60
		a. Horiz pair. Nos. 4783/4784	3·25	3·25
		b. Booklet pane. Nos. 4783/4786 with margins all round	6·50	
4784	3859	(1st) The 'Christmas Dalesman' steam special, Yorkshire Dales National Park, 2019	1·60	1·60
4785	3860	(1st) The 'Cathedrals Express' crossing Ribblehead Viaduct, Yorkshire Dales National Park, 2017	1·60	1·60
		a. Horiz pair. Nos. 4785/4786	3·25	3·25
4786	3861	(1st) Steaming through Blyth, Northumberland, 2016	1·60	1·60
4787	3862	£1·85 In blizzard, Heap Bridge, East Lancashire Railway, 2016	3·00	3·00
		a. Horiz pair. Nos. 4787/4788	6·00	6·00
		b. Booklet pane. Nos. 4787/4790	12·00	
4788	3863	£1·85 The 'Cathedrals Express' crossing the Royal Border Bridge, Berwick-upon-Tweed, 2016	3·00	3·00
4789	3864	£1·85 At Victoria Station, London, 2002	3·00	3·00
		a. Horiz pair. Nos. 4789/4790	6·00	6·00
4790	3865	£1·85 At Shildon, County Dunham, 2019	3·00	3·00
Set of 8			17·00	17·00
Set of 4 Gutter Pairs			34·00	
First Day Cover (Tallents House)				19·00
First Day Cover (Doncaster)				19·00
Presentation Pack (Nos. 4783/4790 and MS4791) (PO Pack No. 628)			19·00	
PHQ Cards (set of 13)			8·75	18·00
MS4791 146×74 mm. 3866 (1st) 'Scotland by the Night Scotsman' poster (Robert Bartlett), 1932; (1st) 'LNER train service to and from Scotland' advertisement (H. L. Oakley), 1923; £1·85 'Refuelling the Flying Scotsman" poster (Frank Newbould), 1932; £1·85 'Mons Meg' poster (Frank Newbould), 1935			10·00	10·00
First Day Cover (Tallents House)				12·00
First Day Cover (Doncaster)				12·00

Nos. 4783/4784, 4785/4786, 4787/4788 and 4789/4790 were each printed together, *se-tenant*, as horizontal pairs in sheets of 60 (2 panes 6×5).

Booklet pane Nos. 4783b and 4787b come from the Flying Scotsman £21·05 premium booklet, No. DY48.

3867 'Scotland by the Night Scotsman' Poster (Robert Bartlett), 1932

3868 'LNER Train Service to and from Scotland' Advertisement (H. L. Oakley), 1923

3869 'Refuelling the Flying Scotsman" Poster (Frank Newbould), 1932

3870 'Mons Meg' Poster (Frank Newbould), 1935

(Litho Cartor)

2023 (9 Mar). Centenary of the *Flying Scotsman* (steam locomotive) (2nd issue). Multicoloured. Two phosphor bands. Perf 14.

4792	3867	(1st) 'Scotland by the Night Scotsman' poster (Robert Bartlett), 1932	1·60	1·60
		a. Booklet pane. Nos. 4792/4795 with margins all round	9·00	
4793	3868	(1st) 'LNER train service to and from Scotland' advertisement (H. L. Oakley), 1923	1·60	1·60
4794	3869	£1·85 'Refuelling the Flying Scotsman' Poster (Frank Newbould), 1932	3·25	3·25
4795	3870	£1·85 'Mons Meg' Poster (Frank Newbould), 1935	3·25	3·25
Set of 5			9·00	9·00

Nos. 4292/4295 came from No. MS4791 and the £21·05 premium booklet, No. DY48.

Decimal Machin Definitives

DENOMINATED STAMPS, PVA, PVAD OR GUM ARABIC, 'STANDARD' PERFORATIONS

356a

357 (Value redrawn)

(Des after plaster cast by Arnold Machin. Recess B.W.)

1970 (17 June)–**72**. Decimal Currency. Chalk-surfaced paper or phosphorised paper (10p.). Perf 12.

829	**356a**	10p. cerise		50	50
830		20p. olive-green		60	20
		a. Thinner uncoated paper*			
831		50p. deep ultramarine		1·25	25
		a. Thinner uncoated paper*		60·00	
831b	**357**	£1 bluish black (6.12.72)		2·25	40
Set of 4				3·25	1·20
First Day Cover (Nos. 829/831)					2·00
First Day Cover (No. 831b)					2·50
Presentation Pack No. 18 (Nos. 829/831)				8·00	
Presentation Pack No. 38 (Nos. 790 (or 831b), 830/831)				12·50	

* These are not as apparent as uncoated photogravure issues where there is normally a higher degree of chalk-surfacing. The 20p. is known only as a block of four with Plate No. 5. The 50p. comes from Plate No. 9.

The 10p. on phosphorised paper continued the experiments which started with the Machin 1s.6d. When the experiment had ended a quantity of the 50p. value was printed on the phosphorised paper to use up the stock. These stamps were issued on 1 February 1973, but they cannot be distinguished from No. 831 by the naked eye. (*Price* £2).

A £1 was also issued in 1970, but it is difficult to distinguish it from the earlier No. 790. In common with the other 1970 values it was issued in sheets of 100.

A whiter paper was introduced in 1973. The £1 appeared on 27 September 1973, the 20p. on 30 November 1973 and the 50p. on 20 February 1974.

Imperforate examples of No. 831b are believed to be printer's waste.

Special First Day of Issue Postmarks

British Philatelic Bureau, Edinburgh (Type C) (Nos. 829/831)	3·00
Windsor, Berks (Type C) (Nos. 829/831)	6·50
Philatelic Bureau, Edinburgh (Type E) (No. 831b)	3·00
Windsor, Berks (Type E) (No. 831b)	8·00

'X' NUMBERS. The following definitive series has been allocated 'X' prefixes to the catalogue numbers to avoid renumbering all subsequent issues

NO VALUE INDICATED. Stamps as Types **367/367a** inscribed '2nd' or '1st' are listed as Nos. 1445/1452, 1511/1516, 1664/1672, 2039/2040 and 2295.

ELLIPTICAL PERFORATIONS. These were introduced in 1993 and stamps showing them will be found listed as Nos. Y1667 etc.

367   **367a**

Printing differences

Litho   Gravure

(Illustrations enlarged×6)

Litho. Clear outlines to value and frame formed by edges of screen.

Gravure. Uneven lines to value and frame formed by edges of screen.

Two types of the 3p., 10p. and 26p.
(Nos. X930/X930c, X886/X886b and X971/971b)

I   II

I   II

Figures of face values as I (all printings of 3p. bright magenta except the multi-value coil No. 930cl and sheets from 21.1.92 onwards, 10p. orange-brown except 1984 Christian Heritage £4 booklet and 26p. rosine except 1987 (£1·04 barcode booklet).

Figures of face value narrower as in II (from coil No. X930cl and in sheets from 21.2.92 (3p.), 1984 Christian Heritage £4 booklet (10p.) or 1987 £1·04 barcode booklet (26p.)). This catalogue includes changes of figure styles on these stamps where there is no other listable difference. Similar changes have also taken place on other values, but only in conjunction with listed colour, paper or perforation changes.

1971 (15 Feb)–**96**. Decimal Currency. T **367**. Chalk-surfaced paper.

(a) Photo Harrison *(except for some printings of Nos. X879 and X913 in sheets produced by Enschedé and issued on 12 December 1979 (8p.) and 19 November 1991 (18p.)). With phosphor bands. Perf 15×14.*

X841	½p. turquoise-blue (2 bands)	20	20
	a. Imperf (pair)†	£2000	
	y. Phosphor omitted	4·00	
	l. Booklet pane. No. X841×2 se-tenant vert with X849×2	3·00	
	ly. Booklet pane. Phosphor omitted	£225	
	la. Booklet pane. No. X841×2 se-tenant horiz with X849×2 (14.7.71)	80	
	lay. Booklet pane. Phosphor omitted	£375	
	m. Booklet pane. No. X841×5 plus label	2·00	
	my. Booklet pane. Phosphor omitted	£120	
	n. Coil strip. No. X849g, X841g×2 and X844g×2	2·50	
	ny. Coil strip. Phosphor omitted	£500	
	nv. Coil strip. PVA gum. No. X849, X841×2 and X844×2 (4.74)	1·00	
	nvy. Coil strip. Phosphor omitted	18·00	
	o. Booklet pane. No. X841, X851, X852, X852a, each×3 (24.5.72)	3·50	
	oy. Booklet pane. Phosphor omitted	£1000	
	p. Booklet pane. No. X841×3, X842 and X852×2 (24.5.72)	45·00	
	py. Booklet pane. Phosphor omitted		
	q. Coil strip. No. X870, X849, X844 and X841×2 (3.12.75)	1·00	
	r. Booklet pane. No. X841×2, X844×3 and X870 (10.3.76)	40	
	s. Booklet pane. No. X841×2, X844×2, X873×2 and X881×4 (8½p. values at right) (26.1.77)	2·00	
	sa. Ditto, but No. X873a and 8½p. values at left	1·40	
	t. Booklet pane. No. X841, X844, X894×3 and X902 (14p. value at right) (26.1.81)	1·40	
	ty. Booklet pane. Phosphor omitted	50·00	
	ta. Booklet pane. No. X841, X844, X894a×3 and X902 (14p. value at left)	1·40	
	tay. Booklet pane. Phosphor omitted	50·00	
	u. Booklet pane. No. X841, X857×4 and X899×3 (12½p. values at left) (1.2.82)	1·60	
	ua. Ditto, but No. X899a and 12½p. values at right	1·60	
	g. Gum arabic (from coil strip, and on 22.9.72 from sheets)	40	
	gy. Phosphor omitted	60·00	
X842	½p. turquoise-blue (1 side band at left) (24.5.72)	45·00	25·00
X843	½p. turquoise-blue (1 centre band) (14.12.77)	20	20
	l. Coil strip. No. X843×2, X875 and X845×2 (14.12.77)	1·00	
	m. Booklet pane. No. X843×2, X845×2 and X875 plus label (8.2.78)	35	
	my. Booklet pane. Phosphor omitted	40·00	
X844	1p. crimson (2 bands)	20	20
	a. Imperf (vert coil)		
	b. Pair, one imperf 3 sides (vert coil)	£750	
	c. Imperf (pair)	£750	
	y. Phosphor omitted	5·00	
	l. Booklet pane. No. X844×2 se-tenant vert with X848×2	3·00	
	m. Ditto, but se-tenant horiz (14.7.71)	80	
	my. Booklet pane. Phosphor omitted	£300	
	n. Booklet pane. No. X844×2, X876×3 and X883×3 (9p. values at right) (13.6.77)	2·25	
	na. Ditto, but No. X876a and 9p. values at left	1·25	
	g. Gum arabic (from coil strip)	50	
	gy. Phosphor omitted	70·00	
X845	1p. crimson (1 centre band) (14.12.77)	20	20
	l. Booklet pane. No. X879 and X845×2 plus label (17.10.79)	30	
	m. Coil strip. No. X879 and X845×2 plus 2 labels (16.1.80)	90	

	n. Booklet pane. No. X845×2, X860 and X898 each×3 (5.4.83)	3·00	
	ny. Booklet pane. Phosphor omitted	22·00	
	p. Booklet pane. No. X845×3, X863×2 and X900×3 (3.9.84)	1·75	
	py. Booklet pane. Phosphor omitted	£250	
	q. Booklet pane. No. X845×2 and X896×4 (29.7.86)	6·00	
	s. Booklet pane. No. X845, X867×2 and X900×3 (20.10.86)	3·00	
	sa. Ditto, but with vertical edges of pane imperf (29.9.87)	1·75	
	say. Booklet pane. Phosphor omitted	£225	
X846	1p. crimson ('all-over') (10.10.79)	20	20
X847	1p. crimson (1 side band at left) (20.10.86)	60	60
	a. Band at right (3.3.87)	4·00	4·00
	l. Booklet pane. No. X847, X901 and X912×2 (20.10.86)	1·40	
	ly. Booklet pane. Phosphor omitted	£110	
	m. Booklet pane. No. X847a, X901×2, X912×5 and X918 with margins all round (3.3.87)	6·00	
X848	1½p. black (2 bands)	20	20
	a. Uncoated paper*	£130	
	b. Imperf (pair)		
	c. Imperf 3 sides (horiz pair)		
	y. Phosphor omitted	60·00	
X849	2p. myrtle-green (2 bands)	20	20
	a. Imperf (horiz pair)	£1800	
	y. Phosphor omitted	12·00	
	l. Booklet pane. No. X849×2, X880×2 and X886×3 plus label (10p. values at right) (28.8.79)	1·25	
	la. Ditto, but No. X880a and 10p. values at left	1·25	
	m. Booklet pane. No. X849×3, X889×2 and X895×2 plus label (12p. values at right) (4.2.80)	1·25	
	my. Booklet pane. Phosphor omitted	50·00	
	ma. Booklet pane. No. X849×3, X889a×2 and X895×2 plus label (12p. values at left)	1·25	
	may. Booklet pane. Phosphor omitted	50·00	
	n. Booklet pane. No. X849, X888×3, X889a and X895×4 with margins all round (16.4.80)	1·75	
	ny. Booklet pane. Phosphor omitted	55·00	
	o. Booklet pane. No. X849×6 with margins all round (16.4.80)	50	
	oy. Booklet pane. Phosphor omitted	60·00	
	p. Booklet pane. No. X849, X857, X898, X899×3 and X899a×3 with margins all round (19.5.82)	2·50	
	py. Booklet pane. Phosphor omitted	£150	
	g. Gum arabic (from coil strip)	1·75	
	gy. Phosphor omitted	£225	
X850	2p. myrtle-green ('all-over' phosphor) (10.10.79)	30	30
X851	2½p. magenta (1 centre band)	20	20
	a. Imperf (pair)†	£225	
	y. Phosphor omitted	10·00	
	l. Booklet pane. No. X851×5 plus label	2·50	
	ly. Booklet pane. Phosphor omitted	55·00	
	m. Booklet pane. No. X851×4 plus two labels	3·00	
	my. Booklet pane. Phosphor omitted	£425	
	n. Booklet pane. No. X851×3, X852a×3 and X855×6 (24.5.72)	3·50	
	ny. Booklet pane. Phosphor omitted		
	g. Gum arabic (13.9.72)	40	
X852	2½p. magenta (1 band at left)	70	70
	a. Band at right (24.5.72)	70	70
	l. Booklet pane. No. X852×2 and X855×4.	3·00	
	ly. Booklet pane. Phosphor omitted	£160	
X853	2½p. magenta (2 bands) (21.5.75)	20	20
X854	2½p. rose-red (2 bands) (26.8.81)	30	30
	l. Booklet pane. No. X854×3, X862×2 and X894×3 (11½p. values at left)	3·75	
	la. Ditto, but No. X894a and 11½p. values at right	5·00	
X855	3p. ultramarine (2 bands)	20	20
	a. Imperf (coil strip of 5)	£1700	
	b. Imperf (pair)†	£300	
	c. Uncoated paper*	45·00	
	y. Phosphor omitted	5·00	
	l. Booklet pane. No. X855×5 plus label	1·50	
	ly. Booklet pane. Phosphor omitted	£325	
	n. Booklet pane. No. X855×12 (24.5.72)	2·00	
	ny. Booklet pane. Phosphor omitted	£250	
	g. Gum arabic (23.8.72)	90	
	gy. Phosphor omitted	10·00	
X856	3p. ultramarine (1 centre band) (10.9.73)	20	20
	a. Imperf (pair)†	£275	
	b. Imperf between (vert pair)†	£475	
	c. Imperf horiz (vert pair)†	£250	
	g. Gum arabic	60	
X857	3p. bright magenta (Type I) (2 bands) (1.2.82)	35	35
	y. Phosphor omitted	£160	

X858	3½p. olive-grey (2 bands) *(shades)*......	50	50
	a. Imperf (pair)......	£375	
	y. Phosphor omitted......	12·00	
	b. *Bronze-green* (18.7.73)......	1·00	1·25
	by. Phosphor omitted......	12·00	
X859	3½p. olive-grey (1 centre band) (24.6.74)......	30	30
X860	3½p. purple-brown (1 centre band) (5.4.83)...	1·50	1·75
	y. Phosphor omitted......	10·00	
X861	4p. ochre-brown (2 bands)......	20	20
	a. Imperf (pair)†......	£1300	
	y. Phosphor omitted......	38·00	
	g. Gum arabic (1.11.72)......	50	
X862	4p. greenish blue (2 bands) (26.8.81)......	2·25	2·25
X863	4p. greenish blue (1 centre band) (3.9.84)......	1·25	1·25
	y. Phosphor omitted......	90·00	
X864	4p. greenish blue (1 side band) (8.1.85)......	4·00	4·25
	a. Band at left......	3·75	4·00
	l. Booklet pane. No. X864, X864a, X901×2, X901a×2, X909×2 and X920 with margins all round (8.1.85)......	8·50	
	ly. Booklet pane. Phosphor omitted......	£1800	
X865	4½p. grey-blue (2 bands) (24.10.73)......	20	20
	a. Imperf (pair)......	£375	
	y. Phosphor omitted......	11·00	
X866	5p. pale violet (2 bands)......	20	20
	y. Phosphor omitted......	£250	
X867	5p. claret (1 centre band) (20.10.86)......	1·00	1·00
	y. Phosphor omitted......	85·00	
X868	5½p. violet (2 bands) (24.10.73)......	30	30
X869	5½p. violet (1 centre band) (17.3.75)......	25	25
	a. Uncoated paper*......	£250	
	y. Phosphor omitted......	22·00	
X870	6p. light emerald (2 bands)......	25	25
	a. Uncoated paper*......	20·00	
	y. Phosphor omitted......	75·00	
	g. Gum arabic (6.6.73)......	2·00	
X871	6½p. greenish blue (2 bands) (4.9.74)......	30	30
X872	6½p. greenish blue (1 centre band) (24.9.75).	30	30
	a. Imperf (vert pair)......	£250	
	b. Uncoated paper*......	£150	
	y. Phosphor omitted......	15·00	
X873	6½p. greenish blue (1 band at right) (26.1.77)	60	60
	a. Band at left......	60	60
X874	7p. purple-brown (2 bands) (15.1.75)......	35	35
	a. Imperf (pair)......	£800	
	y. Phosphor omitted......	4·00	
X875	7p. purple-brown (1 centre band) (13.6.77)......	30	30
	a. Imperf (pair)......	£125	
	l. Booklet pane. No. X875 and X883, each×10 (15.11.78)......	2·50	
X876	7p. purple-brown (1 band at right) (13.6.77)......	40	40
	a. Band at left......	40	40
X877	7½p. pale chestnut (2 bands)......	25	25
	y. Phosphor omitted......	22·00	
X878	8p. rosine (2 bands) (24.10.73)......	25	25
	a. Uncoated paper*......	15·00	
X879	8p. rosine (1 centre band) (20.8.79)......	25	25
	a. Uncoated paper*......	£550	
	b. Imperf (pair)......	—	
	y. Phosphor omitted......	£275	
	l. Booklet pane. No. X879 and X886, each×10 (14.11.79)......	3·00	
X880	8p. rosine (1 band at right) (28.8.79)......	40	50
	a. Band at left......	40	50
X881	8½p. light yellowish green (2 bands) (shades) (24.9.75)......	30	30
	a. Imperf (pair)......	—	
	b. *Yellowish green* (24.3.76)......	1·00	1·00
	y. Phosphor omitted......	6·00	
X882	9p. yellow-orange and black (2 bands)......	40	40
	y. Phosphor omitted......	80·00	
X883	9p. deep violet (2 bands) (25.2.76)......	30	30
	a. Imperf (pair)......	£180	
	y. Phosphor omitted......	4·50	
X884	9½p. purple (2 bands) (25.2.76)......	30	30
	y. Phosphor omitted......	24·00	
X885	10p. orange-brown and chestnut (2 bands) (11.8.71)......	30	30
	a. Orange-brown omitted......	£140	
	b. Imperf (horiz pair)......	£2500	
	y. Phosphor omitted......	12·00	
X886	10p. orange-brown (Type I) (2 bands) (25.2.76)......	30	30
	a. Imperf (pair)......	£350	
	y. Phosphor omitted......	3·00	
	b. Type II (4.9.84)......	12·50	12·50
	by. Phosphor omitted......	£1200	
	bl. Booklet pane. No. X886b, X901a and X909×7 with margins all round......	14·00	
	bly. Booklet pane. Phosphor omitted......	£1600	
X887	10p. orange-brown (Type I) ('all-over') (3.10.79)......	30	30
X888	10p. orange-brown (Type I) (1 centre band) (4.2.80)......	30	30
	a. Imperf (pair)......	£275	
	l. Booklet pane. No. X888×9 with margins all round (16.4.80)......	1·50	
	ly. Booklet pane. Phosphor omitted......	55·00	
	m. Booklet pane. No. X888 and X895, each×10 (12.11.80)......	3·25	
X889	10p. orange-brown (Type I) (1 band at right) (4.2.80)......	1·10	1·10
	a. Band at left......	30	30
X890	10½p. yellow (2 bands) (25.2.76)......	35	35
X891	10½p. deep dull blue (2 bands) (26.4.78)......	35	35
X892	11p. brown-red (2 bands) (25.2.76)......	30	30
	a. Imperf (pair)......	£2000	
	y. Phosphor omitted......	5·00	
X893	11½p. drab (1 centre band) (14.1.81)......	30	30
	a. Imperf (pair)......	£300	
	y. Phosphor omitted......	7·00	
	l. Booklet pane. No. X893 and X902, each×10 (11.11.81)......	4·25	
X894	11½p. drab (1 band at right) (26.1.81)......	40	40
	a. Band at left......	40	40
	l. Booklet pane. No. X894/X894a, each×2 and X902×6 (6.5.81)......	3·50	
X895	12p. yellowish green (2 bands) (4.2.80)......	40	40
	y. Phosphor omitted......	6·00	
	l. Booklet pane. No. X895×9 with margins all round (16.4.80)......	1·75	
	ly. Booklet pane. Phosphor omitted......	55·00	
X896	12p. bright emerald (1 centre band) (29.10.85)......	40	40
	a. Imperf (pair)......	£1700	
	y. Phosphor omitted......	12·00	
	l. Booklet pane. No. X896×9 with margins all round (18.3.86)......	1·75	
	ly. Booklet pane. Phosphor omitted......	£225	
	u. Underprint Type 4 (29.10.85)......	1·00	
X897	12p. bright emerald (1 band at right) (14.1.86)......	40	40
	a. Band at left......	40	40
	l. Booklet pane. No. X897/X897a, each×2 and X909×6 (12p. values at left) (14.1.86)......	3·00	
	la. Ditto, but 12p. values at right......	3·00	
	m. Booklet pane. No. X897/X897a, each×3, X909×6 and X919 with margins all round (18.3.86)......	15·00	
	my. Booklet pane. Phosphor omitted......	£800	
X898	12½p. light emerald (1 centre band) (27.1.82)..	40	40
	a. Imperf (pair)......	70·00	
	y. Phosphor omitted......	6·50	
	u. Underprint Type 1 (10.11.82)......	65	
	uy. Phosphor omitted......	75·00	
	v. Underprint Type 2 (9.11.83)......	65	
	l. Booklet pane. No. X898u and X907u, each×10 (10.11.82)......	5·00	
X899	12½p. light emerald (1 band at right) (1.2.82)..	40	40
	a. Band at left......	40	40
	l. Booklet pane. No. X899/X899a, each×2 and X907×6 (1.2.82)††......	2·50	
	ly. Booklet pane. Phosphor omitted......	£2750	
	m. Booklet pane. No. X899/X899a, each×3 with margins all round (19.5.82)......	1·50	
	my. Booklet pane. Phosphor omitted......	45·00	
	n. Booklet pane. No. X899/X899a, each×2, and X908×6 (12½p. values at left) (5.4.83)......	4·25	
	na. Ditto, but 12½p. values at right......	5·50	
X900	13p. pale chestnut (1 centre band) (28.8.84)......	40	40
	a. Imperf (pair)......	£450	
	u. Underprint Type 2 (2.12.86)......	65	
	y. Phosphor omitted......	6·50	
	l. Booklet pane. No. X900×9 with margins all round (8.1.85)......	1·75	
	ly. Booklet pane. Phosphor omitted......	£425	
	m. Booklet pane. No. X900×6 with margins all round (3.3.87)......	1·40	
	n. Booklet pane. No. X900×4 with margins all round (4.8.87)......	1·90	
	o. Booklet pane. No. X900×10 with margins all round (4.8.87)......	2·50	
X901	13p. pale chestnut (1 band at right) (3.9.84)..	40	40
	a. Band at left......	40	40
	l. Booklet pane. No. X901/X901a, each×2, and X909×6 (13p. values at left)††......	2·50	
	la. Ditto, but 13p. values at right......	2·50	
	m. Booklet pane. No. X901/X901a, each×3 with margins all round (4.9.84)......	1·50	
	my. Booklet pane. Phosphor omitted......	£325	
	n. Booklet pane. No. X901a and X912×5 (20.10.86)......	2·50	
	na. Ditto, but vertical edges of pane imperf (29.9.87)......	2·25	
X902	14p. grey-blue (2 bands) (26.1.81)......	1·00	1·00
	y. Phosphor omitted......	30·00	
X903	14p. deep blue (1 centre band) (23.8.88)......	45	45
	a. Imperf (pair)......	£325	
	y. Phosphor omitted......	9·00	
	l. Booklet pane. No. X903×4 with margins all round......	3·50	
	ly. Booklet pane. Phosphor omitted......	£110	
	m. Booklet pane. No. X903×10 with margins all round......	5·25	

No.	Description		
	n. Booklet pane. No. X903×4 with horizontal edges of pane imperf (11.10.88)	3·75	
	p. Booklet pane. No. X903×10 with horizontal edges of pane imperf (11.10.88)	4·75	
	py. Booklet pane. Phosphor omitted	£160	
	q. Booklet pane. No. X903×4 with three edges of pane imperf (24.1.89)	17·00	
	qy. Booklet pane. Phosphor omitted	35·00	
X904	14p. deep blue (1 band at right) (5.9.88)	3·00	3·00
	l. Booklet pane. No. X904 and X914×2 plus label	5·00	
	ly. Booklet pane. Phosphor omitted	15·00	
	m. Booklet pane. No. X904×2 and X914×4 with vertical edges of pane imperf.	3·75	
	my. Booklet pane. Phosphor omitted	£850	
X905	15p. bright blue (1 centre band) (26.9.89)	40	40
	a. Imperf (pair)	£450	
	y. Phosphor omitted	14·00	
X906	15p. bright blue (1 band at left) (2.10.89)	2·00	2·00
	a. Band at right (20.3.90)	1·50	1·50
	l. Booklet pane. No. X906×2 and X916 plus label	7·00	
	ly. Booklet pane. Phosphor omitted	£450	
	m. Booklet pane. No. X906a, X916, X922, 1446, 1448, 1468a, 1470 and 1472 plus label with margins all round (20.3.90)	10·00	
X907	15½p. pale violet (2 bands) (1.2.82)	40	40
	y. Phosphor omitted	7·00	
	u. Underprint Type 1 (10.11.82)	65	
	l. Booklet pane. No. X907×6 with margins all round (19.5.82)	1·75	
	ly. Booklet pane. Phosphor omitted	85·00	
	m. Booklet pane. No. X907×9 with margins all round (19.5.82)	2·25	
	my. Booklet pane. Phosphor omitted	50·00	
X908	16p. olive-drab (2 bands) (5.4.83)	70	70
	y. Phosphor omitted	£110	
X909	17p. grey-blue (2 bands) (3.9.84)	50	50
	y. Phosphor omitted	£250	
	u. Underprint Type 4 (4.11.85)	65	
	uy. Phosphor omitted	22·00	
	l. Booklet pane. No. X909u×3 plus label (4.11.85)	2·10	
	ly. Booklet pane. Phosphor omitted	65·00	
	la. Booklet pane. No. X909×3 plus label (12.8.86)	2·25	
X910	17p. deep blue (1 centre band) (4.9.90)	70	70
	a. Imperf (pair)	£1500	
X911	17p. deep blue (1 band at right) (4.9.90)	10·00	10·00
	a. Band at left	1·25	1·25
	y. Phosphor omitted	12·00	
	l. Booklet pane. No. X911 and X911a×2 plus label	6·00	
	ly. Booklet pane. Phosphor omitted	55·00	
	m. Booklet pane. No. X911×2 and X917×3 plus three labels with vertical edges of pane imperf	2·25	
	my. Booklet pane. Phosphor omitted	75·00	
X912	18p. deep olive-grey (2 bands) (20.10.86)	60	60
	y. Phosphor omitted	25·00	
X913	18p. bright green (1 centre band) (10.9.91)	50	50
	a. Imperf (pair)	£450	
	y. Phosphor omitted	28·00	
X914	19p. bright orange-red (2 bands) (5.9.88)	1·25	1·25
	y. Phosphor omitted	8·00	
X915	20p. dull purple (2 bands) (25.2.76)	70	70
X916	20p. brownish black (2 bands) (2.10.89)	2·00	2·50
	y. Phosphor omitted	£550	
X917	22p. bright orange-red (2 bands) (4.9.90)	70	70
	y. Phosphor omitted	22·00	
X917a	25p. rose-red (2 bands) (6.2.96)	7·50	8·50
X918	26p. rosine (Type I) (2 bands) (3.3.87)	6·50	7·50
X919	31p. purple (2 bands) (18.3.86)	8·00	9·00
	y. Phosphor omitted	£800	
X920	34p. ochre-brown (2 bands) (8.1.85)	5·50	6·00
	y. Phosphor omitted	£800	
X921	50p. ochre-brown (2 bands) (2.2.77)	1·50	1·75
X922	50p. ochre (2 bands) (20.3.90)	2·75	2·75
	(b) Photo Harrison. On phosphorised paper. Perf 15×14.		
X924	½p. turquoise-blue (10.12.80)	20	20
	a. Imperf (pair)	£120	
	l. Coil strip. No. X924 and X932×3 (30.12.81)	90	
X925	1p. crimson (12.12.79)	20	20
	a. Imperf (pair)	£500	
	l. Coil strip. No. X925 and X932a×3 (14.8.84)	95	
	m. Booklet pane. No. X925 and X969, each×2 (10.9.91)	1·00	
X926	2p. myrtle-green (face value as Type **367**) (12.12.79)	20	20
	a. Imperf (pair)	£1900	
X927	2p. deep green (face value as Type **367a**) (26.7.88)	60	60
	a. Imperf (pair)	£1900	
	l. Booklet pane. No. X927×2 and X969×4 plus 2 labels with vert edges of pane imperf (10.9.91)	1·75	
X928	2p. myrtle-green (face value as Type **367a**) (5.9.88)	7·50	8·00
	l. Coil strip. No. X928 and X932a×3	8·00	
X929	2½p. rose-red (14.1.81)	20	20
	l. Coil strip. No. X929 and X930×3 (6.81)	1·40	
X930	3p. bright magenta (Type I) (22.10.80)	20	20
	a. Imperf (horiz pair)	£1200	
	l. Booklet pane. No. X930, X931×2 and X949×6 with margins all round (14.9.83)	2·75	
	c. Type II (10.10.89)	1·75	2·00
	cl. Coil strip. No. X930c and X933×3	2·25	
X931	3½p. purple-brown (30.3.83)	30	30
X932	4p. greenish blue (30.12.81)	25	25
	a. *Pale greenish blue* (14.8.84)	25	25
X933	4p. new blue (26.7.88)	35	35
	a. Imperf (pair)	£2250	
	l. Coil strip. No. X933×3 and X935 (27.11.90)	1·50	
	m. Coil strip. No. X933 and X935, each×2 (1.10.91)	1·50	
	n. Coil strip. No. X933 and X935×3 (31.1.95)	1·75	
X934	5p. pale violet (10.10.79)	25	25
X935	5p. dull red-brown (26.7.88)	25	25
	a. Imperf (pair)	£3000	
X936	6p. yellow-olive (10.9.91)	25	25
X937	7p. brownish red (29.10.85)	1·25	1·25
X938	8½p. yellowish green (24.3.76)	65	65
X939	10p. orange-brown (Type I) (11.79)	35	35
X940	10p. dull orange (Type II) (4.9.90)	35	35
X941	11p. brown-red (27.8.80)	1·00	1·00
X942	11½p. ochre-brown (15.8.79)	40	40
X943	12p. yellowish green (30.1.80)	35	35
X944	13p. olive-grey (15.8.79)	55	55
X945	13½p. purple-brown (30.1.80)	65	65
X946	14p. grey-blue (14.1.81)	40	40
X947	15p. ultramarine (15.8.79)	45	45
X948	15½p. pale violet (14.1.81)	45	45
	a. Imperf (pair)	£200	
X949	16p. olive-drab (30.3.83)	50	50
	a. Imperf (pair)	£125	
	u. Underprint Type 3 (10.8.83)	65	
	l. Booklet pane. No. X949×9 with margins all round (14.9.83)	2·25	
X950	16½p. pale chestnut (27.1.82)	50	50
X951	17p. light emerald (30.1.80)	45	45
X952	17p. grey-blue (30.3.83)	45	45
	a. Imperf (pair)	£225	
	u. Underprint Type 3 (5.3.85)	65	
	l. Booklet pane. No. X952×6 with margins all round (4.9.84)	1·50	
	m. Booklet pane. No. X952×9 with margins all round (8.1.85)	2·25	
X953	17½p. pale chestnut (30.1.80)	45	45
X954	18p. deep violet (14.1.81)	45	45
X955	18p. deep olive-grey (28.8.84)	45	45
	a. Imperf (pair)	£100	
	l. Booklet pane. No. X955×9 with margins all round (3.3.87)	3·50	
	m. Booklet pane. No. X955×4 with margins all round (4.8.87)	2·25	
	n. Booklet pane. No. X955×10 with margins all round (4.8.87)	4·25	
X956	19p. bright orange-red (23.8.88)	55	60
	a. Imperf (pair)	£325	
	l. Booklet pane. No. X956×4 with margins all round	4·00	
	m. Booklet pane. No. X956×10 with margins all round	6·25	
	n. Booklet pane. No. X956×4 with horizontal edges of pane imperf (11.10.88)	5·00	
	o. Booklet pane. No. X956×10 with horizontal edges of pane imperf (11.10.88)	6·25	
	q. Booklet pane. No. X956×4 with three edges of pane imperf (24.1.89)	20·00	
X957	19½p. olive-grey (27.1.82)	2·00	2·00
X958	20p. dull purple (10.10.79)	1·00	1·00
X959	20p. turquoise-green (23.8.88)	65	65
X960	20p. brownish black (26.9.89)	45	45
	a. Imperf (pair)	£750	
	l. Booklet pane. No. X960×5 plus label with vertical edges of pane imperf (2.10.89)	3·50	
X961	20½p. ultramarine (30.3.83)	60	60
	a. Imperf (pair)	£1400	
X962	22p. blue (22.10.80)	50	50
	a. Imperf (pair)	£325	
X963	22p. yellow-green (28.8.84)	55	55
	a. Imperf (horiz pair)	£1700	
X964	22p. bright orange-red (4.9.90)	55	55
	a. Imperf (pair)	£750	
X965	23p. brown-red (30.3.83)	1·50	1·75

	a. Imperf (horiz pair)	£1300	
X966	23p. bright green (23.8.88)	1·00	1·00
X967	24p. violet (28.8.84)	1·50	1·75
X968	24p. Indian red (26.9.89)	2·00	2·25
	a. Imperf (horiz pair)	£2500	
X969	24p. chestnut (10.9.91)	65	65
	a. Imperf (pair)	£225	
X970	25p. purple (14.1.81)	65	65
X971	26p. rosine (Type I) (27.1.82)	65	65
	a. Imperf (horiz pair)	£675	
	b. Type II (4.8.87)	5·25	6·00
	bl. Booklet pane. No. X971b×4 with margins all round	22·00	
X972	26p. drab (4.9.90)	1·50	1·75
X973	27p. chestnut (23.8.88)	70	70
	l. Booklet pane. No. X973×4 with margins all round	7·00	
	m. Booklet pane. No. X973×4 with horizontal edges of pane imperf (11.10.88)	18·00	
X974	27p. violet (4.9.90)	75	75
X975	28p. deep violet (30.3.83)	75	75
	a. Imperf (pair)	£1600	
X976	28p. ochre (23.8.88)	75	75
X977	28p. deep bluish grey (10.9.91)	75	75
	a. Imperf (pair)	£2000	
X978	29p. ochre-brown (27.1.82)	3·00	3·50
X979	29p. deep mauve (26.9.89)	2·50	3·00
X980	30p. deep olive-grey (26.9.89)	1·00	1·00
X981	31p. purple (30.3.83)	80	80
	a. Imperf (pair)	£975	
X982	31p. ultramarine (4.9.90)	1·50	2·00
X983	32p. greenish blue (23.8.88)	1·70	2·50
	a. Imperf (pair)	£2000	
X984	33p. light emerald (4.9.90)	1·00	1·25
X985	34p. ochre-brown (28.8.84)	1·00	1·50
X986	34p. deep bluish grey (26.9.89)	1·00	1·50
X987	34p. deep mauve (10.9.91)	2·00	2·75
X988	35p. sepia (23.8.88)	1·75	2·25
	a. Imperf (pair)	£1700	
X989	35p. yellow (10.9.91)	2·00	2·75
X990	37p. rosine (26.9.89)	2·00	2·75
X991	39p. bright mauve (10.9.91)	1·00	1·00
X991a	50p. ochre (21.1.92)	13·50	13·50
	ab. Imperf (pair)	£1400	

(c) Photo Harrison. On ordinary paper. Perf 15×14.

X992	50p. ochre-brown (21.5.80)	2·00	2·00
	a. Imperf (pair)	£1000	
X993	50p. ochre (13.3.90)	3·50	4·00
X994	75p. grey-black (face value as Type 367a) (26.7.88)	4·50	4·75

(d) Litho J.W. Perf 14.

X996	4p. greenish blue (2 bands) (30.1.80)	20	20
	y. Phosphor omitted	£1600	
X997	4p. greenish blue (phosphorised paper) (11.81)	30	30
X998	20p. dull purple (2 bands) (21.5.80)	1·50	1·75
X999	20p. dull purple (phosphorised paper) (11.81)	1·50	1·75

(e) Litho Questa. Perf 14 (Nos. X1000, X1003/X1004 and X1023) or 15×14 (others).

X1000	2p. emerald-green (face value as Type 367) (phosphorised paper) (21.5.80)	20	20
	a. Perf 15×14 (10.7.84)	25	25
X1001	2p. bright green and deep green (face value as Type 367a) (phosphorised paper) (23.2.88)	45	45
X1002	4p. greenish blue (phosphorised paper) (13.5.86)	45	45
X1003	5p. light violet (phosphorised paper) (21.5.80)	25	25
X1004	5p. claret (phosphorised paper) (27.1.82)	45	45
	a. Perf 15×14 (21.2.84)	45	45
X1005	13p. pale chestnut (1 centre band) (9.2.88)	45	45
	l. Booklet pane. No. X1005×6 with margins all round	1·75	
X1006	13p. pale chestnut (1 side band at right) (9.2.88)	45	45
	a. Band at left	45	45
	l. Booklet pane. No. X1006/X1006a each×3, X1010, X1015 and X1021 with margins all round	12·00	
	la. Grey-green (on 18p.) ptg double	£2800	
X1007	14p. deep blue (1 centre band) (11.10.88)	2·25	2·75
X1008	17p. deep blue (1 centre band) (19.3.91)	45	45
	y. Phosphor omitted	£240	
	l. Booklet pane. No. X1008×6 with margins all round	1·75	
	ly. Booklet pane. Phosphor omitted	£950	
X1009	18p. deep olive-grey (phosphorised paper) (9.2.88)	40	45
	l. Booklet pane. No. X1009×9 with margins all round	2·50	
	m. Booklet pane. No. X1009×6 with margins all round	1·75	

X1010	18p. deep olive-grey (2 bands) (9.2.88)	5·50	6·50
X1011	18p. bright green (1 centre band) (27.10.92)	45	45
	l. Booklet pane. No. X1011×6 with margins all round	1·50	
X1012	18p. bright green (1 side band at right) (27.10.92)	65	65
	a. Band at left (10.8.93)	1·25	1·25
	y. Phosphor omitted	£450	
	l. Booklet pane. No. X1012×2, X1018×2, X1022×2, 1451a, 1514a and centre label with margins all round	6·25	
	la. Bright blue (on 2nd) printing treble		
	ly. Phosphor omitted	£3500	
	m. Booklet pane. No. X1012a, X1020, X1022 and 1451ab, each×2, with central label and margins all round (10.8.93)	4·75	
	my. Booklet pane. Phosphor omitted	£2500	
X1013	19p. bright orange-red (phosphorised paper) (11.10.88)	1·10	1·10
X1014	20p. dull purple (phosphorised paper) (13.5.86)	1·10	1·10
X1015	22p. yellow-green (2 bands) (9.2.88)	5·50	5·50
X1016	22p. bright orange-red (phosphorised paper) (19.3.91)	65	65
	l. Booklet pane. No. X1016×9 with margins all round	2·75	
	m. Booklet pane. No. X1016×6, X1019×2 and central label with margins all round	5·00	
X1017	24p. chestnut (phosphorised paper) (27.10.92)	65	65
	l. Booklet pane. No. X1017×6 with margins all round	2·00	
X1018	24p. chestnut (2 bands) (27.10.92)	1·50	2·25
	y. Phosphor omitted	£600	
X1019	33p. light emerald (phosphorised paper) (19.3.91)	1·50	2·25
X1020	33p. light emerald (2 bands) (25.2.92)	1·10	1·10
	y. Phosphor omitted	£450	
X1021	34p. bistre-brown (2 bands) (9.2.88)	5·50	6·50
X1022	39p. bright mauve (2 bands) (27.10.92)	2·25	2·75
	y. Phosphor omitted	£450	
X1023	75p. black (face value as Type 367) (ordinary paper) (30.1.80)	2·25	3·00
	a. Perf 15×14 (21.2.84)	2·50	3·25
X1024	75p. brownish grey and black (face value as Type 367a) (ordinary paper) (23.2.88)	7·50	9·00

(f) Litho Walsall. Perf 14.

X1050	2p. deep green (face value as T 367) (phosphorised paper) (9.2.93)	1·10	1·10
	l. Booklet pane. No. X1050×2 and X1053×4 plus 2 labels with vert edges of pane imperf	3·25	
X1051	14p. deep blue (1 side band at right) (25.4.89)	2·75	2·75
	y. Phosphor omitted	£225	
	l. Booklet pane. No. X1051×2 and X1052×4 with vertical edges of pane imperf	7·50	
	ly. Booklet pane. Phosphor omitted	£900	
X1052	19p. bright orange-red (2 bands) (25.4.89)	75	75
	y. Phosphor omitted	£125	
X1053	24p. chestnut (phosphorised paper) (9.2.93)	75	75
X1054	29p. deep mauve (2 bands) (2.10.89)	2·25	2·50
	l. Booklet pane. No. X1054×4 with three edges of pane imperf	9·00	
X1055	29p. deep mauve (phosphorised paper) (17.4.90)	3·50	3·50
	l. Booklet pane. No. X1055×4 with three edges of pane imperf	11·00	
X1056	31p. ultramarine (phosphorised paper) (17.9.90)	1·25	1·25
	l. Booklet pane. No. X1056×4 with horizontal edges of pane imperf	4·00	
X1057	33p. light emerald (phosphorised paper) (16.9.91)	2·00	1·75
	l. Booklet pane. No. X1057×4 with horiz edges of pane imperf	3·50	
X1058	39p. bright mauve (phosphorised paper) (16.9.91)	1·50	1·50
	l. Booklet pane. No. X1058×4 with horiz edges of pane imperf	5·75	

* See footnote after No. 744.

† These come from sheets with gum arabic.

†† Examples of Booklet panes Nos. X899l, X901l and X901la are known on which the phosphor bands were printed on the wrong values in error with the result that the side bands appear on the 15½p. or 17p. and the two bands on the 12½p. or 13p. Similarly examples of the 1p. with phosphor band at right instead of left and of the 13p. with band at left instead of right, exist from 50p. booklet pane No. X847l.

Nos. X844a/X844b come from a strip of eight of the vertical coil. It comprises two normals, one imperforate at sides and bottom, one completely imperforate, one imperforate at top, left and bottom and partly perforated at right due to the bottom three stamps being perforated twice.

No. X844b is also known from another strip having one stamp imperforate at sides and bottom.

Nos. X848b/X848c come from the same sheet, the latter having perforations at the foot of the stamps only.

Multi-value coil strips Nos. X924I, X925I, X928I, X929I, X930cI and X933I/X933n were produced by the Post Office for use by a large direct mail marketing firm. From 2 September 1981 No. X929I was available from the Philatelic Bureau, Edinburgh, and, subsequently from a number of other Post Office counters. Later multi-value coil strips were sold at the Philatelic Bureau and Post Office philatelic counters.

In addition to booklet pane No. X1012m No. X1020 also comes from the *se-tenant* pane in the Wales £6 booklet. This pane is listed under No. W49I in the Wales Regional section.

PANES OF SIX FROM STITCHED BOOKLETS. Nos. X841m, X851I/X851m and X855I include one or two printed labels showing commercial advertisements. These were originally perforated on all four sides, but from the August 1971 editions of the 25p. and 30p. booklets (Nos. DH42, DQ59) and December 1971 edition of the 50p. booklet (No. DT4) the line of perforations between the label and the binding margin was omitted. Similar panes, with the line of perforations omitted, exist for the 3p., 3½p. and 4½p. values (Nos. X856, X858 and X865), but these are outside the scope of this listing as the labels are blank.

PART-PERFORATED SHEETS. Since the introduction of the Jumelle press in 1972 a number of part perforated sheets, both definitives and commemoratives, have been discovered. It is believed that these occur when the operation of the press is interrupted. Such sheets invariably show a number of 'blind' perforations, where the pins have failed to cut the paper. Our listings of imperforate errors from these sheets are for pairs showing no traces whatsoever of the perforations. Examples showing 'blind' perforations are outside the scope of this catalogue.

In cases where perforation varieties affect *se-tenant* stamps, fuller descriptions will be found in Volumes 4 and 5 of the *GB Specialised Catalogue*.

WHITE PAPER. From 1972 printings appeared on fluorescent white paper giving a stronger chalk reaction than the original ordinary cream paper.

PHOSPHOR OMITTED ERRORS. It should be noted that several values listed with phosphor omitted errors also exist on phosphorised paper. These errors can only be identified with certainty by checking for an 'afterglow', using a short-wave ultraviolet lamp.

'ALL-OVER' PHOSPHOR. To improve mechanised handling most commemoratives from the 1972 Royal Silver Wedding 3p. value to the 1979 Rowland Hill Death Centenary set had the phosphor applied by printing cylinder across the entire surface of the stamp, giving a matt effect. Printings of the 1p., 2p. and 10p. definitives, released in October 1979, also had 'all-over' phosphor, but these were purely a temporary expedient pending the adoption of phosphorised paper. Nos. X883, X890 and X921 have been discovered with 'all-over' phosphor in addition to the normal phosphor bands. These errors are outside the scope of this catalogue.

PHOSPHORISED PAPER. Following the experiments on Nos. 743c and 829 a printing of the 4½p. definitive was issued on 13 November 1974, which had, in addition to the normal phosphor bands, phosphor included in the paper coating. Because of difficulties in identifying this phosphorised paper with the naked eye this printing is not listed separately in this catalogue.

No. X938 was the first value printed on phosphorised paper without phosphor bands and was a further experimental issue to test the efficacy of this system. From 15 August 1979 phosphorised paper was accepted for use generally, this paper replacing phosphor bands on values other than those required for the second-class rate.

Stamps on phosphorised paper show a shiny surface instead of the matt areas of those printed with phosphor bands or the overall matt appearance of 'All-over' phosphor.

DEXTRIN GUM. From 1973 printings in photogravure appeared with PVA gum to which dextrin had been added. Because this is virtually colourless a bluish green colouring matter was added to distinguish it from the earlier pure PVA.

The 4p., 5p. (light violet), 20p. and 75p. printed in lithography exist with PVA and PVAD gum. From 1988 Questa printings were with PVAD gum, but did not show the bluish green additive.

VARNISH COATING. Nos. X841 and X883 exist with and without a varnish coating. This cannot easily be detected without the use of an ultraviolet lamp as it merely reduces the fluorescent paper reaction.

POSTAL FORGERIES. In mid-1993 a number of postal forgeries of the 24p. chestnut were detected in the London area. These forgeries, produced by lithography, can be identified by the lack of phosphor in the paper, screening dots across the face value and by the perforations which were applied by a line machine gauging 11.

First Day Covers

15.2.71	½p., 1p., 1½p., 2p., 2½p., 3p., 3½p., 4p., 5p., 6p., 7½p., 9p. (Nos. X841, X844, X848/X849, X851, X855, X858, X861, X866, X870, X877, X882) (Covers carry 'POSTING DELAYED BY THE POST OFFICE STRIKE 1971' cachet)......	2·50
11.8.71	10p. (No. X885)......	1·00
24.5.72	Wedgwood *se-tenant* pane ½p., 2½p. (No. X841p)......	25·00
24.10.73	4½p., 5½p., 8p. (Nos. X865, X868, X878)......	1·00
4.9.74	6½p. (No. X871)......	1·00
15.1.75	7p. (No. X874)......	1·00
24.9.75	8½p. (No. X881)......	1·00
25.2.76	9p., 9½p., 10p., 10½p., 11p., 20p. (Nos. X883/X884, X886, X890, X892, X915)......	2·50
2.2.77	50p. (No. X921)......	1·00
26.4.78	10½p. (No. X891)......	1·00
15.8.79	11½p., 13p., 15p. (Nos. X942, X944, X947)......	1·00
30.1.80	4p., 12p., 13½p., 17p., 17½p., 75p. (Nos. X996, X943, X945, X951, X953, X1023)......	2·00
16.4.80	Wedgwood *se-tenant* pane 2p., 10p., 12p. (No. X849n)......	1·25
22.10.80	3p., 22p. (Nos. X930, X962)......	1·00
14.1.81	2½p., 11½p., 14p., 15½p., 18p., 25p. (Nos. X929, X893, X946, X948, X954, X970)......	1·25
27.1.82	5p., 12½p., 16½p., 19½p., 26p., 29p. (Nos. X1004, X898, X950, X957, X971, X978)......	2·00
19.5.82	Stanley Gibbons *se-tenant* pane 2p., 3p., 12½p. (No. X849p)......	2·00
30.3.83	3½p., 16p., 17p., 20½p., 23p., 28p., 31p. (Nos. X931, X949, X952, X961, X965, X975, X981)......	2·75
14.9.83	Royal Mint *se-tenant* pane 3p., 3½p., 16p. (No. X930l)......	2·50
28.8.84	13p., 18p., 22p., 24p., 34p. (Nos. X900, X955, X963, X967, X985)......	2·00
4.9.84	Christian Heritage *se-tenant* pane 10p., 13p., 17p. (No. X886bl)......	12·00
8.1.85	*The Times se-tenant* pane 4p., 13p., 17p., 34p. (No. X864l)......	8·50
29.10.85	7p., 12p. (Nos. X937, X896)......	2·00
18.3.86	British Rail *se-tenant* pane 12p., 17p., 31p. (No. X897m)......	9·00
3.3.87	P&O *se-tenant* pane 1p., 13p., 18p., 26p. (No. X847m)......	6·00
9.2.88	*Financial Times se-tenant* pane 13p., 18p., 22p., 34p. (No. X1006l)......	12·50
23.8.88	14p., 19p., 20p., 23p., 27p., 28p., 32p., 35p. (Nos. X903, X956, X959, X966, X973, X976, X983, X988)......	3·50
26.9.89	15p., 20p., 24p., 29p., 30p., 34p., 37p. (Nos. X905, X960, X968, X979/X980, X986, X990)......	3·00
20.3.90	London Life *se-tenant* pane 15p., (2nd), 20p., (1st), 15p., 20p., 29p. (No. X906m)......	10·00
4.9.90	10p., 17p., 22p., 26p., 27p., 31p., 33p. (Nos. X910, X940, X964, X972, X974, X982, X984)......	3·00
19.3.91	Alias Agatha Christie *se-tenant* pane 22p., 33p. (No. X1016m)......	6·00
10.9.91	6p., 18p., 24p., 28p., 34p., 35p., 39p. (Nos. X936, X913, X969, X977, X987, X989, X991)......	3·25
27.10.92	Tolkien *se-tenant* pane 18p., (2nd), 24p., (1st), 39p. (No. X1012l)......	6·00
10.8.93	Beatrix Potter *se-tenant* pane 18p., (2nd), 33p., 39p. (No. X1012m)......	5·50

Presentation Packs

15.2.71	PO Pack No. 26. ½p. (2 bands), 1p. (2 bands), 1½p. (2 bands), 2p. (2 bands), 2½p. magenta (1 centre band), 3p. ultramarine (2 bands), 3½p. olive-grey (2 bands), 4p. ochre-brown (2 bands), 5p. pale violet (2 bands), 6p. light emerald (2 bands), 7½p. (2 bands), 9p. yellow-orange and black (2 bands). (Nos. X841, X844, X848/X849, X851, X855, X858, X861, X866, X870, X877, X882)......	9·00
15.4.71**	Scandinavia 71. Contents as above......	25·00
25.11.71	PO Pack No. 37. ½p. (2 bands), 1p. (2 bands), 1½p. (2 bands), 2p. (2 bands), 2½p. magenta (1 centre band), 3p. ultramarine (2 bands) or (1 centre band), 3½p. olive-grey (2 bands) or (1 centre band), 4p. ochre-brown (2 bands), 4½p. (2 bands), 5p. pale violet (2 bands), 5½p. (2 bands) or (1 centre band), 6p. (2 bands), 6½p. (2 bands) or (1 centre band), 7p. (2 bands), 7½p. (2 bands), 8p. (2 bands), 9p. yellow-orange and black (2 bands), 10p. orange-brown and chestnut (2 bands). (Nos. X841, X844, X848/X849, X851, X855 or X856, X858 or X859, X861, X865/X866, X868 or X869, X870, X871 or X872, X874, X877/X878, X881, X882, X885)......	30·00
2.2.77	Later issues of this Pack contained the alternatives PO Pack No. 90. ½p. (2 bands), 1p. (2 bands), 1½p. (2 bands), 2p. (2 bands), 2½p. magenta (1 centre band), 3p. ultramarine (1 centre band), 5p. pale violet (2 bands), 6½p. (1 centre band), 7p. (2 bands) or (1 centre band), 7½p. (2 bands), 8p. (2 bands), 8½p. (2 bands), 9p. deep violet (2 bands), 9½p. (2 bands), 10p. orange-brown (2 bands), 10½p. yellow (2 bands), 11p. (2 bands), 20p. dull purple (2 bands), 50p. ochre-brown (2 bands). (Nos. X841, X844, X848/X849, X851, X856, X866, X872, X874 or X875, X877/X878, X881, X883/X884, X886, X890, X892, X915, X921)......	5·00

28.10.81   PO Pack No. 129a. 10½p. deep dull blue (2 bands), 11½p. (1 centre band), 2½p. (phosphor paper), 3p. (phosphor paper), 11½p. (phosphor paper), 12p. (phosphor paper), 13p. (phosphor paper), 13½p. (phosphor paper), 14p. (phosphor paper), 15p. (phosphor paper), 15½p. (phosphor paper), 17p. light emerald (phosphor paper), 17½p. (phosphor paper), 18p. deep violet (phosphor paper), 22p. blue (phosphor paper), 25p. (phosphor paper), 4p. greenish blue (litho, 2 bands), 75p. (litho) (Nos. X891, X893, X929/X930, X942/X948, X951, X953/X954, X962, X970, X996, X1023).....................   15·00

3.8.83   PO Pack No. 1. 10p. orange-brown (1 centre band), 12½p. (1 centre band), ½p. (phosphor paper), 1p. (phosphor paper), 3p. (phosphor paper), 3½p. (phosphor paper), 16p. (phosphor paper), 16½p. (phosphor paper), 17p. grey-blue (phosphor paper), 20½p. (phosphor paper), 23p. brown-red (phosphor paper), 26p. rosine (phosphor paper), 28p. deep violet (phosphor paper), 31p. purple (phosphor paper), 50p (ordinary paper), 2p. (litho phosphor paper), 4p. (litho phosphor paper), 5p. claret (litho phosphor paper), 20p. (litho phosphor paper), 75p. (litho) (Nos. X888, X898, X924/X925, X930/X931, X949/X950, X952, X961, X965, X971, X975, X981, X992, X997, X999, X1000, X1004, X1023).....................   32·00

23.10.84   PO Pack No. 5. 13p. (1 centre band), ½p. (phosphor paper), 1p. (phosphor paper), 3p. (phosphor paper), 10p. orange-brown (phosphor paper), 16p. (phosphor paper), 17p. grey-blue (phosphor paper), 18p. deep olive-grey (phosphor paper), 22p. yellow-green (phosphor paper), 24p. violet (phosphor paper), 26p. rosine (phosphor paper), 28p. deep violet (phosphor paper), 31p. purple (phosphor paper), 34p. ochre-brown (phosphor paper), 50p. (ordinary paper), 2p. (litho phosphor paper), 4p. (litho phosphor paper), 5p. claret (litho phosphor paper), 20p. (litho phosphor paper), 75p. (litho) (Nos. X900, X924/X925, X930, X939, X949, X952, X955, X963, X967, X971, X975, X981, X985, X992, X1000a, X997, X1004a, X999, X1023a)...............   25·00

3.3.87   PO Pack No. 9. 12p. (1 centre band), 13p. (1 centre band), 1p. (phosphor paper), 3p. (phosphor paper), 7p. (phosphor paper), 10p. orange-brown (phosphor paper), 17p. grey-blue (phosphor paper), 18p. deep olive-grey (phosphor paper), 22p. yellow-green (phosphor paper), 24p. violet (phosphor paper), 26p. rosine (phosphor paper), 28p. deep violet (phosphor paper), 31p. purple (phosphor paper), 34p. ochre-brown (phosphor paper), 50p. (ordinary paper), 2p. (litho phosphor paper), 4p. (litho phosphor paper), 5p. claret (litho phosphor paper), 20p. (litho phosphor paper), 75p. (litho) (Nos. X896, X900, X925, X930, X937, X939, X952, X955, X963, X967, X971, X975, X981, X985, X992, X1000a, X997, X1004a, X999, X1023a)...............   30·00

23.8.88   PO Pack No. 15. 14p. (1 centre band), 19p. (phosphor paper), 20p. turquoise-green (phosphor paper), 23p. bright green (phosphor paper), 27p. chestnut (phosphor paper), 28p. ochre (phosphor paper), 32p. sepia (phosphor paper) (Nos. X903, X956, X959, X966, X973, X976, X983, X988)...............   9·00

26.9.89   PO Pack No. 19. 15p. (centre band), 20p. brownish black (phosphor paper), 24p. Indian red (phosphor paper), 29p. deep mauve (phosphor paper), 30p. (phosphor paper), 34p. deep bluish grey (phosphor paper), 37p. (phosphor paper) (Nos. X905, X960, X968, X979/X980, X986, X990).....................   7·00

4.9.90   PO Pack No. 22. 10p. dull orange (phosphor paper), 17p. (centre band), 22p. bright orange-red (phosphor paper), 26p. drab (phosphor paper), 27p. violet (phosphor paper), 31p. ultramarine (phosphor paper), 33p. (phosphor paper) (Nos. X940, X910, X964, X972, X974, X982, X984).....................   7·00

14.5.91   PO Pack No. 24. 1p. (phosphor paper), 2p. (phosphor paper), 3p. (phosphor paper), 4p. new blue (phosphor paper), 5p. dull red-brown (phosphor paper), 10p. dull orange (phosphor paper), 17p. (1 centre band), 20p. turquoise-green (phosphor paper), 22p. bright orange-red (phosphor paper), 26p. drab (phosphor paper), 27p. violet (phosphor paper), 30p. (phosphor paper), 31p. ultramarine (phosphor paper), 32p. (phosphor paper), 33p. (phosphor paper), 37p. (phosphor paper), 50p. (ordinary paper). (Nos. X925, X927, X930, X933, X935, X940, X910, X959, X964, X972, X974, X980, X982/X984, X990, X993/994).....................   30·00

10.9.91   PO Pack No. 25. 6p (phosphor paper), 18p. (1 centre band), 24p. chestnut (phosphor paper), 28p. deep bluish grey (phosphor paper), 34p. deep mauve (phosphor paper), 35p. yellow (phosphor paper), 39p. (phosphor paper) (Nos. X913, X936, X969, X977, X987, X989, X991).....................   7·00

**   The Scandinavia 71 was a special pack produced for sale during a visit to six cities in Denmark, Sweden and Norway by a mobile display unit between 15 April and 20 May 1971. The pack gives details of this tour and also lists the other stamps which were due to be issued in 1971, the text being in English. A separate insert gives translations in Danish, Swedish and Norwegian. The pack was also available at the Philatelic Bureau, Edinburgh.

For stamps of this design inscribed '2nd' and '1st' see Nos. 1445/1452 and 1511/1516, and for stamps with one elliptical perforation hole on each vertical side see Nos. 1664/1672, Y1667/Y1803, 2039/2040, 2295/2298, 2650/2657, U2941/U2974, U2995/U303, U3010/U3039, U3055/U3067, U2070/U3116, U3150, U3155/U3157, 3271/3278 and U3744/U3747.

508

1977 (2 Feb)–**87**. Perf 14×15.

1026	**508**	£1 bright yellow-green and blackish olive..................	3·00	25
		a. Imperf (pair).................	£1700	
1026*b*		£1·30 pale drab and deep greenish blue (3.8.83).................	5·50	6·00
1026*c*		£1·33 pale mauve and grey-black (28.8.84).................	7·50	8·00
1026*d*		£1·41 pale drab and deep greenish blue (17.9.85).................	8·50	8·50
1026*e*		£1·50 pale mauve and grey-black (2.9.86).................	6·00	5·00
1026*f*		£1·60 pale drab and deep greenish blue (15.9.87).................	6·50	7·00
1027		£2 light emerald and purple-brown....	9·00	50
		a. Imperf (pair).................	£2250	
1028		£5 salmon and chalky blue............	22·00	3·00
		a. Imperf (vert pair).................	£8000	

Set of 8................. 60·00   32·00
Set of 8 Gutter Pairs................. £125
Set of 8 Traffic Light Gutter Pairs................. £150
Presentation Pack (PO Pack No. 91 (small size) (Nos. 1026, 1027/1028)................. 38·00
Presentation Pack (PO Pack No. 13 (large size) (Nos. 1026, 1027/1028)................. £170
Presentation Pack (PO Pack No. 14) (large size) (No. 1026*f*)................. 22·00

Gutter pairs	Plain	Traffic Light
1026, 1027/1028	70·00	75·00
1026*b*	13·00	20·00
1026*c*	16·00	22·00
1026*d*	18·00	25·00
1026*e*	13·00	17·00
1026*f*	14·00	18·00

Special First Day of Issue Postmarks (for illustrations see Introduction)

Philatelic Bureau, Edinburgh (Type F) (£1, £2, £5)............	10·00
Windsor, Berks (Type F) (£1, £2, £5)............	12·00
Philatelic Bureau, Edinburgh (Type F) (£1·30)............	6·50
Windsor, Berks (Type F) (£1·30)............	6·50
British Philatelic Bureau, Edinburgh (Type F) (£1·33)............	8·50
Windsor, Berks (Type F) (£1·33)............	8·50
British Philatelic Bureau, Edinburgh (Type G) (£1·41)............	9·00
Windsor, Berks (Type G) (£1·41)............	9·00
British Philatelic Bureau, Edinburgh (Type G) (£1·50)............	5·50
Windsor, Berks (Type G) (£1·50)............	5·50
British Philatelic Bureau, Edinburgh (Type G) (£1·60)............	7·50
Windsor, Berks (Type G) (£1·60)............	7·50

Decimal Machin Index

(Denominated stamps with 'standard' perforations)

Those booklet stamps shown below with an * after the catalogue number do not exist with perforations on all four sides, but show one or two sides imperforate.

Value.	Process	Colour	Phosphor	Cat. No.	Source
½p.	photo	turquoise-blue	2 bands	X841/X841g	(a) with P.V.A. gum–sheets, 5p. m/v coil (X841nEv), 10p.m/v coil (X841q), 10p. booklets (DN46/DN75, FA1/FA3), 25p. booklets (DH39/DH52), 50p. booklets (DT1/DT12, FB1, FB14/FB16, FB19/FB23), £1 Wedgwood booklet (DX1) (b) with gum arabic—sheets, 5p. m/v coil (X841n)
½p.	photo	turquoise-blue	1 band at left	X842	£1 Wedgwood booklet (DX1)
½p.	photo	turquoise-blue	1 centre band	X843	10p. m/v coil (X843l), 10p. booklets (FA4/FA9)
½p.	photo	turquoise-blue	phos paper	X924	sheets, 12½p. m/v coil (X924l)
1p.	photo	crimson	2 bands	X844/X844g	(a) with P.V.A. gum—sheets, vertical coils, 5p. m/v coil (X841nEv), 10p. m/v coil (X841q), 10p. booklets (DN46/DN75, FA1/FA3), 50p. booklets (FB1/FB8, FB14/FB16) (b) with gum arabic—vertical coils, 5p. m/v coil (X841n)
1p.	photo	crimson	1 centre band	X845	10p. m/v coils (X843l, X845m), 10p. booklets (FA4/FA11), 50p. booklets (FB24/FB30, 34/36, 43/46, 48, 50)
1p.	photo	crimson	'all-over'	X846	sheets
1p.	photo	crimson	phos paper	X925	sheets, horizontal and vertical coils, 13p. m/v coil (X925l), 50p. booklet (FB59/FB66)
1p.	photo	crimson	1 band at left	X847	50p. booklets (FB37/FB42, FB47, FB49)
1p.	photo	crimson	1 band at right	X847a	£5 P. & O. booklet (DX8)
1½p.	photo	black	2 bands	X848	sheets, 10p. booklets (DN46/DN75)
2p.	photo	myrtle-green	2 bands	X849/X849g	(a) with P.V.A. gum—sheets, 5p. m/v coil (X841nEv), 10p. m/v coil (X841q), 10p. booklets (DN46/DN75), 50p. booklets (FB9/FB13), £3 Wedgwood booklet (DX2), £4 SG booklet (DX3) (b) with gum arabic—5p. m/v coil (X841n)
2p.	photo	myrtle-green	'all-over'	X850	sheets
2p.	photo	myrtle-green	phos paper	X926	sheets
2p.	photo	myrtle-green	phos paper	X928	14p. m/v coil (X928l)
2p.	litho	emerald-green	phos paper	X1000/X1000a	sheets
2p.	litho	bright green and deep green	phos paper	X1001	sheets
2p.	photo	deep green	phos paper	X927	sheets, £1 booklets (FH23/FH27)
2p.	litho	deep green	phos paper	X1050*	£1 booklets (FH28/FH30)
2½p.	photo	magenta	1 centre band	X851/X851g	(a) with P.V.A. gum—sheets, horizontal and vertical coils, 25p. booklets (DH39/DH52), 50p. booklets (DT1/DT12), £1 Wedgwood booklet (DX1) (b) with gum arabic—sheets, horizontal coils
2½p.	photo	magenta	1 side band	X852/X852a	(a) band at left—50p. booklets (DT1/DT12), £1 Wedgwood booklet (DX1) (b) band at right—£1 Wedgwood booklet (DX1)
2½p.	photo	magenta	2 bands	X853	sheets
2½p.	photo	rose-red	phos paper	X929	sheets, 11½p. m/v coil (X929l)
2½p.	photo	rose-red	2 bands	X854	50p. booklets (FB17/FB18)
3p.	photo	ultramarine	2 bands	X855/X855g	(a) with P.V.A. gum—sheets, horizontal and vertical coils, 30p. booklets (DQ56/DQ72), 50p. booklets (DT1/DT12), £1 Wedgwood booklet (DX1) (b) with gum arabic—sheets, horizontal coils
3p.	photo	ultramarine	1 centre band	X856/X856g	(a) with P.V.A. gum—sheets, horizontal and vertical coils, 30p. booklets (DQ73/DQ34), 50p. booklets (DT13/DT14) (b) with gum arabic—sheets
3p.	photo	bright magenta	phos paper	X930	Type I. sheets, 11½p. m/v coil (X929l), £4 Royal Mint booklet (DX4)
3p.	photo	bright magenta	phos paper	X930c	Type II. sheets (from 21.1.92), 15p. m/v coil (X930cl)
3p.	photo	bright magenta	2 bands	X857	Type I. 50p. booklets (FB19/FB23), £4 SG booklet (DX3)
3½p.	photo	olive-grey	2 bands	X858/X858b	sheets, horizontal and vertical coils, 35p. booklets (DP1/DP3), 50p. booklets (DT13/DT14)
3½p.	photo	olive-grey	1 centre band	X859	sheet, horizontal coils, 35p. booklet (DP4), 85p. booklet (DW1)
3½p.	photo	purple-brown	phos paper	X931	sheets, £4 Royal Mint booklet (DX4)
3½p.	photo	purple-brown	1 centre band	X860	50p. booklets (FB24/FB26)
4p.	photo	ochre-brown	2 bands	X861/X861g	(a) with P.V.A. gum—sheets. (b) with gum arabic—sheets
4p.	litho	greenish blue	2 bands	X996	sheets
4p.	photo	greenish blue	2 bands	X862	50p. booklets (FB17/FB18)
4p.	litho	greenish blue	phos paper	X997	sheets J.W. ptg.
				X1002	sheets Questa ptg.
4p.	photo	greenish blue	phos paper	X932	12½p. m/v coil (X924l)
				X932a	13p. m/v coil (X925l), 14p. m/v coil (X928l)
4p.	photo	greenish blue	1 centre band	X863	50p. booklets (FB27/FB30)
4p.	photo	greenish blue	1 side band	X864/X864a	(a) band at right—£5 *The Times* booklet (DX6) (b) band at left—£5 *The Times* booklet (DX6)
4p.	photo	new blue	phos paper	X933	sheets, 15p. m/v coil (X930cl), 17p. m/v coil (X933l), 18p. m/v coil (X933m), 19p m/v coil (X933n)
4½p.	photo	grey-blue	2 bands	X865	sheets, horizontal coils, 45p. booklets (DS1/DS2), 85p. booklet (DW1)
5p.	photo	pale violet	2 bands	X866	sheets

Value.	Process	Colour	Phosphor	Cat. No.	Source
5p.	photo	pale violet	phos paper	X934	sheets
5p.	litho	light violet	phos paper	X1003	sheets
5p.	litho	claret	phos paper	X1004/X1004a	sheets
5p.	photo	claret	1 centre band	X867	50p. booklets (FB35/FB36, FB43/FB46, FB48, FB50)
5p.	photo	dull red-brown	phos paper	X935	sheets, 17p. m/v coil (X933l), 18p. m/v coil (X933m), 19p m/v coil (X933n)
5½p.	photo	violet	2 bands	X868	sheets
5½p.	photo	violet	1 centre band	X869	sheets
6p.	photo	light emerald	2 bands	X870/X870g	(a) with P.V.A. gum—sheets, 10p. m/v coil (X841q), 10p. booklets (FA1/FA3) (b) with gum arabic—sheets
6p.	photo	yellow-olive	phos paper	X936	sheets
6½p.	photo	greenish blue	2 bands	X871	sheets
6½p.	photo	greenish blue	1 centre band	X872	sheets, horizontal and vertical coils, 65p. booklet (FC1)
6½p.	photo	greenish blue	1 side band	X873/X873a	(a) band at right—50p. booklet (FB1A). (b) band at left—50p. booklet (FB1B)
7p.	photo	purple-brown	2 bands	X874	sheets
7p.	photo	purple-brown	1 centre band	X875	sheets, horizontal and vertical coils, 10p. m/v coil (X843l), 10p. booklets (FA4/FA9), 70p. booklets (FD1/FD8), £1.60 Christmas booklet (FX1)
7p.	photo	purple-brown	1 side band	X876/X876a	(a) band at right—50p. booklets (FB2A/FB8A) (b) band at left—50p. booklets (FB2B/FB8B)
7p.	photo	brownish red	phos paper	X937	sheets
7½p.	photo	pale chestnut	2 bands	X877	sheets
8p.	photo	rosine	2 bands	X878	sheets
8p.	photo	rosine	1 centre band	X879	sheets, vertical coils, 10p. m/v coil (X845m), 10p. booklets (FA10/FA11), 80p. booklet (FE1), £1.80 Christmas booklet (FX2)
8p.	photo	rosine	1 side band	X880/X880a	(a) band at right—50p. booklets (FB9A/FB10A) (b) band at left—50p. booklets (FB9B/FB10B)
8½p	photo	light yellowish green	2 bands	X881/X881b	sheets, horizontal and vertical coils, 50p. booklet (FB1), 85p. booklet (FF1)
8½p.	photo	yellowish green	phos paper	X938	sheets
9p.	photo	yellow-orange and black	2 bands	X882	sheets
9p.	photo	deep violet	2 bands	X883	sheets, horizontal and vertical coils, 50p. booklets (FB2/FB8), 90p. booklets (FG1/FG8), £1.60 Christmas booklet (FX1)
9½p	photo	purple	2 bands	X884	sheets
10p.	recess	cerise	phos paper	829	sheets
10p.	photo	orange-brown and chestnut	2 bands	X885	sheets
10p.	photo	orange-brown	2 bands	X886	Type I. sheets, 50p. booklets (FB9/FB10), £1.80 Christmas booklet (FX2)
10p.	photo	orange-brown	2 bands	X886b	Type II. £4 Christian Heritage booklet (DX5)
10p.	photo	orange-brown	'all-over'	X887	Type I. sheets, vertical coils, £1 booklet (FH1)
10p.	photo	orange-brown	phos paper	X939	Type I. sheets
10p.	photo	orange-brown	1 centre band	X888	Type I. sheets, vertical coils, £1 booklets (FH2/FH4), £2·20 Christmas booklet (FX3), £3 Wedgwood booklet (DX2)
10p.	photo	orange-brown	1 side band	X889/X889a	Type I. (a) band at right—50p. booklets (FB11A/FB13A) (b) band at left—50p. booklets (FB11B/FB13B), £3 Wedgwood booklet (DX2)
10p.	photo	dull orange	phos paper	X940	sheets
10½p.	photo	yellow	2 bands	X890	sheets
10½p.	photo	deep dull blue	2 bands	X891	sheets
11p.	photo	brown-red	2 bands	X892	sheets
11p.	photo	brown-red	phos paper	X941	sheets
11½p	photo	ochre-brown	phos paper	X942	sheets
11½p.	photo	drab	1 centre band	X893	sheets, vertical coils, £1·15 booklets (FI1/FI4), £2·55 Christmas booklet (FX4)
11½p.	photo	drab	1 side band	X894/X894a	(a) band at right—50p. booklets (FB14A/FB18A), £1.30 booklets (FL1/FL2) (b) band at left—50p. booklets (FB14B/FB18B), £1.30 booklets (FL1/FL2)
12p.	photo	yellowish green	phos paper	X943	sheets, vertical coils, £1·20 booklets (FJ1/FJ3)
12p.	photo	yellowish green	2 bands	X895	50p. booklets (FB11/FB13), £2·20 Christmas booklet (FX3), £3 Wedgwood booklet (DX2)
12p.	photo	bright emerald	1 centre band	X896	sheets, horizontal and vertical coils, 50p. booklet (FB34), £1·20 booklets (FJ4/FJ6), £5 British Rail booklet (DX7)
12p.	photo	bright emerald	1 side band	X897/ X897a	(a) band at right—£1·50 booklets (FP1/FP3), £5 British Rail booklet (DX7) (b) band at left—£1·50 booklets (FP1/FP3), £5 British Rail booklet (DX7)
12p.	photo	bright emerald	1 centre band Underprint T.4	X896u	sheets
12½p.	photo	light emerald	1 centre band	X898	sheets, vertical coils, 50p. booklets (FB24/FB26), £1·25 booklets (FK1/FK8), £4 SG booklet (DX3)
12½p.	photo	light emerald	1 centre band Underprint T.1	X898u	£2·80 Christmas booklet (FX5)
12½p.	photo	light emerald	1 centre band Underprint T.2	X898v	£2·50 Christmas booklet (FX6)
12½p.	photo	light emerald	1 side band	X899/X899a	(a) band at right—50p. booklets (FB19A/FB23A), £1·43 booklets (FN1/FN6), £1·46 booklets (FO1/FO3), £4 SG booklet (DX3), £4 Royal Mint booklet (DX4) (b) band at left—50p. booklets (FB19B/FB23B), £1·43 booklets (FN1/FN6), £1·46 booklets (FO1/FO3), £4 SG booklet (DX3), £4 Royal Mint booklet (DX4)
13p.	photo	olive-grey	phos paper	X944	sheets
13p.	photo	pale chestnut	1 centre band	X900	sheets, horizontal and vertical coils, 50p. booklets (FB27/FB30, FB35/FB36, FB43/FB46, FB48, FB50), 52p. booklet (GA1), £1·30 booklets (FL3/FL14, GI1), £5 *The Times* booklet (DX6), £5 P & O booklet (DX8)
13p.	photo	pale chestnut	1 centre band Underprint T.2	X900u	£1·30 Christmas booklet (FX9)
13p.	photo	pale chestnut	1 side band	X901/X901a	(a) band at right—50p. booklets (FB37/FB42, FB47, FB49), £1·54 booklets (FQ1/FQ4), £4 Christian Heritage booklet (DX5), £5 *The Times* booklet (DX6), £5 P & O booklet (DX8) (b) band at left—£1 booklets (FH6/FH13), £1·54 booklets (FQ1/FQ4), £4 Christian Heritage booklet (DX5), £5 *The Times* booklet (DX6)

Value. Process	Colour	Phosphor	Cat. No.	Source
13p. litho	pale chestnut	1 centre band	X1005	£5 *Financial Times* booklet (DX9)
13p. litho	pale chestnut	1 side band	X1006/X1006a	£5 *Financial Times* booklet (DX9)
13½p. photo	purple-brown	phos paper	X945	sheets
14p. photo	grey-blue	phos paper	X946	sheets, vertical coils, £1·40 booklets (FM1/FM4)
14p. photo	grey-blue	2 bands	X902	50p. booklets (FB14/FB16), £1·30 booklets (FL1/FL2), £2·55 Christmas booklet (FX4)
14p. photo	deep blue	1 centre band	X903	sheets, horizontal and vertical coils, 56p. booklets (GB1/GB4), £1·40 booklets (FM5/FM6, GK1, 3)
14p. photo	deep blue	1 band at right	X904	50p. booklets (FB51/FB4), £1 booklets (FH14/FH15 and 17)
14p. litho	deep blue	1 centre band	X1007	£1·40 booklets (GK2, 4)
14p. litho	deep blue	1 band at right	X1051*	£1 booklet (FH16)
15p. photo	ultramarine	phos paper	X947	sheets
15p. photo	bright blue	1 centre band	X905	sheets, horizontal and vertical coils
15p. photo	bright blue	1 side band	X906/X906a	(a) band at left—50p. booklet (FB55)
				(b) band at right—£5 London Life booklet (DX11)
15½p. photo	pale violet	phos paper	X948	sheets, vertical coils, £1·55 booklets (FR1/FR4)
15½p. photo	pale violet	2 bands	X907	£1·43 booklets (FN1/FN6), £4 SG booklet (DX3)
15½p. photo	pale violet	2 bands Underprint T.1	X907u	£2·80 Christmas booklet (FX5)
16p. photo	olive-drab	phos paper	X949	sheets, vertical coils, £1·60 booklets (FS1, FS3/FS4), £4 Royal Mint booklet (DX4)
16p. photo	olive-drab	phos paper Underprint T.3	X949u	£1·60 booklet (FS2)
16p. photo	olive-drab	2 bands	X908	£1·46 booklets (FO1/FO3)
16½p. photo	pale chestnut	phos paper	X950	sheets
17p. photo	light emerald	phos paper	X951	sheets
17p. photo	grey-blue	phos paper	X952	sheets, vertical coils, £1 booklet (FH5), £1·70 booklets (FT1, FT3 & FT5/FT7), £4 Christian Heritage booklet (DX5), £5 *The Times* booklet (DX6), £5 British Rail booklet (DX7)
17p. photo	grey-blue	phos paper Underprint T.3	X952u	£1.70 booklet (FT2)
17p. photo	grey-blue	2 bands	X909	50p. booklets (FB33a), £1.50 booklets (FP1/FP3), £1·54 booklets (FQ1/FQ4), £4 Christian Heritage booklet (DX5), £5 *The Times* booklet (DX6), £5 British Rail booklet (DX7)
17p. photo	grey-blue	2 bands Underprint T.4	X909u	50p. booklets (FB31/FB33)
17p. photo	deep blue	1 centre band	X910	sheets, vertical coils
17p. photo	deep blue	1 side band	X911/X911a	(a) band at right—50p. booklet (FB57/FB8), £1 booklet (FH21/FH22)
				(b) band at left—50p. booklet (FB57/FB58)
17p. litho	deep blue	1 centre band	X1008	£6 Alias Agatha Christie booklet (DX12)
17½p photo	pale chestnut	phos paper	X953	sheets
18p. photo	deep violet	phos paper	X954	sheets
18p. photo	deep olive-grey	phos paper	X955	sheets, vertical coils, 72p. booklet (GC1), £1·80 booklets (FU1/FU8, GO1), £5 P & O booklet (DX8)
18p. photo	deep olive-grey	2 bands	X912	50p. booklets (FB37/FB42, FB47, FB49), £1 booklet (FH6/FH13), £5 P & O booklet (DX8)
18p. litho	deep olive-grey	phos paper	X1009	£5 *Financial Times* booklet (DX9)
18p. litho	deep olive-grey	2 bands	X1010	£5 *Financial Times* booklet (DX9)
18p. photo/gravure	bright green	1 centre band	X913	sheets, vertical coils
18p. litho	bright green	1 centre band	X1011	£6 Tolkien booklet (DX14)
18p. litho	bright green	1 side band	X1012/X1012a	(a) band at right—£6 Tolkien booklet (DX14).
				(b) band at left—£6 (£5·64) Beatrix Potter booklet (DX15).
19p. photo	bright orange-red	phos paper	X956	sheets, vertical coils, 76p. booklets (GD1/GD4), £1·90 booklets (FV1/FV2, GP1, GP3)
19p. photo	bright orange-red	2 bands	X914	50p. booklets (FB51/FB4), £1 booklets (FH14/FH15, FH17)
19p. litho	bright orange-red	phos paper	X1013	£1·90 booklets (GP2, 4)
19p. litho	bright orange-red	2 bands	X1052*	£1 booklet (FH16)
19½p photo	olive-grey	phos paper	X957	sheets
20p. recess	olive-green	none	830	sheets
20p. photo	dull purple	2 bands	X915	sheets
20p. photo	dull purple	phos paper	X958	sheets
20p. litho	dull purple	2 bands	X998	sheets
20p. litho	dull purple	phos paper	X999	sheets J.W. ptg.
			X1014	sheets Questa ptg.
20p. photo	turquoise-green	phos paper	X959	sheets
20p. photo	brownish black	phos paper	X960	sheets, horizontal and vertical coils, £1 booklet (FH18)
20p. photo	brownish black	2 bands	X916	50p. booklet (FB55), £5 London Life booklet (DX11)
20½p. photo	ultramarine	phos paper	X961	sheets
22p. photo	blue	phos paper	X962	sheets
22p. photo	yellow-green	phos paper	X963	sheets
22p. litho	yellow-green	2 bands	X1015	£5 *Financial Times* booklet (DX9)
22p. photo	bright orange-red	2 bands	X917*	£1 booklet (FH21/FH22)
22p. photo	bright orange-red	phos paper	X964	sheets, vertical coils
22p. litho	bright orange-red	phos paper	X1016	£6 Alias Agatha Christie booklet (DX12)
23p. photo	brown-red	phos paper	X965	sheets
23p. photo	bright green	phos paper	X966	sheets
24p. photo	violet	phos paper	X967	sheets
24p. photo	Indian red	phos paper	X968	sheets
24p. photo	chestnut	phos paper	X969	sheets, vertical coils, 50p. booklets (FB59/FB66), £1 booklets (FH23/FH27)
24p. litho	chestnut	phos paper	X1017	£6 Tolkien booklet (DX14) (Questa ptg)
			X1053*	£1 booklet (FH28/FH30) Walsall ptg
24p. litho	chestnut	2 bands	X1018	£6 Tolkien booklet (DX14)
25p. photo	purple	phos paper	X970	sheets
25p. photo	rose-red	2 bands	X917a	horizontal coils
26p. photo	rosine	phos paper	X971	Type I. sheets
26p. photo	rosine	2 bands	X918	Type I. £5 P & O booklet (DX8)

Value.	Process	Colour	Phosphor	Cat. No.	Source
26p.	photo	rosine	phos paper	X971b	Type II. £1·04 booklet (GE1)
26p.	photo	drab	phos paper	X972	sheets
27p.	photo	chestnut	phos paper	X973	sheets, £1·08 booklets (GF1/GF2)
27p.	photo	violet	phos paper	X974	sheets
28p.	photo	deep violet	phos paper	X975	sheets
28p.	photo	ochre	phos paper	X976	sheets
28p.	photo	deep bluish grey	phos paper	X977	sheets
29p.	photo	ochre-brown	phos paper	X978	sheets
29p.	photo	deep mauve	phos paper	X979	sheets
29p.	litho	deep mauve	2 bands	X1054*	£1·16 booklet (GG1)
29p.	litho	deep mauve	phos paper	X1055*	£1·16 booklet (GG2)
30p.	photo	deep olive-grey	phos paper	X980	sheets
31p.	photo	purple	phos paper	X981	sheets
31p.	photo	purple	2 bands	X919	£5 British Rail booklet (DX7)
31p.	photo	ultramarine	phos paper	X982	sheets
31p.	litho	ultramarine	phos paper	X1056*	£1·24 booklet (GH1)
32p.	photo	greenish blue	phos paper	X983	sheets
33p.	photo	light emerald	phos paper	X984	sheets, vertical coils
33p.	litho	light emerald	phos paper	X1019	£6 Alias Agatha Christie booklet (DX12)
33p.	litho	light emerald	phos paper	X1057*	£1·32 booklet (GJ1)
33p.	litho	light emerald	2 bands	X1020	£6 Wales booklet (DX13), £6 (£5·64) Beatrix Potter booklet (DX15)
34p.	photo	ochre-brown	phos paper	X985	sheets
34p.	photo	ochre-brown	2 bands	X920	£5 *The Times* booklet (DX6)
34p.	litho	bistre-brown	2 bands	X1021	£5 *Financial Times* booklet (DX9)
34p.	photo	deep bluish grey	phos paper	X986	sheets
34p.	photo	deep mauve	phos paper	X987	sheets
35p.	photo	sepia	phos paper	X988	sheets
35p.	photo	yellow	phos paper	X989	sheets
37p.	photo	rosine	phos paper	X990	sheets
39p.	photo	bright mauve	phos paper	X991	sheets, vertical coils
39p.	photo	bright mauve	phos paper	X1058*	78p. booklet (GD4a), £1·56 booklet (GM1)
39p.	litho	bright mauve	2 bands	X1022	£6 Tolkien booklet (DX14), £6 (£5·64) Beatrix Potter booklet (DX15)
50p.	recess	deep ultramarine	none or phos paper	831/831a	sheets
50p.	photo	ochre-brown	2 bands	X921	sheets
50p.	photo	ochre-brown	none	X992	sheets
50p.	photo	ochre	2 bands	X922	£5 London Life (DX11)
50p.	photo	ochre	none	X993	sheets
50p.	photo	ochre	phos paper	X991a	sheets
75p.	litho	black	none	X1023/X1023a	sheets
75p.	litho	brownish grey and black	none	X1024	sheets
75p.	photo	grey-black	none	X994	sheets
£1	recess	bluish black	none	831b	sheets
£1	photo	bright yellow-green and blackish olive	none	1026	sheets
£1.30	photo	drab and deep greenish blue	none	1026b	sheets
£1.33	photo	pale mauve and grey-black	none	1026c	sheets
£1.41	photo	drab and deep greenish blue	none	1026d	sheets
£1.50	photo	pale mauve and grey-black	none	1026e	sheets
£1.60	photo	pale drab and deep greenish blue	none	1026f	sheets
£2	photo	light emerald and purple-brown	none	1027	sheets
£5	photo	salmon and chalky blue	none	1028	sheets

For 1st and 2nd class no value indicated (NVI) stamps, see Nos. 1445/1452, 1511/1516 and 1664/1672.
For table covering Machin stamps with elliptical perforations see after Nos. Y1667, etc, in 1993.
Photo/Gravure stamps were printed from both photogravure and computer engraved (Gravure) cylinders.

DECIMAL MACHIN MULTI-VALUE COIL INDEX

The following is a simplified checklist of horizontal multi-value coils, to be used in conjunction with the main listing as details of stamps listed there are not repeated.

Strip Value	Date	Contents	Cat No.
5p.	15.2.71	½p.×2, 1p.×2, 2p.	X841n
10p.	3.12.75	½p.×2, 1p., 2p., 6p.	X841q
10p.	14.12.77	½p.×2, 1p.×2, 7p.	X843l
10p.	16.1.80	1p.×2, 8p. plus 2 labels	X845m
11½p.	6.81	2½p., 3p.×3	X929l
12½p.	30.12.81	½p., 4p.×3	X924l
13p.	14.8.84	1p., 4p.×3	X925l
14p.	5.9.88	2p., 4p.×3	X928l
15p.	10.10.89	3p., 4p.×3	X930cl
17p.	27.11.90	4p.×3, 5p.	X933l
18p.	1.10.91	4p.×2, 5p.×2	X933m
19p.	31.1.95	4p., 5p.×3	X933n

Decimal Machin Booklet Pane Guide ('X' numbers) the shaded squares represent printed labels.

X841l

X841la

X841m

X841o (DX1)
£1 Wedgwood

X841p (DX1)
£1 Wedgwood

X841r

X841s

X841sa

X841t

X841ta

X841u

X841ua

X843m

X844l

X844m

X844n

X844na

X845l

X845n

X845p

X845q

X845s/sa
X845sa
imperf at left
and right

X847l

X847m (DX8)
£5 P & O

X849l

X849la

X849m

X849ma

X849n (DX2)
£3 Wedgwood

X849o (2 bands) (DX2)
£3 Wedgwood

X849p (DX3)
£4 Stanley Gibbons

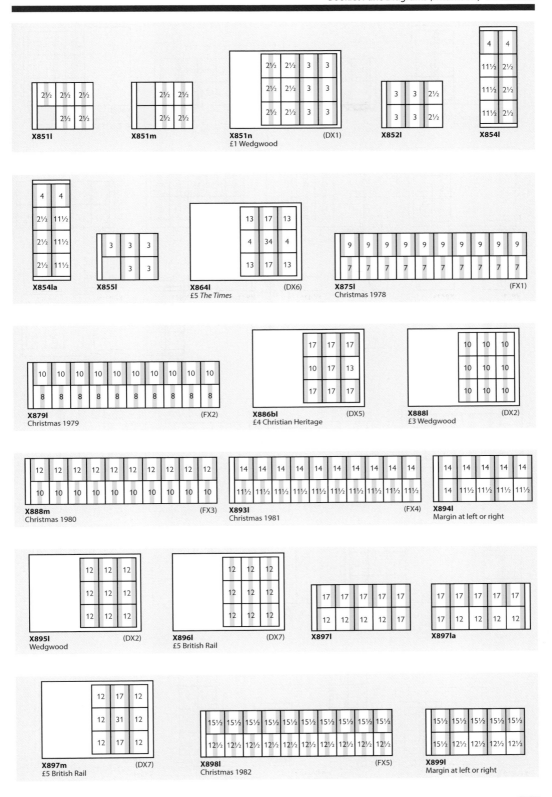

X851l

X851m

X851n (DX1)
£1 Wedgwood

X852l

X854l

X854la

X855l

X864l (DX6)
£5 *The Times*

X875l (FX1)
Christmas 1978

X879l (FX2)
Christmas 1979

X886bl (DX5)
£4 Christian Heritage

X888l (DX2)
£3 Wedgwood

X888m (FX3)
Christmas 1980

X893l (FX4)
Christmas 1981

X894l
Margin at left or right

X895l (DX2)
Wedgwood

X896l (DX7)
£5 British Rail

X897l

X897la

X897m (DX7)
£5 British Rail

X898l (FX5)
Christmas 1982

X899l
Margin at left or right

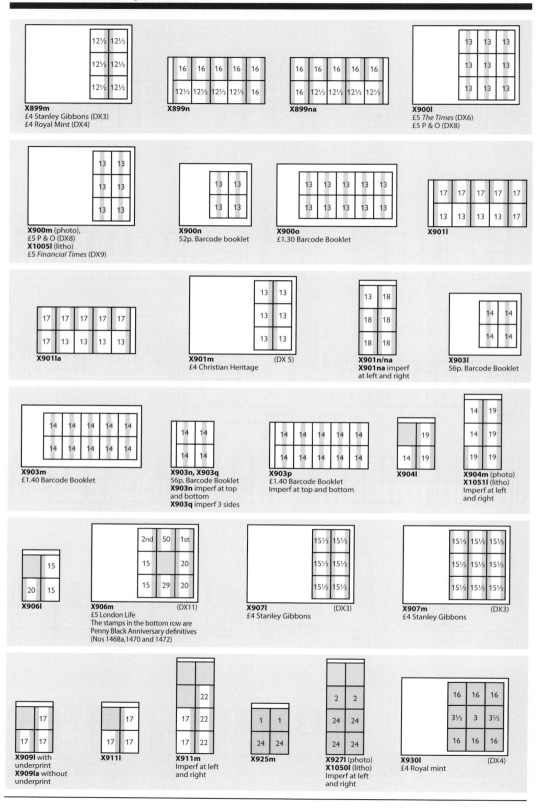

X899m
£4 Stanley Gibbons (DX3)
£4 Royal Mint (DX4)

X899n

X899na

X900l
£5 *The Times* (DX6)
£5 P & O (DX8)

X900m (photo),
£5 P & O (DX8)
X1005l (litho)
£5 *Financial Times* (DX9)

X900n
52p. Barcode booklet

X900o
£1.30 Barcode Booklet

X901l

X901la

X901m   (DX 5)
£4 Christian Heritage

X901n/na
X901na imperf
at left and right

X903l
56p. Barcode Booklet

X903m
£1.40 Barcode Booklet

X903n, X903q
56p. Barcode Booklet
X903n imperf at top
and bottom
X903q imperf 3 sides

X903p
£1.40 Barcode Booklet
Imperf at top and bottom

X904l

X904m (photo)
X1051l (litho)
Imperf at left
and right

X906l

X906m   (DX11)
£5 London Life
The stamps in the bottom row are
Penny Black Anniversary definitives
(Nos 1468a,1470 and 1472)

X907l   (DX3)
£4 Stanley Gibbons

X907m   (DX3)
£4 Stanley Gibbons

X909l with
underprint
X909la without
underprint

X911l

X911m
Imperf at left
and right

X925m

X927l (photo)
X1050l (litho)
Imperf at left
and right

X930l   (DX4)
£4 Royal mint

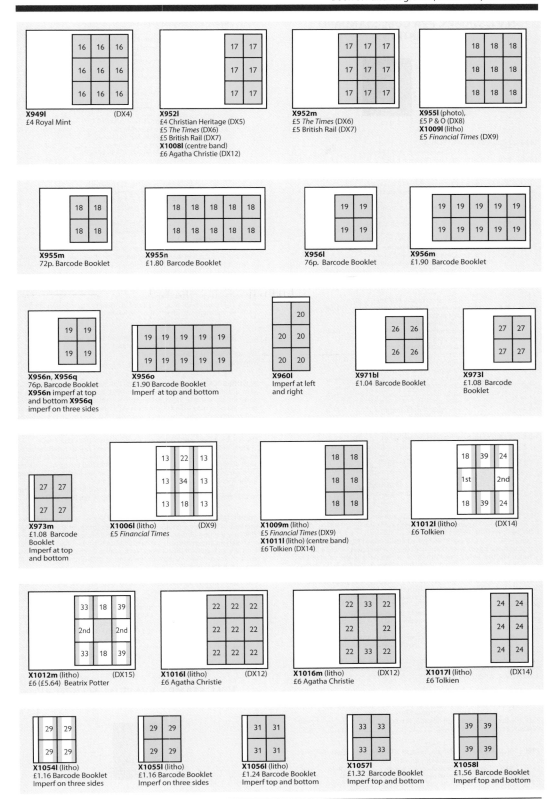

X949l (DX4)
£4 Royal Mint

X952l
£4 Christian Heritage (DX5)
£5 *The Times* (DX6)
£5 British Rail (DX7)
X1008l (centre band)
£6 Agatha Christie (DX12)

X952m (DX6)
£5 *The Times* (DX6)
£5 British Rail (DX7)

X955l (photo),
£5 P & O (DX8)
X1009l (litho)
£5 *Financial Times* (DX9)

X955m
72p. Barcode Booklet

X955n
£1.80 Barcode Booklet

X956l
76p. Barcode Booklet

X956m
£1.90 Barcode Booklet

X956n, X956q
76p. Barcode Booklet
X956n imperf at top
and bottom **X956q**
imperf on three sides

X956o
£1.90 Barcode Booklet
Imperf at top and bottom

X960l
Imperf at left
and right

X971bl
£1.04 Barcode Booklet

X973l
£1.08 Barcode
Booklet

X973m
£1.08 Barcode
Booklet
Imperf at top
and bottom

X1006l (litho) (DX9)
£5 *Financial Times*

X1009m (litho)
£5 *Financial Times* (DX9)
X1011l (litho) (centre band)
£6 Tolkien (DX14)

X1012l (litho) (DX14)
£6 Tolkien

X1012m (litho) (DX15)
£6 (£5.64) Beatrix Potter

X1016l (litho) (DX12)
£6 Agatha Christie

X1016m (litho) (DX12)
£6 Agatha Christie

X1017l (litho) (DX14)
£6 Tolkien

X1054l (litho)
£1.16 Barcode Booklet
Imperf on three sides

X1055l (litho)
£1.16 Barcode Booklet
Imperf on three sides

X1056l (litho)
£1.24 Barcode Booklet
Imperf top and bottom

X1057l
£1.32 Barcode Booklet
Imperf top and bottom

X1058l
£1.56 Barcode Booklet
Imperf top and bottom

N.V.I. STAMPS, PVA GUM, STANDARD PERFORATIONS

913   **914**

1989 (22 Aug)–93. Booklet Stamps.
(a) Photo Harrison. Perf 15×14.

1445	913	(2nd) bright blue (1 centre band).............	1·50	1·50
		l. Booklet pane. No. 1445×10 with horizontal edges of pane imperf....	15·00	
		m. Booklet pane. No. 1445×4 with three edges of pane imperf (28.11.89).........	20·00	
1446		(2nd) bright blue (1 band at right) (20.3.90).........	2·00	2·50
1447	914	(1st) brownish black (phosphorised paper).........	1·60	1·60
		l. Booklet pane. No. 1447×10 with horizontal edges of pane imperf....	13·00	
		m. Booklet pane. No. 1447×4 with three edges of pane imperf (5.12.89).........	21·00	
1448		(1st) brownish black (2 phosphor bands) (20.3.90).........	2·00	2·25

(b) Litho Walsall. Perf 14.

1449	913	(2nd) bright blue (1 centre band).........	1·50	1·50
		a. Imperf between (vert pair).........		
		l. Booklet pane. No. 1449×4 with three edges of pane imperf.........	6·00	
		m. Booklet pane. No. 1449×10 with horiz edges of pane imperf (6.8.91).........	6·50	
		n. Booklet pane. No. 1449×10 with horiz edges of pane imperf (6.8.91).........	10·00	
1450	914	(1st) blackish brown (2 phosphor bands).........	1·75	1·75
		l. Booklet pane. No. 1450×4 with three edges of pane imperf.........	7·75	
		y. Phosphor omitted.........	£400	

(c) Litho Questa. Perf 15×14.

1451	913	(2nd) bright blue (1 centre band) (19.9.89).........	1·75	1·75
		y. Phosphor omitted.........	£160	
1451a		(2nd) bright blue (1 band at right) (25.2.92).........	1·75	1·75
		ab. Band at left (10.8.93).........	1·75	1·75
		al. Booklet pane. Nos. 1451aab and 1514a, each×3, with margins all round (10.8.93).........	8·25	
		ay. Phosphor omitted.........	£450	
1452	914	(1st) brownish black (phosphorised paper) (19.9.89).........	1·25	1·25

First Day Cover (Nos. 1445, 1447)......... 3·00

Nos. 1445, 1447 and 1449/1452 were initially sold at 14p. (2nd) and 19p. (1st), but these prices were later increased to reflect new postage rates.

Nos. 1446 and 1448 come from the *se-tenant* pane in the London Life £5 Booklet. This pane is listed under No. X906m in the Decimal Machin section.

Nos. 1445, 1447 and 1449/1450 do not exist perforated on all four sides, but come with either one or two adjacent sides imperforate.

No. 1450y comes from a pane in which one stamp was without phosphor bands due to a dry print.

No. 1451a comes from the *se-tenant* panes in the Wales and Tolkien £6 booklet. These panes are listed under Nos. X1012al and W49l (Wales Regionals).

No. 1451aab comes from the £6 (£5·64) Beatrix Potter booklet.

For illustrations showing the differences between photogravure and lithography see above T **367**.

For similar designs, but in changed colours, see Nos. 1511/1516, for those with elliptical perforations, Nos. 1664/1671, and for self-adhesive versions Nos. 2039/2040 and 2295.

Special First Day of Issue Postmarks (for illustrations see Introduction)

Philatelic Bureau Edinburgh (Type G) (in red).........	4·50
Windsor, Berks (Type G) (in red).........	4·50

1990 (7 Aug)–92. Booklet stamps. As Types **913/914**, but colours changed.
(a) Photo Harrison. Perf 15×14.

1511	913	(2nd) deep blue (1 centre band).........	1·25	1·25
		l. Booklet pane. No. 1511×10 with horiz edges of pane imperf.........	10·00	

1512	914	(1st) bright orange-red (phosphorised paper).........	1·75	1·75
		l. Booklet pane. No. 1512×10 with horiz edges of pane imperf.........	13·00	

(b) Litho Questa. Perf 15×14.

1513	913	(2nd) deep blue (1 centre band).........	1·75	1·75
1514	914	(1st) bright orange-red (phosphorised paper).........	1·75	1·75
1514a		(1st) bright orange-red (2 bands) (25.2.92).........	1·75	1·75
		ay. Phosphor omitted.........	£700	

(c) Litho Walsall. Perf 14.

1515	913	(2nd) deep blue (1 centre band).........	1·60	1·60
		l. Booklet pane. No. 1515×4 with horiz edges of pane imperf.........	5·00	
		m. Booklet pane. No. 1515×10 with horiz edges of pane imperf.........	10·00	
1516	914	(1st) bright orange-red (phosphorised paper).........	1·75	1·75
		l. Booklet pane. No. 1516×4 with horiz edges of pane imperf.........	6·00	
		m. Booklet pane. No. 1516×10 with horiz edges of pane imperf.........	13·00	
		c. Perf 13.........	3·50	3·50
		cl. Booklet pane. No. 1516c×4 with horiz edges of pane imperf.........	10·00	

First Day Cover (Nos. 1511/1516)......... 3·00

Nos. 1511/1514 and 1515/1516 were initially sold at 15p. (2nd) and 20p. (1st), but these prices were later reduced to reflect new postage rates.

Nos. 1511/1512 and 1515/1516 do not exist with perforations on all four sides, but come with either the top or the bottom edge imperforate.

No. 1514a comes from the *se-tenant* panes in the £6 Wales, £6 Tolkien and £5·64 Beatrix Potter booklets. These panes are listed under Nos. X1012l, 1451al and W49a (Wales Regionals).

No. 1516c was caused by the use of an incorrect perforation comb.

For similar stamps with elliptical perforations see Nos. 1664/1672.

Special First Day of Issue Postmarks (for illustration see Introduction)

Philatelic Bureau, Edinburgh (Type G).........	3·00
Windsor, Berks (Type G).........	3·50

FLUORESCENT PHOSPHOR BANDS. Following the introduction of new automatic sorting machinery in 1991 it was found necessary to substantially increase the signal emitted by the phosphor bands. This was achieved by adding a fluorescent element to the phosphor which appears yellow under UV light. This combination was first used on an experimental sheet printing of the 18p., No. X913, produced by Enschedé in 1991. All values with phosphor bands from the elliptical perforations issue, including the No Value Indicated design, originally showed this yellow fluor.

From mid-1995 printings of current sheet and booklet stamps began to appear with the colour of the fluorescent element changed to blue. As such differences in fluor colour can only be identified by use of a UV lamp they are outside the scope of this catalogue, but full details will be found in the *Great Britain Specialised Catalogue Volume 4*.

The first commemorative/special stamp issue to show the change to blue fluor was the Centenary of Rugby League set, Nos. 1891/1895.

COMPUTER-ENGRAVED CYLINDERS. In 1991 Enschedé introduced a new method of preparing photogravure cylinders for Great Britain stamps. This new method utilised computer-engraving instead of the traditional acid-etching and produced cylinders without the minor flaws which had long been a feature of the photogravure process. Such cylinders were first used on Great Britain stamps for the printing of the 18p. released on 19 November 1991 (see No. X913).

Harrison and Sons continued to use the acid-etching method until mid-1996 after which most Machin values, including NVI's, were produced from computer-engraved cylinders using a very similar process to that of Enschedé. Some values exist in versions from both cylinder production methods and can often be identified by minor differences. Such stamps are, however, outside the scope of this listing, but full details can be found in the current edition of the *Great Britain Specialised Catalogue Volume 4*.

For commemorative stamps the first Harrison issue to use computer-engraved cylinders was the Centenary of Cinema set (Nos. 1920/1924).

When Walsall introduced photogravure printing in 1997 their cylinders were produced using a similar computer-engraved process.

N.V.I. STAMPS, PVA GUM, ELLIPTICAL PERFORATIONS

1093a

1993 (6 Apr)–**2017**. As Types **913/914**, and **1093a**. Perf 14 (No. 1665) or 15×14 (others) (both with one elliptical hole in each vertical side).

(a) Photo/gravure
Harrison No. 1666
Questa Nos. 1664a, 1667a
Walsall/ISP Walsall Nos. 1665, 1668s
Harrison/De La Rue, Questa or Walsall No. 1667
Harrison/De La Rue, Enschedé, Questa or Walsall/ISP Walsall Nos. 1664, 1668, 1669.

1664	**913**	(2nd) bright blue (1 centre band) (7.9.93).............................	1·25	1·25
		a. Perf 14 (1.12.98)..............................	1·50	1·50
		b. Imperf (pair)...................................	£950	
		l. Booklet pane. Nos. 1664 and 1667×3 plus 4 labels ('postcode' on top right label) (27.4.00)..........	6·75	
		la. As No. 1664l, but inscr 'postcodes' on top right label (17.4.01).............................	8·25	
		m. Booklet pane. Nos. 1664×2 and 1667×6 (27.4.00).......................	8·50	
		n. Booklet pane. Nos. 1664 and 1669, each×4, with central label and margins all round (6.2.02)......	14·00	
		o. Booklet pane. Nos. 1664 and 1668, each×4, with central label and margins all round (2.6.03)......	12·00	
		p. Booklet pane. Nos. 1664×4, Y1709×2 and Y1715×2, with central label and margins all round (24.2.05)...........................	6·00	
1665		(2nd) bright blue (1 band at right) (13.10.98)................................	1·60	1·60
		c. Band at left..............................	1·60	1·60
		l. Booklet pane. Nos. 1665×3 and NI81b, S91a and W80a with margins all round....................	6·00	
1666	**914**	(1st) bright orange-red (phosphorised paper).....................	1·20	1·20
1667		(1st) bright orange-red (2 phosphor bands) (4.4.95)........................	1·50	1·50
		y. Phosphor omitted........................	£225	
		a. Perf 14 (1.12.98)..........................	1·50	1·50
		l. Booklet pane. Nos. 1667×8 with central label and margins all round (16.2.99).........................	11·00	
		m. Booklet pane. Nos. 1667×4 plus commemorative label at right (12.5.99)................................	5·00	
1668		(1st) gold (2 phosphor bands) (21.4.97).................................	1·50	1·50
		a. Imperf (pair).............................	£175	
		l. Booklet pane. Nos. 1668 and Y1692, each×4, and central label with margins all round (23.9.97)..	4·50	
		m. Booklet pane. Nos. 1668/1669, each×4, with central label and margins all round (24.9.02)...........	14·00	
		o. Booklet pane. Nos. 1668 and Y1704, each×4, with central label and margins all round (16.3.04)................................	5·00	
		p. Booklet pane. Nos. 1668×4, Y1715×2 and Y1723×2, with central label and margins all round (25.5.04)............................	8·00	
		q. Booklet pane. Nos. 1668×4, Y1726×2 and Y1736×2, with central label and margins all round (18.10.05)............................	6·00	
		r. Booklet pane. Nos. 1668×4, Y1701×2 and Y1711×2, with central label and margins all round (23.2.06)............................	5·00	
1668s		(1st) brownish black (2 phosphor bands) (5.6.17)........................	3·00	3·00
		sl. Booklet pane. Nos. 1668s, 2133×2, 1667/1668, 2124, 2651 and U3067 with central label and margins all round (5.6.17)......	14·00	
1669	**1093a**	(E) deep blue (2 phosphor bands) (19.1.99)................................	3·00	3·00

(b) Litho Questa or Walsall (No. 1670), Enschedé, Questa or Walsall (No. 1671) or De La Rue or Walsall (No. 1672).

1670	**913**	(2nd) bright blue (1 centre band).............	1·40	1·40
		y. Phosphor omitted.......................	£175	
		l. Booklet pane. Nos. 1670 and 1672, each×4, with central label and margins all round (18.9.08)..............	5·00	
1671	**914**	(1st) bright orange-red (2 phosphor bands).................................	1·50	1·50
		y. Phosphor omitted........................	£200	
		l. Booklet pane. Nos. 1671×4 plus commemorative label at left (27.7.94)................................	5·00	

	la. Ditto, but with commemorative label at right (16.5.95)......................	5·00	
	ly. Phosphor omitted...........................	£400	
	m. Pane. No. 1671 with margins all round (roulette 8 across top corners of pane) (Boots logo on margin) (17.8.94).........................	2·00	
	my. Phosphor omitted............................	£1500	
	ma. Without Boots logo above stamp (11.9.95).....................................	2·00	
	mb. Ditto, but roulette 10 across top corners of pane (20.2.97)..................	4·00	
	n. Booklet pane. No. 1671×9 with margins all round (16.2.99)..................	12·00	
1672	(1st) gold (2 phosphor bands) (8.1.08)....	1·50	1·50
	y. Phosphor omitted............................	£1250	
	l. Booklet pane. No. 1672×8 with central label and margins all round (8.1.08)................................	11·00	

For details of sheets, booklets, etc containing these stamps see Decimal Machin Index following the 'Y' numbers.

Nos. 1664/1671 were issued in booklet panes showing perforations on all four edges.

On 6 September 1993 Nos. 1670/1671 printed in lithography by Questa were made available in sheets from post offices in Birmingham, Coventry, Falkirk and Milton Keynes. These sheet stamps became available nationally on 5 October 1993. On 29 April 1997 No. 1664 printed in photogravure by Walsall became available in sheets. On the same date Nos. 1664 and 1667 were issued in coils printed by Harrison. Sheets of No. 1667 were printed by Walsall from 18 November 1997.

No. 1665 exists with the phosphor band at the left or right of the stamp from separate panes of the £6·16 Speed stamp booklet No. DX21.

For pane containing No. 1665c see No. Y1676al.

No. 1668 was originally printed by Harrisons in booklets and Walsall in sheets and booklets for The Queen's Golden Wedding and issued on 21 April 1997. It was printed in coils by Enschedé (5.10.02), when gold became the accepted colour for 1st class definitives, and later in sheets and coils by De La Rue.

Booklet pane No. 1668m was issued on 24 September 2002 in the £6·83 Across the Universe booklet (No. DX29). It was issued again with a different central label on 25 February 2003 in the £6·99 Microcosmos booklet (No. DX30).

No. 1669 was intended for the basic European airmail rate, initially 30p., and was at first only available from Barcode booklet No. HF1, printed by Walsall. It appeared in sheets printed by De La Rue on 5 October 1999.

No. 1671m, printed by Questa, was provided by the Royal Mail for inclusion in single pre-packed greetings cards. The pane shows large margins at top and sides with lines of roulette gauging 8 stretching from the bottom corners to the mid point of the top edge. Examples included with greetings cards show the top two corners of the pane folded over. Unfolded examples were available from the British Philatelic Bureau and from other Post Office philatelic outlets. The scheme was originally limited to Boots and their logo appeared on the pane margin. Other card retailers subsequently participated and later supplies omitted the logo.

A further printing by Enschedé in 1997 showed the roulettes gauging 10 (No. 1671mb). Blank pieces of gummed paper have been found showing the perforation and rouletting of No. 1671mb, but no printing.

No. 1672 was only issued in the following booklets: £7·40 Ian Fleming's James Bond (No. DX41), Pilot to Plane (No. DX42) and Charles Darwin (No. DX45).

For illustration of differences between lithography and gravure see below Types **367** and **367a**.

For self-adhesive stamps in these colours see Nos. 2039/2040 and 2295/2298.

POSTAL FORGERIES. In mid-1994 a number of postal forgeries of the 2nd bright blue printed in lithography were detected after having been rejected by the sorting equipment. These show the Queen's head in bright greenish blue, have a fluorescent, rather than a phosphor, band and show matt, colourless gum on the reverse. These forgeries come from booklets of ten which also have forged covers.

COMMEMORATIVE BOOKLET PANES. Booklets of four 1st Class stamps with *se-tenant* commemorative label were issued for the following anniversaries or events:
  300th Anniversary of the Bank of England (No. 1671l)
  Birth Centenary of R. J. Mitchell (No. 1671la)
  70th Birthday of Queen Elizabeth II (No. 1671la)
  Hong Kong '97 International Stamp Exhibition (No. 1671la)
  Commonwealth Heads of Government Meeting, Edinburgh (No. 1671la)
  50th Birthday of Prince of Wales (No. 1671la)
  50th Anniversary of Berlin Airlift (No. 1667m)
  Rugby World Cup (No. 1667m)

First Day Covers

21.4.97	1st (No. 1668), 26p. (No. Y1692) (Type G) (Philatelic Bureau or Windsor)	3·25
23.9.97	BBC label pane 1st×4, 26p.×4 (No. 1668l), (Philatelic Bureau or London W1)	6·50
19.1.99	E (No. 1669) (Type G) (Philatelic Bureau or Windsor)	2·75
16.2.99	Profile on Print label pane 1st×8 (No. 1671n) (see Nos. 2077/2079) (Philatelic Bureau or London SW1)	5·50
6.2.02	A Gracious Accession label pane 2nd×4 and E×4 (No. 1664n) (see Nos. 2253/2257) (Tallents House or Windsor)	7·00

24.9.02	Across the Universe label pane 1st×4, E×4 (No. 1668m) (Tallents House or Star, Glenrothes)	5·00
25.2.03	Microcosmos label pane 1st×4, E×4 (No. 1668m) (Tallents House or Cambridge)	5·00
2.6.03	A Perfect Coronation label pane 2nd×4, 1st×4 (No. 1664o) (Tallents House or London SW1)	6·50
16.3.04	Letters by Night. A Tribute to the Travelling Post Office label pane 1st×4, 37p.×4 (No. 1668o) (Tallents House or London NW10)	7·50
25.5.04	The Glory of the Garden label pane 1st×4, 42p.×2, 47p.×2 (No. 1668p) (Tallents House or Wisley, Woking)	8·00
24.2.05	The Brontë Sisters label pane 2nd×4, 39p.×2, 42p.×2 (No. 1664p) (Tallents House or Haworth, Keighley)	5·00
18.10.05	Bicentenary of the Battle of Trafalgar label pane 1st×4, 50p.×2 and 68p.×2 (No. 1668q) (Tallents House and Portsmouth)	7·00
23.2.06	Birth Bicentenary of Isambard Kingdom Brunel label pane 1st×4, 35p.×2 and 40p.×2 (No. 1668r) (Tallents House or Bristol)	7·00
8.1.08	James Bond label pane 1st×8 (No. 1672l) (Tallents House or London SE1)	11·00
18.9.08	Pilot to Plane RAF Uniforms label pane 2nd×4 and 1st×4 (No.1670l) (Tallents House or Hendon, London NW9)	5·00
5.6.17	50th Anniversary of the Machin Definitive label pane 1st×6 and 20p.×2 (No. 1668sl). (Tallents House or High Wycombe)	12·00

1390

1390a

1390b

1999 (16 Feb).

(a) Embossed and litho Walsall. Self-adhesive. Die-cut perf 14×15.

2077	**1390**	(1st) grey (face value) (Queen's head in colourless relief) (phosphor background around head)..............	2·00	2·00
		l. Booklet pane. No. 2077×4 with margins all round..............................	8·00	

(b) Eng C. Slania. Recess Enschedé. Perf 14×14½.

2078	**1390a**	(1st) grey-black (2 phosphor bands)....	2·00	2·00
		l. Booklet pane. No. 2078×4 with margins all round.........................	8·00	

(c) Typo Harrison. Perf 14×15.

2079	**1390b**	(1st) black (2 phosphor bands).............	2·00	2·00
		y. Phosphor omitted..........................	£1200	
		l. Booklet pane. No. 2079×4 with margins all round.........................	8·00	
		ly. Booklet pane. Phosphor omitted..	6·00	6·00
Set of 3..			4·00	4·00
First Day Covers (Philatelic Bureau) (3 covers with Nos. 2077l, 2078l, 2079l)...				7·00
First Day Covers (London SW1) (3 covers with Nos. 2077l, 2078l, 2079l)...				7·00

Nos. 2077/2079 were only issued in the £7·54 Profile on Print booklet (No. DX22).

NVI Stamps. Panes with 'standard' perforations

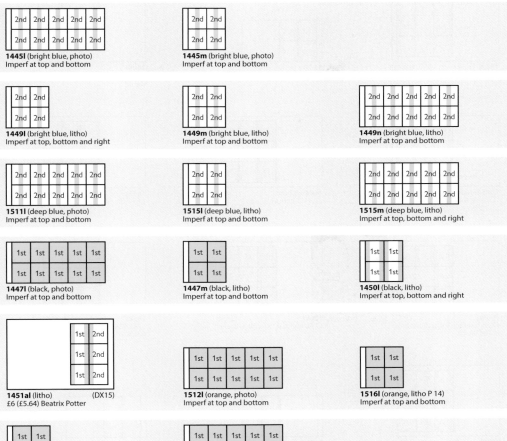

1445l (bright blue, photo)
Imperf at top and bottom

1445m (bright blue, photo)
Imperf at top and bottom

1449l (bright blue, litho)
Imperf at top, bottom and right

1449m (bright blue, litho)
Imperf at top and bottom

1449n (bright blue, litho)
Imperf at top and bottom

1511l (deep blue, photo)
Imperf at top and bottom

1515l (deep blue, litho)
Imperf at top and bottom

1515m (deep blue, litho)
Imperf at top, bottom and right

1447l (black, photo)
Imperf at top and bottom

1447m (black, litho)
Imperf at top and bottom

1450l (black, litho)
Imperf at top, bottom and right

1451al (litho)   (DX15)
£6 (£5.64) Beatrix Potter

1512l (orange, photo)
Imperf at top and bottom

1516l (orange, litho P 14)
Imperf at top and bottom

1516cl (orange, litho, P 13)
Imperf at top and bottom

1516m (orange, litho)
Imperf at top and bottom

NVI Stamps. Panes with **elliptical perforations** the shaded squares represent printed labels.

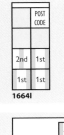

1664l

1664la

1664m

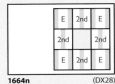

1664n   (DX28)
£7.29 A Gracious Accession

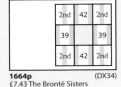

1664o   (DX31)
£7.46 A Perfect Coronation

1664p   (DX34)
£7.43 The Brontë Sisters

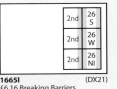

1665l   (DX21)
£6.16 Breaking Barriers

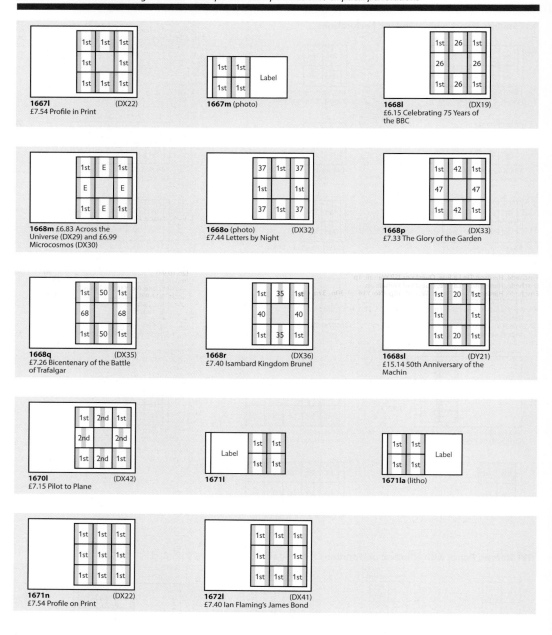

1667l (DX22)
£7.54 Profile in Print

1667m (photo)

1668l (DX19)
£6.15 Celebrating 75 Years of
the BBC

1668m £6.83 Across the
Universe (DX29) and £6.99
Microcosmos (DX30)

1668o (photo) (DX32)
£7.44 Letters by Night

1668p (DX33)
£7.33 The Glory of the Garden

1668q (DX35)
£7.26 Bicentenary of the Battle
of Trafalgar

1668r (DX36)
£7.40 Isambard Kingdom Brunel

1668sl (DY21)
£15.14 50th Anniversary of the
Machin

1670l (DX42)
£7.15 Pilot to Plane

1671l

1671la (litho)

1671n (DX22)
£7.54 Profile on Print

1672l (DX41)
£7.40 Ian Flaming's James Bond

DENOMINATED STAMPS, PVA GUM, ELLIPTICAL PERFORATIONS

Two types of the 54p. (Nos. Y1728/Y1783)

II Normal figures of face value

III Open '4' and open lower curve of '5'

1993 (27 Apr)–**2017**. As Nos. X841, etc, but Perf 15×14 (with one elliptical hole in each vertical side).

Enschedé: 20p. (No. Y1684), 29p., 35p. (No. Y1698), 36p., 38p. (No. Y1706), 41p. (No. Y1712), 43p. (No. Y1716)

Harrison: 20p. (No. Y1686), 25p. (No. Y1689), 26p. (No. Y1692), 35p. (No. Y1699), 41p. (No. Y1713), 43p. (No. Y1717)

Walsall: 10p. (No. Y1676a), 19p. (No. Y1683), 38p. (No. Y1707a), 43p. (No. Y1717a).

Enschedé or Harrison/De La Rue: 4p., 5p., 6p., 25p. (No. Y1690), 31p., 39p. (No. Y1708), £1 (No. Y1743)

Enschedé, Harrison/De La Rue, Questa or ISP Walsall: 1p.

Enschedé, Harrison/De La Rue, Questa or Walsall: 2p.

Enschedé, Harrison/De La Rue or Walsall: 10p. (No. Y1676), 30p., 37p. (No. Y1703), 42p., 50p. (No. Y1726), 63p.

Harrison/De La Rue or Questa: 19p. (No. Y1682), 20p. (No. Y1685), 26p. (No. Y1691)

De La Rue or Walsall: 8p. (No. Y1707), 39p. (No. Y1709), 40p. (No. Y1710), 64p., 65p., 68p.

De La Rue: 7p., 8p., 9p., 12p., 14p., 15p., 16p., 17p., 20p. (No. Y1687), 22p., 33p., 34p., 35p. (No. Y1700), 37p. (Nos. Y1704/Y1705), 41p. (No. Y1714), 43p. (No. Y1718), 44p., 45p., 48p., 49p., 50p., (No. Y1727), 56p., 60p., 62p., 67p., 72p., 78p., 81p., 88p., 90p., 97p., £1 (No. Y1744), £1·46, £1·50, £2, £3, £5

Enschedé or De La Rue: 35p. (No. Y1701), 40p. (No. Y1711), 46p., 47p., 54p.

(a) Photo/gravure.

Y1667	**367**	1p. crimson (2 bands) (8.6.93)................	20	20
		l. Booklet pane. Nos. Y1667×2, Y1685 and Y1691×3 plus 2 labels (1.12.98)................	19·00	
		m. Booklet pane. Nos. Y1667/Y1668, Y1682 and Y1691×3 plus 2 labels (26.4.99)................	6·00	
		n. Booklet pane. Nos. Y1667×4, Y1682×3 and Y1691 with central label and margins all round (21.9.99)................	1·50	
		o. Booklet pane. Nos. Y1667×2, Y1722×4 and Y1728×2 with central label and margins all round (20.9.07)................	4·50	
		p. Booklet pane. Nos. Y1667, Y1668, Y1670, Y1676, Y1687, Y1727, 1664 and U3061, with central label and margins all round (5.6.17)................	30·00	
Y1668		2p. deep green (2 bands) (11.4.95)........	20	20
		a. Imperf (pair)................	£750	
		l. Booklet pane. Nos. Y1668×4 and Nos. Y1722 and Y1724, each×2 with centre label and margins all round (5.6.07)................	6·50	
		m. Booklet pane. Nos. Y1668×2, Y1676×2 and U3060×4 with central label and margins all round (10.1.12)................	15·00	
Y1669		4p. new blue (2 bands) (14.12.93)........	30	30
		a. Imperf................	£950	
Y1670		5p. dull red-brown (Type II) (2 bands) (8.6.93)................	30	30
		l. Booklet pane. Nos. Y1670 and 2651, each×4, with centre label and margins all round (1.3.07)................	3·50	
Y1671		6p. yellow-olive (2 bands)................	40	40
		y. Phosphor omitted................	£180	
Y1672		7p. grey (2 bands) (20.4.99)................	2·00	2·25
		a. Imperf (pair)................	£325	
Y1673		7p. bright magenta (2 bands) (1.4.04)...	45	45
		a. Imperf (pair)................	£100	
Y1674		8p. yellow (2 bands) (25.4.00)................	45	45
Y1675		9p. yellow-orange (2 bands) (5.4.05)......	45	45
Y1676		10p. dull orange (2 bands) (8.6.93)........	45	45
		aa. Imperf pair................	£900	
		a. Perf 14 (13.10.98)................	1·25	1·25
		al. Booklet pane. Nos. Y1676a×2, 1665c and Y1717a, each×3, with centre label and margins all round................	5·00	

Y1677	12p. greenish blue (2 bands) (1.8.06)...	50	60
Y1678	14p. rose-red (2 bands) (1.8.06)................	50	60
Y1679	15p. bright magenta (2 bands) (1.4.08)..	50	60
Y1680	16p. pale cerise (2 bands) (27.3.07)........	50	60
Y1681	17p. brown-olive (2 bands) (31.3.09).......	50	60
	a. Imperf (pair)................	£1300	
Y1682	19p. bistre (1 centre band) (26.10.93).....	50	60
	a. Imperf (pair)................	£475	
	y. Phosphor omitted................	80·00	
	l. Booklet pane. Nos. Y1682 and Y1691×7 (26.4.99)................	6·50	
	ly. Phosphor omitted................	£150	
Y1683	19p. bistre (1 band at right) (perf 14) (15.2.00)................	60	60
	l. Booklet pane. Nos. Y1683×4 and Y1707a×2 with margins all round..	8·50	
Y1684	20p. turquoise-green (2 bands) (14.12.93)................	60	60
Y1685	20p. bright green (1 centre band) (25.6.96)................	60	70
	a. Imperf (horiz pair)................	£175	
	l. Booklet pane. Nos. Y1685 and Y1691×7 (1.12.98)................	18·00	
Y1686	20p. bright green (1 band at right) (23.9.97)................	80	1·10
	l. Booklet pane. Nos. Y1686 and Y1691, each×3 with margins all round................	2·50	
Y1687	20p. bright green (2 bands) (20.4.99)......	60	70
	a. Imperf (pair)................	£175	
Y1688	22p. drab (2 bands) (31.3.09)................	70	70
Y1689	25p. rose-red (phosphorised paper) (26.10.93)................	70	70
	a. Imperf (pair)................	£800	
	l. Booklet pane. No. Y1689×2 plus 2 labels (1.11.93)................	1·00	
Y1690	25p. rose-red (2 bands) (20.12.94)........	70	70
	y. Phosphor omitted................	24·00	
	l. Booklet pane. No. Y1690×2 plus 2 labels (6.6.95)................	1·75	
Y1691	26p. red-brown (2 bands) (25.6.96)........	70	70
	a. Imperf (pair)................	£500	
	y. Phosphor omitted................	10·00	
Y1692	26p. gold (2 bands) (21.4.97)................	80	80
	a. Imperf (horiz pair)................	—	
Y1693	29p. grey (2 bands) (26.10.93)................	80	80
Y1694	30p. deep olive-grey (2 bands) (27.7.93)................	80	80
	a. Imperf (pair)................	£900	
Y1695	31p. deep mauve (2 bands) (25.6.96)......	90	90
Y1696	33p. grey-green (2 bands) (25.4.00)........	90	90
Y1697	34p. yellow-olive (2 bands) (6.5.03)........	4·25	4·75
Y1698	35p. yellow (2 bands) (17.8.93)................	90	90
Y1699	35p. yellow (phosphorised paper) (1.11.93)................	5·25	6·00
Y1700	35p. sepia (2 bands) (1.4.04)................	90	90
	a. Imperf (pair)................	£200	
Y1701	35p. yellow-olive (5.4.05) (1 centre band)................	90	90
Y1702	36p. bright ultramarine (2 bands) (26.10.93)................	90	1·25
Y1703	37p. bright mauve (2 bands) (25.6.96)....	1·00	1·00
Y1704	37p. grey-black (2 bands) (4.7.02)........	1·10	1·25
Y1705	37p. brown-olive (1 centre band) (28.3.06)................	1·10	1·25
Y1706	38p. rosine (2 bands) (26.10.93)................	1·10	1·25
	a. Imperf (pair)................	£375	
Y1707	38p. ultramarine (2 bands) (20.4.99)......	1·10	1·25
	a. Perf 14 (15.2.00)................	3·25	4·50
Y1708	39p. bright magenta (2 bands) (25.6.96)................	1·00	1·00
	a. Imperf (pair)................	£900	
Y1709	39p. grey (2 bands) (1.4.04)................	1·00	1·00
	a. Imperf (pair)................	£200	
Y1710	40p. deep azure (2 bands) (25.4.00).......	1·00	1·10
Y1711	40p. turquoise-blue (2 bands) (1.4.04)...	1·00	1·10
	a. Imperf (pair)................	£200	
Y1712	41p. grey-brown (2 bands) (26.10.93).....	1·00	1·10
Y1713	41p. drab (phosphorised paper) (1.11.93)................	6·25	6·25
Y1714	41p. rosine (2 bands) (25.4.00)................	1·25	1·25
Y1715	42p. deep olive-grey (4.7.02)................	1·00	1·10
Y1716	43p. deep olive-brown (2 bands) (25.6.96)................	1·50	2·50
Y1717	43p. sepia (2 bands) (8.7.96)................	4·00	5·25
	a. Perf 14 (13.10.98)................	1·75	2·50
Y1718	43p. emerald (2 bands) (1.4.04)................	1·75	1·75
	a. Imperf (pair)................	£200	
Y1719	44p. grey-brown (2 bands) (20.4.99)......	3·25	4·00
Y1720	44p. deep bright blue (2 bands) (28.3.06)................	1·25	1·25
Y1721	45p. bright mauve (2 bands) (25.4.00)....	1·25	1·25
Y1722	46p. yellow (2 bands) (5.4.05)................	3·00	3·25
Y1723	47p. turquoise-green (2 bands) (4.7.02)..	1·25	1·25
Y1724	48p. bright mauve (2 bands) (27.3.07)....	1·50	2·25
Y1725	49p. red-brown (2 bands) (28.3.06)........	3·25	4·00
Y1726	50p. ochre (2 bands) (14.12.93)................	1·50	1·50
	a. Imperf (pair)................	£1500	
Y1727	50p. grey (2 bands) (27.3.07)................	1·60	1·60

Y1728		54p. red-brown (Type II) (2 bands) (27.3.07)........	1·50	1·50
Y1729		56p. yellow-olive (2 bands) (1.4.08)........	1·60	1·60
Y1730		60p. light emerald (2 bands) (30.3.10).....	3·25	4·00
Y1731		62p. rosine (2 bands) (31.3.09)........	3·25	4·00
Y1732		63p. light emerald (2 bands) (25.6.96)....	1·60	1·60
Y1733		64p. turquoise-green (2 bands) (20.4.99)........	1·60	1·60
Y1734		65p. greenish blue (2 bands) (25.4.00)...	1·60	1·60
Y1735		67p. bright mauve (2 bands) (30.3.10)....	1·75	1·75
Y1736		68p. grey-brown (2 bands) (4.7.02)........	1·75	1·75
Y1737		72p. rosine (2 bands) (28.3.06)........	3·50	4·00
Y1738		78p. emerald (2 bands) (27.3.07)........	1·90	1·90
Y1739		81p. turquoise-green (2 bands) (1.4.08)...	1·90	1·90
Y1740		88p. bright magenta (2 bands) (30.3.10)........	1·90	1·90
Y1741		90p. ultramarine (2 bands) (31.3.09)......	2·00	2·00
Y1742		97p. violet (2 bands) (30.3.10)........	2·00	2·00
Y1743		£1 bluish violet (2 bands) (22.8.95)........	2·50	2·50
		a. Imperf (horiz pair)........................	£950	
Y1744		£1 magenta (2 bands) (5.6.07).............	2·50	2·50
		l. Booklet pane. No. Y1744×2 with centre label and margins all round	4·00	
Y1745		£1·46 greenish blue (2 bands) (30.3.10)....	3·00	4·25
Y1746		£1·50 brown-red (2 bands) (1.7.03)........	2·50	2·50
Y1747		£2 deep blue-green (2 bands) (1.7.03)...	3·00	3·00
		a. Missing '£' in value (R. 18/1, Cyl D1 no dot)........	£250	
Y1748		£3 deep mauve (2 bands) (1.7.03)........	4·50	4·50
Y1749		£5 azure (2 bands) (1.7.03)........	7·50	7·50

(b) Litho Cartor (1p. (No. Y1761)), 5p. (Nos. Y1763/Y1765), 10p. (No. Y1768),
16p., 17p., 20p., (No. Y1773), 22p., 50p., 54p., 60p. (No. Y1785), 62p., 67p.,
90p., 97p.)
De La Rue (5p. (No. Y1762))
Questa, De La Rue or Cartor (10p. (No. Y1767))
Questa or Walsall (25p., 35p,.)
Walsall (37p., 41p. (No. Y1780) 60p. (No. Y1784), 63p.),
De La Rue (48p.)
Questa (others).

Y1760	**367**	1p. lake (2 bands) (8.7.96)......................	30	30
		y. Phosphor omitted...........................	£500	
		l. Booklet pane. Nos. Y1760×2, Y1772 and Y1776×3 plus 2 labels...	3·50	
		ly. Booklet pane. Phosphor omitted...	£1200	
Y1761		1p. reddish purple (2 bands) (17.9.09)..	2·25	3·00
		l. Booklet pane. Nos. Y1761×2, Y1770×4 and Y1789×2 with central label and margins all round........	8·50	
Y1762		5p. chocolate (2 bands)(Type II) (12.2.09)........	3·00	2·50
		y. Phosphor omitted...........................	£1800	
		l. Booklet pane. Nos. 1672, Y1762, Y1767 and Y1781, each×2 with central label........	7·00	
Y1763		5p. red-brown (*shades*) (13.5.10)............	1·75	3·25
		l. Booklet pane. Nos. Y1763×4, Y1767×2 and Y1785×2, with central label and margins all round........	7·00	
		m. Booklet pane. Nos. Y1763×4, U3155×2 and U3078×2 with central label and margins all round (9.9.11)........	20·00	
Y1764		5p. lake-brown (22.3.11)............	2·50	3·50
		l. Booklet pane. Nos. Y1764×3, Y1767×3, Y1788 and Y1790, with central label and margins all round........	18·00	
Y1765		5p. red-brown (2 bands) (Type III) (7.1.10)........	4·00	5·00
		l. Booklet pane. Nos. Y1765×2, Y1768×5 and Y1774×2 with margins all round........	7·00	
Y1766		6p. yellow-olive (2 bands) (26.7.94)......	6·00	7·25
		l. Booklet pane. Nos. Y1766, Y1771 and Y1775×4 with margins all round........	7·00	
		la. 6p. value misplaced........................	£4000	
Y1767		10p. dull orange (*shades*) (2 bands) (25.4.95)........	2·50	2·50
		y. Phosphor omitted...........................	£1800	
		l. Booklet pane. Nos. Y1767, Y1771/ Y1771a, Y1775×2, Y1777/Y1778, Y1780a and centre label with margins all round........	8·50	
Y1768		10p. pale brownish orange (7.1.10)........	2·50	2·50
Y1769		16p. pale cerise (2 bands) (13.1.09)........	2·25	2·25
		l. Booklet pane. Nos. Y1769 and Y1782, each×10, with central label...	16·00	
Y1770		17p. bistre (2 bands) (18.8.09)............	2·25	2·25
		l. Booklet pane. Nos. Y1770×4, Y1774×2 and Y1786×2 with central label and margins all round........	8·50	
Y1771		19p. bistre (1 band at left) (26.7.94)........	80	80
		a. Band at right (25.4.95)......................	80	80

		l. Booklet pane. Nos. Y1771/Y1771a, each×3 with margins all round (25.4.95)........	3·50	
Y1772		20p. bright yellow-green (1 centre band) (8.7.96)........	2·50	2·50
		y. Phosphor omitted...........................	£125	
		l. Booklet pane. Nos. Y1772 and Y1776×7........	4·00	
		ly. Booklet pane. Phosphor omitted...	£200	
Y1773		20p. light green (2 bands) (7.1.10)........	2·50	2·50
		l. Booklet pane. Nos. Y1773×4, Y1783×2 and Y1786×2 with central label and margins all round........	11·00	
Y1774		22p. olive-brown (2 bands) (18.8.09)......	3·25	4·00
		l. Booklet pane. Nos. Y1774 and Y1783, each×4 with central label and margins all round (25.2.10)........	8·00	
Y1775		25p. red (2 bands) (1.11.93)............	75	75
		l. Booklet pane. Nos. Y1775, NI72, S84 and W73, each×2, with centre label and margins all round (14.5.96)........	2·75	
Y1776		26p. chestnut (2 bands) (8.7.96)............	65	75
		y. Phosphor omitted...........................	20·00	
Y1777		30p. olive-grey (2 bands) (25.4.95)......	2·25	3·00
Y1778		35p. yellow (2 bands) (1.11.93)............	75	90
Y1779		37p. bright mauve (2 bands) (8.7.96)......	2·50	2·50
Y1780		41p. drab (2 bands) (1.11.93)............	1·10	1·10
		a. Grey-brown (25.4.95)........................	1·25	2·00
		y. Phosphor omitted...........................	£800	
Y1781		48p. bright mauve (2 bands) (12.2.09)......	2·50	3·50
		y. Phosphor omitted...........................	£1800	
Y1782		50p. grey (2 bands) (13.1.09)............	3·25	4·00
Y1783		54p. chestnut (2 bands) (Type III) (7.1.10)........	3·25	4·00
Y1784		60p. dull blue-grey (2 bands) (9.8.94)......	1·25	1·25
Y1785		60p. emerald (2 bands) (13.5.10)............	5·50	6·50
Y1786		62p. emerald (2 bands) (18.8.09)............	3·50	4·25
Y1787		63p. light emerald (2 bands) (8.7.96)......	3·25	4·25
		y. Phosphor omitted...........................	£525	
Y1788		67p. bright mauve (2 bands) (22.3.11)......	8·50	12·00
Y1789		90p. bright blue (2 bands) (17.9.09)........	4·00	5·75
Y1790		97p. bluish violet (2 bands) (22.3.11)......	8·50	12·00

(c) Eng C. Slania. Recess Enschedé (until March 2000) or De La Rue (from 11 April 2000).

Y1800	**367**	£1·50 red (9.3.99)........	3·25	3·25
Y1801		£2 dull blue (9.3.99)........	3·75	3·75
Y1802		£3 dull violet (9.3.99)........	5·00	5·00
Y1803		£5 brown (9.3.99)........	7·50	7·50
		a. Imperf (pair)........	£600	

PHQ Card (D7) (No. Y1725)........ 50 / 8·00

PHQ Cards (D30) (Nos. 1664, 1668, Y1667/Y1668, Y1670, Y1675/Y1676, Y1679/Y1680, Y1685/Y1724, Y1727, Y1729, Y1739, Y1744, Y1746/Y1749, 2357a, 2652/2653, 2358/2359)......... 7·00

Nos. Y1743/Y1749 are printed in Iriodin ink which gives a shiny effect to the solid part of the background behind the Queen's head.

A gravure-printed £5 stamp, as No. Y1749 but in sepia is believed to have come from stock stolen from the printer. Both unused and used examples are known.

No. Y1766la shows the 6p. value printed 22 mm to the left so that its position on the booklet pane is completely blank except for the phosphor bands. Other more minor misplacements exist.

The De La Rue printings of the high values, Nos. Y1800/Y1803 cannot easily be identified from the original Enschedé issue as single stamps.

For self-adhesive versions of the 42p. and 68p. see Nos. 2297/2298.

First Day Covers

26.10.93	19p., 25p., 29p., 36p., 38p., 41p. (Nos. Y1682, Y1689, Y1693, Y1702, Y1706, Y1712)........	6·00	
9.8.94	60p. (No. Y1784)........	2·00	
25.4.95	National Trust *se-tenant* pane 10p., 19p., 25p., 30p., 35p., 41p. (No. Y1767l)........	10·00	
22.8.95	£1 (No. Y1743)........	3·00	
14.5.96	European Football Championship *se-tenant* pane 25p.×8 (No. Y1775l)........	5·00	
25.6.96	20p., 26p., 31p., 37p., 39p., 43p., 63p. (Nos. Y1685, Y1691, Y1695, Y1703, Y1708, Y1716, Y1732)........	8·00	
13.10.98	Speed *se-tenant* pane 10p., 2nd, 43p. (No. Y1676al)...	8·00	
9.3.99	£1·50, £2, £3, £5 (Nos. Y1800/Y1803) (Type G) (Philatelic Bureau or Windsor)........	15·00	
20.4.99	7p., 38p., 44p., 64p. (Nos. Y1672, Y1707, Y1719, Y1733) (Type G) (Philatelic Bureau or Windsor)........	5·00	
21.9.99	World Changers *se-tenant* pane 1p.,19p., 26p. (No. Y1667n) (Philatelic Bureau or Downe, Orpington)........	2·50	
25.4.00	8p., 33p., 40p., 41p., 45p., 65p. (Nos. Y1674, Y1696, Y1710, Y1714, Y1721, Y1734) (Type G) (Philatelic Bureau or Windsor)........	5·00	
4.7.02	37p., 42p., 47p., 68p. (Nos. Y1704, Y1715, Y1723, Y1736) (Type K) (Tallents House or Windsor)........	5·00	
6.5.03	34p., (No. Y1697) (Type K) (Tallents House or Windsor)........	4·50	
1.7.03	£1·50, £2, £3, £5 (Nos. Y1746/Y1749) (Type K) (Tallents House or Windsor)........	25·00	

1.4.04	7p., 35p., 39p., 40p., 43p. Worldwide postcard (Nos. Y1673, Y1700, Y1709, Y1711, Y1718, 2357a) (Type K) (Tallents House or Windsor)	9·00
5.4.05	9p., 35p., 46p. (Nos. Y1675, Y1701, Y1722) (Type K) (Tallents House or Windsor)	2·25
28.3.06	37p., 44p., 49p., 72p. (Nos. Y1703, Y1720, Y1725, Y1737) (Type K) (Tallents House or Windsor)	4·25
1.3.07	World of Invention label pane 5p., 1st (No. Y1670l) (Tallents House or Menai Bridge, Gwynedd)	5·00
27.3.07	16p., 48p., 50p., 54p., 78p. (Nos. Y1680, Y1724, Y1727/Y1728, Y1738) (Type K) (Tallents House or Windsor)	6·00
5.6.07	Machin Anniversary se-tenant pane 2p., 46p., 48p. (No. Y1668l) (Tallents House, Windsor or Stoke-on-Trent)	6·50
20.9.07	Army Uniforms se-tenant pane 1p., 46p., 54p. (No. Y1667o) (Tallents House or Boot, Holmrook, Cumbria)	5·00
1.4.08	15p., 56p., 81p. (Nos. Y1679, Y1727, Y1739) (Type K) (Tallents House or Windsor)	4·50
13.1.09	British Design Classics se-tenant pane 16p., 50p. (No. Y1769l) (Tallents House or Longbridge, Birmingham)	16·00
12.2.09	Charles Darwin se-tenant pane 5p., 10p., 1st, 48p. (No. Y1762l) (Tallents House or Shrewsbury)	15·00
31.3.09	17p., 22p., 62p., 90p. (Nos. Y1681, Y1688, Y1731, Y1741) (Type K) (Tallents House or Windsor)	6·00
18.8.09	Treasures of the Archive se-tenant pane 17p., 22p., 62p., (No. Y1770l) (Tallents House or London EC1)	16·00
17.9.09	Royal Navy Uniforms se-tenant pane 1p., 17p., 90p. (No. Y1761l) (Tallents House or Portsmouth)	15·00
7.1.10	Classic Album Covers se-tenant pane 20p., 54p., 52p. (No. Y1773l) (Tallents House or Oldfield, Keighley)	15·00
25.2.10	Royal Society se-tenant pane 22p., 54p. (No. Y1774l) (Tallents House or London SW1)	15·00
30.3.10	60p., 67p., 88p., 97p., £1·46, Europe up to 20 grams, Worldwide up to 20 grams (Nos. Y1730, Y1735, Y1740, Y1742, Y1745, 2357b, 2358a) (Type K) (Tallents House or Windsor)	20·00
13.5.10	Britain Alone se-tenant pane 5p., 10p., 60p., (No. Y1763l) (Tallents House or Dover, Kent)	15·00
22.3.11	WWF se-tenant pane 5p., 10p., 67p., 97p. (No. Y1764l) (Tallents House or Godalming, Surrey)	20·00
9.9.11	Aerial Post Centenary se-tenant pane 5p., 1st, 76p. (No. Y1763m) (Tallents House or Hendon, London NW4)	25·00
10.1.12	Roald Dahl se-tenant pane 2p., 10p., 68p. (No. Y1668m) (Tallents House or Great Missenden, Bucks)	15·00
5.6.17	50th Anniversary of the Machin Definitive se-tenant pane 1p., 2p., 5p., 10p., 20p., 50p. 2nd £1 (No. Y1667p) (Tallents House or High Wycombe)	8·00

For first day covers for Nos. Y1677/Y1678 see under Nos. 2650/2657.

Post Office Presentation Packs

26.10.93	PO Pack No. 30. 19p. (1 centre band), 25p. (phosphor paper), 29p., 36p., 38p. rosine, 41p. grey-brown (Nos. Y1682, Y1689, Y1693, Y1702, Y1706, Y1712)	6·00
21.11.95	PO Pack No. 34. 1p. (photo), 2p., 4p., 5p., 6p. (photo), 10p. (photo), 19p. (1 centre band), 20p. turquoise-green, 25p. (photo) (2 bands), 29p., 30p. (photo), 35p. (photo) (2 bands), 36p., 38p. rosine, 41p. grey-brown, 50p., 60p., £1 (Nos. Y1667/Y1671, Y1676, Y1682, Y1684, Y1690, Y1693/Y1694, Y1698, Y1702, Y1706, Y1712, Y1726, Y1743, Y1784)	35·00
25.6.96	PO Pack No. 35. 20p. bright green (1 centre band), 26p. (photo), 31p., 37p. (photo), 39p., 43p. deep olive brown, 63p. (photo) (Nos. Y1685, Y1691, Y1695, Y1703, Y1708, Y1716, Y1732)	8·00
21.4.97	PO Pack No. 38. 1st, 26p. gold (Nos. 1668, Y1692)	6·00
20.10.98	PO Pack No. 41. 2nd bright blue (1 centre band), 1st bright orange-red (2 phosphor bands), 1p., 2p., 4p., 5p., 6p., 10p., 20p. bright green (1 centre band), 26p., 30p., 31p., 37p., 39p., 43p. sepia, 50p., 63p., £1 (Nos. 1664, 1667, Y1667/Y1671, Y1676, Y1685, Y1691, Y1694/Y1695, Y1703, Y1708, Y1717, Y1726, Y1732)	18·00
9.3.99	PO Pack No. 43 or 43a. £1·50, £2, £3, £5 (Nos. Y1800/Y1803)	38·00
20.4.99	PO Pack No. 44. 7p., 19p., 38p. ultramarine, 44p., 64p. (Nos. Y1672, Y1682, Y1707, Y1719, Y1733)	9·50
25.4.00	PO Pack No. 49. 8p., 33p., 40p., 41p. rosine, 45p., 65p. (Nos. Y1674, Y1696, Y1710, Y1714, Y1721, Y1734)	8·50
12.3.02	PO Pack No. 57. 2nd, 1st, E, 1p., 2p., 4p., 5p., 8p., 10p., 20p., 33p., 40p., 41p., 45p., 50p., 65p., £1 (Nos. 1664, 1667, 1669, Y1667/Y1670, Y1674, Y1676, Y1687, Y1696, Y1710, Y1714, Y1721, Y1726, Y1734, Y1743)	16·00
4.7.02	PO Pack No. 58. 37p., 42p., 47p., 68p. (Nos. Y1704, Y1715, Y1723, Y1736)	6·50
1.7.03	PO Pack No. 62. £1·50, £2, £3, £5 (Nos. Y1746/Y1749).	25·00
1.4.04	PO Pack No. 67. 1st gold (D.L.R. printing), 7p., 35p., 39p., 40p., 43p. Worldwide postcard (Nos. 1668, Y1673, Y1700, Y1709, Y1711, Y1718, 2357a)	10·00

6.9.05	PO Pack No. 71. 1p., 2p., 5p., 9p., 10p., 20p., 35p., 40p., 42p., 46p., 47p., 50p., 68p., £1, 2nd, 1st, Worldwide postcard, Europe up to 40 grams, Worldwide up to 40 grams (Nos. Y1667/Y1668, Y1670, Y1675/Y1676, Y1687, Y1701, Y1711, Y1715, Y1722/Y1723, Y1726, Y1736, Y1743, 2039, 2295, 2357a, 2359)	50·00
28.3.06	PO Pack No. 72. 37p., 44p., 49p., 72p. (Nos. Y1705, Y1720, Y1725, Y1737)	11·00
27.3.07	PO Pack No. 75. 16p., 48p., 50p., 54p., 78p. (Nos. Y1680, Y1724, Y1727, Y1728, Y1738)	10·00
5.6.07	PO Pack No. 77. 2nd, 1st, 1p., 2p., 5p., 10p., 14p., 16p., 20p., 46p., 48p., 50p., 54p., 78p., £1, Worldwide postcard, Europe up to 40 grams, Worldwide up to 40 grams, 2nd Large, 1st Large (Nos. 1664, 1668, Y1667/Y1668, Y1670, Y1676, Y1678/Y1679, Y1687, Y1722, Y1724, Y1727/Y1728, Y1744, 2357a, 2358, 2359, 2652/2653)	45·00
1.4.08	PO Pack No. 78. 15p., 56p., 81p. (Nos. Y1679, Y1729, Y1739)	5·00
31.3.09	PO Pack No. 84 17p., 22p., 62p., 90p. (Nos. Y1681, Y1688, Y1731, Y1741)	8·50
30.3.10	PO Pack No. 86. 60p. 67p., 88p., 97p., £1·46, Europe up to 20 grams, Worldwide up to 20 grams, 1st Recorded Signed For, 1st Large Recorded Signed For (Nos. Y1730, Y1735, Y1740, Y1742, Y1745, 2357b, 2358a, U3045/U3046)	28·00
8.5.10	PO Pack No. 88. 2nd, 1st, 1p., 2p., 5p., 9p., 10p., 20p., 50p., 60p., 67p., 88p., 97p., £1, £1·46, Worldwide postcard, Europe up to 20 grams Worldwide up to 20 grams, Worldwide up to 40 grams, 2nd Large, 1st Large, 1st Recorded Signed For, 1st Large Recorded Signed For (Nos. 1664, 1668, Y1667, Y1668, Y1670, Y1675, Y1676, Y1687, Y1727, Y1730, Y1735, Y1740, Y1742, Y1744, Y1745, 2357a/2359, 2652/2653 and U2981/U2982)	50·00

In 2002 a 'master' presentation pack entitled Royal Mail Definitive Stamps Collection was released, containing packs Nos. 43a, 53, 54, 55, 56 and 57 (Price £120).

1917

(Des Katja Thielan. Gravure De La Rue)

2006 (31 Aug.) 70th Anniversary of the Year of Three Kings. Sheet 127×72 mm containing No. Y1748. Multicoloured. Two phosphor bands. Perf 15×14 (with one elliptical hole in each vertical side).

MS2658 **1917** £3 deep mauve	5·25	5·25
First Day Cover (Tallents House)		5·50
First Day Cover (Threekingham, Sleaford, Lincs)		5·50

Decimal Machin Index

(Stamps with elliptical perforations, including (N.V.Is)

Value	Process	Colour	Phosphor	Cat. No.	Source
2nd	litho Questa or Walsall	bright blue	1 centre band	1670	sheets (Questa), booklets of 4 (Walsall – HA6, Walsall HA9/HA11), booklets of 10 (Questa – HC11, HC13, HC16, HC18, HC20, Walsall – HC12), $7·15 'Pilot to Plane' booklet (Walsall – DX42)
2nd	photo/gravure Harrison/De La Rue), Enschedé, Questa or Walsall	bright blue	1 centre band	1664	sheets (Walsall, De La Rue), horizontal coil (Harrison/De La Rue), vertical coils (Harrison/De La Rue or Enschedé) booklets of 4 (Harrison – HA7/HA8, Walsall – HA12), booklets of 10 (Harrison/De La Rue – HC14/HC15, HC17, HC19, HC21), £1 booklet (Questa – FH44/FH44a), £2 booklet (Questa – FW12), £7·29 'A Gracious Accession' booklet (Enschedé – DX28), £7·46 'A Perfect Coronation' booklet (Walsall – DX31), £7·43 The Brontë Sisters booklet (Walsall – DX34)
2nd	gravure Walsall (*p* 14)	bright blue	1 band at right	1665	£6·16 British Land Speed Record Holders booklet (DX21)
2nd	gravure Walsall (*p* 14)	bright blue	1 band at left	1665c	£6·16 British Land Speed Record Holders booklet (DX21)
2nd	gravure Questa (*p* 14)	bright blue	1 centre band	1664a	booklets of 10 (HC22)
1st	litho Enschedé, Questa or Walsall	bright orange-red	2 bands	1671	sheets (Questa), greetings card panes Questa – Y1671m/ma, Enschedé – Y1671mb), booklets of 4 (Walsall – HB6, HB8/HB13, HB15/HB16, Questa – HB7), booklets of 10 Walsall – HD10, HD12/HD19, HD22/HD23, HD25, HD28, HD34, HD36/HD38, HD40, Questa – HD11, HD21, HD26, HD50), £7·54 'Profile on Print' booklet (Questa – HD22)
1st	photo Harrison	bright orange-red	phos paper	1666	booklets of 4 (HB5), booklets of 10 (HD9, HD20)
1st	photo/gravure Harrison/De La Rue, Questa or Walsall/ISP Walsall	bright orange-red	2 bands	1667	sheets (Walsall), horizontal and vertical coils (Harrison, De La Rue), booklets of 4 (Walsall – HB14, HB17/HB18), booklets of 8 with 2 Millennium commems (Walsall – HBA1/HBA2), booklets of 10 (Harrison/De La Rue – HD24, HD27, HD29/HD33, HD35, HD39, HD45/HD49, Walsall – HD44), £1 booklet (Questa – FH44/FH44a), £2 booklet (Questa – FW12), £7·54 'Profile on Print' booklet (De La Rue – DX22), £15·14 '50th Anniversary of the Machin' booklet (ISP Walsall – DY21)
1st	gravure Questa (*p* 14)	bright orange-red	2 bands	1667a	booklets of 10 (HD51)
1st	gravure De La Rue, Enschedé, Harrison, Questa or Walsall/ISP Walsall	gold	2 bands	1668	sheets (Walsall, De La Rue), vertical coils (Enschedé, De La Rue), booklets of 10 (Harrison – HD41, HD43, Walsall – HD42), £6·15 B.B.C. booklet (Harrison – DX19), £6·83 'Across the Universe' booklet (Questa – DX29, £6·99 'Microcosmos' booklet (Enschedé – DX30), £7·46 'A Perfect Coronation' booklet (Walsall – DX31), £7·44 'Letters by Night' booklet (De La Rue – DX32), £7·23 'The Glory of the Garden' booklet (Enschedé – DX33), £7·26 Trafalgar booklet (Walsall – DX35), £7·40 Brunel booklet (Enschedé – DX36), £15·14 '50th Anniversary of the Machin' booklet (ISP Walsall – DY21)
1st	gravure ISP Walsall	brownish black	2 bands	1668s	£15·14 '50th Anniversary of the Machin' booklet (ISP Walsall – DY21)
1st	litho De La Rue or Walsall	gold	2 bands	1672	£7·40 Ian Fleming's James Bond booklet (De La Rue – DX41), £7·15 'Pilot to Plane' booklet (Walsall – DX42)
E	gravure De La Rue, Enschedé, Questa or Walsall	deep blue	2 bands	1669	sheets (De La Rue), booklets of 4 (Walsall – HF1), £7·29 'A Gracious Accession' booklet (Enschedé – DX28), £6·83 'Across the Universe' booklet (Questa – DX29), £6·99 'Microcosmos' booklet (Enschedé – DX30)
1p.	photo/gravure De La Rue, Enschedé, Harrison, Questa or ISP Walsall	crimson	2 bands	Y1667	sheets, £1 booklets (Questa – FH42/FH43), £6·91 World Changers booklet (Questa – DX23), £7·66 British Army Uniforms booklet (Enschedé – DX40), £15.14 '50th Anniversary of the Machin' booklet (ISP Walsall – DY21)
1p.	litho Questa	lake	2 bands	Y1760	£1 booklet (FH41)
1p.	litho Cartor	reddish purple	2 bands	Y1761	£7·93 Royal Navy Uniforms booklet (DX47)
2p.	photo/gravure De La Rue, Enschedé, Harrison, Questa or Walsall/ISP Walsall	deep green	2 bands	Y1668	sheets, £1 booklets (Questa – FH43), £7·66 'The Machin' booklet (De La Rue – DX39), £11·47 Roald Dahl booklet (Walsall – DY3), £15·14 '50th Anniversary of the Machin' booklet (ISP Walsall – DY21)
4p.	photo/gravure De La Rue, Enschedé or Harrison	new blue	2 bands	Y1669	sheets
4p.	gravure De La Rue	new blue	phos paper	MS2146	Jeffery Matthews Colour Palette miniature sheet
5p.	photo/gravure De La Rue, Enschedé, Harrison or ISP Walsall	dull red-brown	2 bands	Y1670	sheets , £7·49 World of Invention booklet (De La Rue – DX38), £15·14 '50th Anniversary of the Machin' booklet (ISP Walsall – DY21)
5p.	gravure De La Rue	dull red-brown	phos paper	MS2146	Jeffery Matthews Colour Palette miniature sheet
5p.	litho De La Rue	chocolate	2 bands	Y1762	£7·75 Charles Darwin booklet (DX45)
5p.	litho Cartor	red-brown	2 bands	Y1763	£9·76 Great Britain Alone booklet (DX51), £9·97 Aerial Post Centenary booklet (DY2)
5p.	litho Cartor	lake-brown	2 bands	Y1764	£9·05 WWF booklet (DX52)

Value	Process	Colour	Phosphor	Cat. No.	Source
5p.	litho Cartor	red-brown	2 bands	Y1765	Type III. £8·06 Classic Album Covers booklet (DX48)
6p.	photo/gravure Enschedé or Harrison	yellow-olive	2 bands	Y1671	sheets
6p.	litho Questa	yellow-olive	2 bands	Y1766	£6·04 Northern Ireland booklet (DX16)
6p.	gravure De La Rue	yellow-olive	phos paper	**MS**2146	Jeffery Matthews Colour Palette miniature sheet
7p.	gravure De La Rue	grey	2 bands	Y1672	sheets
7p.	gravure De La Rue	bright magenta	2 bands	Y1673	sheets
8p.	gravure De La Rue	yellow	2 bands	Y1674	sheets
9p.	gravure De La Rue	yellow-orange	2 bands	Y1675	sheets
10p.	photo/gravure De La Rue, Enschedé, Harrison or Walsall/ ISP Walsall	dull orange	2 bands	Y1676	sheets, £11·47 Roald Dahl booklet (Walsall – DY3), £15·14 '50th Anniversary of the Machin' booklet (ISP Walsall – DY21)
10p.	litho Questa, De La Rue or Cartor	dull orange	2 bands	Y1767	£6 National Trust booklet (Questa - DX17), £7·75 Charles Darwin booklet (De La Rue - DX45), £9·76 'Britain Alone' booklet (Cartor - DX51), £9·05 WWF booklet (Cartor - DX52)
10p.	litho Cartor	pale brownish orange	2 bands	Y1768	£8·06 Classic Album Covers booklet (DX48)
10p.	gravure Walsall (*p* 14)	dull orange	2 bands	Y1676a	£6·16 British Land Speed Record Holders booklet (DX21)
10p.	gravure De La Rue	dull orange	phos paper	**MS**2146	Jeffery Matthews Colour Palette miniature sheet
12p.	gravure De La Rue	greenish blue	2 bands	Y1677	sheets
14p.	gravure De La Rue	rose-red	2 bands	Y1678	sheets
15p.	gravure De La Rue	bright magenta	2 bands	Y1679	sheets
16p.	gravure De La Rue	pale cerise	2 bands	Y1680	sheets
16p.	litho Cartor	pale cerise	2 bands	Y1769	£7·75 British Design Classics booklet (DX44)
17p.	gravure De La Rue	brown-olive	2 bands	Y1681	sheets
17p.	litho Cartor	bistre	2 bands	Y1770	£8·18 'Treasures of the Archive' booklet (DX46) and £7·93 Royal Navy Uniforms booklet (DX47)
19p.	photo/gravure Harrison or Questa	bistre	1 centre band	Y1682	sheets, vertical coils, £1 booklet (Questa – FH43), £2 booklet (Questa – FW11), £6·99 World Changers booklet (Questa – DX23)
19p.	litho Questa	bistre	1 band at left	Y1771	£6·04 Northern Ireland booklet (DX16), £6 National Trust booklet (DX17)
19p.	litho Questa	bistre	1 band at right	Y1771a	£6 National Trust booklet (DX17)
19p.	gravure Walsall (*p* 14)	bistre	1 band at right	Y1683	£7·50 'Special by Design' booklet (DX24)
20p.	gravure Enschedé	turquoise-green	2 bands	Y1684	sheets
20p.	photo/gravure Harrison or Questa	bright green	1 centre band	Y1685	sheets, £1 booklet (Questa – FH42), £2 booklet (Questa – FW10)
20p.	litho Questa	bright yellow-green	1 centre band	Y1772	£1 booklet (FH41), £2 booklet (FW9)
20p.	gravure Harrison	bright green	1 band at right	Y1686	£6·15 B.B.C. booklet (DX19)
20p.	gravure De La Rue or ISP Walsall	bright green	2 bands	Y1687	sheets, £15·14 '50th Anniversary of the Machin' booklet (ISP Walsall – DY21)
20p.	litho Cartor	light green	2 bands	Y1773	£8·06 Classic Album Covers booklet (DX48)
22p.	gravure De La Rue	drab	2 bands	Y1688	sheets
22p.	litho Cartor	olive-brown	2 bands	Y1774	£8·18 'Treasures of the Archive' booklet (DX46), £8·06 Classic Album Covers booklet (DX48) and £7·72 Royal Society booklet (DX49)
25p.	photo Harrison	rose-red	phos paper	Y1689	sheets, vertical coils, 50p booklets (FB67/FB73), £1 booklets (FH33/FH37), £2 booklets (FW1/FW5)
25p.	litho Walsall or Questa	red	2 bands	Y1775	£1 booklets (Walsall – FH31/FH32), (Questa – FH40), £2 booklet (Questa – FW8), £6·04 Northern Ireland booklet (Questa – DX16), £6 National Trust booklet (Questa – DX17), £6·84 European Football Championship (Questa – DX18)
25p.	photo/gravure Harrison or Enschedé	rose-red	2 bands	Y1690	sheets (Harrison or Enschedé), vertical coils (Harrison), 50p booklets (Harrison – FB74/5), £1 booklets (Harrison – FH38/9), £2 booklets (Harrison – FW6/7)
26p.	photo/gravure Harrison or Questa	red-brown	2 bands	Y1691	sheets, £1 booklets (Questa – FH43), £2 booklets (Questa – FW10/FW11), £6·15 B.B.C. booklet (Harrison – DX19), £6·99 World Changers booklet (Questa – DX23)
26p.	litho Questa	chestnut	2 bands	Y1776	£1 booklet (FH41), £2 booklet (FW9)
26p.	gravure Harrison	gold	2 bands	Y1692	sheets, £6·15 B B.C. booklet (Harrison – DX19)
29p.	gravure Enschedé	grey	2 bands	Y1693	sheets
30p.	photo/gravure Enschedé, Harrison or Walsall	deep olive-grey	2 bands	Y1694	sheets, £1·20 booklets (Walsall – GGAI/GGA2)
30p.	litho Questa	olive-grey	2 bands	Y1777	£6 National Trust booklet (DX17)
31p.	photo/gravure Enschedé or Harrison	deep mauve	2 bands	Y1695	sheets
31p.	gravure De La Rue	deep mauve	phos paper	**MS**2146	Jeffery Matthews Colour Palette miniature sheet
33p.	gravure De La Rue	grey-green	2 bands	Y1696	sheets
34p.	gravure De La Rue	yellow-olive	2 bands	Y1697	sheets
35p.	gravure Enschedé	yellow	2 bands	Y1698	sheets
35p.	photo Harrison	yellow	phos paper	Y1699	vertical coils
35p.	litho Walsall or Questa	yellow	2 bands	Y1778	£1·40 booklets (Walsall – GK5/GK7), £6 National Trust booklet (Questa – DX17)
35p.	gravure De La Rue	sepia	2 bands	Y1700	sheets

Value	Process	Colour	Phosphor	Cat. No.	Source
35p.	gravure Enschedé or De La Rue	yellow-olive	1 centre band	Y1701	sheets, £7·40 Brunel booklet (Enschedé – DX36)
36p.	gravure Enschedé	bright ultramarine	2 bands	Y1702	sheets
37p.	photo/gravure Enschedé, Harrison or Walsall	bright mauve	2 bands	Y1703	sheets (Enschedé or Harrison), vertical coils (Harrison), £1·48 booklets (Walsall – GL3/GL4)
37p.	litho Walsall	bright mauve	2 bands	Y1779	£1·48 booklets (GL1/GL2)
37p.	gravure De La Rue	grey-black	2 bands	Y1704	sheets, £7·44 'Letters by Night' booklet (De La Rue – DX32)
37p.	gravure De La Rue	brown-olive	1 centre band	Y1705	sheets
38p.	gravure Enschedé	rosine	2 bands	Y1706	sheets
38p.	gravure De La Rue or Walsall	ultramarine	2 bands	Y1707	sheets (De La Rue), £1·52 booklet (Walsall – GLAI)
38p.	gravure Walsall (*p* 14)	ultramarine	2 bands	Y1707a	£7·50 'Special by Design' booklet (DX24)
39p.	photo/gravure Enschedé or Harrison	bright magenta	2 bands	Y1708	sheets
39p.	gravure De La Rue	bright magenta	phos paper	MS2146	Jeffery Matthews Colour Palette miniature sheet
39p.	gravure De La Rue or Walsall	grey	2 bands	Y1709	sheets (De La Rue), £7·43 The Brontë Sisters booklet (Walsall – DX34)
40p.	gravure De La Rue or Walsall	deep azure	2 bands	Y1710	sheets (De La Rue), £1·60 booklet (Walsall – GMA1)
40p.	gravure De La Rue or Enschedé	turquoise-blue	2 bands	Y1711	sheets (De La Rue), £7·40 Brunel booklet (Enschedé – DX36)
41p.	gravure Enschedé	grey-brown	2 bands	Y1712	sheets
41p.	photo Harrison	drab	phos paper	Y1713	vertical coils
41p.	gravure De La Rue	rosine	2 bands	Y1714	sheets
41p.	litho Walsall	drab	2 bands	Y1780	£1·64 booklets (GN1/GN3)
41p.	litho Questa	grey-brown	2 bands	Y1780a	£6 National Trust booklet (DX17)
42p.	gravure De La Rue, Enschedé or Walsall	deep olive-grey	2 bands	Y1715	sheets (De La Rue), £7·23 'The Glory of the Garden' booklet (Enschedé – DX33), £7·43 The Brontë Sisters booklet (Walsall – DX34)
43p.	gravure Enschedé	deep olive-brown	2 bands	Y1716	sheets
43p.	photo Harrison	sepia	2 bands	Y1717	sheets, vertical coils
43p.	gravure Walsall (*p* 14)	sepia	2 bands	Y1717a	£6·16 British Land Speed Record Holders booklet (DX21)
43p.	gravure De La Rue	emerald	2 bands	Y1718	sheets
44p.	gravure De La Rue	grey-brown	2 bands	Y1719	sheets
44p.	gravure De La Rue	bright blue	2 bands	Y1720	sheets
45p.	gravure De La Rue	bright mauve	2 bands	Y1721	sheets
46p.	gravure De La Rue or Enschedé	yellow	2 bands	Y1722	sheets (De La Rue), £7·66 'The Machin' booklet (De La Rue – DX39), £7·66 British Army Uniforms booklet (Enschedé – DX40)
47p.	gravure De La Rue or Enschedé	turquoise-green	2 bands	Y1723	sheets (De La Rue), £7·23 'The Glory of the Garden' booklet (Enschedé – DX33)
48p.	gravure De La Rue	bright mauve	2 bands	Y1724	sheets, £7·66 'The Machin' booklet (DX39)
48p.	litho De La Rue	bright mauve	2 bands	Y1781	£7·75 Charles Darwin booklet (DX45)
49p.	gravure De La Rue	red-brown	2 bands	Y1725	sheets
50p.	photo/gravure Enschedé, Harrison or Walsall	ochre	2 bands	Y1726	sheets (Enschedé or Harrison), £7·26 Trafalgar booklet (Walsall–DX35), £7·44 Victoria Cross booklet (Enschedé – DX37)
50p.	gravure De La Rue	grey	2 bands	Y1727	sheets
50p.	litho Cartor	grey	2 bands	Y1782	£7·68 British Design Classics Booklet (DX44)
54p.	gravure De La Rue or Enschedé	red-brown	2 bands	Y1728	sheets (De La Rue), £7·66 British Army Uniforms booklet (Enschedé – DX40)
54p.	litho Cartor	chestnut	2 bands	Y1783	Type III. £8·06 Classic Album Covers booklet (DX48) and £7·72 Royal Society booklet (DX49)
56p.	gravure De La Rue	yellow-olive	2 bands	Y1729	sheets
60p.	litho Walsall	dull blue-grey	2 bands	Y1784	£2·40 booklets (GQ1/GQ4)
60p.	gravure De La Rue	light emerald	2 bands	Y1730	sheets
60p.	litho Cartor	emerald	2 bands	Y1785	'Britain Alone' booklet (DX51)
62p.	gravure De La Rue	rosine	2 bands	Y1731	sheets
62p.	litho Cartor	rosine	2 bands	Y1786	£8·18 'Treasures of the Archive' booklet (DX46) and £8·06 Classic Album Covers booklet (DX48)
63p.	photo/gravure Enschedé, Harrison or Walsall	light emerald	2 bands	Y1732	sheets (Enschedé or Harrison), vertical coils (Harrison) £2·52 booklets (Walsall – GR3/GR4)
63p.	litho Walsall	light emerald	2 bands	Y1787	£2·52 booklets (GR1/GR2)
64p.	gravure De La Rue or Walsall	turquoise-green	2 bands	Y1733	sheets (De La Rue), £2·56 booklet (Walsall – GS1)
64p.	gravure De La Rue	turquoise-green	phos paper	MS2146	Jeffery Matthews Colour Palette miniature sheet
65p.	gravure De La Rue or Walsall	greenish blue	2 bands	Y1734	sheets (De La Rue.), £2·60 booklet (Walsall – GT1)
67p.	gravure De La Rue	bright mauve	2 bands	Y1735	sheets
67p.	litho Cartor	bright mauve	2 bands	Y1788	£9·05 WWF booklet (DX52)
68p.	gravure De La Rue or Walsall	grey-brown	2 bands	Y1736	sheets (De La Rue), £7·26 Trafalgar booklet (Walsall–DX35)
72p.	gravure De La Rue	rosine	2 bands	Y1737	sheets
78p.	gravure De La Rue	emerald	2 bands	Y1738	sheets
81p.	gravure De La Rue	turquoise-green	2 bands	Y1739	sheets
88p.	gravure De La Rue	bright magenta	2 bands	Y1740	sheets

Value	Process	Colour	Phosphor	Cat. No.	Source
90p.	gravure De La Rue	ultramarine	2 bands	Y1741	sheets
90p.	litho Cartor	bright blue	2 bands	Y1789	£7·93 Royal Navy Uniforms booklet (DX47)
97p.	gravure De La Rue	violet	2 bands	Y1742	sheets
97p.	litho Cartor	bluish violet	2 bands	Y1790	£9·05 WWF booklet (DX52)
£1	gravure Enschedé, Harrison or De La Rue	bluish violet	2 bands	Y1743	sheets, **MS**2743 (De La Rue)
£1	gravure De La Rue	magenta	2 bands	Y1744	sheets, £7·66 'The Machin' booklet (DX39), **MS**2743
£1	gravure De La Rue	bluish violet	phos paper	**MS**2146	Jeffery Matthews Colour Palette miniature sheet
£1.46	gravure De La Rue	greenish blue	2 bands	Y1745	sheets
£1.50	recess	red	—	Y1800	sheets (Enschedé then De La Rue)
£1.50	gravure De La Rue	brown-red	2 bands	Y1746	sheets
£2	recess	dull blue	—	Y1801	sheets (Enschedé then De La Rue)
£2	gravure De La Rue	deep blue-green	2 bands	Y1747	sheets
£3	recess	dull violet	—	Y1802	sheets (Enschedé then De La Rue)
£3	gravure De La Rue	deep mauve	2 bands	Y1748	sheets, **MS**2658
£5	recess	brown	—	Y1803	sheets (Enschedé then De La Rue)
£5	gravure De La Rue	azure	2 bands	Y1749	sheets

Note. Harrison and Sons became De La Rue Security Print on 8 September 1997.
Photo/gravure stamps were printed from both photogravure and computor engraved (gravure) cylinders.

Decimal Machin Booklet Pane Guide (ordinary gum) ('Y' numbers) the shaded squares represent printed labels.

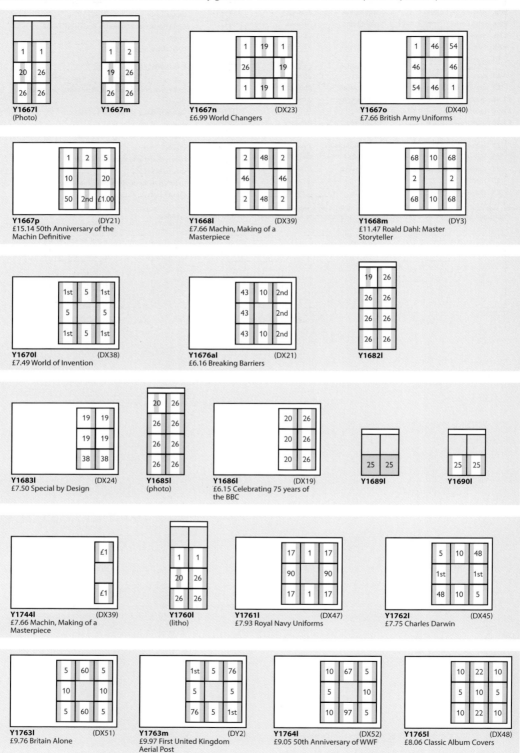

Y1667l
(Photo)

Y1667m

Y1667n   (DX23)
£6.99 World Changers

Y1667o   (DX40)
£7.66 British Army Uniforms

Y1667p   (DY21)
£15.14 50th Anniversary of the
Machin Definitive

Y1668l   (DX39)
£7.66 Machin, Making of a
Masterpiece

Y1668m   (DY3)
£11.47 Roald Dahl: Master
Storyteller

Y1670l   (DX38)
£7.49 World of Invention

Y1676al   (DX21)
£6.16 Breaking Barriers

Y1682l

Y1683l   (DX24)
£7.50 Special by Design

Y1685l
(photo)

Y1686l   (DX19)
£6.15 Celebrating 75 years of
the BBC

Y1689l

Y1690l

Y1744l   (DX39)
£7.66 Machin, Making of a
Masterpiece

Y1760l
(litho)

Y1761l   (DX47)
£7.93 Royal Navy Uniforms

Y1762l   (DX45)
£7.75 Charles Darwin

Y1763l   (DX51)
£9.76 Britain Alone

Y1763m   (DY2)
£9.97 First United Kingdom
Aerial Post

Y1764l   (DX52)
£9.05 50th Anniversary of WWF

Y1765l   (DX48)
£8.06 Classic Album Covers

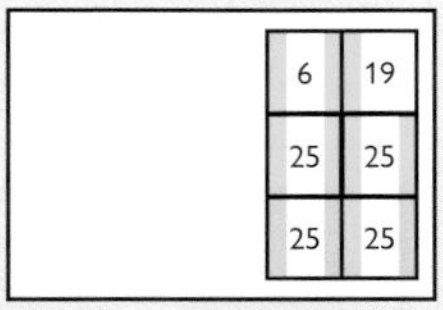

6	19
25	25
25	25

Y1766I (DX16)
£6.04 Northern Ireland

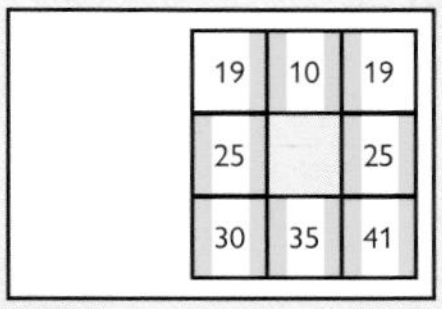

19	10	19
25		25
30	35	41

Y1767I (DX17)
£6.00 The National Trust

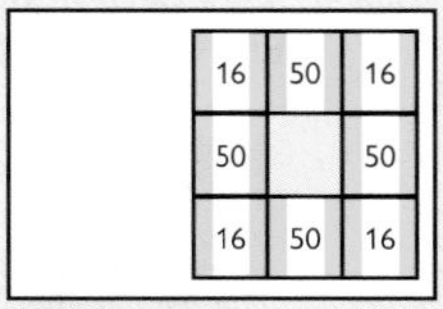

16	50	16
50		50
16	50	16

Y1769I (DX44)
£7.68 British Design Classics

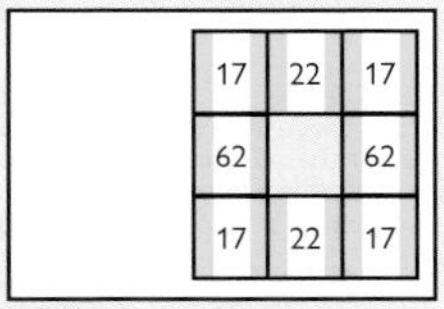

17	22	17
62		62
17	22	17

Y1770I (DX46)
£8.18 Treasures of the Archive

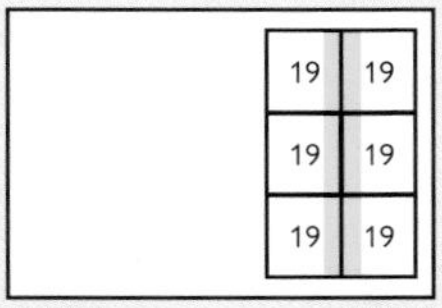

19	19
19	19
19	19

Y1771I (DX17)
£6.00 The National Trust

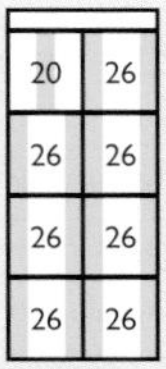

20	26
26	26
26	26
26	26

Y1772I
(litho)

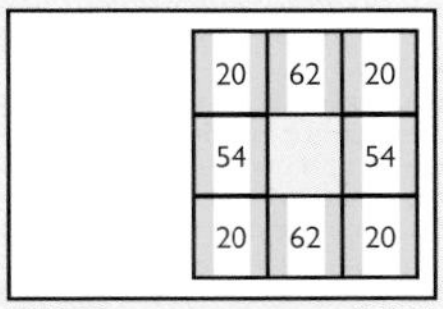

20	62	20
54		54
20	62	20

Y1773I (DX48)
£8.06 Classic Album Covers

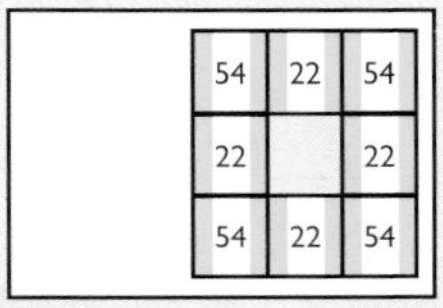

54	22	54
22		22
54	22	54

Y1774I (DX49)
£7.72 350th Anniversary of the
Royal Society

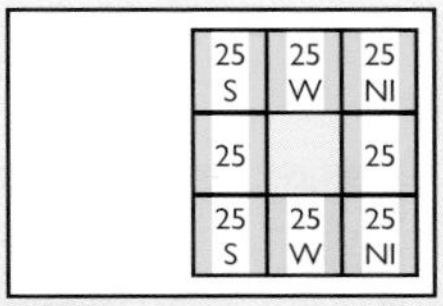

25 S	25 W	25 NI
25		25
25 S	25 W	25 NI

Y1775I (DX18)
£6.48 European Football
Championship

N.V.I. STAMPS, SELF-ADHESIVE, ELLIPTICAL PERFORATIONS

1116

(Des J. Matthews. Litho Walsall)

1993 (19 Oct). Self-adhesive. Two phosphor bands. Die-cut Perf 14×15 (with one elliptical hole on each vertical side).

1789	**1116**	(1st) orange-red	1·50	1·50
		y. Phosphor omitted	£275	
First Day Cover (No. 1789)				2·50
Presentation Pack (PO Pack No. 29) (booklet pane of 20)			18·00	
PHQ Card (D6)			40	2·50

No. 1789 was initially sold at 24p. which was increased to 25p. from November 1993.

It was only issued in booklets containing 20 stamps, each surrounded by die-cut perforations.

For similar 2nd and 1st designs printed in photogravure by Enschedé see Nos. 1976/1977.

Special First Day of Issue Postmarks

British Philatelic Bureau, Edinburgh	2·50
Newcastle upon Tyne	2·50

1301   **1302**

(Des J. Matthews. Gravure Enschedé)

1997 (18 Mar). Self-adhesive. One centre phosphor band (2nd) or two phosphor bands (1st). Perf 14×15 die-cut (with one elliptical hole in each vertical side).

1976	**1301**	(2nd) bright blue	1·40	1·40
1977	**1302**	(1st) bright orange-red	1·40	1·40
Set of 2			2·75	2·75
First Day Cover				3·00
Presentation Pack (PO Pack No. 37)			3·50	

Nos. 1976/1977, which were sold at 20p. and 26p., were in rolls of 100 with the stamps separate on the backing paper.

No. 1976 exists with the printed image in two sizes; the normal stamp is 21.25 mm×17.25 mm, while the scarcer second version is 21.75×17.75 mm.

Special First Day of Issue Postmarks

British Philatelic Bureau, Edinburgh	2·75
Glasgow	2·75

(Gravure Enschedé, Questa or Walsall)

1998 (6 Apr)–**2006** (16 May). Self-adhesive. Designs as Types **913/914**. One centre phosphor band (2nd), or two phosphor bands (1st). Perf 15×14 die-cut (with one elliptical hole in each vertical side).

2039		(2nd) bright blue	1·00	1·00
		a. Imperf (pair, 6 mm gap) (1998)	£275	
		ab. Imperf (pair, 4 mm gap) (2000)	£100	
		b. Perf 14½×14 die-cut (22.6.98)	£225	
2040		(1st) bright orange-red	1·25	1·25
		a. Imperf (pair, 6 mm gap) (1998)	£275	
		ab. Imperf (pair, 4 mm gap) (2000)	£100	
		b. Perf 14½×14 die-cut (22.6.98)	£225	
		y. Phosphor omitted	£130	
		l. Booklet pane No. 2040×6 plus commemorative label at left (29.1.2001)	11·50	

Nos. 2039/2040, initially sold for 20p. and 26p., were in rolls of 200 printed by Enschedé with the surplus self-adhesive paper removed.

2nd and 1st self-adhesive stamps as Nos. 2039/2040 were issued in sheets, printed in photogravure by Walsall Security Printers, on 22 June 1998. These are similar to the previous coil printings, but the sheets retain the surplus self-adhesive paper around each stamp. Stamps from these sheets have square perforation tips instead of the rounded versions to be found on the coils.

No. 2039 exists die-cut through the backing paper from Presentation Pack No. 71.

No. 2039 was issued in rolls of 10,000, printed by Enschedé on yellow backing paper with the surplus self-adhesive paper removed. A number appears on the back of every tenth stamp in the roll.

Nos. 2039a/2040a come from business sheets printed by Walsall and show a 6 mm space between the stamps.

Nos. 2039ab/2040ab come from business sheets printed by Walsall and Questa respectively and have a 4 mm space between stamps. 4 mm pairs also exist from booklets, but are much scarcer from this source.

Nos. 2039b and 2040b come from initial stocks of these Walsall sheet printings sent to the Philatelic Bureau and supplied to collectors requiring single stamps.

They can be indentified by the pointed perforation tips in the corners of the stamp, as illustrated below.

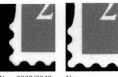

Nos. 2039/2040   Nos. 2039b/2040b

A further printing in business sheets appeared on 4 September 2000 printed by Walsall (2nd) or Questa (1st). These sheets were slightly re-designed to provide a block of four, rather than a strip, in the top panel. Individual stamps cannot be identified as coming from these new sheets as they have rounded perforation tips similar to those on the original coil printings.

The business sheets of 100 were re-issued on 9 May 2002 printed by Enschedé in the same format as used in September 2000. The individual stamps are similar to the Enschedé coil printings of April 1998. A further printing of No. 2039 in sheets of 100 appeared on 4 July 2002 printed by Enschedé. On this printing the top panel reverted to a strip of four with the typography on the label matching that of contemporary stamp booklets.

No. 2039 was issued on 18 March 2003 in stripped matrix sheets of 100, printed by Walsall.

The business sheets of 100 were again issued but without the strapline 'The Real Network' on 15 June 2004. The stamps in stripped matrix sheets of 100 had rounded perforations and were printed by Walsall.

No. 2039 was re-issued in a business sheet on 16 May 2006, in stripped matrix format, printed by Walsall, with an announcement about Pricing in Proportion being introduced on 21 August 2006 in the header.

Both values appeared in stamp booklets from 29 January 2001. No. 2040l comes from self-adhesive booklet No. MB2. The label commemorates the death centenary of Queen Victoria.

See also Nos. 2295/2298.

'MILLENNIUM' MACHINS

1437 Queen Elizabeth II

(Des A. Machin, adapted R. Scholey. Gravure De La Rue, Questa or Walsall/ISP Walsall (No. 2124), Walsall (Nos. 2124bl, 2124dl), Questa or Walsall (No. 2124d))

2000 (6 Jan–Aug). New Millennium. Two phosphor bands. Perf 15×14 (with one elliptical hole in each vertical side).

2124	**1437**	(1st) olive-brown	1·25	1·25
		a. Imperf (pair)	£600	
		l. Booklet pane. No. 2124×4 plus commemorative label at right (21.3.2000)	5·00	
		m. Booklet pane. No. 2124×9 with margins all round (4.8.2000)	12·00	
		y. Phosphor omitted	£450	
		d. Perf 14 (23.5.2000)	1·25	1·25
		dy. Phosphor omitted	10·00	
		dl. Booklet pane. No. 2124d×8 with central label and margins all round (15.2.2000)	11·00	
First Day Cover (Philatelic Bureau) (Type G, see Introduction) (No. 2124)				2·00
First Day Cover (Windsor) (Type G) (No. 2124)				2·00
First Day Cover (Philatelic Bureau) (No. 2124bm)				6·00
First Day Cover (London SW1) (No. 2124bm)				6·00
First Day Cover (Philatelic Bureau) (No. 2124dl)				6·00
First Day Cover (London SW5) (No. 2124dl)				6·00
Presentation Pack (PO Pack No. 48)			2·50	
PHQ Card (D16) (23.5.2000)			40	2·50

No. 2124d comes from stamp booklets printed by Questa.

Similar booklets produced by Walsall have the same perforation as the sheet stamps.

Booklet pane No. 2124dl comes from Prestige Stamp booklet No. DX24.

The labels on booklet pane No. 2124l show either Postman Pat, publicising The Stamp Show 2000, or the National Botanic Garden of Wales.

1459

(Des J. Matthews. Gravure De La Rue)

2000 (22 May). Stamp Show 2000 International Stamp Exhibition, London. Jeffery Matthews Colour Palette. Sheet, 124×70 mm. Phosphorised paper. Perf 15×14 (with one elliptical hole in each vertical side).

MS2146 **1459** 4p. new blue; 5p. dull red-brown; 6p. yellow-olive; 10p. dull orange; 31p. deep mauve; 39p. bright magenta; 64p. turquoise-green; £1 bluish violet ...... 15·00 15·00
First Day Cover (Philatelic Bureau) .... 15·00
First Day Cover (Earls Court, London SW5) .... 15·00
Exhibition Card (wallet, sold at £4·99, containing one mint sheet and one cancelled on postcard) .... 30·00

The £1 value is printed in Iriodin ink which gives a shiny effect to the solid part of the background behind the Queen's head.

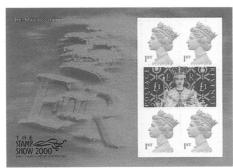

1459a

(Des Delaney Design Consultants. Gravure De La Rue)

2000 (23 May). Stamp Show 2000 International Stamp Exhibition, London. Her Majesty's Stamps. Sheet 121×89 mm. Phosphorised paper. Perf 15×14 (with one elliptical hole in each vertical side of stamps as T **1437**).

MS2147 **1459a** (1st) olive-brown (Type **1437**)×4; £1 slate-green (as Type **163**) .... 9·00 9·00
First Day Cover (Philatelic Bureau) .... 9·25
First Day Cover (City of Westminster, London SW1) .... 9·25
Presentation Pack (PO Pack No. M03) .... 40·00
PHQ Cards (set of 2) (PSM03) .... 80 15·00

The £1 value is an adaptation of the 1953 Coronation 1s.3d. stamp originally designed by Edmund Dulac. It is shown on one of the PHQ cards with the other depicting the complete miniature sheet.

N.V.I. AND DENOMINATED STAMPS, SELF-ADHESIVE GUM, ELLIPTICAL PERFORATIONS

(Gravure Questa, Walsall, Enschedé or De La Rue (1st), Walsall (others))

2002 (5 June–4 July). Self-adhesive. Two phosphor bands. Perf 15×14 die-cut (with one elliptical hole in each vertical side).

2295	**914**	(1st) gold	1·50	1·50
		a. Imperf (pair)	£850	
		y. Phosphor omitted	£225	
2296	**1093a**	(E) deep blue (4.7.02)	2·25	2·25
2297	**367a**	42p. deep olive-grey (4.7.02)	4·50	4·50
2298		68p. grey-brown (4.7.02)	5·00	5·00
Set of 4			12·00	12·00
PHQ Card (D22) (No. 2295) (Walsall) (27.3.03)			40	1·10

No. 2295, sold for 27p., was initially only available in booklets of six or 12, printed by Questa or Walsall, with the surplus self-adhesive paper around each stamp removed. Later booklets were also printed by De La Rue.

No. 2295 exists die-cut through the backing paper from Presentation Pack No. 71

No. 2295 was issued in rolls of 10,000, printed by Enschedé on yellow backing paper with the surplus self-adhesive paper removed. A number appears on the back of every tenth stamp in the roll.

A further printing of No. 2295 in sheets of 100 appeared on 4 July 2002 produced by Enschedé and on 18 March 2003 in stripped matrix sheets of 100 printed by Walsall. The top panel shows a strip of four with the typography of the label matching that of booklet T **ME2**.

Nos. 2296/2298 were only issued in separate booklets, each containing six stamps with the surplus self-adhesive paper around each stamp removed.

POSTAL FORGERIES. A postal forgery of No. 2295 exists, produced in booklets of 12 with a varnish band printed across the centre of the stamps to mimic phosphor bands. A similar forgery is known with the wavy perforations, gauge 10.

OVERSEAS BOOKLET STAMPS

1655

(Des Sedley Place. Gravure Walsall)

2003 (27 Mar)–**10**. Overseas Booklet Stamps. Self-adhesive. As T **1655** Two phosphor bands. Perf 15×14 die-cut with one elliptical hole in each vertical side.

2357a	(Worldwide postcard) grey-black, rosine and ultramarine (1.4.04)	2·50	3·00
2357b	(Europe up to 20 grams) deep blue-green, new blue and rosine (30.3.10)	2·50	3·00
2358	(Europe up to 40 grams) new blue and rosine	3·50	4·00
2358a	(Worldwide up to 20 grams) deep mauve, new blue and rosine (30.3.10)	3·50	4·00
2359	(Worldwide up to 40 grams) rosine and new blue	4·50	3·00
Set of 5		15·00	17·00
First Day Cover (Tallents House) (Type K, see Introduction) (Nos. 2358, 2359)			6·00
First Day Cover (Windsor) (Type K) (Nos. 2358, 2359)			6·00
Presentation Pack (PO Pack No. 60) (Nos. 2358, 2359)		5·50	
PHQ Card (D23) (No. 2358)		40	5·00

No. 2357a was intended to pay postcard rate to foreign destinations (43p.).

No. 2357a was available from philatelic outlets as a single stamp or in PO Packs Nos. 67 and 71 together with other definitive stamps. These single stamps were die-cut through the white backing paper.

Nos. 2358/2359 were intended to pay postage on mail up to 40 grams to either Europe (52p.) or to foreign destinations outside Europe (£1·12).

Nos. 2357b and 2358a were intended to pay postage on mail up to 20 grams to either Europe (initially 56p.) or to foreign destinations outside Europe (90p.).

They were only available in separate booklets of four (Nos. MI3 and MJ3) initially sold at £2·24 and £3·60, with the surplus self-adhesive paper around each stamp removed.

Operationally they were only available in separate booklets of four (Nos. MI1, MJ1 and MJA1), initially sold at £1·72, £2·08 and £4·48, with the surplus self-adhesive paper around each stamp removed.

For listings of first day covers (together with definitives issued on the same day) and presentation packs for Nos. 2357a/2357b and 2358a see after No. Y1803.

Single examples of Nos. 2358/2359 were available from philatelic outlets as sets of two or in PO Pack No. 60. These stamps were die-cut through the backing paper on the back and showed parts of the booklet covers. Nos. 2358a and 2358/2359 from PO Pack No. 67 (No. 2357a only), PO Packs Nos. 71 and 77 were die-cut through on plain white paper, while Nos. 2357b and 2358a in PO Pack No. 86 and all five values in PO Pack No. 88 were guillotined to show an area of margin surrounding the stamps.

The purchase prices of NVI stamps are shown in the introduction of the catalogue.

PRICING IN PROPORTION

1915	1916

(Des J. Matthews)

2006 (1st Aug)–**07**. Pricing in Proportion. Perf 15×14 (with one elliptical hole in each vertical side).

(a) Ordinary gum. Gravure De La Rue, ISP Walsall or Enschedé (No. 2651).

(i) As T **1915**.

2650	(2nd) bright blue (1 centre band)......................	1·00	1·00
	l. Booklet pane. Nos. 2650/2651, and Nos. 2652/2653 each×2, with central label and margins all round (5.6.07).......	7·50	
2651	(1st) gold (2 bands)..	1·25	1·25
	l. Booklet pane. Nos. 2651 and Y1726, each×4, with central label and margins all round (21.9.06).....................................	7·50	

(ii) As T **1916**.

2652	(2nd Large) bright blue (2 bands)...................	1·50	1·50
2653	(1st Large) gold (2 bands)...............................	1·90	1·90

(b) Self-adhesive. Gravure Walsall or Enschedé (No. 2654) or Walsall.

(i) As T **1915**.

2654	(2nd) bright blue (one centre band) (12.9.06)	1·00	1·00
	a. Imperf (pair)..	£275	
2655	(1st) gold (2 bands) (12.9.06)............................	1·25	1·25
	y. Phosphor omitted....................................	£150	

(ii) As T **1916**.

2656	(2nd Large) bright blue (2 bands) (15.8.06)....	1·50	1·50
2657	(1st Large) gold (2 bands) (15.8.06)...............	1·90	1·90
First Day Cover (Type K, see Introduction) (Nos. Y1677/Y1678, 2650/2653)...			5·75
First Day Cover (Windsor) (Type K) (Nos. Y1677/Y1678, 2650/2653)...			5·75
First Day Cover (Tallents House or Cuffley, Potters Bar, Herts) (Victoria Cross label pane 1st×4, 50p.×4 (No. 2651l)..			5·75
Presentation Pack (PO Pack No. 74) (Nos. Y1677/Y1678, 2650/2653)...			6·00

No. 2650 was issued in sheets (1 August) and coils of 500 (15 August).

No. 2654 was issued in rolls of 10,000, printed by Enschedé on yellow backing paper with the surplus self-adhesive paper removed. A number appears on the back of every tenth stamp in the roll.

Nos. 2654/2655 were available in separate booklets of six (No. RC1, *sold at* £1·92) or 12 (Nos. RD1 and RE1, *sold at* £2·76 or £3·84 respectively) and in business sheets of 100.

Nos. 2656/2657 were initially only available in separate booklets of four (Nos. RA1 and RB1), sold at £1·48 and £1·76.

All these booklets had the surplus self-adhesive paper around each stamp removed.

Nos. 2656/2657 were issued in sheets of 50, printed by Walsall, on 27 March 2007.

A postal forgery similar to No. 2651 exists with wavy perforations (gauge 10).

For PHQ cards for Nos. 2652/2653 see below No. Y1803.

NVI Stamps. Panes with elliptical perforations (Self-adhesive) the shaded squares represent printed labels.

2040I

'Millenium Machin' Stamps. Panes with elliptical perforations (Self-adhesive) the shaded squares represent printed labels.

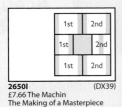

2124I

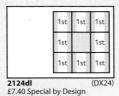

2124dl   (DX24)
£7.40 Special by Design

NVI 'Pricing in Proportion' Stamps. Panes with elliptical perforations (ordinary gum) the shaded squares represent printed labels.

2650I   (DX39)
£7.66 The Machin
The Making of a Masterpiece

2651I   (DX37)
£7.44 150th Anniversary of the
Victoria Cross

SECURITY MACHINS

On 17 February 2009 a new form of Machin definitive appeared, incorporating additional security features to combat the re-use of uncancelled stamps.

The stamps no longer included a water-soluble layer of gum between the paper and the self-adhesive to prevent them being 'soaked off' envelope paper; in addition, four U-shaped slits were die-cut into the stamps to prevent them being peeled off paper and, to make forgery more difficult, an overall iridescent multiple 'ROYALMAIL' overprint was incorporated into the design.

In May 2010 2nd and 1st class stamps were issued in rolls with iridescent overprint but printed on paper with ordinary gum and without U-shaped slits. These are listed as U3065/U3066. Other values in this form subsequently appeared in prestige booklets.

> **USED STAMPS.** Because the self-adhesive stamps in this section do not include a water-soluble layer of gum, we recommend that used stamps are retained on their backing paper and trimmed with a uniform border of 1 mm–2 mm around all sides, taking care not to cut into the perforations.

2132e

Source Codes. In March 2009 stamps were issued with 'codes' incorporated into the iridescent overprint which allowed the source to be identified. The codes may be seen in the words 'ROYALMAIL', usually at the top right of the stamp, although some later Large Letter issues have it at the bottom right (marked 'BR' in the list below) or just to the front of the Queen's hair (marked 'FOH' in the list below).

The codes are:

2nd and 1st		
MAIL		(ie without code letter) – counter sheets
M**B**IL	–	Business sheets
M**C**IL	–	'Custom' booklets, which include special stamps
M**M**IL	–	Miniature sheet (Nos. **MS**3222/**MS**3965) (not listed as individual stamps)
M**P**IL	–	Prestige booklet panes
M**R**IL	–	Rolls
M**S**IL	–	standard booklets of six
M**T**IL	–	booklets of 12
2nd and 1st Large		
ROYALMAIL		(ie without code letter) – counter sheets
Y**B**LM	–	Business sheets (2009)
M**B**I	–	Business sheets (2010)
BIL	–	Business sheets (2011–2013) (BR)
M**B**IL	–	Business sheets (from 2014) (FOH)
FOYAL	–	booklets of Four (2009)
M**F**I	–	booklets of Four (2010)
FIL	–	booklets of Four (2011–2013) (BR)
M**F**IL	–	booklets of Four (from 2014) (FOH)

For the Diamond Jubilee definitive with source codes, which are behind The Queen's head, the end of 'DIAMOND' is adjusted to:

M**B**ND	–	Business sheets
M**C**ND	–	'Custom' booklets of six
M**M**ND	–	Miniature sheet (No. **MS**3272) (not listed as individual stamps)
M**P**ND	–	Prestige booklet pane
M**S**ND	–	standard booklet of six
M**T**ND	–	booklets of 12

And for Large Letter stamps with source codes the end of 'JUBILEE' is adjusted to :

L**B**E	–	Business sheets
L**F**E	–	booklets of four

For the Long to Reign Over Us definitives with source codes, which are behind The Queen's neck, the end of 'REIGN' is adjusted to:

G**C**	–	'Custom' booklets of six
G**M**	–	Miniature sheet (No. **MS**3747) (not listed as individual stamp)
G**P**	–	Prestige booklet pane
G**S**	–	standard booklet of six

Year codes. From 2010 a year code (also sometimes referred to as a date code) was added to the iridescent overprint. Generally it appears in the upper left corner of the stamp, in front of the crown to The Queen's forehead or eye, but on later Large Letter stamps it appears lower down, above the 'ge' of 'Large'. Stamps are listed without or with year codes, and the different codes known are given in checklists at the end of this section. Note that year dates given within the listings are years of issue, not year codes.

> Note that, where stamps exist with more that one year code, the issue date given is for the first release, but prices are for the cheapest code.

U-shaped slits. The first issue featured U-shaped die-cut slits without a break in the middle of each 'U', but subsequent issues have incorporated a break to prevent the stamps tearing while being removed from the backing paper on which they were issued. We no longer list these as separate varieties but details are provided in the checklists at the end of this section.

A 1st gold stamp with U-slits but without iridescent overprint was supplied only to bulk mailing houses.

'ROYAL MAIL' printed backing paper. As an additional security measure, in early 2016 the backing paper on certain booklets appeared with a repeated undulating 'ROYALMAIL' background in two sizes of grey text printed upright on the front of the backing paper (Type PB-Up). This feature extended to business sheets and counter sheets during 2016 and 2017. In early 2017 the background was changed, so that alternate pairs of lines of the repeated 'ROYALMAIL' text were inverted in relation to each other. The pairs of lines can appear with the Large lettering above the small (Type PB-Ls), or with the small above the the Large (Type PB-sL). In October 2018 a fourth type appeared on some No. PM64 booklets. In this type the 'ROYALMAIL' background, in two sizes of grey text, is all inverted (Type PB-Inv). These differences are not listed in this catalogue, unless the stamps themselves are different. Their existence is, however, noted under the sections in which they occur, and in the checklists at the end of this section. For illustrations and further details please refer to the checklists. Booklets with 'ROYALMAIL' security text are listed in the relevant section of this catalogue.

> Details of known source and year-code combinations, and different year code changes, are provided in the series of tables following the listings. For the convenience of collectors, the printer of each combination is also given. We are grateful to John M. Deering for compiling these tables.

367

2009 (17 Feb)–**20**. Self-adhesive. Designs as T **367**. Two phosphor bands. U-shaped slits. Iridescent overprint. Die-cut Perf 14½×14 (with one elliptical hole in each vertical side).

(a) Without source or year codes, gravure De La Rue.

U2911	50p. brownish grey	2·00	1·50
U2912	£1 magenta	3·50	2·75
U2913	£1·50 brown-red	3·25	3·00
U2914	£2 deep blue-green	4·75	4·50
U2915	£3 deep mauve	5·75	5·50
U2916	£5 azure	9·50	9·25

(b) With source and year codes, gravure Walsall.

U2917	50p. brownish grey (MPIL) (8.5.10)	5·00	5·00
	l. Booklet pane Nos. U2917×2, U3011×2 and U3017×4, with central label and margins all round	16·00	

No. U2917 was first issued in £11·15 booklets, No. DX50 with 'MA10' year code. It was issued again in £9·99 premium booklet, No. DY1, with 'M11L' year code, (see also U3075l).

(c) *Without source code, with year code, gravure De La Rue (Nos. U2926/*
U2927, U2929/U2930, U2932/U2933, U2935/U2937, U2939/U2940, U2941,
U2945/U2946, U2948, U2950, U2954, U2956, U2958, U2961, U2968/U2969),
De La Rue or Walsall/ISP Walsall (Nos. U2920/U2925, U2928, U2931/U2934,
U2953, U2955, U2957, U2962) or ISP Walsall (others).

U2920	1p. deep crimson (3.1.13)		40	35
U2921	2p. deep green (3.1.13)		40	35
U2922	5p. dull red-brown (3.1.13)		45	40
U2923	10p. dull orange (3.1.13)		60	50
U2924	20p. bright green (3.1.13)		70	60
U2925	50p. slate (3.1.13)		1·75	1·50
U2926	68p. deep turquoise-green (29.3.11)		2·25	2·00
U2927	76p. bright rose (29.3.11)		2·00	1·75
U2928	78p. bright mauve (27.3.13)		2·00	1·75
U2929	81p. emerald (26.3.14)		3·75	3·50
U2930	87p. yellow-orange (25.4.12)		4·25	4·00
U2931	88p. orange-yellow (27.3.13)		2·25	2·00
U2932	97p. bluish violet (26.3.14)		2·50	2·25
U2933	£1 magenta (10.10.11)		16·00	15·50
U2934	£1 bistre-brown (3.1.13)		3·00	2·75
U2935	£1·05 grey-olive (22.3.16)		2·75	2·50
U2936	£1·10 yellow-olive (29.3.11)		3·25	3·00
U2937	£1·17 orange-red (21.3.17)		3·00	2·75
U2938	£1·25 emerald (20.3.18)		2·75	2·50
U2939	£1·28 emerald (25.4.12)		4·00	3·75
U2940	£1·33 orange-yellow (24.3.15)		2·75	2·50
U2940a	£1·35 bright mauve (19.3.19)		3·00	2·75
U2941	£1·40 grey-green (21.3.17)		3·00	2·75
U2942	£1·42 deep rose-red (17.3.20)		3·00	2·75
U2943	£1·45 lavender-grey (20.3.18)		3·25	3·00
U2945	£1·47 lavender-grey (26.3.14)		3·50	3·25
U2946	£1·52 bright mauve (24.3.15)		3·00	2·75
U2947	£1·55 greenish blue (20.3.18)		3·00	2·75
U2948	£1·57 yellow-olive (21.3.17)		3·25	3·00
U2949	£1·60 orange-yellow (19.3.19)		3·00	2·75
U2949a	£1·63 orange-red (17.3.20)		3·00	2·75
U2950	£1·65 grey-olive (29.3.11)		3·75	3·50
U2951	£1·68 yellow-olive (17.3.20)		3·50	3·25
U2952	£1·70 greenish blue (23.12.20)		3·50	3·25
U2953	£1·88 dull ultramarine (27.3.13)		3·75	3·50
U2954	£1·90 bright mauve (25.4.12)		4·00	3·75
U2955	£2 deep blue-green (4.13)		3·75	3·50
U2956	£2·15 greenish blue (26.3.14)		4·25	4·00
U2957	£2·25 deep violet (24.3.15)		3·75	3·50
U2958	£2·27 bistre (21.3.17)		4·00	3·75
U2959	£2·30 grey-olive (19.3.19)		3·50	3·25
U2960	£2·42 bluish violet (17.3.20)		3·75	3·75
U2961	£2·45 bluish green (24.3.15)		4·00	3·75
U2962	£2·55 deep rose-red (21.3.17)		5·00	4·75
U2963	£2·65 bluish violet (20.3.18)		4·50	4·25
U2964	£2·80 bluish green (19.3.19)		4·25	4·00
U2965	£2·97 bright magenta (17.3.20)		4·50	4·50
U2966	£3 deep mauve (11.9.19)		4·75	4·50
U2968	£3·15 turquoise-blue (24.3.15)		5·00	4·75
U2968a	£3·25 turquoise-green (23.12.20)		4·75	4·50
U2969	£3·30 bright magenta (24.3.15)		5·25	5·00
U2970	£3·45 grey-green (19.3.19)		5·00	4·75
U2971	£3·60 yellow-orange (19.3.19)		5·25	5·00
U2972	£3·66 pale ochre (17.3.20)		5·25	5·25
U2973	£3·82 emerald (17.3.20)		5·50	5·50
U2973a	£4·20 deep violet (23.12.20)		6·25	6·00
U2974	£5 azure (11.9.19)		8·00	7·75
	Set of 57		£195	£185

No. U2936 and U2950 are with 'M11L' year code from stock officially issued/available over the post office counter, and are recorded in the tables following the main listings. A very few examples with an 'M12L' year code are known from a single sheet sent to a specialist catalogue publisher for research purposes. They were never officially issued and are therefore not recorded in the tables following the main listing.

Nos. U2911/U2917, U2926/U2933, U2935/U2936, U2939/U2940, U2945/ U2946, U2950, U2953/U2954, U2956, U2961 and U2968/U2969 only exist on plain backing paper.

Nos. U2920/U2925, U2934, U2937, U2941, U2948, U2955, U2957/ U2958 and U2962 were originally issued on plain backing paper, but later appeared on paper with repeating 'ROYALMAIL' text, with alternate pairs of lines inverted (Types PB-Ls/sL).

Nos. U2938, U2940a, U2942/U2943, U2947, U2949, U2949a, U2951/ U2952, U2959/U2960, U2963/U2966, U2968a, U2970/U2974 only exist on backing paper with repeating 'ROYALMAIL' text, with alternate pairs of lines inverted (Types PB-Ls/sL).

2009 (17 Feb)–**17**. Self-adhesive. Designs as Types **913**/**914** or T **1916**. One centre band (Nos. U2975, U2979/U2981, U2995 and U3010/U3013) two bands (others). U-shaped slits. Iridescent overprint. Die-cut Perf 14½×14 (with one elliptical hole in each vertical side).

(a) *Without source or year codes, gravure De La Rue.*

U2975	(2nd) bright blue		2·50	2·25
U2976	(1st) gold		2·75	2·50
U2977	(2nd Large) bright blue		3·00	2·75
U2978	(1st Large) gold		3·25	3·00

(b) *With source code, without year code, gravure De La Rue (Nos. U2979/*
U2980, U2982, U2984, U2987, U2989) or Walsall (others).

U2979	(2nd) bright blue (MBIL) (31.3.09)		3·75	3·75
U2980	(2nd) bright blue (MRIL) (7.09)		4·50	4·50
U2981	(2nd) bright blue (MTIL) (31.3.09)		2·25	2·25
U2982	(1st) gold (MBIL) (31.3.09)		3·75	3·75
U2983	(1st) gold (MCIL) (10.3.09)		2·25	2·25

U2984	(1st) gold (MRIL) (7.09)		5·00	5·00
U2985	(1st) gold (MSIL) (31.3.09)		4·50	4·50
U2986	(1st) gold (MTIL) (31.3.09)		2·50	2·50
U2987	(2nd Large) bright blue (YBLM) (31.3.09)		3·75	3·75
U2988	(2nd Large) bright blue (FOYAL) (31.3.09)		3·75	3·75
U2989	(1st Large) gold (YBLM) (31.3.09)		3·75	3·75
U2990	(1st Large) gold (FOYAL) (31.3.09)		4·50	4·50

(c) *Without source code, with year code, gravure De La Rue (Nos. U2996/*
U2997 and U3001/U3002), De La Rue or Walsall/ISP Walsall (others).

U2995	(2nd) bright blue (1.7.10)		1·60	1·25
U2996	(1st) gold (20.5.10)		3·50	3·50
U2997	(1st) vermilion (3.1.13)		2·00	1·75
U2998	(1st) bright scarlet (11.4.17)		1·70	1·40
U3000	(2nd Large) bright blue (26.1.11)		1·90	1·50
U3001	(1st Large) gold (3.11.10)		6·00	6·00
U3002	(1st Large) vermilion (3.1.13)		2·75	2·50
U3003	(1st Large) bright scarlet (11.4.17)		2·25	1·75

(d) *With source and year codes, gravure De La Rue or Walsall/ISP Walsall*
(Nos. U3010 and U3031), De La Rue or Enschedé (No. U3018), De La Rue,
Enschedé or Walsall (No. U3012), Enschedé or Walsall (No. U3023), De La
Rue (Nos. U3015 and U3034) or Walsall/ISP Walsall (others).

U3010	(2nd) bright blue (MBIL) (8.10)		2·00	1·75
U3011	(2nd) bright blue (MPIL) (8.5.10)		4·50	4·50
U3012	(2nd) bright blue (MRIL) (7.11)		4·25	4·25
U3013	(2nd) bright blue (MTIL) (2.10)		1·75	1·50
U3015	(1st) gold (MBIL) (6.10)		4·50	4·50
U3016	(1st) gold (MCIL) (25.2.10)		1·75	1·50
U3017	(1st) gold (MPIL) (8.5.10)		2·10	2·10
U3018	(1st) gold (MRIL) (15.7.11)		4·75	4·75
U3019	(1st) gold (MSIL) (26.1.10)		2·00	2·00
U3020	(1st) gold (MTIL) (2.10)		2·25	2·25
U3021	(1st) vermilion (MBIL) (3.1.13)		2·75	2·50
U3022	(1st) vermilion (MCIL) (9.1.13)		1·40	1·20
U3023	(1st) vermilion (MRIL) (3.1.13)		3·00	3·00
U3024	(1st) vermilion (MSIL) (3.1.13)		1·75	1·60
U3025	(1st) vermilion (MTIL) (3.1.13)		1·75	1·60
U3026	(1st) bright scarlet (MBIL) (20.10.16)		2·25	2·00
U3027	(1st) bright scarlet (MCIL) (20.10.16)		1·40	1·20
U3028	(1st) bright scarlet (MSIL) (20.10.16)		1·90	1·75
U3029	(1st) bright scarlet (MTIL) (20.10.16)		2·00	1·75
U3031	(2nd Large) bright blue (MBI/BIL/MBIL) (3.11)		2·75	2·50
U3032	(2nd Large) bright blue (MFI/FIL/MFIL) (8.5.10)		2·50	2·25
U3034	(1st Large) gold (MBI/BIL) (6.10)		4·50	4·50
U3035	(1st Large) gold (MFI/FIL) (8.5.10)		3·25	3·25
U3036	(1st Large) vermilion (BIL/MBIL) (3.1.13)		3·25	3·00
U3037	(1st Large) vermilion (FIL/MFIL) (3.1.13)		3·25	3·00
U3038	(1st Large) bright scarlet (MBIL) (20.10.16)		3·25	3·00
U3039	(1st Large) bright scarlet (MFIL) (20.10.16)		3·25	3·00

Nos. U2975/U2990, U2996/U2997, U3001/U3002, U3011/U3012, U3015/ U3020, U3022/U3023 and U3034/U3035 only exist on plain backing paper.

Nos. U3021, U3024/U3025 and U3036/U3037 were originally issued on plain backing paper, but later appeared on paper with repeating 'ROYALMAIL' text the same way up (Type PB-Up).

Nos. U2995 and U3000 were originally issued on plain backing paper, but later appeared on paper with repeating 'ROYALMAIL' text, with alternate pairs of lines inverted (Types PB-Ls/sL).

Nos. U3010, U3013, U3031 and U3032 were originally issued on plain backing paper, but later appeared on paper with repeating 'ROYALMAIL' text the same way up (Type PB-Up), and subsequently with alternate pairs of lines inverted (Types PB-Ls/sL).

Nos. U3026, U3028/U3029 and U3038/U3039 were originally issued on backing paper with repeating 'ROYALMAIL' text the same way up (Type PB-Up), but later appeared with alternate pairs of lines inverted (Types PB-Ls/sL).

No. U3027 was originally issued on backing paper with repeating 'ROYALMAIL' text the same way up (Type PB-Up), but later appeared with alternate pairs of lines inverted (Types PB-Ls/sL), and subsequently from some No. PM64 booklets with repeating 'ROYALMAIL' text the same way up but inverted (Type PB-Inv).

Nos. U2998 and U3003 only exist on backing paper with repeating 'ROYALMAIL' text, with alternate pairs of lines inverted (Types PB-Ls/sL).

For full details of which stamps and year codes exist on different backing papers, please see the checklists at the end of this section of the catalogue.

2132a	2132b

2132c	2132d

(Gravure De La Rue or from 2018 ISP Walsall)

2009 (17 Nov)–**13**. Self-adhesive. Designs as Types **2132a/2132d**. Two phosphor bands. U-shaped slits. Iridescent overprint. Die-cut Perf 14 (Nos. U3046, U3048, U3050) or 14½×14 (others) (all with one elliptical hole in each vertical side).

(a) Without source or year codes, gravure De La Rue.

U3045	(Recorded Signed for 1st) bright orange-red and lemon............................	4·25	3·75
U3046	(Recorded Signed for 1st Large) bright orange-red and lemon........................	4·75	4·00

(b) Without source code, with year code, gravure De La Rue (Nos. U3047/ U3048), De La Rue or ISP Walsall (others).

U3047	(Recorded Signed for 1st) bright orange-red and lemon (11.4.11)......	13·00	13·00
U3048	(Recorded Signed for 1st Large) bright orange-red and lemon (11.4.11)...........	23·00	23·00
U3049	(Royal Mail Signed for 1st) bright orange-red and lemon (27.3.13)...........	4·50	4·00
U3050	(Royal Mail Signed for 1st Large) bright orange-red and lemon (27.3.13)...........	5·00	4·50
U3051	(Special delivery up to 100g) blue and silver (26.10.10)..........................	11·00	10·50
U3052	(Special delivery up to 500g) blue and silver (26.10.10)..........................	12·00	11·50

No. U3045 was originally sold for £1·14 (£1·15 from 6 April 2010 and £1·23 from 4 April 2011).

No. U3046 was originally sold for £1·36 (£1·40 from 6 April 2010 and £1·52 from 4 April 2011).

No. U3047 was originally sold for £1·23 (£1·55 from 30 April 2012).

No. U3048 was originally sold for £1·52 (£1·85 from 30 April 2012).

No. U3049 was originally sold for £1·55 (£1·70 from 2 April 2013, £1·72 from 31 March 2014, £1·73 from 30 March 2015, £1·74 from 29 March 2016, £1·75 from 27 March 2017, £1·77 from 26 March 2018, £1·90 from 25 March 2019, £2·06 from 23 March 2020 and £2·25 from 1 January 2021).

No. U3050 was originally sold for £1·85 (£2 from 2 April 2013, £2·03 from 31 March 2014, £2·05 from 30 March 2015, £2·06 from 29 March 2016, £2·08 from 27 March 2017, £2·11 from 26 March 2018, £2·26 from 25 March 2019, £2·45 from 23 March 2020 and £2·69 from 1 January 2021).

No. U3051 was originally sold for £5·05 (£5·45 from 4 April 2011, £5·90 from 30 April 2012, £6·22 from 2 April 2013, £6·40 from 31 March 2014, £6·45 from 30 March 2015, £6·50 from 26 March 2018, £6·60 from 25 March 2019, £6·70 from 23 March 2020 and £6·85 from 1 January 2021).

No. U3052 was originally sold for £5·50 (£5·90 from 4 April 2011, £6·35 from 30 April 2012, £6·95 from 2 April 2013, £7·15 from 31 March 2014, £7·25 from 30 March 2015, £7·30 from 26 March 2018, £7·40 from 25 March 2019, £7·50 from 23 March 2020 and £7·65 from 1 January 2021).

Nos. U3045/U3048 only exist on plain backing paper.

Nos. U3049/U3052 were originally issued on plain backing paper, but later appeared on paper with repeating 'ROYALMAIL' text, with alternate pairs of lines inverted (Types PB-Ls/sL).

(Gravure De La Rue or Walsall (Nos. U3057/U3058) or De La Rue (others))

2011 (8 Mar–5 May). Self-adhesive. Designs as T **367**. Two phosphor bands. U-shaped slits. No iridescent overprint. Die-cut Perf 14½×14 (with one elliptical hole in each vertical side).

U3055	1p. crimson.................................	80	80
U3056	2p. deep green..........................	50	50
U3057	5p. dull red-brown.....................	60	60
	l. Booklet pane. Nos. U3057×4, U3058×2 and U2917×2 with central label and margins all round (5.5.11)............	10·50	
U3058	10p. dull orange........................	70	70
U3059	20p. bright green........................	1·00	1·00
Set of 5		3·25	3·25

Nos. U3055/U3059 were issued in counter sheets and do not have an iridescent overprint.

Nos. U3057/U3058 were issued again, but in £9·99 premium booklet, No. DY1.

No. 3057l combines stamps without and with iridescent overprint.

2010 (13 May)–**22**. Ordinary gum. Designs as Types **367** and **913/914**. Without U-shaped slits. Iridescent overprint. One centre phosphor band (Nos. U3065 and U3150) or two bands (others). Perf 14½×14 (with one elliptical hole in each vertical side).

(a) With source and year codes, gravure Walsall (U3060) or ISP Walsall (U3061).

U3060	68p turquoise-green (MPIL) (10.1.12)............	4·00	4·00
U3061	£1 magenta (MPIL) (5.6.17)........................	23·00	23·00

(b) NVIs with source and year codes, gravure De La Rue (Nos. U3065/U3066) or ISP Walsall (No. U3067).

U3065	(2nd) bright blue (MRIL) (13.5.10)................	7·00	7·00
U3066	(1st) gold (MRIL) (13.5.10).......................	7·25	7·25
U3067	(1st) vermilion (MPIL) (5.6.17)...................	11·00	11·00

No. U3060 comes from booklet pane Y1668m in No. DY3 Roald Dahl's Children's Stories premium booklet, and has a 'M11L' year code.

No. U3061 comes from pane Y1667p in No. DY21 50th Anniversary of the Machin Definitive premium booklet, and has a 'M17L' year code.

Nos. U3065/U3066 were issued in separate coils of 500 or 1000, and have 'MA10' year codes.

No. U3066 also exists from Birth Centenary of Arnold Machin miniature sheet No. **MS**3222, from which it has source code 'MMIL' (and 'AM11' year code).

No. U3067 comes from booklet pane 1668ssl in No. DY21 50th Anniversary of the Machin Definitive premium booklet, and has a 'M17L' year code.

No. U3067 also exists printed gravure from 50th Anniversary of the Machin Definitive miniature sheet No. **MS**3965, from which it has source code 'MMIL' and year code 'M17L', but is not separately listed.

A 1st bright scarlet (similar to No. U3067) with 'M21L' year code but without a source code exists from a 95th Birthday of Her Majesty The Queen sheetlet (21.04.21), containing 1st bright scarlet×4, Nos. EN53, S160, W150, NI158 with central label and margins all round. The sheetlet printed by Walsall combines gravure (1st bright scarlet) and litho printing (others and phosphor bands). The sheetlet was commissioned by The Royal Mint for use on cover and was not available unused to the general public.

(c) With source and year codes, litho Enschedé (Nos. U3073, U3076), Cartor/ISP Cartor or Enschedé (Nos. U3071/U3075, U3082) or Cartor/ISP Cartor (others).

U3070	1p. crimson (MPIL) (9.5.13)............................	75	75
	a. Source code without P (M IL) (14.3.19)..	1·25	1·25
	l. Booklet pane. Nos. U3070×2, U3156×2, EN51, NI95, S158 and W148 with central label and margins all round (9.5.13)............................	12·50	
	m. Booklet pane. Nos. U3070×2, U3071×3, U3079 and U3081×2 with central label and margins all round (19.2.15)............................	14·50	
	n. Booklet pane. Nos. U3070, U3072a, U3094 and 3717, each×2 with central label and margins all round (14.5.15).....	14·00	
	o. Booklet pane. Nos. U3070, U3075, U3077a and U3089, each×2 with central label and margins all round (4.12.18)............................	12·50	
	p. Booklet pane. Nos. U3070a×2, U3075a×3, U3089a×2 and U3104, with central label and margins all round (14.3.19)............................	11·75	
	q. Booklet pane. Nos. U3070×2, U3071×4 and U3096×2 with central label and margins all round (11.2.20).....................	10·00	
	r. Booklet pane. Nos. U3070 and 4403, each×4 with central label and margins all round (9.7.20)..	7·50	
U3071	2p. deep green (MPIL) (9.5.13)........................	85	85
	a. Source code without P (M IL) (20.3.18)..	1·00	1·00
	l. Booklet pane. Nos. U3071/U3072 and U3074, each×2 (9.5.13)............................	5·75	
	m. Booklet pane. Nos. U3071/U3072, each×2, and Nos. EN51a, NI95, S158a and W148 with central label and margins all round (20.2.14).....................	12·00	
	n. Booklet pane. Nos. U3071×2, U3074×2, U3157×3 and U3083 with central label and margins all round (15.2.17)...............	11·00	
	o. Booklet pane. Nos. U3071a×3, U3072b×3 and U3084a×2 with central label and margins all round (20.3.18).....	10·50	
	p. Booklet pane. Nos. U3071, U3077 and 3807, each×2 and Nos. 3808/3809 with central label and margins all round (24.5.19).....................	13·50	
	q. Booklet pane. Nos. U3071, U3150, 3786 and S159a, each×2, with central label and margins all round (17.3.20).....	8·00	
	r. Booklet pane. Nos. U3071×2, U3077×3 and U3150×3 with central label and margins all round (13.11.20).....................	8·00	
	s. Booklet pane. Nos. U3071×2, U3074×2, U3077×2 and U3157×2 with central label and margins all round (28.5.21).....................	12·50	
	t. Booklet pane. Nos. U3071, U3074, U3077 and U3108, each×2, with central label and margins all round (4.2.22)........	14·50	
U3072	5p. red-brown (MPIL) (26.3.13)........................	90	90
	a. *Deep brown-red* (MPIL) (14.5.15)............	2·25	2·25
	b. Source code without P (M IL) (20.3.18)..	1·25	1·25
	l. Booklet pane. Nos. U3072, U3074/U3075, U3080 and 3452×4 with central label and margins all round (26.3.13).....	16·00	
	m. Booklet pane. Nos. U3072, U3074, U3077 and U3082, each×2 with central label and margins all round (18.6.15).....	15·00	
	n. Booklet pane. Nos. U3072×3, U3074×2 and U3083×3 with central label and margins all round (28.7.16).....................	9·75	
	o. Booklet pane. Nos. U3072×2, U3075, U3084, NI94×2 and 4049×2 with central label and margins all round (23.1.18).....................	10·50	
	p. Booklet pane. Nos. U3072×2, U3074×4 and U3109×2 with central label and margins all round (13.2.19).....................	30·00	
	q. Booklet pane. Nos. U3072×2 and U3084×2 and U3150×4, with central label and margins all round (26.11.19)..	11·00	

r. Booklet pane. Nos. U3072×2 and
U3074×2 and EN53a, NI158, S160 and
W150 with central label and margins
all round (11.2.20)..................................... 8·00

s. Booklet pane. Nos. U3072×4, U3077×2
and U3110×2 with central label and
margins all round (8.5.20)........................ 15·00

t. Booklet pane. Nos. U3072×2, U3074×3,
U3075×2 and U3116 with central label
and margins all round (12.8.21)............... 18·00

U3073   5p. red-brown (MPIL). Elliptical hole near
the top of sides of stamp (19.9.13)......... 2·00   2·00

l. Booklet pane. Nos. U3073 and U3076,
each×4, with central label and margins
all round (19.9.13)................................... 12·00   12·00

U3074   10p. dull orange (MPIL) (26.3.13)................. 95   95

l. Booklet pane. Nos. U3074×2, U3075×4
and U3082×2 with central label and
margins all round (15.4.14)..................... 10·00

m. Booklet pane. Nos. U3074×2,
U3075×2, EN30, NI95, S131 and W122
with central label and margins all
round (28.7.14).. 9·50

n. Booklet pane. Nos. U3074, U3075,
U3077 and U3082, each×2, with
central label and margins all round
(20.1.22)... 13·50

U3075   20p. bright green (MPIL) (26.3.13)............... 1·10   1·10

a. Source code without P (M IL) (14.3.19).. 1·75   1·75

l. Booklet pane. Nos. U3075×3, U3150×2
and U3157×3 with central label and
margins all round (16.2.21)..................... 13·50

m. Booklet pane. No. U3075×3, U3150×3
and U3157×2 with central label and
margins all round (17.9.21)..................... 10·00

U3076   50p. slate-blue (MPIL). Elliptical hole near
the top sides of stamp (19.9.13)............. 2·00   2·00

U3077   50p. slate (MPIL) (18.6.15)......................... 1·60   1·60

a. *Grey* (MPIL) (4.12.18).......................... 2·00   2·00

U3078   76p. bright rose (MPIL) (9.9.11).................. 9·50   9·50

U3079   81p. deep turquoise-green (MPIL) (19.2.15).. 8·00   8·00

U3080   87p. yellow-orange (MPIL) (26.3.13)............ 6·00   6·00

U3081   97p. bluish violet (MPIL) (19.2.15)............... 3·75   3·75

U3082   £1 sepia (MPIL) (15.4.14)........................... 2·00   2·00

l. Booklet pane. No. U3082 with eight
reproduction King George V 1d.
stamps all round (28.7.14)....................... 4·00

U3083   £1·05 grey-olive (MPIL) (28.7.16)............... 2·75   2·75

U3084   £1·17 bright orange (MPIL) (23.1.18).......... 4·00   4·00

a. Source code without P (M IL) (20.3.18).. 4·50   4·50

U3089   £1·25 emerald (MPIL) (4.12.18).................. 2·75   2·75

a. *Light green.* Source code without P (M
IL) (14.3.19)... 2·75   2·75

U3094   £1·33 orange-yellow (MPIL) (14.5.15)......... 3·00   3·00

U3096   £1·35 bright purple (MPIL) (11.2.20).......... 4·00   4·00

U3099   £1·40 grey-green (MPIL) (14.12.17)............. 4·00   4·00

U3104   £1·45 lavender-grey source code without P
(M IL) (14.3.19).. 7·00   7·00

U3108   £1·50 brown-red (MPIL) (4.2.22)................. 8·50   8·50

U3109   £1·55 greenish blue (MPIL) (13.2.19)........... 15·00   15·00

U3115   £1·63 bright orange (MPIL) (8.5.20)............ 4·50   4·50

U3116   £1·70 greenish blue (MPIL) (12.8.21).......... 15·00   15·00

  (d) NVIs with source and year codes, litho Cartor/ISP Cartor.

U3150   (2nd) bright blue (MPIL) (17.12.15)............ 1·90   1·90

l. Booklet pane. Nos. U3150×2, and
U3156×2 and 3786×4, with central
label and margins all round (17.12.15).. 12·50

m. Booklet pane. Nos. U3150×2, U3156×4
and U3099×2, with central label and
margins all round (14.12.17)................... 13·50

U3155   (1st) gold (MPIL) (9.9.11).......................... 5·25   5·25

U3156   (1st) vermilion (MPIL) (9.5.13)................... 1·75   1·75

l. Booklet pane. Nos. U3156×2,
U3747×2, EN30b, NI95, S131a and
W122, with central label and margins
all round (21.4.16).................................... 14·00

m. Booklet pane. Nos. U3156×4 and
3717×4 with central label and margins
all round (13.9.18)................................... 11·00

U3157   (1st) bright scarlet (MPIL) (15.2.17).......... 2·10   2·10

Nos. U3070/U3157 were all issued in premium booklets.
No. U3070 comes from Nos. DY7, DY12, DY13, DY27, DY32 and DY35.
No. U3070a comes from No. DY29.
No. U3071 comes from Nos. DY7, DY9, DY12, DY20, DY30, DY33, DY36, DY38 and DY42.
No. U3071a comes from No. DY29.
No. U3072 comes from Nos. DY6, DY7 DY9, DY14, DY19, DY24, DY28, DY31, DY32, DY34 and DY39.
No. U3072a comes from No. DY13.
No. U3072b comes from No. DY25.
No. U3073 comes from No. DY8, and has the elliptical hole near the top of sides of stamp.
No. U3074 comes from Nos. DY6, DY7, DY10, DY11, DY14, DY19, DY20, DY28, DY32, DY38, DY39, DY41 and DY42.
No. U3075 comes from Nos. DY6, DY10, DY11, DY24, DY27, DY37, DY39, DY40 and DY41.
No. U3075a comes from No. DY29.

No. U3076 comes from No. DY8, and has the elliptical hole near the top of sides of stamp.
No. U3077 comes from Nos. DY14, DY30, DY34, DY36, DY38, DY41 and DY42.
No. U3077a comes from No. DY27.
No. U3078 comes from booklet pane Y1763m in No. DY2.
No. U3079 comes from No. DY12.
No. U3080 comes from No. DY6.
No. U3081 comes from No. DY12.
No. U3082 comes from Nos. DY10, DY11, DY14 and DY41.
No. U3082l comes from No. DY11 and contains one U3082 with year code M14L, and eight reproduction King George V 1d. stamps.
No. U3083 comes from Nos. DY19 and DY20.
No. U3084 comes from Nos. DY24 and DY31.
No. U3084a comes from No. DY25.
No. U3089 comes from No. DY27.
No. U3089a comes from No. DY29.
No. U3094 comes from No. DY13.
No. U3096 comes from No. DY32.
No. U3099 comes from No. DY23.
No. U3104 comes from No. DY29.
No. U3108 comes from No. DY42.
No. U3109 comes from No. DY28.
No. U3115 comes from No. DY34.
No. U3116 comes from No. DY39.
No. U3150 comes from Nos. DY15, DY23, DY31, DY33, DY36, DY37 and DY40.
No. U3155 comes from booklet pane Y1763m in No. DY2.
No. U3156 comes from Nos. DY7, DY15, DY17, DY23 and DY26.
No. U3157 comes from No. DY20, DY37, DY38 and DY40.
No. U3075, U3089 and U3104 with 'M19L' year code and source codes with P (MPIL) exist from a limited edition 'Marvel 80th Anniversary' premium booklet (*sold at £39·99*). The panes have a simulated pictorial cancellation 'CELEBRATING 80 YEARS OF MARVEL COMICS'.
No. U3075a, U3089a and U3104 from a standard Marvel premium booklet, No. DY29 have 'M18L' year and 'M IL' source codes.
For additional information see Security Machin source and year code tables at the end of this section.

First Day Covers

17.2.09	Nos. U2911/U2912 and U2975/U2978 (Type K, see introduction)..	12·00	
	Nos. U2911/U2912 and U2975/U2978 (Windsor, Type K)...	12·00	
	Nos. U2913/U2916 (Type K)........................	20·00	
	Nos. U2913/U2916 (Windsor)......................	20·00	
17.11.09	Nos. U3045/U3046 (Type K)........................	6·75	
	Nos. U3045/U3046 (Windsor)......................	6·75	
8.5.10	King George V Accession Centenary, *se-tenant* pane No. U2917l (Tallents House or London N1)................	10·00	
26.10.10	Nos. U3051/U3052 (Type K)........................	25·00	
	Nos. U3051/U3052 (Windsor)......................	25·00	
8.3.11	Nos. U3055/U3059 (Type K)........................	4·00	
	Nos. U3055/U3059 (Windsor)......................	4·00	
29.3.11	Nos. U2926/U2927, U2936, U2950 (Type K)...	10·50	
	Nos. U2926/U2927, U2936 and U2950 (Windsor)...	10·50	
5.5.11	Morris & Co, *se-tenant* pane No. U3057l (Tallents House or Walthamstow).................................	6·50	
25.4.12	Nos. U2930, U2939, U2954, U3271 and U3276 (Type K)..	14·00	
	Nos. U2930, U2939, U2954, U3271 and U3276 (Windsor)..	14·00	
3.1.13	Nos. U2920/U2925, U2934, U2997 and U3002 (Type K)..	10·00	
	Nos. U2920/U2925, U2934, U2997 and U3002 (Windsor)..	10·00	
26.3.13	*Dr Who se-tenant* pane No. U3072l (Tallents House or Cardiff)..................................	11·00	
27.3.13	Nos. U2928, U2931, U2953, U3049 and U3050 (Type K)..	16·00	
	Nos. U2928, U2931, U2953, U3049 and U3050 (Windsor)..	16·00	
9.5.13	Football Heroes *se-tenant* pane No. U3070l (Tallents House or Wembley, Middlesex).....................	10·50	
19.9.13	Merchant Navy *se-tenant* pane No. U3073l (Tallents House or Clydebank).................................	8·00	
20.2.14	Classic Locomotives *se-tenant* pane No. U3071m (Tallents House or Newcastle upon Tyne)........	9·00	
26.3.14	Nos. U2929, U2932, U2945 and U2956 (Type K)....	14·00	
	Nos. U2929, U2932, U2945 and U2956 (Windsor)........	14·00	
15.4.14	Buckingham Palace *se-tenant* pane No. U3074l (Tallents House or London SW1).....................	9·00	
28.7.14	First World War Centenary *se-tenant* pane No. U3074m (Tallents House or Newcastle upon Tyne).....	10·00	
19.2.15	Inventive Britain *se-tenant* pane No. U3070m (Tallents House or Harlow)............................	9·00	
24.3.15	Nos. U2940, U2946, U2957, U2961 and U2968/ U2969 (Type K).......................................	25·00	
	Nos. U2940, U2946, U2957, U2961 and U2968/ U2969 (Windsor).....................................	25·00	
14.5.15	First World War Centenary (2nd issue) *se-tenant* pane No. U3070n (Tallents House or Winchester)........	11·00	
18.6.15	Battle of Waterloo Bicentenary *se-tenant* pane No. U3072m (Tallents House or Waterloo, Liverpool).........	9·00	
17.12.15	*Star Wars se-tenant* pane No. U3150l (Tallents House or Elstree, Borehamwood)........................	10·50	

22.3.16	No. U2935 (Type K)..	3·25	
	No. U2935 (Windsor)...	3·25	
21.4.16	90th Birthday of Queen Elizabeth II *se-tenant* pane No. U3156l (Tallents House or Windsor).......................	12·50	
28.7.16	150th Birth Anniversary of Beatrix Potter *se-tenant* pane No. U3072n (Tallents House or Near Sawrey, Ambleside)..	10·00	
15.2.17	Windsor Castle *se-tenant* pane No. U3071n (Tallents House or Windsor)...	8·00	
21.3.17	Nos. U2937, U2941, U2948, U2958 and U2962 (Type K)...	17·00	
	Nos. U2937, U2941, U2948, U2958 and U2962 (Windsor)..	17·00	
14.12.17	*Star Wars* (4th issue) Aliens and Droids *se-tenant* pane No. U3150m (Tallents House or Wookey, Wells).	12·00	
23.1.18	*Game of Thrones se-tenant* pane No. U3072o (Tallents House or Belfast).....................................	9·00	
20.3.18	Nos. U2938, U2943, U2947 and U2963 (Type K)...........	14·00	
	Nos. U2938, U2943, U2947 and U2963 (Windsor).......	14·00	
20.3.18	RAF Centenary *se-tenant* pane No. U3071o (Tallents House or Cranwell, Sleaford).................................	7·00	
13.9.18	First World War Centenary (5th issue) *se-tenant* pane No. U3156m (Tallents House or London SWI)...............	10·50	
4.12.18	Harry Potter *se-tenant* pane No. U3070o (Tallents House or Muggleswick, Consett)...........................	8·75	
13.2.19	Leonardo da Vinci *se-tenant* pane No. U3072p (Tallents House or Windsor)..................................	8·50	
14.3.19	Marvel *se-tenant* pane No. U3070p (Tallents House or Shield Row, Stanley).......................................	9·50	
19.3.19	Nos. U2940a, U2949, U2959, U2964, U2970 and U2971 (Type K)...	23·00	
	Nos. U2940a, U2949, U2959, U2964, U2970 and U2971 (Windsor)..	23·00	
24.5.19	Birth Bicentenary of Queen Victoria *se-tenant* pane No. U3071p (Tallents House or East Cowes)................	8·50	
26.11.19	*Star Wars* The Making of the Vehicles *se-tenant* pane No. U3072q (Tallents House or Maulder, Bedford).......	10·00	
11.2.20	Visions of the Universe. Bicentenary of the Royal Astronomical Society *se-tenant* pane No. U3070q (Tallents House or London W1).............................	7·25	
17.3.20	James Bond *se-tenant* pane No. U3071q (Tallents House or Spy Post, Wellington)............................	8·50	
17.3.20	Nos. U2942, U2949a, U2951, U2960, U2965, U2972 and U2973 (Type K)..	28·00	
	Nos. U2942, U2949a, U2951, U2960, U2965, U2972 and U2973 (Windsor)...	28·00	
8.5.20	75th Anniversary of the End of the Second World War *se-tenant* pane No. U3072s (Tallents House or London SW1)...	8·50	
9.7.20	Queen (rock band) *se-tenant* pane No. 3070r (Tallents House or Knebworth)...........................	10·00	
13.11.20	*Star Trek se-tenant* pane No. 3071r (Tallents House or Beambridge, Craven Arms)................................	8·50	
23.12.20	Nos. U2952, U2968a, and U2973a (Type K).................	16·00	
	Nos. U2952, U2968a, and U2973a (Windsor).............	16·00	
16.2.21	*Only Fools and Horses se-tenant* pane No. U3075l (Tallents House or London SE15).......................	8·50	
28.5.21	Paul McCartney *se-tenant* pane No. U3071s (Tallents House or Liverpool).......................................	15·00	
12.8.21	Industrial Revolutions *se-tenant* pane No. U3072t (Tallents House or Derby).................................	20·00	
17.9.21	DC Collection *se-tenant* pane No. U3075m (Tallents House or Gotham, Nottingham)...........................	12·50	
20.1.22	The Rolling Stones *se-tenant* pane No. U3074n (Tallents House or Dartford)...............................	16·00	
4.2.22	Platinum Jubilee *se-tenant* pane No. U3071t (Tallents House or London SW1)........................	24·00	

Presentation Packs

17.2.09	Nos. U2911/U2912 and U2975/U2978 (PO Pack No. 82)..	7·50	
17.2.09	Nos. U2913/U2916 (PO Pack No. 83)........................	23·50	
26.10.10	Nos. U3051/U3052 (PO Pack No. 89)........................	22·00	
23.3.11	Nos. U2926/U2627, U2936, U2950 and U3055/ U3059 (PO Pack No. 90)....................................	15·00	
25.4.12	Nos. U2930, U2939, U2954, U3271 and U3276 (PO Pack No. 94)...	10·50	
3.1.13	Nos. U2920/U2925, U2934, U2997 and U3002 (PO Pack No. 96)...	7·50	
27.3.13	Nos. U2928, U2931, U2953, U3048 and U3050 (PO Pack No. 97)...	14·00	
26.3.14	Nos. U2929, U2932, U2945 and U2956 (PO Pack No. 99)..	10·00	
24.3.15	Nos. U2940, U2946, U2957, U2961 and U2968/ U2969 (PO Pack No. 101)...................................	22·00	
22.3.16	No. U2935 (PO Pack No. 103)...............................	3·00	
21.3.17	Nos. U2937, U2941, U2948, U2958 and U2962 (PO Pack No. 106)...	17·00	
20.3.18	Nos. U2938, U2943, U2947 and U2963 (PO Pack No. 108)..	12·50	
19.3.19	Nos. U2940a, U2949, U2959, U2964, U2970 and U2971 (PO Pack No. 110)..................................	21·00	
17.3.20	Nos. U2942, U2949a, U2951, U2960, U2965, U2972 and U2973 (PO Pack No. 112).............................	25·00	
23.12.20	Nos. U2952, U2968a, and U2973a (PO Pack No. 114)..	16·00	

For presentation pack containing Nos. U3045/U3046 see after No. Y1803.

2268

(Litho Cartor)

2010 (8 May). London 2010 Festival of Stamps. Jeffery Matthews Colour Palette. Sheet 104×95 mm containing stamps as T**367** with a label. Two phosphor bands. Perf 15×14 (with one elliptical hole in each vertical side).

MS3073 2268 1p. reddish purple; 2p. deep grey-green; 5p. reddish-brown; 9p. bright orange; 10p. orange; 20p. light green; 60p. emerald; 67p. bright mauve; 88p. bright magenta; 97p. bluish violet; £1·46 turquoise-blue.. 50·00   50·00

For details of known source and year-code combinations, and the different year codes, please refer to the tables following these listings.

2408

(Gravure Walsall)

2011 (14 Sept). Birth Centenary of Arnold Machin (sculptor). Sheet 124×71 mm containing stamps as No. U3066×10 but with source code 'MMIL' and year code 'AM11'. Two phosphor bands. Perf 14½×14 (with one elliptical hole in each vertical side).

MS3222 2408 (1st) gold×10.. 13·00   13·50
First Day Cover (Stoke on Trent).......................................   15·00
First Day Cover (Piccadilly, London W1)............................   15·00

914

(Photo De La Rue (U3271, U3276), Walsall (U3272, U3274/U3275, U3277/U3279) or De La Rue and Walsall (U3273))

2012 (6 Feb–1 Oct). Diamond Jubilee. (1st issue). Self-adhesive. Two phosphor bands. U-shaped slits. Iridescent overprint reading 'DIAMOND JUBILEE'. Die-cut perf 14½×14 (with one elliptical hole in each vertical side).

(a) As T**914**.
(i) Without source code.

U3271	(1st) slate-blue..	1·75	1·50

(ii) With source code.

U3272	(1st) slate-blue (MTND)...................................	1·75	1·75
U3273	(1st) slate-blue (MBND)...................................	3·50	3·25
U3274	(1st) slate-blue (MCND) (31.5.12).....................	1·60	1·60
U3275	(1st) slate-blue (MSND) (1.10.12).....................	1·75	1·75

*(b) As T **1916**.*
(i) Without source code.
U3276	(1st Large) slate-blue (25.4.12).....	2·50	2·25

(ii) With source code.
U3277	(1st Large) slate-blue (LFE) (25.4.12).....	3·25	3·25
U3278	(1st Large) slate-blue (LBE) (25.4.12).....	3·50	3·25

(c) Ordinary gum. Without U-shaped slits. With source code.
U3279	(1st) slate-blue (MPND) (31.5.12).....	3·75	3·75
	l. Booklet pane. Nos. U3279/3329, each×4, with central label and margins all round.....	14·00	

Nos. U3271 and U3276 are from counter sheets.
No. U3272 is from booklet of 12, No. MF6.
Nos. U3273 and U3278 are from business sheets.
No. U3274 is from booklets Nos. PM33 and PM34.
No. U3275 is from booklet of six, No. MB11.
No. U3277 is from booklet of four, No. RB3.
No. U3279 is from premium booklet No. DY4.
No. U3279 also exists from Diamond Jubilee miniature sheet No. **MS**3272, from which it has source code 'MMND', but is not separately listed.
For first day cover and presentation pack for Nos. U3271 and U3276 see under U3157.

914

(Gravure De La Rue (No. U3744) or ISP Walsall (Nos. U3745/U3746), or litho ISP Cartor (No. U3747))

2015 (9 Sept)–**16**. Long to Reign Over Us (1st issue). As T**914**. Self-adhesive. Two phosphor bands. U-shaped slits. Iridescent overprint reading 'LONG TO REIGN OVER US'. Die-cut perf 14½×14 (with one elliptical hole in each vertical side).

(a) Without source code, with year code.
U3744	(1st) bright lilac.....	1·75	1·75

(b) With source and year codes.
U3745	(1st) bright lilac (REIGS).....	1·75	1·75
U3746	(1st) bright lilac (REIGC) (18.9.15).....	1·60	1·60

(c) Ordinary gum. Without U-shaped slits. With source and year codes.
U3747	(1st) bright lilac (REIGP) (21.4.16).....	3·50	3·50

No. U3744 comes from counter sheets printed by De La Rue and exists with both O15R and O16R year code.
No. U3745 comes from booklets of six, No. MB14, printed by ISP Walsall. Initial printings had a O15R year code and the front of the self-adhesive backing paper was unprinted. Later printings have repeating 'ROYALMAIL' wording printed on the front of the self-adhesive backing paper and exist with O15R and O16R year code.
No. U3746 comes from booklets Nos. PM49/PM53, printed by ISP Walsall, and has O15R (No. PM49) or O16R (Nos. PM50/PM53) year code.
No. U3747 comes from pane U3156I in £15·11 premium stamp booklet, No. DY17 and has O16R year code.
No. U3747 also exists printed gravure (by FNMT Spain) from Long to Reign Over Us miniature sheet No. **MS**3747, from which it has source code REIGM and year code O15R, but is not separately listed.

3085

(Des Atelier Works. Gravure and gold foil embossed. ISP Walsall)

2017 (5 June). 50th Anniversary of the Machin Definitive. Sheet 202×74 mm containing stamps as T **3085**. Two phosphor bands. Perf 14×14½ (T **1116** and No. U3966) or 14½×14 (others).
MS3965 **3085**	No. X866; No. 1470; As No. 1789 (but ordinary gum); No. 2124; No. 2651; As No. U3067 (but MMIL source code); As No. U3966 (but gravure phosphor bands).....	15·00	15·00
First Day Cover (Tallents House) (No. **MS**3965).....			12·00
First Day Cover (High Wycombe) (No. **MS**3965).....			12·00
Presentation Pack (PO Pack No. 541) (Nos. **MS**3964/ **MS**3865).....		18·00	

On No. **MS**3965 only the £1 gold foil stamp is embossed.
The 5p., 20p. and £1 stamps in No. **MS**3965 do not have an elliptical hole in each vertical side.

3086

(Litho and gold foil embossed. ISP)

2017 (5 June). 50th Anniversary of the Machin Definitive Two narrow phosphor bands. Perf 14×14½.
U3966 **3086**	£1 gold.....	4·50	5·50
	l. Booklet pane. Nos. U3966×4 with margins all round.....	16·00	

No. U3966 was embossed in gold foil, has the phosphor bands printed in litho and does not have an elliptical hole on each vertical side. It was issued in £15·59 booklet No. DY21 and No. **MS**3965.

> Please note that for the convenience of collectors Nos. **MS**3965 and U3966/U3966I are listed additionally in the main section of this catalogue. This duplication is deliberate to ensure that both catalogue sections are complete and can be referenced to independently.

> For the 20p. stamp as T**929** from the 50th Anniversary of the Machin booklet see No. 2133, booklet pane No. 1668ssl.

3041a

(Gravure ISP Walsall)

2017 (6 Feb). 65th Anniversary of Accession of Queen Elizabeth II. As T**3041a**. Two phosphor bands. Iridescent overprint reading '65TH ANNIVERSARY OF ACCESSION' with year code 'ACCE17ION'. Perf 14×14½.
U3920	£5 ultramarine.....	10·00	10·00
First Day Cover (Tallents House).....			12·00
First Day Cover (Windsor).....			12·00
Presentation Pack (PO Pack No. 105).....		11·00	

No. U3920 does not have an elliptical perforation hole on each vertical side.

Decimal Machin Booklet Pane Guide ('U' Numbers) – the shaded squares represent printed labels.

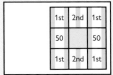

U2917l (DX50)
£11.15 Accession of King George V

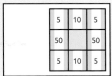

U3057l (DY1)
£9.99 Morris and Company

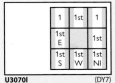

U3070l (DY7)
£11.11 Football Heroes

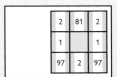

U3070m (DY12)
£14.60 Inventive Britain

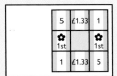

U3070n (DY13)
£13.96 Centenary of the
First World War (2nd Issue)
✿ = Poppy

U3070o (DY27)
£15.50 Harry Potter

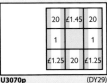

U3070p (DY29)
£17.45 Make mine Marvel

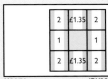

U3070q (DY32)
£16.10 Visions of the Universe

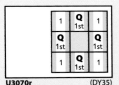

U3070r (DY35)
£19.10 Queen (rock band)
Q = Queen (rock band),
Primrose Hill, London

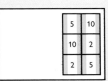

U3071l (DY7)
£11.11 Football Heroes

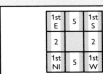

U3071m (DY9)
£13.97 Classic Locomotives

U3071n (DY20)
£14.58 Windsor Castle

U3071o (DY25)
£18.69 Centenary of the RAF

U3071p (DY30)
£17.20 Birth Bicentenary of
Queen Victoria
⊠ = One Penny Black
▲ = One Penny Red
■ = Two Penny Blue

U3071q (DY33)
£16.99 Behind the scenes of
James Bond
✳ = Union Flag

U3071r (DY36)
£18.35 *Star Trek*

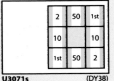

U3071s (DY38)
£20.25 Paul McCartney

U3071t (DY42)
£19.50 Platinum Jubilee

U3072l (DY6)
£13.77 Doctor Who
❖ = Tardis

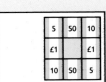

U3072m (DY14)
£14.47 Bicentenary of the
Battle of Waterloo

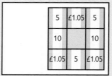

U3072n (DY19)
£15.37 The Tale of Beatrix Potter

U3072o (DY24)
£13.95 *Game of Thrones*

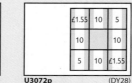

U3072p (DY28)
£13.10 Leonardo Da Vinci
500 Years

U3072q (DY31)
£17.65 Star Wars: The making of
the Vehicles

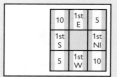

U3072r (DY32)
£16.10 Visions of the Universe

U3072s (DY34)
£19.80 75th Anniversary of the
End of the Second World War

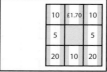

U3072t (DY39)
£18.03 Industrial Revolution

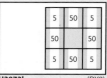

U3073l (DY8)
£11.19 Merchant Navy

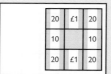

U3074l (DY10)
£11.39 Buckingham Palace

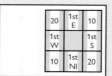

U3074m (DY11)
£11.30 Centenary of the
First World War (1st Issue)

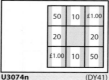

U3074n (DY41)
£20.85 Rolling Stones

U3075l (DY37)
£21.70 *Only Fools and Horses*
(TV sitcom, 1981-2003)

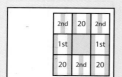

U3075m (DY40)
£21.20 DC Collection

U3082l (DY11)
£11.30 Centenary of the
First World War (1st Issue)

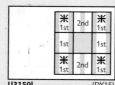

U3150l (DY15)
£16.99 The Making of Star Wars
✳ = Union Flag

U3150m (DY23)
£15.99 Star Wars: The making of
the Droids, Aliens and Creatures

U3156l (DY17)
£15.11 90th Birthday of
Queen Elizabeth II

U3156m (DY26)
£15.65 The Great War 1918
(5th issue) ✿ = Poppy

U3279l (DY4)
£12.77 Diamond Jubilee
▨ = Wilding

The following series of tables gives details of all source and year-code combinations reported at the time of going to press. Each is related to its printer and variations in the U-shaped slits are also noted. These tables are copyright John M Deering and are reproduced with his permission.

'ROYALMAIL' printed backing paper: From early 2016 self-adhesive Security Machins appeared with a repeated undulating 'ROYALMAIL' background in two sizes of grey text printed on the front of the backing paper. Initially the two sizes of grey text were printed upright: Type PB-Up (Printed Backing Upright). In early 2017 the background was changed so that alternate pairs of lines of the repeated 'ROYALMAIL' text were inverted in relation to each other. The pairs of lines can appear with the Large lettering above the small (Type PB-Ls), or with the small above the Large (Type PB-sL). In October 2018 a fourth type appeared on some PM64 booklets. In this type the 'ROYALMAIL' background, in two sizes of grey text, is all inverted (Type PB-Inv). Where there exist these differences are noted in the following tables, and where a stamp is known with both Type PB-Ls and Type PB-sL the price noted is for the cheaper of the two, whichever that is. Type PB-Up and Type PB-Inv are noted and priced separately.

Type PB-Up

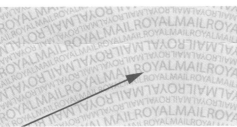

Type PB-Ls

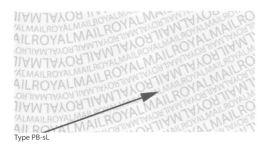

Type PB-sL

Type PB-Inv

SG No.	DESCRIPTION	

Denominated self-adhesive Security Machins, with source and year code *(b)*.

(The source code is at top right, and the year code is to the left of the front of The Queen's forehead.)

(The 'U'-shaped slits are broken.)

U2917	**50p** brownish grey, Walsall 'MPIL' ('U'-shaped slits with break at bottom only) 'MA10' (from DX50)	5·00
	50p brownish grey, Walsall 'MPIL' ('U'-shaped slits with break at top & bottom) 'MA10' (from DX50)	7·75
	50p brownish grey, Walsall 'MPIL' 'M11L' (from DY1 premium booklet)	5·25

SG No.	DESCRIPTION	

Denominated self-adhesive Security Machins, no source code (as from counter sheets), with year code *(c)*.

(Unless noted, front of self-adhesive backing is plain.)

(All have the year code to the left of the front of The Queen's crown.)

(The 'U'-shaped slits are broken.)

U2920	**1p** DLR 'MAIL' (no source code) 'M12L'	50
	1p DLR 'MAIL' (no source code) 'M15L'	1·50
	1p DLR 'MAIL' (no source code) 'M16L'	50
	1p DLR 'MAIL' (no source code) 'M17L', Type PB-Ls/sL	1·50
	1p Walsall 'MAIL' (no source code) 'M18L', Type PB-sL	40
	1p Walsall 'MAIL' (no source code) 'M19L', Type PB-sL	45
	1p Walsall 'MAIL' (no source code) 'M20L', Type PB-Ls/sL	45
	1p Walsall 'MAIL' (no source code) 'M21L', Type PB-sL	45
U2921	**2p** DLR 'MAIL' (no source code) 'M12L'	60
	2p DLR 'MAIL' (no source code) 'M14L'	1·50
	2p DLR 'MAIL' (no source code) 'M15L'	60
	2p DLR 'MAIL' (no source code) 'M16L'	1·50
	2p DLR 'MAIL' (no source code) 'M17L'	1·50
	2p DLR 'MAIL' (no source code) 'M17L', Type PB-Ls/sL	60
	2p Walsall 'MAIL' (no source code) 'M18L', Type PB-Ls/sL	40
	2p Walsall 'MAIL' (no source code) 'M19L', Type PB-sL	45
	2p Walsall 'MAIL' (no source code) 'M20L', Type PB-sL	45
	2p Walsall 'MAIL' (no source code) 'M21L', Type PB-Ls/sL	45
U2922	**5p** DLR 'MAIL' (no source code) 'M12L'	60
	5p DLR 'MAIL' (no source code) 'M14L'	2·50
	5p DLR 'MAIL' (no source code) 'M15L'	2·50
	5p DLR 'MAIL' (no source code) 'M16L'	60
	5p DLR 'MAIL' (no source code) 'M17L', Type PB-Ls/sL	60
	5p Walsall 'MAIL' (no source code) 'M18L', Type PB-Ls/sL	45
	5p Walsall 'MAIL' (no source code) 'M19L', Type PB-Ls/sL	50
	5p Walsall 'MAIL' (no source code) 'M20L', Type PB-sL	50
	5p Walsall 'MAIL' (no source code) 'M21L', Type PB-Ls/sL	50
U2923	**10p** DLR 'MAIL' (no source code) 'M12L'	70
	10p DLR 'MAIL' (no source code) 'MA13'	1·00
	10p DLR 'MAIL' (no source code) 'M14L'	1·00
	10p DLR 'MAIL' (no source code) 'M15L'	1·25
	10p DLR 'MAIL' (no source code) 'M16L'	1·00
	10p DLR 'MAIL' (no source code) 'M17L'	4·00
	10p DLR 'MAIL' (no source code) 'M17L', Type PB-sL	70

SG No.	DESCRIPTION	
U2923 *cont'd*	**10p** Walsall 'MAIL' (no source code) 'M18L', Type PB-Ls/sL	65
	10p Walsall 'MAIL' (no source code) 'M19L', Type PB-Ls/sL	60
	10p Walsall 'MAIL' (no source code) 'M20L', Type PB-Ls/sL	60
	10p Walsall 'MAIL' (no source code) 'M21L', Type PB-sL	60
U2924	**20p** DLR 'MAIL' (no source code) 'M12L'	1·40
	20p DLR 'MAIL' (no source code) 'MA13'	1·60
	20p DLR 'MAIL' (no source code) 'M14L'	1·40
	20p DLR 'MAIL' (no source code) 'M15L'	1·25
	20p DLR 'MAIL' (no source code) 'M16L'	1·00
	20p DLR 'MAIL' (no source code) 'M17L', Type PB-Ls	80
	20p Walsall 'MAIL' (no source code) 'M18L', Type PB-Ls/sL	70
	20p Walsall 'MAIL' (no source code) 'M19L', Type PB-sL	75
	20p Walsall 'MAIL' (no source code) 'M20L', Type PB-Ls/sL	75
	20p Walsall 'MAIL' (no source code) 'M21L', Type PB-sL	75
U2925	**50p** slate DLR 'MAIL' (no source code) 'M12L'	2·25
	50p slate DLR 'MAIL' (no source code) 'M17L', Type PB-Ls	6·50
	50p slate Walsall 'MAIL' (no source code) 'M19L', Type PB-sL	1·75
U2926	**68p** DLR 'MAIL' (no source code) 'M11L'	2·25
	68p DLR 'MAIL' (no source code) 'M12L'	8·00
U2927	**76p** DLR 'MAIL' (no source code) 'M11L'	2·00
	76p DLR 'MAIL' (no source code) 'M12L'	7·75
U2928	**78p** Walsall 'MAIL' (no source code) 'M13L'	2·00
	78p DLR 'MAIL' (no source code) 'MA13'	4·00
U2929	**81p** DLR 'MAIL' (no source code) 'M14L'	3·75
U2930	**87p** DLR 'MAIL' (no source code) 'M12L'	4·25
U2931	**88p** Walsall 'MAIL' (no source code) 'M13L'	2·25
	88p DLR 'MAIL' (no source code) 'MA13'	4·25
U2932	**97p** DLR 'MAIL' (no source code) 'M14L'	2·50
U2933	**£1·00** magenta, DLR 'MAIL' (no source code) 'M11L'	30·00
	£1·00 magenta, DLR 'MAIL' (no source code) 'M12L'	16·00
U2934	**£1·00** bistre-brown, DLR 'MAIL' (no source code) 'M12L'	6·00
	£1·00 bistre-brown, DLR 'MAIL' (no source code) 'M14L'	4·00
	£1·00 bistre-brown, DLR 'MAIL' (no source code) 'M15L'	3·50
	£1·00 bistre-brown, DLR 'MAIL' (no source code) 'M16L'	3·25
	£1·00 bistre-brown, Walsall 'MAIL' (no source code) 'M18L' Type PB-Ls/sL	3·00
	£1·00 bistre-brown, Walsall 'MAIL' (no source code) 'M19L' Type PB-Ls/sL	3·00
	£1·00 bistre-brown, Walsall 'MAIL' (no source code) 'M21L' Type PB-sL	3·00
U2935	**£1·05** DLR 'MAIL' (no source code) 'M16L'	2·75
U2936	**£1·10** DLR 'MAIL' (no source code) 'M11L'	3·25
U2937	**£1·17** DLR 'MAIL' (no source code) 'M17L'	3·00
	£1·17 DLR 'MAIL' (no source code) 'M17L', Type PB-Ls/sL	3·25
U2938	**£1·25** Walsall 'MAIL' (no source code) 'M18L' Type PB-Ls/sL	2·75
U2939	**£1·28** DLR 'MAIL' (no source code) 'M12L'	4·00
	£1·28 DLR 'MAIL' (no source code) 'MA13'	5·00
	£1·28 DLR 'MAIL' (no source code) 'M14L'	12·50
U2940	**£1·33** DLR 'MAIL' (no source code) 'M15L'	2·75
	£1·33 DLR 'MAIL' (no source code) 'M16L'	4·50
U2940a	**£1·35** Walsall 'MAIL' (no source code) 'M19L' Type PB-sL	3·00
U2941	**£1·40** DLR 'MAIL' (no source code) 'M17L'	3·00
	£1·40 DLR 'MAIL' (no source code) 'M17L', Type PB-Ls	3·25
U2942	**£1·42** Walsall 'MAIL' (no source code) 'M20L' Type PB-Ls/sL	3·00
U2943	**£1·45** Walsall 'MAIL' (no source code) 'M18L' Type PB-Ls/sL	3·25

SG No.	DESCRIPTION	
U2945	**£1·47** DLR 'MAIL' (no source code) 'M14L'	3·50
U2946	**£1·52** DLR 'MAIL' (no source code) 'M15L'	3·00
U2947	**£1·55** Walsall 'MAIL' (no source code) 'M18L' Type PB-Ls/sL	3·00
	£1·55 Walsall 'MAIL' (no source code) 'M19L' Type PB-Ls/sL	3·25
U2948	**£1·57** DLR 'MAIL' (no source code) 'M17L'	3·25
	£1·57 DLR 'MAIL' (no source code) 'M17L' Type PB-Ls/sL	4·00
U2949	**£1·60** Walsall 'MAIL' (no source code) 'M19L' Type PB-Ls/sL	3·00
U2949a	**£1·63** Walsall 'MAIL' (no source code) 'M20L' Type PB-sL	3·00
U2950	**£1·65** DLR 'MAIL' (no source code) 'M11L'	3·75
U2951	**£1·68** Walsall 'MAIL' (no source code) 'M20L' Type PB-sL	3·50
U2952	**£1·70** Walsall 'MAIL' (no source code) 'M21L' Type PB-Ls/sL	3·50
U2953	**£1·88** Walsall 'MAIL' (no source code) 'M13L'	3·75
	£1·88 DLR 'MAIL' (no source code) 'MA13'	6·00
U2954	**£1·90** DLR 'MAIL' (no source code) 'M12L'	4·00
U2955	**£2·00** DLR 'MAIL' (no source code) 'MA13'	9·00
	£2·00 Walsall 'MAIL' (no source code) 'M19L' Type PB-Ls/sL	3·75
U2956	**£2·15** DLR 'MAIL' (no source code) 'M14L'	4·25
U2957	**£2·25** DLR 'MAIL' (no source code) 'M15L'	4·00
	£2·25 DLR 'MAIL' (no source code) 'M16L'	13·00
	£2·25 Walsall 'MAIL' (no source code) 'M18L' Type PB-Ls	3·75
U2958	**£2·27** DLR 'MAIL' (no source code) 'M17L'	4·00
	£2·27 DLR 'MAIL' (no source code) 'M17L' Type PB-Ls/sL	5·25
U2959	**£2·30** Walsall 'MAIL' (no source code) 'M19L' Type PB-sL	3·50
U2960	**£2·42** Walsall 'MAIL' (no source code) 'M20L' Type PB-sL	3·75
U2961	**£2·45** DLR 'MAIL' (no source code) 'M15L'	4·00
U2962	**£2·55** DLR 'MAIL' (no source code) 'M17L'	5·00
	£2·55 DLR 'MAIL' (no source code) 'M17L' Type PB-Ls	5·75
	£2·55 Walsall 'MAIL' (no source code) 'M20L' Type PB-sL	5·00
	£2·55 Walsall 'MAIL' (no source code) 'M21L' Type PB-sL	5·00
U2963	**£2·65** Walsall 'MAIL' (no source code) 'M18L' Type PB-Ls/sL	4·50
U2964	**£2·80** Walsall 'MAIL' (no source code) 'M19L' Type PB-sL	4·25
U2965	**£2·97** Walsall 'MAIL' (no source code) 'M20L' Type PB-sL	4·50
U2966	**£3·00** Walsall 'MAIL' (no source code) 'M19L' Type PB-sL	4·75
U2968	**£3·15** DLR 'MAIL' (no source code) 'M15L'	5·00
U2968a	**£3·25** Walsall 'MAIL' (no source code) 'M21L' Type PB-Ls/sL	4·75
U2969	**£3·30** DLR 'MAIL' (no source code) 'M15L'	5·25
U2970	**£3·45** Walsall 'MAIL' (no source code) 'M19L' Type PB-sL	5·00
U2971	**£3·60** Walsall 'MAIL' (no source code) 'M19L' Type PB-sL	5·25
U2972	**£3·66** Walsall 'MAIL' (no source code) 'M20L' Type PB-sL	5·25
U2973	**£3·82** Walsall 'MAIL' (no source code) 'M20L' Type PB-sL	5·50
U2973a	**£4·20** Walsall 'MAIL' (no source code) 'M21L' Type PB-sL	6·25
U2974	**£5·00** Walsall 'MAIL' (no source code) 'M19L' Type PB-sL	8·00

SG No.	DESCRIPTION	

2nd (bright blue) and 1st (as noted) self-adhesive Security Machins, no source code (as from counter sheets), with year code *(c)*.

(Unless noted, front of self-adhesive backing is plain.)

(All have the year code to the left of the front of The Queen's forehead or crown, or for the 'Large' issues from MA11 onwards it is above the 'ge' of 'Large'.)

(The 'U'-shaped slits are broken.)

SG No.	DESCRIPTION	
U2995	**2nd** DLR 'MAIL' (no source code) 'MA10'	6·50
	2nd DLR 'MAIL' (no source code) 'M11L'	4·50
	2nd DLR 'MAIL' (no source code) 'M12L'	2·50
	2nd DLR 'MAIL' (no source code) 'MA13'	2·50
	2nd DLR 'MAIL' (no source code) 'M14L'	2·50
	2nd DLR 'MAIL' (no source code) 'M15L'	2·50
	2nd DLR 'MAIL' (no source code) 'M16L'	2·50
	2nd DLR 'MAIL' (no source code) 'M17L'	3·00
	2nd DLR 'MAIL' (no source code) 'M17L', Type PB-Ls/sL	1·60
	2nd Walsall 'MAIL' (no source code) 'M18L', Type PB-sL	1·60
	2nd Walsall 'MAIL' (no source code) 'M19L', Type PB-sL	1·60
	2nd Walsall 'MAIL' (no source code) 'M20L', Type PB-sL	1·60
	2nd Walsall 'MAIL' (no source code) 'M21L', Type PB-Ls/sL	10·00
U2996	**1st** gold, DLR 'MAIL' (no source code) 'MA10'	3·75
	1st gold, DLR 'MAIL' (no source code) 'M11L'	3·50
U2997	**1st** vermilion, DLR 'MAIL' (no source code) 'M12L'	2·00
	1st vermilion, DLR 'MAIL' (no source code) 'MA13'	2·50
	1st vermilion, DLR 'MAIL' (no source code) 'M14L'	2·50
	1st vermilion, DLR 'MAIL' (no source code) 'M15L'	3·50
	1st vermilion, DLR 'MAIL' (no source code) 'M16L'	2·50
U2998	**1st** bright scarlet, DLR 'MAIL' (no source code) 'M16L', Type PB-sL	6·00
	1st bright scarlet, DLR 'MAIL' (no source code) 'M17L', Type PB-Ls/sL	1·70
	1st bright scarlet, Walsall 'MAIL' (no source code) 'M18L', Type PB-sL	2·00
	1st bright scarlet, Walsall 'MAIL' (no source code) 'M19L', Type PB-sL	2·00
	1st bright scarlet, Walsall 'MAIL' (no source code) 'M20L', Type PB-Ls/sL	2·00
	1st bright scarlet, Walsall 'MAIL' (no source code) 'M21L', Type PB-sL	2·25
U3000	**2nd Large** DLR 'ROYAL' (no source code) 'MA10'	9·50
	2nd Large DLR 'ROYAL' (no source code) 'MA11'	3·00
	2nd Large DLR 'ROYAL' (no source code) 'MA12'	3·00
	2nd Large DLR 'ROYAL' (no source code) 'MA13'	3·00
	2nd Large DLR 'ROYAL' (no source code) 'M14L'	2·75
	2nd Large DLR 'ROYAL' (no source code) 'M15L'	2·75
	2nd Large DLR 'ROYAL' (no source code) 'M16L'	1·90
	2nd Large DLR 'ROYAL' (no source code) 'M17L', Type PB-Ls/sL	2·75
	2nd Large Walsall 'ROYAL' (no source code) 'M18L', Type PB-sL	2·10
	2nd Large Walsall 'ROYAL' (no source code) 'M19L', Type PB-Ls/sL	2·10
	2nd Large Walsall 'ROYAL' (no source code) 'M20L', Type PB-Ls	2·10
	2nd Large Walsall 'ROYAL' (no source code) 'M21L', Type PB-Ls	2·25
U3001	**1st Large**, gold, DLR 'ROYAL' (no source code) 'MA10'	6·00
	1st Large, gold, DLR 'ROYAL' (no source code) 'MA11'	6·50
U3002	**1st Large**, vermilion, DLR 'ROYAL' (no source code) 'MA12'	3·00
	1st Large, vermilion, DLR 'ROYAL' (no source code) 'MA13'	3·50

SG No.	DESCRIPTION	
U3002 *cont'd*	**1st Large**, vermilion, DLR 'ROYAL' (no source code) 'M14L'	5·25
	1st Large, vermilion, DLR 'ROYAL' (no source code) 'M15L'	2·75
	1st Large, vermilion, DLR 'ROYAL' (no source code) 'M16L'	2·75
U3003	**1st Large**, bright scarlet, DLR 'ROYAL' (no source code) 'M17L', Type PB-Ls/sL	2·25
	1st Large, bright scarlet, Walsall 'ROYAL' (no source code) 'M18L', Type PB-sL	2·50
	1st Large, bright scarlet, Walsall 'ROYAL' (no source code) 'M19L', Type PB-Ls/sL	2·75
	1st Large, bright scarlet, Walsall 'ROYAL' (no source code) 'M20L', Type PB-Ls/sL	2·75
	1st Large, bright scarlet, Walsall 'ROYAL' (no source code) 'M21L', Type PB-Ls/sL	2·75

SG No.	DESCRIPTION	

2nd (bright blue) and 1st (as noted) self-adhesive Security Machins, with source and year code *(d)*.

(Unless noted, the source code is at top right, the year code is to the left of the front of The Queen's forehead or crown, or for the 'Large' issues from MA11 onwards it is above the 'ge' of 'Large'.)

(The 'U'-shaped slits are broken.)

SG No.	DESCRIPTION	
U3010	**2nd** DLR 'MBIL' 'MA10'	6·75
	2nd DLR 'MBIL' 'M11L'	5·00
	2nd Walsall 'MBIL' 'M12L'	2·75
	2nd Walsall 'MBIL' 'M13L'	2·75
	2nd Walsall 'MBIL' 'M14L'	5·00
	2nd Walsall 'MBIL' 'M15L'	3·75
	2nd Walsall 'MBIL' 'M15L' Type PB-Up	3·75
	2nd Walsall 'MBIL' 'M16L' Type PB-Up	2·50
	2nd Walsall 'MBIL' 'M16L' Type PB-sL	2·50
	2nd Walsall 'MBIL' 'M17L' Type PB-Ls/sL	2·25
	2nd Walsall 'MBIL' 'M18L' Type PB-Ls/sL	2·00
	2nd Walsall 'MBIL' 'M19L' Type PB-Ls/sL	2·00
	2nd Walsall 'MBIL' 'M20L' Type PB-Ls/sL	2·00
	2nd Walsall 'MBIL' 'M21L' Type PB-Ls/sL	—
U3011	**2nd** Walsall 'MPIL' 'MA10' ('U'-shaped slits with break at bottom only) (from DX50)	4·50
	2nd Walsall 'MPIL' 'MA10' ('U'-shaped slits with break at top & bottom) (from DX50)	7·75
U3012	**2nd** DLR 'MRIL' 'MA10' only known USED from mail posted by bulk mailing houses. *Please note that the 2nd class stamp with these codes on ordinary gummed paper and without U-shaped slits is No. U3065.*	—
	2nd Enschedé 'MRIL' 'MA12'	5·25
	2nd Walsall 'MRIL' 'M12L'	5·25
	2nd Walsall 'MRIL' 'M15L'	4·25
U3013	**2nd** Walsall 'MTIL' 'MA10'	5·50
	2nd Walsall 'MTIL' 'M11L'	2·50
	2nd Walsall 'MTIL' 'M12L'	2·00
	2nd Walsall 'MTIL' 'M13L'	2·00
	2nd Walsall 'MTIL' 'M14L'	1·60
	2nd Walsall 'MTIL' 'M15L',	1·75
	2nd Walsall 'MTIL' 'M15L' Type PB-Up	8·50
	2nd Walsall 'MTIL' 'M16L' Type PB-Up	1·75

SG No.	DESCRIPTION	
U3013 *cont'd*	**2nd** Walsall 'MTIL' 'M16L', Type PB-sL	4·00
	2nd Walsall 'MTIL' 'M17L', Type PB-Ls/sL	2·00
	2nd Walsall 'MTIL' 'M18L', Type PB-Ls/sL	1·75
	2nd Walsall 'MTIL' 'M18L', Type PB-Up	5·00
	2nd Walsall 'MTIL' 'M19L', Type PB-Ls/sL	1·75
	2nd Walsall 'MTIL' 'M20L', Type PB-Ls/sL	1·75
	2nd Walsall 'MTIL' 'M21L', Type PB-Ls/sL	2·00
U3015	**1st** gold, DLR 'MBIL' 'MA10'	8·00
	1st gold, DLR 'MBIL' 'M11L'	4·50
U3016	**1st** gold, Walsall 'MCIL' 'MA10'	1·75
	1st gold, Walsall 'MCIL' 'M11L'	1·75
U3017	**1st** gold, Walsall 'MPIL' 'MA10' ('U'-shaped slits with break at bottom only) (from DX50)	2·10
	1st gold, Walsall 'MPIL' 'MA10' ('U'-shaped slits with break at top & bottom) (from DX50)	6·00
U3018	**1st** gold, DLR 'MRIL' 'MA10'	5·75
	1st gold, Enschedé 'MRIL' 'MA12'	4·75
U3019	**1st** gold, Walsall 'MSIL' 'MA10'	2·00
	1st gold, Walsall 'MSIL' 'M11L'	2·25
U3020	**1st** gold, Walsall 'MTIL' 'MA10'	4·00
	1st gold, Walsall 'MTIL' 'M11L'	2·25
	1st gold, Walsall 'MTIL' 'M12L'	6·75
U3021	**1st** vermilion, Walsall 'MBIL' 'M12L'	3·00
	1st vermilion, Walsall 'MBIL' 'M13L'	6·25
	1st vermilion, Walsall 'MBIL' 'M14L'	3·50
	1st vermilion, Walsall 'MBIL' 'M15L'	2·75
	1st vermilion, Walsall 'MBIL' 'M15L' Type PB-Up	3·75
	1st vermilion, Walsall 'MBIL' 'M16L' Type PB-Up	3·50
U3022	**1st** vermilion, Walsall 'MCIL' 'M12L'	1·90
	1st vermilion, Walsall 'MCIL' 'M13L'	1·40
	1st vermilion, Walsall 'MCIL' 'M14L'	1·40
	1st vermilion, Walsall 'MCIL' 'M15L'	1·40
U3023	**1st** vermilion, Enschedé 'MRIL' 'MA12'	3·95
	1st vermilion, 'MRIL' 'M13L'	3·00
U3024	**1st** vermilion, Walsall 'MSIL' 'M12L'	1·75
	1st vermilion, Walsall 'MSIL' 'M13L'	2·50
	1st vermilion, Walsall 'MSIL' 'M14L'	2·00
	1st vermilion, Walsall 'MSIL' 'M15L'	3·00
	1st vermilion, Walsall 'MSIL' 'M16L' Type PB-Up	2·00
U3025	**1st** vermilion, Walsall 'MTIL' 'M12L'	1·75
	1st vermilion, Walsall 'MTIL' 'M13L'	2·00
	1st vermilion, Walsall 'MTIL' 'M14L'	1·90
	1st vermilion, Walsall 'MTIL' 'M15L'	4·00
	1st vermilion, Walsall 'MTIL' 'M15L' Type PB-Up	9·00
	1st vermilion, Walsall 'MTIL' 'M16L' Type PB-Up	2·50
U3026	**1st** bright scarlet, Walsall 'MBIL' 'M16L' Type PB-Up	2·50
	1st bright scarlet, Walsall 'MBIL' 'M16L' Type PB-sL	3·50
	1st bright scarlet, Walsall 'MBIL' 'M17L' Type PB-Ls/sL	2·25
	1st bright scarlet, Walsall 'MBIL' 'M18L' Type PB-Ls/sL	2·25
	1st bright scarlet, Walsall 'MBIL' 'M19L' Type PB-Ls/sL	2·25
	1st bright scarlet, Walsall 'MBIL' 'M20L' Type PB-Ls/sL	2·25
	1st bright scarlet, Walsall 'MBIL' 'M21L' Type PB-Ls/sL	2·50
U3027	**1st** bright scarlet, Walsall 'MCIL' 'M16L' Type PB-Up	1·60
	1st bright scarlet, Walsall 'MCIL' 'M17L' Type PB-Up	1·60

SG No.	DESCRIPTION	
U3027 *cont'd*	**1st** bright scarlet, Walsall 'MCIL' 'M17L' Type PB-Ls/sL	1·60
	1st bright scarlet, Walsall 'MCIL' 'M18L' Type PB-Ls/sL	1·40
	1st bright scarlet, Walsall 'MCIL' 'M18L' Type PB-Inv	6·00
	1st bright scarlet, Walsall 'MCIL' 'M19L' Type PB-Ls/sL	1·40
	1st bright scarlet, Walsall 'MCIL' 'M20L' Type PB-Ls/sL	1·40
	1st bright scarlet, Walsall 'MCIL' 'M21L' Type PB-Ls/sL	1·40
U3028	**1st** bright scarlet, Walsall 'MSIL' 'M16L' Type PB-Up	2·00
	1st bright scarlet, Walsall 'MSIL' 'M16L' Type PB-Ls/sL	3·25
	1st bright scarlet, Walsall 'MSIL' 'M17L' Type PB-Up	1·90
	1st bright scarlet, Walsall 'MSIL' 'M17L' Type PB-Ls/sL	3·50
	1st bright scarlet, Walsall 'MSIL' 'M18L' Type PB-Ls/sL	2·00
	1st bright scarlet, Walsall 'MSIL' 'M18L' Type PB-Up	4·00
	1st bright scarlet, Walsall 'MSIL' 'M19L' Type PB-Ls/sL	2·00
	1st bright scarlet, Walsall 'MSIL' 'M20L' Type PB-Ls/sL	2·75
	1st bright scarlet, Walsall 'MSIL' 'M21L' Type PB-sL	4·00
U3029	**1st** bright scarlet, Walsall 'MTIL' 'M16L' Type PB-Up	2·00
	1st bright scarlet, Walsall 'MTIL' 'M16L' Type PB-Ls/sL	3·75
	1st bright scarlet, Walsall 'MTIL' 'M17L' Type PB-Ls/sL	2·00
	1st bright scarlet, Walsall 'MTIL' 'M18L' Type PB-Ls/sL	2·00
	1st bright scarlet, Walsall 'MTIL' 'M19L' Type PB-Ls/sL	2·00
	1st bright scarlet, Walsall 'MTIL' 'M20L' Type PB-Ls/sL	2·00
	1st bright scarlet, Walsall 'MTIL' 'M21L' Type PB-sL	2·25
U3031	**2nd Large** DLR 'MBI' 'MA10'	24·00
	2nd Large DLR 'BIL' 'MA11' (source code bottom right)	12·50
	2nd Large Walsall 'BIL' 'MA12' (source code bottom right) (The 'U' slits do not have breaks in them)	3·50
	2nd Large Walsall 'BIL' 'MA13' (source code bottom right)	4·25
	2nd Large Walsall 'BIL' 'MA13' (source code bottom right) (The 'U' slits do not have breaks in them)	5·00
	2nd Large Walsall 'MBIL' 'MA14' (source code in front of hair)	2·75
	2nd Large Walsall 'MBIL' 'MA15' (source code in front of hair)	4·75
	2nd Large Walsall 'MBIL' 'M16L' (not MA16) (source code in front of hair) Type PB-Up	3·25
	2nd Large Walsall 'MBIL' 'M17L' (source code in front of hair) Type PB-Ls/sL	3·00
	2nd Large Walsall 'MBIL' 'M18L' (source code in front of hair) Type PB-sL	2·75
	2nd Large Walsall 'MBIL' 'M19L' (source code in front of hair) Type PB-Ls/sL	2·75
	2nd Large Walsall 'MBIL' 'M20L' (source code in front of hair) Type PB-Ls/sL	2·75
	2nd Large Walsall 'MBIL' 'M21L' (source code in front of hair) Type PB-Ls/sL	3·00
U3032	**2nd Large** Walsall 'MFI' 'MA10'	38·00
	2nd Large Walsall 'FIL' 'MA11' (source code bottom right)	2·50
	2nd Large Walsall 'FIL' 'MA12' (source code bottom right)	3·25
	2nd Large Walsall 'FIL' 'MA13' (source code bottom right)	4·00

SG No.	DESCRIPTION	
U3032 cont'd	**2nd Large** Walsall 'MFIL' 'MA14' (source code in front of hair)	2·75
	2nd Large Walsall 'MFIL' 'MA15' (source code in front of hair)	4·75
	2nd Large Walsall 'MFIL' 'M16L' (not MA16) (source code in front of hair) Type PB-Up	3·25
	2nd Large Walsall 'MFIL' 'M17L' (source code in front of hair) Type PB-Ls	9·00
	2nd Large Walsall 'MFIL' 'M18L' (source code in front of hair) Type PB-Ls/sL	8·00
	2nd Large Walsall 'MFIL' 'M19L' (source code in front of hair) Type PB-Ls/sL	3·00
	2nd Large Walsall 'MFIL' 'M20L' (source code in front of hair) Type PB-sL	3·00
	2nd Large Walsall 'MFIL' 'M21L' (source code in front of hair) Type PB-sL	3·25
U3034	**1st Large**, gold, DLR 'MBI' 'MA10'	8·75
	1st Large, gold, DLR 'BIL' 'MA11' (source code bottom right)	4·50
U3035	**1st Large**, gold, Walsall 'MFI' 'MA10'	8·00
	1st Large, gold, Walsall 'FIL' 'MA11' (source code bottom right)	3·25
U3036	**1st Large**, vermilion, Walsall 'BIL' 'MA12' (source code bottom right) (The 'U' slits do not have breaks in them)	3·25
	1st Large, vermilion, Walsall 'BIL' 'MA13' (source code bottom right)	4·75
	1st Large, vermilion, Walsall 'BIL' 'MA13' (source code bottom right) (The 'U' slits do not have breaks in them)	4·75
	1st Large, vermilion, Walsall 'MBIL' 'MA14' (source code in front of hair)	3·25
	1st Large, vermilion, Walsall 'MBIL' 'MA15' (source code in front of hair)	5·00
	1st Large, vermilion, Walsall 'MBIL' 'MA15' (source code in front of hair) Type PB-Up	10·00
	1st Large, vermilion, Walsall 'MBIL' 'M16L' (not MA16) (source code in front of hair) Type PB-Up	4·00
U3037	**1st Large**, vermilion, Walsall 'FIL' 'MA12' (source code bottom right)	3·25
	1st Large, vermilion, Walsall 'FIL' 'MA13' (source code bottom right)	7·50
	1st Large, vermilion, Walsall 'MFIL' 'MA14' (source code in front of hair)	3·25
	1st Large, vermilion, Walsall 'MFIL' 'MA15' (source code in front of hair)	8·00
	1st Large, vermilion, Walsall 'MFIL' 'MA15' (source code in front of hair) Type PB-Up	8·00
	1st Large, vermilion, Walsall 'MFIL' 'M16L' (not MA16) (source code in front of hair) Type PB-Up	5·50
U3038	**1st Large**, bright scarlet, Walsall 'MBIL' 'M16L' (source code in front of hair) Type PB-Up	3·25
	1st Large, bright scarlet, Walsall 'MBIL' 'M17L' (source code in front of hair) Type PB-Ls/sL	9·00
	1st Large, bright scarlet, Walsall 'MBIL' 'M18L' (source code in front of hair) Type PB-Ls/sL	3·25
	1st Large, bright scarlet, Walsall 'MBIL' 'M19L' (source code in front of hair) Type PB-sL	3·25
	1st Large, bright scarlet, Walsall 'MBIL' 'M20L' (source code in front of hair) Type PB-Ls/sL	3·25
	1st Large, bright scarlet, Walsall 'MBIL' 'M21L' (source code in front of hair) Type PB-Ls/sL	3·50
U3039	**1st Large**, bright scarlet, Walsall 'MFIL' 'M16L' (source code in front of hair) Type PB-Up	7·50
	1st Large, bright scarlet, Walsall 'MFIL' 'M17L' (source code in front of hair) Type PB-Ls/sL	5·25

SG No.	DESCRIPTION	
U3039 cont'd	**1st Large**, bright scarlet, Walsall 'MFIL' 'M18L' (source code in front of hair) Type PB-Ls/sL	3·25
	1st Large, bright scarlet, Walsall 'MFIL' 'M19L' (source code in front of hair) Type PB-Ls	3·25
	1st Large, bright scarlet, Walsall 'MFIL' 'M20L' (source code in front of hair) Type PB-sL	3·75
	1st Large, bright scarlet, Walsall 'MFIL' 'M21L' (source code in front of hair) Type PB-sL	3·75

Note. Where Walsall is stated as the printer, for later year codes the printer is more accurately ISP Walsall. However; being one and the same, later year codes are simply noted here as Walsall. ISP stands for 'International Security Printers' which encompasses both Cartor and Walsall.

SG No.	DESCRIPTION	

'Recorded Signed For', 'Royal Mail Signed For', and 'Special Delivery' self-adhesive Security Machins, no source code (as from counter sheets), with year code *(b).*

(Unless noted, front of self-adhesive backing is plain.)

(Unless noted, the year code is to the left of the front of The Queen's forehead or crown.)

(The U-shaped slits are broken.)

SG No.	DESCRIPTION	
U3047	**'Recorded Signed For' 1st** DLR 'MAIL' (no source code) 'MA10'	13·00
U3048	**'Recorded Signed For' 1st Large** DLR 'MAIL' (no source code) 'MA10'	23·00
U3049	**'Royal Mail Signed For' 1st** DLR (Note. The service name was revised in March 2013.) 'MAIL' (no source code) 'MA13'	4·50
	'Royal Mail Signed For' 1st DLR 'MAIL' (no source code) 'M15L' (not MA15)	6·00
	'Royal Mail Signed For' 1st DLR 'MAIL' (no source code) 'M16L'	6·00
	'Royal Mail Signed For' 1st DLR 'MAIL' (no source code) 'M17L' Type PB-Ls/sL	5·00
	'Royal Mail Signed For' 1st Walsall 'MAIL' (no source code) 'M19L' Type PB-sL	4·75
	'Royal Mail Signed For' 1st Walsall 'MAIL' (no source code) 'M20L' Type PB-sL	4·50
U3050	**'Royal Mail Signed For' 1st Large** DLR (Note. The service name was revised in March 2013.) 'MAIL' (no source code) 'MA13' (year code is above the 'ge' of 'Large')	5·00
	'Royal Mail Signed For' 1st Large DLR 'MAIL' (no source code) 'M15L' (not MA15) (year code is above the 'ge' of 'Large')	9·75
	'Royal Mail Signed For' 1st Large DLR 'MAIL' (no source code) 'M16L' (year code is above the 'ge' of 'Large')	9·00
	'Royal Mail Signed For' 1st Large DLR 'MAIL' (no source code) 'M17L' (year code is above the 'ge' of 'Large')	6·00
	'Royal Mail Signed For' 1st Large Walsall 'MAIL' (no source code) 'M18L' (year code is above the 'ge' of 'Large') Type PB-sL	5·00
	'Royal Mail Signed For' 1st Large Walsall 'MAIL' (no source code) 'M20L' (year code is above the 'ge' of 'Large') Type PB-Ls	5·00
U3051	**'Special Delivery up to 100g'** DLR 'MAIL' (no source code) 'MA10'	11·50
	'Special Delivery up to 100g' DLR 'MAIL' (no source code) 'M14L'	17·00
	'Special Delivery up to 100g' DLR 'MAIL' (no source code) 'M15L'	16·00
	'Special Delivery up to 100g' DLR 'MAIL' (no source code) 'M16L'	17·00
	'Special Delivery up to 100g' DLR 'MAIL' (no source code) 'M17L'	14·00

SG No.	DESCRIPTION	
U3051 *cont'd*	**'Special Delivery up to 100g'** DLR 'MAIL' (no source code) 'M17L' Type PB-Ls	15·00
	'Special Delivery up to 100g' Walsall 'MAIL' (no source code) 'M18L' Type PB-sL	15·00
	'Special Delivery up to 100g' Walsall 'MAIL' (no source code) 'M19L' Type PB-sL	15·00
	'Special Delivery up to 100g' Walsall 'MAIL' (no source code) 'M20L' Type PB-sL	11·00
U3052	**'Special Delivery up to 500g'** DLR 'MAIL' (no source code) 'MA10'	13·00
	'Special Delivery up to 500g' DLR 'MAIL' (no source code) 'M14L'	19·00
	'Special Delivery up to 500g' DLR 'MAIL' (no source code) 'M16L'	16·00
	'Special Delivery up to 500g' Walsall 'MAIL' (no source code) 'M18L' Type PB-sL	13·00
	'Special Delivery up to 500g' Walsall 'MAIL' (no source code) 'M20L' Type PB-sL	12·00

SG No.	DESCRIPTION	

Denominated ordinary gummed (i.e. not self-adhesive) Security Machins, with source and year code *(a)*.

No 'U'-shaped slits. Printed gravure.

| U3060 | **68p** Walsall 'MPIL' 'M11L' (from DY3 premium booklet) | 4·00 |
| U3061 | **£1·00** magenta, ISP Walsall 'MPIL' 'M17L' (from DY21 premium booklet) | 23·00 |

Note. ISP stands for 'International Security Printers' which encompasses both Cartor and Walsall.

SG No.	DESCRIPTION	

NVI ordinary gummed (i.e. not self-adhesive) Security Machins, with source and year code *(b)*.

No 'U'-shaped slits. Printed gravure.

U3065	**2nd** DLR 'MRIL' 'MA10'	7·00
U3066	**1st** gold, DLR 'MRIL' 'MA10'	7·25
U3067	**1st** vermilion, ISP Walsall 'MPIL' 'M17L' (from DY21 premium booklet)	11·00

Note. ISP stands for 'International Security Printers' which encompasses both Cartor and Walsall. No. U3066 also exists from Birth Centenary of Arnold Machin miniature sheet **MS**3222, from which it has source code 'MMIL' (and 'AM11' year code), but is not separately listed. No. U3067 also exists from 50th Anniversary of the Machin Definitive miniature sheet **MS**3965, from which it has source code 'MMIL' and year code 'M17L', but is not separately listed.

SG No.	DESCRIPTION	

Denominated ordinary gummed (i.e. not self-adhesive) Security Machins, with source and year code *(c)*.

No 'U'-shaped slits. Printed litho.

U3070	**1p** Cartor 'MPIL' 'M13L' (from DY7 premium booklet)	1·00
	1p ISP Cartor 'MPIL' 'M14L' (from DY12 premium booklet)	1·00
	1p ISP Cartor 'MPIL' 'M15L' (from DY13 premium booklet)	1·00
	1p ISP Cartor 'MPIL' 'M18L' (from DY27 premium booklet)	1·00

SG No.	DESCRIPTION	
U3070 *cont'd*	**1p** ISP Cartor 'MPIL' 'M19L' (from DY32 premium booklet)	1·00
	1p ISP Cartor 'MPIL' 'M20L' (from DY35 premium booklet)	75
U3070a	**1p** ISP Cartor 'M IL' 'M18L' i.e. source code without P (from DY29 premium booklet)	1·25
U3071	**2p** Cartor 'MPIL' 'M13L' (from DY7 premium booklet)	1·00
	2p Enschedé 'MPIL' 'M13L' (from DY9 premium booklet)	1·00
	2p ISP Cartor 'MPIL' 'M14L' (from DY12 premium booklet)	1·00
	2p ISP Cartor 'MPIL' 'M16L' (from DY20 premium booklet)	1·00
	2p ISP Cartor 'MPIL' 'M19L' (from DY30, DY32 and DY33 premium booklets)	1·00
	2p ISP Cartor 'MPIL' 'M20L' (from DY36 premium booklet)	85
	2p ISP Cartor 'MPIL' 'M21L' (from DY38 and DY42 premium booklets)	85
U3071a	**2p** ISP Cartor 'M IL' 'M18L' i.e. source code without P (from DY25 premium booklet)	1·00
U3072	**5p** Cartor 'MPIL' 'M12L' (from DY6 premium booklet)	1·50
	5p Cartor 'MPIL' 'M13L' (from DY7 premium booklet)	90
	5p Enschedé 'MPIL' 'M13L' (from DY9 premium booklet)	1·00
	5p ISP Cartor 'MPIL' 'M15L' (from DY14 premium booklet)	1·00
	5p ISP Cartor 'MPIL' 'M16L' (from DY19 premium booklet)	1·00
	5p ISP Cartor 'MPIL' 'M17L' (from DY24 premium booklet)	1·25
	5p ISP Cartor 'MPIL' 'M18L' (from DY28 premium booklet)	1·25
	5p ISP Cartor 'MPIL' 'M19L' (from DY31 and DY32 premium booklet)	1·00
	5p ISP Cartor 'MPIL' 'M20L' (from DY34 premium booklets)	1·10
	5p ISP Cartor 'MPIL' 'M21L' (from DY39 premium booklets)	1·10
U3072a	**5p** *deep red-brown*, ISP Cartor 'MPIL' 'M15L' (from DY13 premium booklet)	2·25
U3072b	**5p** ISP Cartor 'M IL' 'M18L' i.e. source code without P (from DY25 premium booklet)	1·25
U3073	**5p** Enschedé 'MPIL' 'M13L'; elliptical perforation near the top of sides of stamp (from DY8 premium booklet)	1·50
U3074	**10p** Cartor 'MPIL' 'M12L' (from DY6 premium booklet)	2·50
	10p Cartor 'MPIL' 'M13L' (from DY7 premium booklet)	1·25
	10p Enschedé 'MPIL' 'M14L' (from DY10 and DY11 premium booklets)	1·10
	10p ISP Cartor 'MPIL' 'M15L' (from DY14 premium booklet)	1·25
	10p ISP Cartor 'MPIL' 'M16L' (from DY19 and DY20 premium booklets)	1·10
	10p ISP Cartor 'MPIL' 'M18L' (from DY28 premium booklet)	1·25
	10p ISP Cartor 'MPIL' 'M19L' (from DY32 premium booklet)	1·25
	10p ISP Cartor 'MPIL' 'M21L' (from DY38, DY39, DY41 and DY42 premium booklets)	95
U3075	**20p** Cartor 'MPIL' 'M12L' (from DY6 premium booklet)	3·75
	20p Enschedé 'MPIL' 'M14L' (from DY10 and DY11 premium booklets)	1·10
	20p ISP Cartor 'MPIL' 'M17L' (from DY24 premium booklet)	2·00
	20p ISP Cartor 'MPIL' 'M18L' (from DY27 premium booklet)	1·75
	20p ISP Cartor 'MPIL' 'M20L' (from DY37 premium booklet)	1·50
	20p ISP Cartor 'MPIL' 'M21L' (from DY39, DY40 and DY41 premium booklets)	1·10
U3075a	**20p** ISP Cartor 'M IL' 'M18L' i.e. source code without P (from DY29 premium booklet)	1·75

SG No.	DESCRIPTION	
U3076	**50p** slate, Enschedé 'MPIL' 'M13L'; elliptical perforation near the top of sides of stamp (from DY8 premium booklet)	2·00
U3077	**50p** slate, ISP Cartor 'MPIL' 'M15L' (from DY14 premium booklet)	2·00
	50p slate, ISP Cartor 'MPIL' 'M19L' (from DY30 premium booklet)	1·75
	50p slate, ISP Cartor 'MPIL' 'M20L' (from DY34 and DY36 premium booklets)	1·75
	50p slate, ISP Cartor 'MPIL' 'M21L' (from DY38, DY41 and DY42 premium booklets)	1·60
U3077a	**50p** *grey*, ISP Cartor 'MPIL' 'M18L' (from DY27 premium booklet)	2·00
U3078	**76p** Cartor 'MPIL' 'M11L' (from DY2 premium booklet)	9·50
U3079	**81p** ISP Cartor 'MPIL' 'M14L' (from DY12 premium booklet)	8·00
U3080	**87p** Cartor 'MPIL' 'M12L' (from DY6 premium booklet)	6·00
U3081	**97p** ISP Cartor 'MPIL' 'M14L' (from DY12 premium booklet)	3·75
U3082	**£1·00** Enschedé 'MPIL' 'M14L' (from DY10 and DY11 premium booklets)	2·25
	£1·00 ISP Cartor 'MPIL' 'M15L' (from DY14 premium booklet)	2·25
	£1·00 ISP Cartor 'MPIL' 'M21L' (from DY41 premium booklet)	2·00
U3083	**£1·05** ISP Cartor 'MPIL' 'M16L' (from DY19 and DY20 premium booklets)	2·75
U3084	**£1·17** ISP Cartor 'MPIL' 'M17L' (from DY24 premium booklet)	15·00
	£1·17 ISP Cartor 'MPIL' 'M19L' (from DY31 premium booklet)	4·00
U3084a	**£1·17** ISP Cartor 'M IL' 'M18L' i.e. source code without P (from DY25 premium booklet)	4·50
U3089	**£1·25** ISP Cartor 'MPIL' 'M18L' (from DY27 premium booket)	2·75
U3089a	**£1·25** ISP Cartor 'M IL' 'M18L' i.e. source code without P. *Light green* (from DY29 premium booklet)	2·75
U3094	**£1·33** ISP Cartor 'MPIL' 'M15L' (from DY13 premium booklet)	3·00
U3096	**£1·35** ISP Cartor 'MPIL' 'M19L' (from DY32 premium booklet)	4·00
U3099	**£1·40** ISP Cartor 'MPIL' 'M17L' (from DY23 premium booklet)	4·00
U3104	**£1·45** ISP Cartor 'M IL' 'M18L' i.e. source code without P (from DY29 premium booklet)	7·00
U3108	**£1·50** ISP Cartor 'MPIL' 'M21L' (from DY42 premium booklet)	8·50
U3109	**£1·55** ISP Cartor 'MPIL' 'M18L' (from DY28 premium booklet)	15·00
U3115	**£1·63** ISP Cartor 'MPIL' 'M20L' (from DY34 premium booklet)	4·50
U3116	**£1·70** ISP Cartor 'MPIL' 'M21L' (from DY39 premium booklet)	15·00

SG No.	DESCRIPTION	
	NVI ordinary gummed (i.e. not self-adhesive) Security Machins, with source and year code *(d)*.	
	No 'U'-shaped slits. Printed litho.	
U3150	**2nd** ISP Cartor 'MPIL' 'M15L' (from DY15 premium booklet)	4·25
	2nd ISP Cartor 'MPIL' 'M17L' (from DY23 premium booklet)	2·25
	2nd ISP Cartor 'MPIL' 'M19L' (from DY31 and DY33 premium booklets)	1·90
	2nd ISP Cartor 'MPIL' 'M20L' (from DY36 and DY37 premium booklets)	2·00
	2nd ISP Cartor 'MPIL' 'M21L' (from DY40 premium booklet)	2·00
U3155	**1st** gold, Cartor 'MPIL' 'M11L' (from DY2 premium booklet)	5·25
U3156	**1st** vermilion, Cartor 'MPIL' 'M13L' (from DY7 premium booklet)	1·75

SG No.	DESCRIPTION	
U3156 *cont'd*	**1st** vermilion, ISP Cartor 'MPIL' 'M15L' (from DY15 premium booklet)	6·00
	1st vermilion, ISP Cartor 'MPIL' 'M16L' (from DY17 premium booklet)	2·50
	1st vermilion, ISP Cartor 'MPIL' 'M17L' (from DY23 premium booklet)	2·00
	1st vermilion, ISP Cartor 'MPIL' 'M18L' (from DY26 premium booklet)	2·00
U3157	**1st** bright scarlet, ISP Cartor 'MPIL' 'M16L' (from DY20 premium booklet)	2·25
	1st bright scarlet, ISP Cartor 'MPIL' 'M20L' (from DY37 premium booklet)	2·25
	1st bright scarlet, ISP Cartor 'MPIL' 'M21L' (from DY38 and DY40 premium booklets)	2·10

Note. ISP stands for 'International Security Printers' which encompasses both Cartor and Walsall.

SG No.	DESCRIPTION	
	1st 'Long to Reign Over Us' self-adhesive Security Machins, no source code (as from counter sheets), with year code *(a)*.	
	(All have the year code to the left of The Queen's neck, just above the front of the necklace.)	
	(The 'U'-shaped slits are broken.)	
U3744	**1st** bright lilac, DLR 'REIGN' (no source code) 'O15R'	1·75
	1st bright lilac, DLR 'REIGN' (no source code) 'O16R'	7·25

SG No.	DESCRIPTION	
	1st 'Long to Reign Over Us' self-adhesive Security Machins, with source and year code *(b)*.	
	(Unless noted, front of self-adhesive backing is plain.)	
	(All have the source code behind the back of the Queen's hair at the bottom, the year code is to the left of The Queen's neck, just above the front of the necklace.)	
	(The 'U'-shaped slits are broken.)	
U3745	**1st** bright lilac, ISP Walsall 'REIGS' 'O15R'	1·75
	1st bright lilac, ISP Walsall 'REIGS' 'O15R' Type PB-Up	35·00
	1st bright lilac, ISP Walsall 'REIGS' 'O16R' Type PB-Up	4·50
U3746	**1st** bright lilac, ISP Walsall 'REIGC' 'O15R'	1·60
	1st bright lilac, ISP Walsall 'REIGC' 'O16R' Type PB-Up	1·75

Note. ISP stands for 'International Security Printers' which encompasses both Cartor and Walsall.

SG No.	DESCRIPTION	
	1st 'Long to Reign Over Us' ordinary gum (i.e. not self-adhesive) Security Machin, with source and year code (c). No 'U'-shaped slits. Printed litho.	
	(Source code behind the back of the Queen's hair at the bottom, year code is to the left of The Queen's neck, just above the front of the necklace.)	
U3747	**1st** bright lilac, ISP Cartor 'REIGP' 'O16R' (from DY17 premium booklet)	3·50

Note. ISP stands for 'International Security Printers' which encompasses both Cartor and Walsall. 1st bright lilac with ordinary gum but gravure (by FNMT Spain), with source code REIGM and year code O15R, exists from the Long to Reign Over Us miniature sheet **MS**3747, but is not separately listed.

BARCODED SECURITY MACHINS

Please note that the 'V' numbers in this section are temporary and subject to change.

On 23 March 2021, Royal Mail piloted their first-ever barcoded postage stamp, in the form of a self-adhesive 2nd class Security Machin definitive, issued in 50×2nd class business sheets.

Replacing non-barcoded Security Machins, on 1 February 2022, 2nd and 1st class Security Machins in new colours with barcodes were introduced in retail booklets and counter sheets. The range was expanded on 28 February 2022 when business sheets of NVIs were issued. Then, barcoded versions of denominated Security Machins, some in a new design with The Queen's portrait set against a white background, with coloured borderline, were issued on 4 April 2022 in counter sheets.

Like non-barcoded Security Machins, the barcoded versions have the usual security features of U-shaped slits, an overall iridescent overprint, sometimes with source codes, year codes, and self-adhesive backing paper with 'ROYALMAIL' printed backing.

Barcoded Machins are nearly 50% larger than a traditional Machin definitive, partly due to the adjacent barcode. The main features, such as the value, iridescent overprint and U-shaped slits, are scaled up accordingly.

Unlike the non-barcoded versions, barcoded Large Letter stamps are the same size as standard letter stamps. They have the value instead placed at the top left, and at the lower left have the word Large printed sideways and reading upwards.

Each stamp's (2D) barcode (also known as a data matrix) is unique and printed alongside the stamp design's main body, and a simulated perforation line separates the two elements. The simulated perforation line and 2D barcode are printed in the same colour as the stamp. Barcode stamps are a two-process printing, the main design and simulated perforation in gravure, and each stamp's barcode is separately digitally printed. The barcode enables tracking and further helps combat counterfeiting.

USED STAMPS. Because the self-adhesive stamps in this section do not include a water-soluable layer of gum, we recommend that used stamps are retained on their backing paper and trimmed with a uniform border of 1 mm–2 mm around all sides, taking care not to cut into the perforations.

Source Codes: similarly to non-barcoded Security Machins, codes may be seen in the words 'ROYALMAIL' at the top right of the stamp.

The codes are:

MAIL	–	(ie without code letter) – counter sheets
MBIL	–	Business sheets
MEIL	–	standard booklets of eight
MFIL	–	standard booklets of four
MPIL	–	Prestige booklet panes

Note that, where stamps exist with more than one year code, the issue date given is for the first release, but prices are for the cheapest code.

'ROYALMAIL' printed backing paper. Barcoded stamps' self-adhesive backing paper has the repeating 'ROYALMAIL' wording, first introduced as an additional security measure in 2016. It is described at the beginning of the non-barcoded Security Machin section. Please refer to the Security Machin checklists for further details and illustrations of the pre-existing 'ROYALMAIL' backing Types.

Barcoded stamps from counter sheets have the 'ROYALMAIL' backing at 90 degrees to the stamp design, which brings about a new (fifth) backing Type. With the stamp design positioned upright (as a stamp is intended to be used), reading the backing from the left, the pairs of lines can appear with the Large lettering before (as opposed to over) the small (Type PB(L)-Ls), or with the small before the Large (Type PB(L)-sL). These differences are not listed in this catalogue unless the barcoded stamps themselves are different. However, their existence is noted under the sections in which they occur and in the checklists at the end of this section where the new Type is illustrated.

Details of known source and year-code combinations, and different year code changes, are provided in the series of tables following the listings. For the convenience of collectors, the printer of each combination is also given. We are grateful to John M. Deering for compiling these tables.

3578	3719

2021 (23 Mar)–**22**. Barcoded Security Machins. Design as T **3578** or T **3719**. Self-adhesive. One centre band (Nos. V4500/V4502, V4510, V4525) or two bands (others). U-shaped slits. Iridescent overprint . Die-cut perf 15×14½ with one elliptical hole in each vertical side).

(a) With source and year code.
*(i) Gravure and digital ISP Walsall as T **3578**.*

V4500	(2nd) bright blue (MBIL) (23.3.21)	2·00	2·00
V4501	(2nd) emerald (MBIL) (28.2.22)	1·50	1·50
V4502	(2nd) emerald (MEIL) (1.2.22)	1·30	1·30
V4505	(1st) deep violet (MBIL) (28.2.22)	2·00	2·00
V4506	(1st) deep violet (MEIL) (1.2.22)	1·80	1·80
V4507	(1st) deep violet (MFIL) (1.2.22)	1·80	1·80

*(ii) Litho and digital Cartor as Type **3578**.*

V4510	(2nd) emerald (MPIL) (16.2.23)	2·00	2·00
	I. Booklet pane. Nos. V4510 and V4849 each×2, with 2 central labels (16.2.23)	9·00	

*(iii) As T **3719**.*

V4511	(2nd Large) grey-green (MBIL) (28.2.22)	2·25	2·25
V4512	(2nd Large) grey-green (MFIL) (1.2.22)	2·10	2·10
V4515	(1st Large) greenish blue (MBIL) (28.2.22)	3·00	3·00
V4516	(1st Large) greenish blue (MFIL) (1.2.22)	2·75	2·75

(b) Without source code, with yearcode.
*(i) As T **3578**.*

V4525	(2nd) emerald (1.2.22)	1·10	1·10
V4526	(1st) deep violet (1.2.22)	1·60	1·60

*(ii) As T **3719**.*

V4527	(2nd Large) grey-green (1.2.22)	1·90	1·90
V4528	(1st Large) greenish blue (1.2.22)	2·50	2·50

No. V4500 came from business sheets of 50 stamps sold only through Royal Mail Philatelic Bureau, Edinburgh and through a volume retailer of business sheets. Philatelic customers could also purchase from the Philatelic Bureau, Edinburgh, a maximum of five loose single stamps.

Presentation packs were not made available for No. V4500.

Nos. V4500/V4502, V4505/V4507, V4511/V4512, and V4515/V4516 have backing paper with repeating 'ROYALMAIL' text, with alternate pairs of lines inverted (Type PB-Ls/sL).

Nos. V4525/V4528 have backing paper with repeating 'ROYALMAIL' text, with alternate pairs of lines inverted, at 90 degrees to the stamp design, (Type PB(L)-Ls/sL).

3720

(Gravure and digital ISP Walsall)

2022 (4 Apr). Barcoded Security Machins. Design as T **3720**. Self-adhesive. Two bands. U-shaped slits. Iridescent overprint. Die-cut perf 15×14½ (with one elliptical hole in each vertical side).

(a) Without source code, with year code, gravure and digital ISP Walsall.

V4600	£1·85 grey-brown	2·50	2·50
V4610	£2·55 blue	3·50	3·50
V4620	£3·25 purple	4·50	4·50
V4630	£4·20 bright green	5·75	5·75

(b) With source and year codes, litho and digital ISP Cartor.

V4640	£1·85 grey-brown (MPIL) (24.11.22)	4·50	4·50

Nos. V4600, V4610, V4620, and V4630 have backing paper with repeating 'ROYALMAIL' text, with alternate pairs of lines inverted, at 90 degrees to the stamp design, (Type PB(L)-Ls/sL).

3721

(Gravure and digital ISP Walsall)

2022 (4 Apr–1 Sept). Barcoded Security Machins. Design as T **3721**. Self-adhesive. Two bands. U-shaped slits. Iridescent overprint. Die-cut perf 15×14½ (with one elliptical hole in each vertical side).

(a) Without source code, with year code, gravure and digital ISP Walsall.

V4700	1p. blue	10	10
V4702	2p. deep green	10	10
V4705	5p. dull violet-blue	10	10
V4710	10p. turquoise-green	15	15
V4720	20p. bright green (MPIL)	30	30
V4750	50p. slate	90	90
	l. Booklet pane. Nos. V4750×2 and		
	V4780×3 with horiz label (5.5.22)	8·50	
V4780	£1 grey-brown	1·75	1·75
V4800	£2 new blue	3·00	3·00
V4820	£3 purple	4·25	4·25
V4840	£5 emerald	7·00	7·00

(b) With source and year codes, gravure and digital ISP Walsall.

V4841	50p. slate (MPIL) (1.9.22)	1·50	1·50
	l. Booklet pane. Nos. V4841/V4842		
	each×2, with 2 central labels (1.9.22)	9·00	
V4842	£1 grey-brown (MPIL) (1.9.22)	2·00	2·00

(c) With source and year codes, litho and digital ISP Cartor.

V4845	10p. turquoise-green (MPIL) (24.11.22)	1·00	1·00
	l. Booklet pane. Nos. V4640, V4845×2		
	and V4846×2, with horiz label		
	(24.11.22)	10·00	
V4846	20p. bright green (MPIL) (24.11.22)	1·25	1·25
	l. Booklet pane. Nos. V4846×3 and		
	V4850, with 2 central labels (9.3.23)	9·00	
V4849	£1 grey-brown (MPIL) (16.2.23)	2·00	2·30
V4850	£2 new blue (MPIL) (9.3.23)	3·50	3·50

Nos. V4700, V4702, V4705, V4710, V4720, V4750, V4780, V4800, V4820, and V4840 have backing paper with repeating 'ROYALMAIL' text, with alternate pairs of lines inverted, at 90 degrees to the stamp design, (Type PB(L)-Ls/sL).

First Day Covers

23.3.21	No. V4500 (Type K)	4·25
23.3.21	No. V4500 (Windsor)	4·25
1.2.22	No. V4525/V4528 (Type K)	9·00
1.2.22	No. V4525/V4528 (Windsor)	9·00
4.4.22	Nos. V4600, V4610, V4620, V4630 (Type K)	17·00
4.4.22	Nos. V4600, V4610, V4620, V4630 (Windsor)	17·00
4.4.22	Nos. V4700, V4702, V4705, V4710, V4720, V4750, V4780 (Type K)	5·50
4.4.22	Nos. V4700, V4702, V4705, V4710, V4720, V4750, V4780 (Windsor)	5·50
4.4.22	Nos. V4800, V4820, V4840 (Type K)	16·00
4.4.22	Nos. V4800, V4820, V4840 (Windsor)	16·00
5.5.22	Unsung Heroes. Women of World War II *se-tenant* pane No. V4750l (Tallents House or London SW1)	10·00
1.9.22	Transformers *se-tenant* pane No. V4750l (Tallents House or Arkholme, Carnforth)	11·00
24.11.22	Tutankhamun *se-tenant* pane No. V4845l (Tallents House or Oxford)	12·00
16.2.23	X-Men *se-tenant* pane No. V4510l (Tallents House or Muir of Ord)	11·00
9.3.23	Flying Scotsman *se-tenant* pane No. 4846l (Tallents House or Doncaster)	11·00

Presentation Packs

1.2.22	Nos. V4525/V4528 (PO Pack No. 116)	8·50
4.4.22	Nos. V4600, V4610, V4620, V4630 (PO Pack No. 117)	17·00
4.4.22	Nos. V4700, V4702, V4705, V4710, V4720, V4750, V4780 (PO Pack No. 118)	5·50
4.4.22	Nos. V4800, V4820, V4840 (PO Pack No. 119)	16·00

Barcoded Security Machins Booklet Guide ('V' Numbers) – the shaded squares represent printed labels.

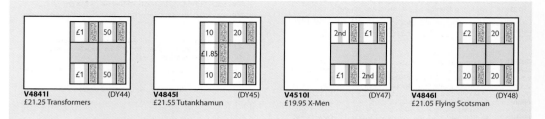

V4841I   (DY44)
£21.25 Transformers

V4845I   (DY45)
£21.55 Tutankhamun

V4510I   (DY47)
£19.95 X-Men

V4846I   (DY48)
£21.05 Flying Scotsman

The following series of tables gives details of all source and year-code combinations reported at the time of going to press. Each is related to its printer and variations in the U-shaped slits are also noted. These tables are copyright John M Deering and are reproduced with his permission.

'ROYALMAIL' printed backing paper: Barcoded stamps from counter sheets have the 'ROYALMAIL' backing at 90 degrees to the stamp design, which brings about new backing Types. With the stamp design positioned upright (as a stamp is intended to be used), reading the backing from the left, the pairs of lines can appear with the Large lettering before (as opposed to over) the small (Type PB(L)-Ls), or with the small before the Large (Type PB(L)-sL). For further details and illustrations of the pre-existing 'ROYALMAIL' backing Types, please refer to the Security Machin checklists.

Type PB (L)-Ls

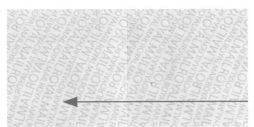

Type PB (L)-sL

SG No.	DESCRIPTION	

NVI self-adhesive Barcoded Security Machins, with source and year code *(a).*

(Unless noted, the self-adhesive backing paper has repeating 'ROYALMAIL' text, with alternate pairs of lines inverted)

(The source code is at top right, the year code is to the left of the front of The Queen's forehead or crown.)

(The 'U'-shaped slits are broken.) Printed gravure unless noted.

V4500	**2nd** ISP Walsall 'MBIL' 'M21L', Type PB-Ls/sL	2·00
V4501	**2nd** ISP Walsall 'MBIL' 'M22L', Type PB-Ls/sL	1·50
V4502	**2nd** ISP Walsall 'MEIL' 'M22L', Type PB-sL	1·30
V4505	**1st** ISP Walsall 'MBIL' 'M22L', Type PB-sL	2·00
V4506	**1st** ISP Walsall 'MEIL' 'M22L', Type PB-sL	1·80
V4507	**1st** ISP Walsall 'MFIL' 'M22L', Type PB-Ls/sL	1·80
V4510	**2nd** Cartor printed litho 'MPIL' 'M23L', (from DY46 premium booklet)	2·00
V4511	**2nd Large** ISP Walsall 'MBIL' 'M22L', Type PB-sL	2·25
V4512	**2nd Large** ISP Walsall 'MFIL' 'M22L', Type PB-Ls/sL	2·10
V4515	**1st Large** ISP Walsall 'MBIL' 'M22L', Type PB-Ls/sL	3·00
V4516	**1st Large** ISP Walsall 'MFIL' 'M22L', Type PB-sL	2·75

SG No.	DESCRIPTION	

NVI self-adhesive Barcoded Security Machins, no source code (as from counter sheets), with year code *(b).*

(Unless noted, the self-adhesive backing paper has repeating 'ROYALMAIL' text, with alternate pairs of lines inverted, at 90 degrees to the stamp design.)

(The year code is to the left of the front of The Queen's forehead or crown.)

(The 'U'-shaped slits are broken.) Printed gravure.

V4525	**2nd** ISP Walsall 'MAIL' (no source code) 'M22L' Type PB(L)-Ls/sL	1·10
V4526	**1st** ISP Walsall 'MAIL' (no source code) 'M22L' Type PB(L)-Ls/sL	1·60
V4527	**2nd Large** ISP Walsall 'MAIL' (no source code) 'M22L' Type PB(L)-Ls	1·90
V4528	**1st Large** ISP Walsall 'MAIL' (no source code) 'M22L' Type PB(L)-Ls	2·50

SG No.	DESCRIPTION	

Denominated self-adhesive Barcoded Security Machins, with source and year code *(b).*

(The year code is to the left of the front of The Queen's forehead or crown.)

(The 'U'-shaped slits are broken.) Printed litho.

V4600	**£1.85** Cartor 'MPIL' 'M22L', (from DY45 premium booklet)	4·50
V4610	**£2.55** ISP Walsall 'MAIL' (no source code) 'M22L' Type PB(L)-Ls	3·50
V4620	**£3.25** ISP Walsall 'MAIL' (no source code) 'M22L' Type PB(L)-Ls	4·50
V4630	**£3.40** ISP Walsall 'MAIL' (no source code) 'M22L' Type PB(L)-Ls	5·75

SG No.	DESCRIPTION	

Denominated self-adhesive Barcoded Security Machins, white background, no source code (as from counter sheets), with year code .

(Unless noted, the self-adhesive backing paper has repeating 'ROYALMAIL' text, with alternate pairs of lines inverted, at 90 degrees to the stamp design.)

(The year code is to the left of the front of The Queen's forehead or crown.)

(The 'U'-shaped slits are broken.) Printed gravure.

V4700	**1p** ISP Walsall 'MAIL' (no source code) 'M22L' Type PB(L)-Ls	10
V4702	**2p** ISP Walsall 'MAIL' (no source code) 'M22L' Type PB(L)-Ls	10
V4705	**5p** ISP Walsall 'MAIL' (no source code) 'M22L' Type PB(L)-Ls	10
V4710	**10p** ISP Walsall 'MAIL' (no source code) 'M22L' Type PB(L)-Ls	15
V4720	**20p** ISP Walsall 'MAIL' (no source code) 'M22L' Type PB(L)-Ls	30
V4750	**50p** ISP Walsall 'MAIL' (no source code) 'M22L' Type PB(L)-Ls	90
V4780	**£1** ISP Walsall 'MAIL' (no source code) 'M22L' Type PB(L)-Ls	1·75
V4800	**£2** ISP Walsall 'MAIL' (no source code) 'M22L' Type PB(L)-Ls	3·00
V4820	**£3** ISP Walsall 'MAIL' (no source code) 'M22L' Type PB(L)-Ls	4·25
V4840	**£5** ISP Walsall 'MAIL' (no source code) 'M22L' Type PB(L)-Ls	7·00

SG No.	DESCRIPTION	

Denominated self-adhesive Barcoded Security Machins, white background, with source and year codes *(b)* **or** *(c)*.

(The year code is to the left of the front of The Queen's forehead or crown.)

(The 'U'-shaped slits are broken.) Printed litho unless noted.

V4841	**50p** ISP Walsall printed gravure 'MPIL' 'M22L' (from DY44 premium booklet)	1·50
V4842	**£1** ISP Walsall printed gravure 'MPIL' 'M22L' (from DY44 premium booklet)	2·00
V4845	**10p** Cartor 'MPIL' 'M22L' (from DY45 premium booklet)	1·00
V4846	**20p** Cartor 'MPIL' 'M22L' (from DY45 premium booklet)	1·25
V4849	**£1** Cartor 'MPIL' 'M23L' (from DY46 premium booklet)	2·00
V4850	**£2** Cartor 'MPIL' 'M23L' (from DY47 premium booklet)	3·50

We may have a new look, but at the heart of everything we do, it's still all about stamps.

Our dedicated shop team are here to help with all philatelic enquiries, from fulfilling everyday lists and new GB issues to recommending the best albums and stamp accessories to suit your collection.

Call on +44 (0)20 7557 4436 or email them at shop@stanleygibbons.com

STANLEY GIBBONS
THE HOME OF STAMP COLLECTING

King Charles III

9 September 2022

(Des Charlie Smith Design. Litho Cartor SP)

2023 (22 Mar). Flowers. Self-adhesive. Multicoloured. Two phosphor bands. Die-cut perf 14½×14.

5000	**5000**	(1st) Sweet Pea..	1·60	1·60
		a. Horiz strip of 5. Nos. 5002/5006.....	8·00	8·00
5001	**5001**	(1st) Iris...	1·60	1·60
5002	**5002**	(1st) Lily..	1·60	1·60
5003	**5003**	(1st) Sunflower..	1·60	1·60
5004	**5004**	(1st) Fuschia...	1·60	1·60
5005	**5005**	(1st) Tulip...	1·60	1·60
		a. Horiz strip of 5. Nos. 5005/5009.....	8·00	8·00
5006	**5006**	(1st) Peony..	1·60	1·60
5007	**5007**	(1st) Nasturtium..	1·60	1·60
5008	**5008**	(1st) Rose..	1·60	1·60
5009	**5009**	(1st) Dahlia...	1·60	1·60
Set of 10..			16·00	16·00
Set of 2 Gutter Strips of 10..................................			32·00	
First Day Cover (Tallents House)............................				18·00
First Day Cover (Bloomfield, Tipton).....................				18·00
Presentation Pack (PO Pack No. 519)......................			18·00	
PHQ Cards (set of 10) (335).....................................			6·50	18·00

Nos. 5000/5004 and 5005/5009 were each printed together, *se-tenant*, as horizontal strips of five stamps in sheets of 50 (2 panes 5×5).

5000 Sweet Pea

5001 Iris

5002 Lily

5003 Sunflower

5004 Fuschia

5005 Tulip

5006 Peony

5007 Nasturtium

5008 Rose

5009 Dahlia

King Charles III Definitives

Like the Queen Elizabeth II barcoded definitives they have the usual security features of U-shaped slits, an overall iridescent overprint, sometimes with source codes, year codes, and self-adhesive backing paper with 'ROYALMAIL' printed backing. Barcoded definitives are nearly 50% larger than a traditional definitive, partly due to the adjacent barcode. The main features, such as the value, iridescent overprint and U-shaped slits, are scaled up accordingly.

Each stamp's (2D) barcode (also known as a data matrix) is unique and printed alongside the stamp design's main body, and a simulated perforation line separates the two elements. The simulated perforation line and 2D barcode are printed in the same colour as the stamp. Barcode stamps are a two-process printing, the main design and simulated perforation in gravure, and each stamp's barcode is separately digitally printed. The barcode enables tracking and further helps combat counterfeiting.

USED STAMPS. Because the self-adhesive stamps in this section do not include a water-soluable layer of gum, we recommend that used stamps are retained on their backing paper and trimmed with a uniform border of 1-2 mm around all sides, taking care not to cut into the perforations.

Source Codes: similarly to Queen Elizabeth II barcoded definitives, codes may be seen in the words 'ROYALMAIL' at the top right of the stamp. The codes are:

MAIL	-	(ie without code letter) – counter sheets
MEIL	-	standard booklets of eight
MFIL	-	standard booklets of four

Note that, where stamps exist with more than one year code, the issue date given is for the first release, but prices are for the cheapest code.

'ROYALMAIL' printed backing paper. Barcoded stamps' self-adhesive backing paper has the repeating 'ROYALMAIL' wording, first introduced as an additional security measure in 2016. It is described at the beginning of the non-barcoded Security Machin section.

Barcoded stamps from counter sheets have the 'ROYALMAIL' backing at 90 degrees to the stamp design. With the stamp design positioned upright (as a stamp is intended to be used), reading the backing from the left, the pairs of lines can appear with the Large lettering before (as opposed to over) the small (Type PB(L)-Ls), or with the small before the Large (Type PB(L)-sL). These differences are not listed in this catalogue unless the barcoded stamps themselves are different.

5010	5011

(Des after portrait by Martin Jennings)

2023 (4 Apr). Barcoded Security Definitives. Design as T **5010** or T **5011**. Self-adhesive. One centre band (Nos. V5000, V5010) or two bands (others). U-shaped slits. Iridescent overprint. Die-cut perf 15×14½ (with one elliptical hole in each vertical side).

*(a) Without source code, with yearcode. (i) Gravure and digital Cartor SP as Type **5010**.*

V5000	(2nd) emerald (4.4.23)	1·10	1·10
V5001	(1st) deep violet (4.4.23)	1·60	1·60

*(ii) As Type **5011**.*

V5002	(2nd Large) grey-green (4.423)	1·90	1·90
V5003	(1st Large) greenish blue (4.4.23)	2·50	2·50

*(b) With source and year code. (i) Gravure and digital Cartor SP as Type **5010**.*

V5010	(2nd) emerald (MEIL) (4.4.23)	1·30	1·30
V5015	(1st) deep violet (MEIL) (4.4.23)	1·80	1·80
V5016	(1st) deep violet (MFIL) (4.4.23)	1·80	1·80

*(c) With source and year code. (i) Gravure and digital Cartor ISP as Type **5011**.*

V5017	(2nd Large) grey-green (MFIL) (4.4.23)	2·10	2·10
V5018	(1st Large) greenish blue (MFIL) (4.4.23)	2·75	2·75

Nos. V5000/V5018 have backing paper with repeating 'ROYALMAIL' text, with alternate pairs of lines inverted, at 90 degrees to the stamp design, (Type PB(L)-Ls/sL).

5012

(Des after portrait by Martin Jennings)

2023 (4 Apr). Barcoded Security Definitives. Design as T **5012**. Self-adhesive. Two bands. U-shaped slits. Iridescent overprint. Die-cut perf 14½×15.

(a) Without source code, with year code, gravure and digital Cartor ISP.

V5025	£2.20 dark green (4.4.23)	3·75	3·75

No. V5025 has backing paper with repeating 'ROYALMAIL' text, with alternate pairs of lines inverted, at 90 degrees to the stamp design, (Type PB(L)-Ls/sL).

First Day Covers

4.4.23	Nos. V5000/5003 (Type K)	9·00
4.4.23	Nos. V5000/5003 (Windsor)	9·00
4.4.23	No. V5025 (Type K)	5·50
4.4.23	No. V5025 (Windsor)	5·50

Presentation Packs

4.4.23	Nos. V5000/V5003 (PO Pack No. 121)	8·50
4.4.23	No. V5025 (PO Pack No. 122)	5·50

ROYAL MAIL POSTAGE LABELS ('FRAMAS')

These imperforate labels were issued as an experiment by the Post Office. Special microprocessor-controlled machines were installed at post offices in Cambridge, London, Shirley (Southampton) and Windsor to provide an after-hours sales service to the public. The machines printed and dispensed the labels according to the coins inserted and the buttons operated by the customer. Values were initially available in ½p. steps to 16p. and in addition, the labels were sold at philatelic counters in two packs containing either three values (3½p., 12½p., 16p.) or 32 values (½p. to 16p.).

From 28 August 1984 the machines were adjusted to provide values up to 17p. After 31 December 1984 labels including ½p. values were withdrawn. The machines were taken out of service on 30 April 1985.

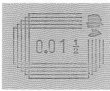

L1 *Machine postage-paid impression in red on phosphorised paper with grey-green background design. No watermark. Imperforate.*

1984 (1 May–28 Aug).

Set of 32 (½p. to 16p.)	15·00	22·00
Set of 3 (3½p., 12½p., 16p.)	2·50	3·00
Set of 3 on First Day Cover (1.5.84)		6·50
Set of 2 (16½p., 17p.) (28.8.84)	4·00	3·00

ROYAL MAIL POST & GO STAMPS

Post & Go stamps were a new sort of postage stamp, introduced on 8 October 2008 at the Galleries post office in Bristol. The stamps are dispensed from self-service Post & Go machines which are stocked with rolls of partly-printed stamps which already have the design and background pre-printed in gravure. Once a transaction has completed the machine thermally prints a two-line service indicator (i.e. the value) and a four-part code into the stamp's background, and dispenses the finished ready-to-use stamp(s). The four-part code represents the branch in which the machine is sited, the machine number within the branch, and session and transaction numbers.

The Bristol installation followed trials of several self-service machines capable of dispensing postage labels. The Post & Go machine installed at Bristol was manufactured by Wincor Nixdorf, and dispensed postage labels as well as Post & Go stamps. Wincor Nixdorf machines were subsequently rolled out to other large post offices and remained in service until they were decommissioned in March 2015. A new series of machines, manufactured by NCR, made their appearance from 28 February 2014, dispensing Type IIA stamps (see below). From 28 February 2014 through to March 2015 both Wincor Nixdorf and NCR machines were in use within the network of post offices, but not at the same time in the same office.

In the interim, self-service on-demand Post & Go postage stamps have become commonplace, with some post offices having several machines.

Initially, and until autumn 2011 (see below, Tariff changes), five different tariff stamps were in the available range; 1st Class Up to 100g., 1st Large Up to 100g., Europe Up to 20g., Worldwide Up to 10g. and Worldwide Up to 20g.

Large and small typeface (Wincor): when the machines were first installed they were programmed to dispense five denominations and the service indicator lines were in a large size typeface (Type I), as T **FT1**. The large typeface remained current until September 2010 when the first pictorial Post & Go stamps, depicting British Birds, were released.

The larger pictorial element in the new design necessitated machines to be upgraded to print the service indicator both repositioned to the left and in a reduced size (Type II). The four-part code was also significantly reduced in size. Initially the pictorials were only available from 30 offices nationwide, and because the upgrading was phased over many months, the early pictorial issues had limited availability. The Machin design ran concurrently with the pictorials and started appearing with the smaller service indicator from 8 September 2010, when machines in London were the first to be upgraded in advance of the first pictorial issue. The smaller service indicator became the norm after all machines were upgraded.

Tariff changes: in the autumn of 2011 a new value, 'Worldwide up to 40g', was added to the range and began to appear whilst Birds (4th series) was current. The Machin design was the first to be seen with it though, having been trialled in one London office from 13 October.

Birds (4th series) appeared with 'Worldwide up to 40g' later in the year and due to the late use of earlier Birds issues they too are known with it, although it is not included in set prices for Birds, series 1 to 3.

Second class stamps were introduced to the range on 20 February 2013 but only in Special Packs, and from machines at Spring Stampex 2013. They were finally released at a postal location (a mobile 'pop-up' Christmas post shop in Newcastle-upon-Tyne) on 20 November 2013 (see below).

On 31 March 2014, the 'Worldwide up to 10g' and 'Worldwide up to 40g' stamps were withdrawn and replaced by new tariff stamps with 'Europe up to 60g' and 'Worldwide up to 60g' service indicators.

On 5 June 2014, the individual 'Europe up to 20g' and the 'Worldwide up to 10g' stamps were withdrawn and replaced with a combined tariff or 'dual value' stamp with the service indicator 'Euro 20g World 10g'.

On 30 March 2015 the 'Europe up to 60g' and 'Worldwide up to 60g' tariff stamps were withdrawn and replaced by 'Europe up to 100g' and 'Worldwide up to 100g' stamps.

On 1 September 2020, the 'Europe up to 100g' and 'Worldwide up to 20g' stamps were withdrawn and replaced by a second combined tariff stamp 'Euro 100g World 200g'. Simultaneously the 'Worldwide up to 100g' stamp was withdrawn and replaced by two new 'Zoned' worldwide tariff stamps: 'World up to 100g Zone 1-3' and 'World up to 100g Zone 2'.

On 1 January 2021 after a service life of only four months, both 'Zoned' stamps were withdrawn along with the original 'Euro 20g World 10g' stamp. They were replaced by the reintroduction of the 'Worldwide up to 100g' stamp and two new 'Large Letter' tariff stamps with service indicators 'Europe Large 100g' and 'Worldwide Large 100g'.

From 1 January 2021 following the numerous changes, the range of available values remained at six: 1st Class up to 100g, 1st Large up to 100g, Euro 100g World 20g, Worldwide up to 100g, Europe Large 100g and Worldwide Large 100g.

Worldwide up to 100g Zone 1-3: during the four months until superseded on 1 January 2021, machines sited in post offices generated the stamp 'Worldwide up to 100g Zone 1-3' using a hyphen between the 1 and the 3. The hyphen was far from satisfactory as the stamp could be misinterpreted to be also valid for Zone 2. However, post offices machines' could not be amended to replace the hyphen with anything more appropriate. Similar stamps from museums machines', which all bear inscriptions (see tables elsewhere in this listing), had the hyphen replaced by and ampersand from 18 September.

Following the introduction of the new values on 1 September 2020 and 1 January 2021 a miscellany of material is coming to light as post office stocks of older pictorial issues are gradually used up. This catalogue edition includes the material that we have verified to date, the editors welcome feedback from readers and listings will be expanded as appropriate in due course.

Special Packs: 1st stamps of the different 'Post & Go' pictorial designs are available in Special Packs from the Philatelic Bureau Edinburgh. For the Birds series these packs contained sheetlets of the six designs which were printed in gravure and had the two lines of the service indicator '1st Class' and 'up to 100g' printed much closer together (2 mm). From Farm Animals onwards the sheetlets were replaced by strips of six thermally printed from Hytech/Royal Mail Series I machines which also had the two lines of the service indicator printed closer together (3 mm). First day covers sold by the Philatelic Bureau Edinburgh use these types of stamps.

Year codes: codes first appeared on the 2012 Christmas Robin issue where there is an 'MA12' in the background to the left of the main pictorial design. The February 2013 2nd class stamps also have an MA12 year code and the year code became a standard feature from 2013.

For machin issue year code positions, see illustrations in the main listings.

Digitally-printed stamps: since November 2015 some stamp designs have been produced in single-design rolls, digitally printed instead of being printed by gravure. To date, these have been available from Post & Go machines sited at exhibitions and at The Postal Museum (see below), and at other locations that are outside the scope of this catalogue. Details may be found in the relevant tables.

Machines at exhibitions: from Spring Stampex 2011 through to and including Autumn Stampex 2017, Royal Mail sited Post & Go machines at stamp exhibitions. The machines were initially manufactured by Hytech International. Stamps from the early exhibition machines are easily identifiable from the (post offices') Wincor machine versions because the two lines of their service indicator are printed much closer together. Those from Wincor machines are spaced 4 mm apart. There are other minor differences.

Marking particular events (from autumn 2011 through to and including autumn 2017) machines at exhibitions have produced stamps with special inscriptions. Owing to their restricted availability stamps from exhibition machines with and without inscriptions are not listed separately. However, details are provided in tables following the Royal Mail Post & Go stamps listings. Machines for use at locations other than post offices have evolved. Following Hytech's version came a Royal Mail Series I machine, and from Spring Stampex 2014 the Royal Mail Series II machine was introduced.

Machines at The Postal Museum: The Postal Museum (previously The British Postal Museum & Archive, London), has two Post & Go machines permanently available. One machine is sited in the main gift shop area and the second is in the Mail Rail area. The purchase of a museum ticket is not necessary to use the machines. The machines are used by collectors to obtain material and also serve a local postal need for those preferring to buy their postage stamps there. Stamps from these machines always bear inscriptions of one sort or another. These are recorded in the tables at the end of this section.

Temporary pop-up Christmas post shops: in November 2012 a new type of post office, a temporary, pop-up, Christmas post shop, appeared in Camden, London. It had a Royal Mail Series I Post & Go machine that the public could use to buy postage stamps.

The availability of this type of machine at this sort of office resulted in the first publicly available versions from a Royal Mail Series I machine in a post office location. The olive-brown Machin and 2012 Christmas Robin designs were on sale at this post office. They differ from Wincor (Type II) versions through their code line, which consists of letters and numerals (Type III). Wincor-generated stamps have a code line entirely of numerals. Type III stamps also differ through their two service indicator lines which are printed much closer together (2.6 mm). See Nos. FS1b/FS3b, FS4b, FS5b, FS5eb, and FS51a/FS56a. The following year, in November/December 2013, the pop-up Christmas post shop evolved into a mobile version and went to several locations. It also had a Royal Mail Series I machine from which the 'new blue' (second class) Machin (Nos. FS93/FS94) and 2012 Christmas Robin designs were on sale.

Royal Mail Enquiry Offices: some Royal Mail enquiry offices had Royal Mail Series II machines installed from December 2014 through to October 2019. The machines dispensed stamps with a Type IIIA service indicator, and are given a full listing.

Unintentional use of large typeface: after upgrading machines to produce the smaller service indicator, some machines experienced software glitches resulting in the unintentional part reversion to the large typeface, or a semi corrupted version of it, and in some instances a mixture of both large and small on the same denomination. Machines at varying locations were affected and some went unchanged for several months, or were quickly amended and then simply reverted again. Such glitches seem to have continued on and off until December 2012 when all machines nationwide seemed to be functioning correctly.

There are two main types of part-reversion. The first type resulted in the 'Worldwide up to 10g' having the 'Up to 10g' in the larger typeface whilst 'Worldwide' was still in the smaller typeface (Fig. 1). At the same time and although still in the smaller typeface, the '1st Class', '1st Large' and 'Europe' were also affected by the glitch and had the service indicator lines positioned a little too far to the right. The 'Worldwide up to 20g' was similarly affected and results in the 'e' of Worldwide being printed on the pictorial design. Additionally, all five values show the (Type II) four-part code incorrectly spaced so that there is a large gap between the branch and machine number (see the four-part code on Fig. 1). The 'Worldwide up to 40g' had not been introduced at this point.

The second type of reversion is more significant and is of a complete return to the large typeface across the

five original denominations, but with the 'Worldwide Up to 10g' stamp having the second line, 'Up to 10g', completely missing (Fig. 2). Note that the glitch has caused the (Type I) four-part code to be compressed.

The problems continued after the introduction of the 'Worldwide up to 40g' which when affected by the glitch caused the 'Worldwide' to be in the large typeface and the 'up to 40g' in the small typeface (Fig. 3). This is the opposite of the 'Worldwide up to 10g' from the first type of reversion.

Such reversions are outside the scope of this catalogue, but are footnoted for the interest of collectors.

Figure 1

Figure 2

Figure 3

Incorrect design/service indicator combinations: following the introduction of 2nd Class units and stamps specifically designed for the use in them it was almost inevitable that 2nd Class designs would be found with 1st Class or International service indicators and vice-versa. These versions may have occurred because units were loaded by mistake with the wrong roll of designs. Sometimes a post office may have deemed it necessary to use an alternative design when the correct stock was not available. Irrespective of the reason for their existence, these stamps are outside the scope of this catalogue. However, for the interest of collectors, and where the provenance has been confirmed, some of them are footnoted.

Open value labels: In addition to Post & Go stamps, post offices' NCR machines dispense so-called 'Open Value' labels. Depending on the service purchased, these are generated either on non-stamp stock (a large self-adhesive label) or on the same pre-printed (Machin or pictorial) illustrated background stock as Post & Go stamps.

The labels have a thermally printed service indicator to specify the service selected, e.g. '1L' (1st Letter), '1LG' (1st Large Letter), '2SP' (2nd Small Parcel). Also printed on each label are the weight of the letter/parcel, the prevailing price of the service purchased, a VAT code and a four-part code.

Labels are generated by putting a single piece of mail onto the scales of the machine and selecting the destination and service. The labels are not designed to be taken away from the office, but are instead meant to be used straight away. With some services the process of generating the label automatically calls for the intervention of staff who apply the label and take the item away.

Such items are outside the scope of this catalogue. Note, however, that on 7 July 2014 Royal Mail released a special pack containing five 'Open Value' labels in the Machin Head design, as Types **FT1** and **FT14** (P&G 15) (Price £29).

Five Types of Post & Go service indicator, including subtypes of Types II and III:

FT1 (Type I)

Type I: As T **FT1**, with large, bold service indicator and four-part code consisting entirely of numerals (Wincor)

Type II

Type II: Smaller service indicator with lines 4 mm apart and code consisting entirely of numerals (Wincor)

Type IIA

Type IIA: Similar to Type II but with service indicator and code in changed typeface and ranged left with service indicator lines 3.3 mm apart and code consisting entirely of numerals (NCR)

Type III

Type III: Smaller service indicator with lines 2.6 mm apart and code consisting of letters and numerals (Royal Mail Series I).

Type IIIA

Type IIIA: As Type III, with the code being a mixture of letters and numerals and all wording ranged left. However, the top line of the service indicator is noticeably smaller and slightly further away from the second line, at 2.7 mm (Royal Mail Series II with revised typeface).

(Gravure Walsall, thermally printed service indicator)

2008 (8 Oct)–**20.** T **FT1.** Olive-brown background. Self-adhesive. Two phosphor bands. Multicoloured. Perf 14×14½.

FS1	(1st Class Up to 100g) (Type I)	9·00	9·00
	a. Type II (8.9.10)	3·25	3·25
	b. Type III (17.11.12)	10·50	10·50
	c. Type IIA (6.14)	6·50	6·50
	d. Type IIIA (3.6.15)	5·25	5·25
FS2	(1st Large Up to 100g) (Type I)	9·75	9·75
	a. Type II (8.9.10)	3·50	3·50
	b. Type III (17.11.12)	11·00	11·00
	c. Type IIA (6.14)	7·00	7·00
	d. Type IIIA (3.6.15)	5·50	5·50
FS3	(Europe Up to 20g)(Type I)	9·75	9·75
	a. Type II (8.9.10)	4·00	4·00
	b. Type III (17.11.12)	11·50	11·50
FS3c	(Euro 20g World 10g) (TIIA) (6.14)	7·00	7·00
	ca. Type II (20.10.14)	8·50	8·50
	cb. Type IIIA (3.6.15)	5·50	5·50
FS3d	(Europe up to 60g) (Type II) (31.3.14)	9·75	9·75
	dc. Type IIA (6.14)	8·50	8·50
FS3e	(Europe up to 100g) (Type IIA) (4.15)	9·75	9·75
	ea. Type IIIA (3.6.15)	8·50	8·50
FS3f	(Euro 100g World 20g) (Type IIA) (4.9.20)	13·00	13·00
FS4	(Worldwide Up to 10g) (Type I) (9.10.08)	11·00	11·00
	a. Type II (8.9.10)	6·00	6·00
	b. Type III (17.11.12)	11·50	11·50
FS5	(Worldwide Up to 20g) (Type I)	11·00	11·00
	a. Type II (8.9.10)	4·75	4·75
	b. Type III (17.11.12)	12·00	12·00
	c. Type IIA (6.14)	7·25	7·25
	d. Type IIIA (3.6.15)	6·00	6·00

FS5e	(Worldwide Up to 40g) (Type II) (13.10.11)	13·00	13·00
	eb. Type III (17.11.12)	14·00	14·00
FS5f	(Worldwide Up to 60g) (Type II) (31.3.14)	10·50	10·50
	fc. Type IIA (6.14)	9·25	9·25
FS5g	(Worldwide Up to 100g) (Type IIA) (4.15)	10·50	10·50
	ga. Type IIIA (3.6.15)	9·25	9·25
FS5h	(World 100g Zone 1-3) (Type IIA) (4.9.20)	14·00	14·00
FS5i	(World 100g Zone 2) (Type IIA) (4.9.20)	14·00	14·00
FS1/FS5 Set of 5 (Type I)		45·00	45·00
FS1a/FS3a, FS4a, FS5a, FS5e Set of 6 (Type II)		32·00	32·00
FS1b/FS3b, FS4b, FS5b, FS5eeb Set of 6 (Type III)		65·00	65·00
FS1c, FS2c, FS3c, FS3ddc, FS5c, FS5ffc Set of 6 (Type IIA)		42·00	42·00
FS1d, FS2d, FS3ccb, FS3fa, FS5d, FS5gga Set of 6 (Type IIIA)		35·00	35·00
Special Pack (As Nos. FS1/FS5 but service indicator and code lines in gravure) (Type I)		£100	

Although the very first Post & Go machines went live at the Galleries post office, Bristol, on 8 October 2008, one particular machine function had not been properly enabled and the Worldwide Up to 10g version was not available until 9 October.

The five stamps from the special pack and first day cover sold by the Philatelic Bureau, Edinburgh differ from machine-printed stamps in having the service indicator and branch code printed in gravure and have a narrow gap between the two lines of the service indicator. Also, they are easily identified through the code lines which are unique to the gravure printing: 020511 1-08445-01 (to -05).

Smaller service indicator versions similar to Type II were available from Hytech machines at Spring Stampex 2011. Subsequently, versions similar to Type II or Type III were available from exhibition machines, additionally with inscriptions. Details are provided in separate tables at the end of this section. Versions with various inscriptions have been available at the BPMA (now The Postal Museum) since December 2012.

Nos. FS1/FS5e are known printed unintentionally from Wincor machines with the typeface varieties resulting from software glitches causing a reversion to the large typeface; see notes to 'Unintentional use of large typeface'.

Nos. FS4a and FS5e were replaced on 31 March 2014 by Nos. FS3d and FS5f.

No. FS3a was replaced on 20 October 2014 by No. FS3cca.

Nos. FS3ddc and FS5ffc were replaced on in April 2015 by Nos. FS3e and FS5g.

No. FS3f was introduced on 1 September 2020 and replaced No. FS3e and FS5c. The substitution of two values by one was deliberate so as to accommodate FS5h.

Nos. FS5h and FS5i were introduced on 1 September 2020 to replace No. FS5g and to fill the space left by No. FS5c.

No. FS3c was available until 31 December 2020 (inclusive).

All Wincor machines, producing Type II stamps, were decommissioned before the 30 March 2015 tariff change.

T **FT1** (olive-brown) are known thermally printed with 2nd Class up to 100g and 2nd Large up to 100g, Type IIA, when put in a machine's second class unit. This may have occurred because it was mistakenly put in the wrong unit, or because standard second class (new blue Machin) T **FT14** stock were not available, and it was deemed necessary to use the other design instead.

No. FS3ccb exists with the 20g weight missing and is instead shown as Euro World 10g, and results from a software glitch. Only from Mount Pleasant Royal Mail enquiry office 29/31 March 2016.

For full details of Post & Go stamps dispensed from machines at locations other than post offices and post shops, please refer to the tables following these listings.

FT2 Blue Tit

(Des Robert Gillmor and Kate Stephens. Gravure Walsall, thermally printed service indicator).

2010 (17 Sept)–**14.** Birds of Britain (1st series). Garden Birds. Self-adhesive. Two phosphor bands. Multicoloured Perf 14×14½.

FS6	(1st Class up to 100g) (Type II)	6·50	6·50
FS7	(1st Large up to 100g) (Type II)	7·00	7·00
FS8	(Europe up to 20g) (Type II)	8·50	8·50
FS8a	(Europe up to 60g) (Type II) (5.14)	80·00	80·00
FS9	(Worldwide up to 10g) (Type II)	14·00	14·00
FS10	(Worldwide up to 20g) (Type II)	10·00	10·00
FS10a	(Worldwide up to 40g) (Type II) (2.12)	40·00	40·00
FS10b	(Worldwide up to 60g) (Type II) (5.14)	80·00	80·00
FS6/FS8, FS9, FS10 Set of 5 (Type I)		40·00	40·00
First Day Cover (No. FS6 in 6 designs)			20·00
Special Pack (No. FS6 in sheet*let of* 6 gravure designs) (Type II)			20·00

Nos. FS6/FS10b were each available in six different designs: T **FT2**, Goldfinch, Wood Pigeon, Robin, House Sparrow and Starling.

Nos. FS6/FS10 were available from Post & Go terminals, initially in 30 post offices.

Nos. FS6/FS10 are known printed unintentionally from Wincor machines with both typeface varieties resulting from software glitches causing a reversion to the large typeface; see notes to 'Unintentional use of large typeface'.

Nos. FS8a, 10a, 10b resulted from the late use of old stock.

FT3 Blackbird

(Des Robert Gillmor and Kate Stephens. Gravure Walsall, thermally printed service indicator)

2011 (24 Jan)–**14**. Birds of Britain (2nd series). Garden Birds. Self-adhesive. Two phosphor bands. Multicoloured Perf 14×14½.

FS11	(1st class up to 100g) (Type II)	3·50	3·50
FS12	(1st Large up to 100g) (Type II)	3·75	3·75
FS13	(Europe up to 20g) (Type II)	4·25	4·25
FS13a	(Europe up to 60g) (Type II) (4.14)	20·00	20·00
FS14	(Worldwide up to 10g) (Type II)	8·50	8·50
FS15	(Worldwide up to 20g) (Type II)	4·25	4·25
FS15a	(Worldwide up to 40g) (Type II) (12.11)	20·00	20·00
FS15b	(Worldwide up to 60g) (Type II) (4.14)	20·00	20·00
FS11/FS13, FS14, FS15 Set of 5 (Type II)		20·00	20·00
First Day Cover (No. FS11 in 6 designs)			20·00
Special Pack (No. FS11 in sheetlet of 6 gravure designs)			
(Type II)		35·00	

Nos. FS11/FS15b were each available in six different designs: T **FT3**, two Magpies, Long-tailed Tit, Chaffinch, Collared Dove and Greenfinch.

Nos. FS11/FS15a are known printed unintentionally from Wincor machines with the first type of software glitch causing a part reversion to the large typeface on Up to 10g. The issue is also known printed with the large typeface because a roll was supplied to an office yet to have its machine upgraded for the smaller service indicator. See notes to 'Unintentional use of large typeface'.

Nos. FS13a, FS15a, FS15b resulted from the late use of old stock.

FT4 Mallard

(Des Robert Gillmor and Kate Stephens. Gravure Walsall, thermally printed service indicator)

2011 (19 May)–**14**. Birds of Britain (3rd series). Water Birds. Self-adhesive. Two phosphor bands. Multicoloured. Perf 14×14½.

FS16	(1st Class up to 100g) (Type II)	2·50	2·50
FS17	(1st Large up to 100g) (Type II)	3·00	3·00
FS18	(Europe up to 20g) (Type II)	3·50	3·50
FS18a	(Europe up to 60g) (Type II) (4.14)	27·00	27·00
FS19	(Worldwide up to 10g) (Type II)	5·00	5·00
FS20	(Worldwide up to 20g) (Type II)	4·00	4·00
FS20a	(Worldwide up to 40g) (Type II) (12.11)	10·00	10·00
FS20b	(Worldwide up to 60g) (Type II) (4.14)	27·00	27·00
FS16/FS18, FS19, FS20 Set of 5 (Type II)		15·00	15·00
First Day Cover (No. FS16 in 6 designs)			8·75
Special Pack (No. FS16 in sheetlet of 6 gravure designs)			
(Type II)		8·00	

Nos. FS16/FS20b were each available in six different designs: T **FT4**, Greylag Goose, Kingfisher, Moorhen, Mute Swan and Great Crested Grebe.

Nos. FS16/FS20 are known printed unintentionally from Wincor machines with both typeface varieties resulting from software glitches causing a reversion to the large typeface; see notes to 'Unintentional use of large typeface'.

Nos. FS18a, FS20a and FS20b resulted from the late use of old stock.

FT5 Puffin

(Des Robert Gillmor and Kate Stephens. Gravure Walsall, thermally printed service indicator)

2011 (16 Sept)–**14**. Birds of Britain (4th series). Sea Birds. Self-adhesive. Two phosphor bands. Multicoloured. Perf 14×14½.

FS21	(1st class up to 100g) (Type II)	2·25	2·25
FS22	(1st Large up to 100g) (Type II)	2·75	2·75
FS23	(Europe up to 20g) (Type II)	3·25	3·25
FS23a	(Europe up to 60g) (Type II) (31.3.14)	8·00	8·00
FS24	(Worldwide up to 10g) (Type II)	4·75	4·75
FS25	(Worldwide up to 20g) (Type II)	3·75	3·75
FS26	(Worldwide up to 40g) (Type II)	7·50	7·50
FS26a	(Worldwide up to 60g) (Type II)		
	(31.3.14)	8·50	8·50
FS21/FS23, FS24/FS26 Set of 6 (Type II)		20·00	20·00
First Day Cover (No. FS21 in 6 designs)			7·25
Special Pack (No. FS21 in sheetlet of 6 gravure designs)			
(Type II)		9·00	

Nos. FS21/FS26a were each available in six different designs: T **FT5**, Gannet, Oystercatcher, Ringed Plover, Cormorant and Arctic Tern.

Nos. FS21/FS25 are known printed unintentionally from Wincor machines with both typeface varieties resulting from software glitches causing a reversion to the large typeface. Additionally No. FS26 is known with the second type mixing both sizes of typeface; see notes to 'Unintentional use of large typeface'.

Nos. FS23a and FS26a resulted from the late use of old stock.

FT6 Welsh Mountain Badger Face

(Des Robert Gillmor and Kate Stephens. Gravure Walsall, thermally printed service indicator)

2012 (24 Feb)–**14**. British Farm Animals (1st series). Sheep. Self-adhesive. Two phosphor bands. Multicoloured Perf 14×14½.

FS27	(1st Class up to 100g) (Type II)	2·75	2·75
FS28	(1st Large up to 100g) (Type II)	3·25	3·25
FS29	(Europe up to 20g) (Type II)	3·25	3·25
FS29a	(Euro 20g World 10g) (Type II) (10.14)	10·00	10·00
FS29b	(Europe up to 60g) (Type II) (31.3.14)	12·00	12·00
FS30	(Worldwide up to 10g) (Type II)	5·25	5·25
FS31	(Worldwide up to 20g) (Type II)	4·00	4·00
FS32	(Worldwide up to 40g) (Type II)	5·75	5·75
FS32b	(Worldwide up to 60g) (Type II)		
	(31.3.14)	13·00	13·00
FS27/FS29, FS30/FS32 Set of 6 (Type II)		22·00	22·00
First Day Cover (No. FS27 in 6 designs)			8·75
Special Pack (P&G 6) (No. FS27 in strip of 6 designs)			
(Type II)		8·00	

Nos. FS27/FS32b were each available in six different designs: T **FT6**, Dalesbred, Jacob, Suffolk, Soay, Leicester Longwool.

Nos. FS27/FS32 are known printed unintentionally from Wincor machines with the second typeface variety resulting from software glitches causing a reversion to the large typeface; see notes to 'Unintentional use of large typeface'.

Nos. FS29a, FS29b and FS32b resulted from the late use of old stock.

FT7 Berkshire

(Des Robert Gillmor and Kate Stephens. Gravure Walsall, thermally printed service indicator)

2012 (24 Apr)–**14**. British Farm Animals (2nd series). Pigs. Multicoloured. Self-adhesive. Two phosphor bands. Multicoloured. Perf 14×14½.

FS33	(1st class up to 100g) (Type II)	2·75	2·75
FS34	(1st Large up to 100g) (Type II)	3·25	3·25
FS35	(Europe up to 20g) (Type II)	3·25	3·25
FS35a	(Euro 20g World 10g) (Type II) (10.14)	8·75	8·75
FS35b	(Europe up to 60g) (Type II) (31.3.14)	13·00	13·00
FS36	(Worldwide up to 10g) (Type II)	5·25	5·25
FS37	(Worldwide up to 20g) (Type II)	4·00	4·00
FS38	(Worldwide up to 40g) (Type II)	5·75	5·75
FS38b	(Worldwide up to 60g) (Type II)		
	(31.3.14)	13·00	13·00
FS33/FS35, FS36/FS38 Set of 6 (Type II)		22·00	22·00
First Day Cover (No. FS33 in 6 designs)			8·50
Special Pack (P&G 7) (No. FS33 in strip of 6 designs)			
(Type II)		8·00	

Nos. FS33/FS38b were each available in six different designs: T **FT7**, Gloucestershire Old Spots, Oxford Sandy and Black, Welsh, Tamworth, British Saddleback.

Nos. FS33/FS38 are known in Type III and come from Post & Go machines used at exhibitions. Details are provided in separate tables at the end of this section.

Nos. FS33/FS38 are known printed unintentionally from Wincor machines with the second typeface variety resulting from software glitches causing a reversion to the large typeface; see notes to 'Unintentional use of large typeface'.

Nos. FS35a, FS35b and FS38b resulted from the late use of old stock.

FT8 Union Flag

(Des Anton Morris and Dick Davies. Gravure Walsall, thermally printed service indicator)

2012 (21 May)–**20**. Union Flag T **FT8**. Self-adhesive. Two phosphor bands. Multicoloured Perf 14×14½.

FS39	(1st Class up to 100g) (Type II)	2·75	2·75
	a. Type IIA	3·00	3·00
FS40	(1st Large up to 100g) (Type II)	3·25	3·25
	a. Type IIA	3·25	3·25
FS41	(Europe up to 20g) (Type II)	3·50	3·50
FS41a	(Euro 20g World 10g) (Type IIA) (7.14)	3·50	3·50
	ab. Type II (10.14)	9·00	9·00
FS41b	(Europe up to 60g) (Type II) (31.3.14)	9·75	9·75
	ba. Type IIA (7.14)	11·50	11·50
FS41c	(Europe up to 100g) (Type IIA) (30.3.15)	9·50	9·50
FS41d	(Euro 100g World 20g) (Type IIA) (9.20)	13·00	13·00
FS42	(Worldwide up to 10g) (Type II)	5·25	5·25
FS43	(Worldwide up to 20g) (Type II)	4·50	4·50
	a. Type IIA (7.14)	4·50	4·50
FS44	(Worldwide up to 40g) (Type II)	6·00	6·00
FS44b	(Worldwide up to 60g) (Type II) (31.3.14)	10·50	10·50
	ba. Type IIA (7.14)	12·50	12·50
FS44c	(Worldwide up to 100g) (Type IIA) (30.3.15)	10·50	10·50
FS44d	(World 100g zone 1-3) (Type IIA) (9.20)	27·00	27·00
FS44e	(World 100g zone 2) (Type IIA) (9.20)	35·00	35·00
FS39/FS41, FS42/FS44 Set of 6 (Type II)		23·00	23·00
FS39a, FS40a, FS41a, FS41bba, FS43a, FS44bba Set of 6 (Type IIA)		35·00	35·00
First Day Cover (No. FS39 only)			2·50
Special Pack (P&G 8) (No. FS39 only) (Type IIA)		3·00	

When first printed the Special Pack stamps had the upper service indicator line, 1st Class, in a slightly larger typeface and ranged left with the code line, and are therefore a Type II sub-type (Price £3·50). A reprint of the Special Packs has stamps in a smaller typeface, with all lines ranged left, and are therefore similar to Type IIA.

Nos. FS39/FS44 are known printed unintentionally from Wincor machines with the second typeface variety resulting from software glitches causing a reversion to the large typeface; see notes to 'Unintentional use of large typeface'.

T **FT8** is known thermally printed with 2nd Class up to 100g and 2nd Large up to 100g, Type IIA, when put in a machine's second class unit. This may have occurred because it was mistakenly put in the wrong unit, or because standard second class (new blue Machin) T **FT14** stock were not available, and it was deemed necessary to use the other design instead.

All Wincor machines, producing Type II stamps, were decommissioned before the 30 March 2015 tariff change.

FT9 Irish Moiled

(Des Robert Gillmor and Kate Stephens. Gravure Walsall, thermally printed service indicator)

2012 (28 Sept)–**14**. British Farm Animals (3rd series). Cattle. Self-adhesive. Two phosphor bands. Multicoloured Perf 14×14½.

FS45	(1st Class up to 100g) (Type II)	4·00	4·00
FS46	(1st Large up to 100g) (Type II)	4·75	4·75
FS47	(Europe up to 20g) (Type II)	5·00	5·00
FS47a	(Euro 20g World 10g) (Type II) (10.14)	10·00	10·00
FS47b	(Europe up to 60g) (Type II) (31.3.14)	12·00	12·00
FS48	(Worldwide up to 10g) (Type II)	6·00	6·00
FS49	(Worldwide up to 20g) (Type II)	5·25	5·25

FS50	(Worldwide up to 40g) (Type II)	7·00	7·00
FS50b	(Worldwide up to 60g) (Type II) (31.3.14)	13·00	13·00
FS45/FS47, FS48/FS50 Set of 6 (Type II)		29·00	29·00
First Day Cover (No. FS45 in 6 designs) (Type III)			8·50
Special Pack (P&G 9) (No. FS45 in strip of 6 designs) (Type III)		8·00	

Nos. FS45/FS50b were each available in six different designs: T **FT9**, Welsh Black, Highland, White Park, Red Poll, Aberdeen Angus.

Nos. FS45/FS50 are known in Type III and come from Post & Go machines used at exhibitions. Details are provided in separate tables at the end of this section.

Nos. FS45/FS50 are known printed unintentionally from Wincor machines with the second typeface variety resulting from software glitches causing a reversion to the large typeface; see notes to 'Unintentional use of large typeface'.

Nos. FS47a, FS47b and FS50b resulted from the late use of old stock.

FT10 Robin

(Des Robert Gillmor and Kate Stephens. Gravure Walsall, thermally printed service indicator)

2012 (6 Nov)–**15**. Christmas Robin with year code in background. T **FT10**. Self-adhesive. Two phosphor bands. Multicoloured Perf 14×14½.

FS51	(1st Class up to 100g) (Type II)	2·75	2·75
	a. Type III (17.11.12)	4·25	4·25
	b. Type IIA (7.14)	4·50	4·50
FS52	(1st Large up to 100g) (Type II)	3·25	3·25
	a. Type III (17.11.12)	4·75	4·75
	b. Type IIA (7.14)	5·00	5·00
FS53	(Europe up to 20g) (Type II)	3·50	3·50
	a. Type III (17.11.12)	5·25	5·25
FS53c	(Euro 20g World 10g) (Type IIA) (7.14)	5·00	5·00
	ca. Type II (20.10.14)	9·00	9·00
FS53d	(Europe up to 60g) (Type II) (4.14)	10·00	10·00
	da. Type IIA (7.14)	9·00	9·00
FS53e	(Europe up to 100g) (Type IIA) (4.15)	13·00	13·00
FS54	(Worldwide up to 10g) (Type II)	4·00	4·00
	a. Type III (17.11.12)	5·25	5·25
FS55	(Worldwide up to 20g) (Type II)	4·50	4·50
	a. Type III (17.11.12)	5·50	5·50
	b. Type IIA (7.14)	5·25	5·25
FS56	(Worldwide up to 40g) (Type II)	5·75	5·75
	a. Type III (17.11.12)	6·50	6·50
FS56d	(Worldwide up to 60g) (Type II) (4.14)	11·00	11·00
	da. Type IIA (7.14)	9·75	9·75
FS56e	(Worldwide up to 100g) (Type IIA) (4.15)	14·00	14·00
FS51/FS53, FS54/FS56 Set of 6 (Type II)		22·00	22·00
FS51a/FS56a Set of 6 (Type III)		29·00	29·00
FS51b, FS52b, FS53c, FS53dda, FS55b, FS56dda Set of 6 (Type IIA)		35·00	35·00

Nos. FS51/FS56 are known printed unintentionally from Wincor machines with the second typeface variety resulting from software glitches causing a reversion to the large typeface; see notes to 'Unintentional use of large typeface'.

Nos. FS51/FS56, FS53cca, FS53d and FS56d exist with both MA12 and MA13 year codes (Type II).

Nos. FS51a/FS56a exist with both MA12 and MA13 year codes (Type III).

Nos. FS51b, FS52b, FS53c, FS53dda, FS53e, FS55b, FS56dda and FS56e exist with both MA12 and MA13 year codes (Type IIA).

Nos. FS53c, FS53d, FS56d resulted from the late use of old stock.

T **FT10** with year code MA12 and MA13 are known thermally printed with 2nd Class up to 100g and 2nd Large up to 100g, Type IIA, when put in a machine's second class unit. This may have occurred because it was mistakenly put in the wrong unit, or because standard second class (new blue Machin) T **FT14** stock was temporarily unavailable and it was deemed necessary to use alternative stock.

All Wincor machines, producing Type II stamps, were decommissioned before the 30 March 2015 tariff change.

T **FT10** was not made available in a Special Pack and was only available from Post & Go machines.

Nos. FS57 and FS58 are vacant.

FT11 Lesser Silver Water Beetle

(Des Kate Stephens. Illustrations by Chris Wormell. Gravure Walsall, thermally printed service indicator)

2013 (22 Feb)–**19**. Freshwater Life (1st series). Ponds. Self-adhesive. Two phosphor bands. Multicoloured Perf 14×14½.

FS59	(1st Class up to 100g) (Type II)..............	2·25	2·25
	a. Type IIA (5.19).............................	4·75	3·75
FS60	(1st Large up to 100g) (Type II)..............	2·50	2·50
	a. Type IIA (5.19).............................	5·25	4·25
FS61	(Europe up to 20g) (Type II)...................	4·00	4·00
FS61a	(Euro 20g World 10g) (Type II) (10.14)...	7·50	7·50
	ab. Type IIA (5.19)............................	7·50	7·50
FS61b	(Europe up to 60g) (Type II) (4.14)..........	9·00	9·00
FS61c	(Europe up to 100g) (Type IIA) (5.19).....	30·00	30·00
FS62	(Worldwide up to 10g) (Type II)............	4·00	4·00
FS63	(Worldwide up to 20g) (Type II)............	4·00	4·00
	a. Type IIA (5.19).............................	6·00	4·75
FS64	(Worldwide up to 40g) (Type II)............	5·00	5·00
FS64b	(Worldwide up to 60g) (Type II) (4.14)...	9·50	9·50
FS64c	(Worldwide up to 100g) (Type IIA) (5.19)...	30·00	30·00
FS59/FS61, FS62/FS64 *Set of* 6 (Type II).............................		20·00	20·00
FS59a/FS60a, FS61aab, FS61c, FS63a, FS64c *Set of* 6 (Type IIA)..		70·00	70·00
First Day Cover (No. FS59 in 6 designs) (Type III)...............			9·50
Special Pack (P&G 11) (No. FS59 in strip of 6 designs) (Type III)..		8·00	

Nos. FS59/FS64c were each available in six different designs: T **FT11**, Three-spined Stickleback, Smooth Newt, Fairy Shrimp, Emperor Dragonfly and Glutinous Snail.

Nos. FS59/FS64 are known in Type III and come from Post & Go machines used at exhibitions. Details are provided in separate tables at the end of this section.

Nos. FS59a/FS60a, FS61aab, FS61c, FS63a, and FS64c resulted from the late use of old stock.

Nos. FS61a, FS61b, FS64b and FS64c resulted from the late use of old stock.

FT12 Perch

(Des Kate Stephens. Illustrations by Chris Wormell. Gravure Walsall, thermally printed service indicator)

2013 (25 June)–**19**. Freshwater Life (2nd series). Lakes. Self-adhesive. Two phosphor bands. Multicoloured. Perf 14×14½.

FS65	(1st Class up to 100g) (Type II)..............	2·75	2·75
	a. Type IIA (5.19).............................	3·50	3·50
FS66	(1st Large up to 100g) (Type II)..............	3·25	3·25
	a. Type IIA (5.19).............................	4·00	4·00
FS67	(Europe up to 20g) (Type II)...................	4·25	4·25
FS67a	(Euro 20g World 10g) (Type II) (10.14)...	6·50	6·50
	ab. Type IIA (5.19)............................	6·50	6·50
FS67b	(Europe up to 60g) (Type II) (31.3.14)......	8·25	8·25
FS67c	(Europe up to 100g) (Type IIA) (5.19).....	24·00	24·00
FS68	(Worldwide up to 10g) (Type II)............	4·25	4·25
FS69	(Worldwide up to 20g) (Type II)............	4·25	£425
	a. Type IIA (5.19).............................	4·50	4·50
FS70	(Worldwide up to 40g) (Type II)............	5·25	5·25
FS70b	(Worldwide up to 60g) (Type II) (31.3.14)...	8·75	8·75
FS70c	(Worldwide up to 100g) (Type IIA) (5.19)...	24·00	24·00
FS65/FS67, FS68/FS70 *Set of* 6 (Type II).............................		21·00	21·00
FS65a/FS66a, FS67aab, FS67c, FS69a, FS70c *Set of* 6 (Type IIA)..		55·00	55·00
First Day Cover (No. FS65 in 6 designs) (Type III)...............			9·50
Special Pack (P&G 12) (No. FS65 in strip of 6 designs) (Type III)..		8·00	

Nos. FS65/FS70c were each available in six different designs: T **FT12**, European Eel, Crucian Carp, Caddis Fly Larva, Arctic Char and Common Toad.

Nos. FS65/FS70 are known in Type III and come from Post & Go machines used at exhibitions. Details are provided in separate tables at the end of this section.

Nos. FS65a/FS66a, FS67aab, FS67c, FS69a, and FS70c resulted from the late use of old stock.

Nos. FS67a, FS67b, and FS70b resulted from the late use of old stock.

FT13 Minnow

(Des Kate Stephens. Illustrations by Chris Wormell. Gravure Walsall, thermally printed service indicator)

2013 (20 Sept)–**19**. Freshwater Life (3rd series). Rivers. Self-adhesive. Two phosphor bands. Multicoloured. Perf 14×14½.

FS71	(1st Class up to 100g) (Type II)..............	2·25	2·25
	a. Type IIA (5.19).............................	3·50	3·50
FS72	(1st Large up to 100g) (Type II)..............	2·50	2·50
	a. Type IIA (5.19).............................	4·00	4·00
FS73	(Europe up to 20g) (Type II)...................	4·00	4·00
FS73a	(Euro 20g World 10g) (Type II) (10.14)...	10·00	10·00
	ab. Type IIA (5.19)............................	6·50	6·50
FS73b	(Europe up to 60g) (Type II) (31.3.14)......	7·50	7·50
FS73c	(Europe up to 100g) (Type IIA) (5.19).....	24·00	24·00
FS74	(Worldwide up to 10g) (Type II)............	4·00	4·00
FS75	(Worldwide up to 20g) (Type II)............	4·00	4·00
	a. Type IIA (5.19).............................	4·50	4·50
FS76	(Worldwide up to 40g) (Type II)............	5·00	5·00
FS76b	(Worldwide up to 60g) (Type II) (31.3.14)...	8·00	8·00
FS76c	(Worldwide up to 100g) (Type IIA) (5.19)...	24·00	24·00
FS71/FS73, FS74/FS76 *Set of* 6 (Type II).............................		20·00	20·00
FS71a/FS72a, FS73aab, FS73c, FS75a, FS76c *Set of* 6 (Type IIA)..		55·00	55·00
First Day Cover (No. FS71 in 6 designs) (Type III)...............			9·50
Special Pack (P&G 13) (No. FS71 in strip of 6 designs) (Type III)..		9·00	

Nos. FS71/FS76c were each available in six different designs: T **FT13**, Atlantic Salmon, White-clawed Crayfish, River Lamprey, Blue-winged Olive Mayfly Larva, Brown Trout.

Nos. FS71/FS76 are known in Type III and come from Post & Go machines used at exhibitions. Details are provided in separate tables at the end of this section.

Nos. FS71a/FS72a, FS73aab, FS73c, FS75a, FS76b and FS76c resulted from the late use of old stock.

No. FS73a resulted from the late use of old stock.

(Gravure Walsall, thermally printed service indicator)

2013 (19 Nov)–**21**. T **FT1** with year code in background. Olive-brown background. Self-adhesive. Two phosphor bands. Perf 14×14½.

FS77	(1st Class up to 100g) (Type II)..............	3·50	3·50
	a. Type IIA (28.2.14)...........................	2·25	2·25
	b. Type IIIA (30.3.15)..........................	3·50	3·50
FS78	(1st Large up to 100g) (Type II)..............	3·75	3·75
	a. Type IIA (28.2.14)...........................	3·00	3·00
	b. Type IIIA (30.3.15)..........................	4·00	4·00
FS79	(Europe up to 20g) (Type II)...................	5·50	5·50
	a. Type IIA (28.2.14)...........................	8·00	8·00
FS79b	(Euro 20g World 10g) (Type II) (20.10.14)..	8·00	8·00
	ba. Type IIIA (5.6.14)..........................	3·75	3·75
	bb. Type IIIA (30.3.15)........................	4·25	4·25
FS80	(Europe up to 60g) (Type II) (31.3.14)......	6·50	6·50
	a. Type IIA (1.4.14)............................	6·00	6·00
FS80c	(Europe up to 100g) (Type IIA) (30.3.15)..	4·00	4·00
	ca. Type IIIA (30.3.15)........................	5·50	5·50
FS80d	(Euro 100g World 20g) (Type IIA) (1.9.20)...	3·75	3·75
FS80e	(Europe Large 100g) (Type IIA) (2.1.21)...	9·50	9·50
FS81	(Worldwide up to 10g) (Type II)............	—	—
	a. Type IIA (28.2.14)...........................	—	—
FS82	(Worldwide up to 20g) (Type II)............	5·00	5·00
	a. Type IIA (28.2.14)...........................	3·75	3·75
	b. Type IIIA (30.3.15)..........................	4·75	4·75
FS83	(Worldwide up to 40g) (Type II)............	—	—
	a. Type IIA (28.2.14)...........................	—	—
FS84	(Worldwide up to 60g) (Type II) (31.3.14)..	7·50	7·50
	a. Type IIA (1.4.14)............................	7·00	7·00
FS84c	(Worldwide up to 100g) (Type IIA) (30.3.15)..	4·75	4·75
	ca. Type IIIA (30.3.15)........................	6·75	6·75
FS84d	(World 100g zone 1 & 3) (Type IIA) (1.9.20)...	9·75	9·75
FS84e	(World 100g zone 2) (Type IIA) (1.9.20)...	9·75	9·75
FS84f	(Worldwide Large 100g) (Type IIA) (2.1.21)...	10·50	10·50
FS77/FS80, FS82, FS84 *Set of* 6 (Type II).............................		20·00	20·00

FS77a, FS78a, FS79ba, FS80c, FS82a, FS84c Set of 6
(Type IIA).. 20·00   20·00
FS77b, FS78b, FS79bbb, FS80cca, FS82b, FS84cca Set of
6 (Type IIIA)... 25·00   25·00

From FS77 onwards all Post & Go stamps incorporate a year code unless otherwise stated.

Year codes in the format of MA** are positioned to the left of the front of the Queen's forehead. Year codes in the format of R**Y are positioned further to the left of the design, approximately half way between the left edge of the stamp and the Queen's nose.

> For full details of the different year codes, the values, the types and periods of use associated with these issues, please refer to the separate table at the end of this section.

Nos. FS81 and FS83 were replaced on 31 March 2014 by Nos. FS80 and FS84.

Nos. FS81a and FS83a were replaced on 1 April 2014 by Nos. FS80a and FS84a.

No. FS79a was replaced on 5 June 2014 by No. FS79bba.

No. FS79 was replaced on 20 October 2014 by No. FS79b.

Nos. FS80a and FS84a were replaced on 30 March 2015 by Nos. FS80c and FS84c.

No. FS80d was introduced on 1 September 2020 and replaced Nos. FS80c and FS82a. The substitution of the two values by one was deliberate so as to accommodate FS84d.

Nos. FS84d and FS84e were introduced on 1 September 2020 to replace No. FS84a and to fill the space left by No. FS82a.

No. FS79bba was available until 31 December 2020 (inclusive).

No. FS80c was reinstated on 1 January 2021, filling the space left by No. FS79bba.

Nos. FS80e and FS84f were introduced on 1 January 2021 to replace Nos. FS84d and FS84e.

All Wincor machines, producing Type II stamps, were decommissioned before the 30 March 2015 tariff change.

T **FT1** (olive-brown) with year code MA13, MA14, MA15, MA16, R17Y and R18Y are known thermally printed with 2nd Class up to 100g and 2nd Large up to 100g, Type IIA, when put in a machine's second class unit. Similarly, T **FT1** MA15, Type IIIA are known from Kingston enquiry office. This may have occurred because it was mistakenly put in the wrong unit, or because standard second class (new blue Machin) T **FT14** stock was temporarily unavailable and it was deemed necessary to use alternative stock.

No. FS79bbb exists with the 20g weight missing and is instead shown as Euro World 10g, and results from a software glitch. Only from Bradford Royal Mail enquiry office 29/31 March 2016.

T **FT1** (olive-brown) with year code was not made available in a Special Pack and is only available from Post & Go machines.

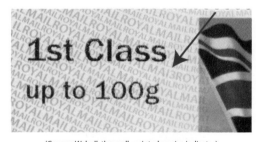

(Gravure Walsall, thermally printed service indicator)
2013 (17 Nov)–**16**. Union Flag T **FT8** with year code in background. Multicoloured. Self-adhesive. Two phosphor bands. Perf 14×14½.

FS85	(1st Class up to 100g) (Type II)................	—	—
	a. Type IIA (10.8.16).....................................	4·00	4·00
FS86	(1st Large up to 100g) (Type II).............	—	—
	a. Type IIA (10.8.16).....................................	4·25	4·25
FS87	(Europe up to 20g) (Type II).....................	—	—
FS87a	(Euro 20g World 10g) (Type IIA)		
	(10.8.16)..	4·50	4·50
FS88	(Europe up to 60g) (Type II) (31.3.14).....	20·00	20·00
FS88a	(Europe up to 100g) (Type IIA)		
	(10.8.16)..	5·50	5·50
FS89	(Worldwide up to 10g) (Type II).............	—	—
FS90	(Worldwide up to 20g) (Type II)		
	a. Type IIA (10.8.16).....................................	4·75	4·75
FS91	(Worldwide up to 40g) (Type II).............	—	—
FS92	(Worldwide up to 60g) (Type II)		
	(31.3.14)..	21·00	21·00
FS92a	(Worldwide up to 100g) (Type IIA)		
	(10.8.16)..	6·75	6·75
FS85/FS87, FS89/FS91 Set of 6 (Type II)..........................		—	—
FS85a, FS86a, FS87a, FS88a, FS90a, FS92a Set of 6			
(Type IIA)..		27·00	27·00

Nos. FS85/FS92a are MA13.

Nos. FS85, FS86, FS87, and FS90 are known from the Ludgate Circus post office in late 2013, and from Harrogate and Dorchester post offices following the 31 March 2014 tariff change.

Nos. FS89 and FS91 are only known from Ludgate Circus post office in late 2013.

(Worldwide up to 10g) and (Worldwide up to 40g) were replaced on 31 March 2014 by (Europe up to 60g) and (Worldwide up to 60g).

All Wincor machines, producing Type II stamps, were decommissioned before the 30 March 2015 tariff change.

T **FT8** with year code in background is known thermally printed with 2nd Class up to 100g and 2nd Large up to 100g, Type IIA, when put in a machine's second class unit. This may have occurred because it was mistakenly put in the wrong unit, or because standard second class (new blue Machin) T **FT14** stock was temporarily unavailable and it was deemed necessary to use alternative stock.

FT8 with year code was not made available in a Special Pack and was only available from Post & Go machines.

FT14

(Gravure Walsall, thermally printed service indicator)
2013 (20 Nov)–**15**. T **FT14** with background text reading 'ROYALMAIL' in alternate lines of large and small lettering with year code in background. New blue background. Self-adhesive. One phosphor band (over the Queen's head). Perf 14×14½.

FS93	(2nd Class up to 100g) (Type III).............	3·50	3·50
	a. Type IIA (2.14)...	2·50	2·50
	b. Type IIIA (30.3.15)....................................	3·50	3·50
FS94	(2nd Large up to 100g) (Type III).............	4·00	4·00
	a. Type IIA (2.14)...	2·75	2·75
	b. Type IIIA (30.3.15)....................................	3·75	3·75
Special Pack (P&G 10) (As Nos. FS93/FS94 but weight			
line inset at left) (Type III)		10·00	

Post & Go stamps as T **FT14** were issued by the Philatelic Bureau, Edinburgh on 20 February 2013 in packs and on first day covers (price £7·00 per pack and £3·00 on first day cover). They were sold from Royal Mail Series I machines at Spring Stampex 2013 but were not made available through post offices until November 2013.

Nos. FS93/FS94 exist MA12 from Special Pack and Spring Stampex 2013, and MA12/MA13 from Christmas post shop.

Nos. FS93a/FS94a exist MA12, MA13, MA14 and MA15 (Type IIA)

Nos. FS93b/FS94b are MA12 and MA15 (Type IIIA).

T **FT14** with year code MA12 is known thermally printed with 1st Class up to 100g, 1st Class Large up to 100g, Euro 20g World 10g, Europe up to 60g, Worldwide up to 20g and Worldwide up to 60g, Type IIA, when mistakenly put in machine's first class unit.

T **FT14** with year code MA14 and MA15 are known thermally printed with 1st Class up to 100g, 1st Class Large up to 100g, Euro 20g World 10g, Europe up to 100g, Worldwide up to 20g and Worldwide up to 100g, Type IIA, when mistakenly put in machine's first class unit.

For the 2nd Class Machin design with the background text reading '2ndCLASS' in large lettering, alternating with 'ROYALMAIL' in small lettering, see Nos. FS157/FS158.

FT15 Primrose

(Des Kate Stephens. Illustrations by Julia Trickey. Gravure ISP Walsall, thermally printed service indicator)
2014 (19 Feb)–**15**. British Flora (1st series). Spring Blooms. Self-adhesive. Two phosphor bands. Multicoloured. Perf 14×14½.

FS95	(1st Class up to 100g) (Type II).............	4·50	4·50
	a. Type IIA (5.14)...	4·50	4·50
FS96	(1st Large up to 100g) (Type II).............	5·25	5·25
	a. Type IIA (5.14)...	5·25	5·25
FS97	(Europe up to 20g) (Type II).....................	5·50	5·50
	a. Type IIA (5.14)...	15·00	15·00
FS97b	(Euro 20g World 10g) (Type IIA)		
	(5.6.14)..	6·00	6·00
	ba. Type II (10.14)...	8·50	8·50
FS98	(Europe up to 60g) (Type II) (31.3.14)....	10·00	10·00
	a. Type IIA (5.14)...	7·50	7·50
FS98b	(Europe up to 100g) (Type IIA)		
	(30.3.15)...	11·50	11·50
FS99	(Worldwide up to 10g) (Type II).............	6·50	6·50
FS100	(Worldwide up to 20g) (Type II).............	5·75	5·75
	a. Type IIA (5.14)...	5·75	5·75
FS101	(Worldwide up to 40g) (Type II).............	7·50	7·50

FS102   (Worldwide up to 60g) (Type II)

                (31.3.14) .... 11·00   11·00

          a. Type IIA (5.14) .... 8·50   8·50

FS102*b*   (Worldwide up to 100g) (Type IIA)

                (30.3.15) .... 12·50   12·50

FS95/FS97 and FS99/FS101 *Set of* 6 (Type II).................... 32·00   32·00

FS95a, FS96a, FS97*b*, FS98a, FS100a, FS102a *Set of* 6

(Type IIA) .... 35·00   35·00

First Day Cover (No. FS95 in 6 designs) (Type III)................   9·50

Special Pack (P&G 14) (No. FS95 in strip of 6 designs)

(Type III) .... 8·00

Nos. FS95/FS102*b* were each available in six different designs: T **FT15**, Snowdrop, Lesser Celandine, Dog Violet, Wild Daffodil, Blackthorn.

Nos. FS95/FS102*b* have year code MA14.

There was a late reprint of the Special Packs containing Type IIIA stamps (*Price* £20).

Nos. FS95/FS97, FS99/FS101 are known in Type III and come from Post & Go machines used at exhibitions. Details are provided in separate tables at the end of this section.

No. FS97a was replaced on 5 June 2014 by No. FS97*b*.

Nos. FS98*b* and FS102*b* resulted from the late use of old stock.

All Wincor machines, producing Type II stamps, were decommissioned before the 30 March 2015 tariff change.

FT16 Forget-me-not

(Des Kate Stephens. Illustrations by Julia Trickey. Gravure ISP Walsall, thermally printed service indicator)

2014 (17 Sept)–**21**. British Flora (2nd series). Symbolic Flowers. Self-adhesive. Two phosphor bands. Multicoloured Perf 14×14½.

FS103	(1st Class up to 100g) (Type IIA)............	3·00	3·00
	a. Type II (17.9.14)...........................	5·25	5·25
FS104	(1st Large up to 100g) (Type IIA)..........	3·25	3·25
	a. Type II (17.9.14)...........................	5·50	5·50
FS104*b*	Europe up to 20g (Type II) (17.9.14).....	25·00	25·00
FS105	(Euro 20g World 10g) (Type IIA)...........	3·50	3·50
	a. Type II (20.10.14)..........................	9·25	9·25
FS106	(Europe up to 60g) (Type IIA)..............	6·75	6·75
	a. Type II (17.9.14)...........................	6·75	6·75
FS106*b*	(Europe up to 100g) (Type IIA)		
	(30.3.15)......................................	10·00	10·00
FS106*c*	(Euro 100g World 20g) (Type IIA)		
	(9.20)..	4·50	4·50
FS106*d*	(Europe Large 100g) (Type IIA) (1.21)...	10·00	10·00
FS107	(Worldwide up to 20g) (Type IIA)..........	4·50	4·50
	a. Type II (17.9.14)...........................	6·00	6·00
FS108	(Worldwide up to 60g) (Type IIA).........	7·25	7·25
	a. Type II (17.9.14)...........................	7·25	7·25
FS108*b*	(Worldwide up to 100g) (Type IIA)		
	(30.3.15)......................................	11·00	11·00
FS108*c*	(World 100g zone 1 & 3) (Type IIA)		
	(9.20)..	14·50	14·50
FS108*d*	(World 100g zone 2) (Type IIA) (9.20)...	17·50	17·50
FS108*e*	(Worldwide Large 100g) (Type IIA)		
	(1.21)..	11·00	11·00

FS103/FS104, FS105/FS106, FS107/FS108 *Set of* 6 (Type

IIA)... 26·00   26·00

FS103a, FS104a, FS104*b*, FS106a, FS107a, FS108a *Set of*

6 (Type II).. 50·00   50·00

First Day Cover (No. FS103 in 6 designs) (Type IIIA)..........   9·50

Special Pack (P&G 16) (No. FS103 in strip of 6 designs)

(Type IIIA).. 8·00

Nos. FS103/FS108*e* were each available in six different designs (all with year code MA14): T **FT16**, Common Poppy, Dog Rose, Spear Thistle, Heather and Cultivated Flax.

Nos. FS103/FS108 are known in Type IIIA and come from Post & Go machines used at exhibitions. Details are provided in separate tables at the end of this section.

No. FS104*b* was replaced on 20 October 2014 by No. FS105a.

Nos. FS106 and FS108 were replaced on 30 March 2015 by Nos. FS106*b* and FS108*b*.

Wincor machines, producing Type II stamps, were decommissoned before the 30 March 2015 tariff change.

In the run-up to Remembrance Sunday 2014, the Common Poppy design was made available on 21 October 2014 from single-design rolls for use in post offices and other locations for a limited period after that. When distributed to post offices in 2014 the single-design roll stock had year code MA14. Nos. FS103/FS108 (Type IIA) and Nos. FS103a/FS108a (Type II) exist in this form.

In subsequent years the Common Poppy from single-design rolls has been re-issued and usually only available for a limited period. It was available in post offices from 19 October 2015, 24 October 2016, 24 October 2017 and 23 October 2018. It does not appear that stock was automatically distributed in 2019/2020 with only some offices having it available from different day. The availability of Common Poppy is not limited to October/November as post offices may use it at any time of year.

The Common Poppy design in FS103/FS105, FS106*b*, FS07 and FS108*b* have year codesMA14, MA15, MA16, R17Y and R18Y.

There was a reprint of the Common Poppy in 2019 with R19Y, but this stock was not supplied to post offices but instead went to The National Museum Royal Navy for use in their machine, which only dispensed stamps with an inscription. Details are provided in tables at the end of this section. See also FS137/FS142 which are Type IIIA also for single-design rolls.

Nos. FS106*c*, FS106*d*, FS108*c*/FS108*e* only exist on Common Poppy from single-design rolls. They have year codes R17Y or R18Y.

T **FT16**, Common Poppy, Dog Rose, Spear Thistle, Heather and Cultivated Flax are each known thermally printed with 2nd Class up to 100g and 2nd Large up to 100g, Type IIA, when put in a machine's second class unit. This may have occurred because they were mistakenly put in the wrong unit, or because standard second class (new blue Machin) T **FT14** stock were not available, and it was deemed necessary to use the other design instead.

Single-design rolls of the Common Poppy, code MA14, MA15, MA16, R17Y, and R18Y are known thermally printed with 2nd Class up to 100g and 2nd Large up to 100g, Type IIA, when put in a machine's second class unit. This may have occurred because they were mistakenly put in the wrong unit, or because standard second class (new blue Machin) T **FT14** stock were not available, and it was deemed necessary to use the other design instead.

FT17 Common Ivy

(Des Kate Stephens. Illustrations by Julia Trickey. Gravure ISP Walsall, thermally printed service indicator)

2014 (13 Nov)–**15**. British Flora (3rd series). Winter Greenery. Blue background with one phosphor band at right (Nos. FS109/FS109b and FS110/FS110b) or olive-brown background with two phosphor bands (others). Self-adhesive. Multicoloured Perf 14×14½.

FS109	(2nd Class up to 100g) (Type IIA)..........	3·50	3·50
	b. Type IIIA (3.12.14).........................	4·50	4·50
FS110	(2nd Large up to 100g) (Type IIA).........	4·00	4·00
	b. Type IIIA (3.12.14).........................	5·00	5·00
FS111	(1st Class up to 100g) (Type IIA)..........	3·50	3·50
	a. Type II (13.11.14)..........................	7·25	7·25
	b. Type IIIA (3.12.14).........................	4·75	4·75
FS112	(1st Large up to 100g) (Type IIA)..........	4·00	4·00
	a. Type II (13.11.14)..........................	7·50	7·50
	b. Type IIIA (3.12.14).........................	5·25	5·25
FS113	(Euro 20g World 10g) (Type IIA)..........	4·00	4·00
	b. Type IIIA (3.12.14).........................	7·75	7·75
FS113*c*	(Europe up to 20g) (Type II) (12.14)....	25·00	25·00
FS114	(Europe up to 60g) (Type IIA).............	4·50	4·50
	a. Type II (13.11.14)..........................	8·25	8·25
	b. Type IIIA (3.12.14).........................	6·00	6·00
FS114*c*	(Europe up to 100g) (Type IIA) (5.15)...	10·00	10·00
FS115	(Worldwide up to 20g) (Type IIA).........	4·25	4·25
	a. Type II (13.11.14)..........................	8·00	8·00
	b. Type IIIA (3.12.14).........................	5·75	5·75
FS116	(Worldwide up to 60g) (Type IIA).........	5·75	5·75
	a. Type II (13.11.14)..........................	9·00	9·00
	b. Type IIIA (3.12.14).........................	6·75	6·75
FS116*c*	(Worldwide up to 100g) (Type IIA)		
	(5.15)..	11·00	11·00

FS109/FS113, FS114, FS115, FS116 *Set of* 8 (Type IIA)...... 30·00   30·00

FS111a/FS113a, FS114a, FS115a, FS116a *Set of* 6 (Type II) 45·00   45·00

FS109b/FS113b, FS114b, FS115b, FS116b *Set of* 8 (Type

IIIA).. 40·00   40·00

First Day Cover (Nos. FS109b/FS112b; 4 designs) (Type

IIIA)..   9·50

Special Pack (P&G 17) (Nos. FS109b/FS112b; 4 designs

as two pairs) (Type IIIA).. 7·00

Nos. FS109/FS109b and FS110/FS110b were each available in two different designs: T **FT17** and Mistletoe.

Nos. FS111/FS111b through to No. FS116c were each available in two different designs: Butcher's Broom and Holly.

No. FS109 through to No. FS116c have year code MA14.

Defining their intended second class status, T **FT17** and Mistletoe have repeating background 'ROYALMAIL' wording in blue and a single phosphor band placed at the right-hand side.

The Special Pack stamps are No. FS109b T **FT17**; No. FS110b Mistletoe; No. FS111b Butcher's Broom, and No. FS112b Holly.

No. FS113*c* only came from a single Wincor machine in Keighley during December 2014.

Nos. FS109b/FS116b came from Royal Mail Series II machines situated at Royal Mail enquiry offices, and the stamps are easily identified by the code being a mixture of letters and numerals.

All Wincor machines, producing Type II stamps, were decommissioned before the 30 March 2015 tariff change.

T **FT17** and Mistletoe are also each known thermally printed with 1st Class up to 100g, 1st Class Large up to 100g, Euro 20g World 10g, Europe up to 60g, Worldwide up to 20g and Worldwide up to 60g, Type II, having been mistakenly sent to post offices using Wincor machines. Wincor machines did not dispense 2nd Class and 2nd Large.

Butcher's Broom and Holly are each known thermally printed with 2nd Class up to 100g and 2nd Large up to 100g, Type IIA, when put in a machine's second class unit. This may have occurred because they were mistakenly put in the wrong unit, or because T **FT17** and Mistletoe or standard second class (new blue Machin) T **FT14** stock were not available, and it was deemed necessary to use the other design instead.

For T **FT17** and the Mistletoe design with the blue background text reading '2ndCLASS' in large lettering, alternating with 'ROYALMAIL' in small lettering, see Nos. FS191/FS191a and FS192/FS192a.

For Butcher's Broom and Holly with the background text in greenish grey, see Nos. FS193/FS193a and FS198/FS198a.

FT18 *Falcon*

(Des Osborne Ross. Gravure ISP Walsall, thermally printed service indicator)

2015 (18 Feb–30 Mar). Working Sail. Self-adhesive. Two phosphor bands. Multicoloured. Perf 14×14½.

FS117	(1st Class up to 100g) (Type IIA)	3·75	3·75
FS118	(1st Large up to 100g) (Type IIA)	4·25	4·25
FS119	(Euro 20g World 10g) (Type IIA)	4·50	4·50
FS120	(Europe up to 60g) (Type IIA)	7·50	7·50
FS121	(Europe up to 100g) (Type IIA)		
	(30.03.15)	14·00	14·00
FS122	(Worldwide up to 20g) (Type IIA)	5·25	5·25
FS123	(Worldwide up to 60g) (Type IIA)	8·25	8·25
FS124	(Worldwide up to 100g) (Type IIA)		
	(30.03.15)	15·00	15·00
FS117/FS120, FS122, FS123 *Set of 6* (Type IIA)		30·00	30·00
First Day Cover (No. FS117 in 6 designs) (Type IIIA)			9·50
Special Pack (P&G 18) (No. FS117 in strip of 6 designs)			
(Type IIIA)			8·00

Nos. FS117/FS124 were each available in six different designs: T **FT18**, *Briar, Harry, Margaret, Stag, Nell Morgan*.

Nos. FS117/FS124 have year code MA15.

Nos. FS117/FS120, FS122/FS123 are known in Type IIIA and come from Post & Go machines used at exhibitions. Details are provided in separate tables at the end of this section.

Nos. FS120 and FS123 were replaced on 30 March 2015 by Nos. FS121 and FS124.

T **FT18**, *Briar, Harry, Margaret, Stag* and *Nell Morgan* are each known thermally printed with 2nd Class up to 100g and 2nd Large up to 100g, Type IIA, when put in a machine's second class unit. This may have occurred because they were mistakenly put in the wrong unit, or because standard second class (new blue Machin) T **FT14** stock was temporarily unavailable and it was deemed necessary to use alternative stock.

FT19 *Lion*

(Des Osborne Ross. Illustrations by Chris Wormell, Gravure ISP Walsall, thermally printed service indicator)

2015 (13 May). Heraldic Beasts Self-adhesive. Two phosphor bands. Multicoloured Perf 14×14½.

FS125	(1st Class up to 100g) (Type IIA)	3·75	3·75
FS126	(1st Large up to 100g) (Type IIA)	4·25	4·25
FS127	(Euro 20g World 10g) (Type IIA)	4·50	4·50
FS128	(Europe up to 100g) (Type IIA)	5·50	5·50
FS129	(Worldwide up to 20g) (Type IIA)	5·25	5·25
FS130	(Worldwide up to 100g) (Type IIA)	6·75	6·75
FS125/FS130, *Set of 6* (Type IIA)		27·00	27·00
First Day Cover (No. FS125 in 6 designs) (Type IIIA)			9·50
Special Pack (P&G 19) (No. FS125 in strip of 6 designs)			
(Type IIIA)			8·00

Nos. FS125/FS130 were each available in six different designs: T **FT19**, Unicorn, Yale, Dragon, Falcon and Griffin.

Nos. FS125/FS130 have year code MA15.

Nos. FS125/FS130 are known in Type IIIA and come from Post & Go machines used at exhibitions. Details are provided in separate tables at the end of this section.

T **FT19**, Unicorn, Yale, Dragon, Falcon and Griffin are each known thermally printed with 2nd Class up to 100g and 2nd Large up to 100g, Type IIA, when put in a machine's second class unit. This may have occurred because they were mistakenly put in the wrong unit, or because standard second class (new blue Machin) T **FT14** stock was temporarily unavailable and it was deemed necessary to use alternative stock.

FT20 *Dover*

(Des Osborne Ross. Illustrations by Andy Tuohy, Gravure ISP Walsall, thermally printed service indicator)

2015 (16 Sept). Sea Travel. Self-adhesive. Two phosphor bands. Multicoloured Perf 14×14½.

FS131	(1st Class up to 100g) (Type IIA)	3·75	3·75
FS132	(1st Large up to 100g) (Type IIA)	4·25	4·25
FS133	(Euro 20g World 10g) (Type IIA)	4·50	4·50
FS134	(Europe up to 100g) (Type IIA)	5·50	5·50
FS135	(Worldwide up to 20g) (Type IIA)	5·25	5·25
FS136	(Worldwide up to 100g) (Type IIA)	6·75	6·75
FS131/FS136, *Set of 6*		27·00	27·00
First Day Cover (No. FS131 in 6 designs) (Type IIIA)			9·50
Special Pack (P&G 20) (No. FS131 in strip of 6 designs)			
(Type IIIA)			8·00

Nos. FS131/FS136 were each available in six different designs: T **FT20**, Hong Kong, Sydney, Ha Long Bay, New York City and Venice.

Nos. FS131/FS136 have year code MA15.

T **FT20**, Hong Kong, Sydney, Ha Long Bay, New York City and Venice are each known thermally printed with 2nd Class up to 100g and 2nd Large up to 100g, Type IIA, when put in a machine's second class unit. This may have occurred because the issue was mistakenly put in the wrong unit, or because standard second class (new blue Machin) T **FT14** stock was temporarily unavailable and it was deemed necessary to use alternative stock.

Nos. FS131/FS136 are known in Type IIIA and come from Post & Go machines used at exhibitions. Details are provided in separate tables at the end of this section.

FT21 Common Poppy

(Des Kate Stephens. Illustrations by Julia Trickey. Gravure ISP Walsall, thermally printed service indicator)

2015 (19 Oct). Common Poppy in Type IIIA. Self-adhesive. Two phosphor bands. Multicoloured Perf 14×14½.

FS137	(1st Class up to 100g) (Type IIIA)	3·75	3·75
FS138	(1st Large up to 100g) (Type IIIA)	4·25	4·25
FS139	(Euro 20g World 10g) (Type IIIA)	4·50	4·50
FS140	(Europe up to 100g) (Type IIIA)	5·50	5·50
FS141	(Worldwide up to 20g) (Type IIIA)	5·25	5·25
FS142	(Worldwide up to 100g) (Type IIIA)	6·75	6·75
FS137/FS142 *Set of 6* (Type IIIA)		27·00	27·00

Nos. FS137/FS142 came from Royal Mail Series II machines situated at Royal Mail enquiry offices, and the stamps are easily identified by the code being a mixture of letters and numerals.

In the run-up to Remembrance Sunday 2015 the Common Poppy design was for the first time offered through Royal Mail enquiry offices in single-design rolls. The annual tradition of re-issuing the Common Poppy in single-design rolls continued, with short-term availability from Royal Mail enquiry offices from 24 October 2016 and 24 October 2017. The Common Poppy design was not made available from Royal Mail enquiry offices in 2018 or 2019.

Nos. FS137/FS142 only exist with year code MA15.

T **FT21** was not made available in a Special Pack and was only available from Post & Go machines.

See also FS103/FS108b.

FT22 Mountain Hare

(Des Osborne Ross. Illustrations by Robert Gillmor, Gravure ISP Walsall, thermally printed service indicator)

2015 (16 Nov). Winter Fur and Feathers. Self-adhesive. One phosphor band at right (Nos. FS143/FS143a and FS144/FS144a) or two phosphor bands (others). Multicoloured Perf 14×14½.

FS143	(2nd Class up to 100g) (Type IIA)	2·25	2·25
	a. Type IIIA (16.11.15)	4·00	4·00

FS144	(2nd Large up to 100g) (Type IIA)..........	3·00	3·00
	a. Type IIIA (16.11.15)............	4·25	4·25
FS145	(1st Class up to 100g) (Type IIA)..........	3·75	3·75
	a. Type IIIA (16.11.15)............	4·25	4·25
FS146	(1st Large up to 100g) (Type IIA)..........	4·25	4·25
	a. Type IIIA (16.11.15)............	4·50	4·50
FS147	(Euro 20g World 10g) (Type IIA)........	4·50	4·50
	a. Type IIIA (16.11.15)............	5·25	5·25
FS148	(Europe up to 100g) (Type IIA)..........	5·50	5·50
	a. Type IIIA (16.11.15)............	6·50	6·50
FS149	(Worldwide up to 20g) (Type IIA)........	5·25	5·25
	a. Type IIIA (16.11.15)............	6·25	6·25
FS150	(Worldwide up to 100g) (Type IIA)........	6·75	6·75
	a. Type IIIA (16.11.15)............	7·50	7·50
FS143/FS150, Set of 8 (Type IIA).............................		28·00	28·00
FS143a/FS150a, Set of 8 (Type IIIA)........................		38·00	38·00
First Day Cover (Nos. FS143a/FS146a; 4 designs) (Type IIIA).............			8·00
Special Pack (P&G 21) (Nos. FS143a/FS146a; 4 designs as two pairs) (Type IIIA)............			7·25

Nos. FS143/FS143a and FS144/FS144a were each available in two different designs: T **FT22** and Redwing.

Nos. FS145/FS145a to FS150/FS150a were each available in two different designs: Red Fox and Squirrel.

Defining their intended second class status, T **FT22** and Redwing have repeated background text in blue, reading '2ndCLASS' (large typeface) and 'ROYALMAIL' (small typeface) in alternate lines and a single phosphor band placed at the right-hand side.

The Special Pack stamps are No. FS143a T **FT22**, No. FS144a Redwing, No. FS145a Red Fox, and No. FS146a Red Squirrel.

Nos. FS143/FS143a and FS144/FS144a have year code CL15S.

Nos. FS145/FS145a through to FS150/FS150a have year code MA15.

Nos. FS143a/FS150a came from Royal Mail Series II machines situated at Royal Mail enquiry offices, and the stamps are easily identified by the code being a mixture of letters and numerals.

No. FS147a in Red Fox and Squirrel exist with the 20g weight missing and is instead shown as Euro World 10g, and results from a software glitch. Only from Bradford Royal Mail enquiry office 29/31 March 2016.

T **FT22** and Redwing are also both known thermally printed with 1st Class up to 100g, 1st Class Large up to 100g, Euro 20g World 10g, Europe up to 100g, Worldwide up to 20g and Worldwide up to 100g, Type IIA, when mistakenly put in machine's first class unit. Similarly, in Type IIIA are known from Bradford enquiry office.

Red Fox and Squirrel are each known thermally printed with 2nd Class up to 100g and 2nd Large up to 100g, Type IIA, when put in a machine's second class unit. Similarly, in Type IIIA are known from Bradford enquiry office. This may have occurred because they were mistakenly put in the wrong unit, or because T **FT22** and Redwing or standard second class (new blue Machin) T **FT14** stock were not available, and it was deemed necessary to use the other design instead.

2016 (5 Aug). T **FT14** with background text reading, alternately, '2ndCLASS' in large lettering and 'ROYALMAIL' in small lettering, with year code. New blue background. Self-adhesive. One phosphor band (over the Queen's head). Perf 14×14½.

FS157	(2nd Class up to 100g) (Type IIA)...........	2·10	2·10
FS158	(2nd Large up to 100g) (Type IIA)..........	2·75	2·75

Nos. FS157/FS158 have year code CL16S, CL17S, CL18S, CL19S or CL21S with the code positioned half-way between the left edge of the stamp and the Queen's nose.

T **FT14** with background text reading, alternately, '2ndCLASS' in large lettering and 'ROYALMAIL' in small lettering, with year code CL16S and CL18S is known thermally printed with 1st Class up to 100g, 1st Class Large up to 100g, Euro 20g World 10g, Europe up to 100g, Worldwide up to 20g and Worldwide up to 100g, Type IIA, when mistakenly put in machine's first class unit.

Nos. FS157/FS158 were not made available in a Special Pack and are only available from Post & Go machines.

Nos. FS151/FS156 in Type IIIA exist digitally printed in the Mail Coach, 1790s design from single-design rolls used in Post & Go machines at The Postal Museum. These stamps only exist with a museum inscription. Details are provided in separate tables at the end of this section.

The Mail Coach, 1790s design from digitally printed single-design rolls exists with Euro 100g World 20g, World up to 100g zone 1-3 and World up to 100g zone 2 values (Type IIIA). These stamps only exist from the Post & Go machine at The Postal Museum from 29 October 2020 and all bear a museum inscription. Details are provided in separate tables at the end of this section.

FT23 Post Boy, 1640s

(Des Howard Brown. Illustrations by Andrew Davidson. Gravure ISP Walsall, thermally printed service indicator)

2016 (17 Feb). Royal Mail Heritage. Transport. Self-adhesive. Two phosphor bands. Multicoloured Perf 14×14½.

FS151	(1st Class up to 100g) (Type IIA)..............	3·25	3·25
FS152	(1st Large up to 100g) (Type IIA)...........	3·50	3·50
FS153	(Euro 20g World 10g) (Type IIA)...........	3·75	3·75
FS154	(Europe up to 100g) (Type IIA)...........	4·50	4·50
FS155	(Worldwide up to 20g) (Type IIA)..........	4·25	4·25
FS156	(Worldwide up to 100g) (Type IIA)........	6·25	6·25
FS151/156, Set of 6 (Type IIA).............................		23·00	23·00
First Day Cover (No. FS151 in 6 designs) (Type IIA)........			9·50
Special Pack (P&G 22) (No. FS151 in strip of 6 designs) (Type IIIA)............			10·00

Nos. FS151/FS156 were each available in six different designs: T **FT23**; Mail coach, 1790s; Falmouth packet ship, 1820s; Travelling Post Office, 1890s; Airmail, 1930s and Royal Mail Minivan, 1970s.

Nos. FS151/FS156 have year code MA16.

T **FT23**; Mail coach, 1790s; Falmouth packet ship, 1820s; Travelling Post Office, 1890s; Airmail, 1930s and Royal Mail Minivan, 1970s are each known thermally printed with 2nd Class up to 100g and 2nd Large up to 100g, Type IIA, when put in a machine's second class unit. This may have occurred because the issue was mistakenly put in the wrong unit, or because standard second class (new blue Machin) T **FT14** stock was temporarily unavailable and it was deemed necessary to use alternative stock.

Nos. FS151/FS156 are known from Post & Go machines used at exhibitions. Details are provided in separate tables at the end of this section.

Nos. FS151/FS156 in Type IIIA exist digitally printed in the Travelling Post Office, 1890s (Locomotive) design from single-design rolls used in Post & Go machines at exhibitions. Details are provided in separate tables at the end of this section.

FT24 Seven-spot Ladybird

(Des Osborne Ross. Illustrations by Chris Wormell, Gravure ISP Walsall, thermally printed service indicator)

2016 (14 Sept). Ladybirds. Self-adhesive. Two phosphor bands. Multicoloured Perf 14×14½.

FS159	(1st Class up to 100g) (Type IIA).............	2·50	2·50
	a. Type IIIA............	4·25	4·25
FS160	(1st Large up to 100g) (Type IIA)...........	2·75	2·75
	a. Type IIIA............	4·50	4·50
FS161	(Euro 20g World 10g) (Type IIA)...........	4·25	4·25
	a. Type IIIA............	4·75	4·75
FS162	(Europe up to 100g) (Type IIA)...........	4·25	4·25
	a. Type IIIA............	5·50	5·50
FS163	(Worldwide up to 20g) (Type IIA)..........	4·25	4·25
	a. Type IIIA............	5·25	5·25
FS164	(Worldwide up to 100g) (Type IIA)........	5·75	5·75
	a. Type IIIA............	7·50	7·50
FS159/FS164, Set of 6 (Type IIA)............................		21·00	21·00
FS159a/FS164a, Set of 6 (Type IIIA)........................		29·00	29·00
First Day Cover (No. FS159a in 6 designs) (Type IIIA)........			9·50
Special Pack (P&G 23) (No. FS159a in strip of 6 designs) (Type IIIA)............			9·00

Nos. FS159/FS164a were each available in six different designs: T **FT24**, 14-spot Ladybird, Orange Ladybird, Heather Ladybird, Striped Ladybird and Water Ladybird.

No. FS159 through to No. FS164a have year code MA16.

T **FT24**, 14-spot Ladybird, Orange Ladybird, Heather Ladybird, Striped Ladybird and Water Ladybird are each known thermally printed with 2nd Class up to 100g and 2nd Large up to 100g, Type IIA, when put in a machine's second class unit. This may have occurred because the issue was mistakenly put in the wrong unit, or because standard second class (new blue Machin) T **FT14** stock was temporarily unavailable and it was deemed necessary to use alternative stock.

Nos. FS159a/FS164a (Type IIIA) come from Royal Mail Series II machines situated at Royal Mail enquiry offices. These may be identified by the code M00 at the beginning of the second group of data within the code line at the foot of the stamp. Stamps with codes other than M00 either come from machines at stamp exhibitions (see tables), or in the case of No. FS159a with code C00 come from special packs.

FT25 Hedgehog

(Des Osborne Ross. Illustrations by Chris Wormell, Gravure ISP Walsall, thermally printed service indicator)

2016 (14 Nov). Hibernating Animals. Self-adhesive. One phosphor band at right (Nos. FS165/FS165a and FS166/FS166a) or two phosphor bands (others). Multicoloured Perf 14×14½.

FS165	(2nd Class up to 100g) (Type IIA)............	2·50	2·50
	a. Type IIIA............	3·00	3·00
FS166	(2nd Large up to 100g) (Type IIA)............	2·75	2·75
	a. Type IIIA............	3·25	3·25
FS167	(1st Class up to 100g) (Type IIA)............	2·75	2·75
	a. Type IIIA............	4·25	4·25
FS168	(1st Large up to 100g) (Type IIA)............	3·00	3·00
	a. Type IIIA............	4·50	4·50
FS169	(Euro 20g World 10g) (Type IIA)............	3·25	3·25
	a. Type IIIA............	4·75	4·75
FS170	(Europe up to 100g) (Type IIA)............	4·50	4·50
	a. Type IIIA............	5·50	5·50
FS171	(Worldwide up to 20g) (Type IIA)............	4·25	4·25
	a. Type IIIA............	5·25	5·25
FS172	(Worldwide up to 100g) (Type IIA)........	6·00	6·00
	a. Type IIIA............	7·50	7·50
FS165/FS172, *Set* of 8 (Type IIA)............		25·00	25·00
FS165a/FS172a, *Set* of 8 (Type IIIA)............		32·00	32·00
First Day Cover (Nos. FS165a/FS168a in 4 designs) (Type IIIA)............			8·00
Special Pack (P&G 24) (Nos. FS165a/FS168a; 4 designs as two pairs) (Type IIIA)............		9·00	

Nos. FS165/FS165a and FS166/FS166a were each available in two different designs: T **FT25** or Grass Snake.

Nos. FS167/FS167a through to Nos. FS172/FS172a were each available in two different designs: Dormouse or Brown Long-eared Bat.

Defining their intended second class status, T **FT25** and Grass Snake have repeated background text in blue, reading '2ndCLASS' (large typeface) and 'ROYALMAIL' (small typeface) in alternate lines and a single phosphor band placed at the right-hand side.

The Special Pack stamps are No. FS165a T **FT25**, No. FS166a Grass Snake, No. FS167a Dormouse, and No. FS168a Long-eared Bat.

Nos. FS165/FS165a and FS166/FS166a have year code CL16S.

Nos. FS167/FS167a through to Nos. FS172/FS172a have year code MA16.

Dormouse and Brown Long-eared Bat are each known thermally printed with 2nd Class up to 100g and 2nd Large up to 100g, Type IIA, when put in a machine's second class unit. This may have occurred because they were mistakenly put in the wrong unit, or because T **FT25** and Grass Snake or standard second class (new blue Machin) T **FT14** stock were not available, and it was deemed necessary to use the other design instead.

Nos. FS165a/FS172a (Type IIIA) come from Royal Mail Series II machines situated at Royal Mail enquiry offices. These may be identified by the code M00 at the beginning of the second group of data within the code line at the foot of the stamp.

No. FS165a with code C00 come from special packs.

FT26 Travelling Post Office: bag exchange

(Des Osborne Ross. Gravure ISP Walsall, thermally printed service indicator)

2017 (15 Feb). Royal Mail Heritage. Mail by Rail. Self-adhesive. Two phosphor bands. Multicoloured Perf 14×14½.

FS173	(1st Class up to 100g) (Type IIA)............	2·50	2·50
	a. Type IIIA............	4·25	4·25
FS174	(1st Large up to 100g) (Type IIA)............	2·75	2·75
	a. Type IIIA............	4·50	4·50
FS175	(Euro 20g World 10g) (Type IIA)............	4·75	4·75
	a. Type IIIA............	4·75	4·75

FS176	(Europe up to 100g) (Type IIA)............	4·75	4·75
	a. Type IIIA............	5·50	5·50
FS177	(Worldwide up to 20g) (Type IIA)............	4·75	4·75
	a. Type IIIA............	5·25	5·25
FS178	(Worldwide up to 100g) (Type IIA)........	5·75	5·75
	a. Type IIIA............	7·50	7·50
FS173/FS178, *Set* of 6 (Type IIA)............		23·00	23·00
FS173a/FS178a, *Set* of 6 (Type IIIA)............		27·00	27·00
First Day Cover (No. FS173a in 6 designs) (Type IIIA)........			7·50
Special Pack (P&G 25) (No. FS173a in strip of 6 designs) (Type IIIA)............		9·00	

Nos. FS173/FS178a were each available in six different designs: T **FT26**; Post Office (London) Railway; Night Mail: poster; Travelling Post Office: loading; Travelling Post Office: sorting and Travelling Post Office: on the move.

Nos. FS173/FS178a have year code MA17.

T **FT26**; Post Office (London) Railway; Night Mail: poster; Travelling Post Office: loading; Travelling Post Office: sorting and Travelling Post Office: on the move are each known thermally printed with 2nd Class up to 100g and 2nd Large up to 100g, Type IIA, when put in a machine's second class unit. This may have occurred because the issue was mistakenly put in the wrong unit, or because standard second class (new blue Machin) T **FT14** stock was temporarily unavailable and it was deemed necessary to use alternative stock.

Nos. FS173a/FS178a (Type IIIA) come from Royal Mail Series II machines situated at Royal Mail enquiry offices. These may be identified by the code M00 at the beginning of the second group of data within the code line at the foot of the stamp. Stamps with codes other than M00 either come from machines at stamp exhibitions (see tables), or in the case of No. FS173a with code C00 come from special packs.

FS173a/FS178a exist digitally printed in the Post Office (London) Railway design from single-design rolls used in the Post & Go machine at The Postal Museum. These stamps are known with an MA17, MA18 (FS173a/FS175a only) or R19Y year codes, and only exist with a museum inscription. Details are provided in separate tables at the end of this section.

The Post Office (London) Railway design from digitally printed single-design rolls exists with Euro 100g World 20g, World up to 100g zone 1-3 and World up to 100g zone 2 values (Type IIA). These stamps are known with MA17, MA18 or R19Y year codes and only exist from the Post & Go machine at The Postal Museum from 29 October 2020, and all bear a museum inscription. Details are provided in separate tables at the end of this section.

FT27 Machin Commemorative Head

(Gravure ISP Walsall, thermally printed service indicator)

2017 (5 June)–**21**. Machin Anniversary 1967–2017. Self-adhesive. Two phosphor bands. Multicoloured. Perf 14×14½.

FS179	(1st Class up to 100g) (Type IIA)............	3·00	3·00
	a. Type IIIA............	3·00	3·00
FS180	(1st Large up to 100g) (Type IIA)............	3·25	3·25
	a. Type IIIA............	3·25	3·25
FS181	(Euro 20g World 10g) (Type IIA)............	4·25	4·25
	a. Type IIIA............	4·25	4·25
FS182	(Europe up to 100g) (Type IIA)............	4·25	4·25
	a. Type IIIA............	4·25	4·25
FS182*b*	(Euro 100g World 20g) (Type IIA) (9.20)............	9·75	9·75
FS182*c*	(Europe Large 100g) (Type IIA) (1.21)...	12·00	10·50
FS183	(Worldwide up to 20g) (Type IIA)........	4·25	4·25
	a. Type IIIA............	4·25	4·25
FS184	(Worldwide up to 100g) (Type IIA).......	5·75	5·75
	a. Type IIIA............	5·75	5·75
FS184*b*	(World 100g zone 1-3) (Type IIA) (9.20)............	—	—
FS184*c*	(World 100g zone 2) (Type IIA) (9.20)...	—	—
FS184*d*	(Worldwide Large 100g) (Type IIA) (1.21)............	13·00	13·00
FS179/FS184, *Set* of 6 (Type IIA)............		22·00	22·00
FS179a/FS184a, *Set* of 6 (Type IIIA)............		22·00	22·00
First Day Cover (No. FS179a in 6 designs) (Type IIIA)........			7·50
Special Pack (P&G 26) (No. FS179a in strip of 6 designs) (Type IIIA)............		17·00	

Nos. FS179/FS184*d* were each available in six different colours: T **FT27**, light olive, violet, deep sepia, bright emerald and drab.

Nos. FS179/FS184*d* do not have a year code as such, but have repeated background text, reading MACHIN ANNIVERSARY, 1967 - 2017 (large typeface) and 'ROYALMAIL' (small typeface) in alternate lines.

T **FT27**, light olive, violet, deep sepia, bright emerald and drab are each known thermally printed with 2nd Class up to 100g and 2nd Large up to 100g, Type IIA, when put in a machine's second class unit. This may have occurred because the issue was mistakenly put in the wrong unit, or because standard second class (new blue Machin) T **FT14** stock was temporarily unavailable and it was deemed necessary to use alternative stock.

Nos. FS179a/FS184a (Type IIIA) come from Royal Mail Series II machines situated at Royal Mail enquiry offices. These may be identified by the code M00 at the beginning of the second group of data within the code line at the foot of the stamp. Stamps with codes other than M00 either come from machines at stamp exhibitions (see tables), or in the case of No. FS179a with code C00 come from special packs.

FT28 First UK Aerial Mail, 1911

Des Osborne Ross. Illustrations by Andrew Davidson. Gravure ISP Walsall, thermally printed service indicator)

2017 (13 Sept). Royal Mail Heritage. Mail by Air. Self-adhesive. Two phosphor bands. Multicoloured Perf 14×14½.

FS185	(1st Class up to 100g) (Type IIA)............	2·25	2·25
	a. Type IIIA......................................	3·25	3·25
FS186	(1st Large up to 100g) (Type IIA)...........	2·75	2·75
	a. Type IIIA......................................	3·75	3·70
FS187	(Euro 20g World 10g) (Type IIA)............	4·00	4·00
	a. Type IIIA......................................	4·00	4·00
FS188	(Europe up to 100g) (Type IIA).............	4·00	4·00
	a. Type IIIA......................................	4·50	4·50
FS189	(Worldwide up to 20g) (Type IIA)...........	4·00	4·00
	a. Type IIIA......................................	4·25	4·25
FS190	(Worldwide up to 100g) (Type IIA)........	5·25	5·25
	a. Type IIIA......................................	6·25	6·25
FS185/FS190, *Set of* 6 (Type IIA)................................		20·00	20·00
FS185a/FS190a, *Set of* 6 (Type IIIA)...........................		22·00	22·00
First Day Cover (No. FS185a in 6 designs) (Type IIIA)........			7·50
Special Pack (P&G 27) (No. FS185a in strip of 6 designs) (Type IIIA)			9·00

Nos. FS185/FS190a were each available in six different designs: T **FT28**; Military Mail Flight, 1919; International Airmail, 1933; Domestic Airmail, 1934; Flying Boat Airmail, 1937 and Datapost Service, 1980s.

Nos. FS185/FS190a have year code R17Y.

T **FT28**; Military Mail Flight, 1919; International Airmail, 1933; Domestic Airmail, 1934; Flying Boat Airmail, 1937 and Datapost Service, 1980s are each known thermally printed with 2nd Class up to 100g and 2nd Large up to 100g, Type IIA, when put in a machine's second class unit. This may have occurred because the issue was mistakenly put in the wrong unit, or because standard second class (new blue Machin) T **FT14** stock was temporarily unavailable and it was deemed necessary to use alternative stock.

Nos. FS185a/FS190a (Type IIIA) come from Royal Mail Series II machines situated at Royal Mail enquiry offices. These may be identified by the code M00 at the beginning of the second group of data within the code line at the foot of the stamp. Stamps with codes other than M00 either come from machines at stamp exhibitions (see tables), or in the case of No. FS185a with code C00 come from special packs.

No. FS185a in all six designs exist from digitally printed rolls used in the Post & Go machine at The Postal Museum. These stamps have an R19Y year code and only exist with a museum inscription. Details are provided in separate tables at the end of this section.

(Des Kate Stephens. Illustrations by Julia Trickey. Gravure ISP Walsall, thermally printed service indicator)

2017 (13 Nov)–**21**. British Flora (3rd series). Winter Greenery, 2017 re-issue. T **FT17** with blue background text reading, alternately, '2ndCLASS' in large lettering and 'ROYALMAIL' in small lettering, with one phosphor band at right (Nos. FS191/FS191a and Nos. FS192/FS192a), or greenish grey 'ROYALMAIL' background, with two phosphor bands (others). Self-adhesive. Multicoloured Perf 14×14½.

FS191	(2nd Class up to 100g) (Type IIA)..........	2·10	2·10
	a. Type IIIA......................................	4·75	4·75
FS192	(2nd Large up to 100g) (Type IIA)........	2·75	2·75
	a. Type IIIA......................................	5·00	5·00

FS193	(1st Class up to 100g) (Type IIA)............	2·25	2·25
	a. Type IIIA......................................	4·75	4·75
FS194	(1st Large up to 100g) (Type IIA)..........	3·00	3·00
	a. Type IIIA......................................	5·25	5·25
FS195	(Euro 20g World 10g) (Type IIA)............	5·50	5·50
	a. Type IIIA......................................	5·50	5·50
FS196	(Europe up to 100g) (Type IIA).............	5·50	5·50
	a. Type IIIA......................................	5·75	5·75
FS196*b*	(Euro 100g World 20g) (Type IIA) (3.11.20)......................................	4·00	4·00
FS196*c*	(Europe Large 100g) (Type IIA) (2.1.21)..	10·50	10·50
FS197	(Worldwide up to 20g) (Type IIA).........	5·50	5·50
	a. Type IIIA......................................	5·75	5·75
FS198	(Worldwide up to 100g) (Type IIA).......	5·50	5·50
	a. Type IIIA......................................	6·50	6·50
FS198*b*	(World 100g zone 1-3) (Type IIA) (3.11.20)......................................	11·00	11·00
FS198*c*	(World 100g zone 2) (Type IIA) (3.22.20)......................................	11·00	11·00
FS198*d*	(Worldwide Large 100g) (Type IIA) (2.1.21)..	11·50	11·50
FS191/FS198, *Set of* 8 (Type IIA).................................		30·00	30·00
FS191a/FS198a, *Set of* 8 (Type IIIA)............................		40·00	40·00

Nos. FS191/FS191a and FS192/FS192a were each available in two different designs: T **FT17** and Mistletoe.

No. FS193 through to No. FS198*d* were each available in two different designs: Butcher's Broom and Holly.

No. FS191 through to No. FS198*d* are a re-issue of the 13 November 2014 designs, but with differences necessitating a separate listing.

For the 2014 issue see No. FS109 through to No. FS116*c*.

Nos. FS191/FS191a and FS192/FS192a may be differentiated from the 2014 issue through their repeated blue background text, reading '2ndCLASS' (large typeface) and 'ROYALMAIL' (small typeface) in alternate lines.

Nos. FS191/FS191a and FS192/FS192a may also be differentiated through the year code which is the CL**S format (the 2014 issue has year code MA14).

No. FS193 through to No. FS198*d* may be differentiated from the 2014 issue through their repeated greenish grey background text (the 2014 issue has olive-brown background text).

No. FS193 through to No. FS198*d* may also be differentiated through the year code which is in the R**Y format (the 2014 issue has year code MA14).

T **FT17** and Mistletoe, Butcher's Broom and Holly have been re-issued in November of each year since 2017. In each successive year there has been a reprint and new year codes.

Year codes for Nos. FS191/FS192 (Type IIA) are CL17S, CL18S, CL19S and CL20S.

Year codes for Nos. FS193/FS198 (Type IIA) are R17Y, R18Y and R19Y.

Year codes for Nos. FS196*b*, FS198*b*/FS198*c* are R17Y, R19Y and R20Y.

Year codes for Nos. FS196*c* and FS198*d* are R19Y and R19Y.

Nos. FS191a/FS198a (Type IIA) come from Royal Mail Series II machines situated at Royal Mail enquiry offices. These may be identified by the code M00 at the beginning of the second group of data within the code line at the foot of the stamp. Nos. FS191a/FS198a were available at Royal Mail enquiry offices in 2017 but were not made available in 2018 or 2019.

Year codes for Nos. FS191a/FS198a (Type IIA) are R17Y.

T **FT17** and Mistletoe with blue background text reading, alternately, '2ndCLASS' in large lettering and 'ROYALMAIL' in small lettering, with year code CL17 and CL18, are each known thermally printed with 1st Class up to 100g, 1st Class Large up to 100g, Euro 20g World 10g, Europe up to 100g, Worldwide up to 20g and Worldwide up to 100g, Type IIA, when mistakenly put in machine's first class unit.

Butcher's Broom and Holly with year code R17Y and R18Y are each known thermally printed with 2nd Class up to 100g and 2nd Large up to 100g, Type IIA, when put in a machine's second class unit. This may have occurred because they were mistakenly put in the wrong unit, or because T **FT17** or Mistletoe or standard second class (new blue Machin) T **FT14** stock were not available, and it was deemed necessary to use the other design instead.

Winter Greenery 2017 re-issue was not made available in a Special Pack and was only available from Post & Go machines.

FT29 The Iron Throne–Ice

(Design GBH. Illustrations by Rob Ball. Gravure ISP Walsall, thermally printed service indicator)

2018 (23 Jan)–**20**. Game of Thrones. Self-adhesive. One phosphor band at right (Nos. FS199/FS199a and FS200/FS200a) or two phosphor bands (others). Multicoloured Perf 14×14½.

FS199	(2nd Class up to 100g) (Type IIA)..........	7·75	7·75
	a. Type IIIA......................................	5·25	5·25
FS200	(2nd Large up to 100g) (Type IIA)........	8·00	8·00
	a. Type IIIA......................................	5·50	5·50

FS201	(1st Class up to 100g) (Type IIA)...........	3·25	3·25
	a. Type IIIA.......................................	5·25	5·25
FS202	(1st Large up to 100g) (Type IIA).........	3·75	3·75
	a. Type IIIA.......................................	5·75	5·75
FS203	(Euro 20g World 10g) (Type IIA)...........	12·00	12·00
	a. Type IIIA.......................................	9·00	9·00
FS204	(Europe up to 100g) (Type IIA).............	27·00	27·00
	a. Type IIIA.......................................	9·00	9·00
FS204b	(Euro 100g World 20g) (Type IIA)		
	(9.20)...	16·00	16·00
FS205	(Worldwide up to 20g) (Type IIA).........	27·00	27·00
	a. Type IIIA.......................................	9·00	9·00
FS206	(Worldwide up to 100g) (Type IIA).......	16·00	16·00
	a. Type IIIA.......................................	9·00	9·00
FS206b	(World 100g zone 1-3 (Type IIA) (9.20)	19·00	19·00
FS206c	(World 100g zone 2) (Type IIA) (9.20)..	23·00	23·00
FS199/FS206, Set of 8 (Type IIA).................		95·00	95·00
FS199a/FS206a, Set of 8 (Type IIIA).............		50·00	50·00
First Day Cover (Nos. FS199 and FS201a) (Type IIIA).......			4·00
Special Pack (P&G 28) (Nos. FS199a and FS201a) (Type IIIA)......			
			5·00

Nos. FS199/FS199a and FS200/FS200a were each available in one design: T **FT29** in blue (Ice).

No. FS201 through to No. FS206c were each available in one design: T **FT29** in yellow-orange (Fire).

Defining their intended second class status, T **FT29** has repeated background text in blue, reading '2ndCLASS' (large typeface) and 'ROYALMAIL' (small typeface) in alternate lines, and a single phosphor band placed at the right-hand side.

No. FS201 through to No. FS206c have repeated background text in yellow-orange with 'ROYALMAIL' in alternate lines of large and small typeface.

Nos. FS199/FS199a and FS200/FS200a have year code CL18S.

No. FS201 through to No. FS206c have year code R18Y.

The Iron Throne–Fire design is known thermally printed with 2nd Class up to 100g and 2nd Large up to 100g, Type IIA, when put in a machine's second class unit. This may have occurred because the issue was mistakenly put in the wrong unit, or because standard second class (new blue Machin) T **FT14** stock was temporarily unavailable and it was deemed necessary to use alternative stock.

T **FT29** The Iron Throne–Ice design is known thermally printed with 1st Class up to 100g, 1st Class Large up to 100g, Euro 20g World 10g, Europe up to 100g, Worldwide up to 20g and Worldwide up to 100g, Type IIA, when mistakenly put in machine's first class unit.

Nos. FS199a/FS206a (Type IIIA) come from Royal Mail Series II machines situated at Royal Mail enquiry offices. These may be identified by the code M00 at the beginning of the second group of data within the code line at the foot of the stamp.

Nos. FS199a and FS201a with code C00 come from special packs.

FT30 Packet *Antelope*, 1780

(Illustrations by Andrew Davidson. Gravure ISP Walsall, thermally printed service indicator)

2018 (14 Feb)–**20**. Royal Mail Heritage. Mail by Sea. Self-adhesive. Two phosphor bands. Multicoloured Perf 14×14½.

FS207	(1st Class up to 100g) (Type IIA).........	2·25	2·25
	a. Type IIIA.......................................	3·25	3·25
FS208	(1st Large up to 100g) (Type IIA)........	2·75	2·75
	a. Type IIIA.......................................	3·75	3·75
FS209	(Euro 20g World 10g) (Type IIA)..........	4·00	4·00
	a. Type IIIA.......................................	4·00	4·00
FS210	(Europe up to 100g) (Type IIA).............	4·00	4·00
	a. Type IIIA.......................................	4·50	4·50
FS210b	(Euro 100g World 20g) (9.20)...............	13·50	13·50
FS211	(Worldwide up to 20g) (Type IIA).......	4·00	4·00
	a. Type IIIA.......................................	4·25	4·25
FS212	(Worldwide up to 100g) (Type IIA).....	5·25	5·25
	a. Type IIIA.......................................	6·25	6·25
FS212b	(World 100g zone 1-3) (Type IIA)		
	(9.20)...	14·50	14·50
FS212c	(World 100g zone 2) (Type IIA) (9.20)		
	....	16·50	16·50
FS207/FS212 Set of 6 (Type IIA)...................		20·00	20·00
FS207a/FS212a Set of 6 (Type IIIA)...............		23·00	23·00
First Day Cover (No. FS207a in 6 designs) (Type IIIA)......			7·50
Special Pack (P&G 29) (No. FS207a in strip of 6 designs)			
(Type IIIA)..			7·00

Nos. FS207/FS212c were each available in six different designs: T **FT30**; SS *Great Western*, 1838; SS *Britannia*, 1887; RMS *Olympic*, 1911; RMS *Queen Mary*, 1936; RMS *St Helena*, 1990.

Nos. FS207/FS212c have year code R18Y.

T **FT30**; SS *Great Western*, 1838; SS *Britannia*, 1887; RMS *Olympic*, 1911; RMS *Queen Mary*, 1936; RMS *St Helena*, 1990 are each known thermally printed with 2nd Class up to 100g and 2nd Large up to 100g, Type IIA, when put in a machine's second class unit. This may have occurred because the issue was mistakenly put in the wrong unit, or because standard second class (new blue Machin) T **FT14** stock was temporarily unavailable and it was deemed necessary to use alternative stock.

Nos. FS207a/FS212a (Type IIIA) come from Royal Mail Series II machines situated at Royal Mail enquiry offices. These may be identified by the code M00 at the beginning of the second group of data within the code line at the foot of the stamp.

No. FS207a with code C00 comes from special packs.

FT31 Pentacycle, 1882

(Illustrations by Andrew Davidson. Gravure ISP Walsall, thermally printed service indicator)

2018 (12 Sept)–**20**. Royal Mail Heritage. Mail by Bike. Self-adhesive. Two phosphor bands. Multicoloured Perf 14×14½.

FS213	(1st Class up to 100g) (Type IIA)............	2·25	2·25
FS214	(1st Large up to 100g) (Type IIA)............	2·75	2·75
FS215	(Euro 20g World 10g) (Type IIA).............	4·00	4·00
FS216	(Europe up to 100g) (Type IIA)...............	4·00	4·00
FS216a	(Euro 100g World 20g) (Type IIA)		
	(9.20)...	12·50	16·00
FS217	(Worldwide up to 20g) (Type IIA)..........	4·00	4·00
FS218	(Worldwide up to 100g) (Type IIA)........	5·25	5·25
FS218a	(World 100g zone 1-3) (Type IIA)		
	(9.20)...	13·50	19·00
FS218b	(World 100g zone 2) (Type IIA) (9.20)...	13·50	23·00
FS213/FS218 Set of 6 (Type IIA)....................		20·00	20·00
First Day Cover (No. FS213 in 6 designs) (Type IIIA)......			7·50
Special Pack (P&G 30) (No. FS213 in strip of 6 designs)			
(Type IIIA)..			9·50

Nos. FS213/FS218b were each available in six different designs: T **FT31**; Motorcycle and trailer, 1902; Tricycle and basket, 1920; Bicycle, 1948; Motorcycle, 1965; Quad bike, 2002.

Nos. FS213/FS218b have year code R18Y.

T **FT31**; Motorcycle and trailer, 1902; Tricycle and basket, 1920; Bicycle, 1949; Motorcycle, 1965; Quad bike, 2002. are each known thermally printed with 2nd Class up to 100g and 2nd Large up to 100g, Type IIA, when put in a machine's second class unit. This may have occurred because the issue was mistakenly put in the wrong unit, or because standard second class (new blue Machin) T **FT14** stock was temporarily unavailable and it was deemed necessary to use alternative stock.

Nos. FS213/FS218 were not available from the Royal Mail Series II machines (Type IIIA) situated at Royal Mail enquiry offices.

No. FS213 with code C00 comes from special packs.

Post & Go Machin design Type FT **1** but with year code in background. Olive-brown background. Self-adhesive. Two phosphor bands. Perf 14×14½.
A simplified list of the different year codes, but shown listed in the range of six values/weights (and Types) available at the time (or current).

Service indicator	SG No.	Year code	Availability (inclusive) [1]
1st Class up to 100g, 1st Large up to 100g, Europe up to 20g, Worldwide up to 10g, Worldwide up to 20g, and Worldwide up to 40g:			
Type II	FS77, FS78, FS79, FS81, FS82, and FS83	MA13	19.11.13 – 30.3.14
Type IIA	FS77a, FS78a, FS79a, FS81a, FS82a, and FS83a	MA13	28.2.14 – 31.3.14
1st Class up to 100g, 1st Large up to 100g, Europe up to 20g, Europe up to 60g, Worldwide up to 20g, and Worldwide up to 60g:			
Type II	FS77, FS78, FS79, FS80, FS82, and FS84	MA13	31.3.14 – 19.10.14
Type IIA	FS77a, FS78a, FS79a, FS80a, FS82a, and FS84a	MA13	1.4.14 – 4.6.14
1st Class up to 100g, 1st Large up to 100g, Euro 20g World 10g, Europe up to 60g, Worldwide up to 20g, and Worldwide up to 60g:			
Type II	FS77, FS78, FS79b, FS80, FS82, and FS84	MA13	20.10.14 – 3.15
Type IIA	FS77a, FS78a, FS79ba, FS80a, FS82a, and FS84a	MA13	5.6.14 – 29.3.15
		MA14	
1st Class up to 100g, 1st Large up to 100g, Euro 20g World 10g, Europe up to 100g, Worldwide up to 20g, and Worldwide up to 100g:			
Type IIA	FS77a, FS78a, FS79ba, FS80c, FS82a, and FS84c	MA13	30.3.15 – 31.8.20
		MA14	
		MA15	
		MA16	
		R17Y	
		R18Y	
		R19Y	
		R20Y	
1st Class up to 100g, 1st Large up to 100g, Euro 20g World 10g, Euro 100g World 20g, World 100g Zone 1-3, and World 100g Zone 2:			
Type IIA	FS77a, FS78a, FS79ba, FS80d, FS84d, and FS84e	MA13	1.9.20 – 31.12.20
		MA14	
		MA15	
		MA16	
		R17Y	
		R18Y	
		R19Y	
		R20Y	
1st Class up to 100g, 1st Large up to 100g, Euro 100g World 20g, Worldwide up to 100g, Europe Large 100g, and Worldwide Large 100g:			
Type IIA	FS77a, FS78a, FS80d, FS84c, FS80e, and FS84f	MA14	from 1.1.21
		MA15	
		MA16	
		R17Y	
		R18Y	
		R19Y	
		R20Y	
1st Class up to 100g, 1st Large up to 100g, Euro 20g World 10g, Europe up to 100g, Worldwide up to 20g, and Worldwide up to 100g:			
Type IIIA	FS77b, FS78b, FS79bb, FS80ca, FS82b, and FS84ca	MA13	30.5.15 – 10.19
		MA15	

Note. When Machin Post & Go stamps first appeared with a year code it was in the format of MA** and positioned to the left of the front of The Queen's forehead (MA13 through to and including MA16). From 2017, the format and position changed simultaneously to R**Y and positioned further to the left of the design, approximately half way between the left edge and the Queen's forehead. The range of six values/weights noted are also the range that would appear in a collectors' strip of six (or, in the case of Type II, a pair of collectors' strips of three).
[1] Date of availability (inclusive) of the range of six values/weights (and Types). The dates do not take account of the availability of particular year codes which are randomly available and dependent on the stock that is available from a machine at the time.

Post & Go tables. The tables on the next few pages list Post & Go stamps with inscriptions from the following primary locations: UK and international stamp exhibitions, the UK's national Postal Museum (formerly The BPMA, and since 1 February 2016, The Postal Museum), Royal Mail Enquiry Offices and the Armed Forces' museums which have (or had) Post & Go machines. Inscriptions from other (secondary) locations are not within the scope of these tables. The final table lists Post & Go stamps from exhibitions and stamp fairs which were generated without inscriptions.

The tables have been compiled from information available at time of going to press. Note that the lists of dates of availability/duration are not exhaustive and are merely intended as a guide to the availability of the inscriptions. However, if you have additional relevant information (or spot any mistakes) please do get in touch in the usual way. The tables are intended to be a simplified record and do not attempt to list Post & Go stamps from the specified locations with errors, as such items are beyond the scope of this particular listing. Note that some of the catalogue numbers shown are provisional and may be subject to change.

In the 2018 catalogue these tables included prices for the first time. The prices shown are provided for the information of collectors and indicate what one might expect to pay for the said items in the retail market place. Unless noted to the contrary they are for Collectors' Strips (or for Collectors' Pairs of 2nd/2nd Large). If no price is given then at the time of publication the market price was not sufficiently established. (These tables are copyright John M Deering and for the convenience of collectors are reproduced in catalogue style with his permission.)

Post & Go stamps – the different exhibition issues with inscriptions to April 2021: A simplified checklist

Post and Go stamps – the inscriptions from UK and international stamp exhibitions, September 2011–September 2017: A simplified checklist of the Machin, Union Flag and pictorial issues

Stamp Design, Values, **Inscriptions** (see **bold** text) & Note(s)	Year Code	Availability (dates inclusive) & Note(s)	Cat. No. of Stamp Issue Without Inscription, or Closest Match	Collectors' Strip Price
Machin: 1st/1st L/E 20g/WW 10g/WW 20g/WW 40g				
Autumn Stampex 2011, 14–17 September 2011				
Arnold Machin **1911–1999**	None	Available throughout exhibition	FS1a/3a, 4a, 5a & 5e (Type II)	17.00
Spring Stampex 2012, 22–25 February 2012				
Diamond Jubilee **1952–2012**	None	Available throughout exhibition	FS1a/3a, 4a, 5a & 5e (Type II)	15.00
The National Philatelic Exhibition Perth 2012 (Scotland), 19–22 October 2012				
Perth 2012 **19–22 October**	None	Available to non-delegates only on 19–20 October	FS1b/3b, 4b, 5b & 5eb (Type III)	80.00
Spring Stampex 2013, 20–23 February 2013				
The Coronation **60th Anniversary**	None	Available throughout exhibition	FS1b/3b, 4b, 5b & 5eb (Type III)	15.00
The Coronation **60th Anniversary** First line slightly inset.	None	Only known from stock produced in advance of the exhibition for sale at Royal Mail exhibition stand. Available throughout exhibition	FS1b/3b, 4b, 5b & 5eb (Type III)	20.00
84th Annual Congress of Association of Scottish Philatelic Societies (Perth, Scotland),19–20 April 2013				
84th Scottish **Congress 2013**	None	Available throughout exhibition	FS1b/3b, 4b, 5b & 5eb (Type III)	20.00
Australia 2013 World Stamp Exhibition (Melbourne, Australia), 10–15 May 2013				
Australia 2013 **World Stamp Expo** with '**GB**' code	None	Issued to coincide with the exhibition and only available from Royal Mail, Tallents House, Edinburgh	FS1b/3b, 4b, 5b & 5eb (Type III)	18.00
Australia 2013 **Stamp Expo** '**World**' missing, with '**AU**' code	None	Only available from machines at the exhibition	FS1b/3b, 4b, 5b & 5eb (Type III)	29.00
Spring Stampex 2014, 19–22 February 2014				
Stampex 2014 **19–22 February**	None	Available for the majority of the exhibition	FS1b/3b, 4b, 5b & 5eb (Type III)	23.00
	MA13	Sometimes available from the machine	FS77/79, 81/83 (but Type III)	25.00
Machin: 1st/1st L/E 20g/E 60g/WW 20g/WW 60g				
85th Annual Congress of Association of Scottish Philatelic Societies (Perth, Scotland), 11–12 April 2014				
85th Scottish **Congress 2014**	None	Available for the majority of the exhibition	FS1b/3b, 3d, 5b, 5f (but Type III)	30.00
	MA13	Sometimes available from the machine	FS77/80, 82 & 84 (but Type III)	28.00

Post and Go stamps – the inscriptions from UK and international stamp exhibitions, September 2011–September 2017: A simplified checklist of the Machin, Union Flag and pictorial issues

Stamp Design, Values, **Inscriptions** (see **bold** text) & Note(s)	Year Code	Availability (dates inclusive) & Note(s)	Cat. No. of Stamp Issue Without Inscription, or Closest Match	Collectors' Strip Price
Machin: 1st/1st L/E 20g WW 10g/E 60g/WW 20g/WW 60g				
PhilaKorea World Stamp Exhibition, Seoul, Korea 2014, 7–12 August 2014				
PhilaKorea 2014 World Stamp Expo	None	Available from Royal Mail, Tallents House, Edinburgh. Also available from machines throughout exhibition	FS1d, 2d, 3cb, 3d, 5d & 5f (Type IIIA)	18.00[1]
Issued to coincide with the exhibition and available from Royal Mail, Tallents House, Edinburgh, with '**GB**' code. Also available throughout exhibition, with '**KR**' code.	MA13	Available from Royal Mail, Tallents House, Edinburgh. Also available from machines throughout exhibition	FS77b, 78b, 79bb, 80, 82b & 84 (Type IIIA)	20.00[1]
Machin: 1st/1st L/E 20g WW 10g/E 100g/WW 20g/WW 100g				
86th Annual Congress of Association of Scottish Philatelic Societies (Perth, Scotland), 17–18 April 2015				
86th Scottish Congress 2015	MA13	Only available from machines at the exhibition	FS77b, 78b, 79bb, 80ca, 82b & 84ca (Type IIIA)	23.00
	None	Only available from machines at the exhibition	FS1d, 2d, 3cb, 3ea, 5d & 5ga (Type IIIA)	25.00
86th Scottish Congress '**2015**' missing after '**Congress**'.	MA13	Only available from stock produced in advance and for collection from the Post & Go stand at the exhibition	FS77b, 78b, 79bb, 80ca, 82b & 84ca (Type IIIA)	40.00
	None	Only available from stock produced in advance and for collection from the Post & Go stand at the exhibition (Only known from a very small part of this stock)	FS1d, 2d, 3cb, 3ea, 5d & 5ga (Type IIIA)	80.00
LONDON 2015 EUROPHILEX, 13–16 May 2015				
Europhilex London Penny Black 175	MA13	Available for the majority of the exhibition	FS77b, 78b, 79bb, 80ca, 82b & 84ca (Type IIIA)	15.00
	None	Sometimes available from the machine	FS1d, 2d, 3cb, 3ea, 5d & 5ga (Type IIIA)	19.00
SINGAPORE 2015 World Stamp Exhibition, 14–19 August 2015				
Singpex 2015 World Stamp Expo	None	Available from Royal Mail, Tallents House, Edinburgh.	FS1d, 2d, 3cb, 3ea, 5d & 5ga (Type IIIA)	18.00
Issued to coincide with the exhibition and available from Royal Mail, Tallents House, Edinburgh, with '**GB**' code. Also available throughout exhibition, with '**SG**' code.	MA13	Available from Royal Mail, Tallents House, Edinburgh. Also available from machines throughout exhibition	FS77b, 78b, 79bb, 80ca, 82b & 84ca (Type IIIA)	19.00[1]
Autumn Stampex 2015, 16–19 September 2015				
Queen Elizabeth II Longest Reign	None	Available for the majority of the exhibition	FS1d, 2d, 3cb, 3ea, 5d & 5ga (Type IIIA)	15.00
	MA13	Only available from a machine for a very short period on 18 September 2015. Apparently from one roll only	FS77b, 78b, 79bb, 80ca, 82b & 84ca (Type IIIA)	30.00
Spring Stampex 2016, 17–20 February 2016				
500 Years of Royal Mail	None	Available for the majority of the exhibition	FS1d, 2d, 3cb, 3ea, 5d & 5ga (Type IIIA)	15.00
	MA13	Sometimes available from the machine	FS77b, 78b, 79bb, 80ca, 82b & 84ca (Type IIIA)	22.00
87th Annual Congress of Association of Scottish Philatelic Societies (Perth, Scotland), 15–16 April 2016				
87th Scottish Congress 2016 Dual value correctly shown as '**Euro 20g World 10g**'.	MA13	Only available from machines at the exhibition	FS77b, 78b, 79bb, 80ca, 82b & 84ca (Type IIIA)	23.00
87th Scottish Congress 2016 Dual value with '**20g weight**' missing, and instead shown as '**Euro World 10g**'	None	Only available from stock produced in advance and for collection from the Post & Go stand at the exhibition (Stock without a year code is only known without the '**20g weight**' and is from the material produced in advance of the exhibition)	FS1d, 2d, 3cb, 3ea, 5d & 5ga (Type IIIA)	60.00

Post and Go stamps – the inscriptions from UK and international stamp exhibitions, September 2011–September 2017: A simplified checklist of the Machin, Union Flag and pictorial issues

Stamp Design, Values, **Inscriptions** (see **bold** text) & Note(s)	Year Code	Availability (dates inclusive) & Note(s)	Cat. No. of Stamp Issue Without Inscription, or Closest Match	Collectors' Strip Price
Machin: 1st/1st L/E 20g WW 10g/E 100g/WW 20g/WW 100g *continued*				
Spring Stampex 2017, 15–18 February 2017				
65th Anniversary of HM The Queen's Accession	MA14	Available for the majority of the exhibition	FS77b, 78b, 79bb, 80ca, 82b & 84ca (Type IIIA)	16.00
	MA13	Only known from a small part of the stock produced in advance of the exhibition for sale at Royal Mail exhibition stand	FS77b, 78b, 79bb, 80ca, 82b & 84ca (Type IIIA)	40.00
Machin Anniversary 1967–2017	MA14	Available for the majority of the exhibition	FS77b, 78b, 79bb, 80ca, 82b & 84ca (Type IIIA)	16.00
	None	Only available from a machine for a very short period on 16 February 2017. Apparently from one roll only	FS1d, 2d, 3cb, 3ea, 5d & 5ga (Type IIIA)	42.00
88th Annual Congress of Association of Scottish Philatelic Societies (Perth, Scotland), 21–22 April 2017				
88th Scottish Congress	MA15	Available from the machine for part of the exhibition	FS77b, 78b, 79bb, 80ca, 82b & 84ca (Type IIIA)	35.00
'2017' missing after **'Congress'** All stock dispensed from the exhibition's machine(s) was missing '2017'. (See also 50th Anniversary Machin design which has '2017').	None	Available from the machine for part of the exhibition	FS1d, 2d, 3cb, 3ea, 5d & 5ga (Type IIIA)	35.00
	MA13	Only available from the machine for a very short period. Apparently a part or single roll only	FS77b, 78b, 79bb, 80ca, 82b & 84ca (Type IIIA)	—
50th Anniversary Machin design in six different colours: 1st/1st L/E 20g WW 10g/E 100g/WW 20g/WW 100g				
88th Annual Congress of Association of Scottish Philatelic Societies (Perth, Scotland), 21–22 April 2017				
88th Scottish Congress 2017 Stock bearing '2017' only came from stock produced in advance of the exhibition.	n/a	The 50th Anniversary Machin design only came from stock produced in advance and for collection from the Post & Go stand at the exhibition. This design used was: i) Used by mistake (intended design was the standard Machin which was not used for stock produced in advance, instead could only be obtained from the exhibition's machine(s) [See elsewhere in this table]). ii) Had not been officially issued (it was pre-released – official issue date was the 5 June 2017)	FS179a/184a (Type IIIA)	95.00
50th Anniversary Machin design: 1st x 6 different colours				
Autumn Stampex 2017, 13–16 September 2017				
Autumn Stampex 2017	n/a	Available throughout exhibition	FS179a/184a (Type IIIA)	9.00
Union Flag: 1st/1st L/E 20g/WW 10g/WW 20g/WW 40g				
Autumn Stampex 2012, 26–29 September 2012				
Diamond Jubilee 1952–2012	None	Available throughout exhibition	FS39/44 (but Type III)	15.00
The National Philatelic Exhibition Perth 2012 (Scotland), 19–22 October 2012				
Perth 2012 19–22 October	None	Available to non-delegates only on 19–20 October	FS39/44 (but Type III)	80.00
84th Annual Congress of Association of Scottish Philatelic Societies (Perth, Scotland), 19–20 April 2013				
84th Scottish Congress 2013	None	Available throughout exhibition	FS39/44 (but Type III)	20.00
Australia 2013 World Stamp Exhibition (Melbourne, Australia), 10–15 May 2013				
Australia 2013 World Stamp Expo with **'GB'** code.	None	Issued to coincide with the exhibition and only available from Royal Mail, Tallents House, Edinburgh	FS39/44 (but Type III)	18.00
Australia 2013 Stamp Expo **'World'** missing, with **'AU'** code.	None	Only available from machines at the exhibition	FS39/44 (but Type III)	28.00
Autumn Stampex 2013, 18–21 September 2013				
The Coronation 60th Anniversary	MA13	Available throughout exhibition	FS85/7 & 89/91 (but Type III)	15.00

1st Class
up to 100g
Arnold Machin
1911-1999
002011 94-000185-37

1st Large
up to 100g
Diamond Jubilee
1952 - 2012
002012 23-000109-80

Worldwide
up to 10g
Perth 2012
19-22 October
AOGB12 A2-000643-10

Worldwide
up to 20g
The Coronation
60th Anniversary
A2GB13 B1-001689-77

Worldwide
up to 20g
The Coronation
60th Anniversary
A2GB13 B1-003087-17

Worldwide
up to 40g
84th Scottish
Congress 2013
A4GB13 A4-001108-54

Worldwide
up to 40g
Australia 2013
World Stamp Expo
A5GB13 B1-003875-42

Worldwide
up to 40g
Australia 2013
Stamp Expo
A5AU13 A3-001510-12

1st Large
up to 100g
Stampex 2014
19-22 February
B2GB14 A004-0405-236

Europe
up to 20g
85th Scottish
Congress 2014
B4GB14 B002-0135-141

Europe
up to 60g
PhilaKorea 2014
World Stamp Expo
B8KR14 A003-1030-226

Europe
up to 100g
86th Scottish
Congress 2015
B4GB15 A006-0267-064

Europe
up to 100g
86th Scottish
Congress
B4GB15 B001-2974-118

Europe
up to 100g
Europhilex London
Penny Black 175
B5GB15 B001-2714-058

Worldwide
up to 100g
Singpex 2015
World Stamp Expo
B8GB15 B001-1621-066

Worldwide
up to 100g
Queen Elizabeth II
Longest Reign
89GB15 B001-1788-108

Euro 20g
World 10g
500 Years of Royal Mail
B2GB16 B001-4379-003

Euro 20g
World 10g
87th Scottish
Congress 2016
B4GB16 A011-2463-543

Euro
World 10g
87th Scottish
Congress 2016
B4GB16 B001-4624-067

Europe
up to 100g
65th Anniversary of
HM The Queen's Accession
B2GB17 B001-8185-238

Worldwide
up to 20g
Machin Anniversary
1967-2017
B2GB17 B001-8163-215

The different inscriptions from exhibitions. Where the same inscription exists on more than one design only one may be pictured.

Post and Go stamps – the inscriptions from UK and international stamp exhibitions, September 2011–September 2017: A simplified checklist of the Machin, Union Flag and pictorial issues

Stamp Design, Values, **Inscriptions** (see **bold text**) & Note(s)	Year Code	Availability (dates inclusive) & Note(s)	Cat. No. of Stamp Issue Without Inscription, or Closest Match	Collectors' Strip Price
Union Flag: 1st/1st L/E 20g/E 60g/WW 20g/WW 60g				
85th Annual Congress of Association of Scottish Philatelic Societies (Perth, Scotland), 11–12 April 2014				
85th Scottish Congress 2014	MA13	Available for the majority of the exhibition	FS85/8, 90 & 92 (but Type III)	30.00
	None	Sometimes available from the machine	FS39/41, 41*b*, 43 & 44*b* (but Type III)	27.00
Union Flag: 1st/1st L/E 20g WW 10g/E 60g/WW 20g/WW 60g				
PhilaKorea World Stamp Exhibition, Seoul, Korea 2014, 7–12 August 2014				
PhilaKorea 2014 World Stamp Exhibition Issued to coincide with the exhibition and available from Royal Mail, Tallents House, Edinburgh, with '**GB**' code. Also available throughout exhibition, with '**KR**' code.	None	Available from Royal Mail, Tallents House, Edinburgh. Also available from machines throughout exhibition	FS39, 40, 41*a*, 41*b*, 43 & 44*b* (but Type IIIA)	20.00[1]
	MA13	Only known from a very small part of the stock available from Royal Mail, Tallents House, Edinburgh	FS85/6, 87*a*, 88, 90 & 92 (but Type IIIA)	£125
Spring Stampex 2015, 18–21 February 2015				
Spring Stampex February 2015	None	Available throughout exhibition	FS39, 40, 41*a*, 41*b*, 43 & 44*b* (but Type IIIA)	15.00
Union Flag: 1st/1st L/E 20g WW 10g/E 100g/WW 20g/WW 100g				
86th Annual Congress of Association of Scottish Philatelic Societies (Perth, Scotland), 17–18 April 2015				
86th Scottish Congress 2015	None	Only available from machines at the exhibition	FS39, 40, 41*a*, 41*c*, 43 & 44*c* (but Type IIIA)	20.00
86th Scottish Congress '**2015**' missing after '**Congress**'.	None	Only available from stock produced in advance and for collection from the Post & Go stand at the exhibition	FS39, 40, 41*a*, 41*c*, 43 & 44*c* (but Type IIIA)	40.00
SINGAPORE 2015 World Stamp Exhibition, 14–19 August 2015				
Singpex 2015 World Stamp Expo Issued to coincide with the exhibition and available from Royal Mail, Tallents House, Edinburgh, with '**GB**' code. Also available throughout exhibition, with '**SG**' code.	None	Available from Royal Mail, Tallents House, Edinburgh. Also available from machines throughout exhibition	FS39, 40, 41*a*, 41*c*, 43 & 44*c* (but Type IIIA)	17.00[1]
HONG KONG 2015 (31st Asian International Stamp Exhibition), 20–23 November 2015				
Hong Kong November 2015 Issued to coincide with the exhibition and available from Royal Mail, Tallents House, Edinburgh, with '**GB**' code. Also available throughout exhibition, with '**HK**' code.	None	Available from Royal Mail, Tallents House, Edinburgh. Also available from machines throughout exhibition	FS39, 40, 41*a*, 41*c*, 43 & 44*c* (but Type IIIA)	16.00[1]
87th Annual Congress of Association of Scottish Philatelic Societies (Perth, Scotland), 15–16 April 2016				
87th Scottish Congress 2016 Dual value correctly shown as '**Euro 20g World 10g**'.	None	Only available from machines at the exhibition	FS39, 40, 41*a*, 41*c*, 43 & 44*c* (but Type IIIA)	20.00
87th Scottish Congress 2016 Dual value with '**20g weight**' missing, and instead shown as '**Euro World 10g**'.	None	Only available from stock produced in advance and for collection from the Post & Go stand at the exhibition	FS39, 40, 41*a*, 41*c*, 43 & 44*c* (but Type IIIA)	40.00

Post and Go stamps – the inscriptions from UK and international stamp exhibitions, September 2011–September 2017: A simplified checklist of the Machin, Union Flag and pictorial issues

Stamp Design, Values, **Inscriptions** (see **bold** text) & Note(s)	Year Code	Availability (dates inclusive) & Note(s)	Cat. No. of Stamp Issue Without Inscription, or Closest Match	Collectors' Strip Price
Union Flag: 1st/1st L/E 20g WW 10g/E 100g/WW 20g/WW 100g *continued*				
World Stamp Show-NY 2016 (New York), 28 May–4 June 2016				
World Stamp Show NY2016 Issued to coincide with the exhibition and available from Royal Mail, Tallents House, Edinburgh, with '**GB**' code. Also available throughout exhibition, with '**US**' code.	None	Available from Royal Mail, Tallents House, Edinburgh. Also available from machines throughout exhibition	FS39, 40, 41*a*, 41*c*, 43 & 44*c* (but Type IIIA)	19.00¹
Poppy: 1st/1st L/E 20g WW 10g/E 60g/WW 20g/WW 60g				
Autumn Stampex 2014, 17–20 September 2014				
First World War Centenary	MA14	Available throughout exhibition	FS103, 104, 105, 106, 107 & 108 (but Type IIIA)	18.00
Poppy: 1st/1st L/E 20g WW 10g/E 100g/WW 20g/WW 100g				
Autumn Stampex 2016, 14–17 September 2016				
The Battle of the Somme (+ tank logo)	MA15	Available throughout exhibition	FS137/142 (Type IIIA)	19.00
Autumn Stampex 2017, 13–16 September 2017				
WWI Battle of Passchendaele	MA15	Available throughout exhibition	FS137/142 (Type IIIA)	18.00
Hong Kong Sea Travel: 1st/1st L/E 20g WW 10g/E 100g/WW 20g/WW 100g				
HONG KONG 2015 (31st Asian International Stamp Exhibition), 20–23 November 2015				
Hong Kong November 2015 Issued to coincide with the exhibition and available from Royal Mail, Tallents House, Edinburgh, with '**GB**' code. Also available throughout exhibition, with '**HK**' code.	MA15	Available from Royal Mail, Tallents House, Edinburgh. Also available from machines throughout exhibition	FS131/136 (but Type IIIA & stamps digitally printed)	16.00¹

The different inscriptions from exhibitions. Where the same inscription exists on more than one design only one may be pictured.

Post and Go stamps – the inscriptions from UK and international stamp exhibitions, September 2011–September 2017: A simplified checklist of the Machin, Union Flag and pictorial issues

Stamp Design, Values, **Inscriptions** (see **bold** text) & Note(s)	Year Code	Availability (dates inclusive) & Note(s)	Cat. No. of Stamp Issue Without Inscription, or Closest Match	Collectors' Strip Price
New York Sea Travel: 1st/1st L/E 20g WW 10g/E 100g/WW 20g/WW 100g				
World Stamp Show-NY 2016 (New York), 28 May–4 June 2016				
World Stamp Show NY2016 Issued to coincide with the exhibition and available from Royal Mail, Tallents House, Edinburgh, with '**GB**' code. Also available throughout exhibition, with '**US**' code.	MA15	Available from Royal Mail, Tallents House, Edinburgh. Also available from machines throughout exhibition	FS131/136 (but Type IIIA & stamps digitally printed)	19.00¹
Lion (Heraldic Beast): 1st/1st L/E 20g WW 10g/E 100g/WW 20g/WW 100g				
87th Annual Congress of Association of Scottish Philatelic Societies (Perth, Scotland), 5–16 April 2016				
87th Scottish Congress 2016 Dual value correctly shown as '**Euro 20g World 10g**'.	MA15	Only available from machines at the exhibition	FS125/130 (but Type IIIA)	20.00
87th Scottish Congress 2016 Dual value without '**20g weight**', and instead shown as '**Euro World 10g**'.	MA15	Only available from stock produced in advance and for collection from the Post & Go stand at the exhibition	FS125/130 (but Type IIIA)	36.00
88th Annual Congress of Association of Scottish Philatelic Societies (Perth, Scotland), 21–22 April 2017				
88th Scottish Congress '**2017**' missing after '**Congress**'.	MA15	Only available from machines at the exhibition, but different to stock produced in advance (see below) which was not fully appreciated until after exhibition had ended	FS125/130 (but Type IIIA)	—
88th Scottish Congress 2017	MA15	Stock bearing '**2017**' only came from stock produced in advance and for collection from the Post & Go stand at the exhibition	FS125/130 (but Type IIIA)	50.00
Thistle (Symbolic Flower): 1st/1st L/E 20g WW 10g/E 100g/WW 20g/WW 100g				
88th Annual Congress of Association of Scottish Philatelic Societies (Perth, Scotland), 21–22 April 2017				
88th Scottish Congress '**2017**' missing after '**Congress**'.	MA17	Only available from machines at the exhibition, but different to stock produced in advance (see below) which was not fully appreciated until after exhibition had ended	FS103, 104, 105, 106b, 107, 108b (but Type IIIA & stamps digitally printed)	—
88th Scottish Congress 2017	MA17	Stock bearing '**2017**' only came from stock produced in advance and for collection from the Post & Go stand at the exhibition	FS103, 104, 105, 106b, 107, 108b (but Type IIIA & stamps digitally printed)	50.00

¹ When a similar item is available from more than one location the price given is for the cheaper of the two.

Autumn Stampex 2017, 13–16 September 2017, was the last time Post & Go kiosks were at exhibitions.

Glitches affecting inscriptions and lasting only a very short time and/or which exist in small quantities are beyond the scope of these tables.

The different inscriptions from exhibitions. Where the same inscription exists on more than one design only one may be pictured.

Post & Go stamps – the different issues and inscriptions from '*The Postal Museum*' (formerly 'The BPMA'), to April 2022: A simplified checklist

Stamp Design, Values, **Inscriptions** (see **bold** text) & Note(s)	Year Code	Availability (dates inclusive) & Note(s)	Cat. No. of Stamp Issue Without Inscription, or Closest Match	Collectors' Strip Price
Post & Go stamps – the inscriptions from *The Postal Museum* (formerly 'The BPMA'), December 2012–April 2022: A simplified checklist of the Machin, Union Flag and pictorial issues				
Machin: 1st/1st L/E 20g/WW 10g/WW 20g/WW 40g				
The B.P.M.A. Low set; inscription is immediately above code line.	None	3 December 2012–18 February 2014	FS1b/3b, 4b, 5b & 5eb (Type III)	17.00
The B.P.M.A. Postage Due 1914 An RMS II machine replaced existing machine from 24 March 2014. The stamps from it have a subtly different typeface.	None	Sometimes available between 19 February–21 March 2014	FS1b/3b, 4b, 5b & 5eb (Type III)	23.00
	MA13	Sometimes available between 19 February–21 March 2014 24–28 March 2014 (RMS II machine)	FS77/79, 81/83 (but Type III)	30.00[1]
Machin: 1st/1st L/E 20g/E 60g/WW 20g/WW 60g				
The B.P.M.A. Postage Due 1914	MA13	31 March–25 April 2014	FS77/80, 82 & 84 (but Type III)	25.00
Machin: 1st/1st L/E 20g WW 10g/E 60g/WW 20g/WW 60g				
The B.P.M.A. High set; inscription is immediately below service indicator. E 20g WW 10g in large typeface.	MA13	28 April–19 August 2014	FS77, 78, 79b, 80, 82 & 84 (but Type III)	30.00
The B.P.M.A. Inland Airmail 1934 + Airmail logo	None	Sometimes available between 20 August–20 October 2014	FS1d, 2d, 3cb, 3d, 5d & 5f (Type IIIA)	25.00
	MA13	Sometimes available between 20 August–20 October 2014	FS77b, 78b, 79bb, 80, 82b & 84 (Type IIIA)	20.00
The B.P.M.A. Low set; inscription is immediately above code line. All six values have a revised (smaller) typeface.	None	21 October 2014–17 February 2015	FS1d, 2d, 3cb, 3d, 5d & 5f (Type IIIA)	23.00
The B.P.M.A. Trollope 200 + Postbox logo	MA13	18 February–28 March 2015	FS77b, 78b, 79bb, 80, 82b & 84 (Type IIIA)	19.00

Europe up to 20g
The B.P.M.A.
ADGB12 A1-001063-69

Worldwide up to 40g
The B.P.M.A.
Postage Due 1914
A2GB14 A1-003615-96

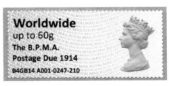

Worldwide up to 60g
The B.P.M.A.
Postage Due 1914
B4GB14 A001-0247-210

Euro 20g World 10g
The B.P.M.A.
B6GB14 A001-0694-171

Europe up to 100g
The B.P.M.A.
B8GB15 A001-3598-136

Worldwide up to 100g
The B.P.M.A.
Penny Black 175
B5GB15 A001-3336-024

Worldwide up to 100g
The Postal Museum
B2GB16 A001-4883-204

1st Class up to 100g
The Postal Museum
B2GB16 A001-4571-343

Euro World 10g
The Postal Museum
B3GB16 A001-5079-226

Euro 20g World 10g
The Postal Museum
B7GB18 A001-0658-015

The different inscriptions from *The Postal Museum*. Where the same inscription exists on more than one design only one may be pictured.

Post & Go stamps – the inscriptions from *The Postal Museum* (formerly 'The BPMA'), December 2012–April 2022:
A simplified checklist of the Machin, Union Flag and pictorial issues

Stamp Design, Values, **Inscriptions** (see **bold text**) & Note(s)	Year Code	Availability (dates inclusive) & Note(s)	Cat. No. of Stamp Issue Without Inscription, or Closest Match	Collectors' Strip Price
Machin: 1st/1st L/E 20g WW 10g/E 100g/WW 20g/WW 100g				
The B.P.M.A. **Trollope 200** + Postbox logo	MA13	30 March–30 April 2015	FS77b, 78b, 79bb, 80ca, 82b & 84ca (Type IIIA)	35.00
The B.P.M.A. Low set; inscription is immediately above code line. All six values have a revised (smaller) typeface.	MA13	1–5 May 2015 8 August 2015–29 January 2016	FS77b, 78b, 79bb, 80ca, 82b & 84ca (Type IIIA)	22.00
The B.P.M.A. **Penny Black 175** + Maltese Cross logo	MA13	6 May–7 August 2015	FS77b, 78b, 79bb, 80ca, 82b & 84ca (Type IIIA)	18.00
The Postal Museum + Museum's Envelope logo (small format) logo positioned before the wording. Envelope logo originally positioned inset from the left. From 17 February 2016 Envelope logo repositioned ranged left.	MA13	1 February–28 March 2016 1 April–19 August 2016 Late August–13 September 2016 Sometimes available between 14 November 2016–2 June 2017	FS77b, 78b, 79bb, 80ca, 82b & 84ca (Type IIIA)	20.00[1]
	None	Available for a short time sometime between 19 August–late August 2016	FS1d, 2d, 3cb, 3ea, 5d & 5ga (Type IIIA)	—
	MA15	Sometimes available between 14 November 2016–2 June 2017	FS77b, 78b, 79bb, 80ca, 82b & 84ca (Type IIIA)	21.00
The Postal Museum + Museum's Envelope logo (small format) logo positioned before the wording. Dual value without '**20g weight**', and instead shown as '**Euro World 10g**'	MA13	29–31 March 2016	FS77b, 78b, 79bb *var*, 80ca, 82b & 84ca (Type IIIA)	—
			Single: i.e. Euro World 10g/FS79bb *var* (but TIIIA)	30.00
The Postal Museum **King Edward VIII 1936** + ERI VIII Cypher logo, + Museum's Envelope logo (small format) logo positioned before the wording.	None	14 September–24 October 2016	FS1d, 2d, 3cb, 3ea, 5d & 5ga (Type IIIA)	19.00
	MA13	Apparently available for a few hours only on 14 September 2016	FS77b, 78b, 79bb, 80ca, 82b & 84ca (Type IIIA)	—
	MA15	24 October–11 November 2016	FS77b, 78b, 79bb, 80ca, 82b & 84ca (Type IIIA)	23.00
The Postal Museum Revised generic inscription without Envelope logo.	MA14	2 July–11 September 2018 Late autumn/winter 2019–18 March 2020 except when 'MA15' available	FS77b, 78b, 79bb, 80ca, 82b & 84ca (Type IIIA)	19.00
	None	Apparently available for a few hours only on 29 August 2018.	FS1d, 2d, 3cb, 3ea, 5d & 5ga (Type IIIA)	—
	MA15	1 January 2019–12 February 2019 Mid October–early 2020 except when 'MA14' available	FS77b, 78b, 79bb, 80ca, 82b & 84ca (Type IIIA)	19.00
The Postal Museum **'F' box 50** + Postbox logo	None	Apparently available for a few hours only on 12 September 2018	FS1d, 2d, 3cb, 3ea, 5d & 5ga (Type IIIA)	—
	MA14	12 September–22 October 2018	FS77b, 78b, 79bb, 80ca, 82b & 84ca (Type IIIA)	19.00
	MA15	22 October–7 November 2018	FS77b, 78b, 79bb, 80ca, 82b & 84ca (Type IIIA)	19.00
The Postal Museum **NPM 50** Unintentional issue when the Machin design was loaded into the machine and the return of the generic inscription (i.e. '**The Postal Museum**') was delayed due to a technical reason.	None	Apparently available for a few hours only on 11 October 2019	FS1d, 2d, 3cb, 3ea, 5d & 5ga (Type IIIA)	—
	MA14	Available for a few hours only on 11 October 2019	FS77b, 78b, 79bb, 80ca, 82b & 84ca (Type IIIA)	20.00
	MA15	11 October 2019–mid October 2019	FS77b, 78b, 79bb, 80ca, 82b & 84ca (Type IIIA)	22.00
Mail Rail	MA14	29 October–1 December 2019 except when 'MA15' available (see below) 1 January–18 March 2020	FS77b, 78b, 79bb, 80ca, 82b & 84ca (Type IIIA)	20.00
	MA15	Available for a few hours only on 9 November 2019	FS77b, 78b, 79bb, 80ca, 82b & 84ca (Type IIIA)	24.00

Post & Go stamps – the inscriptions from *The Postal Museum* (formerly 'The BPMA'), December 2012–April 2022:
A simplified checklist of the Machin, Union Flag and pictorial issues

Stamp Design, Values, **Inscriptions** (see **bold** text) & Note(s)	Year Code	Availability (dates inclusive) & Note(s)	Cat. No. of Stamp Issue Without Inscription, or Closest Match	Collectors' Strip Price
Machin: 1st/1st L/E 20g WW 10g/E 100g WW 20g/WW 100g Zone 1 & 3/WW 100g Zone 2 *[Dual-zone value with ampersand i.e. 'World 100g Zone 1 & 3']*				
The Postal Museum Virtual Stampex 2020	MA14	Only available via mail order from The Postal Museum London online shop between 1–3 October 2020[2], i.e. duration Virtual Autumn Stampex 2020	FS77b, 78b, 79bb (Type IIIA), 80d, 84d var & 84e (but Type IIIA)	25.00
The Postal Museum	MA14	29 October–1 November 2020[2]	FS77b, 78b, 79bb (Type IIIA), 80d, 84d var & 84e (but Type IIIA)	25.00
Mail Rail	MA14	29 October–1 November 2020[2] 3 November 2020[2] 3–19 December 2020[2]	FS77b, 78b, 79bb (Type IIIA), 80d, 84d var & 84e (but Type IIIA)	25.00
Machin: 1st/1st Large/E 100g WW 20g/WW 100g/E Large 100g/WW Large 100g				
The Postal Museum Wish You Were Here + Postcard logo	MA13	20 May 2021–2 January 2022	FS77b, 78b, 80d (but Type IIIA), 84ca, 80e (but Type IIIA) and 84f (but Type IIIA)	30.00
The Postal Museum	MA14	5 January–18 February 2022	FS77b, 78b, 80d (but Type IIIA), 84ca, 80e (but Type IIIA) and 84f (but Type IIIA) Set of two singles: i.e. E Large 100g/FS80e & WW Large 100g/FS84f (but TIIIA)	32.00 / 20.00
	MA13	27 February–27 March 2022 30 April–1 June 2022 2 July–10 November 2022	FS77b, 78b, 80d (but Type IIIA), 84ca, 80e (but Type IIIA) and 84f (but Type IIIA)	32.00
The Postal Museum London 2022	MA13	19–26 February 2022	FS77b, 78b, 80d (but Type IIIA), 84ca, 80e (but Type IIIA) and 84f (but Type IIIA)	32.00
The Postal Museum Sorting Britain	MA13	30 March–22 April 2022	FS77b, 78b, 80d (but Type IIIA), 84ca, 80e (but Type IIIA) and 84f (but Type IIIA)	32.00
	R20Y	From 23 April 2022	FS77b, 78b, 80d (but Type IIIA), 84ca, 80e (but Type IIIA) and 84f (but Type IIIA)	32.00
Mail Rail	MA14	20 May–10 Novemeber 2021	FS77b, 78b, 80d (but Type IIIA), 84ca, 80e (but Type IIIA) and 84f (but Type IIIA) Set of two singles: i.e. E Large 100g/FS80e & WW Large 100g/FS84f (but TIIIA)	20.00
	MA13	8 December 2021–1 June 2022	FS77b, 78b, 80d (but Type IIIA), 84ca, 80e (but Type IIIA) and 84f (but Type IIIA)	32.00
	R20Y	1–2 June 2022 2 July–30 November 2022	FS77b, 78b, 80d (but Type IIIA), 84ca, 80e (but Type IIIA) and 84f (but Type IIIA)	32.00
Mail Rail The Queen's Platinum Jubilee	R20Y	3 June–1 July–2022	FS77b, 78b, 80d (but Type IIIA), 84ca, 80e (but Type IIIA) and 84f (but Type IIIA)	32.00

The different inscriptions from *The Postal Museum*. Where the same inscription exists on more than one design only one may be pictured.

Post & Go stamps – the inscriptions from *The Postal Museum* (formerly 'The BPMA'), December 2012–April 2022: A simplified checklist of the Machin, Union Flag and pictorial issues

Stamp Design, Values, **Inscriptions** (see **bold text**) & Note(s)	Year Code	Availability (dates inclusive) & Note(s)	Cat. No. of Stamp Issue Without Inscription, or Closest Match	Collectors' Strip Price
50th Anniversary Machin design: 1st x 6 different colours				
The Postal Museum + Museum's Envelope logo (small format) logo positioned before the wording.	n/a	5 June–12 July 2017	FS179a x 6 (Type IIIA)	9.50
The Postal Museum Official Opening 2017	n/a	25 July 2017 28 July–12 September 2017	FS179a x 6 (Type IIIA)	9.50
The Postal Museum Revised generic inscription without Envelope logo.	n/a	13 September–23 October 2017 2–22 January 2018 23 February–1 July 2018 For a brief time on 26 March 2018 Collectors' Strips of 1st WW 100g were dispensed in error	FS179a x 6 (Type IIIA)	9.00
The Postal Museum NPM 50	n/a	13 February 2019–10 October 2019	FS179a x 6 (Type IIIA)	9.00
The Postal Museum The Queen's Platinum Jubilee	n/a	3 June–1 July–2022	FS179a x 6 (Type IIIA)	9.00
Machin: 2nd/2nd L				
The B.P.M.A. Inland Airmail 1934 + Airmail logo	MA12	20 August–20 October 2014	FS93b/94b (Type IIIA)	10.00
The B.P.M.A. Inland Airmail 1934 + Airmail logo in '**1st/1stL**' values. '**1st/1stL**' on (blue-coloured FT **14**) second class stock, due to a software glitch.	MA12	Available for a few hours only on 16 September 2014	FT **14** in 1st/1stL (Type IIIA) Set of two singles: i.e. 1st/1stL/FT 14 (TIIIA)	n/a 50.00
The B.P.M.A.	MA12	21 October–12 November 2014 29 December 2014–17 February 2015 1–5 May 2015 8 August–13 November 2015 4–29 January 2016	FS93b/94b (Type IIIA)	6.50
	MA13	Apparently available for a few hours only on 5 May 2015	FS93b/94b (Type IIIA)	—
The B.P.M.A. Trollope 200 + Postbox logo	MA12	18 February–30 April 2015	FS93b/94b (Type IIIA)	6.50
The B.P.M.A. Penny Black 175 + Maltese Cross logo	MA13	6 May–7 July 2015 10 July–(early) August 2015	FS93b/94b (Type IIIA)	6.50
The B.P.M.A. Penny Black 175 + Maltese Cross logo Maltese Cross logo set lower and to right (following a software upgrade).	MA12	Available (early) August–7 August 2015 (Repositioned Maltese Cross logo obscures 'MA12')	FS93b/94b (Type IIIA)	13.00

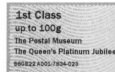

The different inscriptions from *The Postal Museum*. Where the same inscription exists on more than one design only one may be pictured.

Post & Go stamps – the inscriptions from *The Postal Museum* (formerly 'The BPMA'), December 2012–April 2022: A simplified checklist of the Machin, Union Flag and pictorial issues

Stamp Design, Values, Inscriptions (see **bold text**) & Note(s)	Year Code	Availability (dates inclusive) & Note(s)	Cat. No. of Stamp Issue Without Inscription, or Closest Match	Collectors' Strip Price
Machin: 2nd/2nd L *continued*				
The Postal Museum + Museum's Envelope logo (small format) logo positioned before the wording. Envelope logo originally positioned inset from the left. From 17 February 2016 Envelope logo repositioned range left.	MA12	1 February–13 September 2016 3–24 January 2017 25 January–12 July 2017 except when 'CL16S' available (see below)	FS93b/94b (Type IIIA)	5.50[1]
	CL16S	Sometimes available between 25 January–12 July 2017	FS157/8 (but Type IIIA)	5.75
The Postal Museum King Edward VIII 1936 + ERI VIII Cypher logo, + Museum's Envelope logo (small format) logo positioned before the wording.	MA12	14 September–11 November 2016	FS93b/94b (Type IIIA)	6.00
The Postal Museum Official Opening 2017	CL16S	25 July 2017 28 July–12 September 2017	FS157/158 (but Type IIIA)	6.00
	MA15	(Early) September–12 September 2017	FS93b/94b (Type IIIA)	6.00
The Postal Museum Revised generic inscription without Envelope logo.	MA15	13 September–12 November 2017 2–22 January 2018 23 February–11 September 2018 1 January 2019–18 March 2020 29 October–1 November 2020[2] 3 January–30 November 2022	FS93b/94b (Type IIIA)	6.00
The Postal Museum 'F' box 50 + Postbox logo	MA15	12 September–7 November 2018	FS93b/94b (Type IIIA)	6.00
The Postal Museum Wish You Were Here + Postcard logo	MA15	20 May–30 November 2022	FS93b/94b (Type IIIA)	5.00
Union Flag: 1st/1st L/E 20g/WW 10g/WW 20g/WW 40g				
The B.P.M.A. Low set; inscription is immediately above code line.	None	21 February–4 November 2013 30 December 2013–18 February 2014	FS39/44 (but Type III)	17.00
The B.P.M.A. Postage Due 1914 An RMS II machine replaced existing machine from 24 March 2014. The stamps from it have a subtly different typeface.	None	Sometimes available between 19–21 February 2014 22 February–21 March 2014 24–28 March 2014 (RMS II machine)	FS39/44 (but Type III)	23.00[1]
	MA13	Sometimes available between 19–21 February 2014	FS85/7 & 89/91 (but Type III)	55.00
Union Flag: 1st/1st L/E 20g/E 60g/WW 20g/WW 60g				
The B.P.M.A. Postage Due 1914	None	31 March–25 April 2014	FS39/41, 41b, 43 & 44b (but Type III)	20.00
Union Flag: 1st/1st L/E 20g WW 10g/E 60g/WW 20g/WW 60g				
The B.P.M.A. High set; inscription is immediately below service indicator. E 20g WW 10g in large typeface.	None	28 April–19 August 2014	FS39, 40, 41*a*, 41*b*, 43 & 44*b* (but Type III)	25.00
The B.P.M.A. Low set; inscription is immediately above code line. All six values have a revised (smaller) typeface.	None	21 October 2014–17 February 2015	FS39, 40, 41*a*, 41*b*, 43 & 44*b* (but Type IIIA)	25.00

The different inscriptions from *The Postal Museum*. Where the same inscription exists on more than one design only one may be pictured.

Post & Go stamps – the inscriptions from *The Postal Museum* (formerly 'The BPMA'), December 2012–April 2022:
A simplified checklist of the Machin, Union Flag and pictorial issues

Stamp Design, Values, **Inscriptions** (see **bold text**) & Note(s)	Year Code	Availability (dates inclusive) & Note(s)	Cat. No. of Stamp Issue Without Inscription, or Closest Match	Collectors' Strip Price
Union Flag: 1st/1st L/E 20g WW 10g/E 60g/WW 20g/WW 60g *continued*				
The B.P.M.A. High set; inscription is immediately below service indicator. All six values have a revised (smaller) typeface.	None	18 February–28 March 2015	FS39, 40, 41*a*, 41*b*, 43 & 44*b* (but Type IIIA)	45.00
Union Flag: 1st/1st L/E 20g WW 10g/E 100g/WW 20g/WW 100g				
The B.P.M.A. Low set; inscription is immediately above code line. All six values have a revised (smaller) typeface.	None	30 March 2015–29 January 2016	FS39, 40, 41*a*, 41*c*, 43 & 44*c* (but Type IIIA)	25.00
The **Postal** **Museum** + Museum's large format Envelope logo positioned before wording.	None	1 February–28 March 2016 1 April 2016–12 July 2017	FS39, 40, 41*a*, 41*c*, 43 & 44*c* (but Type IIIA)	19.00
The **Postal** **Museum** + Museum's large format Envelope logo positioned before wording. Dual value without '**20g weight**', and instead shown as '**Euro** **World 10g**'	None	29–31 March 2016	FS39, 40, 41*a* var, 41*c*, 43 & 44*c* (but Type IIIA) Single: i.e. Euro World 10g/FS41*a* var (but TIIIA)	— 25.00
The Postal Museum **Official Opening**[3]	None	25 July 2017 28 July–12 September 2017	FS39, 40, 41*a*, 41*c*, 43 & 44*c* (but Type IIIA)	19.00
The Postal Museum Revised generic inscription without Envelope logo.	None	30 November 2018–10 September 2019	FS39, 40, 41*a*, 41*c*, 43 & 44*c* (but Type IIIA)	19.00
Union Flag: 1st/1st L/E 20g WW 10g/E 100g WW 20g/WW 100g Zone 1 & 3/WW 100g Zone 2 *[Dual-zone value with ampersand i.e. '**World 100g Zone 1 & 3**']*				
The Postal Museum	None	29 October–1 November 2020[2] 3 November 2020[2] 3–19 December 2020[2]	FS39, 40, 41*a*, 41*d*, 44*d* & 44*e* (but Type IIIA)	25.00
Union Flag: 1st/1st Large/E 100g WW 20g/WW 100g/E Large 100g/WW Large 100g				
The Postal Museum	None	20 May–30 November 2021 05 January–27 March 2022 30 April–1 June 2022 2 July–10 November 2022	FS39, 40, 41*d*, 44*c*, 41 var & 44 var (but Type IIIA) Set of two singles: i.e. E Large 100g/FS41 var & WW Large 100g/FS44 var (but TIIIA)	32.00 20.00
	MA19	Available for a few hours only on 11 November 2022	FS85a, 86a, 87a, 88 var, 92 var & 92 var (but Type IIIA & stamps digitally printed)	—
The Postal Museum **Sorting Britain**	MA19	From 30 March 2022–1 January 2023	FS85a, 86a, 87a, 88 var, 92 var & 92 var (but Type IIIA & stamps digitally printed)	30.00

The different inscriptions from *The Postal Museum*. Where the same inscription exists on more than one design only one may be pictured.

Post & Go stamps – the inscriptions from *The Postal Museum* (formerly 'The BPMA'), December 2012–April 2022: A simplified checklist of the Machin, Union Flag and pictorial issues

Stamp Design, Values, **Inscriptions** (see **bold text**) & Note(s)	Year Code	Availability (dates inclusive) & Note(s)	Cat. No. of Stamp Issue Without Inscription, or Closest Match	Collectors' Strip Price
Common Poppy: 1st/1st L/E 20g WW 10g/E 60g/WW 20g/WW 60g				
The B.P.M.A.	MA14	21 October–12 November 2014	FS103, 104, 105, 106, 107 & 108 (but Type IIIA)	20.00
Common Poppy: 1st/1st L/E 20g WW 10g/E 100g/WW 20g/WW 100g				
The B.P.M.A.	MA15	19 October–13 November 2015	FS137/142 (Type IIIA)	20.00
The Postal Museum + Museum's large format Envelope logo positioned before wording.	MA15	24 October–11 November 2016	FS137/142 (Type IIIA)	20.00
The Postal Museum Revised generic inscription without Envelope logo.	MA15	24 October–12 November 2017	FS137/142 (Type IIIA)	19.00
The Postal Museum WWI 1918-2018	MA15	23 October–29 November 2018	FS137/142 (Type IIIA)	20.00
Common Poppy: 1st/1st Large/E 100g WW 20g/WW 100g/E Large 100g/WW Large 100g				
Mail Rail	MA15	11 November–5 December 2021	FS137/142 (Type IIIA)	32.00
The Postal Museum Lest We Forget	MA15	11–30 November 2022	FS137, 138, 140 *var*, 142, 140 *var*, 142 *var* (Type IIIA)	32.00
Lion (Heraldic Beast): 1st/1st L/E 20g WW 10g/E 100g/WW 20g/WW 100g				
The B.P.M.A.	MA15	16 September–16 October 2015 4–29 January 2016	FS125/130 (but Type IIIA)	20.00
The Postal Museum + Museum's large format Envelope logo positioned before wording.	MA15	1–16 February 2016	FS125/130 (but Type IIIA)	19.00
Game of Thrones: **2nd/2nd L, and 1st/1st L/E 20g WW 10g/E 100g/WW 20g/WW 100g**				
The Postal Museum[4]	CL18S/ R18Y	23 January–22 February 2018	FS199a/206a (Type IIIA) Set of 8:	24.00

The different inscriptions from *The Postal Museum*. Where the same inscription exists on more than one design only one may be pictured.

Post & Go stamps – the inscriptions from *The Postal Museum* (formerly 'The BPMA'), December 2012–April 2022:
A simplified checklist of the Machin, Union Flag and pictorial issues

Stamp Design, Values, **Inscriptions** (see **bold text**) & Note(s)	Year Code	Availability (dates inclusive) & Note(s)	Cat. No. of Stamp Issue Without Inscription, or Closest Match	Collectors' Strip Price
Royal Mail Heritage – Transport: 1st × 6 designs				
The Postal Museum + Museum's large format Envelope logo positioned before wording.	MA16	17 February–31 March 2016	FS151×6 (but Type IIIA)	9.00
Royal Mail Heritage – Mail Coach design: 1st/1st L/E 20g WW 10g/E 100g/WW 20g/WW 100g				
The Postal Museum + Museum's large format Envelope logo positioned before wording.	MA16	1 April 2016–12 July 2017	FS151/156 (but Type IIIA & stamps digitally printed)	19.00
The Postal Museum Official Opening³	MA16	25 July 2017 28 July–12 September 2017	FS151/156 (but Type IIIA & stamps digitally printed)	19.00
The Postal Museum Revised generic inscription without Envelope logo.	MA16	13 September 2017–11 September 2018 30 November 2018–12 February 2019	FS151/156 (but Type IIIA & stamps digitally printed)	20.00
The Postal Museum NPM 50	MA16	13 February–10 October 2019	FS151/156 (but Type IIIA & stamps digitally printed)	19.00
The Postal Museum New exhibit 2019	MA16	11 October 2019–18 March 2020	FS151/156 (but Type IIIA & stamps digitally printed)	19.00
Royal Mail Heritage – Mail Coach design: 1st/1st L/E 20g WW 10g/E 100g WW 20g/WW 100g Zone 1 & 3/WW 100g Zone 2 [Dual-zone value with ampersand i.e. **'World 100g Zone 1 & 3'**]				
The Postal Museum Postcards 150	MA16	29 October–1 November 2020² 3 November 2020² 3–19 December 2020²	FS151, 152, 153, 154 *var*, 156 *var*, 156 *var* (but Type IIIA & stamps digitally printed)	25.00
Royal Mail Heritage – Mail Coach design: 1st/1st Large/E 100g WW 20g/WW 100g/E Large 100g/WW Large 100g				
The Postal Museum Postcards 150	MA16	20 May–21 July 2021	FS151, 152, 154 *var*, 156, 156 *var*, 156 *var* (but Type IIIA & stamps digitally printed)	32.00
			Set of two singles: i.e. E Large 100g/FS156 *var* & WW Large 100g/FS156 *var* (TIIIA)	20.00
The Postal Museum	MA16	22 July 2021–27 March 2022	FS151, 152, 154 *var*, 156, 156 *var*, 156 *var* (but Type IIIA & stamps digitally printed)	32.00
Royal Mail Heritage – Mail by Rail: 1st × 6 designs				
The Postal Museum + Museum's large format Envelope logo positioned before wording.	MA17	15 February–31 March 2017	FS173a x6 (Type IIIA)	8.75
Royal Mail Heritage – Mail by Rail: 1st/1st L/E 20g WW 10g/E 100g/WW 20g/WW 100g				
The Postal Museum Revised generic inscription without Envelope logo. Unintentional issue because machine was loaded with Royal Mail Heritage – Mail by Rail design, instead of Royal Mail Heritage – Post Office (London) Railway single-design issue.	MA17	Available for a few hours only on 4 October 2018	FS173a/178a (Type IIIA)	£125
The Postal Museum New exhibit 2019	MA17	Never available to the public via the museum's Post & Go kiosk. Only from a limited edition special pack entitled 'The Great Train Robbery: Crime & the Post' through the museum's gift shop	FS173a/178a (Type IIIA)	35.00

Post & Go stamps – the inscriptions from *The Postal Museum* (formerly 'The BPMA'), December 2012–April 2022:
A simplified checklist of the Machin, Union Flag and pictorial issues

Stamp Design, Values, **Inscriptions** (see **bold** text) & Note(s)	Year Code	Availability (dates inclusive) & Note(s)	Cat. No. of Stamp Issue Without Inscription, or Closest Match	Collectors' Strip Price
Royal Mail Heritage – Post Office (London) Railway design: 1st/1st L/E 20g WW 10g/E 100g/WW 20g/WW 100g				
The Postal Museum + Museum's large format Envelope logo positioned before wording.	MA17	3 April–12 July 2017	FS173a/178a (Type IIIA & stamps digitally printed)	19.00
The Postal Museum Official Opening³	MA17	25 July 2017 28 July–12 September 2017	FS173a/178a (Type IIIA & stamps digitally printed)	19.00
The Postal Museum Revised generic inscription without Envelope logo.	MA17	13 September 2017–18 March 2020	FS173a/178a (Type IIIA & stamps digitally printed)	19.00
Mail Rail	MA17	29 October 2019–18 March 2020 except when 'R19Y' available (see below)	FS173a/178a (Type IIIA & stamps digitally printed)	25.00
	R19Y	29 October 2019–18 March 2020 except when 'MA17' available (see above)	FS173a/178a (Type IIIA & stamps digitally printed)	19.00
Royal Mail Heritage – Post Office (London) Railway design: 1st/1st L/E 20g WW 10g/E 100g WW 20g/WW 100g Zone 1 & 3/WW 100g Zone 2 *[Dual-zone value with ampersand i.e. 'World 100g Zone 1 & 3']*				
The Postal Museum	R19Y	29 October–1 November 2020² 3 November 2020²	FS173a, 174a, 175a, 175 *var*, 178 *var*, 178 *var* (Type IIIA & stamps digitally printed)	25.00
	MA18	Late on 3 November² 3–19 December 2020²	FS173a, 174a, 175a, 175 *var*, 178 *var*, 178 *var* (Type IIIA & stamps digitally printed)	39.00
Mail Rail	MA18	29 October–1 November 2020²	FS173a, 174a, 175a, 175 *var*, 178 *var*, 178 *var* (Type IIIA & stamps digitally printed)	25.00
	MA17	Late on 1 November 2020² 3 November 2020² 3–19 December 2020²	FS173a, 174a, 175a, 175 *var*, 178 *var*, 178 *var* (Type IIIA & stamps digitally printed)	39.00
Royal Mail Heritage – Post Office (London) Railway design: 1st/1st Large/E 100g WW 20g/WW 100g/E Large 100g/WW Large 100g				
The Postal Museum	MA18	20 May–September 2021 23 April–10 November 2022	FS173a, 174a, FS176 *var*, 178a, 176 *var*, 178 *var* (Type IIIA & stamps digitally printed)	32.00
			Set of two singles: i.e. E Large 100g/FS176 *var* & WW Large 100g/FS178 *var* (TIIIA)	20.00
	R19Y	From September 2021–22 April 2022	FS173a, 174a, FS176 *var*, 178a, 176 *var*, 178 *var* (Type IIIA & stamps digitally printed)	32.00
			Set of two singles: i.e. E Large 100g/FS176 *var* & WW Large 100g/FS178 *var* (TIIIA)	20.00

The different inscriptions from *The Postal Museum*. Where the same inscription exists on more than one design only one may be pictured.

Post & Go stamps – the inscriptions from *The Postal Museum* (formerly 'The BPMA'), December 2012–April 2022:
A simplified checklist of the Machin, Union Flag and pictorial issues

Stamp Design, Values, **Inscriptions** (see **bold text**) & Note(s)	Year Code	Availability (dates inclusive) & Note(s)	Cat. No. of Stamp Issue Without Inscription, or Closest Match	Collectors' Strip Price
Mail Rail	MA17	20 May–July 2021 27 February 2022–22 April 2022	FS173a, 174a, FS176 *var*, 178a, 176 *var*, 178 *var* (Type IIIA & stamps digitally printed)	32.00
			Set of two singles: i.e. E Large 100g/FS176 *var* & WW Large 100g/FS178 *var* (TIIIA)	20.00
	R19Y	Sometimes available between 22 July 2021–18 February 2022	FS173a, 174a, FS176 *var*, 178a, 176 *var*, 178 *var* (Type IIIA & stamps digitally printed)	32.00
	MA18	Sometimes available between 21 November 2021–18 February 2022 From 23 April 2022	FS173a, 174a, FS176 *var*, 178a, 176 *var*, 178 *var* (Type IIIA & stamps digitally printed)	35.00
			Set of two singles: i.e. E Large 100g/FS176 *var* & WW Large 100g/FS178 *var* (TIIIA)	23.00
Mail Rail **London 2022**	R19Y	19–26 February 2022	FS173a, 174a, FS176 *var*, 178a (but Type IIIA), 176 *var*, 178 *var* (but Type IIIA & stamps digitally printed)	32.00
Royal Mail Heritage – Mail by Air: 1st × 6 designs				
The Postal Museum[4]	R17Y	13 September 2017–13 February 2018	FS185a x 6 (Type IIIA)	12.50
	R19Y	From 30 March–2 June 2022 From 2 July 2022	FS185a x 6 (Type IIIA but stamps digitally printed)	12.50
The Postal Museum **Airmail 1919**	R17Y	Available for a few hours only on 11 September 2019	FS185a x 6 (Type IIIA)	33.00
	R19Y	11 September 2019–18 March 2020	FS185a x 6 (but Type IIIA but stamps digitally printed)	12.50
Royal Mail Heritage – Mail by Air: 1st/1st Large/E 100g WW 20g/WW 100g/E Large 100g/WW Large 100g *[Six designs in six values as single value strips of six]*				
The Postal Museum Unintentionally, all six values could be dispensed after this issue was made available in place of Royal Mail Heritage – Mail Coach. Each value could be dispensed in single value strips of six. Collectors' strips could not be dispensed.	R19Y	30 March–22 April 2022	FS185a, 186a, 188 *var*, 190a, 188 *var*, 190 *var* (Type IIIA & stamps digitally printed)	
			Set of 36: i.e. six strips available in six issues	170.00
Royal Mail Heritage – Mail by Sea: 1st × 6 designs				
The Postal Museum[4]	R18Y	14 February–28 March 2018 12 September–22 October 2018	FS207a x6 (Type IIIA)	9.50
Voices from the Deep **The Postal Museum**	R18Y	29 March–11 September 2018	FS207a x6 (Type IIIA)	10.00
Royal Mail Heritage – Mail by Bike: 1st × 6 designs				
The Postal Museum[4]	R18Y	12 September–29 November 2018	FS213 x6 (but Type IIIA)	9.50

The different inscriptions from *The Postal Museum*. Where the same inscription exists on more than one design only one may be pictured.

Post & Go stamps – the inscriptions from *The Postal Museum* (formerly 'The BPMA'), December 2012–April 2022:
A simplified checklist of the Machin, Union Flag and pictorial issues

Stamp Design, Values, **Inscriptions** (see **bold** text) & Note(s)	Year Code	Availability (dates inclusive) & Note(s)	Cat. No. of Stamp Issue Without Inscription, or Closest Match	Collectors' Strip Price
Robin: 1st/1st L/E 20g/WW 10g/WW 20g/WW 40g				
The B.P.M.A.	MA12	3 December 2012–20 February 2013	FS51a/56a (Type III)	20.00
	MA13	5 November–24 December 2013	FS51a/56a (Type III)	18.00
Fur & Feathers: 2nd/2nd L, and 1st/1st L/E 20g WW 10g/E 100g/WW 20g/WW 100g				
The B.P.M.A.	CL15S/ MA15	16 November–31 December 2015	FS143a/150a (Type IIIA) Set of 16: i.e. eight values in two designs	45.00
Hibernating Animals: 2nd/2nd L, and 1st/1st L/E 20g WW 10g/E 100g/WW 20g/WW 100g				
The Postal Museum + Museum's large format Envelope logo positioned before wording.	CL16S/ MA16	14 November–30 December 2016	FS165a/172a (Type IIIA) Set of 16: i.e. eight values in two designs	45.00
Winter Greenery: 2nd/2nd L, and 1st/1st L/E 20g WW 10g/E 60g/WW 20g/WW 60g				
The B.P.M.A.	MA14/ MA14	13 November–23 December 2014 29 October–1 November 2020[2]	FS109b/116b (Type IIIA) Set of 16: i.e. eight values in two designs	45.00
Winter Greenery 2017 issue: 2nd/2nd L, and 1st/1st L/E 20g WW 10g/E 100g/WW 20g/WW 100g				
The Postal Museum[4]	CL17S/ R17Y	13 November 2017–1 January 2018 8 November–31 December 2018 3 November 2020 (2nd/2nd L only)[2] 3–19 December 2020 (2nd/2nd L only)[2] 1 December 2021–2 January 2022 (2nd/2nd L only)	FS191a/198a (Type IIIA) Set of 16: i.e. eight values in two designs	48.00
Winter Greenery 2017 issue: 1st/1st L/E 20g WW 10g/E 100g/WW 20g/WW 100g				
Mail Rail	R17Y	2–31 December 2019	FS193a/198a (Type IIIA) Set of 16: i.e. eight values in two designs	40.00
Winter Greenery 2017 issue: 1st/1st L/E 20g WW 10g/E 100g WW 20g/WW 100g Zone 1 & 3/WW 100g Zone 2 *[Dual-zone value with ampersand i.e. '**World 100g Zone 1 & 3**']*				
The Postal Museum	R17Y	3 November 2020[2] 3–19 December 2020[2]	FS193a/195a (Type IIIA), 196b, 198b/198c (but Type IIIA) Set of 16: i.e. eight values in two designs	48.00
Winter Greenery: 1st/1st Large/E 100g WW 20g/WW 100g/E Large 100g/WW Large 100g				
The Postal Museum	R17Y	1 December 2021–2 January 2022 1–31 December 2022	FS193a, 194a, 196b (but Type IIIA), 198a, 196c (but Type IIIA), 198d (but Type IIIA) Set of 12: i.e. six values in two designs Set of 4: i.e. two values in two designs i.e. E Large 100g/FS196c & WW Large 100g/FS198d (TIIIA)	60.00 35.00
Mail Rail (1st Class design only)	R19Y	1–31 December 2022	FS193a, 194a, 196b (but Type IIIA), 198a, 196c (but Type IIIA), 198d (but Type IIIA)	32.00

[1] When two similar items are available, the price given is for the cheaper of the two.

[2] Owing to COVID 19 restrictions, *The Postal Museum* closed its doors to the general public on 18 March 2020. It temporarily reopened between 29 October–4 November 2020 and 3–19 December 2020; both periods with a much-reduced Thursday to Sunday opening schedule. There was also a special one-day opening on Tuesday, 3 November 2020, for the museum's annual 'Winter Greenery' offering. *The Postal Museum* reopened on 20 May 2021.

[3] When used on the pictorial issue, the *The Postal Museum*'s official opening inscription deliberately omitted '**2017**'.

[4] Revised generic inscription without a large Envelope logo and the current norm. Note: Issue does not exist with large Envelope logo.)

Glitches affecting inscriptions and lasting only a very short time and/or which exist in small quantities are beyond the scope of these tables.

The different inscriptions from exhibitions. Where the same inscription exists on more than one design only one may be pictured.

Post & Go stamps – the inscriptions from Royal Mail Enquiry Offices, February 2015–March 2015: A simplified checklist of the Machin issues

Stamp Design, Values, **Inscriptions** (see **bold text**) & Note(s)	Year Code	Location of machine, Availability (dates inclusive) & Note(s)	Cat. No. of Stamp Issue Without Inscription, or Closest Match	Collectors' Strip Price
Machin: 1st/1st L/E 20g WW 10g/E 60g/WW 20g/WW 60g				
Bradford N This inscription was the result of a two office trial which ended very quickly, and Enquiry Office inscriptions ceased	MA13	Bradford North Royal Mail Enquiry Office 9 February–28 March 2015	FS77b, 78b, 79bb, 80*var*, 82b, & 84*var* (Type IIIA)	25.00
Crewe This inscription was the result of a two office trial which ended very quickly, and Enquiry Office inscriptions ceased	MA13	Crewe Royal Mail Enquiry Office 9 February–28 March 2015	FS77b, 78b, 79bb, 80*var*, 82b, & 84*var* (Type IIIA)	25.00
Machin: 2nd/2nd L				
Bradford N This inscription was the result of a two office trial which ended very quickly, and Enquiry Office inscriptions ceased	MA12	Bradford North Royal Mail Enquiry Office 9 February–28 March 2015	FS93b/94b (Type IIIA)	11.50
Crewe This inscription was the result of a two office trial which ended very quickly, and Enquiry Office inscriptions ceased	MA12	Crewe Royal Mail Enquiry Office 9 February–28 March 2015	FS93b/94b (Type IIIA)	11.50

The different inscriptions from exhibitions. Where the same inscription exists on more than one design only one may be pictured.

Post & Go stamps – the different issues and inscriptions from *National Museum Royal Navy,* Portsmouth to April 2022: A simplified checklist

Post & Go stamps – the inscriptions from *The National Museum Royal Navy*, Portsmouth, July 2014–April 2022: A simplified checklist of the Machin, Union Flag and Common Poppy issues				
Stamp Design, Values, **Inscriptions** (see **bold** text) & Note(s)	Year Code	Location of dispensing machine, Availability (dates inclusive) & Note(s)	Cat. No. of Stamp Issue Without Inscription, or Closest Match	Collectors' Strip Price
Machin: 1st/1st L/E 20g WW 10g/E 60g/WW 20g/WW 60g				
The NMRN	None	*The National Museum of the Royal Navy*, Portsmouth[1] 28 July–20 October 2014 14 November 2014–29 March 2015	FS1d, 2d, 3cb, 3d, 5d & 5f (Type IIIA)	22.00
	MA13	*The National Museum of the Royal Navy*, Portsmouth[1] Apparently available for a few hours only on 8 May 2015 Only known on 8 May 2015 due to a reversion to the pre 30 March 2015 weight bands	FS77, 78, 79b, 80, 82 & 84 (but Type III) Set of two singles: i.e. E 60g/FS80 & WW 60g/FS84 (but TIII)	75.00 50.00
Machin: 1st/1st L/E 20g WW 10g/E 100g/WW 20g/WW 100g				
The NMRN	MA13	*The National Museum of the Royal Navy*, Portsmouth[1] 30 March–18 October 2015	FS77b, 78b, 79bb, 80ca, 82b & 84ca (Type IIIA)	20.00
	None	*The National Museum of the Royal Navy*, Portsmouth[1] Available for a few hours only on 30 March 2015	FS1d, 2d, 3cb, 3ea, 5d & 5ga (Type IIIA)	50.00
Royal Navy + large circle logo Generic inscription revised, i.e. '**Royal Navy**' replaces acronym, and large logo introduced.	MA13	*The National Museum of the Royal Navy*, Portsmouth[1] 16 November 2015–30 May 2016 1 July–15 August 2016 except when 'No year code' available (see below) 15 August 2016–18 August 2017 except when 'MA15' available (see below)	FS77b, 78b, 79bb, 80ca, 82b & 84ca (Type IIIA)	19.00
	None	*The National Museum of the Royal Navy*, Portsmouth[1] Sometimes available between 1 July 2016–18 August 2017 *Explosion Museum of Naval Firepower*, Gosport[4] 16 August 2016–18 May 2017 19 June–18 August 2017	FS1d, 2d, 3cb, 3ea, 5d and 5ga (Type IIIA)	20.00[5]
	MA15	*The National Museum of the Royal Navy*, Belfast[2] *HMS Caroline* 1 July 2016–spring/summer 2017 *The National Museum of the Royal Navy*, Hartlepool[3] *HMS Trincomalee* 1 July 2016–15 June 2017 *The National Museum of the Royal Navy*, Portsmouth[1] Sometimes available between 15 August 2016–18 August 2017	FS77b, 78b, 79bb, 80ca, 82b & 84ca (Type IIIA)	20.00[5]
Royal Navy Battle of Jutland + large circle logo	None	*The National Museum of the Royal Navy*, Portsmouth[1] 31 May–30 June 2016	FS1d 2d, 3cb, 3ea, 5d and 5ga (Type IIIA)	20.00
	MA13	*The National Museum of the Royal Navy*, Portsmouth[1] Apparently available for a few hours only on 31 May 2016	FS77b, 78b, 79bb, 80ca, 82b & 84ca (Type IIIA)	—
	MA15	*The National Museum of the Royal Navy*, Belfast[2] *HMS Caroline* *The National Museum of the Royal Navy*, Hartlepool[3] *HMS Trincomalee* 1–30 June 2016 (Note: Not 31 May)	FS77b, 78b, 79bb, 80ca, 82b & 4ca (Type IIIA)	20.00
Heligoland 'Big Bang' 1947 + large circle logo	MA15	*Explosion Museum of Naval Firepower*, Gosport[4] 19 May–18 June 2017	FS77b, 78b, 79bb, 80ca, 82b & 84ca (Type IIIA)	20.00
HMS Trincomalee 200 Years + large circle logo	MA15	*The National Museum of the Royal Navy*, Hartlepool[3] *HMS Trincomalee* 16 June–18 August 2017	FS77b, 78b, 79bb, 80ca, 82b & 84ca (Type IIIA)	20.00
Royal Navy Queen Elizabeth II Carrier + small circle logo	MA15	*The National Museum of the Royal Navy*, Portsmouth[1] 19–28 August 2017 The carrier is named *Queen Elizabeth* and not *Queen Elizabeth II* From 29 August 2017, the erroneous '**II**' was removed	FS77b, 78b, 79bb, 80ca, 82b & 84ca (Type IIIA)	23.00
Royal Navy Queen Elizabeth Carrier 2017 + small circle logo	MA15	*The National Museum of the Royal Navy*, Portsmouth[1] 29 August–17 September 2017 At the same time the erroneous '**II**' was removed from the inscription the date '**2017**' was added	FS77b, 78b, 79bb, 80ca, 82b & 84ca (Type IIIA)	24.00

Post & Go stamps – the inscriptions from *The National Museum Royal Navy*, Portsmouth, July 2014–April 2022:
A simplified checklist of the Machin, Union Flag and Common Poppy issues

Stamp Design, Values, Inscriptions (see **bold text**) & Note(s)	Year Code	Location of dispensing machine, Availability (dates inclusive) & Note(s)	Cat. No. of Stamp Issue Without Inscription, or Closest Match	Collectors' Strip Price
Machin: 1st/1st L/E 20g WW 10g/E 100g/WW 20g/WW 100g *continued*				
HMS Trincomalee 200 Years + small circle logo	MA14	*The National Museum of the Royal Navy*, Hartlepool[3] *HMS Trincomalee* 19 August–19 October 2017	FS77b, 78b, 79bb, 80ca, 82b & 84ca (Type IIIA)	22.00
	MA15	*The National Museum of the Royal Navy*, Hartlepool[3] *HMS Trincomalee* Available for a few hours only on 19 August 2017	FS77b, 78b, 79bb, 80ca, 82b & 84ca (Type IIIA)	45.00
Royal Navy + small circle logo Small circle logo introduced in place of large version.	MA15	*Explosion Museum of Naval Firepower*, Gosport[4] 19 August–19 October 2017 20 November 2017–31 October 2019 *The National Museum of the Royal Navy*, Portsmouth[1] 18 September–19 October 2017 20 November 2017–31 October 2019 1 December 2019–18 March 2020[†] 24 August–1 September 2020[†]	FS77b, 78b, 79bb, 80ca, 82b & 84ca (Type IIIA)	20.00[5]
	MA14	*The National Museum of the Royal Navy*, Hartlepool[3] *HMS Trincomalee* 22 February 2018–31 October 2019 except when 'MA13' and 'No year code' available (see below) 3 December 2019–18 March 2020[†]	FS77b, 78b, 79bb, 80ca, 82b & 84ca (Type IIIA)	23.00
	MA13	*The National Museum of the Royal Navy*, Hartlepool[3] *HMS Trincomalee* Available for a short time sometime between 17 September–late September 2018	FS77b, 78b, 79bb, 80ca, 82b & 84ca (Type IIIA)	40.00
	None	*The National Museum of the Royal Navy*, Hartlepool[3] *HMS Trincomalee* Available for a short time sometime between 17 September–late September 2018 *Explosion Museum of Naval Firepower*, Gosport[4] 7 December 2019–18 March 2020[†] 29 August–1 September 2020[†]	FS1d 2d, 3cb, 3ea, 5d and 5ga (Type IIIA)	40.00[5]
HMS Trincomalee 12th Oct 1817 + small circle logo	MA14	*The National Museum of the Royal Navy*, Hartlepool[3] *HMS Trincomalee* 20 October–31 December 2017 except when 'MA15' available (see below)	FS77b, 78b, 79bb, 80ca, 82b & 84ca (Type IIIA)	20.00
	MA15	*The National Museum of the Royal Navy*, Hartlepool[3] *HMS Trincomalee* Available for a short time sometime between 20 October–late October 2017	FS77b, 78b, 79bb, 80ca, 82b & 84ca (Type IIIA)	28.00
HMS Trincomalee 19th Oct 1817 + small circle logo '**19th Oct**' instead of '**12th Oct**' for less than one hour on the first day of the '**12th Oct 1817**' inscription.	MA14	*The National Museum of the Royal Navy*, Hartlepool[3] *HMS Trincomalee* 20 October 2017	FS77b, 78b, 79bb, 80ca, 82b & 84ca (Type IIIA)	50.00
HMS Trincomalee + small circle logo	MA14	*The National Museum of the Royal Navy*, Hartlepool[3] *HMS Trincomalee* 2–14 January 2018	FS77b, 78b, 79bb, 80ca, 82b & 84ca (Type IIIA)	20.00
Royal Navy Lest We Forget 100 Unintentional issue when the Machin design was loaded into the machine and the return of the generic inscription (i.e. '**Royal Navy**' + small circle logo) was delayed due to a technical reason.	MA13	*The National Museum of the Royal Navy*, Hartlepool[3] *HMS Trincomalee* Available for a few hours only on 2 December 2019	FS77b, 78b, 79bb, 80ca, 82b & 84ca (Type IIIA)	40.00
	MA14	*The National Museum of the Royal Navy*, Hartlepool[3] *HMS Trincomalee* Available for a few hours on 2 December and 3 December 2019	FS77b, 78b, 79bb, 80ca, 82b & 84ca (Type IIIA)	45.00

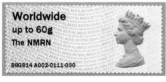

The different inscriptions from *National Museum Royal Navy*. Where the same inscription exists on more than one design only one may be pictured.

Europe
up to 100g
Heligoland
'Big Bang' 1947
B5GB17 A007-0125-004

Worldwide
up to 100g
HMS Trincomalee
200 Years
B6GB17 A006-2152-006

Worldwide
up to 20g
Royal Navy
Queen Elizabeth II Carrier
B6GB17 A002-3440-257

Euro 20g
World 10g
Royal Navy
Queen Elizabeth Carrier 2017
B9GB17 A002-3495-483

Worldwide
up to 20g
HMS Trincomalee
200 Years
B6GB17 A006-2229-287

Worldwide
up to 100g
Royal Navy
B9GB17 A007-0188-030

Euro 20g
World 10g
HMS Trincomalee
12th Oct 1817
BOiB17 A006-2309-411

Worldwide
up to 100g
HMS Trincomalee
19th Oct 1817
BOGB17 A006-2284-060

Worldwide
up to 20g
HMS Trincomalee
B1GB18 A006-2388-071

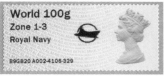

World 100g
Zone 1-3
Royal Navy
B9GB20 A002-4106-329

World 100g
Zone 1 & 3
Royal Navy
B9GB20 A006-2835-041

Worldwide
Large 100g
Royal Navy
BNGB21 A006-3009-210

The different inscriptions from *National Museum Royal Navy*. Where the same inscription exists on more than one design only one may be pictured.

Post & Go stamps – the inscriptions from *The National Museum Royal Navy*, Portsmouth, July 2014–April 2022:
A simplified checklist of the Machin, Union Flag and Common Poppy issues

Stamp Design, Values, **Inscriptions** (see **bold** text) & Note(s)	Year Code	Location of dispensing machine, Availability (dates inclusive) & Note(s)	Cat. No. of Stamp Issue Without Inscription, or Closest Match	Collectors' Strip Price
Machin: 1st/1st L/E 20g WW 10g/E 100g WW 20g/WW 100g Zone 1-3/WW 100g Zone 2 *[Dual value of E 100g WW 20g and two World Zoned stamps introduced on 1 September 2020]*				
Royal Navy + small circle logo Dual-zone value with hyphen i.e. **'World 100g Zone 1-3'**	MA15	*The National Museum of the Royal Navy*, Portsmouth[1] 1–17 September 2020[†] *Explosion Museum of Naval Firepower*, Gosport[4] 5–17 September 2020[†]	FS77b, 78b, 79bb (Type IIIA), 80d, 84d & 84e (but Type IIIA)	35.00[5]
	MA14	*The National Museum of the Royal Navy*, Hartlepool[3] *HMS Trincomalee* 4 September 2020[†]	FS77b, 78b, 79bb (Type IIIA), 80d, 84d & 84e (but Type IIIA)	45.00
	MA13	*The National Museum of the Royal Navy*, Hartlepool[3] *HMS Trincomalee* 4–17 September 2020[†]	FS77b, 78b, 79bb (Type IIIA), 80d, 84d & 84e (but Type IIIA)	40.00
	None	*Explosion Museum of Naval Firepower*, Gosport[4] 5 September 2020[†]	FS1d, 2d, 3cb, and 3f, 5h, 5i (but all Type IIIA)	45.00
Machin: 1st/1st L/E 20g WW 10g/E 100g WW 20g/WW 100g Zone 1 & 3/WW 100g Zone 2 *[Service indicator for 'World Zones 1 and 3' revised on 18 September 2020]*				
Royal Navy + small circle logo Dual-zone value with ampersand i.e. **'World 100g Zone 1 & 3'**	MA15	*The National Museum of the Royal Navy*, Portsmouth[1] 18 September–4 October 2020[†] *Explosion Museum of Naval Firepower*, Gosport[4] 20 September–4 November 2020[†] 3–19 December 2020[†] *The National Museum of the Royal Navy*, Hartlepool[3] *HMS Trincomalee* 23 September–4 November 2020[†]	FS77b, 78b, 79bb (Type IIIA), 80d, 84d var & 84e (but Type IIIA) Single: i.e. Zone1 & 3/FS84d var	35.00[5] 13.50[5]
	MA14	*The National Museum of the Royal Navy*, Hartlepool[3] *HMS Trincomalee* 23 September 2020[†]	FS77b, 78b, 79bb (Type IIIA), 80d, 84d var & 84e (but Type IIIA) Single: i.e. Zone1 & 3/FS84d var	— 20.00
	MA13	*The National Museum of the Royal Navy*, Hartlepool[3] *HMS Trincomalee* 23 September 2020[†]	FS77b, 78b, 79bb (Type IIIA), 80d, 84d var & 84e (but Type IIIA) Single: i.e. Zone1 & 3/FS84d var	45.00 17.00
	None	*The National Museum of the Royal Navy*, Portsmouth[1] 4 October–4 November 2020[†] 3–19 December 2020[†]	FS1d, 2d, 3cb, and 3f, 5h var, 5i (but all Type IIIA) Single: i.e. Zone1 & 3/FS5h var	45.00 15.00

Post & Go stamps – the inscriptions from *The National Museum Royal Navy*, Portsmouth, July 2014–April 2022:
A simplified checklist of the Machin, Union Flag and Common Poppy issues

Stamp Design, Values, **Inscriptions** (see **bold** text) & Note(s)	Year Code	Location of dispensing machine, Availability (dates inclusive) & Note(s)	Cat. No. of Stamp Issue Without Inscription, or Closest Match	Collectors' Strip Price
Machin: 1st/1st Large/E 100g WW 20g/WW 100g/E Large 100g/WW Large 100g				
Royal Navy + small circle logo	None	*The National Museum of the Royal Navy*, Portsmouth[1] 17 May–30 July 2021	FS1d, 2d, 3f (but Type IIIA), 5ga, 3 *var* and 5 *var* (Type IIIA)	35.00
			Set of two singles: i.e. E Large 100g/FS3 *var* & WW Large 100g/FS5 *var* (but TIIIA)	23.00
	MA13	*The National Museum of the Royal Navy*, Hartlepool[3] *HMS Trincomalee* 17 May 2021 only	FS77b, 78b, 80d (but Type IIIA), 84ca, 80e (but Type IIIA) and 84f (but Type IIIA)	35.00[5]
		The National Museum of the Royal Navy, Portsmouth[1] 1 September–20 October 2021	Set of two singles: i.e. E Large 100g/FS80e & WW Large 100g/FS84f (but TIIIA)	23.00[5]
	MA14	*The National Museum of the Royal Navy*, Hartlepool[3] *HMS Trincomalee* 17 May 2021 1 September–10 November 2021	FS77b, 78b, 80d (but Type IIIA), 84ca, 80e (but Type IIIA) and 84f (but Type IIIA)	35.00[5]
		The National Museum of the Royal Navy, Portsmouth[1] 1 November 2021 only (2 November 2021 ♦♦)	Set of two singles: i.e. E Large 100g/FS80e & WW Large 100g/FS84f (but TIIIA)	23.00[5]
	MA15	*The National Museum of the Royal Navy*, Hartlepool[3] *HMS Trincomalee* 17 May–30 July 2021	FS77b, 78b, 80d (but Type IIIA), 84ca, 80e (but Type IIIA) and 84f (but Type IIIA)	35.00[5]
		Explosion Museum of Naval Firepower, Gosport[4] (19 May–15 June 2021♦) 16 June–30 July 2021 1 September–1 November 2021 (2 November 2021 ♦♦)	Set of two singles: i.e. E Large 100g/FS80e & WW Large 100g/FS84f (but TIIIA)	23.00[5]
	R20Y	*The National Museum of the Royal Navy*, Hartlepool[3] *HMS Trincomalee* 10–25 November 2021 11 December 2021–31 March 2022 30 April–1 June 2022 2 July–10 November 2022	FS77b, 78b, 80d (but Type IIIA), 84ca, 80e (but Type IIIA) and 84f (but Type IIIA)	32.00
Royal Navy **Black Tot Day 31st July 1970** + circle logo	MA13	*The National Museum of the Royal Navy*, Portsmouth[1] 31 July–31 August 2021	FS77b, 78b, 80d (but Type IIIA), 84ca, 80e (but Type IIIA) and 84f (but TIIIA)	32.00
	MA15	*The National Museum of the Royal Navy*, Hartlepool[3] *HMS Trincomalee* 31 July–31 August 2021	FS77b, 78b, 80d (but Type IIIA), 84ca, 80e (but Type IIIA) and 84f (but Type IIIA)	32.00[5]
		Explosion Museum of Naval Firepower, Gosport[4] 31 July–31 August 2021		
	None	*The National Museum of the Royal Navy*, Hartlepool[3] *HMS Trincomalee* Sometimes available between 24–31 August 2021	FS1d, 2d, 3f (but Type IIIA), 5ga, 3 *var* and 5 *var* (Type IIIA)	—
	MA14	*The National Museum of the Royal Navy*, Hartlepool[3] *HMS Trincomalee* Sometimes available between 24–31 August 2021	FS77b, 78b, 80d (but Type IIIA), 84ca, 80e (but Type IIIA) and 84f (but Type IIIA)	—
Royal Navy **Trafalgar Day** + circle logo	MA14	*National Museum of the Royal Navy*, Portsmouth[1] 21–31 October 2021	FS77b, 78b, 80d (but Type IIIA), 84ca, 80e (but Type IIIA) and 84f (but Type IIIA)	35.00

The different inscriptions from *National Museum Royal Navy*. Where the same inscription exists on more than one design only one may be pictured.

Post & Go stamps – the inscriptions from *The National Museum Royal Navy*, Portsmouth, July 2014–April 2022: A simplified checklist of the Machin, Union Flag and Common Poppy issues

Stamp Design, Values, **Inscriptions** (see **bold** text) & Note(s)	Year Code	Location of dispensing machine, Availability (dates inclusive) & Note(s)	Cat. No. of Stamp Issue Without Inscription, or Closest Match	Collectors' Strip Price
Machin: 1st/1st Large/E 100g WW 20g/WW 100g/E Large 100g/WW Large 100g *continued*				
Royal Navy Falklands 40th + circle logo	None	*The National Museum of the Royal Navy*, Hartlepool[3] *HMS Trincomalee* Apparently available for a few hours only on 1 April 2022	FS1d, 2d, 3f (but Type IIIA), 5ga, 3 *var* and 5 *var* (Type IIIA)	—
	MA13	*The National Museum of the Royal Navy*, Hartlepool[3] *HMS Trincomalee* Apparently available for a few hours only on 1 and 29 April 2022	FS77b, 78b, 80d (but Type IIIA), 84ca, 80e (but Type IIIA) and 84f (but Type IIIA)	—
	MA14	*The National Museum of the Royal Navy*, Hartlepool[3] *HMS Trincomalee* Apparently available for a few hours only on 29 April 2022	FS77b, 78b, 80d (but Type IIIA), 84ca, 80e (but Type IIIA) and 84f (but Type IIIA)	—
	MA15	*The National Museum of the Royal Navy*, Hartlepool[3] *HMS Trincomalee* Apparently available for a few hours only on 29 April 2022	FS77b, 78b, 80d (but Type IIIA), 84ca, 80e (but Type IIIA) and 84f (but Type IIIA)	—
	R20Y	*The National Museum of the Royal Navy*, Hartlepool[3] *HMS Trincomalee* Sometimes available between 1–29 April 2022	FS77b, 78b, 80d (but Type IIIA), 84ca, 80e (but Type IIIA) and 84f (but Type IIIA)	35.00
Royal Navy Queen's Platinum Jubilee (without 'The') + circle logo	MA13	*The National Museum of the Royal Navy*, Portsmouth[1] 3 June–1 July 2022	FS77b, 78b, 80d (but Type IIIA), 84ca, 80e (but Type IIIA) and 84f (but Type IIIA)	35.00
Royal Navy The Queen's Platinum Jubilee + circle logo	MA14	*The National Museum of the Royal Navy*, Hartlepool[3] *HMS Trincomalee* 3 June–1 July 2022 *Explosion Museum of Naval Firepower*, Gosport[4] 3 June–1 July 2022	FS77b, 78b, 80d (but Type IIIA), 84ca, 80e (but Type IIIA) and 84f (but Type IIIA)	35.00
	MA15	*The National Museum of the Royal Navy*, Hartlepool[3] *HMS Trincomalee* 3 June–1 July 2022 *Explosion Museum of Naval Firepower*, Gosport[4] 3 June–1 July 2022	FS77b, 78b, 80d (but Type IIIA), 84ca, 80e (but Type IIIA) and 84f (but Type IIIA)	35.00
	R20Y	*The National Museum of the Royal Navy*, Hartlepool[3] *HMS Trincomalee* 3 June–1 July 2022 *Explosion Museum of Naval Firepower*, Gosport[4] 3 June–1 July 2022	FS77b, 78b, 80d (but Type IIIA), 84ca, 80e (but Type IIIA) and 84f (but Type IIIA)	35.00

The different inscriptions from *National Museum Royal Navy*. Where the same inscription exists on more than one design only one may be pictured.

Post & Go stamps – the inscriptions from *The National Museum Royal Navy*, Portsmouth, July 2014–April 2022:
A simplified checklist of the Machin, Union Flag and Common Poppy issues

Stamp Design, Values, **Inscriptions** (see **bold** text) & Note(s)	Year Code	Location of dispensing machine, Availability (dates inclusive) & Note(s)	Cat. No. of Stamp Issue Without Inscription, or Closest Match	Collectors' Strip Price
Union Flag: 1st/1st L/E 20g WW 10g/E 60g/WW 20g/WW 60g				
The NMRN	None	*The National Museum of the Royal Navy*, Portsmouth[1] 28 July–20 October 2014 11 November 2014–29 March 2015	FS39, 40, 41*a*, 41*b*, 43 & 44*b* (but Type IIIA)	20.00
The NMRN **Trafalgar Day**	None	*The National Museum of the Royal Navy*, Portsmouth[1] 21 October–10 November 2014	FS39, 40, 41*a*, 41*b*, 43 & 44*b* (but Type IIIA)	35.00
The NMRN **V.E. Day 70**	None	*The National Museum of the Royal Navy*, Portsmouth[1] Apparently available for a few hours only on 8 May 2015. Only known on 8 May 2015 due to a reversion to the pre 30 March 2015 weight bands	FS39, 40, 41*a*, 41*b*, 43 & 44*b* (but Type IIIA) Set of two singles: i.e. E 60g/FS41*b* & WW 60g/FS44*b* (but TIII)	75.00 50.00
Union Flag: 1st/1st L/E 20g WW 10g/E 100g/WW 20g/WW 100g				
The NMRN	None	*The National Museum of the Royal Navy*, Portsmouth[1] 30 March–7 May 2015 30 May–18 October 2015	FS39, 40, 41a, 41c, 43 and 44c (but Type IIIA)	25.00
The NMRN **V.E. Day 70**	None	*The National Museum of the Royal Navy*, Portsmouth[1] 8–29 May 2015	FS39, 40, 41a, 41c, 43 and 44c (but Type IIIA)	20.00
Royal Navy **Trafalgar Day** Generic inscription revised, i.e. '**Royal Navy Trafalgar Day**' replaces acronym.	None	*The National Museum of the Royal Navy*, Portsmouth[1] 19 October–15 November 2015 23 September–23 October 2016 – all sites	FS39, 40, 41a, 41c, 43 and 44c (but Type IIIA)	20.00[5]
Royal Navy Generic inscription revised, i.e. '**Royal Navy**' replaces acronym.	None	*The National Museum of the Royal Navy*, Portsmouth[1] 16 November 2015–30 May 2016 14 November 2016–18 August 2017 18 September 2017–18 March 2020[†] 24 August–1 September 2020[†] *The National Museum of the Royal Navy*, Belfast[2] *HMS Caroline* 1 July 2016–spring/summer 2017 *The National Museum of the Royal Navy*, Hartlepool[3] *HMS Trincomalee* 1 July 2016–15 June 2017 22 February 2018–18 March 2020[†] *Explosion Museum of Naval Firepower*, Gosport[4] 16 August 2016–18 May 2017 19 June 2017–18 March 2020[†] 29 August–1 September 2020[†]	FS39, 40, 41a, 41c, 43 and 44c (but Type IIIA)	20.00[5]
Royal Navy **Battle of Jutland**	None	*The National Museum of the Royal Navy*, Portsmouth[1] 31 May–30 June 2016 1–30 June 2016 – all sites	FS39, 40, 41a, 41c, 43 and 44c (but Type IIIA)	20.00[5]
Heligoland **'Big Bang' 1947**	None	*Explosion Museum of Naval Firepower*, Gosport[4] 19 May–18 June 2017	FS39, 40, 41a, 41c, 43 and 44c (but Type IIIA)	20.00

The different inscriptions from *National Museum Royal Navy*. Where the same inscription exists on more than one design only one may be pictured.

Post & Go stamps – the inscriptions from *The National Museum Royal Navy*, Portsmouth, July 2014–April 2022:
A simplified checklist of the Machin, Union Flag and Common Poppy issues

Stamp Design, Values, **Inscriptions** (see **bold** text) & Note(s)	Year Code	Location of dispensing machine, Availability (dates inclusive) & Note(s)	Cat. No. of Stamp Issue Without Inscription, or Closest Match	Collectors' Strip Price
Union Flag: 1st/1st L/E 20g WW 10g/E 100g/WW 20g/WW 100g *continued*				
HMS Trincomalee **200 Years**	None	*The National Museum of the Royal Navy*, Hartlepool[3] *HMS Trincomalee* 16 June–19 November 2017	FS39, 40, 41a, 41c, 43 and 44c (but Type IIIA)	20.00
Royal Navy **QE II Carrier**	None	*The National Museum of the Royal Navy*, Portsmouth[1] 19–28 August 2017 The Carrier is named *Queen Elizabeth* and not *Queen Elizabeth II*. From 29 August 2017 the erroneous '**II**' was removed	FS39, 40, 41a, 41c, 43 and 44c (but Type IIIA)	23.00
Royal Navy **QE Carrier 2017**	None	*The National Museum of the Royal Navy*, Portsmouth[1] 29 August–17 September 2017 At the same time the erroneous '**II**' was removed from the inscription the date '**2017**' was added	FS39, 40, 41a, 41c, 43 and 44c (but Type IIIA)	24.00
HMS Trincomalee **12th Oct 1817**	None	*The National Museum of the Royal Navy*, Hartlepool[3] *HMS Trincomalee* 20 November–31 December 2017	FS39, 40, 41a, 41c, 43 and 44c (but Type IIIA)	20.00
HMS Trincomalee	None	*The National Museum of the Royal Navy*, Hartlepool[3] *HMS Trincomalee* 2–14 January 2018	FS39, 40, 41a, 41c, 43 and 44c (but Type IIIA)	20.00
Union Flag: 1st/1st L/E 20g WW 10g/E 100g WW 20g/WW 100g Zone 1-3/WW 100g Zone 2 *[Dual value of E 100g WW 20g and two World Zoned stamps introduced on 1 September 2020]*				
Royal Navy Dual-zone value with hyphen i.e. '**World 100g Zone 1-3**'	None	*The National Museum of the Royal Navy*, Portsmouth[1] 1–17 September 2020[†] *The National Museum of the Royal Navy*, Hartlepool[3] *HMS Trincomalee* 4–17 September 2020[†] *Explosion Museum of Naval Firepower*, Gosport[4] 5–17 September 2020[†]	FS39, 40, 41a, 41d, 44d & 44e (but Type IIIA)	35.00[5]

Euro 20g
World 10g
Royal Navy
QE Carrier 2017
B9GB17 A002-3492-297

Worldwide
up to 100g
HMS Trincomalee
B1GB18 A006-2390-042

Worldwide
Large 100g
Black Tot Day
31st July 1970
B7GB21 A006-2947-012

The different inscriptions from *National Museum Royal Navy*. Where the same inscription exists on more than one design only one may be pictured.

Post & Go stamps – the inscriptions from *The National Museum Royal Navy*, Portsmouth, July 2014–April 2022:
A simplified checklist of the Machin, Union Flag and Common Poppy issues

Stamp Design, Values, **Inscriptions** (see **bold** text) & Note(s)	Year Code	Location of dispensing machine, Availability (dates inclusive) & Note(s)	Cat. No. of Stamp Issue Without Inscription, or Closest Match	Collectors' Strip Price
Union Flag: 1st/1st L/E 20g WW 10g/E 100g WW 20g/WW 100g Zone 1 & 3/WW 100g Zone 2 *[Service indicator for 'World Zones 1 and 3' revised on 18 September 2020]*				
Royal Navy Dual-zone value with ampersand i.e. **'World 100g Zone 1 & 3'**	None	*The National Museum of the Royal Navy*, Portsmouth[1] 18 September–4 November 2020[†] 3–19 December 2020[†]	FS39, 40, 41*a*, 41*d*, 44*d* var & 44*e* (but Type IIIA)	30.00[5]
		Explosion Museum of Naval Firepower, Gosport[4] 20 September–4 November 2020[†] 3–19 December 2020[†]		
		The National Museum of the Royal Navy, Hartlepool[3] *HMS Trincomalee* 23 September–4 November 2020[†]	Single: i.e. Zone1 & 3/FS44*d* var	12.00[5]
Union Flag: 1st/1st Large/E 100g WW 20g/WW 100g/E Large 100g/WW Large 100g				
Royal Navy	None	*The National Museum of the Royal Navy*, Portsmouth[1] 17 May–30 July 2021 1 September–20 October 2021 1 November 2021 only (2 November 2021 [♦♦])	FS39, 40, 41d, 44c, 41 var & 44 var (but all Type IIIA)	32.00[5]
		National Museum of the Royal Navy, Hartlepool[3] *HMS Trincomalee* 17 May–30 July 2021 1 September–25 November 2021 11 December 2021–31 March 2022 30 April–1 June 2022 2 July–10 November 2022		
		Explosion Museum of Naval Firepower, Gosport[4] (19 May–15 June 2021[♦]) 16 June–30 July 2021 1 September–31 October 2021 (2 November 2021[♦♦])	Set of two singles: i.e. E Large 100g/FS41 var & WW Large 100g/FS44 var (but TIIIA)	20.00[5]
Black Tot Day 31st July 1970 (Note: **'Royal Navy'** not included on this issue)	None	*The National Museum of the Royal Navy*, Portsmouth[1] 31 July–31 August 2021	FS39, 40, 41d, 44c, 41 var & 44 var (but all Type IIIA)	32.00[5]
		The National Museum of the Royal Navy, Hartlepool[3] *HMS Trincomalee* 31 July–31 August 2021		
		Explosion Museum of Naval Firepower, Gosport[4] 31 July–31 August 2021		
		Note: These stamps are identifiable only through their machine code i.e. *National Museum of the Royal Navy*, Portsmouth = 002 *National Museum of the Royal Navy*, Hartlepool = 006 *Explosion Museum of Naval Firepower*, Gosport = 007		
Royal Navy Trafalgar Day	None	*National Museum of the Royal Navy*, Portsmouth[1] 21–31 October 2021	FS39, 40, 41d, 44c, 41 var & 44 var (but all Type IIIA)	35.00
Royal Navy Lest We Forget	None	*The National Museum of the Royal Navy*, Hartlepool[3] *HMS Trincomalee* 26 November–10 December 2021 11 November 2022 until roll was finished	FS39, 40, 41d, 44c, 41 var & 44 var (but all Type IIIA)	35.00
		The National Museum of the Royal Navy, Portsmouth[1] 11 November 2022 until roll was finished		
		Explosion Museum of Naval Firepower, Gosport[4] 11–30 November 2022		
	MA19	*The National Museum of the Royal Navy*, Portsmouth[1] Available from when the undated stock ran out to the 30 November 2022	FS39, 40, 41d, 44c, 41 var & 44 var (but all Type IIIA)	35.00
		The National Museum of the Royal Navy, Hartlepool[3] *HMS Trincomalee* Available from when the undated stock ran out to the 30 November 2022		
Royal Navy Falklands 40th	None	*The National Museum of the Royal Navy*, Hartlepool[3] *HMS Trincomalee* 1–29 April 2022	FS39, 40, 41d, 44c, 41 var & 44 var (but all Type IIIA)	35.00

Post & Go stamps – the inscriptions from *The National Museum Royal Navy*, Portsmouth, July 2014–April 2022:
A simplified checklist of the Machin, Union Flag and Common Poppy issues

Stamp Design, Values, **Inscriptions** (see **bold** text) & Note(s)	Year Code	Location of dispensing machine, Availability (dates inclusive) & Note(s)	Cat. No. of Stamp Issue Without Inscription, or Closest Match	Collectors' Strip Price
***Common Poppy:* 1st/1st L/E 20g WW 10g/E 60g/WW 20g/WW 60g**				
The NMRN Remembrance	MA14	*The National Museum of the Royal Navy*, Portsmouth[1] 21 October–13 November 2014	FS103, 104, 105, 106, 107 & 108 (but Type IIIA)	35.00
***Common Poppy:* 1st/1st L/E 20g WW 10g/E 100g/WW 20g/WW 100g**				
Royal Navy	MA15	*The National Museum of the Royal Navy*, Portsmouth[1] 19 October–15 November 2015 24 October–13 November 2016 – all sites apart from *The National Museum of the Royal Navy*, Belfast[2] – *HMS Caroline* which was closed at the time 20 October–19 November 2017 – all sites apart from *The National Museum of the Royal Navy*, Belfast[2] – *HMS Caroline* owing to the machine having been taken out of service spring/summer 2017	FS137, 138, 139, 140, 141 & 142 (Type IIIA)	20.00[5]
Royal Navy	MA15	*The National Museum of the Royal Navy*, Portsmouth[1] 19 October–15 November 2015 24 October–13 November 2016 – all sites apart from *The National Museum of the Royal Navy*, Belfast[2] – *HMS Caroline* which was closed at the time 20 October–19 November 2017 – all sites apart from *The National Museum of the Royal Navy*, Belfast[2] – *HMS Caroline* owing to the machine having been taken out of service spring/summer 2017	FS137, 138, 139, 140, 141 & 142 (Type IIIA)	20.00[5]
HMS Trincomalee 12th Oct 1817 With the introduction of this inscription, the Machin design should have replaced the *Common Poppy* design. Instead, the *Common Poppy* design was left in the machine resulting in an unintentional issue.	MA15	*The National Museum of the Royal Navy*, Hartlepool[3] *HMS Trincomalee* 20 November 2017	FS137, 138, 139, 140, 141 & 142 (Type IIIA)	45.00
Royal Navy Lest We Forget 100	MA15	*The National Museum of the Royal Navy*, Portsmouth[1] 1–30 November 2019 *The National Museum of the Royal Navy*, Hartlepool[3] *HMS Trincomalee* 1 November–2 December 2019	FS137, 138, 139, 140, 141 & 142 (Type IIIA)	20.00[5]
	MA16	*The National Museum of the Royal Navy*, Hartlepool[3] *HMS Trincomalee* Available for a few hours only on 27 November 2019	FS137, 138, 139, 140, 141 & 142 (Type IIIA)	30.00
	MA19	*The National Museum of the Royal Navy*, Hartlepool[3] *HMS Trincomalee* Available for a few hours only on 1 November 2019 *Explosion Museum of Naval Firepower*, Gosport[4] 1–30 November 2019	FS137, 138, 139, 140, 141 & 142 (Type IIIA)	21.00[5]

The different inscriptions from *National Museum Royal Navy*. Where the same inscription exists on more than one design only one may be pictured.

Post & Go stamps – the inscriptions from *The National Museum Royal Navy*, Portsmouth, July 2014–April 2022:
A simplified checklist of the Machin, Union Flag and Common Poppy issues

Stamp Design, Values, **Inscriptions** (see **bold** text) & Note(s)	Year Code	Location of dispensing machine, Availability (dates inclusive) & Note(s)	Cat. No. of Stamp Issue Without Inscription, or Closest Match	Collectors' Strip Price
Common Poppy: 1st/1st Large/E 100g WW 20g/WW 100g/E Large 100g/WW Large 100g				
Royal Navy **Lest We Forget**	MA15	*The National Museum of the Royal Navy*, Hartlepool[3] *HMS Trincomalee* 26 November–10 December 2021	FS137, 138, 140 *var*, 142, 140 *var*, and 142 *var* (Type IIIA)	45.00
	MA19	*The National Museum of the Royal Navy*, Hartlepool[3] *HMS Trincomalee* Apparently available for a few hours only on 26 November 2021	FS137, 138, 140 *var*, 142, 140 *var*, and 142 *var* (Type IIIA)	38.00

Post & Go machines at Royal Navy Museums and the dates they were available from:

[1] *The National Museum of the Royal Navy* (NMRN), Portsmouth (machine code 002) – from 28 July 2014.

[2] *The National Museum of the Royal Navy*, Belfast – *HMS Caroline* (machine code 008) – from 1 June 2016–spring/summer 2017.
Note: Machine taken out of service with no plans for it to be reinstated.

[3] *The National Museum of the Royal Navy*, Hartlepool – *HMS Trincomalee* (machine code 006) – from 1 June 2016.

[4] *Explosion Museum of Naval Firepower*, Gosport (machine code 007) – from 16 August 2016.

[5] When a similar item is available from more than one location the price given is for the cheaper version.

The machines at all the *National Museum Royal Navy* sites dispense stamps with the same generic inscription, although sometimes a particular site will mark a specific event through a unique inscription that is only available for a limited period.

[†] Owing to COVID 19 restrictions, the *Royal Navy* sites at Portsmouth, Hartlepool and *Explosion* at Gosport, closed their doors to the general public on 18 March 2020. The Portsmouth site reopened on 24 August 2020, Hartlepool on 4 September 2020, and Gosport on 29 August 2020. All sites closed again on 5 November 2020. The Portsmouth site temporarily reopened 3–19 December 2020 and Gosport 5–19 December 2020. Hartlepool remained closed. Portsmouth and Hartlepool sites reopened on 17 May 2021 and Gosport on 19 May 2021.

[♦] Post & Go machine out-of service between 19 May–15 June 2021.

[♦♦] Post & Go machine out-of service from 2 November 2021 up to, and including, the end date of this table i.e. April 2022.

Note: Each of *The Royal Navy Museum* sites has individual opening days outside the scope of this listing.

Glitches affecting inscriptions and lasting only a very short time and/or which exist in small quantities are beyond the scope of these tables.

The different inscriptions from *National Museum Royal Navy*. Where the same inscription exists on more than one design only one may be pictured.

Post & Go stamps – the different issues and inscriptions from *The Royal Marines Museum*, Portsmouth to February 2017: A simplified checklist

Post & Go stamps – the inscriptions from *The Royal Marines Museum*, Southsea, January 2015–February 2017: A simplified checklist of the Machin, Union Flag and Common Poppy issues

Stamp Design, Values, Inscriptions (see bold text) & Note(s)	Year Code	Availability (dates inclusive) & Note(s)	Cat. No. of Stamp Issue Without Inscription, or Closest Match	Collectors' Strip Price
Machin: 1st/1st L/E 20g WW 10g/E 60g/WW 20g/WW 60g				
The RMM	MA13	13 January–29 March 2015	FS77b, 78b, 79bb, 80, 82b & 84 (Type IIIA)	19.00
	None	Apparently available for a few hours only on 13 January 2015	FS1d, 2d, 3cb, 3d, 5d & 5f (Type IIIA)	75.00
Machin: 1st/1st L/E 20g WW 10g/E 100g/WW 20g/WW 100g				
The RMM	MA13	30 March–18 October 2015	FS77b, 78b, 79bb, 80ca, 82b & 84ca (Type IIIA)	25.00
Royal Marines + circle logo Generic inscription revised, i.e. '**Royal Marines**' replaces acronym, and circle logo introduced.	MA13	16 November 2015–30 May 2016 1 July 2016–24 February 2017 after which the machine was relocated owing to the closure of the museum	FS77b, 78b, 79bb, 80ca, 82b & 84ca (Type IIIA)	19.00
Royal Marines Battle of Jutland + circle logo	MA13	31 May–30 June 2016	FS77b, 78b, 79bb, 80ca, 82b & 84ca (Type IIIA)	20.00
	MA15	Apparently available for a few hours only on 31 May 2016	FS77b, 78b, 79bb, 80ca, 82b & 84ca (Type IIIA)	—
Union Flag: 1st/1st L/E 20g WW 10g/E 60g/WW 20g/WW 60g				
The RMM	None	13 January–29 March 2015	FS39, 40, 41a, 41b, 43 & 44b (but Type IIIA)	19.00
Union Flag: 1st/1st L/E 20g WW 10g/E 100g/WW 20g/WW 100g				
The RMM	None	30 March–7 May 2015 1 June–18 October 2015	FS39, 40, 41a, 41c, 43 & 44c (but Type IIIA)	25.00
The RMM V.E. Day 70	None	8–31 May 2015	FS39, 40, 41a, 41c, 43 & 44c (but Type IIIA)	20.00
Royal Marines Trafalgar Day	None	19 October–15 November 2015 23 September–23 October 2016	FS39, 40, 41a, 41c, 43 & 44c (but Type IIIA)	20.00
Union Flag: 1st/1st L/E 20g WW 10g/E 100g/WW 20g/WW 100g				
Royal Marines Generic inscription revised, i.e. '**Royal Marines**' replaces acronym.	None	16 November 2015–30 May 2016 1 July–22 September 2016 14 November 2016–24 February 2017 after which the machine was relocated owing to the closure of the museum	FS39, 40, 41a, 41c, 43 & 44c (but Type IIIA)	19.00
Royal Marines Battle of Jutland	None	31 May–30 June 2016	FS39, 40, 41a, 41c, 43 & 44c (but Type IIIA)	20.00
Common Poppy: 1st/1st L/E 20g WW 10g/E 100g/WW 20g/WW 100g				
Royal Marines	MA15	19 October–15 November 2015 24 October–13 November 2016	FS137, 138, 139, 140, 141 & 142 (Type IIIA)	20.00

Glitches affecting inscriptions and lasting only a very short time and/or which exist in small quantities are beyond the scope of these tables.

The different inscriptions from *The Royal Marines Museum*. Where the same inscription exists on more than one design only one may be pictured.

Post & Go stamps – the different issues and inscriptions from *The Royal Navy Submarine Museum,* Gosport to April 2022: A simplified checklist

Stamp Design, Values, Inscriptions (see bold text) & Note(s)	Year Code	Availability (dates inclusive) & Note(s)	Cat. No. of Stamp Issue Without Inscription, or Closest Match	Collectors' Strip Price
Post & Go stamps – the inscriptions from *The Royal Navy Submarine Museum,* July 2015–April 2022: A simplified checklist of the Machin, Union Flag and Common Poppy issues				
Machin: 1st/1st L/E 20g WW 10g/E 100g WW 20g/WW 100g				
The RNSM	MA13	28 July–18 October 2015	FS77b, 78b, 79bb, 80ca, 82b & 84ca (Type IIIA)	20.00
RN Submarine + circle logo Generic inscription revised, i.e. **'RN Submarine'** replaces acronym, and logo introduced	MA13	16 November 2015–30 May 2016 1 July 2016–18 May 2017 except when 'MA15' available (see below) 19 June 2017–31 October 2019 5 December 2019–18 March 2020 26 August–1 September 2020	FS77b, 78b, 79bb, 80ca, 82b & 84ca (Type IIIA)	19.00
	MA15	Sometimes available between 1 July 2016–18 May 2017	FS77b, 78b, 79bb, 80ca, 82b & 84ca (Type IIIA)	20.00
RN Submarine **Battle of Jutland** + circle logo	MA15	31 May–30 June 2016	FS77b, 78b, 79bb, 80ca, 82b & 84ca (Type IIIA)	20.00
	MA13	Apparently available for a short time between 1–3 June 2016	FS77b, 78b, 79bb, 80ca, 82b & 84ca (Type IIIA)	—
HMS Alliance **14th May 1947** + circle logo	MA15	Only available for a short time on 19 May 2017	FS77b, 78b, 79bb, 80ca, 82b & 84ca (Type IIIA)	23.00
	MA13	19 May–18 June 2017	FS77b, 78b, 79bb, 80ca, 82b & 84ca (Type IIIA)	20.00
Machin: 1st/1st L/E 20g WW 10g/E 100g WW 20g/WW 100g Zone 1-3/WW 100g Zone 2 *[Dual value of E 100g WW 20g and two World Zoned stamps introduced on 1 September 2020]*				
RN Submarine + circle logo Dual-zone value with hyphen i.e. **'World 100g Zone 1-3'**	MA13	2–17 September 2020[1]	FS77b, 78b, 79bb (Type IIIA), 80d, 84d & 84e (but Type IIIA)	35.00
Machin: 1st/1st L/E 20g WW 10g/E 100g WW 20g/WW 100g Zone 1 & 3/WW 100g Zone 2 *[Service indicator for 'World Zones 1 and 3' revised on 18 September 2020]*				
RN Submarine + circle logo Dual-zone value with ampersand i.e. **'World 100g Zone 1 & 3'**	MA13	18 September–4 November 2020[1] 3–19 December 2020[1]	FS77b, 78b, 79bb (Type IIIA), 80d, 84d var & 84e (but Type IIIA) Single: i.e. Zone 1 & 3/FS84d var	— 15.00
Machin: 1st/1st Large/E 100g WW 20g/WW 100g/E Large 100g/WW Large 100g: *continued*				
RN Submarine + circle logo	MA15	19 May–30 July 2021	FS77b, 78b, 80d (but Type IIIA), 84ca, 80e (but Type IIIA) and 84f (but Type IIIA)	35.00
	MA13	1 September–1 November 2021 (2–18 November 2021 ♦ ♦) 19–25 November 2021	FS77b, 78b, 80d (but Type IIIA), 84ca, 80e (but Type IIIA) and 84f (but Type IIIA) Set of two: i.e. E Large 100g/FS80e & WW Large 100g/FS84f (but TIIIA)	32.00 20.00
	R20Y	11 December 2021–31 March 2022 30 April–1 June 2022 2 July–22 November 2022	FS77b, 78b, 80d (but Type IIIA), 84ca, 80e (but Type IIIA) and 84f (but Type IIIA)	32.00
RN Submarine **Black Tot Day 31st July 1970** + circle logo	MA15	Available for a few hours only on 31 July 2021	FS77b, 78b, 80d (but Type IIIA), 84ca, 80e (but Type IIIA) and 84f (but Type IIIA)	—
	MA13	31 July–31 August 2021	FS77b, 78b, 80d (but Type IIIA), 84ca, 80e (but Type IIIA) and 84f (but Type IIIA)	32.00
RN Submarine **Falklands 40th** + circle logo	MA13	1–29 April 2022	FS77b, 78b, 80d (but Type IIIA), 84ca, 80e (but Type IIIA) and 84f (but Type IIIA)	35.00
RN Submarine **The Queen's Platinum Jubilee** + circle logo	MA13	3 June–1 July 2022	FS77b, 78b, 80d (but Type IIIA), 84ca, 80e (but Type IIIA) and 84f (but Type IIIA)	35.00

Post & Go stamps – the inscriptions from *The Royal Navy Submarine Museum*, July 2015–April 2022:
A simplified checklist of the Machin, Union Flag and Common Poppy issues

Stamp Design, Values, Inscriptions (see bold text) & Note(s)	Year Code	Availability (dates inclusive) & Note(s)	Cat. No. of Stamp Issue Without Inscription, or Closest Match	Collectors' Strip Price
Union Flag: 1st/1st L/E 20g WW 10g/E 100g/WW 20g/WW 100g				
The RNSM	None	28 July–18 October 2015	FS39, 40, 41*a*, 41*c*, 43 & 44*c* (but Type IIIA)	20.00
RN Submarine Generic inscription revised, i.e. '**RN Submarine**' replaces acronym.	None	19 October 2015–30 May 2016 1 July–23 October 2016 14 November 2016–18 May 2017 19 June–19 October 2017 20 November 2017–18 March 2020 26 August–1 September 2020	FS39, 40, 41*a*, 41*c*, 43 & 44*c* (but Type IIIA)	19.00
RN Submarine **Battle of Jutland**	None	31 May–30 June 2016	FS39, 40, 41*a*, 41*c*, 43 & 44*c* (but Type IIIA)	20.00
HMS Alliance **14th May 1947**	None	19 May–18 June 2017	FS39, 40, 41*a*, 41*c*, 43 & 44*c* (but Type IIIA)	20.00
Union Flag: 1st/1st L/E 20g WW 10g/E 100g WW 20g/WW 100g Zone 1-3/WW 100g Zone 2 *[Dual value of E 100g WW 20g and two World Zoned stamps introduced on 1 September 2020]*				
RN Submarine Dual-zone value with hyphen i.e. '**World 100g Zone 1-3**'	None	2–17 September 2020[1]	FS39, 40, 41*a*, 41*d*, 44*d* & 44*e* (but Type IIIA)	35.00
Union Flag: 1st/1st L/E 20g WW 10g/E 100g WW 20g/WW 100g Zone 1 & 3/WW 100g Zone 2 *[Service indicator for 'World Zones 1 and 3' revised on 18 September 2020]*				
RN Submarine Dual-zone value with ampersand i.e. '**World 100g Zone 1 & 3**'	None	18 September–4 November 2020[1] 3–19 December 2020[1]	FS39, 40, 41*a*, 41*d*, 44*d* var & 44*e* (but Type IIIA) Single: i.e. Zone 1 & 3/FS44*d* var	— 15.00

The different inscriptions from *The Royal Navy Submarine Museum*. Where the same inscription exists on more than one design only one may be pictured.

Post & Go stamps – the inscriptions from *The Royal Navy Submarine Museum*, July 2015–April 2022:
A simplified checklist of the Machin, Union Flag and Common Poppy issues

Stamp Design, Values, Inscriptions (see bold text) & Note(s)	Year Code	Availability (dates inclusive) & Note(s)	Cat. No. of Stamp Issue Without Inscription, or Closest Match	Collectors' Strip Price
Union Flag: 1st/1st Large/E 100g WW 20g/WW 100g/E Large 100g/WW Large 100g				
RN Submarine	None	19 May–30 July 2021 1 September–1 November 2021 (2–18 November 2021 ♦ ♦) 19–25 November 2021	FS39, 40, 41*d*, 44*c*, 41 *var* & 44 *var* (but all Type IIIA)	35.00
			Set of two singles: i.e. E Large 100g/FS41 *var* & WW Large 100g/FS44 *var* (but TIIIA)	23.00
	MA19	11 December 2021–31 March 2022 30 April–1 June 2022 2 July–22 November 2022	FS85a, 86a, 87 *var*, 88 *var*, 92 *var* & 92 *var* (but all Type IIIA & stamps digitally printed)	32.00
Black Tot Day 31st July 1970 (Note: '**RN Submarine**' not included on this issue)	None	31 July–31 August 2021 (Note: These stamps from *The Royal Navy Submarine Museum*, identifiable only through their machine code, i.e. 004	FS39, 40, 41*d*, 44*c*, 41 *var* & 44 *var* (but all Type IIIA)	32.00
RN Submarine Lest We Forget	None	Available for a few hours only on 26 November 2021	FS39, 40, 41*d*, 44*c*, 41 *var* & 44 *var* (but all Type IIIA)	42.00
	MA19	26 November–10 December 2021 23 November–30 November 2022	FS85a, 86a, 87 *var*, 88 *var*, 92 *var* & 92 *var* (but all Type IIIA & stamps digitally printed)	35.00
RN Submarine Falklands 40th	MA19	1–29 April 2022	FS85a, 86a, 87 *var*, 88 *var*, 92 *var* & 92 *var* (but all Type IIIA & stamps digitally printed)	35.00
Common Poppy: 1st/1st L/E 20g WW 10g/E 100g/WW 20g/WW 100g				
RN Submarine	MA15	19 October–15 November 2015 24 October–13 November 2016 20 October–19 November 2017	FS137, 138, 139, 140, 141 & 142 (Type IIIA)	20.00
RN Submarine Lest We Forget 100	MA15	1–30 November 2019	FS137, 138, 139, 140, 141 & 142 (Type IIIA)	20.00
RN Submarine + circle logo With the return of the generic inscription, the Machin design should have replaced the *Common Poppy* design. Instead, the *Common Poppy* was left in the machine resulting in an unintentional issue.	MA15	1–5 December 2019	FS137, 138, 139, 140, 141 & 142 (Type IIIA)	35.00
Common Poppy: 1st/1st Large/E 100g WW 20g/WW 100g/E Large 100g/WW Large 100g				
RN Submarine Lest We Forget	MA15	26 November–10 December 2021	FS137, 138, 140 *var*, 142, 140 *var*, and 142 *var* (Type IIIA)	35.00

[1] Owing to COVID 19 restrictions, *The Royal Navy Submarine Museum* closed its doors to the general public on 18 March 2020. It temporarily reopened between 26 August–4 November and 3–19 December 2020, both periods with a Wednesday to Sunday opening schedule, and remained closed until 19 May 2021.
♦ ♦ Post & Go machine out-of service

Glitches affecting inscriptions and lasting only a very short time and/or which exist in small quantities are beyond the scope of these tables.

The different inscriptions from *The Royal Navy Submarine Museum*. Where the same inscription exists on more than one design only one may be pictured.

Post & Go stamps – the different issues and inscriptions from *The Royal Navy Fleet Air Arm Museum*, RNAS Yeovilton to April 2022: A simplified checklist

Post & Go stamps – the inscriptions from *The Royal Navy Fleet Air Arm Museum*, RNAS Yeovilton, Ilchester, Yeovil, April 2015–April 2022: A simplified checklist of the Machin, Union Flag and Common Poppy issues

Stamp Design, Values, Inscriptions (see bold text) & Note(s)	Year Code	Availability (dates inclusive) & Note(s)	Cat. No. of Stamp Issue Without Inscription, or Closest Match	Collectors' Strip Price
Machin: 1st/1st L/E 20g WW 10g/E 100g/WW 20g/WW 100g				
The FAAM	MA13	14 April–18 October 2015	FS77b, 78b, 79bb, 80ca, 82b & 84ca (Type IIIA)	20.00
Fleet Air Arm + large circle logo Generic inscription revised, i.e. '**Fleet Air Arm**' replaces acronym, and large logo introduced.	MA13	16 November 2015–30 May 2016 1 July–2 December 2016 4 January–18 July 2017 except when 'MA15' available (see below) 22 August 2017–June 2018	FS77b, 78b, 79bb, 80ca, 82b & 84ca (Type IIIA)	19.00
	MA15	Available for a short time in early January 2017	FS77b, 78b, 79bb, 80ca, 82b & 84ca (Type IIIA)	20.00
	MA14	June 2018–5 November 2019	FS77b, 78b, 79bb, 80ca, 82b & 84ca (Type IIIA)	24.00
Fleet Air Arm **Battle of Jutland** + small circle logo	MA13	31 May–30 June 2016	FS77b, 78b, 79bb, 80ca, 82b & 84ca (Type IIIA)	20.00
Fleet Air Arm **LZ551/G 1st Jet Carrier Landing**	MA13	Only available for a short time on 3 December 2016	FS77b, 78b, 79bb, 80ca, 82b & 84ca (Type IIIA)	75.00
	MA15	3 December 2016–3 January 2017	FS77b, 78b, 79bb, 80ca, 82b & 84ca (Type IIIA)	20.00
Fleet Air Arm **Sea King ZA298 Junglie** + large circle logo	MA13	Only available for a short time on 19 July 2017	FS77b, 78b, 79bb, 80ca, 82b & 84ca (Type IIIA)	90.00
	MA15	19 July–21 August 2017	FS77b, 78b, 79bb, 80ca, 82b & 84ca (Type IIIA)	20.00
Fleet Air Arm **Concorde 50 Years** + Concorde 50 logo Due to poor thermal printing, the right-hand part of the Concorde logo is faintly printed, which is the norm for this issue. Conveniently, this allows the 'MA14' year code to be seen, which otherwise, would have been obscured.	MA14	6 November 2019–18 March 2020[1] 14 August–1 September 2020[1]	FS77b, 78b, 79bb, 80ca, 82b & 84ca (Type IIIA)	20.00

The different inscriptions from *The Royal Navy Fleet Air Arm Museum*. Where the same inscription exists on more than one design only one may be pictured.

Post & Go stamps – the inscriptions from *The Royal Navy Fleet Air Arm Museum*, RNAS Yeovilton, Ilchester, Yeovil, April 2015–April 2022:
A simplified checklist of the Machin, Union Flag and Common Poppy issues

Stamp Design, Values, Inscriptions (see bold text) & Note(s)	Year Code	Availability (dates inclusive) & Note(s)	Cat. No. of Stamp Issue Without Inscription, or Closest Match	Collectors' Strip Price
Machin: 1st/1st L/E 20g WW 10g/E 100g WW 20g/WW 100g Zone 1-3/WW 100g Zone 2 *[Dual value of E 100g WW 20g and two World Zoned stamps introduced on 1 September 2020]*				
Fleet Air Arm + large circle logo	MA14	1–2 September 2020[1]	FS77b, 78b, 79bb (Type IIIA), 80d, 84d & 84e (but Type IIIA)	—
Dual-zone value with hyphen i.e. '**World 100g Zone 1-3**'	MA13	2–17 September 2020[1]	FS77b, 78b, 79bb (Type IIIA), 80d, 84d & 84e (but Type IIIA)	35.00
Machin: 1st/1st L/E 20g WW 10g/E 100g WW 20g/WW 100g Zone 1 & 3/WW 100g Zone 2 *[Service indicator for 'World Zones 1 and 3' revised on 18 September 2020]*				
Fleet Air Arm + large circle logo Dual-zone value with ampersand i.e. '**World 100g Zone 1 & 3**'	MA13	18 September–6 October 2020[1] During this period, partly owing to a shortage of stock, the machine was rarely in service	FS77b, 78b, 79bb (Type IIIA), 80d, 84d var & 84e (but Type IIIA) Single: i.e. Zone 1 & 3/FS84d var	— —
Fleet Air Arm + small circle logo Small circle logo replaced large version Dual-zone value with ampersand i.e. '**World 100g Zone 1 & 3**'	MA13	7 October–4 November 2020[1] 3–11 December 2020[1] 18–20 December 2020[1]	FS77b, 78b, 79bb (Type IIIA), 80d, 84d var & 84e (but Type IIIA)	30.00
Machin: 1st/1st L/E 20g WW 10g/E 100g/WW 20g/WW 100g *(reversion to pre-September 2020 tariff stamps)*				
Fleet Air Arm + small circle logo Reversion to pre-September 2020 tariff stamp, but with small logo	MA13	12–17 December 2020[1]	FS77b, 78b, 79bb, 80ca, 82b & 84ca (Type IIIA)	38.00
Machin: 1st/1st Large/E 100g WW 20g/WW 100g/E Large 100g/WW Large 100g				
Fleet Air Arm + small circle logo	MA13	19 May–30 July 2021 1 September–1 November 2021 (2–18 November 2021 ♦♦) 19–25 November 2021 11 December 2021–31 March 2022 30 May–2 June 2022 2 July–10 November 2022	FS77b, 78b, 80d (but Type IIIA), 84ca, 80e (but Type IIIA) & 84f (but Type IIIA) Set of two singles: i.e. E Large 100g/FS80e & WW Large 100g/FS84f (but TIIIA)	32.00 20.00
	MA14	From sometime late 2022	FS77b, 78b, 80d (but Type IIIA), 84ca, 80e (but Type IIIA) & 84f (but Type IIIA)	35.00
Fleet Air Arm **Black Tot Day 31st July 1970** + circle logo	MA13	31 July–31 August 2021	FS77b, 78b, 80d (but Type IIIA), 84ca, 80e (but Type IIIA) & 84f (but Type IIIA)	32.00
Fleet Air Arm **Falklands 40th** + circle logo	MA13	1–29 April 2022	FS77b, 78b, 80d (but Type IIIA), 84ca, 80e (but Type IIIA) & 84f (but Type IIIA)	35.00
Fleet Air Arm **The Queen's Platinum Jubilee** + circle logo	MA13	3 June–1 July 2022	FS77b, 78b, 80d (but Type IIIA), 84ca, 80e (but Type IIIA) & 84f (but Type IIIA)	35.00

The different inscriptions from *The Royal Navy Fleet Air Arm Museum*. Where the same inscription exists on more than one design only one may be pictured.

Post & Go stamps – the inscriptions from *The Royal Navy Fleet Air Arm Museum*, RNAS Yeovilton, Ilchester, Yeovil, April 2015–April 2022: A simplified checklist of the Machin, Union Flag and Common Poppy issues

Stamp Design, Values, Inscriptions (see bold text) & Note(s)	Year Code	Availability (dates inclusive) & Note(s)	Cat. No. of Stamp Issue Without Inscription, or Closest Match	Collectors' Strip Price
Union Flag: 1st/1st L/E 20g WW 10g/E 100g/WW 20g/WW 100g				
The FAAM	None	14 April–7 May 2015 30 May–18 October 2015	FS39, 40, 41*a*, 41*c*, 43 & 44*c* (but Type IIIA)	20.00
The FAAM **V.E. Day 70**	None	8–29 May 2015	FS39, 40, 41*a*, 41*c*, 43 & 44*c* (but Type IIIA)	20.00
Fleet Air Arm Generic inscription revised, i.e. **'Fleet Air Arm'** replaces acronym.	None	19 October 2015–30 May 2016 1 July–23 October 14 November–2 December 2016 4 January–18 July 2017 22 August–19 October 2017 20 November 2017–5 November 2019 12–17 December 2020[1] due to a temporary reversion to the pre-September 2020 tariff stamps	FS39, 40, 41*a*, 41*c*, 43 & 44*c* (but Type IIIA)	19.00
	MA19	Only available for a short time on 12 December 2020[1] due to a temporary reversion to the pre-September 2020 tariff stamps	FS85a, 86a, 87*a*, 88*a*, 90*a* & 92*a* (but Type IIIA & stamps digitally printed)	—
Union Flag: 1st/1st L/E 20g WW 10g/E 100g/WW 20g/WW 100g:				
Fleet Air Arm **Battle of Jutland**	None	31 May–30 June 2016	FS39, 40, 41*a*, 41*c*, 43 & 44*c* (but Type IIIA)	20.00
Fleet Air Arm **LZ551/G 03Dec45**	None	3 December 2016–3 January 2017	FS39, 40, 41*a*, 41*c*, 43 & 44*c* (but Type IIIA)	20.00
Fleet Air Arm **LZ551/G 03Dec45** Second line of inscription slightly inset	None	Only available for a short time on 3 December 2016 and then corrected	FS39, 40, 41*a*, 41*c*, 43 & 44*c* (but Type IIIA)	25.00
Fleet Air Arm **GR9A Harrier ZD433**	None	19 July–21 August 2017	FS39, 40, 41*a*, 41*c*, 43 & 44*c* (but Type IIIA)	19.00
Fleet Air Arm **Concorde 50 Years**	None	6 November 2019–18 March 2020[1] 14 August–1 September 2020[1]	FS39, 40, 41*a*, 41*c*, 43 & 44*c* (but Type IIIA)	20.00
Union Flag: 1st/1st L/E 20g WW 10g/E 100g WW 20g/WW 100g Zone 1-3/WW 100g Zone 2 *[Dual value of E 100g WW 20g and two World Zoned stamps introduced on 1 September 2020]*				
Fleet Air Arm Dual-zone value with hyphen i.e. **'World 100g Zone 1-3'**	None	1–17 September 2020[1]	FS39, 40, 41*a*, 41*d*, 44*d* & 44*e* (but Type IIIA)	35.00
Union Flag: 1st/1st L/E 20g WW 10g/E 100g WW 20g/WW 100g Zone 1 & 3/WW 100g Zone 2 *[Service indicator for 'World Zones 1 and 3' revised on 18 September 2020]*				
Fleet Air Arm Dual-zone value with ampersand i.e. **'World 100g Zone 1 & 3'**	None	18 September–6 October 2020[1] During this period, partly owing to a shortage of stock, the machine was rarely in service 18–20 December 2020[1]	FS39, 40, 41*a*, 41*d*, 44*d* var & 44*e* (but Type IIIA) Single: i.e. Zone 1 & 3/FS44*d* var (but TIIIA)	— —
	MA19	7 October–4 November 2020[1] 3–12 December 2020[1]	FS85a, 86a, 87*a*, 88 var, 92 var & 92 var (but Type IIIA & stamps digitally printed)	30.00
Union Flag: 1st/1st Large/E 100g WW 20g/WW 100g/E Large 100g/WW Large 100g				
Fleet Air Arm	None	19 May–30 July 2021 1 September–1 November 2021 (2–18 November 2021 ♦♦) 19–25 November 2021 11 December 2021–31 March 2022 30 May–2 June 2022 2 July–1 November 2022	FS39, 40, 41*d*, 44*c*, 41 var & 44 var (but all Type IIIA) Set of two singles: i.e. E Large 100g/FS41 var & WW Large 100g/FS44 var (but TIIIA)	35.00 23.00
Black Tot Day **31st July 1970** (Note: **'Fleet Air Arm'** not included on this issue)	None	31 July–31 August 2021 (Note: These stamps from *The Royal Navy Fleet Air Arm Museum* identifiable only through their machine code, i.e. 003	FS39, 40, 41*d*, 44*c*, 41 var & 44 var (but all Type IIIA)	32.00
Fleet Air Arm **Lest We Forget**	None	26 November–10 December 2021 11 November–30 November 2022	FS39, 40, 41*d*, 44*c*, 41 var & 44 var (but all Type IIIA)	35.00
Fleet Air Arm **Falklands 40th**	None	Only available for a short time on 1 April 2022	FS39, 40, 41*d*, 44*c*, 41 var & 44 var (but all Type IIIA)	—
	MA19	1–29 April 2022	FS85a, 86a, 87 var, 88 var, 92 var & 92 var (but all Type IIIA & stamps digitally printed)	35.00

Euro 20g
World 10g
The FAAM
V.E. Day 70
B5GB15 A003-2175-093

Europe
up to 100g
Fleet Air Arm
B0GB15 A003-2326-010

Worldwide
up to 100g
Fleet Air Arm
Battle of Jutland
B6GB16 A003-2607-084

Worldwide
up to 100g
Fleet Air Arm
LZ551/G 03Dec45
BDGB16 A003-2813-006

Worldwide
up to 100g
Fleet Air Arm
LZ551/G 03Dec45
BDGB16 A003-2770-120

Worldwide
up to 100g
Fleet Air Arm
GR9A Harrier ZD433
B7GB17 A003-3027-180

1st Large
up to 100g
Fleet Air Arm
Concorde 50 Years
BNGB19 A003-3740-440

World 100g
Zone 1-3
Fleet Air Arm
B9GB20 A003-3835-011

World 100g
Zone 1 & 3
Fleet Air Arm
B0GB20 A003-3909-191

World 100g
Zone 2
Fleet Air Arm
B9GB20 A003-3835-012

Worldwide
Large 100g
Black Tot Day
31st July 1970
B7GB21 A003-4016-006

Worldwide
Large 100g
Fleet Air Arm
Lest We Forget
BNGB21 A003-4108-054

Worldwide
up to 100g
Fleet Air Arm
Falklands 40th
B4GB22 A003-4192-016

The different inscriptions from
The Royal Navy Fleet Air Arm Museum.
Where the same inscription exists on
more than one design only one may
be pictured.

Post & Go stamps – the inscriptions from *The Royal Navy Fleet Air Arm Museum*, RNAS Yeovilton, Ilchester, Yeovil, April 2015–April 2022:
A simplified checklist of the Machin, Union Flag and Common Poppy issues

Stamp Design, Values, Inscriptions (see bold text) & Note(s)	Year Code	Availability (dates inclusive) & Note(s)	Cat. No. of Stamp Issue Without Inscription, or Closest Match	Collectors' Strip Price
Common Poppy: **1st/1st L/E 20g WW 10g/E 100g/WW 20g/WW 100g**				
Fleet Air Arm	MA15	19 October–15 November 2015 24 October–13 November 2016 20 October–19 November 2017	FS137, 138, 139, 140, 141 & 142 (Type IIIA)	20.00
Common Poppy: **1st/1st Large/E 100g WW 20g/WW 100g/E Large 100g/WW Large 100g**				
Fleet Air Arm Lest We Forget	MA15	26 November–10 December 2021	FS137, 138, 140 *var*, 142, 140 *var*, & 142 *var* (Type IIIA)	35.00

¹ Owing to COVID 19 restrictions, *The Royal Navy Fleet Air Arm Museum* closed its doors to the general public on 18 March 2020. It temporarily reopened between 14 August–4 November and 3–20 December 2020 (sometimes only opening Wednesday to Sunday), and remained closed until 19 May 2021.
✦✦ Post & Go machine out-of service

Glitches affecting inscriptions and lasting only a very short time and/or which exist in small quantities are beyond the scope of these tables.

Euro 100g
World 20g
Fleet Air Arm
Lest We Forget
BNGB21 A003-4109-003

The different inscriptions from
The Royal Navy Fleet Air Arm Museum.
Where the same inscription exists on
more than one design only one may
be pictured.

Post & Go stamps – the different issues and inscriptions from The Royal Signals Museum to April 2021: A simplified checklist

Post and Go stamps – the inscriptions from The Royal Signals Museum, Royal School of Signals, Blandford Camp, Blandford Forum, November 2016–April 2021: A simplified checklist of the Machin, Union Flag and Common Poppy issues

Stamp Design, Values, Inscriptions (see bold text) & Note(s)	Year Code	Availability (dates inclusive) & Note(s)	Cat. No. of Stamp Issue Without Inscription, or Closest Match	Collectors' Strip Price
Machin: 1st/1st L/E 20g WW 10g/E 100g/WW 20g/WW 100g				
Royal Corps of Signals + Jimmy logo	None	From 3 November 2016[1]	FS1d, 2d, 3cb, 3ea, 5d & 5ga (Type IIIA)	20.00
	MA13	At different times, no year code and 'MA13' have been available	FS77b, 78b, 79bb, 80ca, 82b & 84ca (Type IIIA)	25.00
Union Flag: 1st/1st L/E 20g WW 10g/E 100g/WW 20g/WW 100g				
Royal Corps of Signals	None	3 November 2016–8 June 2017 From 20 November 2017[1]	FS39, 40, 41a, 41c, 43 & 44c (but Type IIIA)	20.00
Royal Signals White Helmets + Motorcycle logo	None	9 June–19 October 2017	FS39, 40, 41a, 41c, 43 & 44c (but Type IIIA)	20.00
Poppy: 1st/1st L/E 20g WW 10g/E 100g/WW 20g/WW 100g				
Royal Corps of Signals	MA15	20 October–19 November 2017	FS137, 138, 139, 140, 141 & 142 (Type IIIA)	20.00

[1] Owing to COVID 19 restrictions, The Royal Signals Museum closed its doors to the general public on 18 March 2020 and remains closed.

Glitches affecting inscriptions and lasting only a very short time and/or which exist in small quantities are beyond the scope of these tables.

The different inscriptions from The Royal Signals Museum. Where the same inscription exists on more than one design only one may be pictured.

Post & Go stamps – the different printings from exhibitions and stamp fairs in the United Kingdom but without inscriptions (February 2011 – September 2017): a simplified checklist

Stamp Design, Values, Machine Type & Note(s)	Format produced		Event the stamps were available from, the date and duration (all the dates are inclusive)	Space between service indicator lines	Code string is numerals only (Type II)	Code string is letters & numerals (Type III)	Cat. No. of Stamp Issue Without Inscription, or Closest Match
	CS	Set of 36					
Machin, 1st/1stL/E-20g/WW-10g/WW-20g without year code (N.B. five values only):-							
Hytech Postal Vision (trial machine) Weight line inset †	✓	n/a	**Spring Stampex** 2011 23–26 February: 4 days	3mm	yes		FS1a/5a
Machin, 1st/1stL/E-20g/WW-10g/WW-20g/WW-40g without year code:							
Royal Mail 'Series I' (sometimes known as Hytech 'next generation')	✓	n/a	**York Stamp Fair** 18–19 January 2013: 2 days **Salisbury Stamp Fair** 15–16 March 2013: 2 days **Midpex Exhibition** 6 July 2013: 1 day (N.B. similar stamps were first issued in November 2012 from a pop-up Christmas Post Shop in Camden, London)	2.6mm		yes	FS1b/3b, 4b, 5b & 5eb
Royal Mail 'Series II'	✓	n/a	**Salisbury Stamp Fair** 14–15 March 2014: 2 days	2.4mm		yes	FS1b/3b, 4b, 5b & 5eb
Machin, 1st/1stL/E-20g/WW-10g/WW-20g/WW-40g with MA13 year code:							
Royal Mail 'Series I' (sometimes known as Hytech 'next generation')	✓	n/a	**York Stamp Fair** 19–20 July 2013: 2 days **Autumn Stampex** 2013 18–21 September: 4 days **Stafford Stamp Fair** 8–9 November 2013: 2 days **York Stamp Fair** 17–18 January 2014: 2 days	2.6mm		yes	FS77/79, 81/83 (but Type III)
Royal Mail 'Series II'	✓	n/a	**Salisbury Stamp Fair** 14–15 March 2014: 2 days	2.4mm		yes	FS77/79, 81/83 (but Type III)
Machin, 1st/1stL/E-20g WW-10g/E-60g/WW-20g/WW-60g without year code:							
Royal Mail 'Series II' Euro 20g large typeface World 10g small typeface	✓	n/a	**York Stamp Fair** 18–19 July 2014: 2 days	2.4mm		yes	FS1b, 2b, 3c, 3d, 5b, & 5f
Royal Mail 'Series II' All values have a revised (smaller) typeface	✓	n/a	**Autumn Stampex** 2014 17–20 September: 4 days **Stafford Stamp Fair** 7–8 November 2014: 2 days **Spring Stampex** 2015 18–21 February: 4 days (N.B. limited availablilty and only known from stock produced in advance of the exhibition)	2.7mm		yes (Type IIIA)	FS1d, 2d, 3cb, 3d, 5d & 5f
Machin, 1st/1stL/E-20g WW-10g/E-60g/WW-20g/WW-60g with MA13 year code:							
Royal Mail 'Series II' Euro 20g large typeface World 10g small typeface	✓	n/a	**York Stamp Fair** 18–19 July 2014: 2 days	2.4mm		yes	FS77/78, 79b, 80, 82 & 84 (but Type III)
Royal Mail 'Series II' All values have a revised (smaller) typeface	✓	n/a	**Autumn Stampex** 2014 17–20 September: 4 days **Stafford Stamp Fair** 7–8 November 2014: 2 days **Spring Stampex** 2015 18–21 February: 4 days	2.7mm		yes (Type IIIA)	FS77b, 78b, 79bb, 80, 82b & 84
Machin, 1st/1stL/E-20g WW-10g/E-100g/WW-20g/WW-100g without year code:							
Royal Mail 'Series II' All values have a revised (smaller) typeface	✓	n/a	**Midpex Exhibition** 4 July 2015: 1 day (N.B. similar stamps were (officially) issued on 3 June 2015 from Royal Mail Enquiry offices	2.7mm		yes (Type IIIA)	FS1d, 2d, 3cb, 3ea, 5d & 5ga

Stamp Design, Values, Machine Type & Note(s)	Format produced		Event the stamps were available from, the date and duration (all the dates are inclusive)	Space between service indicator lines	Code string is numerals only (Type II)	Code string is letters & numerals (Type III)	Cat. No. of Stamp Issue Without Inscription, or Closest Match
	CS	Set of 36					
Machin, 1st/1stL/E-20g WW-10g/E-100g/WW-20g/WW-100g with MA13 year code:							
Royal Mail 'Series II' All values have a revised (smaller) typeface	✓	n/a	**Midpex Exhibition** 4 July 2015: 1 day (N.B. similar stamps were (officially) issued on 30 March 2015 from Royal Mail Enquiry offices)	2.7mm		yes (Type IIIA)	FS77b, 78b, 79bb, 80ca, 82b & 84ca
Machin, 2nd/2ndL with MA12 year code:							
Royal Mail 'Series I' (sometimes known as Hytech 'next generation')	✓	n/a	**Spring Stampex** 2013 20–23 February: 4 days (N.B. similar stamps, but not identical, were (officially) issued in November 2013 from a travelling pop-up Christmas post office)	2.6mm		yes	FS93, 94
Union Flag, 1st/1stL/E-20g/WW-10g/WW-20g/WW-40g without year code:							
Royal Mail 'Series I' (sometimes known as Hytech 'next generation')	✓	n/a	**Autumn Stampex** 2012 26–29 September: 4 days **York Stamp Fair** 18–19 January 2013: 2 days **Salisbury Stamp Fair** 15–16 March 2013: 2 days **Midpex Exhibition** 6 July 2013: 1 day	2.6mm		yes	FS39/44 (but Type III)
Royal Mail 'Series II'	✓	n/a	**Spring Stampex** 2014 19–22 February: 4 days (N.B. This design only available on 21–22 February: 2 days) **Salisbury Stamp Fair** 14–15 March 2014: 2 days	2.4mm		yes	FS39/44 (but Type III)
Union Flag, 1st/1stL/E-20g/WW-10g/WW-20g/WW-40g with MA13 year code:							
Royal Mail 'Series I' (sometimes known as Hytech 'next generation')	✓	n/a	**York Stamp Fair** 19–20 July 2013: 2 days **York Stamp Fair** 17–18 January 2014: 2 days	2.6mm		yes	FS85/90 (but Type III)
Royal Mail 'Series II'	✓	n/a	**Spring Stampex** 2014 19–22 February: 4 days **Salisbury Stamp Fair** 14–15 March 2014: 2 days	2.4mm		yes	FS85/90 (but Type III)
Union Flag, 1st/1stL/E-20g/E-60g/WW-20g/WW-60g without year code:							
Royal Mail 'Series II'	✓	n/a	**85th Annual Congress of Association of Scottish Philatelic Societies (Perth, Scotland)** 11–12 April 2014: 2 days	2.4mm		yes	FS39/41, 41b, 43, & 44b (but Type III)
Union Flag, 1st/1stL/E-20g/E-60g/WW-20g/WW-60g with MA13 year code:							
Royal Mail 'Series II'	✓	n/a	**85th Annual Congress of Association of Scottish Philatelic Societies (Perth, Scotland)** 11–12 April 2014: 2 days	2.4mm		yes	FS85/91 (but Type III)
Union Flag, 1st/1stL/E-20g WW-10g/E-60g/WW-20g/WW-60g without year code :							
Royal Mail 'Series II' Euro 20g large typeface World 10g small typeface	✓	n/a	**York Stamp Fair** 18–19 July 2014: 2 days	2.4mm		yes	FS39, 40, 41a, 41b, 43, & 44b (but Type III)
Royal Mail 'Series II' All values have a revised (smaller) typeface	✓	n/a	**Autumn Stampex** 2014 17–20 September: 4 days **Stafford Stamp Fair** 7–8 November 2014: 2 days	2.7mm		yes (Type IIIA)	FS39, 40, 41a, 41b, 43, & 44b (but Type IIIA)
Union Flag, 1st/1stL/E-20g WW-10g/E-100g/WW-20g/WW-100g without year code :							
Royal Mail 'Series II' All values have a revised (smaller) typeface	✓	n/a	**Europhilex** 2015 13–16 May: 4 days **Midpex Exhibition** 4 July 2015: 1 day **Autumn Stampex** 2015 16–19 September: 4 days	2.7mm		yes (Type IIIA)	FS39, 40, 41a, 41c, 43 & 44c (but Type IIIA)

Stamp Design, Values, Machine Type & Note(s)	Format produced		Event the stamps were available from, the date and duration (all the dates are inclusive)	Space between service indicator lines	Code string is numerals only (Type II)	Code string is letters & numerals (Type III)	Cat. No. of Stamp Issue Without Inscription, or Closest Match
	CS	Set of 36					
Robin, 1st/1stL/E-20g/WW-10g/WW-20g/WW-40g with MA13 year code:							
Royal Mail 'Series I' (sometimes known as Hytech 'next generation')	✓	n/a	**Stafford Stamp Fair** 8–9 November 2013: 2 days (N.B. similar MA13 stamps were (officially) issued later in November 2013 from a travelling pop-up Christmas post office)	2.6mm		yes	FS51a/56a
Birds of Britain 3rd series, 1st/1stL/E-20g/WW-10g/WW-20g/1st (N.B. only produced in collectors' strips of six with additional '1st Class' value at bottom so all six designs represented):							
Royal Mail 'Series I' (sometimes known as Hytech 'next generation') Weight line inset †	✓	n/a	**Autumn Stampex** 2011 14–17 September: 4 days (N.B. This design only available on 14 September: 1 day)	3mm	yes		FS16/20
Birds of Britain 4th series, 1st/1stL/E-20g/WW-10g/WW-20g/WW-40g:							
Royal Mail 'Series I' (sometimes known as Hytech 'next generation') Weight line inset †	✓	✓	**Autumn Stampex** 2011 14–17 September: 4 days (N.B. This design only available on 16–17 September: 2 days) **Spring Stampex** 2012 22–25 February: 4 days (N.B. This design only available on 22–23 September: 2 days)	3mm	yes		FS21/26
Sheep (British Farm Animals 1st series), 1st/1stL/E-20g/WW-10g/WW-20g/WW-40g:							
Royal Mail 'Series I' (sometimes known as Hytech 'next generation') Weight line inset †	✓	✓	**Spring Stampex** 2012 22–25 February: 4 days (N.B. This design only available on 24–25 February: 2 days)	3mm	yes		FS27/32
Pigs (British Farm Animals 2nd series), 1st/1stL/E-20g/WW-10g/WW-20g/WW-40g:							
Royal Mail 'Series I' (sometimes known as Hytech 'next generation')	✓	✓	**Autumn Stampex** 2012 26–29 September: 4 days (N.B. This design only available on 26–27 September: 2 days)	2.6mm		yes	FS33/38 (but Type III)
Cattle (British Farm Animals 3rd series), 1st/1stL/E-20g/WW-10g/WW-20g/WW-40g:							
Royal Mail 'Series I' (sometimes known as Hytech 'next generation')	✓	✓	**Autumn Stampex** 2012 26–29 September: 4 days (N.B. This design only available on 28–29 September: 2 days)	2.6mm		yes	FS45/50 (but Type III)
Ponds (Freshwater Life 1st series), 1st/1stL/E-20g/WW-10g/WW-20g/WW-40g:							
Royal Mail 'Series I' (sometimes known as Hytech 'next generation')	✓	✓	**Spring Stampex** 2013 20–23 February: 4 days (N.B. This design only available on 22–23 February: 2 days)	2.6mm		yes	FS59/64 (but Type III)
Lakes (Freshwater Life 2nd series), 1st/1stL/E-20g/WW-10g/WW-20g/WW-40g:							
Royal Mail 'Series I' (sometimes known as Hytech 'next generation')	✓	✓	**Midpex Exhibition** 06 July 2013: 1 day **York Stamp Fair** 19–20 July 2013: 2 days	2.6mm		yes	FS65/70 (but Type III)
Rivers (Freshwater Life 3rd series), 1st/1stL/E-20g/WW-10g/WW-20g/WW-40g:							
Royal Mail 'Series I' (sometimes known as Hytech 'next generation')	✓	✓	**Autumn Stampex** 2013 18–21 September: 4 days (N.B. This design only available on 20–21 September: 2 days) **Stafford Stamp Fair** 8–9 November 2013: 2 days	2.6mm		yes	FS71/76 (but Type III)
Spring Blooms (British Flora 1st series), 1st/1stL/E-20g/WW-10g/WW-20g/WW-40g:							
Royal Mail 'Series II'	✓	✓	**Spring Stampex** 2014 19–22 February: 4 days	2.4mm		yes	FS95/97, 99/101 (but Type III)
Symbolic Flowers (British Flora 2nd series), 1st/1stL/E-20g WW-10g/E-60g/WW-20g/WW-60g:							
Royal Mail 'Series II'	✓	✓	**Autumn Stampex** 2014 17–20 September: 4 days	2.7mm		yes (Type IIIA)	FS103/108 (but Type IIIA)

Stamp Design, Values, Machine Type & Note(s)	Format produced		Event the stamps were available from, the date and duration (all the dates are inclusive)	Space between service indicator lines	Code string is numerals only (Type II)	Code string is letters & numerals (Type III)	Cat. No. of Stamp Issue Without Inscription, or Closest Match
	CS	Set of 36					
Working Sail, 1st/1stL/E-20g WW-10g/E-60g/WW-20g/WW-60g:							
Royal Mail 'Series II'	✓	✓	Spring Stampex 2015 18–21 February: 4 days	2.7mm		yes (Type IIIA)	FS117/120, 122/123 (but Type IIIA)
Heraldic Beasts, 1st/1stL/E-20g WW-10g/E-100g/WW-20g/WW-100g:							
Royal Mail 'Series II'	✓	✓	Europhilex 2015 13–16 May: 4 days	2.7mm		yes (Type IIIA)	FS125/130 (but Type IIIA)
Lion design (from Heraldic Beasts issue) in single design rolls, 1st/1stL/E-20g WW-10g/E-100g/WW-20g/WW-100g:							
Royal Mail 'Series II'	✓	n/a	Autumn Stampex 2015 16–19 September: 4 days	2.7mm		yes (Type IIIA)	FS125/130 (but Type IIIA)
Sea Travel, 1st/1stL/E-20g WW-10g/E-100g/WW-20g/WW-100g:							
Royal Mail 'Series II'	✓	✓	Autumn Stampex 2015 16–19 September: 4 days	2.7mm		yes (Type IIIA)	FS131/136 (but Type IIIA)
Royal Mail Heritage: Transport, 1st/1stL/E-20g WW-10g/E-100g/WW-20g/WW-100g:							
Royal Mail 'Series II'	✓	✓	Spring Stampex 2016 17–20 February: 4 days	2.7mm		yes (Type IIIA)	FS151/156 (but Type IIIA)
Locomotive design (from Royal Mail Heritage: Transport issue) from single-design rolls, 1st/1stL/E-20g WW-10g/E-100g/WW-20g/WW-100g:							
Royal Mail 'Series II' Stamps digitally printed	✓	n/a	Spring Stampex 2016 17–20 February: 4 days Spring Stampex 2017 15–18 February: 4 days	2.7mm		yes (Type IIIA)	FS151/156 (but Type IIIA)
Ladybirds, 1st/1stL/E-20g WW-10g/E-100g/WW-20g/WW-100g:							
Royal Mail 'Series II'	✓	✓	Autumn Stampex 2016 14–17 September: 4 days	2.7mm		yes (Type IIIA)	FS159a/164a
Royal Mail Heritage: Mail by Rail, 1st/1stL/E-20g WW-10g/E-100g/WW-20g/WW-100g:							
Royal Mail 'Series II'	✓	✓	Spring Stampex 2017 15–18 February: 4 days	2.7mm		yes (Type IIIA)	FS173a/178a
Royal Mail Heritage: Mail by Air, 1st/1stL/E-20g WW-10g/E-100g/WW-20g/WW-100g:							
Royal Mail 'Series II'	✓	✓	Autumn Stampex 2017 13–16 September: 4 days	2.7mm		yes (Type IIIA)	FS185a/195a

Hytech Postal Vision was a trial machine introduced at Spring Stampex 2011. Machines referred to as Hytech version 1 were used at Autumn Stampex 2011 and Spring Stampex 2012. From Autumn Stampex 2012 modified machines were instead brought into use, sometimes referred to as Hytech 'next generation', Hytech version 2, and also Royal Mail Series I which is used in the above table. At Spring Stampex 2014 a new machine was brought into use and it is classified as a Royal Mail 'Series II' (although it is sometimes referred to as Royal Mail Series B).

† = Stamps generated from Hytech Postal Vision and Hytech version I machines have their weight lines inset, whereas stamps from Royal Mail 'Series I' and Royal Mail 'Series II' have their weight lines ranged left. From Autumn Stampex 2014, Royal Mail 'Series II' machines at exhibitions produced stamps with a smaller typeface. In place of gravure, digital printing is sometimes used for some single-design rolls. Stamps produced by this process are very shiny and have poor background definition, especially in the repeating 'ROYALMAIL' wording.

CS = Collectors' strips: the Machins from the Hytech Postal Vision trial machine are in strips of five, the Machin 2nds are in pairs, and all other collectors' strips are of six stamps. Sets of 36 (from and including Birds of Britain 4th series): all six denominations were available in all six designs making a complete set 36 stamps. Some of the catalogue numbers shown are provisional and may be subject to change

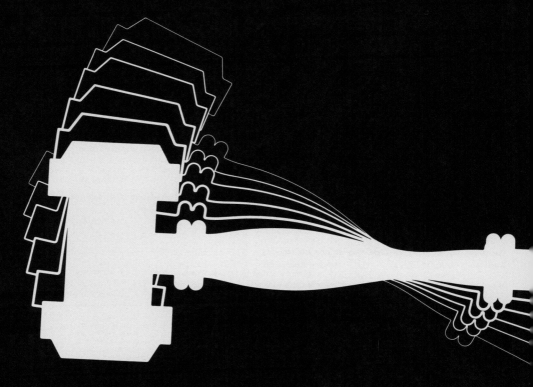

Regional Issues

PRINTERS (£.s.d. stamps of all regions): Photo Harrison & Sons. Portrait by Dorothy Wilding Ltd.

DATES OF ISSUE. Conflicting dates of issue have been announced for some of the regional issues, partly explained by the stamps being released on different dates by the Philatelic Bureau in Edinburgh or the Philatelic Counter in London and in the regions. We have adopted the practice of giving the earliest known dates, since once released the stamps could have been used anywhere in the United Kingdom.

I. ENGLAND

'Emblem' Regional colours. Where the Queen's head has been printed in a black screen, this appears as grey. Where stamps exist with either silver or grey heads, this is stated in the catalogue entries.

EN1 Three Lions of England

EN3 English Oak Tree

EN2 Crowned Lion, Supporting the Shield of St George

EN4 English Tudor Rose

(Des Sedley Place, from sculptures by David Dathan. Gravure Questa (No. EN1b) or De La Rue (others))

2001 (23 Apr)–**02**. One centre phosphor band (2nd) or two phosphor bands (others). Perf 15×14 (with one elliptical hole in each vertical side). All heads Type I.

EN1	**EN1**	(2nd) Three lions of England......................	1·25	1·00
		a. Imperf (pair)...		
		I. Booklet pane. Nos. EN1/EN2, each×4, and No. S95, with margins all round (24.9.02)..............	8·50	
		Ia. Imperf pane...	—	—
EN2	**EN2**	(1st) Lion and shield..............................	1·50	1·00
		a. Imperf pair..	£350	
EN3	**EN3**	(E) English oak tree.............................	2·00	2·00
EN4	**EN4**	65p. English Tudor rose...........................	2·10	2·10
EN5		68p. English Tudor rose (4.7.02)...........	2·10	2·10
Presentation Pack (PO Pack No. 54) (Nos. EN1/EN4)........			7·00	
PHQ Cards (set of 4) (D20) (Nos. EN1/EN4)................			1·25	7·00

Nos. EN1/EN3 were initially sold at 19p., 27p. and 36p., the latter representing the basic European airmail rate.

First Day Covers

23.4.01	2nd, 1st, E, 65p. (Nos. EN1/EN4) Philatelic Bureau, (Type G, see Introduction)		2·50
	Windsor		2·00
4.7.02	68p. (No. EN5) Tallents House (Type K, see Introduction)		2·50
	London		1·50

Combined Presentation Pack for England, Northern Ireland, Scotland and Wales

4.7.02	PO Pack No. 59. 68p. (Nos. EN5, NI93, S99, W88)	8·50

I	II

Head Types

Type I:	Ribbon at back of the head appears as two separate and distinct strands
Type II:	Ribbon solid and firmly joined to the head

2003 (14 Oct)–**17**. As Nos. EN1/EN3 and EN5, and new values, but with white borders. One centre phosphor band (2nd) or two phosphor bands (others). Type I heads unless otherwise stated. Perf 15×14 (with one elliptical hole in each vertical side).

(a) *Walsall or De La Rue (No. EN10), De La Rue (others).*

EN6	**EN1**	(2nd) Three lions of England. Type II........	1·25	1·00
		a. Imperf (pair)..	£175	
		I. Booklet pane. Nos. EN6 and EN9, each×2, with central label and margins all round (24.2.05).............	5·50	
		b. Type I (2006).......................................	5·50	5·50
EN7	**EN2**	(1st) Lion and shield. Type II...................	1·50	1·25
		a. Imperf (pair)..	£250	
		b. Type I (2006).......................................	5·50	5·50
EN8	**EN3**	(E) English oak tree. Type II...................	2·00	2·00
EN9		40p. English oak tree Type II (11.5.04).....	1·25	1·25
EN10		42p. English oak tree Type II (5.4.05).....	1·75	1·75
EN11		44p. English oak tree Type II (28.3.06).....	1·25	1·25
		a. Imperf (pair)..	£1200	
		b. Type I (2006).......................................	40·00	40·00
EN12		48p. English oak tree (27.3.07)................	1·00	1·00
EN13		50p. English oak tree (1.4.08)..................	1·25	1·25
EN14		56p. English oak tree (31.3.09)................	1·25	1·25
EN15		60p. English oak tree (30.3.10)................	1·50	1·50
EN16	**EN4**	68p. English Tudor rose. Type II.............	1·75	1·75
EN17		72p. English Tudor rose Type II (28.3.06)...	1·75	1·75
		a. Type I (2006).......................................	25·00	25·00
EN18		78p. English Tudor rose (27.3.07)............	2·00	2·00
EN19		81p. English Tudor rose (1.4.08).............	2·00	2·00
EN20		90p. English Tudor rose (31.3.09)...........	2·25	2·25
EN21		97p. English Tudor rose (30.3.10)............	2·50	2·50

(b) *Litho Enschedé or ISP Cartor (No. EN30) or ISP Cartor (others). Queen's head in grey (Nos. EN29, EN30b and EN36) or silver (others).*

EN29	**EN1**	(2nd) Three lions of England (3.1.13)........	1·25	1·00
EN30	**EN2**	(1st) Lion and shield (Queen's head silver) (20.9.07).................................	1·50	1·50
		I. Booklet pane. Nos. EN30, NI95 S131 and W122 with five labels and margins all round.....................	14·00	
EN30b		(1st) Lion and shield (Queen's head grey) (3.1.13).....................................	2·00	1·75
EN31	**EN3**	68p. English oak tree (29.3.11)................	1·75	1·75
EN32		87p. English oak tree (25.4.12)................	2·25	2·25
EN33		88p. English oak tree (27.3.13)................	2·25	2·25
EN34		97p. English oak tree (26.3.14)................	2·40	2·40
EN35		£1 English oak tree (24.3.15)..................	2·40	2·40
EN36		£1·05 English oak tree (22.3.16).............	2·75	2·75
EN41	**EN4**	£1·10 English Tudor rose (29.3.11)............	2·50	2·50
EN43		£1·28 English Tudor rose (25.4.12)...........	2·60	2·60
EN44		£1·33 English Tudor rose (24.3.15)...........	2·75	2·75
Presentation Pack (PO Pack No. 63) (Nos. EN6/EN8, EN16)..			6·00	
PHQ Cards (set of 4) (D24) (Nos. EN6/EN8, EN16)...............			1·25	6·50

The 72p. stamp from the 2006 Lest We Forget miniature sheet, No. **MS**2685, has the Type I head.

The price for No. EN17a is for the Type I stamp from counter sheets. Collectors should obtain this stamp from a reliable source.

No. EN6I comes from booklet No. DX34.

Stamps as Nos. EN18/EN19 but printed in lithography were only issued within No. **MS**2796 (No. EN18) or No. **MS**2886 (No. EN19).

No. EN30 was first issued for £7·66 stamp booklets, No. DX40, printed by Enschedé. No. EN30b was issued in sheets printed by ISP Cartor in January 2013.

A design as No. EN30 but self-adhesive was issued on 23 April 2007 in sheets of 20, each stamp accompanied by a *se-tenant* label showing an English scene (No. LS38). These sheets were printed in lithography by Cartor, perforated 15×14 without the elliptical holes, and sold at £7·35 each. They were also available with personalised photographs on the labels at £14·95 from the Royal Mail in Edinburgh.

Stamps as Nos. EN30, NI95, S131 and W122 but self-adhesive were issued on 29 September 2008 in sheets of 20 containing five of each design with *se-tenant* labels (No. LS49). These sheets were printed in lithography by Cartor and perforated 15×14 with one elliptical hole on each vertical side.

First Day Covers

14.10.03	2nd, 1st, E, 68p. (Nos. EN6/EN8, EN16) Tallents House (Type K, see Introduction)	5·50	
	London	5·50	
11.5.04	40p. (No. EN9) Tallents House (Type K)	2·00	
	London	2·00	
5.4.05	42p. (No. EN10) Tallents House (Type K)	2·00	
	London	2·00	
28.3.06	44p., 72p., (Nos. EN11, EN17) Tallents House (Type K)	3·50	
	London	3·50	
27.3.07	48p., 78p. (Nos. EN12, EN18) Tallents House (Type K)	3·00	
	London	3·00	
1.4.08	50p., 81p., (Nos. EN13, EN19) Tallents House (Type K)	3·00	
	London	3·00	
31.3.09	56p., 90p. (Nos. EN14, EN20) Tallents House (Type K)	3·50	
	London	3·50	
30.3.10	60p., 97p. (Nos. EN15, EN21) Tallents House (Type K)	4·00	
	London	4·00	
29.3.11	68p., £1·10 (Nos. EN31, EN41) Tallents House (Type K)	4·50	
	London	4·50	
25.4.12	87p., £1·28 (Nos. EN32, EN43) Tallents House (Type K)	4·75	
	London	4·75	
27.3.13	88p. (No. EN33) Tallents House (Type K)	2·25	
	London	2·25	
26.3.14	97p. (No. EN34) Tallents House (Type K)	2·25	
	London	2·25	
24.3.15	£1, £1·33 (Nos. EN35, EN44) Tallents House (Type K)	5·50	
	London	5·50	
22.3.16	£1·05 (No. EN36) Tallents House (Type K)	2·50	
	London	2·50	

Combination Presentation Packs for England, Northern Ireland, Scotland and Wales

11.5.04	PO Pack No. 68. 40p. (Nos. EN9, NI97, S112, W101)	6·50
5.4.05	PO Pack No. 70. 42p. (Nos. EN10, NI98, S113, W102)	6·25
28.3.06	PO Pack No. 73. 44p. and 72p. (Nos. EN11, EN17, NI99, NI102, S114, S120, W103, W109)	10·00
27.3.07	PO Pack No. 76. 48p. and 78p. (Nos. EN12, EN18, NI124, NI128, S115, S121, W104, and W110)	10·00
1.4.08	PO Pack No. 79. 50p. and 81p. (Nos. EN13, EN19, NI125, NI129, S116, S122, W105, W111)	10·00
29.9.08	PO Pack No. 81. 2nd, 1st, 50p. and 81p. (Nos. EN6/EN7, EN13, EN19, NI122/NI123, NI125, NI129, S109/S110, S116, S122, W98/W99, W105, W111)	40·00
31.3.09	PO Pack No. 85. 56p. and 90p. (Nos. EN14, EN20, NI126, NI130, S117, S123, W106, W112)	13·00
30.3.10	PO Pack No. 87. 60p. and 97p. (Nos. EN15, EN21, NI127, NI131, S118, S124, W107, W113)	14·00
29.3.11	PO Pack No. 91. 68p. and £1·10 (Nos. EN31, EN41, NI101, NI111, S132, S138 W123, W129)	15·00
25.4.12	PO Pack No. 95. 87p. and £1·28 (Nos. EN32, EN43, NI103, NI113, S133, S143, W124, W134)	18·00
27.3.13	PO Pack No. 98. 88p. (Nos. EN33, NI104, S134, W125)	8·50
26.3.14	PO Pack No. 100. 97p. (Nos. EN34, NI105, S135, W126)	8·50
24.3.15	PO Pack No. 102 £1 and £1·33 (Nos. EN35, EN44, NI106, NI114, S136, S144, W127, W135)	18·00
22.3.16	PO Pack No. 104. £1·05 (Nos. EN36, NI 107, S137 and W128)	10·00

EN5

(Des Peter Crowther, Clare Melinsky and Silk Pearce. Gravure De La Rue)

2007 (23 Apr). Celebrating England. Sheet 123×70 mm. Two phosphor bands. Perf 15×14 (with one elliptical hole in each vertical side) (1st) or 15×14½ (78p.).

MSEN50 **EN5** (1st) No. EN7b; (1st) St George's flag; 78p. St George; 78p. Houses of Parliament, London	4·00	4·00
First Day Cover (Tallents House)		4·50
First Day Cover (St Georges, Telford)		4·50
Presentation Pack (PO Pack No. M15)	5·00	
PHQ Cards (set of 5) (CGB2)	2·00	8·00

No. **MS**EN50 was on sale at post offices throughout the UK.

Stamps as the 1st class St George's flag stamp within No. **MS**EN50 but self-adhesive were issued on 23 April 2009 in sheets of 20 with *se-tenant* labels showing English Castles, No. LS59.

These sheets were printed in lithography by Cartor and sold for £8·35 each.

The five PHQ cards show the four individual stamps and the complete miniature sheet.

EN6 St George's Flag

(Des Peter Crowther and Silk Pearce. Litho ISP Cartor (No. EN51) or Enschedé (No. EN51a))

2013 (9 May)–**14**. England Flag. Two phosphor bands. Perf 14½×14 (with one elliptical hole in each vertical side).

EN51	**EN6**	(1st) St George's Flag (Queen's head silver)	4·50	4·50
		a. St George's Flag (Queen's head grey) (20.2.14)	3·50	3·50

No. EN51 was issued in £11·11 Football Heroes booklet (No. DY7, booklet pane No. U3073I) and £16.49 Centenary of the First World War (3rd issue) booklet (No. DY18, booklet pane No. 3717a).

No. EN51a was issued in £13·97 Classic Locomotives booklet (No. DY9, booklet pane No. U3071m).

EN7 Three Lions of England   **EN8** Crowned Lion, Supporting the Shield of St George

EN9 English Oak Tree   **EN10** English Tudor Rose

(Des Sedley Place, from sculptures by David Dathan. Litho ISP Cartor)

2017 (21 Mar)–**20**. As previous set but with value indicated in revised typeface. One centre phosphor band (No. EN52) or two phosphor bands. Perf 15×14 (with one elliptical hole in each vertical side).

EN52	**EN7**	(2nd) Three Lions of England (20.3.18)	1·00	75
EN53	**EN8**	(1st) Lion and shield (Indian red) (20.3.18)	1·25	75
		a. Venetian red (11.2.20)	1·50	1·50
EN54	**EN9**	£1·17 English Oak tree (21.3.17)	2·75	2·75
EN55		£1·25 English Oak tree (20.3.18)	2·75	2·75
EN56		£1·35 English Oak tree (19.3.19)	3·00	3·00
EN60	**EN10**	£1·40 English Tudor Rose (21.3.17)	3·00	3·00
EN61	**EN9**	£1·42 English Oak tree (17.3.20)	2·50	2·50
EN62	**EN10**	£1·45 English Tudor Rose (20.3.18)	3·25	3·25
EN63		£1·55 English Tudor Rose (19.3.19)	3·25	3·25
EN64		£1·63 English Tudor Rose (17.3.20)	2·75	2·75
EN65	**EN9**	£1·70 English Oak Tree (23.12.20)	2·40	2·40

No. EN53a was issued in £16·10 Visions of the Universe booklet, No. DY32, booklet pane No. U3072r.

EN11 Three Lions of England   **EN12** Crowned Lion, Supporting the Shield of St George

EN13 English Oak Tree

(Des Sedley Place, from sculptures by David Dathan. Litho ISP Cartor)

2022 (11 Aug). As Types **EN11**, **EN12** and **EN13** with barcoded strip at right. Self-adhesive. One centre phosphor band (2nd) or two phosphor bands (others). Die-cut perf 15×14½ (with one elliptical hole in each vertical side).

EN66	**EN11**	(2nd) Three Lions of England....................	1·10	1·10
EN67	**EN12**	(1st) Lion and shield................................	1·60	1·60
EN68	**EN13**	£1·85 English oak tree.............................	2·50	2·50

First Day Covers

21.3.17	£1·17, £1·40. (Nos. EN54, EN60) Tallents House (Type K)..	6·00
	London (as Windsor)..	6·00
20.3.18	2nd, 1st, £1·25, £1·45. (Nos. EN52/EN53, EN55, EN61) Tallents House (Type K)........................	9·00
	London (as Windsor)..	9·00
19.3.19	£1·35, £1·55 (Nos. EN56, EN62) Tallents House (Type K)...	7·00
	London (as Windsor)..	7·00
17.3.20	£1·42, £1·63 (Nos. EN60a, EN63) Tallents House (Type K)...	7·00
	London...	7·00
23.12.20	£1·70 (No. EN64) Tallents House (Type K)...........	3·75
	London...	3·75
11.8.22	2nd, 1st, £1·85 (Nos. EN66/EN68) Tallents House (Type K)...	7·50
	London...	7·50

Combination Presentation Packs for England, Northern Ireland, Scotland and Wales

21.3.17	PO Pack No. 107. £1·17 and £1·40 (Nos. EN54, EN60, NI159, NI165, S161, S166, W151, W156).....................	22·00
20.3.18	PO Pack No. 109. 2nd, 1st, £1·25 and £1·45 (Nos. EN52/EN53, EN55, EN62, NI157/NI158, NI160, NI166, S159/S160, S162, S168, W149/W150, W152, W158).....	25·00
19.3.19	PO Pack No. 111. £1·35, £1·55 (Nos. EN56, EN63, NI161, NI167, S163, S169, W153, W159).....................	26·00
17.3.20	PO Pack No. 113. £1·42, £1·63 (Nos. EN61, EN64, NI165, NI168, S167, S170, W157, W160).....................	28·00
23.12.20	PO Pack No. 115. £1·70 (Nos. EN65, NI169, S171, W161)...	11·00
11.8.22	PO Pack No. 120. 2nd, 1st, £1·85 (EN66/EN68, NI170/NI172, S18/S182 and W162/W164)..............................	25·00

II. NORTHERN IRELAND

N1 **N2** **N3**

White spot on flower (Cyl. 1, no dot, R. 7/7) Dot under 'S' of POSTAGE (Cyl. 1, dot, R. 2/4)

(Des W. Hollywood (3d., 4d., 5d.), L. Pilton (6d., 9d.), T. Collins (1s.3d., 1s.6d.))

1958–67. W **179**. Perf 15×14.

NI1	**N1**	3d. deep lilac (18.8.58)............................	15	15
		p. One centre phosphor band (9.6.67)...	25	25
NI2		4d. ultramarine (7.2.66).........................	15	15
		a. Flower flaw...............................	25·00	

		b. Dot under 'S' of POSTAGE.................	25·00	
		p. Two phosphor bands (10.67)..........	15	15
NI3	**N2**	6d. deep claret (29.9.58)........................	50	50
NI4		9d. bronze-green (2 phosphor bands) (1.3.67).......................................	40	40
NI5	**N3**	1s.3d. green (29.9.58)................................	50	50
NI6		1s.6d. grey-blue (2 phosphor bands) (1.3.67).......................................	40	40
		y. Phosphor omitted.............................	£225	

For Nos. NI1, NI3 and NI5 in Presentation Pack, see below Wales No. W6.

1968–69. No watermark. Chalk-surfaced paper. One centre phosphor band (Nos. NI8/NI9) or two phosphor bands (others). Gum arabic (No. NI7) or PVA gum (others). Perf 15×14.

NI7	**N1**	4d. deep bright blue (27.6.68)...............	25	25
		v. PVA gum (23.10.68)......................	30·00	
NI8		4d. olive-sepia (4.9.68)........................	25	25
		y. Phosphor omitted......................		
NI9		4d. bright vermilion (26.2.69)................	30	30
		y. Phosphor omitted......................	4·50	
NI10		5d. royal blue (4.9.68)........................	40	40
		y. Phosphor omitted......................	25·00	
NI11	**N3**	1s.6d. grey-blue (20.5.69)........................	1·50	1·50
		y. Phosphor omitted......................	£500	

* No. NI7v was never issued in Northern Ireland. After No. NI7 (gum arabic) had been withdrawn from Northern Ireland but while still on sale at the philatelic counters elsewhere, about 50 sheets with PVA gum were sold over the London Philatelic counter on 23 October, 1968, and some were also on sale at the British Philatelic Exhibition Post Office.

There was no post office first day cover for No. NI9.

First Day Covers

18.8.58	3d. (No. NI1)...	30·00
29.9.58	6d., 1s.3d. (Nos. NI3, NI5)...............................	35·00
7.2.66	4d. (No. NI2)..	7·00
1.3.67	9d., 1s.6d. (Nos. NI4, NI6)...............................	4·00
4.9.68	4d., 5d. (Nos. NI8, NI10)................................	3·00

Presentation Pack

9.12.70	PO Pack No. 25. 3d., 9d., 1s.3d., 1s.6d., 4d., 5d. (Nos. NI1p, NI4/NI6, NI8/NI10)...	3·50

N4

I II

Redrawn design of T **N4** (litho printings)

Two Types of Crown

Type I Crown with all pearls individually drawn.

Type II Crown with clear outlines, large pearls and strong white line below them. First 3 pearls at left are joined, except on Nos. NI39 and NI49.

The following stamps printed in lithography show a screened background behind and to the left of the emblem: 11½p., 12½p., 14p. (No. NI38), 15½p., 16p., 18p. (No. NI45), 19½p., 22p. (No. NI53) and 28p. (No. NI62). The 13p. and 17p. (No. NI43) also showed screened backgrounds in Type I, but changed to solid backgrounds for Type II. The 31p. had a solid background in Type I, but changed to a screened background for Type II. All other values printed in lithography have solid backgrounds.

(Des Jeffery Matthews after plaster cast by Arnold Machin)

1971 (7 July)–**93**. Decimal Currency. Chalk-surfaced paper. T **N4**.

(a) Photo Harrison. With phosphor bands. Perf 15×14.

NI12		2½p. bright magenta (1 centre band)...............	45	45
NI13		3p. ultramarine (2 bands).........................	30	30
		y. Phosphor omitted................................	50·00	
NI14		3p. ultramarine (1 centre band) (23.1.74)........	20	20
NI15		3½p. olive-grey (2 bands) (23.1.74).................	20	20
NI16		3½p. olive-grey (1 centre band) (6.11.74)..........	40	40
NI17		4½p. grey-blue (2 bands) (6.11.74).................	30	30
NI18		5p. reddish violet (2 bands)......................	90	90
NI19		5½p. violet (2 bands) (23.1.74).....................	25	25
		y. Phosphor omitted................................	£250	

NI20	5½p. violet (1 centre band) (21.5.75)...............	25	25
NI21	6½p. greenish blue (1 centre band) (14.1.76)....	20	20
NI22	7p. purple-brown (1 centre band) (18.1.78)........	30	30
NI23	7½p. chestnut (2 bands).................................	1·25	1·25
	y. Phosphor omitted....................................	£100	
NI24	8p. rosine (2 bands) (23.1.74)........................	40	40
	y. Phosphor omitted....................................	75·00	
NI25	8½p. yellow-green (2 bands) (14.1.76)...............	40	40
NI26	9p. deep violet (2 bands) (18.1.78)................	40	40
	y. Phosphor omitted....................................	25·00	
NI27	10p. orange-brown (2 bands) (20.10.76)...........	40	40
NI28	10p. orange-brown (1 centre band) (23.7.80).....	40	40
NI29	10½p. steel-blue (2 bands) (18.1.78)................	50	50
NI30	11p. scarlet (2 bands) (20.10.76)...................	50	50
	y. Phosphor omitted....................................	5·00	

(b) Photo Harrison. On phosphorised paper. Perf 15×14.

NI31	12p. yellowish green (23.7.80)........................	50	50
NI32	13½p. purple-brown (23.7.80).........................	60	60
NI33	15p. ultramarine (23.7.80).............................	60	60

(c) Litho Questa (Type II, unless otherwise stated). Perf 14 (11½p., 12½p., 14p. (No. NI38), 15½p., 16p., 18p. (No. NI45), 19½p., 20½p., 22p. (No. NI53), 26p. (No. NI60), 28p. (No. NI62)) or 15×14 (others).

NI34	11½p. drab (Type I) (1 side band) (8.4.81)........	85	85
NI35	12p. bright emerald (1 side band) (7.1.86)......	90	90
NI36	12½p. light emerald (Type I) (1 side band) (24.2.82)..	50	50
	a. Perf 15×14 (28.2.84)...............................	3·50	3·50
NI37	13p. chestnut (Type I) (1 side band) (23.10.84)..	60	60
	a. Type II (28.11.86)...................................	1·10	1·10
	y. Phosphor omitted (Type I).......................	£375	
NI38	14p. grey-blue (Type I) (phosphorised paper) (8.4.81)...	60	60
NI39	14p. deep blue (1 centre band) (8.11.88)........	50	50
NI40	15p. bright blue (1 centre band) (28.11.89)...	60	60
NI41	15½p. pale violet (Type I) (phosphorised paper) (24.2.82)............................	80	80
NI42	16p. drab (Type I) (phosphorised paper) (27.4.83)...	1·00	1·00
	a. Perf 15×14 (28.2.84)...............................	5·00	5·00
NI43	17p. grey-blue (Type I) (phosphorised paper) (23.10.84)............................	80	80
	a. Type II (9.9.86)......................................	£140	£140
NI44	17p. deep blue (1 centre band) (4.12.90).........	60	60
NI45	18p. deep violet (Type I) (phosphorised paper) (8.4.81).................................	80	80
NI46	18p. deep olive-grey (phosphorised paper) (6.1.87)..	80	80
NI47	18p. bright green (1 centre band) (3.12.91)......	80	80
	a. Perf 14 (31.12.92*)................................	6·00	6·00
NI48	18p. bright green (1 side band) (10.8.93).......	1·50	1·50
	l. Booklet pane. Nos. NI48, NI59, S61, S71, W49b and W60 with margins all round..	8·00	
NI49	19p. bright orange-red (phosphorised paper) (8.11.88).................................	80	80
NI50	19½p. olive-grey (Type I) (phosphorised paper) (24.2.82)............................	1·50	1·50
NI51	20p. brownish black (phosphorised paper) (28.11.89)..	80	80
NI52	20½p. ultramarine (Type I) (phosphorised paper) (27.4.83).................................	2·75	2·75
NI53	22p. blue (Type I) (phosphorised paper) (8.4.81)..	80	80
NI54	22p. yellow-green (Type I) (phosphorised paper) (23.10.84)............................	80	80
NI55	22p. bright orange-red (phosphorised paper) (4.12.90).................................	80	80
NI56	23p. bright green (phosphorised paper) (8.11.88)...	80	80
NI57	24p. Indian red (phosphorised paper) (28.11.89)..	90	90
NI58	24p. chestnut (phosphorised paper) (3.12.91)...	80	80
NI59	24p. chestnut (2 bands) (10.8.93)...................	1·50	1·50
NI60	26p. rosine (Type I) (phosphorised paper) (24.2.82)..	90	90
	a. Perf 15×14 (Type II) (27.1.87).................	2·00	2·00
NI61	26p. drab (phosphorised paper) (4.12.90).........	1·10	1·10
NI62	28p. deep violet-blue (Type I) (phosphorised paper) (27.4.83).....................	1·00	1·00
	a. Perf 15×14 (Type II) (27.1.87).................	1·40	1·40
NI63	28p. deep bluish grey (phosphorised paper) (3.12.91)...	90	90
NI64	31p. bright purple (Type I) (phosphorised paper) (23.10.84).................................	1·40	1·40
	a. Type II (14.4.87)....................................	1·75	1·75
NI65	32p. greenish blue (phosphorised paper) (8.11.88)...	1·40	1·40
NI66	34p. deep bluish grey (phosphorised paper) (28.11.89)...	1·40	1·40
NI67	37p. rosine (phosphorised paper) (4.12.90).....	1·50	1·50
NI68	39p. bright mauve (phosphorised paper) (3.12.91)...	1·50	1·50

* Earliest known date of issue.

No. NI47a was caused by the use of a reserve perforating machine for some printings in the second half of 1992.

Nos. NI48 and NI49 only come from booklet pane No. NI48l from the £5·64 The Story of Beatrix Potter booklet, No. DX15.

From 1972 printings were made on fluorescent white paper and from 1973 most printings had dextrin added to the PVA gum (see notes after 1971 Decimal Machin issue).

First Day Covers

7.7.71	2½p., 3p., 5p., 7½p. (Nos. NI12/NI13, NI18, NI23)..........	2·50
23.1.74	3p., 3½p., 5½p., 8p. (Nos. NI14/NI15, NI19, NI24)........	2·00
6.11.74	4½p. (No. NI17)..	80
14.1.76	6½p., 8½p. (Nos. NI21, NI25)............................	80
20.10.76	10p., 11p. (Nos. NI27, NI30).............................	90
18.1.78	7p., 9p., 10½p. (Nos. NI22, NI26, NI29).............	90
23.7.80	12p., 13½p., 15p. (Nos. NI31/NI33)..................	1·50
8.4.81	11½p., 14p., 18p., 22p. (Nos. NI34, NI38, NI45, NI53)....	1·25
24.2.82	12½p., 15½p., 19½p., 26p. (Nos. NI36, NI41, NI50, NI60)....	2·00
27.4.83	16p., 20½p., 28p. (Nos. NI42, NI52, NI62)........	2·00
23.10.84	13p., 17p., 22p., 31p. (Nos. NI37, NI43, NI54, NI64)......	2·25
7.1.86	12p. (No. NI35)..	90
6.1.87	18p. (No. NI46)..	90
8.11.88	14p., 19p., 23p., 32p. (Nos. NI39, NI49, NI56, NI65)......	2·50
28.11.89	15p., 20p., 24p., 34p. (Nos. NI40, NI51, NI57, NI66)......	3·00
4.12.90	17p., 22p., 26p., 37p. (Nos. NI44, NI55, NI61, NI67)......	3·00
3.12.91	18p., 24p., 28p., 39p. (Nos. NI47, NI58, NI63, NI68)......	3·00

Presentation Packs

7.7.71	PO Pack No. 29. 2½p., 3p. (2 bands), 5p., 7½p. (Nos. NI12/NI13, NI18, NI23)...............................	2·00
29.5.74	PO Pack No. 61. 3p. (1 centre band), 3½p. (2 bands) or (1 centre band), 5½p. (2 bands) or (1 centre band), 8p. (Nos. NI14, NI15 or NI16, NI19 or NI20, NI24). The 4½p. (No. NI17) was added later.	3·00
20.10.76	PO Pack No. 84. 6½p., 8½p., 10p. (2 bands), 11p. (Nos. NI21, NI25, NI27, NI30)...............................	1·50
28.10.81	PO Pack No. 129d. 7p., 9p., 10½p., 12p. (gravure), 13½p., 15p. (gravure), 11½p., 14p. grey-blue, 18p. deep violet, 22p. blue (Nos. NI22, NI26, NI29, NI31/NI34, NI38, NI45, NI53)...............................	7·00
3.8.83	PO Pack No. 4. 10p. (1 centre band), 12½p., 16p., 20½p., 26p. rosine, 28p. deep violet-blue (Nos. NI28, NI36, NI42, NI52, NI60, NI62)...........................	15·00
23.10.84	PO Pack No. 8. 10p. (1 centre band), 13p., 16p., 17p. grey-blue, 22p. yellow-green, 26p. rosine, 28p. deep violet-blue, 31p. (Nos. NI28, NI37, NI42a, NI43, NI54, NI60, NI62, NI64)...........................	12·50
3.3.87	PO Pack No. 12. 12p. (litho), 13p., 17p. grey-blue, 18p. deep olive-grey, 22p. yellow-green, 26p. rosine, 28p. deep violet-blue, 31p. (Nos. NI35, NI37, NI43, NI46, NI54, NI60a, NI62a, NI64)......................	16·00

Combined Presentation Packs for Northern Ireland, Scotland and Wales

8.11.88	PO Pack No. 17. 14p. deep blue, 19p., 23p., 32p. (Nos. NI39, NI49, NI56, NI65), 14p. (1 centre band), 19p. (phosphorised paper), 23p. (phosphorised paper), 32p. (Nos. S54, S62, S67, S77), 14p. deep blue, 19p., 23p., 32p. (Nos. W40, W50, W57, W64).................	12·50
28.11.89	PO Pack No. 20. 15p. (litho), 20p., 24p. Indian red, 34p. (Nos. NI40, NI51, NI57, NI66), 15p. (litho), 20p., 24p. Indian red, 34p. (Nos. S56, S64, S69, S78), 15p. (litho), 20p., 24p. Indian red, 34p. (Nos. W41, W52, W58, W67).................	12·00
4.12.90	PO Pack No. 23. 17p. deep blue, 22p. bright orange-red, 26p. drab, 37p. (Nos. NI44, NI55, NI61, NI67), 17p. deep blue, 22p. bright orange-red, 26p. drab, 37p. (Nos. S58, S66, S73, S79), 17p. deep blue, 22p. bright orange-red, 26p. drab, 37p. (Nos. W45, W56, W62, W68).................	12·00
3.12.91	PO Pack No. 26. 18p. bright green, 24p. chestnut, 28p. deep bluish grey, 39p. (Nos. NI47, NI58, NI63, NI68), 18p. bright green, 24p. chestnut, 28p. deep bluish grey, 39p. (Nos. S60, S70, S75, S80), 18p. bright green, 24p. chestnut, 28p. deep bluish grey, 39p. (Nos. W48, W59, W64, W69).................	12·00

(Des Jeffery Matthews after plaster cast by Arnold Machin)

1993 (7 Dec)–**2000**. Chalk-surfaced paper.

(a) Litho Questa. Perf 15×14 (with one elliptical hole in each vert side).

NI69	**N4**	19p. bistre (1 centre band)........................	80	80
NI70		19p. bistre (1 band at left) (26.7.94)............	1·25	1·25
		y. Phosphor omitted................................	£500	
		l. Booklet pane. Nos. NI70×2, NI72×4, NI74, NI76 and centre label with margins all round...............................	4·50	
		m. Booklet pane. Nos. NI70, NI72, NI74 and NI76 with margins all round..........	3·50	
		my. Booklet pane. Phosphor omitted.......	£3000	
		c. Band at right (25.4.95)...........................	1·75	1·75
		n. Booklet pane. Nos. NI70c, NI72, S82, S84, W71 and W73 with margins all round (25.4.95).....................................	4·75	
		na. Part perf pane*...................................	£3500	
NI71		20p. bright green (1 centre band) (23.7.96)..	1·25	1·25

NI72	25p. red (2 bands)........................	75	75
	y. Phosphor omitted........................	£275	
NI73	26p. red-brown (2 bands) (23.7.96)......	1·50	1·50
NI74	30p. deep olive-grey (2 bands)...........	1·10	1·10
	y. Phosphor omitted........................	£750	
NI75	37p. bright mauve (2 bands) (23.7.96).....	2·25	2·25
NI76	41p. grey-brown (2 bands)..................	1·50	1·50
	y. Phosphor omitted........................	£750	
NI77	63p. light emerald (2 bands) (23.7.96)......	3·50	3·50

(b) *Gravure Walsall (19p., 20p., 26p. (No. NI81b), 38p., 40p., 63p., 64p., 65p.), Harrison or Walsall (26p. (No. NI81), 37p.). Perf 14 (No. NI80) or 15×14 (others) (both with one elliptical hole in each vertical side).*

NI78	**N4**	19p. bistre (1 centre band) (8.6.99).........	2·50	2·50
NI79		20p. bright green (1 centre band)		
		(1.7.97)................................	2·50	2·50
NI80		20p. bright green (1 side band at right)		
		(13.10.98).............................	3·00	3·00
		l. Booklet pane. Nos. NI80, S90a,		
		W79a and Y1717a×3 with margins		
		all round.............................	7·00	
NI81		26p. chestnut (2 bands) (1.7.97).............	1·60	1·60
		l. Booklet pane. Nos. NI81/NI82,		
		S91/S92 and W80/W81 with		
		margins all round (23.9.97).........	6·00	
		b. Perf 14 (13.10.98).................	3·00	3·00
NI82		37p. bright mauve (2 bands) (1.7.97)......	1·90	1·90
NI83		38p. ultramarine (2 bands) (8.6.99)........	5·50	5·50
NI84		40p. deep azure (2 bands) (25.4.2000)....	3·50	3·50
NI85		63p. light emerald (2 bands) (1.7.97)......	3·50	3·50
NI86		64p. turquoise-green (2 bands) (8.6.99)..	6·50	6·50
NI87		65p. greenish blue (2 bands) (25.4.2000)..	3·00	3·00

* No. NI70na, which comes from he 1995 National Trust £6 booklet, shows the top two values in the pane of six (Nos. S82, S84) completely imperforate and the two Wales values below partly imperforate.
Nos. NI70, NI80 and NI81b only come from booklets.
The listed booklet panes come from the following Sponsored Booklets:
Nos. NI70l/NI70m Booklet No. DX16
No. NI70n Booklet No. DX17
No. NI80l Booklet No. DX21
No. NI81l Booklet No. DX19

First Day Covers

7.12.93	19p., 25p., 30p., 41p. (Nos. NI69, NI72, NI74, NI76)......	4·00
26.7.94	Northern Ireland *se-tenant* pane 19p., 25p., 30p.,	
	41p. (No. NI70l)................................	5·00
23.7.96	20p., 26p., 37p., 63p. (Nos. NI71, NI73, NI75, NI77)..	5·00
8.6.99	38p., 64p. (Nos.NI83, NI86)........................	10·00
25.4.00	1st, 40p., 65p. (Nos. NI84, NI87, NI88b)............	12·50

Presentation Packs

8.6.99	PO Pack No. 47. 19p., 26p., 38p., 64p. (Nos. NI78,	
	NI81, NI83, NI86)...........................	15·00
25.4.00	PO Pack No. 52. 1st, 40p., 65p. (Nos. NI88b, NI84,	
	NI87)......................................	16·00

Combined Presentation Packs for Northern Ireland, Scotland and Wales

7.12.93	PO Pack No. 31. 19p., 25p., 30p., 41p., each×3 (Nos.	
	NI69, NI72, NI74, NI76, S81, S84, S86, S88, W70, W73,	
	W75, W77).................................	20·00
23.7.96	PO Pack No. 36. 20p., 26p., 37p., 63p., each×3 (Nos.	
	NI71, NI73, NI75, NI77, S83, S85, S87, S89, W72, W74,	
	W76, W78).................................	16·00
20.10.98	PO Pack No. 42. 20p. (1 centre band), 26p., 37p.,	
	63p., each×3 (Nos. NI79, NI81/NI82, NI85, S90/S93,	
	W79/W82).................................	18·00

N5

(Des Jeffery Matthews. Gravure Walsall)

2000 (15 Feb–25 Apr). T **N4** redrawn with '1st' face value as T **N5**. Two phosphor bands. Perf 14 (with one elliptical hole in each vertical side).

NI88	**N5**	(1st) bright orange-red.....................	1·60	1·60
		l. Booklet pane. Nos. NI88, S108		
		and W97, each×3 with margins all		
		round................................	12·00	
		b. Perf 15×14 (25.4.2000).............	7·00	7·00

First Day Cover (Philatelic Bureau) (*se-tenant* pane No.
NI88l).. 7·00   7·00
First Day Cover (London SW5) (*se-tenant* pane No.
NI88l).. 7·00

No. NI88 was issued in £7·50 stamp booklet (No. DX24).
No NI88b was issued in sheets.

N6 Basalt Columns, Giant's Causeway   **N7** Aerial View of Patchwork Fields

N8 Linen Pattern   **N9** Vase Pattern from Belleek

(Des Rodney Miller Associates (Basalt columns), Richard Cooke (Aerial view of fields), David Pauley (Linen pattern), Tiff Hunter (Vase pattern). Litho Walsall or Enschedé (1st, 2nd), De La Rue or Walsall (E), Walsall (65p.), De La Rue (68p.))

2001 (6 Mar)–**03**. One centre phosphor band (2nd) or two phosphor bands (others). Perf 15×14 (with one elliptical hole in each vertical side).

NI89	**N6**	(2nd) Basalt columns, Giant's Causeway..	1·25	1·25
		l. Booklet pane. No. NI89×5 and No.		
		NI90×4 with margins all round		
		(25.2.2003)...........................	7·00	
		y. Phosphor omitted..................	£625	
NI90	**N7**	(1st) Aerial view of patchwork fields.......	1·50	1·50
		y. Phosphor omitted..................	35·00	
NI91	**N8**	(E) Linen pattern...........................	2·25	2·25
NI92	**N9**	65p. Vase pattern from Belleek..............	2·25	2·25
NI93		68p. Vase pattern from Belleek		
		(4.7.2002)...........................	2·75	2·75

PHQ Cards (*set of 4*) (D19) (Nos. NI89/NI92)............ 1·25   7·50

Nos. NI89, NI90 and NI91 were initially sold at 19p., 27p. and 36p., the latter representing the basic European airmail rate.
A new printing of No. NI91, produced by De La Rue instead of Walsall, was issued on 15 October 2002. Stamps from this printing do not differ from those produced by Walsall.
Booklet pane No. NI89l was printed by Enschedé. For combined presentation pack for all four Regions, see under England.

First Day Covers

6.3.01	2nd, 1st, E, 65p. (Nos. NI89/NI92) Tallents House.........	2·75
	Belfast..	3·00
4.7.02	68p. (Nos NI93) Tallents House (Type K, see Introduction)	2·50
	Belfast..	2·75

Presentation Pack

| 6.3.01 | PO Pack No. 53. 2nd, 1st, E, 65p., 68p. (Nos. NI89/ | |
| | NI92) Tallents House.......................... | 6·00 |

2003 (14 Oct)–**17**. As Nos. NI89/NI91 and NI93, and new values, but with white borders. One centre phosphor band (2nd) or two phosphor bands (others). Perf 15×14 (with one elliptical hole in each vertical side).

(a) *Litho Walsall (No. NI98), De La Rue or Enschedé (No. NI95), Cartor (Nos. NI101 and NI103/NI115) or De La Rue (others)).*

NI94	**N6**	(2nd) Basalt columns, Giant's Causeway..	1·25	1·25
NI95	**N7**	(1st) Aerial view of patchwork fields.......	1·50	1·50
		a. black omitted.....................	£6000	
NI96	**N8**	(E) Linen pattern...........................	2·25	2·25
NI97		40p. Linen pattern (11.5.04)...............	1·60	1·60
NI98		42p. Linen pattern bluish grey and		
		black (5.4.05)........................	2·25	2·25
		a. Linen pattern *olive-grey and black*		
		(26.7.05).............................	2·50	2·50
NI99		44p. Linen pattern (28.3.06)...............	1·40	1·40
NI100	**N9**	68p. Vase pattern from Belleek.............	2·50	2·50
NI101	**N8**	68p. Linen pattern (29.3.11)...............	2·00	2·00
NI102	**N9**	72p. Vase pattern from Belleek		
		(28.3.06).............................	2·75	2·75
NI103	**N8**	87p Linen pattern (25.4.12)...............	2·25	2·25
NI104		88p. Linen pattern (27.3.13)...............	2·25	2·25
NI105		97p. Linen pattern (26.3.14)...............	2·50	2·50
NI106		£1 Linen pattern (24.3.15)...............	2·50	2·50
NI107		£1·05 Linen pattern (22.3.16)...............	2·75	2·75

NI111	**N9**	£1·10 Vase pattern from Belleek		
		(29.3.11)..................................	2·50	2·50
NI113		£1·28 Vase pattern from Belleek		
		(25.4.12)..................................	2·75	2·75
NI114		£1·33 Vase pattern from Belleek		
		(24.3.15)..................................	2·75	2·75
		(b) Gravure De La Rue.		
NI122	**N6**	(2nd) Basalt columns, Giant's Causeway		
		(20.9.07).................................	1·25	1·25
NI123	**N7**	(1st) Aerial view of patchwork fields		
		(20.9.07).................................	1·50	1·50
NI124	**N8**	48p. Linen pattern (27.3.07)............	1·25	1·25
NI125		50p. Linen pattern (1.4.08).............	1·25	1·25
NI126		56p. Linen pattern (31.3.09)............	1·25	1·25
NI127		60p. Linen pattern (30.3.10)............	1·40	1·40
NI128	**N9**	78p. Vase pattern from Belleek		
		(27.3.07).................................	1·60	1·60
NI129		81p. Vase pattern from Belleek		
		(1.4.08)..................................	2·00	2·00
NI130		90p. Vase pattern from Belleek		
		(31.3.09).................................	2·25	2·25
NI131		97p. Vase pattern from Belleek		
		(30.3.10).................................	2·50	2·50
PHQ Cards (set of 4) (D27) (Nos. NI94/NI96, NI100)..........			1·25	10·00

* The bright magenta used on the 68p. is fluorescent.

No. NI95 was printed in sheets and in £9·72 booklet, No. DX43 by De La Rue and was also issued in £7·66 booklet, No. DX40, printed by Enschedé and in premium booklets Nos. DY17 and DY18 (ISP Cartor) and Nos. DY9 and DY11 (Enschedé).

No. NI95a originates from an example of booklet pane NI154m with a progressive dry print of black.

No NI98 (Walsall printing) appears bluish grey and No. NI98a (De La Rue printing) appears olive-grey.

Nos. NI122/NI123 went on philatelic sale on 20 September 2007. They went on sale in Northern Ireland post offices as supplies of Nos. NI94/NI95 were used up.

A stamp as No. NI102 but printed in gravure was only issued within No. **MS**2685.

Stamps as Nos. NI128/NI129 but printed in lithography were only issued within No. **MS**2796 (No. NI128) or No. **MS**2886 (No. NI129).

A design as No. NI95 but self-adhesive was issued on 11 March 2008 in sheets of 20, each stamp accompanied by a *se-tenant* label showing a Northern Ireland scene (No. LS46). These sheets, perforated 15×14 without the elliptical holes, were printed in lithography by Cartor and sold at £7·35 each. They were also available with personalised photographs on the labels at £14·95 from the Royal Mail in Edinburgh.

Stamps as Nos. EN30, NI95, S131 and W122 but self-adhesive were issued on 29 September 2008 in sheets of 20 containing five of each design with *se-tenant* labels (No. LS49).

Stamps as No. NI95 but self-adhesive were issued again on 17 March 2009 in sheets of 20 with *se-tenant* labels showing Northern Ireland Castles, No. LS58. These sheets were printed in lithography by Cartor and originally sold at £7·74 each (£8·35 from 6 April 2009).

First Day Covers

14.10.03	2nd, 1st, E, 68p. (Nos. NI94/NI96, NI100) Tallents House		
	(Type K, see Introduction)..............................	3·25	
	Belfast...	3·25	
11.5.04	40p. (No. NI97) Tallents House (Type K)................	1·75	
	Belfast...	1·75	
5.4.05	42p. (No. NI98) Tallents House (Type K)................	2·25	
	Belfast...	2·25	
28.3.06	44p., 72p. (Nos. NI99, NI102) Tallents House (Type K)..	3·50	
	Belfast...	3·50	
27.3.07	48p., 78p. (Nos. NI124, NI128) Tallents House,		
	(Type K)..	2·50	
	Belfast...	2·50	
1.4.08	50p., 81p. (Nos. NI125, NI129) Tallents House		
	(Type K)..	3·00	
	Belfast...	3·00	
31.3.09	56p., 90p. (Nos. NI126, NI130) Tallents House		
	(Type K)..	3·50	
	Belfast...	3·50	
30.3.10	60p., 97p. (Nos. NI127, NI131) Tallents House		
	(Type K)..	4·00	
	Belfast...	4·00	
29.3.11	68p., £1·10 (Nos. NI101, NI111) Tallents House		
	(Type K)..	4·25	
	Belfast...	4·25	
25.4.12	87p., £1·28 (Nos. NI103, NI113) Tallents House		
	(Type K)..	5·00	
	Belfast...	5·00	
27.3.13	88p. (No. NI104) Tallents House (Type K).............	2·25	
	Belfast...	2·25	
26.3.14	97p. (No. NI105) Tallents House (Type K).............	2·25	
	Belfast...	2·25	
24.3.15	£1, £1·33 (Nos. NI106, NI114) Tallents House (Type K)	5·00	
	Belfast...	5·00	
22.3.16	£1·05 (No. NI107) Tallents House (Type K)............	2·50	
	Belfast...	2·50	

N10

(Des David Lyons, Clare Melinsky, Ric Ergenhright and Silk Pearce. Litho De La Rue)

2008 (11 Mar). Celebrating Northern Ireland. Sheet 123×70 mm. Two phosphor bands. Perf 15×14½ (with one elliptical hole in each vertical side) (1st) or 15×14½ (78p).

MSNI152 **N10** (1st) Carrickfergus Castle; (1st) Giant's Causeway; 78p. St Patrick; 78p. Queen's Bridge and *Angel of Thanksgiving* sculpture, Belfast....................	4·00	4·00
First Day Cover (Tallents House)..		4·75
First Day Cover (Downpatrick, Co. Down)...........................		4·75
Presentation Pack (PO Pack No. 410).................................	5·00	
PHQ Cards (set of 5) (CGB3)..	1·50	7·00

No. **MS**NI152 was on sale at post offices throughout the UK.

The five PHQ cards depict the complete miniature sheet and the four stamps within it.

N11

(Des Sedley Place. Gravure De La Rue)

2008 (29 Sept). 50th Anniversary of the Country Definitives. Sheet 124×70 mm, containing designs as Nos. NI1, NI3, NI5, S1, S3, S5, W1, W3 and W5 (regional definitives of 1958) but inscribed 1st and printed on pale cream. Two phosphor bands. Perf 15×14 (with one elliptical hole in each vertical side).

MSNI153 **N11** (1st)×9 As No. W1; As No. S1; As No. W5; As No. S5; As No. NI1; As No. W3; As No. S3; As No. NI3; As No. NI5..	7·00	7·00
First Day Cover (Tallents House)..		9·25
First Day Cover (Gloucester)...		9·25
Presentation Pack (PO Pack No. 80)...................................	10·00	
PHQ Cards (set of 10)..	3·00	12·50

No. **MS**NI153 was on sale at post offices throughout the UK.

The ten PHQ cards show the nine individual stamps and the complete sheet.

N11a **N11b** **N11c**

(Litho De La Rue)

2008 (29 Sept). 50th Anniversary of the Country Definitives (2nd issue). Two phosphor bands. Perf 15×14½ (with one elliptical hole in each vertical side).

NI154 **N11a** (1st) deep lilac.................................	1·60	1·60
l. Booklet pane. Nos. NI154/NI156, S154/S156 and W144/W146..........	15·00	
m. Booklet pane. Nos. NI154/NI156 and NI95×3........................	6·50	
NI155 **N11b** (1st) deep claret................................	1·60	1·60
NI156 **N11c** (1st) green.......................................	1·60	1·60
First Day Cover (Tallents House) (No. NI154l).....................		6·00
First Day Cover (Gloucester) (No. NI154l)..........................		6·00

Nos. NI154/NI156 come from £9·72 booklet, No. DX43.

N12 Basalt Columns, Giant's Causeway

N13 Aerial View of Patchwork Fields

N14 Linen Pattern

N15 Vase Pattern from Belleek

(Des Rodney Miller Associates (Basalt columns), Richard Cooke (Aerial view of fields), David Pauley (Linen pattern), Tiff Hunter (Vase pattern). Litho ISP Cartor.)

2017 (21 Mar)–**20**. As previous set but with value indicated in revised typeface. One centre phosphor band (2nd) or two phosphor bands. Perf 15×14 (with one elliptical hole in each vertical side).

NI157	**N12**	(2nd) Basalt columns, Giant's Causeway		
		(20.3.18)................	1·00	75
NI158	**N13**	(1st) Aerial view of patchwork fields		
		(20.3.18)................	1·25	75
NI159	**N14**	£1·17 Linen pattern (21.3.17)................	2·75	2·75
NI160		£1·25 Linen pattern (20.3.18)................	2·75	2·75
NI161		£1·35 Linen pattern (19.3.19)................	2·75	2·75
NI164	**N15**	£1·40 Vase pattern from Belleek (21.3.17)...	3·00	3·00
NI165	**N14**	£1·42 Linen pattern (17.3.20)................	2·50	2·50
NI166	**N15**	£1·45 Vase pattern from Belleek (20.3.18)...	3·25	3·25
NI167		£1·55 Vase pattern from Belleek (19.3.19)...	3·25	3·25
NI168		£1·63 Vase pattern from Belleek (17.3.20)...	2·75	2·75
NI169	**N14**	£1·70 Linen pattern (23.12.20)................	2·40	2·40

N16 Basalt Columns, Giant's Causeway

N17 Aerial View of Patchwork Fields

N18 Linen Pattern

(Des Rodney Miller Associates. Litho ISP Cartor)

2022 (11 Aug). As Types **N16**, **N17** and **N18** with barcoded strip at right. Self-adhesive. One centre phosphor band (2nd) or two phosphor bands (others). Die-cut perf 15×14½ (with one elliptical hole in each vertical side).

NI170	**N16**	(2nd) Basalt columns, Giant's Causeway..	1·10	1·10
NI171	**N17**	(1st) Aerial view of patchwork fields.......	1·60	1·60
NI172	**N18**	£1·85 Linen pattern............	2·50	2·50

First Day Covers

21.3.17	£1·17, £1·40. (Nos. NI159, NI165) (Tallents House) (Type K)................	6·00	
	Belfast................	6·00	
20.3.18	2nd, 1st, £1·25, £1·45. (Nos. NI157/NI158, NI160, NI166) Tallents House (Type K)................	9·00	
	Belfast................	9·00	
13.9.19	2nd, 1st, £1·35, £1·55. (Nos. NI161/NI167) Tallents House (Type K)................	7·00	
	Belfast................	7·00	
17.3.20	£1·42, £1·63 (Nos. NI164a, NI168) Tallents House (Type K)................	7·00	
	Belfast................	7·00	

23.12.20	£1·70 (No. NI169) Tallents House (Type K)................	3·75	
	Belfast................	3·75	
11.8.22	2nd, 1st, £1·85 (Nos. NI170/NI172) Tallents House (Type K)................	7·50	
	Belfast................	7·50	

III. SCOTLAND

S1

S2

S3

Dot before second 'E' of 'REVENUE' (cyl. 2 dot, R.10/9)

Broken 'V' of 'REVENUE' (Cyl. 1 no dot, R. 11/2)

(Des G. Huntly (3d., 4d., 5d.), J. Fleming (6d., 9d.), A. Imrie (1s.3d., 1s.6d.))

1958–67. W **179**. Perf 15×14.

S1	**S1**	3d. deep lilac (18.8.58)................	15	15
		p. Two phosphor bands (29.1.63).......	7·50	6·00
		pa. One phosphor band at right (30.4.65)................	25	25
		pb. Band at left................	25	25
		pc. Horizontal pair. Nos. S1pa/pb....	60	75
		pd. One centre phosphor band (9.11.67)................	15	15
S2		4d. ultramarine (7.2.66)................	20	20
		a. dot before second 'E' of 'REVENUE'..	25·00	
		p. Two phosphor bands................	20	20
		pa. dot before second 'E' of 'REVENUE'..	25·00	
S3	**S2**	6d. deep claret (29.9.58)................	25	25
		a. Broken 'V' of 'REVENUE'................	25·00	
		p. Two phosphor bands (29.1.63).......	25	25
		pa. Broken 'V' of 'REVENUE'................	25·00	
S4		9d. bronze-green (2 phosphor bands) (1.3.67)................	40	40
S5	**S3**	1s.3d. green (29.9.58)................	40	40
		p. Two phosphor bands (29.1.63).......	50	50
S6		1s.6d. grey-blue (2 phosphor bands) (1.3.67)................	60	60

The one phosphor band on No. S1pa was produced by printing broad phosphor bands across alternate vertical perforations. Individual stamps show the band at right or left (same prices either way).

For Nos. S1, S3 and S5 in Presentation Pac, see below Wales No. W6.

1967–70. No wmk. Chalk-surfaced paper. One centre phosphor band (Nos. S7, S9/S10) or two phosphor bands (others). Gum Arabic (Nos. S7, S8) or PVA gum (others). Perf 15×14.

S7	**S1**	3d. deep lilac (16.5.68)................	15	15
		y. Phosphor omitted................	7·00	
		v. PVA gum................	10	
		vy. Phosphor omitted (No. S7v)........	4·00	
S8		4d. deep bright blue (28.11.67).........	30	30
		y. Phosphor omitted................	10·00	
		v. PVA gum (25.7.68)................	10	
S9		4d. olive-sepia (4.9.68)................	15	15
		y. Phosphor omitted................	3·00	
S10		4d. bright vermilion (26.2.69).........	15	15
		y. Phosphor omitted................	2·50	
S11		5d. royal blue (4.9.68)................	25	25
		y. Phosphor omitted................	55·00	
S12	**S2**	9d. bronze-green (28.9.70)................	4·00	4·00
		y. Phosphor omitted................	£275	
S13	**S3**	1s.6d. grey-blue (12.12.68)................	1·25	1·25
		y. Phosphor omitted................	£125	

Presentation Pack (PO Pack No. 23) Nos. S3, S5p., S7, S9/S13) (9.12.70)................ 8·00

There was no Post Office first day cover for No. S10.

First Day Covers

18.8.58	3d. (No. S1)................	17·00	
29.9.58	6d., 1s.3d. (Nos. S3, S5)................	25·00	
7.2.66	4d. (No. S2)................	7·00	
1.3.67	9d., 1s.6d. (Nos. S4, S6)................	6·00	
4.9.68	4d., 5d. (Nos. S9, S11)................	3·00	

Presentation Pack

9.12.70	PO Pack No. 23. 6d., 3d., 4d., 5d., 9d. 1s.3d., 1s.6d. (Nos. S3, S5p, S7, S9/S13)................	8·00	

S4

I   II

Redrawn design of T S4 (litho printings.)

The introduction of the redrawn lion took place in 1983 when Waddington's had the contract and therefore the 13p., 17p., 22p. and 31p. exist in both types and perforated 14. The Questa printings, perforated 15×14, are all Type II.

The Types of Lion.

Type I: The eye and jaw appear larger and there is no line across the bridge of the nose.

Type II: The tongue is thick at the point of entry to the mouth and the eye is linked to the background by a solid line.

The following stamps printed in lithography show a screened background behind and to the left of the emblem: 12½p., 15½p., 16p., 19½p., 28p. (Nos. S50 and S74) and 31p. (Nos. S51 and S76). The 13p. and 17p. (No. S43) also showed screened backgrounds for both Type I and Type II of the John Waddington printings, but changed to solid backgrounds for the Questa Type II. All other values printed in lithography have solid backgrounds.

(Des Jeffery Matthews after plaster cast by Arnold Machin)

1971 (7 July)–**93**. Decimal Currency. Chalk-surfaced paper. T **S4**.

(a) Photo Harrison. With phosphor bands. Perf 15×14.

S14	2½p. bright magenta (1 centre band).............		25	20
	y. Phosphor omitted........................		10·00	
	g. Gum arabic (22.9.72)......................		30	
	gy. Phosphor omitted........................		20·00	
S15	3p. ultramarine (2 bands)......................		25	15
	y. Phosphor omitted........................		17·00	
	g. Gum arabic (14.12.72).....................		30	
	ga. Imperf (pair)...........................		£575	
	gy. Phosphor omitted........................		50·00	
S16	3p. ultramarine (1 centre band) (23.1.74)....		15	15
S17	3½p. olive-grey (2 bands) (23.1.74)............		20	20
	y. Phosphor omitted........................		50·00	
S18	3½p. olive-grey (1 centre band) (6.11.74).......		20	20
S19	4½p. grey-blue (2 bands) (6.11.74)........		25	25
S20	5p. reddish violet (2 bands)..................		90	90
S21	5½p. violet (2 bands) (23.1.74).............		25	25
S22	5½p. violet (1 centre band) (21.5.75)........		20	25
	a. Imperf (pair)............................		£450	
S23	6½p. greenish blue (2 bands) (14.1.76)....		20	25
S24	7p. purple-brown (1 centre band) (18.1.78)...		25	25
S25	7½p. chestnut (2 bands)......................		90	90
	y. Phosphor omitted........................		7·00	
S26	8p. rosine (2 bands) (23.1.74).............		35	35
S27	8½p. yellow-green (2 bands) (14.1.76)........		35	35
S28	9p. deep violet (2 bands) (18.1.78)........		35	35
S29	10p. orange-brown (2 bands) (20.10.76).......		35	35
S30	10p. orange-brown (1 centre band) (23.7.80).....................		35	35
S31	10½p. steel-blue (2 bands) (18.1.78).............		45	45
S32	11p. scarlet (2 bands) (20.10.76)................		40	40
	y. Phosphor omitted........................		3·50	

(b) Photo Harrison. On phosphorised paper. Perf 15×14.

S33	12p. yellowish green (23.7.80)............		45	45
S34	13½p. purple-brown (23.7.80).............		60	60
S35	15p. ultramarine (23.7.80)............		50	50

(c) Litho Waddington. (Type I unless otherwise stated.) One side phosphor band (11½p., 12p., 12½p., 13p.) or phosphorised paper (others). Perf 14.

S36	11½p. drab (8.4.81)......................		55	55
	y. Phosphor omitted........................		£750	
S37	12p. bright emerald (Type II) (7.1.86).............		1·25	1·25
S38	12½p. light emerald (24.2.82)................		45	45
S39	13p. pale chestnut (Type I) (23.10.84).........		75	75
	y. Phosphor omitted........................		£750	
	a. Type II (1.85)...........................		8·00	8·00
	ay. Phosphor omitted.......................		£750	
S40	14p. grey-blue (8.4.81)..................		45	45
S41	15½p. pale violet (24.2.82).....................		50	50
S42	16p. drab (Type II) (27.4.83).................		50	50

S43	17p. grey-blue (Type I) (23.10.84)..................		1·25	1·25
	a. Type II (1.85)...........................		1·10	1·10
S44	18p. deep violet (8.4.81).............		70	70
S45	19½p. olive-grey (24.2.82).............		1·25	1·25
S46	20½p. ultramarine (Type II) (27.4.83).............		2·25	2·25
S47	22p. blue (8.4.81).............		75	75
S48	22p. yellow-green (Type I) (23.10.84).............		2·25	2·25
	a. Type II (1.86)...........................		16·00	16·00
S49	26p. rosine (24.2.82).............		70	70
S50	28p. deep violet-blue (Type II) (27.4.83).............		70	70
S51	31p. bright purple (Type I) (23.10.84).............		1·50	1·50
	a. Type II (11.85*)...........................		£150	£150

(d) Litho Questa (Type II). Perf 15×14.

S52	**S4**	12p. bright emerald (1 side band) (29.4.86).........................		1·25	1·25
S53		13p. pale chestnut (1 side band) (4.11.86).........................		70	70
S54		14p. deep blue (1 centre band) (8.11.88).........................		45	45
		l. Booklet pane. No. S54×6 with margins all round (21.3.89)......		1·50	
S55		14p. deep blue (1 side band) (21.3.89)....		50	50
		l. Booklet pane. No. S55×5, S63×2, S68 and centre label with margins all round.........................		9·00	
		la. Error. Booklet pane imperf.............		£1750	
S56		15p. bright blue (1 centre band) (28.11.89).........................		50	50
		a. Imperf (three sides) (block of four).		£275	
S57		17p. grey-blue (phosphorised paper) (29.4.86).........................		2·40	2·40
S58		17p. deep blue (1 centre band) (4.12.90).........................		70	70
S59		18p. deep olive-grey (phosphorised paper) (6.1.87).................		70	70
S60		18p. bright green (1 centre band) (3.12.91).........................		60	60
		a. Perf 14 (26.9.92*).....................		1·00	1·00
		ay. Phosphor omitted.....................		£900	
S61		18p. bright green (1 side band) (10.8.93).........................		1·40	1·40
S62		19p. bright orange-red (phosphorised paper) (8.11.88).................		50	50
		l. Booklet pane. No. S62×9 with margins all round (21.3.89)......		2·75	
		m. Booklet pane. No. S62×6 with margins all round (21.3.89)......		2·25	
S63		19p. bright orange-red (2 bands) (21.3.89).........................		1·40	1·40
S64		20p. brownish black (phosphorised paper) (28.11.89).................		70	70
S65		22p. yellow-green (phosphorised paper) (27.1.87).................		1·10	1·10
S66		22p. bright orange-red (phosphorised paper) (4.12.90).................		60	60
S67		23p. bright green (phosphorised paper) (8.11.88).................		80	80
S68		23p. bright green (2 bands) (21.3.89)....		9·00	9·00
S69		24p. Indian red (phosphorised paper) (28.11.89).................		1·00	1·00
S70		24p. chestnut (phosphorised paper) (3.12.91).........................		75	75
		a. Perf 14 (10.92*).....................		6·00	6·00
S71		24p. chestnut (2 bands) (10.8.93)........		1·40	1·40
S72		26p. rosine (phosphorised paper) (27.1.87).........................		2·25	2·25
S73		26p. drab (phosphorised paper) (4.12.90).........................		1·00	1·00
S74		28p. deep violet-blue (phosphorised paper) (27.1.87).................		1·00	1·00
S75		28p. deep bluish grey (phosphorised paper) (3.12.91).................		1·00	1·00
		a. Perf 14 (18.2.93*).....................		9·00	9·00
S76		31p. bright purple (phosphorised paper) (29.4.86).................		1·50	1·50
S77		32p. greenish blue (phosphorised paper) (8.11.88).................		1·00	1·00
S78		34p. deep bluish grey (phosphorised paper) (28.11.89).................		1·25	1·75
S79		37p. rosine (phosphorised paper) (4.12.90).........................		1·25	1·25
S80		39p. bright mauve (phosphorised paper) (3.12.91).................		1·50	1·50
		a. Perf 14 (11.92).....................		12·50	12·50

* Earliest known date of issue.

Nos. S55, S63 and S68 only come from booklet pane S55l from the £5 Scots Connection booklet, No. DX10.

The listed booklet panes come from the Sponsored Booklet No. DX10; Nos. S54l, S55l, S62l/S62m.

No. S56a occured in the second vertical row of two sheets. It is best collected as a block of four including the left-hand vertical pair imperforate on three sides.

Nos. S60a, S70a, S75a and S80a were caused by the use of a reserve perforating machine for some printings in the second half of 1992.

From 1972 printings were on fluorescent white paper. From 1973 most printings had dextrin added to the PVA gum (see notes after the 1971 Decimal Machin issue).

7.7.71	2½p., 3p., 5p., 7½p. (Nos. S14/S15, S20, S25)............	1·50
23.1.74	3p., 3½p., 5½p., 8p. (Nos. S16/S17, S21, S26).............	1·25
6.11.74	4½p. (No. S19)...	1·00
14.1.76	6½p., 8½p. (Nos. S23, S27)..................................	1·00
20.10.76	10p., 11p. (Nos. S29, S32)..................................	1·00
18.1.78	7p., 9p., 10½p. (Nos. S24, S28, S31).....................	1·00
23.7.80	12p., 13½p., 15p. (Nos. S33/S35).........................	1·50
8.4.81	11½p., 14p., 18p., 22p. (Nos. S36, S40, S44, S47)..........	1·50
24.2.82	12½p., 15½p., 19½p., 26p. (Nos. S38, S41, S45, S49).....	1·75
27.4.83	16p., 20½p., 28p. (Nos. S42, S46, S50)..................	2·00
23.10.84	13p., 17p., 22p., 31p. (Nos. S39, S43, S48, S51).....	2·00
7.1.86	12p. (No. S37)..	1·00
6.1.87	18p. (No. S59)..	1·00
8.11.88	14p., 19p., 23p., 32p. (Nos. S54, S62, S67, S77)......	2·00
21.3.89	Scots Connection *se-tenant* pane 14p., 19p., 23p. (No. S55l)...	10·00
28.11.89	15p., 20p., 24p., 34p. (Nos. S56, S64, S69, S78)......	2·50
4.12.90	17p., 22p., 26p., 37p. (Nos. S58, S66, S73, S79)......	2·50
3.12.91	18p., 24p., 28p., 39p. (Nos. S70, S75, S80)............	2·50

7.7.71	PO Pack No. 27. 2½p., 3p. (2 bands), 5p., 7½p. (Nos. S14/S15, S20, S25)....................	2·00
29.5.74	PO Pack No. 62. 3p. (1 centre band), 3½p. (2 bands) or (1 centre band), 5½p. (2 bands) or (1 centre band), 8p. (Nos. S16, S17 or S18, S21 or S22, S26). The 4½p. (No. S19) was added later...................	2·00
20.10.76	PO Pack No. 85. 6½p., 8½p., 10p. (2 bands), 11p. (Nos. S23, S27, S29, S32)........................	1·50
28.10.81	PO Pack No. 129b. 7p., 9p., 10½p., 12p. (gravure), 13½p. (gravure), 11½p., 14p. grey-blue, 18p. deep violet, 22p. blue (Nos. S24, S28, S31, S33/S36, S40, S44, S47)........................	6·00
3.8.83	PO Pack No. 2. 10p. (1 centre band), 12½p., 16p., 20½p., 26p. (J.W.), 28p. (J.W.), (Nos. S30, S38, S42, S46, S49/S50)........................	14·00
23.10.84	PO Pack No. 6. 10p. (1 centre band), 13p. (J.W.), 16p., 17p. (J.W.), 22p. yellow-green, 26p. (J.W.), 28p. (J.W.), 31p. (J.W.), (Nos. S30, S39, S42/S43, S48/S51).........	12·00
3.3.87	PO Pack No. 10. 12p. (litho), 13p. (Questa), 17p. grey-blue (Questa), 18p. deep olive-grey, 22p. yellow-green, 26p. rosine (Questa), 28p. deep violet-blue (Questa), 31p. (Questa) (Nos. S52/S53, S57, S59, S65, S72, S74, S76)........................	15·00

Presentation Packs containing stamps of Northern Ireland, Scotland and Wales are listed after those for Northern Ireland.

1977–1978 EXPERIMENTAL MACHINE PACKETS. These are small cartons containing loose stamps for sale in vending machines. The experiment was confined to the Scottish Postal Board area, where six vending machines were installed, the first becoming operational in Dundee about February 1977.

The cartons carry labels inscribed 'ROYAL MAIL STAMPS', their total face value (30p. or 60p.) and their contents.

At first the 30p. packet contained two 6½p. and two 8½p. Scottish Regional stamps and the 60p. packet had four of each. The stamps could be in pairs or blocks, but also in strips or singles.

With the change in postal rates on 13 June 1977 these packets were withdrawn on 11 June and on 13 June the contents were changed, giving three 7p. and one 9p. for the 30p. packet and double this for the 60p. packet. However, this time ordinary British Machin stamps were used. Moreover the Edinburgh machine, situated in an automatic sorting area, was supplied with 7p. stamps with two phosphor bands instead of the new centre band 7p. stamps, despite instructions having been given to withdraw the two phosphor bands. However, the demand for these packets was too great to be filled and by 27 June the machine was closed down. It was brought back into use on 16 August 1977, supplying 7p. stamps with the centre band.

The 6½p. and 8½p. Scottish Regional packets were put on sale at the Edinburgh Philatelic Bureau in June 1977 and withdrawn in April 1978. The packets with the 7p. and 9p. Machin stamps were put on sale at the Bureau in June 1977 and withdrawn in December 1978.

Such machine packets are outside the scope of this catalogue.

(Des Jeffery Matthews after plaster cast by Arnold Machin)

1993 (7 Dec)–**98**. Chalk-surfaced paper.

(a) Litho Questa. Perf 15×14 (with one elliptical hole in each vert side).

S81	**S4**	19p. bistre (1 centre band)....................	70	70
S82		19p. bistre (1 band at right) (25.4.95)......	2·00	2·00
S83		20p. bright green (1 centre band) (23.7.96)......................	1·25	1·25
S84		25p. red (2 bands)............................	80	80
S85		26p. red-brown (2 bands) (23.7.96)........	1·40	1·40
S86		30p. deep olive-grey (2 bands).............	1·25	1·25
S87		37p. bright mauve (2 bands) (23.7.96).....	1·75	1·75
S88		41p. grey-brown (2 bands)...................	1·25	1·25
		y. Phosphor omitted........................	£325	
S89		63p. light emerald (2 bands) (23.7.96)....	2·50	2·50

(b) Gravure Walsall (20p., 26p. (No. S91a), 63p.), Harrison or Walsall (26p. (No. S91), 37p.). Perf 14 (No. S90a) or 15×14 (others) (both with one elliptical hole in each vertical side).

S90	**S4**	20p. bright green (1 centre band) (1.7.97)......................	1·00	1·00
S90*a*		20p. bright green (1 side band at right) (13.10.98)......................	3·00	3·00
S91		26p. chestnut (2 bands) (1.7.97)............	1·40	1·40
		a. Perf 14 (13.10.98)........................	3·00	3·00
S92		37p. bright mauve (2 bands) (1.7.97).......	1·60	1·60
S93		63p. light emerald (2 bands) (1.7.97)......	3·50	3·50

Nos. S82, S90*a* and S91*a* only come from booklets. The Harrison printings of Nos. S91/S92 come from booklet pane No. NI81l.

7.12.93	19p., 25p., 30p., 41p. (Nos. S81, S84, S86, S88)............	3·50
23.7.96	20p. 26p., 37p., 63p. (Nos. S83, S85, S87, S89)............	4·00

For Presentation Pack containing stamps of Northern Ireland, Scotland and Wales see after No. NI87 of Northern Ireland.

S5 Saltire    **S6** Lion Rampant of Scotland

S7 Thistle    **S8** Tartan

(Des Anton Morris (Saltire), Frank Pottinger (Lion Rampant of Scotland), Tim Chalk (Thistle) and Tartan, supplied by Kinloch Anderson; adapted by Tayburn of Edinburgh. Gravure Questa (Nos. S94l, S95l), De La Rue (No. S99), De La Rue or Walsall (Nos. S94/S95), Walsall (others))

1999 (8 June)–**2002**. One centre phosphor band (2nd) or two phosphor bands (others). Perf 15×14 (with one elliptical hole in each vertical side).

S94	**S5**	(2nd) Saltire..................................	1·25	1·25
		l. Booklet pane. Nos. S94×6 and S98×2 with centre label and margins all round (4.8.00)............	6·00	
S95	**S6**	(1st) Lion Rampant of Scotland.............	1·50	1·50
		l. Booklet pane. Nos. S95/S96, each×4, with centre label and margins all round (22.10.01)..........	7·50	
S96	**S7**	(E) Thistle....................................	2·25	2·25
S97	**S8**	64p. Tartan....................................	5·50	5·50
S98		65p. Tartan (25.4.00).........................	2·00	2·00
S99		68p. Tartan (4.7.02)..........................	2·25	2·25
PHQ Cards (set of 4) (D12) (Nos. S94/S97).........			1·25	10·00

Nos. S94, S95 and S96 were initially sold at 19p., 26p. and 30p., the latter representing the basic European airmail rate.

New printings of Nos. S94/S95, produced by De La Rue instead of Walsall were issued on 5 June 2002. Stamps from this printing do not differ from those produced by Walsall.

No. S94l comes from booklet No. DX25.

No. S95l comes from booklet No. DX27.

For combined presentation pack for all four Regions, see under England.

8.6.99	2nd, 1st, E, 64p. (Nos. S94/S97) Tallents House............	3·50
	Edinburgh...	4·00
25.4.00	65p. (No. S98) Tallents House.............................	2·50
	Edinburgh...	2·50
4.8.00	Queen Elizabeth the Queen Mother *se-tenant* pane 2nd, 65p. (No. S94l) Tallents House (as for Nos. 2160/2161)........................	4·75
	London SW1 (as for Nos. 2160/2161).................	4·75
22.10.01	Unseen and Unheard *se-tenant* pane (1st), E, (No. S95l) Tallents House (as for No. **MS**2206)...............	7·00
	Rosyth, Dunfermline (as for No. **MS**2206)........	7·00
4.7.02	68p. (No. S99) Tallents House (Type K) (see Introduction)........................	2·00
	Edinburgh...	2·00

08.06.99	PO Pack No. 45. 2nd, 1st, E, 64p. (Nos. S94/S97)..........	9·50
25.04.00	PO Pack No. 50. 65p. (No. S98)...........................	10·00
12.03.02	PO Pack No. 55. 2nd, 1st, E, 65p. (Nos. S94/S96, S98)...	15·00

S9

(Des Jeffery Matthews. Gravure Walsall)

2000 (15 Feb). T **S4** redrawn with '1st' face value as T **S9**. Two phosphor bands. Perf 14 (with one elliptical hole in each vertical side).

S108	**S9**	(1st) bright orange-red.............	1·60	1·60

No. S108 was only issued in £7·50 stamp booklet (No. DX24).

2003 (14 Oct)–**17**. As Nos. S94/S96 and S99, and new values, but with white borders. One centre phosphor band (2nd) or two phosphor bands (others). Perf 15×14 (with one elliptical hole in each vertical side).

(a) Gravure Walsall or De La Rue (42p.) or De La Rue (others).

S109	**S5**	(2nd) Saltire.............	1·25	1·25
		l. Booklet pane. Nos. S109 and EN16, each×3, with margins all round (16.3.04).............	5·50	
		m. Booklet pane. Nos. S109 and W103, each×3, with margins all round (1.3.07).............	5·00	
S110	**S6**	(1st) Lion Rampant of Scotland.............	1·50	1·50
S111	**S7**	(E) Thistle.............	2·10	2·10
S112		40p. Thistle (11.5.04).............	1·40	1·40
S113		42p. Thistle (5.4.05).............	1·75	1·75
S114		44p. Thistle (28.3.06).............	1·40	1·40
S115		48p. Thistle (27.3.07).............	1·25	1·25
S116		50p. Thistle (1.4.08).............	1·25	1·25
S117		56p. Thistle (31.3.09).............	1·40	1·40
S118		60p. Thistle (30.3.10).............	1·50	1·50
S119	**S8**	68p. Tartan.............	1·60	1·60
S120		72p. Tartan (28.3.06).............	1·75	1·75
S121		78p. Tartan (27.3.07).............	1·75	1·75
S122		81p. Tartan (1.4.08).............	2·00	2·00
S123		90p. Tartan (31.3.09).............	2·25	2·25
S124		97p. Tartan (30.3.10).............	2·40	2·40

(b) Litho Enschedé, De La Rue or ISP Cartor (1st) or ISP Cartor (others). Queen's head in grey (Nos. S130a and S131a) or silver (others).

S130	**S5**	(2nd) Saltire (Queen's head silver) (27.6.12).............	1·25	1·25
		a. Saltire (Queen's head grey) (5.16).............	1·75	1·50
S131	**S6**	(1st) Lion Rampant of Scotland (Queen's head silver) (20.9.07).............	1·50	1·50
		a. Lion Rampant of Scotland (Queen's head grey) (19.5.16).............	2·00	2·00
S132	**S7**	68p. Thistle (29.3.11).............	1·90	1·90
S133		87p Thistle (25.4.12).............	2·25	2·25
S134		88p. Thistle (27.3.13).............	2·25	2·25
S135		97p Thistle (26.3.14).............	2·40	2·40
S136		£1 Thistle (24.3.15).............	2·40	2·40
S137		£1·05 Thistle (22.3.16).............	2·60	2·60
S138	**S8**	£1·10 Tartan (29.3.11).............	2·40	2·40
S143		£1·28 Tartan (25.4.12).............	2·60	2·60
S144		£1·33 Tartan (24.3.15).............	2·75	2·75
PHQ Cards (set of 4) (D25) (Nos. S109/S111, S119).............			1·25	6·50

No. S109l comes from booklet No. DX32.

No. S109m from booklet No. DX38.

The Walsall printing of No. S113 was issued on 5 April 2005, and the De La Rue printing on 24 May 2005.

Stamps as No. S121/S122 but printed in lithography were only issued within No. **MS**2796 (No. S121) or No. **MS**2886 (No. S122).

No. S131 was issued on 20 September 2007 in £7·66 stamp booklets printed by Enschedé, No. DX40 and on 29 September 2008 in £9·72 booklets (No. DX43) printed by De La Rue. It was issued in sheets printed by ISP Cartor on 27 June 2012.

A design as No. S131 but self-adhesive was issued on 30 November 2007 in sheets of 20, each stamp accompanied by a *se-tenant* label showing a Scottish scene (No. LS44). These sheets were printed in lithography by Cartor, perforated 15×14 without the elliptical holes, and sold at £7·35. They were also available with personalised photographs on the labels at £14·95 from the Royal Mail in Edinburgh.

Stamps as Nos. EN30, NI95, S131 and W122 but self-adhesive were issued on 29 September 2008 in sheets of 20 containing five of each design with *se-tenant* labels (No. LS49).

Numbers have be left for possible additions to this definitive series.

First Day Covers

14.10.03	2nd, 1st, E, 68p. (Nos. S109/S111, S119) Tallents House (Type K, see Introduction).............	2·00	
	Edinburgh.............	2·00	
11.5.04	40p. (No. S112) Tallents House (Type K).............	1·50	
	Edinburgh.............	1·50	
5.4.05	42p. (No. S113) Tallents House (Type K).............	1·75	
	Edinburgh.............	1·75	
28.3.06	44p., 72p. (Nos. S114, S120) Tallents House (Type K).............	3·00	
	Edinburgh.............	3·00	
27.3.07	48p., 78p. (Nos. S115, S121) Tallents House (Type K).............	3·00	
	Edinburgh.............	3·00	

1.4.08	50p., 81p. (S116, S122) Tallents House (Type K).............	3·25	
	Edinburgh.............	3·25	
31.3.09	56p., 90p. (Nos. S117, S123) Tallents House (Type K).............	3·50	
	Edinburgh.............	3·50	
30.3.10	60p., 97p. (Nos. S118, S124) Tallents House (Type K).............	3·75	
	Edinburgh.............	3·75	
29.3.11	68p., £1·10 (Nos. S132, S138) Tallents House (Type K).............	4·25	
	Edinburgh.............	4·25	
25.4.12	87p., £1·28 (Nos. S133, S143) Tallents House (Type K).............	4·50	
	Edinburgh.............	4·50	
27.3.13	88p. (No. S134) Tallents House (Type K).............	2·00	
	Edinburgh.............	2·00	
26.3.14	97p. (No. S135) Tallents House (Type K).............	2·25	
	Edinburgh.............	2·25	
24.3.15	£1, £1·33 (Nos. S136, S144) Tallents House (Type K).............	5·25	
	Edinburgh.............	5·25	
22.3.16	£1·05 (No. S137) Tallents House (Type K).............	2·50	
	Edinburgh.............	2·50	

Presentation Pack

14.10.03	PO Pack No. 64. 2nd, 1st, E, 68p. (Nos. S109/S111, S119).............	6·00	

S9a

(Des Howard Brown. Gravure De La Rue)

2004 (5 Oct). Opening of New Scottish Parliament, Edinburgh. Sheet 123×70 mm. Printed in gravure by De La Rue. One centre phosphor band (2nd) or two phosphor bands (others). Perf 15×14 (with one elliptical hole on each vertical side).

MSS152 **S9a** Nos. S109, S110×2 and S112×2.............		5·00	5·00
First Day Cover (Tallents House).............			5·50
First Day Cover (Edinburgh).............			5·50

S10

(Des Peter Crowther, Clare Melinsky and Silk Pearce. Gravure De La Rue)

2006 (30 Nov). Celebrating Scotland. Sheet 124×71 mm. Two phosphor bands. Perf 15×14 (with one elliptical hole in each vertical side) (1st) or 14½×14 (72p.).

MSS153 **S10** (1st) As No. S110; (1st) Saltire; 72p. St Andrew; 72p. Edinburgh Castle.............		4·00	4·00
First Day Cover (Tallents House).............			4·25
First Day Cover (St Andrews, Fife).............			4·75
Presentation Pack (PO Pack No. M14).............		5·25	
PHQ Cards (set of 5) (CGB1).............		1·50	4·00

No. **MS**S153 was on sale at post offices throughout the UK.

Stamps as the 1st class Saltire stamp within No. **MS**S153 but self-adhesive were issued on 30 November 2009 in sheets of 20 with *se-tenant* labels showing Scottish Castles, No. LS68. These sheets were printed in lithography by Cartor and sold for £8·35 each.

The five PHQ cards depict the complete miniature sheet and the four stamps within it.

S10a   **S10b**   **S10c**

(Litho De La Rue)

2008 (29 Sept). 50th Anniversary of the Country Definitives. Two phosphor bands. Perf 15×14½ (with one elliptical hole in each vertical side).

S154	**S10a**	(1st) deep lilac..	1·60	1·60
		I. Booklet pane. Nos. S154/S156		
		and S131×3........................	6·50	
S155	**S10b**	(1st) deep claret......................................	1·60	1·60
S156	**S10c**	(1st) green...	1·60	1·60

Nos. S154/S156 come from £9·72 booklets, No. DX43.

S11

(Des Tayburn. Gravure Enschedé)

2009 (22 Jan). 250th Birth Anniversary of Robert Burns (poet). Sheet 145×74 mm. One centre phosphor band (2nd) or two phosphor bands (others). Perf 14½ (size 34×34 mm) or 15×14 (with one elliptical hole in each vertical side) (others).

MSS157	**S11**	(2nd) No. S109; (1st) 'A Man's a Man for a' that' and Burns ploughing (detail) (James Sargent Storer) (34×34 mm); (1st) No. S110; (1st) Portrait of Burns (Alexander Nasmyth) (34×34 mm); 50p. No. S116; 81p. S122.	5·00	5·00
First Day Cover (Tallents House)............................				5·50
First Day Cover (Alloway, Ayr)................................				5·50
Presentation Pack (PO Pack No. 422).....................			6·00	
PHQ Cards (set of 3) (319).....................................			90	7·00

No. **MS**S157 was on sale at post offices throughout the UK.

The three PHQ cards show the two 34×34 mm Robert Burns stamps and the complete miniature sheet.

S12 Saltire

Des Peter Crowther (illustration) and Silk Pierce. Litho ISP Cartor or Enschedé)

2013 (9 May)–**14**. Scotland Flag. Two phosphor bands. Perf 14½×14 (with one elliptical hole in each vertical side).

S158	**S12**	(1st) Saltire (Queen's head silver).............	4·75	4·75
		a. Saltire (Queen's head grey)		
		(20.2.14).........................	3·50	3·50

No. S158 was issued in £11·11 Football Heroes booklet (No. DY7, booklet pane No. U3070I).

No. S158a was issued in £13.97 Classic Locomotives booklet (No. DY9, booklet pane No. U307lm) and £16·49 Centenary of the First World War (3rd issue) booklet (No. DY18, booklet pane 3717a).

S13 Saltire   **S14** Lion Rampant of Scotland   **S15** Thistle   **S16** Tartan

(Des Des Anton Morris (Saltire), Frank Pottinger (Lion Rampant of Scotland), Tim Chalk (Thistle) and Tartan, supplied by Kinloch Anderson; adapted by Tayburn of Edinburgh. Litho ISP Cartor)

2017 (21 Mar)–**2020**. As previous set but with value indicated in revised typeface. One centre phosphor band (2nd) or two phosphor bands (others). Perf 15×14 (with one elliptical hole in each vertical side).

S159	**S13**	(2nd) Saltire (silver-grey head) (20.3.18)...	1·00	75
		a. Saltire (Queens head dull grey)		
		(17.3.20)	1·50	1·50
S160	**S14**	(1st) Lion of Scotland (20.3.18)................	1·25	75
S161	**S15**	£1·17 Thistle (21.3.17).............................	2·75	2·75
S162		£1·25 Thistle (20.3.18).............................	2·75	2·75
S163		£1·35 Thistle (19.3.19).............................	2·75	2·75
S166	**S16**	£1·40 Tartan (21.3.17).............................	3·00	3·00
S167	**S15**	£1·42 Thistle (17.3.20).............................	2·50	2·50
S168	**S16**	£1·45 Tartan (20.3.18).............................	3·25	3·25
S169		£1·55 Tartan (19.3.19).............................	3·25	3·25
S170		£1·63 Tartan (17.3.20).............................	2·75	2·75
S171		£1·70 Thistle (23.12.20)............................	2·40	2·40

S159 and S159a are both printed from black plates but owing to variations in the relative intensity, No. 159 gives a silver-grey effect while 159a is a duller grey.

No. S159a was issued in £16.99 James Bond booklet (No. DY33), booklet pane U3071q.

S17

(Des Tayburn. Litho ISP Cartor)

2020 (6 Apr). 700th Anniversary of the Declaration of Arbroath. Sheet 133×70 mm. Printed in lithography by ISP Cartor. One centre phosphor band (2nd) or two phosphor bands (others). Perf 15×14 (with one elliptical hole in each vertical side).

MSS180	**S17**	Nos. S159/S160, S167 and S170...................	7·00
First Day Cover (Tallents House)............................			9·00
First Day Cover (Arbroath)...................................			9·00

S18 Saltire   **S19** Lion Rampant of Scotland

S20 Thistle

(Des Anton Morris (Saltire), Frank Pottinger (Lion Rampant of Scotland), Tim Chalk (Thistle), adapted by Tayburn of Edinburgh. Litho ISP Cartor)

2022 (11 Aug). As Types **S18**, **S19** and **S20** with barcoded strip at right. Self-adhesive. One centre phosphor band (2nd) or two phosphor bands (others). Die-cut perf 15×14½ (with one elliptical hole in each vertical side).

S181	**S18**	(2nd) Saltire..	1·10	1·10
S182	**S19**	(1st) Lion of Scotland.............................	1·60	1·60
S183	**S20**	£1·85 Thistle..	2·50	2·50

First Day Covers

21.3.17	£1·17, £1·40 (Nos. S161, S166) Tallents House	
	(Type K)..	5·00
	Edinburgh..	5·00
20.3.18	2nd, 1st, £1·25, £1·45 (S159/S160, S162, S168)	
	Tallents House (Type K)...............................	9·00
	Edinburgh..	9·00
19.3.19	£1·35, £1·55 (Nos. S163/S169) Tallents House	
	(Type K)..	7·00
	Edinburgh..	7·00
17.3.20	£1·42, £1·63 (Nos. S167, S170) Tallents House	
	(Type K)..	7·00
	Edinburgh..	7·00
23.12.20	£1·70 (No. S171) Tallents House (Type K)......	3·75
	Edinburgh..	3·75
11.8.22	2nd, 1st, £1·85 (Nos. S181/S183) Tallents House	
	(Type K)..	7·50
	Edinburgh..	7·50

W4 With 'p'

I   II

Redrawn design of T W4 (litho printings)

IV. WALES

From the inception of the Regional stamps, the Welsh versions were tendered to members of the public at all Post Offices within the former County of Monmouthshire but the national alternatives were available on request. By August 1961 the policy of 'dual stocking' of definitive stamps was only maintained at Abergavenny, Chepstow, Newport and Pontypool. Offices with a Monmouthshire postal address but situated outside the County, namely Beachley, Brockweir, Redbrook, Sedbury, Welsh Newton and Woodcroft, were not supplied with the Welsh Regional stamps. With the re-formation of Counties, Monmouthshire became known as Gwent and was also declared to be part of Wales. From 1 July 1974, therefore, except for the offices mentioned above, only Welsh Regional stamps were available at the offices under the jurisdiction of Newport, Gwent.

Two Types of Dragon

Type I: The eye is complete with white dot in the centre. Wing-tips, tail and tongue are thin.

Type II: The eye is joined to the nose by a solid line. Tail, wing-tips, claws and tongue are wider than in Type I.

The following stamps printed in lithography show a screened background behind and to the left of the emblem: 11½p., 12½p., 14p. (No. W39), 15½p., 16p., 18p. (No. W46), 19½p., 22p. (No. W54) and 28p. (No. W63). The 13p. and 17p. (No. W44) also show screened backgrounds in Type I, but changed to solid backgrounds for Type II. All other values printed in lithography have solid backgrounds.

W1   W2   W3

(Des Reynolds Stone)

1958–67. W **179.** Perf 15×14.

W1	**W1**	3d. deep lilac (18.8.58)...........................	15	15
		p. One centre phosphor band		
		(16.5.67)......................................	20	15
W2		4d. ultramarine (7.2.66).........................	20	20
		p. Two phosphor bands (10.67)..........	20	20
W3	**W2**	6d. deep claret (29.9.58).........................	35	35
W4		9d. bronze-green (2 phosphor bands)		
		(1.3.67)..	35	35
		y. Phosphor omitted...........................	£375	
W5	**W3**	1s.3d. green (29.9.58).............................	40	40
W6		1s.6d. grey-blue (2 phosphor bands)		
		(1.3.67)..	40	40
		y. Phosphor omitted...........................	50·00	
Presentation Pack*..			£100	

* This was issued in 1960 and comprises Guernsey No. 7, Jersey No. 10, Isle of Man No. 2, Northern Ireland Nos. NI1, NI3 and NI5, Scotland Nos. S1, S3 and S5 and Wales Nos. W1, W3 and W5 together with a 6 page printed leaflet describing the stamps. There exist two forms: (a) inscribed '7s.3d.' for sale in the UK; and (b) inscribed '$1.20' for sale in the USA.

1967–69. No wmk. Chalk-surfaced paper. One centre phosphor band (Nos. W7, W9/W10) or two phosphor bands (others). Perf 15×14.

W7	**W1**	3d. deep lilac (6.12.67)...........................	15	15
		y. Phosphor omitted...........................	70·00	
W8		4d. ultramarine (21.6.68)........................	15	15
		a. White spot before 'E' of 'POSTAGE'.	25·00	
		b. White spot above dragon's hind		
		leg...	25·00	
W9		4d. olive-sepia (4.9.68)...........................	15	15
		a. White spot before 'E' of 'POSTAGE'.	22·00	
		b. White spot above dragon's hind		
		leg...	22·00	
W10		4d. bright vermilion (26.2.69).................	15	15
		y. Phosphor omitted...........................	2·00	
W11		5d. royal blue (4.9.68).............................	15	15
		y. Phosphor omitted...........................	3·00	
W12	**W3**	1s.6d. grey-blue (1.8.69).........................	2·75	2·75

The 3d. exists with gum arabic only; the remainder with PVA gum only. There was no Post Office first day cover for No. W10.

4.9.68	First Day Cover (Nos. W9, W11).....................	3·00
9.12.70	Presentation Pack (PO Pack No. 24) Nos. W4, W6/	
	W7, W9/W11..	5·50

Types of 5½p.

Cyl. 1 (W21)   Cyl. 2 (W21b)

(Des Jeffery Matthews after plaster cast by Arnold Machin)

1971 (7 July)**–93.** Decimal Currency. Chalk-surfaced paper. T **W4.**

(a) Gravure Harrison. With phosphor bands. Perf 15×14.

W13	2½p. bright magenta (1 centre band)................	20	20
	y. Phosphor omitted...........................	7·50	
	g. Gum arabic (22.9.72).......................	20	
	ga. Imperf (pair).................................	£575	
W14	3p. ultramarine (2 bands).........................	25	20
	y. Phosphor omitted...........................	30·00	
	g. Gum arabic (6.6.73).........................	25	
	gy. Phosphor omitted...........................	12·00	
W15	3p. ultramarine (1 centre band) (23.1.74)........	25	25
W16	3½p. olive-grey (2 bands) (23.1.74)..................	20	30
W17	3½p. olive-grey (1 centre band) (6.11.74)...........	20	20
W18	4½p. reddish violet (2 bands) (6.11.74).............	25	25
W19	5p. reddish violet (2 bands)......................	80	80
	y. Phosphor omitted...........................	20·00	
W20	5½p. violet (2 bands) (23.1.74).....................	25	25
	y. Phosphor omitted...........................	£180	
W21	5½p. violet (1 centre band) (21.5.75)..............	25	25
	a. Imperf (pair).................................	£550	
	b. Low emblem and value (cyl. 2) (1977)....	£180	£180
W22	6½p. greenish blue (1 centre band) (14.1.76).....	20	20
W23	7p. purple-brown (1 centre band) (18.1.78).....	25	25
W24	7½p. chestnut (2 bands)............................	1·25	1·25
	y. Phosphor omitted...........................	75·00	
W25	8p. rosine (2 bands) (23.1.74)....................	30	30
	y. Phosphor omitted...........................	£600	
W26	8½p. yellow-green (2 bands) (14.1.76).............	35	35
W27	9p. deep violet (2 bands) (18.1.78)..............	35	35
W28	10p. orange-brown (2 bands) (20.10.76).........	35	35
W29	10p. orange-brown (1 centre band) (23.7.80)...	35	35
W30	10½p. steel-blue (2 bands) (18.1.78)...............	45	45
W31	11p. scarlet (2 bands) (20.10.76)..................	40	40

(b) Gravure Harrison. On phosphorised paper. Perf 15×14.

W32	12p. yellowish green (23.7.80).....................	45	45
W33	13½p. purple-brown (23.7.80)......................	55	55
W34	15p. ultramarine (23.7.80).........................	55	55

(c) Litho Questa (Type II unless otherwise stated). Perf 14 (11½p., 12½p., 14p. (No. W39), 15½p., 16p., 18p. (No. W46), 19½p., 20½p., 22p. (No. W54), 26p. (No. W61), 28p. (No. W63)) or 15×14 (others).

W35	11½p. drab (Type I) (1 side band) (8.4.81)...............	70	70
W36	12p. bright emerald (1 side band) (7.1.86)...............	1·00	1·00
W37	12½p. light emerald (Type I) (1 side band) (24.2.82)...............................	50	50
	a. Perf 15×14 (Type I) (10.1.84)............	2·75	2·75
W38	13p. pale chestnut (Type I) (1 side band) (23.10.84)........................	50	50
	a. Type II (1.87).......................	1·40	1·40
W39	14p. grey-blue (Type I) (phosphorised paper) (8.4.81)............................	55	55
W40	14p. deep blue (1 centre band) (8.11.88)...	55	55
W41	15p. bright blue (1 centre band) (28.11.89)...	60	60
	y. Phosphor omitted............................	£125	
W42	15½p. pale violet (Type I) (phosphorised paper) (24.2.82)........................	70	70
W43	16p. drab (Type I) (phosphorised paper) (27.4.83)........................	1·10	1·10
	a. Perf 15×14 (10.1.84).............	1·10	1·10
W44	17p. grey-blue (Type I) (phosphorised paper) (23.10.84)...............	80	80
	a. Type II (18.8.86)........................	40·00	40·00
W45	17p. deep blue (1 centre band) (4.12.90)......	60	60
	y. Phosphor omitted............................	18·00	
W46	18p. deep violet (Type I) (8.4.81)...................	80	80
W47	18p. deep olive-grey (phosphorised paper) (6.1.87)..........................	80	80
W48	18p. bright green (1 centre band) (3.12.91)...	55	55
	y. Phosphor omitted............................	£225	
	l. Booklet pane. No. W48×6 with margins all round (25.2.92)........................	1·75	
	ly. Phosphor omitted........................	£225	
	b. Perf 14 (12.1.93*).............	7·50	7·50
W49	18p. bright green (1 side band at right) (25.2.92)........................	1·75	1·75
	l. Booklet pane. No. X1020×2, 1451a, 1514a, W49×2, W60×2 and centre label with margins all round........................	8·50	
	ly. Phosphor omitted........................	£225	
	b. Band at left (10.8.93).............	1·60	1·60
W50	19p. bright orange-red (phosphorised paper) (8.11.88)........................	70	70
W51	19½p. olive-grey (Type I) (phosphorised paper) (24.2.82)........................	1·25	1·25
W52	20p. brownish black (phosphorised paper) (28.11.89)........................	70	70
W53	20½p. ultramarine (Type I) (phosphorised paper) (27.4.83)........................	2·50	2·50
W54	22p. blue (Type I) (phosphorised paper) (8.4.81)............................	80	80
W55	22p. yellow-green (Type I) (phosphorised paper) (23.10.84)........................	80	80
W56	22p. bright orange-red (phosphorised paper) (4.12.90)........................	80	80
W57	23p. bright green (phosphorised paper) (8.11.88)........................	80	80
W58	24p. Indian red (phosphorised paper) (28.11.89)........................	90	90
W59	24p. chestnut (phosphorised paper) (3.12.91)........................	70	70
	l. Booklet pane. No. W59×6 with margins all round (25.2.92)........................	2·50	
	b. Perf 14 (14.9.92*)........................	6·00	6·00
W60	24p. chestnut (2 bands) (25.2.92)........................	90	90
W61	26p. rosine (Type I) (phosphorised paper) (24.2.82)........................	80	80
	a. Perf 15×14 (Type II) (27.1.87).............	3·00	3·00
W62	26p. drab (phosphorised paper) (4.12.90)...	1·25	1·25
W63	28p. deep violet-blue (Type I) (phosphorised paper) (27.4.83)........................	90	90
	a. Perf 15×14 (Type II) (27.1.87).............	1·25	1·25
W64	28p. deep bluish grey (phosphorised paper) (3.12.91)........................	80	80
W65	31p. bright purple (Type I) (phosphorised paper) (23.10.84)........................	1·00	1·00
W66	32p. greenish blue (phosphorised paper) (8.11.88)........................	1·25	1·25
W67	34p. deep bluish grey (phosphorised paper) (28.11.89)........................	1·25	1·25
W68	37p. rosine (phosphorised paper) (4.12.90)...	1·25	1·25
W69	39p. bright mauve (phosphorised paper) (3.12.91)........................	1·25	1·25

* Earliest known date of issue.

Nos. W48b and W59b were caused by the use of a reserve perforating machine for some printings in the second half of 1992.

No. W49 only comes from booklet pane W49l from the £6 Cymru Wales booklet, No. DX13.

Nos. W49b and W60 only come from booklet pane NI48l from the £5·64 The Story of Beatrix Potter booklet, No. DX15.

The listed booklet panes come from the Sponsored Booklet No. DX13; Nos. W48l, W49l, W59l.

No. W60 exists with the phosphor omitted, but cannot be identified without the use of ultraviolet light (*Price £300 unused*).

From 1972 printings were on fluorescent white paper.

From 1973 most printings had dextrin added to the PVA gum (see notes after 1971 Decimal Machin issue).

First Day Covers

7.7.71	2½p., 3p., 5p., 7½p. (Nos. W13/W14, W19, W24)..........	2·00
23.1.74	3p., 3½p., 5½p., 8p. (Nos. W15/W16, W20, W25)..	1·50
6.11.74	4½p. (No. W18)........	80
14.1.76	6½p., 8½p. (Nos. W22, W26)........	80
20.10.76	10p., 11p. (Nos. W28, W31)........	80
18.1.78	7p., 9p., 10½p. (Nos. W23, W27, W30)........	1·00
23.7.80	12p., 13½p., 15p. (Nos. W30/W34)..........	2·00
8.4.81	11½p., 14p., 22p. (Nos. W35, W39, W46, W54)..	2·00
24.2.82	12½p., 15½p., 19½p., 26p. (Nos. W37, W42, W51, W61)..	2·00
27.4.83	16p., 20½p., 28p. (Nos. W43, W53, W63)......	2·50
23.10.84	13p., 17p., 22p., 31p. (Nos. W38, W44, W55, W65).......	3·00
7.1.86	12p. (No. W36)........	1·00
6.1.87	18p. (No. W47)........	1·00
8.11.88	14p., 19p., 23p., 32p. (Nos. W40, W50, W57, W66).......	3·00
28.11.89	15p., 20p., 24p., 34p. (Nos. W41, W52, W58, W67).......	4·00
4.12.90	17p., 22p., 26p., 37p (Nos. W45, W56, W62, W68)........	4·00
3.12.91	18p., 24p., 28p., 39p. (Nos. W48, W59, W64, W69).......	4·25
25.2.92	Cymru-Wales se-tenant pane 18p. (2nd), 24p. (1st), 33p. (No. W49a)........................	8·50

Presentation Packs

7.7.71	PO Pack No. 28. 2½p., 3p. (2 bands) 5p., 7½p. (Nos. W13/W14, W19, W24)........................	2·00
29.5.74	PO Pack No. 63. 3p. (1 centre band), 3½p. (2 bands) or (1 centre band), 5½p. (2 bands) or (1 centre band), 8p. (Nos. W15, W16 or W17, W20 or W21, W25). The 4½p. (No. W18) was added later........................	2·25
20.10.76	PO Pack No. 86. 6½p., 8½p., 10p. (2 bands), 11p. (Nos. W22, W26, W28, W31)........................	1·40
28.10.81	PO Pack No. 129c. 7p., 9p., 10½p., 12p. (photo), 13½p., 15p. (photo), 11½p., 14p. grey-blue, 18p. deep violet, 22p. blue (Nos. W23, W27, W30, W32/W35, W39, W46, W54)........................	6·00
3.8.83	PO Pack No. 3. 10p. (1 centre band), 12½p., 16p., 20½p., 26p. rosine, 28p. deep violet-blue (Nos. W29, W37, W43, W53, W61)........................	14·00
23.10.84	PO Pack No. 7. 10p. (1 centre band), 13p., 16p., 17p. grey-blue, 22p. yellow-green, 26p. rosine, 28p. deep violet-blue, 31p. (Nos. W29, W38, W43a, W44, W55, W61, W65)........................	12·00
3.3.87	PO Pack No. 11. 12p. (litho), 13p., 17p. grey-blue, 18p. deep olive-grey, 22p. yellow-green, 26p. rosine, 28p. deep violet-blue, 31p. (Nos. W36, W38, W44, W47, W55, W61a, W63a, W65)........................	15·00

Presentation Packs containing stamps of Northern Ireland, Scotland and Wales are listed after those for Northern Ireland.

(Des Jeffery Matthews after plaster cast by Arnold Machin. Litho Questa)

1993 (7 Dec)–**96**. Chalk-surfaced paper. Perf 15×14 (with one elliptical hole in each vertical side).

W70	**W4**	19p. bistre (1 centre band)........................	60	60
W71		19p. bistre (1 band at right) (25.4.95)......	1·90	1·90
W72		20p. bright green (1 centre band) (23.7.96)........................	1·00	1·00
W73		25p. red (2 bands)........................	75	75
W74		26p. red-brown (2 bands) (23.7.96)........	1·20	1·20
W75		30p. deep olive-grey (2 bands)........	80	80
W76		37p. bright mauve (2 bands) (23.7.96)........	1·60	1·60
W77		41p. grey-brown (2 bands)........	1·40	1·40
W78		63p. light emerald (2 bands) (23.7.96)....	3·50	3·50

No. W71 only comes from booklets.

First Day Covers

7.12.93	19p., 25p., 30p., 41p. (Nos. W70, W73, W75, W77)........	3·75
23.7.96	20p., 26p., 37p., 63p., (Nos. W72, W74, W76, W78)........	6·00

For Presentation Packs containing stamps of Northern Ireland, Scotland and Wales see after No. NI85 of Northern Ireland.

W5 Without 'p'

(Gravure Walsall (20p., 26p. (No. W80a), 63p.), Harrison or Walsall (26p. (No. W80), 37p.))

1997 (1 July)–**98**. Chalk-surfaced paper. Perf 14 (No. W79a) or 15×14 (others) (both with one elliptical hole in each vertical side).

W79	**W5**	20p. bright green (1 centre band)............	80	80
W79a		20p. bright green (1 side band at right) (13.10.98)........................	3·25	3·25
W80		26p. chestnut (2 bands)........................	1·40	1·40
		a. Perf 14 (13.10.98)........................	3·25	3·25
W81		37p. bright mauve (2 bands)........................	1·75	1·75
W82		63p. light emerald (2 bands)........................	3·50	3·50

Nos. W79a and W80a were only issued in booklets.

The Harrison printings of Nos. W80/W81 come from booklet pane No. NI81l.

First Day Cover

1.7.97	20p., 26p., 37p., 63p. (Nos. W79, W80/W82).................	6·00

Presentation Pack

1.7.97	PO Pack No. 39. 20p., 26p., 37p., 63p. (Nos. W79, W80/W82)..	12·00

W6 Leek **W7** Welsh Dragon **W8** Daffodil **W9** Prince of Wales' Feathers

(Des David Petersen (Leek), Toby & Gideon Petersen (Welsh Dragon), Ieuan Rees (Daffodil), Rhiannon Evans (Prince of Wales' Feathers). Adapted Tutssels. Gravure De La Rue or Walsall (2nd, 1st), De La Rue (68p.), Walsall (others))

1999 (8 June)–**2002**. One phosphor band (2nd) or two phosphor bands (others). Perf 14 (No. W83a) or 15×14 (others) (both with one elliptical hole in each vertical side).

W83	**W6**	(2nd) Leek (1 centre band)........................	1·10	1·10
W83a		(2nd) Leek (1 band at right) (Perf 14) (18.9.2000)...	2·25	2·25
		al. Booklet pane. No. 2124d and W83a, each×4, with centre label and margins all round......................	9·00	
W84	**W7**	(1st) Welsh dragon...............................	1·75	1·75
W85	**W8**	(E) Daffodil..	2·10	2·10
W86	**W9**	64p. Prince of Wales' Feathers.................	5·50	5·50
W87		65p. Prince of Wales' Feathers (25.4.2000)..	2·50	2·50
W88		68p. Prince of Wales' Feathers (4.7.2002)..	2·25	2·25

PHQ Cards (set of 4) (D13) (Nos. W83, W84/W86)........... 1·25 10·00

Nos. W83, W84 and W85 were initially sold at 19p., 26p. and 30p., the latter representing the basic European airmail rate.

New printings of Nos. W83 and W84, produced by De La Rue instead of Walsall, were issued on 28 May 2003 and 4 March 2005. Stamps from these printings do not differ from those produced by Walsall.

No. W83a comes from the £7 Treasury of Trees booklet (No. DX26).

For combined presentation pack for all four Regions, see under England.

First Day Covers

8.6.99	2nd (centre band), 1st, E, 64p. (Nos. W83, W84/W86) Philatelic Bureau......................................	3·00
	Cardiff...	3·25
25.4.00	65p. (No. W87) Philatelic Bureau..................	3·00
	Cardiff...	3·50
18.9.00	Treasury of Trees se-tenant pane 1st (Millennium), 2nd (Nos. 2124d, W83a) Philatelic Bureau................	5·00
	Llangernyw, Abergele.......................................	5·00
4.7.02	68p. (Nos. W88) Tallents House (Type K) (see Introduction)...	2·50
	Cardiff...	2·50

W10

(Des Jeffery Matthews. Gravure Walsall)

2000 (15 Feb). T **W4** redrawn with 1af/st face value as T **W10**. Two phosphor bands. Perf 14 (with one elliptical hole in each vertical side).

W97	**W10**	(1st) bright orange-red..............................	1·60	1·60

No. W97 was only issued in £7·50 stamp booklet (No. DX24).

2003 (14 Oct)–**17**. As Nos. W83, W84/W85 and W88, and new values, but with white borders. One centre phosphor band (2nd) or two phosphor bands (others). Perf 15×14 (with one elliptical hole in each vertical side).

(a) (Gravure Walsall or De La Rue (42p.) or De La Rue (others)).

W98	**W6**	(2nd) Leek..	1·10	1·10
W99	**W7**	(1st) Welsh Dragon................................	1·60	1·60
W100	**W8**	(E) Daffodil..	2·25	2·25
W101		40p. Daffodil (11.5.04)..........................	1·40	1·40

W102		42p. Daffodil (5.4.05).............................	2·00	2·00
W103		44p. Daffodil (28.3.06)............................	1·60	1·60
W104		48p. Daffodil (27.3.07)............................	1·10	1·10
W105		50p. Daffodil (1.4.08)..............................	1·40	1·40
W106		56p. Daffodil (31.3.09)............................	1·50	1·50
W107		60p. Daffodil (30.3.10)............................	1·70	1·70
W108	**W9**	68p. Prince of Wales' Feathers..................	1·60	1·60
W109		72p. Prince of Wales' Feathers (28.3.06)..	1·60	1·60
W110		78p. Prince of Wales' Feathers (27.3.07)....	2·00	2·00
W111		81p. Prince of Wales' Feathers (1.4.08)....	2·25	2·25
W112		90p. Prince of Wales' Feathers (31.3.09)....	2·40	2·40
W113		97p. Prince of Wales' Feathers (30.3.10)...	2·50	2·50

(b) Litho Enschedé, De La Rue or ISP Cartor (1st) or ISP Cartor (others).

W121	**W6**	(2nd) Leek (1.13).....................................	1·40	1·40
W122	**W7**	(1st) Welsh Dragon (20.9.07)....................	1·60	1·60
W123	**W8**	68p. Daffodil (29.3.11)............................	1·75	1·75
W124		87p Daffodil (25.4.12).............................	2·25	2·25
W125		88p. Daffodil (27.3.13)............................	2·25	2·25
W126		97p. Daffodil (26.3.14)............................	2·50	2·50
W127		£1 Daffodil (24.3.15)..............................	2·50	2·50
W128		£1·05 Daffodil (22.3.16).........................	2·75	2·75
W129	**W9**	£1·10 Prince of Wales' Feathers (29.3.11)...	2·50	2·50
W134		£1·28 Prince of Wales' Feathers (25.4.12)...	2·75	2·75
W135		£1·33 Prince of Wales' Feathers (24.3.15)...	2·75	2·75

PHQ Cards (set of 4) (D26) (Nos. W98/W100, W108).......... 5·00

The Walsall printing of No. W102 was issued on 5 April 2005 and the De La Rue on 24 May 2005.

Stamps as Nos. W110/W111 but printed in lithography were only issued within No. MS2796 (No. W110) or No. MS2886 (No. W111).

No. W122 was first issued in £7·66 stamp booklet, No. DX40 printed by Enschedé, then on 29 September 2008 in £9·72 booklet (No. DX43) printed by De La Rue and on 26 February 2009 in No. MSW147. It was issued in sheets printed by ISP Cartor in January 2013.

A design as No. W122 but self-adhesive was issued on 1 March 2007 in sheets of 20, each stamp accompanied by a se-tenant label showing a Welsh scene (No. LS37). These sheets were printed in lithography by Cartor, perforated 15×14 without the elliptical holes, and sold at £6·55 each. They were also available with personalised photographs on the labels at £14·95 from Royal Mail in Edinburgh.

Stamps as Nos. EN30, NI95, S131 and W122 but self-adhesive were issued on 29 September 2008 in sheets of 20 containing five of each design with se-tenant labels (No. LS49).

First Day Covers

14.10.03	2nd, 1st, E, 68p. (Nos. W98/W100, W108) Tallents House (Type K) (see Introduction).................................	3·25
	Cardiff...	3·25
11.5.04	40p. (No. W101) Tallents House (Type K)..........	1·75
	Cardiff...	1·75
5.4.05	42p. (No. W102) Tallents House (Type K)..........	2·00
	Cardiff...	2·00
28.3.06	44p., 72p. (Nos. W103, W109) Tallents House (Type K)..	3·25
	Cardiff...	3·25
27.3.07	48p., 78p. (Nos. W104, W110) Tallents House (Type K)..	3·50
	Cardiff...	3·50
1.4.08	50p., 81p. (Nos. W105, W111) Tallents House (Type K)..	3·75
	Cardiff...	3·75
31.3.09	56p., 90p. (Nos. W106, W112) Tallents House (Type K)..	4·00
	Cardiff...	4·00
30.3.10	60p., 97p. (Nos. W107, W113) Tallents House (Type K)..	4·00
	Cardiff...	4·00
29.3.11	68p., £1·10 (Nos. W123, W129) Tallents Househ (Type K)..	4·25
	Cardiff...	4·25
25.4.12	87p. £1·28 (Nos. W124, W134) Tallents House (Type K)..	5·00
	Cardiff...	5·00
27.3.13	88p. (No. W125) Tallents House (Type K).......................	2·25
	Cardiff...	2·25
26.3.14	97p. (No. W126) Tallents House (Type K).......................	2·50
	Cardiff...	2·50
24.3.15	£1, £1·33 (Nos. W127, W135) Tallents House (Type K)..	5·25
	Cardiff...	5·25
22.3.16	£1·05 (No. W128) Tallents House (Type K).....................	2·75
	Cardiff...	2·75

W10a

(Des Silk Pearce. Gravure De La Rue)

2006 (1 Mar). Opening of New Welsh Assembly Building, Cardiff. Sheet 123×70 mm. One centre phosphor band (2nd) or two phosphor bands (others). Perf 15×14 (with one elliptical hole in each vertical side).

MSW143 **W10a** Nos. W98, W99×2 and W108×2		4·50	4·50
First Day Cover (Tallents House)			5·00
First Day Cover (Cardiff)			5·00

W10b　　　　　**W10c**　　　　　**W10d**

(Litho De La Rue)

2008 (29 Sept). 50th Anniversary of the Country Definitives. Two phosphor bands. Perf 15×14½ (with one elliptical hole in each vertical side).

W144	**W10b**	(1st) deep lilac	1·60	1·60
		l. Booklet pane. Nos. W144/W146		
		and W122×3	7·00	
W145	**W10c**	(1st) deep claret	1·60	1·60
W146	**W10d**	(1st) green	1·60	1·60

Nos. W144/W146 come from £9·72 booklet, No. DX43.

DATHLU CYMRU · CELEBRATING WALES

W11

(Des Clare Melinsky and Silk Pearce. Litho De La Rue)

2009 (26 Feb). Celebrating Wales. Sheet 123×70 mm. Two phosphor bands. Perf 15×14 (with one elliptical hole in each vertical side (1st) or 14½×14 (81p.)).

MSW147 **W11** (1st) Red Dragon; (1st) No. W122; 81p. St		
David; 81p. National Assembly for Wales, Cardiff	4·25	4·25
First Day Cover (Tallents House)		5·25
First Day Cover (St Davids)		5·25
Presentation Pack (PO Pack No. 424)	5·00	
PHQ Cards (set of 5) (CGB4)	1·50	8·00

No. **MS**W147 was on sale at post offices throughout the UK.

Stamps as the 1st class Red Dragon stamp from No. **MS**W147 but self-adhesive were issued on 1 March 2010 in sheets of 20 with *se-tenant* labels showing Welsh Castles, No. LS71. These sheets were printed in lithography by ISP Cartor and sold for £8·35 each.

Miniature sheet collection containing Nos. **MS**EN50, **MS**NI152, **MS**S153 and **MS**W147 in a folder was available from 6 March 2009, sold at £31·95.

The five PHQ cards show the four individual stamps and the complete miniature sheet.

W12 Red Dragon

(Des Peter Crowther (illustrations) and Silk Pearce. Litho ISP Cartor or Enschedé)

2013 (9 May). Wales Flag. Two phosphor bands. Perf 14½×14 (with one elliptical hole in each vertical side).

W148	**W12**	(1st) Red Dragon	4·00	4·00

No. W148 was issued in £11·11 Football Heroes booklet, No. DY7 (see booklet pane No. U3070l), £13·97 Classic Locomotives booklet, No. DY9 (see booklet pane No. U3071m) and £16·49 Centenary of the First World War (3rd issue), No. DY18 (booklet pane No. 3717a).

W13 Leek　　**W14** Dragon　　**W15** Daffodil　　**W16** Prince of Wales' Feathers

(Des David Petersen (Leek), Toby & Gideon Petersen (Welsh Dragon), Ieuan Rees (Daffodil), Rhiannon Evans (Prince of Wales' Feathers). Adapted Tutssels. Litho Cartor)

2017 (21 Mar)–**20**. As previous set but with value indicated in revised typeface. One centre band (2nd) or two phosphor bands. Perf 15×14 (with one elliptical hole in each vertical side).

W149	**W13**	(2nd) Leek (20.3.18)	1·00	75
W150	**W14**	(1st) Dragon (20.3.18)	1·25	75
W151	**W15**	£1·17 Daffodil (21.3.17)	2·75	2·75
W152		£1·25 Daffodil (20.3.18)	2·75	2·75
W153		£1·35 Daffodil (19.3.19)	2·75	2·75
W156	**W16**	£1·40 Prince of Wales Feathers (21.3.17)	3·00	3·00
W157	**W15**	£1·42 Daffodil (17.3.20)	2·50	2·50
W158	**W16**	£1·45 Prince of Wales Feathers (20.3.18)	3·25	3·25
W159		£1·55 Prince of Wales' Feathers (19.3.19)	3·25	3·25
W160		£1·63 Prince of Wales Feathers (17.3.20)	2·75	2·75
W161	**W15**	£1·70 Daffodil (23.12.20)	2·40	2·40

W17 Leek　　　　　　**W18** Dragon

W19 Daffodil

(Des David Petersen (Leek), Toby & Gideon Petersen (Welsh Dragon), Leuan Rees (Daffodil). Adapted by Tutssels. Litho ISP Cartor)

2022 (11 Aug). As Types **W17**, **W18** and **W19** with barcoded strip at right. Self-adhesive. One centre phosphor band (2nd) or two phosphor bands (others). Die-cut perf 15×14½ (with one elliptical hole in each vertical side).

W162	**W17**	(2nd) Leek	1·10	1·10
W163	**W18**	(1st) Dragon	1·60	1·60
W164	**W19**	£1·85 Daffodil	2·50	2·50

The stamps produced for Royal Mail First Day Covers come from an entirely different set of cylinders. The 'AF' is in a sans serif font compared to those sold in Post Offices or supplied mint by the Philatelic Bureau which are in a serifed font.

First Day Covers

21.3.17	£1·17, £1·40 (Nos. W151, W156) Tallents House (Type K)	6·00
	Cardiff	6·00
20.3.18	2nd, 1st, £1·25, £1·45. (Nos. W149/W150, W152, W158) Tallents House (Type K)	9·00
	Cardiff	9·00
19.3.19	£1·35, £1·55. (Nos. W153, W159) Tallents House (Type K)	7·00
	Cardiff	7·00
17.3.20	£1·42, £1·63 (Nos. W157, W160) Tallents House (Type K)	7·00
	Cardiff	7·00
23.12.20	£1·70 (W61) Tallents House (Type K)	3·75
	Cardiff	3·75
11.8.22	2nd, 1st, £1·85 (Nos. W162/W164) Tallents House (Type K)	7·50
	Cardiff	7·50

V. Isle of Man

Although specifically issued for use in the Isle of Man, these issues were also valid for use throughout Great Britain.

1 **2**

(Des John Hobson Nicholson. Portrait by Dorothy Wilding Ltd. Photo Harrison)

1958 (18 Aug)–**68**. W **179**. Perf 15×14.
1	**1**	2½d. carmine-red (8.6.64)	70	70
2	**2**	3d. deep lilac (18.8.58)	50	50
		a. Chalk-surfaced paper (17.5.63)	6·50	6·50
		p. One centre phosphor band (27.6.68)	20	20
3		4d. ultramarine (7.2.66)	1·00	1·00
		p. Two phosphor bands (5.7.67)	30	30
1/3		*Set of 3 (cheapest)*	1·00	1·00

No. 2a was released in London sometime after 17 May 1963, this being the date of issue in Douglas.

For No. 2 in Presentation Pack, see Regional issues below Wales No. W6.

First Day Covers

18.8.58	No. 2 (3d.)	32·00
8.6.64	No. 1 (2½d.)	45·00
7.2.66	No. 3 (4d.)	15·00

Frame flaw (Cyl. 1 no dot, R. 20/1) **3**

1968–69. No wmk, Chalk-surfaced paper. One centre phosphor band (Nos. 5/6) or two phosphor bands (others). Perf 15×14.
4	**2**	4d. blue (24.6.68)	25	25
5		4d. olive-sepia (4.9.68)	30	30
		y. Phosphor omitted	25·00	
6		4d. bright vermilion (26.2.69)	45	45
7		5d. royal blue (4.9.68)	45	45
		a. Frame flaw	25·00	
		y. Phosphor omitted	£175	
4/7		*Set of 4*	1·25	1·25

First Day Cover

4.9.68	Nos. 5 and 7 (4d., 5d.)	4·00

(Des Jeffrey Matthews. Portrait after plaster cast by Arnold Machin. Photo Harrison)

1971 (7 July). Decimal Currency. Chalk-surfaced paper. One centre phosphor band (2½p.) or two phosphor bands (others). Perf 15×14.
8	**3**	2½p. bright magenta	30	30
		y. Phosphor omitted	£1500	
9		3p. ultramarine	30	30
10		5p. reddish violet	70	70
		y. Phosphor omitted	£275	
11		7½p. chestnut	80	80
8/11		*Set of 4*	1·90	1·90
		Presentation Pack (PO Pack No. 30)	2·50	

All values were originally issued on ordinary cream paper, but the 2½p. and 3p. later appeared on white fluorescent paper.

Nos. 8/11 and current stamps of Great Britain were withdrawn from sale on the island from 5 July 1973 when the independent postal administration was established bt remained valid for use there for a time. They also remained on sale at the Philatelic Sales counters in the United Kingdom until 4 July 1974.

First Day Cover

7.7.71	Nos. 8/11 (2½p., 3p., 5p., 7½p.)	3·50

VI. Channel Islands

GENERAL ISSUE

C1 Gathering Vraic (seaweed) **C2** Islanders gathering Vraic

C2a Broken Wheel (R.20/5)

(Des J. R. R. Stobie (1d.) or from drawing by Edmund Blampied (2½d.). Photo Harrison and Sons)

1948 (10 May). Third Anniversary of Liberation. W **127** of Great Britain. Perf 15×14.
C1	**C1**	1d. scarlet	25	55
C2	**C2**	2½d. ultramarine	25	60
		a. Broken wheel	75·00	

First Day Cover

10.05.48	Nos. C1/C2 (1d., 2½d.)	35·00

VII. Guernsey

GERMAN OCCUPATION ISSUES, 1940–1945

BISECTS. On 24 December 1940 authority was given, by Post Office notice, that prepayment of penny postage could be effected by using half a British 2d. stamp, diagonally bisected. Such stamps were first used on 27 December 1940.

The 2d. stamps generally available were those of the Postal Centenary issue, 1940 (No. SG 482) and the first colour of the King George VI issue (No. SG 465). These are listed under Nos. 482a and 465b. A number of the 2d. King George V, 1912–1922, and of the King George V photogravure stamp (No. SG 442) which were in the hands of philatelists, were also bisected and used.

1 Arms of Guernsey

1a Loops (*half actual size*)

(Des E. W. Vaudin. Typo Guernsey Press Co Ltd)

1941–44. Rouletted.
		(a) White paper. No wmk.		
1	**1**	½d. light green (7.4.41)	6·00	3·50
		a. Emerald-green (6.41)	6·00	3·50
		b. Bluish green (11.41)	35·00	15·00
		c. Bright green (2.42)	25·00	12·00
		d. Dull green (9.42)	5·00	3·50

	e. Olive-green (2.43).....................................	45·00	25·00	
	f. Pale yellowish green (7.43 and later)			
	(shades)..	5·00	3·50	
	g. Imperf (pair)...	£250		
	h. Imperf between (horizontal pair)........	£800		
	i. Imperf between (vertical pair).............	£950		
2	1d. scarlet (18.2.41)....................................	3·25	2·00	
	a. Pale vermilion (7.43) (etc)......................	5·00	2·00	
	b. Carmine (1943)......................................	3·50	2·00	
	c. Imperf (pair)...	£200	90·00	
	d. Imperf between (horizontal pair)........	£800		
	da. Imperf vert (centre stamp of			
	horizontal strip of 3).....................			
	e. Imperf between (vertical pair).............	£950		
	f. Printed double (scarlet shade).............	£150		
3	2½d. ultramarine (12.4.44)........................	18·00	15·00	
	a. Pale ultramarine (7.44)...........................	15·00	10·00	
	b. Imperf (pair)...	£550		
	c. Imperf between (horizontal pair)........	£1250		
1/3 Set of 3...		22·00	14·00	

*(b) Bluish French banknote paper. W **1a** (sideways).*

4	**1**	½d. bright green (11.3.42)...............	32·00	25·00
5		1d. scarlet (9.4.42)...........................	18·00	25·00

First Day Covers

18.2.1941	No. 2 (1d.)..		15·00
7.4.1941	No. 1 (½d.).......................................		10·00
12.4.1941	No. 3 (2½d.).....................................		20·00
11.3.1942	No. 4 (½d.).......................................		£325
9.4.1942	No. 5 (1d.)..		£125

REGIONAL ISSUES

2	**3**	Stem flaw (Cyl. 1 no dot, R. 12/8).

(Des Eric A Piprell. Portrait by Dorothy Wilding Ltd. Photo Harrison & Sons)

1958 (18 Aug)–**67**. W **179** of Great Britain. Perf 15×14.

6	**2**	2½d. rose-red (8.6.64)...............................	40	40
7	**3**	3d. deep lilac..	30	30
		p. One centre phosphor band		
		(24.5.67)...	30	30
8		4d. ultramarine (7.2.66)...........................	40	40
		a. Stem Flaw..	25·00	
		p. Two phosphor bands (24.10.67).....	20	20
		pa. Stem flaw...	25·00	
6/8p Set of 3...			1·00	1·00

For No. 7 in Presentation Pack, see Regional Issues below Wales No. W6.

First Day Covers

18.8.1958	No. 7 (3d.)..		20·00
8.6.1964	No. 6 (2½d.).....................................		30·00
7.2.1966	No. 8 (4d.)..		8·00

1968–69. No wmk. Chalk-surfaced paper. PVA gum*. One centre phosphor band (Nos. 10/11) or two phosphor bands (others). Perf 15×14.

9	**3**	4d. pale ultramarine (16.4.68)...............	20	20
		y. Phosphor omitted............................	50·00	
		a. Stem Flaw..	25·00	
		y. Phosphor omitted............................	50·00	
10		4d. olive-sepia (4.9.68).........................	20	20
		y. Phosphor omitted............................	50·00	
		a. Stem Flaw..	25·00	
		y. Phosphor omitted............................	50·00	
11		4d. bright vermilion (26.2.69)...............	20	20
12		5d. royal blue (4.9.68)............................	30	30
9/12 Set of 4...			80	80

* PVA Gum. See note after No. 722 of Great Britain. No. 9 was not issued in Guernsey until 22 April.

First Day Cover

4.9.1971	4d. (No. 10), 5d. (No. 12)	3·00

VIII. Jersey

GERMAN OCCUPATION ISSUES, 1940–1949

5 Arms of Jersey

(Des Major Norman Victor Lacey Rybot. Typo *Jersey Evening Post*)

1941–43. Stamps issued during the German Occupation White paper. No wmk. Perf 11 (line).

1	**5**	½d. bright green (29.1.42).....................	8·00	6·00
		a. Imperf between (vertical pair).........	£900	
		b. Imperf between (horizontal pair)....	£800	
		c. Imperf (pair).......................................	£300	
		d. On greyish paper (1.43)......................	12·00	12·00
2		1d. scarlet (1.4.41)..................................	8·00	5·00
		a. Imperf between (vertical pair).........	£900	
		b. Imperf between (horizontal pair)....	£800	
		c. Imperf (pair).......................................	£325	
		d. On chalk-surfaced paper (9.41)........	55·00	48·00
		e. On greyish paper (1.43)........................	14·00	14·00

First Day Covers

1.4.41	1d. (No. S2)..		8·00
29.1.42	½d. (No. S1).......................................		7·50

6 Old Jersey Farm	**7** Portelet Bay

8 Corbière Lighthouse	**9** Elizabeth Castle

10 Mont Orgueil Castle	**11** Gathering Vraic (seaweed)

(Des Edmund Blampied. Eng H. Cortot. Typo French Govt Ptg Works, Paris)

1943–44. No wmk. Perf 13½.

3	**6**	½d. Old Jersey Farm (1.6.43)..................	12·00	12·00
		a. Rough, grey paper (6.10.43)...............	15·00	14·00
4	**7**	1d. Portelet Bay (1.6.43)........................	3·00	50
		a. On newsprint (28.2.44)........................	3·50	75
5	**8**	1½d. Corbière Lighthouse (8.6.43)..........	8·00	5·75
6	**9**	2d. Elizabeth Castle (8.6.43).................	7·50	2·00
7	**10**	2½d. Mont Orgueil Castle (29.6.43)........	3·00	1·00
		a. On newsprint (25.2.44)........................	1·00	1·75
		ba. Thin paper* (design shows		
		through on reverse)........................	£225	
8	**11**	3d. Gathering Vraic (seaweed)		
		(29.6.43)...	3·00	2·75
3/8 Set of 6..			30·00	21·00
Set of 6 Gutter Pairs...			80·00	

* On No. 7ba the design shows clearly through the back of the stamp.

First Day Covers

01.06.43	Nos. 3/4 (½d., 1d.)............................		36·00
08.06.43	Nos. 5/6 (1½d., 2d.)..........................		36·00
20.06.43	Nos. 7/8 (2½d., 3d.)..........................		36·00

12   13

Halberd flaw (Cyl. 1 no dot,   Leaf flaw (cyl. 1 no dot,
R. 20/23)   R. 3/6)

(Des. Edmund Blampied (T **12**), W. Gardner (T **13**). Portrait by Dorothy
Wilding Ltd. Photo Harrison & Sons)

1958 (18 Aug)–**67**. W **179** of Great Britain. Perf 15×14.

9	**12**	2½d. carmine-red (8.6.64)............................	45	45
		a. Imperf three sides (pair)...................	£3250	
10	**13**	3d. deep lilac (18.8.58)............................	30	30
		a. Halberd Flaw......................................	25·00	
		p. One centre phosphor band		
		(9.6.67)..	20	20
11		4d. ultramarine (7.2.66)...........................	25	25
		a. Leaf Flaw...	25·00	
		p. Two phosphor bands (5.9.67).........	25	25
9/11 *Set of* 3...			80	80

First Day Covers

18.5.58	3d. (No. S10)..	20·00
8.6.64	2½d. (No. S9)...	30·00
7.2.66	4d. (No. S11)..	10·00

1968–**69**. No wmk. Chalk-surfaced paper. PVA gum*. One centre phosphor
band (4d. values) or two phosphor bands (5d.). Perf 15×14.

12	**13**	4d. olive-sepia (4.9.68)............................	20	20
		y. Phosphor omitted............................	£1100	
13		4d. bright vermilion (26.2.69)................	20	20
14		5d. royal blue (4.9.68).............................	20	20
12/14 *Set of* 3..			50	50

*   PVA Gum. See note after No. 722 of Great Britain.

First Day Cover

4.9.68	4d., 5d. (Nos. 12, 14)...	3·00

POSTAL FISCAL STAMPS

PRICES. Prices in the used column are for stamps with genuine postal cancellations dated from the time when they were authorised for use as postage stamps. Beware of stamps with fiscal cancellations removed and fraudulent postmarks applied.

VALIDITY. The 1d. surface-printed stamps were authorised for postal use from 1 June 1881 and at the same time the 1d. postage issue, No. 166, was declared valid for fiscal purposes. The 3d. and 6d. values together with the embossed issues were declared valid for postal purposes by another Act effective from 1 January 1883.

SURFACE-PRINTED ISSUES

(Typo Thomas De La Rue & Co)

F1 Rectangular Buckle   **F2**

F3 Octagonal Buckle   **F4**

F5 Double-lined Anchor   **F6** Single-lined Anchor

1853–57. Perf 15½×15.

*(a) Wmk **F5** (inverted) (1853–1855).*

			Unused	Used	Used on cover
F1	**F1**	1d. light blue (10.10.53)............	50·00	65·00	£225
		Wi. Watermark upright............	£180	—	
		Wj. Watermark reversed*........	£180	—	
F2	**F2**	1d. ochre (10.53)......................	£130	£160	£600
		a. Tête-bêche (in block of four)...............................	—	—	
		Wi. Watermark upright............	—	—	
F3	**F3**	1d. pale turquoise-blue (12.53)................................	45·00	60·00	£350
F4		1d. light blue/*blue* (12.53)........	90·00	95·00	£550
		Wi. Watermark upright............	£160	£225	
F5	**F4**	1d. reddish lilac/*blue glazed paper* (25.3.55)....................	£130	£160	£450
		Wi. Watermark upright............	£200	£300	

* Watermark reversed: with the stamp upright and viewed from the front, the cable finishes to the right of the base of the anchor shaft. Only one example is known of No. F2a outside The Postal Museum and the Royal Philatelic Collection.

*(b) Wmk **F6** (1856–1857).*

F6	**F4**	1d. reddish lilac (*shades*).........	12·00	9·50	£180
		Wi. Watermark inverted..........	£160	—	
		Wj. Watermark reversed..........	£180	—	
		s. Optd 'SPECIMEN' (2)...........	£170		
F7		1d. reddish lilac/*bluish* (*shades*) (1857)..................	12·00	9·50	£180
		Wj. Watermark reversed..........	£180	—	

INLAND REVENUE

(**F7**)

1860 (3 Apr). No. F7 optd with T **F7**, in red

			Unused	Used	Used on cover
F8	**F4**	1d. dull reddish lilac/*blue*........	£950	£725	£1500
		Wj. Wmk reversed...................	—	—	

BLUE PAPER. In the following issues we no longer distinguish between bluish and white paper. There is a range of papers from white or greyish to bluish.

F8   **F9**

F10

1860–67. Bluish to white Paper. Perf 15½×15.

*(a) Wmk **F6** (1860).*

			Unused	Used	Used on cover
F9	**F8**	1d. reddish lilac (5.60).............	14·00	18·00	£180
		Wi. Watermark inverted..........	£130	—	
		s. Optd 'SPECIMEN' (2)..........	£180		
F10	**F9**	3d. reddish lilac (6.60).............	£550	£340	£550
		s. Optd 'SPECIMEN' (2)..........	£240		
F11	**F10**	6d. reddish lilac (10.60)...........	£225	£225	£450
		Wi. Watermark inverted..........	£275	£225	
		Wj. Watermark reversed..........	£275	£225	
		s. Optd 'SPECIMEN' (2)..........	£225		

*(b) W **40**. (Anchor 16 mm high) (1864).*

F12	**F8**	1d. pale reddish lilac (11.64).....	12·00	14·00	£180
		Wi. Watermark inverted..........	—	—	
F13	**F9**	3d. pale reddish lilac...............	£275	£200	£550
		s. Optd 'SPECIMEN' (9)..........	£225		
F14	**F10**	6d. pale reddish lilac...............	£250	£200	£550
		Wi. Watermark inverted..........	£350	—	

*(c) W **40**. (Anchor 18 mm high) (1867).*

F15	**F8**	1d. reddish lilac......................	25·00	27·00	£275
F16	**F9**	3d. reddish lilac......................	£120	£120	£450
		s. Optd 'SPECIMEN' (9, 10).....	£190		
F17	**F10**	6d. reddish lilac......................	£110	95·00	£300
		s. Optd 'SPECIMEN' (9, 10).....	£190		

For stamps perf 14, see Nos. F24/F27.

F11   **F12**

Nos. F19/F21 show 'O' of 'ONE' circular. No. F22 (Die 4) shows a horizontal oval

Four Dies of T **F12**

Round 'O' (Dies 1 to 3)

Four lines of shading in left-hand ribbon
(Die 1)

Ovel 'O' (Die 4)

Two lines of shading in left-hand ribbons
(Die 2)

Small corner ornaments (Dies 1 and 2)

Three lines of shading in left-hand ribbon
(Die 3)

Medium corner ornaments (Die 3)

Heavy shading in both ribbons (Die 4)

Large corner ornaments (Die 4)

Band of crown shaded (Dies 1 and 2)

Band of crown unshaded (Die 3)

F13

F14

F15

Band of crown unshaded at front only (Die 4)

Die 1:	Round 'O' in 'ONE'. Small corner ornaments. Four lines of shading in left-hand ribbon. Band of crown shaded
Die 2:	Round 'O' in 'ONE'. Small corner ornaments. Two lines of shading in left-hand ribbon. Band of crown shaded
Die 3:	Round 'O' in 'ONE'. Medium corner ornaments. Three lines of shading in left-hand ribbon. Band of crown unshaded
Die 4:	Oval 'O' in 'ONE'. Large corner ornaments. Heavy shading in both ribbons. Band of crown unshaded at front only

1867–81. White to bluish paper. Perf 14.

(a) W 47 (Small Anchor).

			Unsed	Used	Used on cover
F18	**F11**	1d. purple (1.9.67).....................	22·00	24·00	£140
		Wi. Watermark inverted..........	£130	—	
F19	**F12**	1d. purple (Die I) (6.68)..........	7·50	9·00	£140
		s. Optd 'SPECIMEN' (6, 9, 10).	60·00		
		Wi. Watermark inverted..........	90·00	—	
F20		1d. purple (Die 2) (6.76)..........	27·00	22·00	£300
		s. Optd 'SPECIMEN' (9)...........	£110		
F21		1d. purple (Die 3) (3.77)..........	14·00	18·00	£220
		s. Optd 'SPECIMEN' (9)...........	90·00		
F22		1d. purple (Die 4) (7.78)..........	8·50	10·00	£120

(b) W 48 (Orb).

| F23 | **F12** | 1d. purple (Die 4) (1.81).......... | 8·50 | 5·00 | £110 |
| | | Wi. Watermark inverted.......... | £130 | — | |

1881. White to bluish paper. Perf 14.

(a) W 40 (Anchor 18 mm high) (January).

			Unused	Used	Used on cover
F24	**F9**	3d. reddish lilac......................	£850	£525	£1000
F25	**F10**	6d. reddish lilac......................	£400	£225	£450

(b) W 40 (Anchor 20 mm high) (May).

F26	**F9**	3d. reddish lilac......................	£625	£425	£700
		s. Optd 'SPECIMEN' (9)..........	£350		
F27	**F10**	6d. reddish lilac......................	£350	£200	£450
		s. Optd 'SPECIMEN' (9)..........	£300		

ISSUES EMBOSSED IN COLOUR

(Made at Somerset House)

The embossed stamps were struck from dies not appropriated to any special purpose on paper which had the words 'INLAND REVENUE' previously printed, and thus became available for payment of any duties for which no special stamps had been provided.

The die letters are included in the embossed designs and holes were drilled for the insertion of plugs showing figures indicating dates of striking.

1860 (3 Apr)–**71**. Types **F13/F14** and similar types embossed on bluish paper. No wmk. Imperf.

F28	2d. pink (Die A) (1.1.71)................	£775
	s. Optd 'SPECIMEN' (2, 9)............	£200
F29	3d. pink (Die C)...........................	£200
	a. Tête-bêche (vertical pair).........	£1700
F30	3d. pink (Die D)..........................	£775
F31	6d. pink (Die T)..........................	£200
F32	6d. pink (Die U)..........................	£400
	a. Tête-bêche (vertical pair).........	
F33	9d. pink (Die C) (1.1.71)...............	£1000
	s. Optd 'SPECIMEN' (2, 9)............	£200
F34	1s. pink (Die E) (28.6.61).............	£775
	a. Tête-bêche (vertical pair).........	
F35	1s. pink (Die F) (28.6.61).............	£300
	a. Tête-bêche (vertical pair).........	£1200
	s. Optd 'SPECIMEN' (2, 9)............	£200
F36	2s. pink (Die K) (6.8.61)...............	£775
F37	2s.6d. pink (Die N) (28.6.61)........	£400
F38	2s.6d. pink (Die O) (28.6.61)........	£400
	s. Optd 'SPECIMEN' (2, 9)............	£200

1871 (Aug). As last but perf 12½.

F39	2d. pink (Die A).........................	£500
	a. Tête-bêche (vertical pair).........	
	s. Optd 'SPECIMEN' (9)...............	£120
F42	9d. pink (Die C).........................	£1200
	s. Optd 'SPECIMEN' (9)...............	£200
F43	1s. pink (Die E).........................	£775
F44	1s. pink (Die F).........................	£700
	s. Optd 'SPECIMEN' (9)...............	£200
F45	2s.6d. pink (Die O).....................	£400
	s. Optd 'SPECIMEN' (9)...............	£200

1874 (Nov). T **F15** embossed on white paper. Underprint in green. W **47** (Small Anchor). P 12½.

F48	1s. vermilion (Die F)...................	£775

1875 (Nov)–**80**. Types **F13/F15** and similar but colour changed and underprint as T **F15**. On white or bluish paper.

F50	2d. vermilion (Die A) (1880).........	£600
	s. Optd 'SPECIMEN' (9)...............	£200
F51	9d. vermilion (Die C) (1876).........	£775
	s. Optd 'SPECIMEN' (9, 10).........	£200
F52	1s. vermilion (Die E)...................	£500
	s. Optd 'SPECIMEN' (9, 10).........	£200
F53	1s. vermilion (Die F)...................	£1200
F54	2s.6d. vermilion (Die O) (1878).....	£500
	s. Optd 'SPECIMEN' (9)...............	£200

1882 (Oct). As last but W **48** (Orbs).

F55	2d. vermilion (Die A)...................	†
	s. Optd 'SPECIMEN' (9)...............	£225
F56	9d. vermilion (Die C)...................	†
	s. Optd 'SPECIMEN' (9)...............	£225
F57	1s. vermilion (Die E)...................	†
	s. Optd 'SPECIMEN' (9)...............	£225
F58	2s.6d. vermilion (Die O)...............	£1000 £775
	s. Optd 'SPECIMEN' (9)...............	£225

Although specimen overprints of Nos. F55/F57 are known there is some doubt if these values were issued.

The sale of Inland Revenue stamps up to the 2s. value ceased from 30 December 1882 and stocks were called in and destroyed. The 2s.6d. value remained on sale until 2 July 1883 when it was replaced by the 2s.6d. 'Postage & Revenue' stamp. Inland Revenue stamps still in the hands of the public continued to be accepted for revenue and postal purposes.

POSTAGE DUE STAMPS

PERFORATIONS. All postage due stamps to No. D101 are perf 14×15.

WATERMARK. The watermark always appears sideways and this is the 'normal' listed in this Catalogue for Nos. D1/D68. Varieties occur as follows. The point of identification is which way the top of the crown points, but (where they occur) the disposition of the letters needs to be noted also. The meaning of the terms is given below: (1) as described and illustrated in the Catalogue, i.e. as read through the front of the stamp, and (2) what is seen during watermark detection when the stamp is face down and the back is under examination.

Watermark	Crown pointing	Letters reading
	(1) As described	
Sideways	left	upwards
Sideways-inverted	right	downwards
Sideways and reversed	left	downwards, back to front
Sideways-inverted and reversed	right	upwards, back to front
	(2) As detected (stamp face down)	
Sideways	right	upwards, back to front
Sideways-inverted	left	downwards, back to front
Sideways and reversed	right	downwards
Sideways-inverted and reversed	left	upward

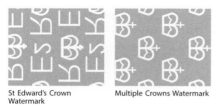

St Edward's Crown Watermark   Multiple Crowns Watermark

Sideways watermarks *as viewed from the back of the stamp*

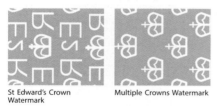

St Edward's Crown Watermark   Multiple Crowns Watermark

Sideways inverted watermarks *as viewed from the back of the stamp*

D1   **D2**

(Des G. Eve. Typo Somerset House (early trial printings of ½d., 1d., 2d. and 5d.; all printings of 1s.) or Harrison (later printings of all values except 1s.)).

1914 (20 Apr)–**22**. W **100** (Simple Cypher) sideways.

			Unmtd mint	Mtd mint	Used
D1	**D1**	½d. emerald	1·50	50	25
		Wi. Watermark sideways-inverted	5·00	2·00	2·00
		Wj. Watermark sideways and reversed	30·00	18·00	20·00
		Wk. Watermark sideways-inverted and reversed			20·00
		s. Overprinted '*SPECIMEN*' (23)		45·00	
D2		1d. carmine	1·50	50	25
		a. *Pale carmine*	1·50	75	50
		Wi. Watermark sideways-inverted	5·00	2·00	2·00
		Wj. Watermark sideways and reversed			20·00
		Wk. Watermark sideways-inverted and reversed	30·00	18·00	20·00
		s. Overprinted '*SPECIMEN*' (23)		45·00	

			Unmtd mint	Mtd mint	Used
D3		1½d. chestnut (1922)	£150	48·00	20·00
		Wi. Watermark sideways-inverted	£190	70·00	24·00
		s. Overprinted '*SPECIMEN*' (23)		75·00	
D4		2d. agate	1·50	50	25
		Wi. Watermark sideways-inverted	7·00	3·75	3·75
		Wk. Watermark sideways-inverted and reversed	28·00	18·00	18·00
		s. Overprinted '*SPECIMEN*' (23, 26)		40·00	
D5		3d. violet (1918)	28·00	9·00	75
		a. *Bluish violet*	28·00	10·00	2·75
		Wi. Watermark sideways-inverted	80·00	40·00	40·00
		Wk. Watermark sideways-inverted and reversed			
		s. Overprinted '*SPECIMEN*' (23, 26)		45·00	
D6		4d. dull grey-green (12.20)	£300	£150	50·00
		Wi. Watermark sideways-inverted	£150	40·00	5·00
		s. Overprinted '*SPECIMEN*' (23)		45·00	
D7		5d. brownish cinnamon	23·00	7·00	3·50
		Wi. Watermark sideways-inverted	45·00	20·00	20·00
		s. Overprinted '*SPECIMEN*' (23, 30)		45·00	
D8		1s. bright blue (1915)	£150	40·00	5·00
		a. *Deep bright blue*	£150	40·00	5·00
		Wi. Watermark sideways-inverted	£150	40·00	40·00
		Wk. Watermark sideways-inverted and reversed			
		s. Overprinted '*SPECIMEN*' (23, 26)		45·00	
D1/D8 *Set of 8*			£450	£130	32·00

Stamps from the above issue are known bisected and used for half their face value at the following sorting offices:

1d. Barrhead (1922), Bristol (1918), Cowes (1923), Elgin (1921), Kidlington (1922, 1923), Kilburn, London NW (1923), Malvern (1915), Palmers Green, London N (1922), Plaistow, London E (1916), River, Dover (1922), Rock Ferry, Birkenhead (1915, 1918), St Ouens, Jersey (1924), Salford, Manchester (1914), South Tottenham, London N (1921), Warminster (1922), Wavertree, Liverpool (1921), Whitchurch (1922), Winton, Bournemouth (1921), Wood Green, London N (1921)

2d. Anerley, London SE (1921), Bethnal Green, London E (1918), Christchurch (1921), Didcot (1919), Ealing, London W (1921), Hythe, Southampton (1923), Kirkwall (1922), Ledbury (1922), Malvern (1921, 1923), Sheffield (1921), Shipley (1921), Streatham, London SW (1921), Victoria Docks and North Woolwich (1921), West Kensington, London W (1921, 1922)

3d. Malvern (trisected and used for 1d.) (1921), Warminster (1922)

(Typo Waterlow)

1924. As 1914–1922, but on thick chalk-surfaced paper.

			Unmtd mint	Mtd mint	Used
D9	**D1**	1d. carmine	15·00	6·00	6·00
		Wi. Watermark sideways-inverted			

(Typo Waterlow and (from 1934) Harrison)

1924–31. W **111** (Block Cypher) sideways.

			Unmtd mint	Mtd mint	Used
D10	**D1**	½d. emerald (6.25)	2·50	1·25	75
		Wi. Watermark sideways-inverted	10·00	5·00	2·50
		s. Overprinted '*SPECIMEN*' (23, 26, 30)		45·00	
D11		1d. carmine (4.25)	2·50	60	25
		Wi. Watermark sideways-inverted	—	—	30·00
		s. Overprinted '*SPECIMEN*' (23, 26, 30)		55·00	
D12		1½d. chestnut (10.24)	£160	48·00	22·00
		Wi. Watermark sideways-inverted	—	—	75·00
		s. Overprinted '*SPECIMEN*' (23)		55·00	
D13		2d. agate (7.24)	9·00	1·00	25
		Wi. Watermark sideways-inverted	—	—	30·00
		s. Overprinted '*SPECIMEN*' (23, 30)		45·00	
D14		3d. dull violet (10.24)	15·00	1·50	25
		a. Printed on gummed side	£150	£125	†
		Wi. Wmk sideways-inverted	—	—	40·00

		Unmtd mint	Mtd mint	Used

	s. Overprinted 'SPECIMEN' (23)................		55·00	
	c. Experimental paper W 111a............	£175	95·00	95·00
D15	4d. dull grey-green (10.24)........	70·00	15·00	4·25
	Wi. Watermark sideways-inverted........	£100	40·00	40·00
	s. Overprinted 'SPECIMEN' (23, 26)........	£175		
D16	5d. brownish cinnamon (1.31)........	£175	65·00	45·00
D17	1s. deep blue (9.24)........	60·00	8·50	50
	Wi. Watermark sideways-inverted........			
	s. Overprinted 'SPECIMEN' (23)........			
D18	**D2** 2s.6d. purple/*yellow* (5.24)........	£275	85·00	1·75
	Wi. Watermark sideways-inverted........	£750	—	90·00
	s. Overprinted 'SPECIMEN' (23, 30)........		55·00	
D10/D18	*Set of 9*........	£725	£200	70·00

Stamps from the above issue are known bisected and used for half their face value at the following sorting offices:
1d. Ashton under Lyne (1932), Hastings (1930), Penryn, Cornwall (1928), Shenfield (1926), Wimbledon, London SW (1925)
2d. Perranwell Station (1932)

1936–37. W **125** (E 8 R) sideways.

D19	**D1** ½d. emerald (6.37)........		15·00	11·00
D20	1d. carmine (5.37)........		2·00	1·75
D21	2d. agate (5.37)........		15·00	12·00
D22	3d. dull violet (3.37)........		2·00	2·00
	s. Overprinted 'SPECIMEN' (30)........			—
	Wi. Watermark sideways-inverted........			
D23	4d. dull grey-green (12.36)........		65·00	35·00
	s. Overprinted 'SPECIMEN' (30)........			
D24	5d. brownish cinnamon (11.36)........		90·00	30·00
	a. Yellow-brown (1937)........		40·00	28·00
	s. Overprinted 'SPECIMEN' (30)........			
D25	1s. deep blue (12.36)........		25·00	8·50
	s. Overprinted 'SPECIMEN' (30)........			
D26	**D2** 2s.6d. purple/*yellow* (5.37)........		£325	12·00
D19/D26	*Set of 8 (cheapest)*........		£450	£100

The 1d. of the above issue is known bisected and used for half its face value at the following sorting office:
1d. Solihull (1937)

1937–38. W **127** (G VI R) sideways.

D27	**D1** ½d. emerald (5.38)........		13·00	3·75
	s. Overprinted 'SPECIMEN' (9, 30)........			
D28	1d. carmine (5.38)........		3·00	50
	Wi. Watermark sideways-inverted........		£250	—
	s. Overprinted 'SPECIMEN' (9, 30)........			
D29	2d. agate (5.38)........		2·75	30
	Wi. Watermark sideways-inverted........		£150	—
	s. Overprinted 'SPECIMEN' (9, 30)........			
D30	3d. violet (12.37)........		11·00	30
	Wi. Watermark sideways-inverted........		£150	—
	s. Overprinted 'SPECIMEN' (9, 30)........			
D31	4d. dull grey-green (9.37)........		£110	10·00
	Wi. Watermark sideways-inverted........		£300	—
	s. Overprinted 'SPECIMEN' (9, 30)........			
D32	5d. yellow-brown (11.38)........		17·00	75
	Wi. Watermark sideways-inverted........		£150	—
	s. Overprinted 'SPECIMEN' (9, 30)........			
D33	1s. deep blue (10.37)........		80·00	75
	Wi. Watermark sideways-inverted........		£150	—
	s. Overprinted 'SPECIMEN' (9, 30)........			
D34	**D2** 2s.6d. purple/*yellow* (9.38)........		85·00	1·25
D27/D34	*Set of 8*........		£300	16·00

The 2d. from the above issue is known bisected and used for half its face value at the following sorting offices:
2d. Robin Hood's Bay Station, Yorks (1938), Boreham Wood (1951), Camberley (1951), Harpenden (1951, 1954), St Albans (1951)

DATES OF ISSUE. The dates for Nos. D35/D39 are those on which stamps were first issued by the Supplies Department to postmasters.

1951–54. Colours changed and new value (1½d.). W **127** (G VI R) sideways.

D35	**D1** ½d. yellow-orange (18.9.51)........		3·50	3·50
	a. Bright orange (5.54)........		75·00	
D36	1d. violet-blue (6.6.51)........		1·50	75
	Wi. Watermark sideways-inverted........		—	—
D37	1½d. green (11.2.52)........		2·00	2·00
	Wi. Watermark sideways-inverted........		£140	£140
D38	4d. blue (14.8.51)........		50·00	22·00
	Wi. Watermark sideways inverted........		†	£1000
D39	1s. ochre (6.12.51)........		28·00	5·25
	Wi. Watermark sideways-inverted........		£2800	—
D35/D39	*Set of 5*........		75·00	30·00

The 1d. of the above issue is known bisected and used for half its face value at the following sorting office:
1d. Camberley (1954), Capel, Dorking (1952)

1954–55. W **153** (Tudor Crown) sideways.

D40	**D1** ½d. bright orange (8.6.55)........		7·00	5·25
	Wi. Watermark sideways-inverted........		£150	£150
D41	2d. agate (28.7.55)........		26·00	23·00
	Wi. Watermark sideways-inverted........		—	—
D42	3d. violet (4.5.55)........		75·00	60·00
D43	4d. blue (14.7.55)........		26·00	32·00
	a. Imperf (pair)........		£250	
D44	5d. yellow-brown (19.5.55)........		20·00	20·00
D45	**D2** 2s.6d. purple/*yellow* (11.54)........		£150	5·75
	Wi. Watermark sideways-inverted........		—	—
D40/D45	*Set of 6*........		£250	£130

1955–57. W **165** (St Edward's Crown) sideways.

D46	**D1** ½d. bright orange (16.7.56)........		2·75	3·25
	Wi. Watermark sideways-inverted........		£125	—
D47	1d. violet-blue (7.6.55)........		5·00	1·50
D48	1½d. green (13.2.56)........		8·50	7·00
	Wi. Watermark sideways-inverted........		85·00	—
D49	2d. agate (22.5.56)........		45·00	3·50
D50	3d. violet (5.3.56)........		6·00	1·50
	Wi. Watermark sideways-inverted........		£100	—
D51	4d. blue (24.4.56)........		25·00	6·00
	Wi. Watermark sideways-inverted........		£175	—
D52	5d. brown-ochre (23.3.56)........		26·00	20·00
D53	1s. ochre (22.11.55)........		65·00	2·25
	Wi. Watermark sideways-inverted........		—	—
D54	**D2** 2s.6d. purple/*yellow* (28.6.57)........		£200	8·25
	Wi. Watermark sideways-inverted........		—	—
D55	5s. scarlet/*yellow* (25.11.55)........		£150	32·00
	Wi. Watermark sideways-inverted........		—	£375
D46/D55	*Set of 10*........		£475	75·00

Stamps from the above issue are known bisected and used for half their face value at the following sorting offices:
1d. Beswick, Manchester (1958), Huddersfield (1956), London SE (1957)
2d. Eynsham, Oxford (1956), Garelochhead, Helensburgh (1956), Harpenden (1956), Hull (1956), Kingston on Thames (1956), Leicester Square, London WC (1956), London WC (1956)
3d. London SE (1957)
4d. Poplar, London E (1958)

1959–63. W **179** (Multiple Crowns) sideways.

D56	**D1** ½d. bright orange (18.10.61)........		15	1·25
	Wi. Watermark sideways-inverted........		2·50	2·50
D57	1d. violet-blue (9.5.60)........		15	50
	Wi. Watermark sideways-inverted........		£125	—
D58	1½d. green (5.10.60)........		2·50	2·50
D59	2d. agate (14.9.59)........		1·10	50
	Wi. Watermark sideways-inverted........		£200	—
D60	3d. violet (24.3.59)........		30	30
	Wi. Watermark sideways-inverted........		85·00	85·00
D61	4d. blue (17.12.59)........		30	30
	Wi. Watermark sideways-inverted........		£300	—
D62	5d. yellow-brown (6.11.61)........		45	60
	Wi. Watermark sideways-inverted........		5·00	6·00
D63	6d. purple (29.3.62)........		50	30
	Wi. Watermark sideways-inverted........		£400	£400
D64	1s. ochre (11.4.60)........		90	30
	Wi. Watermark sideways-inverted........		75·00	75·00
D65	**D2** 2s.6d. purple/*yellow* (11.5.61)........		3·00	50
	Wi. Watermark sideways-inverted........		15·00	15·00
D66	5s. scarlet/*yellow* (8.5.61)........		8·25	1·00
D67	10s. blue/*yellow* (2.9.63)........		11·50	5·75
	Wi. Watermark sideways-inverted........		40·00	25·00
D68	£1 black/*yellow* (2.9.63)........		45·00	8·25
D56/D68	*Set of 13*........		65·00	20·00

Whiter paper. The note after No. 586 also applies to Postage Due stamps.
Stamps from the above issue are known bisected and used for half their face value at the following sorting offices:
1d. Chieveley, Newbury (1962, 1963), Henlan, Llandyssil (1961), Mayfield (1962), St Albans (1964)
2d. Doncaster (?)

1968–69. Typo. No wmk. Chalk-surfaced paper.

D69	**D1** 2d. agate (11.4.68)........		75	1·00
	v. PVA gum (26.11.68)........		75·00	
D70	3d. violet (9.9.68)........		1·00	1·00
D71	4d. blue (6.5.68)........		1·00	1·00
	v. PVA gum........		£2250	
D72	5d. orange-brown (3.1.69)........		8·00	11·00
D73	6d. purple (9.9.68)........		2·25	1·75
D74	1s. ochre (19.11.68)........		4·00	2·50
D69/D74	*Set of 6*........		15·00	16·00

The 2d. and 4d. exist with gum arabic and PVA gum; the remainder with PVA gum only.
Stamps from the above issue are known bisected and used for half their face value at the following sorting offices:
4d. Northampton (1970)
6d. Kilburn, London NW (1968)

1968–69. Photo. No wmk. Chalk-surfaced paper. PVA gum.

D75	**D1** 4d. blue (12.6.69)........		7·00	6·75
D76	8d. red (3.10.68)........		50	1·00

Nos. D75/D76 are smaller, 21½×17½ mm.
The 4d. is known bisected in April 1970 (Northampton).

D3 **D4**

(Des Jeffery Matthews. Photo Harrison)

1970 (17 June)–**75**. Decimal Currency. Chalk-surfaced paper.

D77	D3	½p. turquoise-blue (15.2.71)..................	15	2·50
D78		1p. deep reddish purple (15.2.71).........	15	15
D79		2p. myrtle-green (15.2.71)......................	20	15
D80		3p. ultramarine (15.2.71)........................	20	15
D81		4p. yellow-brown (15.2.71).....................	25	15
D82		5p. violet (15.2.71).................................	25	15
D83		7p. red-brown (21.8.74).........................	35	1·00
D84	D4	10p. carmine..	30	30
D85		11p. slate-green (18.6.75).......................	50	1·00
D86		20p. olive-brown....................................	60	25
D87		50p. ultramarine....................................	2·00	1·25
D88		£1 black...	4·00	1·00
D89		£5 orange-yellow and black (2.4.73)......	25·00	1·50
D77/D89 *Set of* 13..			30·00	7·75

Presentation Pack (PO Pack No. 36) (Nos. D77/D82, D84, D86/D88 (3.11.71).. 28·00

Presentation Pack (PO Pack No. 93) (Nos. D77/D88) (30.3.77)... 9·00

Later printings were on fluorescent white paper, some with dextrin added to the PVA gum (see notes after X1058).

The 2p. from the above issue is known bisected and used for half its face value at Exeter (1977).

D5 **D6**

(Des Sedley Place Design Ltd. Photo Harrison)

1982 (9 June). Chalk-surfaced paper.

D90	D5	1p. lake..	10	30
D91		2p. bright blue.......................................	30	30
D92		3p. deep mauve.....................................	15	30
D93		4p. deep blue...	15	25
D94		5p. sepia..	20	25
D95	D6	10p. light brown.....................................	30	40
D96		20p. olive-green......................................	50	60
D97		25p. deep greenish blue.........................	80	90
D98		50p. grey-black.......................................	1·75	1·75
D99		£1 red..	3·00	1·25
D100		£2 turquoise-blue..................................	5·00	4·25
D101		£5 dull orange......................................	10·00	2·25
D90/D101 *Set of* 12..			19·00	10·00
D90/D101 *Set of* 12 *Gutter Pairs*......................			38·00	
Presentation Pack (PO Pack No.135).................			24·00	

D7

(Des Sedley Place Design Ltd. Litho Questa)

1994 (15 Feb). Perf 15×14 (with one elliptical hole in each vertical side).

D102	D7	1p. red, yellow and black........................	10	75
D103		2p. magenta, purple and black..............	10	75
D104		5p. yellow, red-brown and black...........	15	50
D105		10p. yellow, emerald and black..............	30	75
D106		20p. blue-green, violet and black...........	75	1·50
D107		25p. cerise, rosine and black..................	1·50	2·00
D108		£1 violet, magenta and black.................	7·00	7·00
D109		£1·20 greenish blue, blue-green and black..	8·00	9·00
D110		£5 greenish black, blue-green and black..	20·00	20·00
D102/D110 *Set of* 9..			35·00	35·00
First Day Cover..				45·00
Presentation Pack (PO Pack No.32)...................			38·00	

Special First Day of Issue Postmarks

London EC3.. 45·00

Following changes in the method of collecting money due on unpaid or underpaid mail the use of postage due stamps was restricted from April 1995 to mail addressed to business customers and to Customs/VAT charges levied by the Royal Mail on behalf of the Customs and Excise. The use of postage due stamps ceased on 28 January 2000.

Subscribe & Save Money

on the cover price*

Post Office Stamp Booklets

The following listing covers all the booklets sold by post offices from 1904.

All major variations of contents and cover are included, but minor changes to the covers and differences on the interleaves have been ignored.

From 1913 each booklet carried an edition number, linked to an internal Post Office system of identification which divided the various booklets into series. In 1943 these edition numbers were replaced by edition dates. No attempt has been made to list separate edition numbers for booklets prior to 1943, although notes giving their extent are provided for each booklet.

Edition dates from August 1943 are listed separately and exist for all £.s.d. and most Decimal Stitched booklets (except for the 1s. booklets, the 2s. booklets (Nos. N1/N3), the 5s. Philympia booklets (No. HP34), the £1 Stamps for Cooks booklet (No. ZP1) and the Decimal Sponsored booklets). They are those found printed upon the booklets, either on the outer back cover or on the white leaves.

Note that the date of issue may not coincide with the edition date given on the booklet, thus No. DW1, issued on 13 November 1974 has an edition date of SEPT 1974.

ERRORS OF MAKE-UP of booklets exist but we do not list them here. More detailed listings can be found in the 2nd, 3rd and 4th volumes of the *Great Britain Specialised Catalogue*.

ILLUSTRATIONS. The illustrations of the covers are ¾ size except where otherwise stated. Those in Queen Elizabeth II Decimal Sections C to H are ⅔ size, except where otherwise stated.

PRICES quoted are for complete booklets containing stamps with average perforations (i.e. full perforations on two edges of the pane only). Booklets containing panes with complete perforations are worth more.

KING EDWARD VII

2s. Booklets

BA1

1904 (Mar). Red cover printed in black as T **BA1**. Panes of six stamps: 24×1d. Wmk Imperial Crown (No. 219).
BA1 .... £325

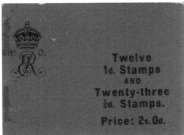

BA2

1906 (June). Red cover printed in black as T **BA2**. As before but make-up changed to include 12×1d. and 23×½d. and label showing one green cross (Nos. 217 and 219).
BA2 .... £1500

1907 (Aug). Red cover printed in black as T **BA2**. Make-up changed to include 18×1d. and 11×½d. and label showing one green cross (Nos. 217 and 219).
BA3 .... £2000

1908 (Aug). As before, but interleaves used for post office adverts printed in red.
BA4 .... £2200

1909 (Aug). As before, but interleaves used for trade advert printed in green.
BA5 .... £1750

BA6

1911 (June). Red cover printed in black as T **BA6** showing a larger Post Office cypher on cover. As before, but containing stamps by Harrison & Sons (Nos. 267 and 272).
BA6 .... £1800

KING GEORGE V

2s. Booklets

BB1

1911 (Aug). Red cover printed in black as T **BA2** showing King George V cypher. Panes of six stamps: 18×1d. and 12×½d. Wmk Crown (Nos. 325, 329) Die 1B.
BB1 .... £1000

BB2

1912 (Apr). As before, but red cover printed in black as T **BB2**.
BB2 .... £1200

1912 (Sept). As before, but wmk Simple Cypher (Nos. 334, 336) Die 1B.
BB3 .... £850

BB5

1912 (Nov). As before, but red cover printed in black as T **BB5** but without edition number.
BB4 .... £1000

1913 (Jan). As before, but red cover printed in black as T **BB5**.
BB5 Edition numbers 8 or 9............................. £900

1913 (Apr). As before, but 1912–1922 wmk Simple Cypher (Nos. 351, 357).
BB6 Edition numbers 10 to 35......................... £900

1915 (Nov). As before, except lower panel of front cover which was changed to show New rates of postage.
BB7 Edition numbers 36 to 42........................ £1000

1916 (May). As before, but interleave adverts printed in black instead of green.
BB8 Edition numbers 43 to 45........................ £1300

1916 (July). As before, but orange cover printed in black as T **BB5**.
BB9 Edition numbers 46 to 64........................ £950

BB10

1917 (Sept). As before, but orange cover printed in black as T **BB10**.
BB10 Edition numbers 65 to 81........................ £875

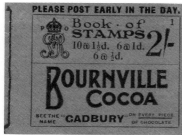

BB11

1924 (Feb). Blue cover printed in black as T **BB11**. Panes of six stamps: 10×1½d. (first completed by two perforated labels), 6×1d. and 6×½d. 1912–1922 wmk Simple Cypher (Nos. 351, 357, 362).
BB11 Edition numbers 1 or 2............................ £1200

1924 (Mar). As before, but 1924–1926 wmk Block Cypher (Nos. 418/420).
BB12 Edition numbers 3 to 102 and 108 to
254... £700

BB13

1929 (May). Postal Union Congress issue. Cover of special design as T **BB13** printed in blue on buff as before but containing stamps of the PUC issue (Nos. 434/436).
BB13 Edition numbers 103 to 107................... £400

1934 (Feb). Blue cover printed in black as T **BB11**, but containing stamps with Block Cypher wmk printed by Harrison & Sons (Nos. 418/420).
BB14 Edition numbers 255 to 287................... £850

1935 (Jan). As before, but containing stamps of the photogravure issue (intermediate format) with the se-tenant advertisements printed in brown (Nos. 439/441).
BB15 Edition numbers 288 to 297................... £2100

BB16

1935 (May). Silver Jubilee issue. Larger size cover printed in blue on buff as T **BB16** and containing pages of four stamps with no se-tenant advertisements: 12×1½d., 4×1d. and 4×½d. (Nos. 453/455).
BB16 Edition numbers 298 to 304................... 70·00

1935 (July). As No. BB15, but containing stamps of the photogravure (small format) issue with se-tenant advertisements printed in black (Nos. 439/441).
BB17 Edition numbers 305 to 353................... £350

3s. Booklets

BB19

1918 (Oct). Orange cover printed in black as T **BB19**. Panes of six stamps: 12×1½d., 12×1d. and 12×½d. 1912–1922 wmk Simple Cypher (Nos. 351, 357, 362).
BB18 Edition numbers 1 to 11......................... £1250

1919 (July). As before, but make-up altered to contain 18×1½d., 6×1d. and 6×½d.
BB19 Edition numbers 12 to 26....................... £1300

BB20

1921 (Apr). Experimental booklet bound in blue covers as T **BB20**, containing pages of six stamps: 18×2d. (Die I) (No. 368).
BB20   Edition numbers 35 and part 37............ £1700

1921 (Dec). As before, but containing 2d. (Die II) (No. 370).
BB21   Edition numbers 12, 13 and part 37....... £2400

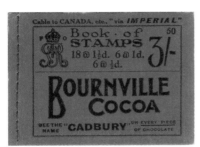

BB22

1922 (May). Scarlet cover printed in black as T **BB22**. Panes of six stamps: 18×1½d., 6×1d. and 6×½d. (Nos. 351, 357, 362).
BB22   Edition numbers 19, 20, 22, 23 and 25
              to 54.. £1700

BB23

1922 (June). Experimental booklet as Edition numbers 12 and 13 bound in blue covers as T **BB23**, containing panes of six stamps: 24×1½d. (No. 362).
BB23   Edition numbers 21 or 24....................... £1700

1924 (Feb). Scarlet cover printed in black as T **BB22**, but containing stamps with Block Cypher wmk, printed by Waterlow & Sons (Nos. 418/420).
BB24   Edition numbers 55 to 167 and 173 to
              273.. £425

1929 (May). Postal Union Congress issue. Cover of special design as T **BB13** printed in red on buff as before but containing stamps of the PUC issue (Nos. 434/436).
BB25   Edition numbers 168 to 172.................... £350

1934 (Mar). Scarlet cover printed in black as T **BB22**, but containing stamps with the Block Cypher wmk printed by Harrison & Sons (Nos. 418/420).
BB26   Edition numbers 274 to 288.................... £500

1935 (Jan). As No. BB29, but containing stamps of the photogravure issue (intermediate format).
BB27   Edition numbers 289 to 293.................... £1400

1935 (May). Silver Jubilee issue. Larger size cover printed in red on buff as T **BB16** and containing panes of four stamps: 20×1½d., 4×1d. and 4×½d. (Nos. 453/455).
BB28   Edition numbers 294 to 297.................... 70·00

1935 (July). As No. BB26, but containing stamps of the photogravure issue (small format) (Nos. 439/441).
BB29   Edition numbers 298 to 319.................... £425

3s.6d. Booklets

BB30

1920 (July). Orange cover printed in black as T **BB30**, containing panes of six stamps: 18×2d. and 6×1d. (Nos. 357, 368).
BB30   Edition numbers 27 to 32........................ £1600

BB31

1921 (Jan). Orange-red cover printed in black as T **BB31**, as before but make-up changed to include stamps of 1912–1922 issue with the Simple Cypher wmk: 12×2d. (Die I), 6×1½d., 6×1d. and 6×½d. (Nos. 351, 357, 362, 368).
BB31   Edition numbers 33, 34, 36 and 38........ £2200

1921 (July). As No. BB31 including stamps of the 1912–1922 issue with Simple Cypher wmk: 12×2d. (Die I or Die II), 6×1½d., 6×1d. and 6×½d. (Nos. 351, 357, 362, 368 or 370).
BB32   Edition numbers 1 to 11, 14 to 18.......... £2200

5s. Booklets

BB33

1931 (Aug). Green cover printed in black as T **BB33**. Panes of six stamps: 34×1½d., 6×1d. and 6×½d. The first 1½d. pane completed by two *se-tenant* advertisements. Printed by Waterlow & Sons on paper with Block Cypher wmk (Nos. 418/420).
BB33   Edition number 1.. £4500

1932 (June). As before, but buff cover printed in black.
BB34   Edition numbers 2 to 6............................. £3600

1934 (July). As before, but containing stamps with Block Cypher wmk printed by Harrison & Sons (Nos. 418/420).
BB35   Edition numbers 7 or 8............................ £1600

1935 (Feb). As before, but containing stamps of the photogravure issue (intermediate format) with *se-tenant* advertisements printed in brown (Nos. 439/441).
BB36   Edition number 9.. £4500

1935 (July). As before, but containing stamps of the photogravure issue (small format) with *se-tenant* advertisements printed in black (Nos. 439/441).
BB37   Edition numbers 10 to 15........................... £500

KING EDWARD VIII

6d. Booklet

1936 . Buff unglazed cover without inscription containing 4×1½d. stamps, in panes of two (No. 459).
BC1   Edition numbers 354 to 385.................... 40·00

2s. Booklet

BC2

1936 (Oct). Blue cover printed in black as T **BC2**, containing pages of six stamps: 10×1½d., 6×1d. and 6×½d. (Nos. 457/459).
BC2   Edition numbers 354 to 385.................... 90·00

3s. Booklet

1936 (Nov). As No. BB29, except for the KEVIII cypher on the cover but without 'P' and 'O' on either side of the crown, and containing Nos. 457/459.
BC3   Edition numbers 320 to 332.................... 75·00

5s. Booklet

1937 (Mar). As No. BB37, but with the KEVIII cypher on the cover and containing Nos. 457/459.
BC4   Edition numbers 16 or 17......................... £180

KING GEORGE VI

6d. Booklets

1938 (Jan). As No. BC1, but containing stamps in the original dark colours. Buff cover without inscription (No. 464).
BD1   .... 50·00

1938 (Feb). As before, but pink unprinted cover and make-up changed to contain 2×1½d., 2×1d. and 2×½d. in the original dark colours (Nos. 462/164).
BD2   .... £225

1940 (June). Pale green unprinted cover and make-up changed to include two panes of four stamps with wmk sideways. Stamps in original dark colours with binding margin either at the top or bottom of the pane: 4×1d., 4×½d. (Nos. 462a/463a).
BD3   .... 85·00

1s. Booklets with Panes of 2

1947 (Dec). Cream cover, unglazed and without inscription containing panes of two stamps in pale shades, all with wmk normal. Panes of two stamps: 4×½d., 4×1d. and 4×1½d. (Nos. 485/487).
BD4   .... 18·00

1951 (May). As before, but containing stamps in changed colours (Nos. 503/505).
BD5   .... 18·00

1s. Booklets with Panes of 4

1948. Cream cover as before, but make-up changed to contain 4×1½d., 4×1d. and 4×½d. in panes of four of the pale shades with wmk normal (Nos. 485/487).
BD6   .... £5750

1951 (May). As before, but stamps in new colours all wmk normal, margins at either top or at the bottom. (Nos. 503/505).
BD7   .... 35·00

BD8

1952 (Dec). Cream cover printed in black as T **BD8**. Make-up as before but with wmk either upright or inverted and margins only at the top (Nos. 503/505).
BD8   .... 18·00

BD10

1954 . As before but cover showing GPO emblem with St Edward's crown and oval frame as T **BD10** (Nos. 503/505).
BD10   .... 20·00

2s. Booklets

BD11

1937 (Aug). Blue cover printed in black as T **BB11**, but with KGVI cypher on the cover and containing stamps in the original dark colours. Panes of six stamps: 10×1½d., 6×1d. and 6×½d. The first 1½d. pane completed by two *se-tenant* advertisements.(Nos. 462/464).
BD11   Edition numbers 386 to 412.................... £750

BD12

1938 (Mar). Blue cover printed in black as T **BD12** (Nos. 462/464).
BD12   Edition numbers 413 to 508.................... £750

2s.6d. Booklets

BD13

1940 (June). Scarlet cover printed in black as T **BD13**, containing panes of six stamps in original dark colours: 6×2½d., 6×2d. and 6×½d. (Nos. 462, 465/466).
BD13   Edition numbers 1 to 8 (part)................. £1100

1940 (Sept). As before, but blue cover printed in black as T **BD13**.
BD14   Edition numbers 8 (part) to 13................ £1100

BD15

1940 (Oct). As before, but with green cover printed in black as T **BD15** (Nos. 462, 465/466).
BD15   Edition numbers 14 to 94......................... £650

1942 (Mar). As before, but containing stamps in pale shades (Nos. 485, 488/189).
BD16   Edition numbers 95 to 146 (Part)........... £650

1942 (Oct). Composition as before, but with unglazed green covers.
BD17   Edition numbers 146 (Part) to 214.......... £650

BD20 Type A Circular GPO Cypher

1943 (Aug). As before, but green cover printed in black as Type A, with different contents details (Nos. 485, 488/489).
BD18   Edition dates August 1943 to February 1951.. 65·00

(1) AUG 1943	70·00
(2) OCT 1943	90·00
(3) NOV 1943	£115
(4) DEC 1943	£110
(5) JAN 1944	£100
(6) FEB 1944	£100
(7) MAR 1944	£100
(8) APR 1944	£100
(9) MAY 1944	£100
(10) JUNE 1944	£100
(11) JULY 1944	£100
(12) AUG 1944	£100
(13) SEPT 1944	£100
(14) OCT 1944	£100
(15) NOV 1944	£100
(16) DEC 1944	£100
(17) JAN 1945	£100
(18) FEB 1945	£100
(19) MAR 1945	£100
(20) APR 1945	£100
(21) MAY 1945	£100
(22) JUNE 1945	£100
(23) JULY 1945	£100
(24) AUG 1945	£100
(25) SEPT 1945	£100
(26) OCT 1945	£100
(27) NOV 1945	£100
(28) DEC 1945	£100
(29) JAN 1946	90·00
(30) FEB 1946	90·00
(31) MAR 1946	90·00
(32) APR 1946	90·00
(33) MAY 1946	90·00
(34) JUNE 1946	90·00
(35) JULY 1946	90·00
(36) AUG 1946	90·00
(37) SEPT 1946	90·00
(38) OCT 1946	£250
(39) NOV 1946	90·00
(40) DEC 1946	90·00
(41) JAN 1947	90·00
(42) FEB 1947	90·00
(43) MAR 1947	90·00
(44) APR 1947	90·00
(45) MAY 1947	90·00
(46) JUNE 1947	90·00
(47) JULY 1947	90·00
(48) AUG 1947	90·00
(49) SEPT 1947	90·00
(50) OCT 1947	90·00
(51) NOV 1947	90·00
(52) DEC 1947	90·00
(53) JAN 1948	£115
(54) FEB 1948	90·00
(55) MAR 1948	90·00
(56) APR 1948	90·00
(57) MAY 1948	90·00
(58) JUNE 1948	90·00
(59) JULY 1948	90·00
(60) AUG 1948	90·00
(61) OCT 1948	85·00
(62) NOV 1948	85·00
(63) DEC 1948	85·00
(64) JAN 1949	85·00
(65) FEB 1949	90·00
(66) MAR 1949	90·00
(67) APR 1949	90·00
(68) MAY 1949	90·00

(69) JUNE 1949	90·00
(70) JULY 1949	90·00
(71) AUG 1949	90·00
(72) OCT 1949	90·00
(73) NOV 1949	90·00
(74) DEC 1949	90·00
(75) JAN 1950	75·00
(76) FEB 1950	75·00
(77) MAR 1950	75·00
(78) APR 1950	75·00
(79) MAY 1950	75·00
(80) JUNE 1950	75·00
(81) JULY 1950	65·00
(82) AUG 1950	65·00
(83) SEPT 1950	65·00
(84) OCT 1950	65·00
(85) NOV 1950	65·00
(86) DEC 1950	65·00
(87) JAN 1951	65·00
(88) FEB 1951	65·00

1951 (May). As before, but containing stamps in the new colours (Nos. 503, 506/507).

BD19	Edition dates May 1951 to February 1952	35·00

(1) MAY 1951	35·00
(2) JUNE 1951	50·00
(3) JULY 1951	£130
(4) AUG 1951	35·00
(5) SEPT 1951	£110
(6) OCT 1951	35·00
(7) NOV 1951	35·00
(8) DEC 1951	35·00
(9) JAN 1952	35·00
(10) FEB 1952	35·00

1952 (Mar). As before, but make-up changed to contain: 6×2½d., 6×1½d., 3×1d. and 6×½d. The 1d. pane was completed by three perforated labels in the lower row inscribed MINIMUM INLAND PRINTED PAPER RATE 1½d. (Nos. 503/505, 507).

BD20	Edition dates March 1952 to May 1953.	32·00

(1) MAR 1952	32·00
(2) APR 1952	35·00
(3) MAY 1952	32·00
(4) JUNE 1952	32·00
(5) JULY 1952	32·00
(6) AUG 1952	32·00
(7) SEPT 1952	32·00
(8) OCT 1952	32·00
(9) NOV 1952	32·00
(10) DEC 1952	32·00
(11) JAN 1953	32·00
(12) FEB 1953	32·00
(13) MAR 1953	32·00
(14) APR 1953	32·00
(15) MAY 1953	35·00

3s. Booklets

BD21

1937 (Aug). Scarlet cover printed black as T **BD21**, containing panes of six stamps: 18×1½d., 6×1d. and 6×½d. in the original dark colours (Nos. 462/464).

BD21	Edition numbers 333 to 343	£1200

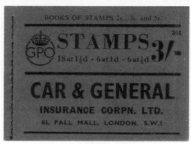

BD22

1938 (Apr). As before, but scarlet cover printed in black as T **BD22** (Nos. 462/464).

BD22	Edition numbers 344 to 377	£1200

5s. Booklets

1937 (Aug). Buff cover printed in black as T **BB33**, containing stamps of the new reign in the original dark colours. Panes of six stamps: 34×1½d., 6×1d. and 6×½d. The first 1½d. pane completed by two *se-tenant* advertisements. (Nos. 462/464).

BD23	Edition numbers 18 to 20	£1300

BD24

1938 (May). As before, but with redesigned front cover showing GPO emblem as T **BD24** instead of royal cypher.

BD24	Edition numbers 21 to 29	£1300

1940 (July). As before, but make-up changed to contain: 18×2½d., 6×2d. and 6×½d. in the original dark colours (Nos. 462, 465/466).

BD25	Edition numbers 1 to 16 (part)	£1300

1942 (Mar). As before, but containing stamps in pale shades (Nos. 485, 488/489).

BD26	Edition numbers 16 (part) to 36	£1300

1943 (Sept). As before, but buff cover printed in black as Type A (see No. BD18, 2s.6d.) (Nos. 485, 488/489).

BD28	Edition dates September 1943 to December 1950	85·00

(1) SEPT 1943	£100
(2) OCT 1943	£145
(3) NOV 1943	£115
(4) DEC 1943	£145
(5) FEB 1944	£120
(6) MAR 1944	£120
(7) AUG 1944	£120
(8) OCT 1944	£120
(9) NOV 1944	£120
(10) JAN 1945	£120
(11) FEB 1945	£130
(12) APR 1945	£130
(13) JUNE 1945	£130
(14) AUG 1945	£130
(15) OCT 1945	£130
(16) DEC 1945	£130
(17) JAN 1946	£130
(18) MAR 1946	£115
(19) MAY 1946	£115
(20) JUNE 1946	£115
(21) AUG 1946	£115
(22) OCT 1946	£115
(23) DEC 1946	£115
(24) FEB 1947	£115
(25) APR 1947	£115
(26) JUNE 1947	£115

(27) AUG 1947		£115
(28) OCT 1947		£115
(29) DEC 1947		£115
(30) FEB 1948		£115
(31) APR 1948		£115
(32) JUNE 1948		£115
(33) JULY 1948		£115
(34) AUG 1948		£115
(35) OCT 1948		£115
(36) DEC 1948		£130
(37) FEB 1949		£130
(38) APR 1949		£130
(39) JUNE 1949		£120
(40) AUG 1949		£120
(41) SEPT 1949		£120
(42) OCT 1949		£120
(43) DEC 1949		£120
(44) FEB 1950		85·00
(45) APR 1950		85·00
(46) JUNE 1950		85·00
(47) AUG 1950		85·00
(48) OCT 1950		85·00
(49) DEC 1950		85·00

BD29

1944 (Apr). As before, but buff cover printed in black as T **BD29** (Nos. 485, 488/489).

BD29	Edition dates April or June 1944	£3500

(1) APR 1944		£3500
(2) JUNE 1944		£3500

1951 (May). As before, but buff cover changed back to Type A (see No. BD18, 2s.6d.) and containing stamps in the new colours (Nos. 503, 506/507).

BD30	Edition dates May 1951 to January 1952	50·00

(1) MAY 1951		50·00
(2) JULY 1951		50·00
(3) SEPT 1951		50·00
(4) NOV 1951		50·00
(5) JAN 1952		50·00

1952 (Mar). As before, make-up changed to contain: 18×2½d., 6×1½d., 3×1d. and 6×½d. The 1d. pane was completed by three perforated labels in the lower row inscribed MINIMUM INLAND PRINTED PAPER RATE 1½d. (Nos. 503/505, 507).

BD31	Edition dates March to November 1952	40·00

(1) MAR 1952		40·00
(2) MAY 1952		40·00
(3) JULY 1952		40·00
(4) SEPT 1952		40·00
(5) NOV 1952		40·00

1953 (Jan). As before, but make-up changed again to include the 2d. value and containing: 12×2½d., 6×2d., 6×1½d., 6×1d. and 6×½d. (Nos. 503/507).

BD32	Edition dates January or March 1953	50·00

(1) JAN 1953		50·00
(2) MAR 1953		50·00

QUEEN ELIZABETH II

I. £.s.d. BOOKLETS, 1953–1970.

TYPES OF BOOKLET COVER WITH GPO CYPHER

Type A Circular GPO Cypher

Type B Oval Type GPO Cypher

Type C New GPO Cypher (small)

Type D New GPO Cypher (large)

1s. Booklets

1953 (2 Sept)–**59**.
  I. White unprinted cover. Panes of two stamps: 4×1½d., 4×1d., 4×½d.
     For use in experimental 'D' machines.
     A. Wmk Tudor Crown (Nos. 515/517) EE.

E1	No date	5·00

	B. Wmk St Edward's Crown (Nos. 540/542).	
E2	No date (11.57)	35·00

II. White printed cover as Type B. Panes of four stamps: 4×1½d. 4×1d., 4×½d. For use in 'E' machines.
A. Wmk Tudor Crown (Nos. 515/517).

K1	No date (22.7.54).........................	8·00

B. Wmk St Edward's Crown (Nos. 540/542).

K2	No date (5.7.56)...........................	5·00

C. Wmk Crowns (Nos. 570/572).

K3	No date (13.8.59).........................	5·00

2s. Booklets

1959 (22 Apr)–**65**. Panes of four stamps: 4×3d., 4×1½d., 4×1d., 4×½d.
I. Salmon cover as Type B. Wmk. St Edward's Crown (Nos. 540/542 and 545).

N1	No date..	6·00

II. Salmon cover as Type C. Wmk Crowns (Nos. 570/572 and 575).

N2	No date (2.11.60).........................	6·50

III. Lemon cover as Type C. Wmk Crowns (Nos. 570/572 and 575).

N3	No date (2.61)...............................	6·50

IV. Lemon cover as Type C. Wmk Crowns (sideways) (Nos. 570a, 571a, 572b, 575a) or phosphor (Nos. 610a, 611a, 612a, 615b).

N4	APR 1961.................................	22·00
	p. With phosphor bands................	40·00
N5	SEPT 1961................................	35·00
N6	JAN 1962..................................	32·00
N7	APR 1962.................................	40·00
N8	JULY 1962................................	35·00
	p. With phosphor bands................	60·00
N9	NOV 1962.................................	50·00
	p. With phosphor bands................	60·00
N10	JAN 1963..................................	40·00
	p. With phosphor bands................	£125
N11	MAR 1963.................................	40·00
N12	JUNE 1963................................	40·00
	p. With phosphor bands................	75·00
N13	AUG 1963.................................	40·00
	p. With phosphor bands................	70·00
N14	OCT 1963.................................	55·00
	p. With phosphor bands................	90·00
N15	FEB 1964.................................	40·00
N16	JUNE 1964................................	40·00
	p. With phosphor bands................	85·00
N17	AUG 1964.................................	55·00
	p. With phosphor bands................	85·00
N18	OCT 1964.................................	40·00
	p. With phosphor bands................	50·00
N19	DEC 1964.................................	65·00
	p. With phosphor bands................	50·00
N20	APR 1965.................................	40·00
	p. With phosphor bands................	45·00

1965 (16 Aug)–**67**. New Composition. Pages of four stamps: 4×4d. and pane of 2×1d. and 2×3d. arranged *se-tenant* horiz. Orange-yellow cover as Type C printed in black. Wmk Crowns (sideways) (Nos. 571a, 575a and 576ab) or phosphor (Nos. 611a, 615cd or 615cda (one side phosphor band) and 616ab).

N21	JULY 1965................................	3·50
	p. With phosphor bands................	12·00
N22	OCT 1965.................................	3·75
	p. With phosphor bands................	12·00
N23	JAN 1966..................................	6·25
	p. With phosphor bands................	16·00
N24	APR 1966.................................	6·25
	p. With phosphor bands................	8·00
N25	JULY 1966................................	7·50
	p. With phosphor bands................	£150
N26	OCT 1966.................................	6·00
	p. With phosphor bands................	10·00
N27	JAN 1967..................................	8·00
	p. With phosphor bands................	5·00
N28p	APR 1967. With phosphor bands.........	6·00
N29p	JULY 1967. With phosphor bands.........	4·00
N30p	OCT 1967. With phosphor bands.........	4·00

In the *se-tenant* pane the 3d. appears at left or right to facilitate the application of phosphor bands.

The following illustration shows how the *se-tenant* stamps with one phosphor band on 3d. were printed and the arrows indicate where the guillotine fell. The result gives 1d. stamps with two bands and the 3d. stamps with one band either at left or right.

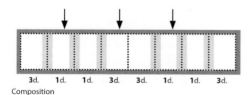

| 3d. | 1d. | 1d. | 3d. | 3d. | 1d. | 1d. | 3d. |

Composition

1967 (Nov)–**68**. Composition and cover as Nos. N21/N30. Wmk Crowns (sideways) (Nos. 611a, 615b (two phosphor bands) and 616ab).

N31p	JAN 1968..................................	4·00
N32p	MAR 1968.................................	4·50

2s. Booklets with Machin type stamps

1968 (6 Apr–Aug). Orange-yellow cover as Type C. Panes of four stamps: 4×4d. and pane of 2×1d. and 2×3d. arranged *se-tenant* horiz. PVA gum (Nos. 724, 730, 731v).

NP27	MAY 1968.................................	1·20
NP28	JULY 1968................................	1·00
NP29	AUG 1968.................................	3·75

1968 (16 Sept)–**70**. Grey cover as Type C. New Composition. 4d. stamps only comprising pane of 4×4d. with two phosphor bands (No. 731v) and pane of 2×4d. with one centre phosphor band (No. 732) *se-tenant* with two printed labels.

NP30	SEPT 1968................................	75
NP31	JAN 1969..................................	£175

Same composition but all 6×4d. stamps have one centre phosphor band (No. 732).

NP31a	SEPT 1968................................	£425
NP32	NOV 1968.................................	80
NP33	JAN 1969..................................	75

Same composition but change to 4d. bright vermilion with one centre phosphor band (No. 733).

NP34	MAR 1969.................................	1·10
NP35	MAY 1969.................................	1·25
NP36	JULY 1969................................	1·75
NP37	SEPT 1969................................	1·50
NP38	NOV 1969.................................	1·25
NP39	JAN 1970..................................	2·00
NP40	MAR 1970.................................	2·00
NP41	MAY 1970.................................	2·00
NP42	JULY 1970................................	2·00
NP43	AUG 1970.................................	2·00
NP44	OCT 1970.................................	2·00
NP45	DEC 1970.................................	2·00

2s. Booklets for Holiday Resorts

1963 (15 July)–**64**.
I. Lemon cover as Type C printed in red. New composition. Panes of four stamps: two of 4×2½d. and one of 3×½d. and 1×2½d. arranged se-tenant. Chalk-surfaced paper. Wmk Crowns (Nos. 570k and 574k).

NR1	No date, black stitching.................	4·00
	a. White stitching (3.9.63).............	4·00

II. Lemon cover as Type C printed in red. Composition changed again. Panes of four stamps 2×½d. and 2×2½d. arranged sideways, vertically se-tenant. Wmk Crowns (sideways) (No. 570mn×4).

NR2	1964 (1.7.64).............................	1·50

2s. Booklet for Christmas Cards

1965 (6 Dec). Orange-yellow cover as Type C printed in red. Two panes of 4×3d. arranged sideways. Wmk Crowns (sideways) (No. 575a).

NX1	1965..	1·00

2s.6d. Booklets

Green cover. Panes of six stamps: 6×2½d., 6×1½d., 3×1d. (page completed by three perforated labels), 6×½d.

LABELS. The wording printed on the labels differs as follows:

'PPR' = MINIMUM INLAND PRINTED PAPER RATE 1½d.

Two types exist:

A. Printed in photogravure, 17 mm high.

B. Typographed, 15 mm high.

'Shorthand' = SHORTHAND IN 1 WEEK (covering all three labels).

'Post Early' = PLEASE POST EARLY IN THE DAY.

'PAP' = PACK YOUR PARCELS SECURELY (1st label)

ADDRESS YOUR LETTERS CORRECTLY (2nd label),

AND POST EARLY IN THE DAY (3rd label).

1953–54. Composite booklets containing stamps of King George VI and Queen Elizabeth II.
A. KGVI ½d. and 1d. (Nos. 503/504) and QEII 1½d. and 2½d. (Nos. 517 and 519b). Cover as Type A. No interleaving pages.

F1	MAY 1953 (PPR 17 mm).....................	20·00
F2	JUNE 1953 (PPR 17 mm)...................	25·00
F3	JULY 1953 (PPR 17 mm)...................	30·00
F4	AUG 1953 (PPR 17 mm)...................	27·00

B. Same composition but with addition of two interleaving pages, one at each end. Cover as Type A.

F5	SEPT 1953 (PPR 17 mm)...................	£175
F6	SEPT 1953 (PPR 15 mm)...................	90·00

C. Same composition and with interleaving pages but with cover as Type B.

F7	OCT 1953 (PPR 17 mm)...................	40·00
F8	OCT 1953 (PPR 15 mm)...................	£100
F9	NOV 1953 (PPR 17 mm)...................	45·00
F10	NOV 1953 (PPR 15 mm)...................	£175

F11	DEC 1953 (PPR 17 mm)	40·00
F12	JAN 1954 (Shorthand)	50·00
F13	FEB 1954 (Shorthand)	55·00

D. New composition: KGVI 1d. (No. 504) and QEII ½d., 1½d. and 2½d. (Nos. 515, 517 and 519b).

F14	MAR 1954 (PPR 17 mm)	£450
F14a	MAR 1954 (Shorthand)	

1954–57. Booklets containing only Queen Elizabeth II stamps. All covers as Type B.

A. Wmk Tudor Crown (Nos. 515/517 and 519b).

F15	MAR 1954 (PPR 15 mm)	£225
F16	APR 1954 (Post Early)	45·00
F17	MAY 1954 (Post Early)	45·00
F18	JUNE 1954 (Post Early)	45·00
F19	JULY 1954 (Post Early)	45·00
F20	AUG 1954 (Post Early)	45·00
F21	SEPT 1954 (Post Early)	45·00
F22	OCT 1954 (Post Early)	35·00
F23	NOV 1954 (Post Early)	35·00
F24	DEC 1954 (Post Early)	35·00

B. Same composition but with interleaving pages between each pane of stamps.

F25	JAN 1955 (Post Early)	50·00
F26	JAN 1955 (PAP)	£140
F27	FEB 1955 (PAP)	35·00
F28	MAR 1955 (PAP)	35·00
F29	APR 1955 (PAP)	35·00
F30	MAY 1955 (PAP)	45·00
F31	JUNE 1955 (PAP)	35·00
F32	JULY 1955 (PAP)	35·00
F33	AUG 1955 (PAP)	35·00

C. Mixed watermarks. Wmk Tudor Crown (Nos. 515/517 and 519b) and wmk St Edward's Crown (Nos. 540/542 and 544b) in various combinations.

F34	SEPT 1955 (PAP)............from	42·00

2s.6d. booklets dated AUGUST, OCTOBER, NOVEMBER and DECEMBER 1955, JANUARY, MAY and JUNE 1956 exist both as listed and with the two watermarks mixed. There are so many different combinations that we do not list them separately, but when in stock selections can be submitted. The SEPTEMBER 1955 booklet (No. F34) only exists in composite form.

D. Wmk St Edward's Crown (Nos. 540/542 and 544b).

F35	OCT 1955 (PAP)	25·00
F36	NOV 1955 (PAP)	25·00
F37	DEC 1955 (PAP)	25·00
F38	JAN 1956 (PAP)	25·00
F39	FEB 1956 (PAP)	25·00
F40	MAR 1956 (PAP)	25·00
F41	APR 1956 (PAP)	32·00
F42	MAY 1956 (PAP)	25·00
F43	JUNE 1956 (PAP)	25·00
F44	JULY 1956 (PAP)	18·00
F45	AUG 1956 (PAP)	18·00
F46	SEPT 1956 (PAP)	32·00
F47	OCT 1956 (PAP)	25·00
F48	NOV 1956 (PAP)	25·00
F49	DEC 1956 (PAP)	25·00
F50	JAN 1957 (PAP)	25·00
F51	FEB 1957 (PAP)	25·00
F52	MAR 1957 (PAP)	25·00

E. Same wmk but new composition. Panes of six stamps: 6×2½d. (No. 544b), 6×2d. (No. 543b) and 6×½d. (No. 540).

F53	APR 1957	25·00
F54	MAY 1957	25·00
F55	JUNE 1957	22·00
F56	JULY 1957	22·00
F57	AUG 1957	22·00
F58	SEPT 1957	22·00
F59	OCT 1957	22·00
F60	NOV 1957	18·00
F61	DEC 1957	32·00

3s. Booklets

1958–65. Panes of six stamps: 6×3d., 6×1½d., 6×1d., 6×½d.

I. Red cover as Type B.
A. Wmk St Edward's Crown (Nos. 540/542 and 545).

M1	JAN 1958	20·00
M2	FEB 1958	25·00
M3	MAR 1958	22·00
M4	APR 1958	20·00
M5	MAY 1958	20·00
M6	JUNE 1958	20·00
M7	JULY 1958	22·00
M8	AUG 1958	25·00
M9	NOV 1958	25·00

The 3s. booklets dated NOVEMBER 1958, DECEMBER 1958 and JANUARY 1959 exist both as listed and with mixed St Edward's Crown and Crowns watermarks.

B. Wmk Crowns (Nos. 570/572 and 575) or graphite lines (Nos. 587/589 and 592).

M10	DEC 1958	25·00
M11	JAN 1959	25·00
M12	FEB 1959	25·00

M13	AUG 1959	28·00
	g. With graphite lines	£175
M14	SEPT 1959	28·00
	g. With graphite lines	£225

II. Brick-red cover as Type C. Wmk Crowns (Nos. 570/572 and 575), graphite lines (Nos. 587/589 and 592) or phosphor (Nos. 610/612 and 615).

M15	OCT 1959	25·00
	g. With graphite lines	£250
M16	NOV 1959	25·00
M17	DEC 1959	25·00
M18	JAN 1960	25·00
M19	FEB 1960	35·00
	g. With graphite lines	£225
M20	MAR 1960	35·00
	g. With graphite lines	£250
M21	APR 1960	32·00
	g. With graphite lines	£225
M22	MAY 1960	42·00
M23	JUNE 1960	42·00
M24	JULY 1960	35·00
M25	AUG 1960	32·00
	p. With phosphor bands	50·00
M26	SEPT 1960	35·00
M27	OCT 1960	35·00
M28	NOV 1960	25·00
	p. With phosphor bands	50·00

III. Brick-red cover as Type D. Wmk Crowns (Nos. 570/572 and 575) or phosphor (Nos. 610/612 and 615).

M29	DEC 1960	35·00
	p. With phosphor bands	50·00
M30	JAN 1961	42·00
M31	FEB 1961	42·00
M32	MAR 1961	42·00
M33	APR 1961	42·00
	p. With phosphor bands	50·00
M34	MAY 1961	42·00
M35	JUNE 1961	42·00
M36	JULY 1961	40·00
	p. With phosphor bands	50·00
M37	AUG 1961	42·00
	p. With phosphor bands	50·00
M38	SEPT 1961	42·00
	p. With phosphor bands	55·00
M39	OCT 1961	42·00
	p. With phosphor bands	70·00
M40	NOV 1961	42·00
M41	DEC 1961	42·00
M42	JAN 1962	42·00
M43	FEB 1962	42·00
	p. With phosphor bands	70·00
M44	MAR 1962	35·00
	p. With phosphor bands	70·00
M45	APR 1962	35·00
	p. With phosphor bands	70·00
M46	MAY 1962	42·00
	p. With phosphor bands	70·00
M47	JUNE 1962	42·00
	p. With phosphor bands	70·00
M48	JULY 1962	42·00
M49	AUG 1962	42·00
	p. With phosphor bands	60·00
M50	SEPT 1962	40·00
	p. With phosphor bands	70·00
M51	OCT 1962	50·00
	p. With phosphor bands	70·00
M52	NOV 1962	50·00
	p. With phosphor bands	70·00
M53	DEC 1962	50·00
	p. With phosphor bands	70·00
M54	JAN 1963	50·00
M55	FEB 1963	50·00
	p. With phosphor bands	70·00
M56	MAR 1963	50·00
	p. With phosphor bands	70·00
M57	APR 1963	50·00
	p. With phosphor bands	70·00
M58	MAY 1963	50·00
	p. With phosphor bands	£350
M59	JUNE 1963	55·00
	p. With phosphor bands	50·00
M60	JULY 1963	42·00
	p. With phosphor bands	70·00
M61	AUG 1963	50·00
	p. With phosphor bands	70·00
M62	SEPT 1963	50·00
M63	OCT 1963	55·00
M64	NOV 1963	50·00
	p. With phosphor bands	70·00
M65	DEC 1963	50·00
	p. With phosphor bands	£140
M66	JAN 1964	55·00
	p. With phosphor bands	50·00
M67	MAR 1964	55·00
	p. With phosphor bands	70·00
M68	MAY 1964	55·00
	p. With phosphor bands	85·00
M69	JULY 1964	42·00
	p. With phosphor bands	70·00

M70	SEPT 1964..	42·00
	p. With phosphor bands..........................	70·00
M71	NOV 1964..	32·00
	p. With phosphor bands..........................	40·00
M72	JAN 1965...	32·00
	p. With phosphor bands..........................	50·00
M73	MAR 1965...	25·00
	p. With phosphor bands..........................	48·00
M74	MAY 1965..	48·00
	p. With phosphor bands..........................	70·00

3s.9d. Booklets

1953–57. Red cover as Type B. Panes of six stamps: 18×2½d.

A. Wmk Tudor Crown (No. 519b).

G1	NOV 1953..	28·00
G2	JAN 1954...	42·00
G3	MAR 1954...	28·00
G4	DEC 1954...	28·00
G5	FEB 1955...	28·00
G6	APR 1955...	28·00
G7	JUNE 1955...	28·00
G8	AUG 1955...	28·00
G9	OCT 1955...	28·00
G10	DEC 1955...	28·00

3s.9d. booklets dated OCTOBER and DECEMBER 1955 exist both as listed and with the two watermarks mixed.

B. Wmk St Edward's Crown (No. 544b). Same composition but with interleaving pages between each pane of stamps.

G12	FEB 1956...	22·00
G13	APR 1956...	22·00
G14	JUNE 1956...	22·00
G15	AUG 1956...	22·00
G16	OCT 1956...	22·00
G17	DEC 1956...	22·00
G18	FEB 1957...	22·00
G19	APR 1957...	22·00
G20	JUNE 1957...	12·00
G21	AUG 1957...	28·00

4s.6d. Booklets

1957–65. Panes of six stamps: 18×3d.

I. Purple cover as Type B.
A. Wmk St Edward's Crown (No. 545).

L1	OCT 1957...	22·00
L2	DEC 1957...	22·00
L3	FEB 1958...	25·00
L4	APR 1958...	22·00
L5	JUNE 1958...	24·00
L6	OCT 1958...	22·00
L7	DEC 1958...	22·00

B. Wmk Crowns (No. 575).

L8	DEC 1958...	90·00

II. Purple cover as Type C. Wmk Crowns (No. 575) or graphite lines (No. 592).

L9	FEB 1959...	25·00
L10	JUNE 1959...	28·00
L11	AUG 1959...	22·00
	g. With graphite lines.............................	32·00
L12	OCT 1959...	32·00
L13	DEC 1959...	25·00

III. Violet cover as Type C. Wmk Crowns (No. 575), graphite lines (No. 592) or phosphor (No. 615).

L14	FEB 1959...	70·00
L15	APR 1959...	25·00
	g. With graphite lines.............................	22·00
L16	JUNE 1959...	42·00
	g. With graphite lines.............................	22·00
L17	DEC 1959...	42·00
L18	FEB 1960...	25·00
	g. With graphite lines.............................	42·00
L19	APR 1960...	25·00
	g. With graphite lines.............................	25·00
L20	JUNE 1960...	28·00
L21	AUG 1960...	28·00
	p. With phosphor bands..........................	42·00
L22	OCT 1960...	50·00

IV. Violet cover as Type D. Wmk Crowns (No. 575) or phosphor (No. 615).

L23	DEC 1960...	50·00
L24	FEB 1961...	50·00
	p. With phosphor bands..........................	35·00
L25	APR 1961...	35·00
	p. With phosphor bands..........................	32·00
L26	JUNE 1961...	50·00
L27	AUG 1961...	50·00
	p. With phosphor bands..........................	55·00
L28	OCT 1961...	50·00
	p. With phosphor bands..........................	42·00
L29	DEC 1961...	50·00
L30	FEB 1962...	45·00
	p. With phosphor bands..........................	28·00
L31	APR 1962...	50·00
	p. With phosphor bands..........................	55·00
L32	JUNE 1962...	55·00
	p. With phosphor bands..........................	60·00

L33	AUG 1962...	42·00
	p. With phosphor bands..........................	60·00
L34	OCT 1962...	42·00
	p. With phosphor bands..........................	£200
L35	DEC 1962...	50·00
	p. With phosphor bands..........................	55·00
L36	FEB 1963...	50·00
	p. With phosphor bands..........................	55·00
L37	APR 1963...	50·00
	p. With phosphor bands..........................	40·00
L38	JUNE 1963...	50·00
	p. With phosphor bands..........................	40·00
L39	AUG 1963...	55·00
	p. With phosphor bands..........................	45·00
L40	OCT 1963...	50·00
	p. With phosphor bands..........................	70·00
L41	NOV 1963..	55·00
	p. With phosphor bands..........................	45·00
L42	DEC 1963...	50·00
	p. With phosphor bands..........................	£210
L43	JAN 1964...	85·00
L44	FEB 1964...	55·00
	p. With phosphor bands..........................	40·00
L45	MAR 1964...	85·00
	p. With phosphor bands..........................	£125
L46	APR 1964...	85·00
	p. With phosphor bands..........................	45·00
L47	MAY 1964..	55·00
	p. With phosphor bands..........................	70·00
L48	JUNE 1964...	55·00
	p. With phosphor bands..........................	70·00
L49	JULY 1964..	55·00
	p. With phosphor bands..........................	45·00
L50	AUG 1964...	55·00
	p. With phosphor bands..........................	40·00
L51	SEPT 1964..	55·00
	p. With phosphor bands..........................	45·00
L52	OCT 1964...	55·00
	p. With phosphor bands..........................	70·00
L53	NOV 1964..	55·00
	p. With phosphor bands..........................	45·00
L54	DEC 1964...	55·00
	p. With phosphor bands..........................	45·00
L55	JAN 1965...	50·00
	p. With phosphor bands..........................	42·00
L56	FEB 1965...	42·00
	p. With phosphor bands..........................	55·00
L57	MAR 1965...	25·00
	p. With phosphor bands..........................	£350
L58	APR 1965...	40·00

1965 (26 July)–**67**. New composition. Panes of six stamps: 12×4d., 6×1d. Slate-blue cover as Type D. Wmk Crowns (Nos. 571 and 576a) or phosphor (Nos. 611 and 616a).

L59	JULY 1965..	22·00
	p. With phosphor bands..........................	24·00
L60	SEPT 1965..	22·00
	p. With phosphor bands..........................	24·00
L61	NOV 1965..	22·00
	p. With phosphor bands..........................	25·00
L62	JAN 1966...	25·00
	p. With phosphor bands..........................	24·00
L63	MAR 1966...	22·00
	p. With phosphor bands..........................	22·00
L64	JAN 1967...	28·00
	p. With phosphor bands..........................	22·00
L65	MAR 1967...	50·00
	p. With phosphor bands..........................	17·00
L66p	MAY 1967. With phosphor bands..........	12·00
L67p	JULY 1967. With phosphor bands..........	17·00
L68p	SEPT 1967. With phosphor bands..........	15·00
L69p	NOV 1967. With phosphor bands..........	12·00
L70p	JAN 1968. With phosphor bands..........	12·00
L71p	MAR 1968. With phosphor bands..........	10·00

4s.6d. Booklets with Machin type stamps

1968–70. Slate-blue cover as Type D. Panes of six stamps: 12×4d., 6×1d. PVA gum (Nos. 724, 731v).

LP45	MAY 1968..	4·00

LP46 Ships series with GPO Cypher

(Des S. Rose)

Blue cover as Type **LP46**. Ships series. Composition as last.

LP46	JULY 1968 (*Cutty Sark*)............................	70

Same composition but changed to 4d. with one centre phosphor band (No. 732).

LP47	SEPT 1968 (*Golden Hind*)..........................	70
LP48	NOV 1968 (*Discovery*)..............................	70

Same composition but changed to 4d. bright vermilion with one centre phosphor band (No. 733).

LP49	JAN 1969 (*Queen Elizabeth 2*)...................	90
LP50	MAR 1969 (*Sirius*)..................................	2·00
LP51	MAY 1969 (*Sirius*)..................................	1·25
LP52	JULY 1969 (*Dreadnought*)........................	1·25
LP53	SEPT 1969 (*Dreadnought*)........................	5·00
LP54	NOV 1969 (*Mauretania*)..........................	1·50
LP55	JAN 1970 (*Mauretania*)...........................	5·00
LP56	MAR 1970 (*Victory*)................................	1·50
LP57	MAY 1970 (*Victory*)................................	5·00

LP58 Ships Series with Post Office Corporation Crown Symbol

(Des S. Rose)

As last but cover changed to T **LP58**.

LP58	AUG 1970 (*Sovereign of the Seas*)............	4·50
LP59	OCT 1970 (*Sovereign of the Seas*)............	5·00

5s. Booklets

1953–57. Buff cover. Panes of six stamps. 12×2½d., 6×2d., 6×1½d., 6×1d., 6×½d.

I. Composite booklets containing stamps of King George VI and Queen Elizabeth II.

A. KGVI ½d., 1d. and 2d. (Nos. 503/504 and 506) and QEII 1½d. and 2½d. (Nos. 517 and 519b). Cover as Type A. No interleaving pages.

H1	MAY 1953..	32·00
H2	JULY 1953...	35·00

B. Same composition but with addition of two interleaving pages, one at each end. Cover as Type A.

H3	SEPT 1953...	45·00

C. Same composition and with interleaving pages but cover as Type B.

H4	NOV 1953..	35·00
H5	JAN 1954..	45·00

D. New composition: KGVI 1d. and 2d. (Nos. 504 and 506) and QEII ½d., 1½d.and 2½d. (Nos. 515, 517 and 519b).

H6	MAR 1954..	£675

E. New composition: KGVI 2d. (No. 506) and QEII ½d. 1d., 1½d. and 2½d. (Nos. 515/517 and 519b).

H7	MAR 1954..	£190

II. Booklets containing only Queen Elizabeth II stamps. Buff cover as Type B. Two interleaving panes as before.

A. Wmk Tudor Crown (Nos. 515/518 and 519b).

H8	MAR 1954..	£160
H9	MAY 1954..	85·00
H10	JULY 1954...	90·00
H11	SEPT 1954...	65·00
H12	NOV 1954..	85·00

B. Same composition but with interleaving pages between each pane of stamps.

H13	JAN 1955..	65·00
H14	MAR 1955..	50·00
H15	MAY 1955..	55·00
H16	JULY 1955...	85·00

C. Wmk St Edward's Crown (Nos. 540/543 and 544b).

H17	SEPT 1955...	28·00
H18	NOV 1955..	30·00
H19	JAN 1956..	32·00
H20	MAR 1956..	40·00
H21	MAY 1956..	35·00
H22	JULY 1956...	32·00
H23	SEPT 1956...	35·00
H24	NOV 1956..	35·00
H25	JAN 1957..	40·00

5s. booklets dated SEPTEMBER and NOVEMBER 1955 and JANUARY 1956 exist both as listed and with the two watermarks mixed. There are so many different combinations that we do not list them separately, but when in stock selections can be submitted.

D. Same watermark. Introduction of 2d. light red-brown (No. 543b) in place of No. 543.

H26	JAN 1957..	35·00
H27	MAR 1957..	45·00
H28	MAY 1957..	35·00
H29	JULY 1957...	28·00
H30	SEPT 1957...	28·00
H31	NOV 1957..	28·00

1958–65.

E. New composition. Panes of six stamps: 12×3d. (No. 545), 6×2½d. (No. 544b), 6×1d. (No. 541), 6×½d. (No. 540). Wmk St Edward's Crown.

H32	JAN 1958..	28·00
H33	MAR 1958..	28·00
H34	MAY 1958..	30·00
H35	JULY 1958 (11.58)..................................	20·00
H36	NOV 1958..	20·00

5s. booklets dated JULY 1958, NOVEMBER 1958 and JANUARY 1959 exist with mixed watermarks.

F. Blue cover as Type C. Wmk Crowns (Nos. 570/571, 574/575), graphite lines (Nos. 587/588 and 591/592) or phosphor (Nos. 610/611, 614 and 615).

H37	JAN 1959..	25·00
H38	MAR 1959..	32·00
H39	JULY 1959...	30·00
	g. With graphite lines.............................	90·00
H40	SEPT 1959...	32·00
H41	NOV 1959..	32·00
H42	JAN 1960..	32·00
H43	MAR 1960..	32·00
	g. With graphite lines.............................	£120
H44	MAY 1960..	35·00
H45	JULY 1960...	40·00
H46	SEPT 1960...	55·00
	g. With graphite lines.............................	£120
	p. With phosphor bands.........................	85·00
H47	NOV 1960..	42·00

G. As last but blue cover as Type D. Same composition.
I. Phosphor has two bands on 2½d. (No. 614).

H48	JAN 1961..	42·00
H49	MAR 1961..	42·00
	p. With phosphor bands.........................	£110
H50	MAY 1961..	42·00
H51	JULY 1961...	65·00
	p. With phosphor bands.........................	£120
H52	SEPT 1961...	42·00
	p. With phosphor bands.........................	£160
H53	NOV 1961..	42·00
H54	JAN 1962..	65·00
	p. With phosphor bands.........................	£160

II. As last but phosphor has one band on 2½d. (No. 614a).

H55	MAR 1962..	55·00
	p. With phosphor bands.........................	£125
H56	MAY 1962..	42·00
	p. With phosphor bands.........................	£140
H57	JULY 1962...	65·00
	p. With phosphor bands.........................	£125
H58	SEPT 1962...	60·00
	p. With phosphor bands.........................	£175
H59	NOV 1962..	60·00
	p. With phosphor bands.........................	£175
H60	JAN 1963..	42·00
	p. With phosphor bands.........................	£425
H61	MAR 1963..	42·00
	p. With phosphor bands.........................	£175
H62	MAY 1963..	55·00
	p. With phosphor bands.........................	£175
H63	JULY 1963...	65·00
	p. With phosphor bands.........................	£120
H64	SEPT 1963...	42·00
	p. With phosphor bands.........................	£175
H65	NOV 1963..	42·00
	p. With phosphor bands.........................	£175
H66	JAN 1964..	42·00
	p. With phosphor bands.........................	85·00
H67	MAR 1964..	42·00
	p. With phosphor bands.........................	85·00
H68	MAY 1964..	65·00
	p. With phosphor bands.........................	£160
H69	JULY 1964...	65·00
	p. With phosphor bands.........................	£140
H70	SEPT 1964...	42·00
	p. With phosphor bands.........................	£140
H71	NOV 1964..	65·00
	p. With phosphor bands.........................	85·00
H72	JAN 1965..	35·00
	p. With phosphor bands.........................	85·00
H73	MAR 1965..	35·00
	p. With phosphor bands.........................	£160
H74	MAY 1965..	32·00
	p. With phosphor bands.........................	£100

5s. Booklets with Machin type stamps

HP26 English Homes Series with GPO Cypher

(Des S. Rose)

1968 (27 Nov)–**70**. Cinnamon cover as T **HP26** (English Homes Series). Panes of six stamps: 12×5d. (No. 735).

HP26	DEC 1968 (Ightham Mote)	2·00
HP27	FEB 1969 (Little Moreton Hall)	2·00
HP28	APR 1969 (Long Melford Hall)	2·00
HP29	JUNE 1969 (Long Melford Hall)	2·00
HP30	AUG 1969 (Long Melford Hall)	5·00

HP31 English Homes Series with Post Office Corporation Crown Symbol

(Des S. Rose)

As last but cover changed to T **HP31**.

HP31	OCT 1969 (Mompesson House)	2·25
HP32	DEC 1969 (Mompesson House)	2·50
HP33	FEB 1970 (Cumberland Terrace)	2·25

HP34

(Des P. Gauld)

As last but cover changed to T **HP34** *(special edition to advertise Philympia International Philatelic Exhibition, London, September 1970).*

HP34	(no date) (3.3.70)	2·25

As last but cover changed to T **HP31**.

HP35	JUNE 1970 (The Vineyard, Saffron Walden)	2·50
HP36	AUG 1970 (The Vineyard, Saffron Walden)	3·25
HP37	OCT 1970 (Mereworth Castle)	3·25
HP38	DEC 1970 (Mereworth Castle)	3·25

6s. Booklets

1965 (21 June)–**67**. Claret cover as Type D. Wmk Crowns (No. 576a) or phosphor (No. 616a). Panes of six stamps: 18×4d.

Q1	JUNE 1965	32·00
	p. With phosphor bands	32·00
Q2	JULY 1965	32·00
	p. With phosphor bands	32·00
Q3	AUG 1965	55·00
	p. With phosphor bands	55·00
Q4	SEPT 1965	42·00
	p. With phosphor bands	42·00

Q5	OCT 1965	60·00
	p. With phosphor bands	60·00
Q6	NOV 1965	60·00
	p. With phosphor bands	60·00
Q7	DEC 1965	60·00
	p. With phosphor bands	70·00
Q8	JAN 1966	60·00
	p. With phosphor bands	60·00
Q9	FEB 1966	60·00
	p. With phosphor bands	60·00
Q10	MAR 1966	60·00
	p. With phosphor bands	70·00
Q11	APR 1966	60·00
	p. With phosphor bands	£140
Q12	MAY 1966	60·00
	p. With phosphor bands	70·00
Q13	JUNE 1966	60·00
	p. With phosphor bands	60·00
Q14	JULY 1966	60·00
	p. With phosphor bands	60·00
Q15	AUG 1966	60·00
	p. With phosphor bands	£175
Q16	SEPT 1966	40·00
	p. With phosphor bands	40·00
Q17	OCT 1966	70·00
	p. With phosphor bands	£120
Q18	NOV 1966	50·00
	p. With phosphor bands	32·00
Q19	DEC 1966	32·00
	p. With phosphor bands	55·00
Q20	JAN 1967	60·00
	p. With phosphor bands	60·00
Q21	FEB 1967	60·00
	p. With phosphor bands	35·00
Q22	MAR 1967	42·00
	p. With phosphor bands	35·00
Q23	APR 1967	32·00
	p. With phosphor bands	35·00
Q24p	MAY 1967. With phosphor bands	28·00
Q25p	JUNE 1967. With phosphor bands	28·00
Q26p	JULY 1967. With phosphor bands	70·00
Q27p	AUG 1967. With phosphor bands	50·00

6s. Booklets with Machin type stamps

1967–**70**. Claret cover as Type D. Panes of six stamps: 18×4d. Two phosphor bands. Gum arabic (No. 731).

QP28	SEPT 1967	35·00
QP29	OCT 1967	42·00
QP30	NOV 1967	35·00
QP31	DEC 1967	35·00
QP32	JAN 1968	35·00
QP33	FEB 1968 (No. 731a)	35·00
QP34	MAR 1968 (No. 731a)	35·00
QP35	APR 1968 (No. 731a)	25·00
QP36	MAY 1968 (No. 731a)	12·00

Change to PVA gum (No. 731v).

QP37	MAY 1968	£325

QP38 Birds Series with GPO Cypher

(Des S. Rose)

Orange-red cover as T **QP38** *(Birds Series). Same composition. Two phosphor bands. PVA gum (No. 731v).*

QP38	JUNE 1968 (Kingfisher) (4.6.68)	2·00
QP39	JULY 1968 (Kingfisher)	10·00
QP40	AUG 1968 (Peregrine Falcon)	2·00

Change to one centre phosphor band (No. 732).

QP41	SEPT 1968 (Peregrine Falcon) (16.9.68)	1·40
QP42	OCT 1968 (Pied Woodpecker)	2·00
QP43	NOV 1968 (Pied Woodpecker)	1·50
QP44	DEC 1968 (Great Crested Grebe)	1·50
QP45	JAN 1969 (Barn Owl)	2·75

Change to 4d. bright vermilion with one centre phosphor band (No. 733).

QP46	FEB 1969 (Barn Owl) (20.2.69)	3·50
QP47	MAR 1969 (Jay)	2·50
QP48	MAY 1969 (Jay)	3·25
QP49	JULY 1969 (Puffin)	2·50
QP50	SEPT 1969 (Puffin)	5·00

QP51 Birds Series with Post Office Corporation Crown Symbol

(Des S. Rose)

*As last but cover changed to T **QP51**.*

QP51	NOV 1969 (Cormorant)............................	3·25
QP52	JAN 1970 (Cormorant)............................	3·75
QP53	APR 1970 (Wren)...................................	3·00
QP54	AUG 1970 (Golden Eagle)......................	3·00
QP55	OCT 1970 (Golden Eagle)......................	3·00

10s. Booklets

1961 (10 Apr–Oct). Green cover as Type D. Panes of six stamps: 30×3d., 6×2d., 6×1½d., 6×1d., 6×½d. Wmk Crowns (Nos. 570/573 and 575).

X1	No date..	£100
X2	OCT 1961...	£210

1962–64. New Composition. Panes of six stamps: 30×3d., 6×2½d., 6×1½d., 6×1d. (Nos. 571/572 and 574/575).

X3	APR 1962...	90·00
X4	AUG 1962...	£125
X5	MAR 1963...	£190
X6	JULY 1963...	£125
X7	DEC 1963..	£110
X8	JULY 1964...	90·00
X9	DEC 1964..	£425

1965 (23 Aug)–**66.** Ochre cover as Type D. Panes of six stamps: 24×4d., 6×3d., 6×1d. Wmk Crowns (Nos. 571, 575, 576a).

X10	AUG 1965...	28·00
X11	DEC 1965..	55·00
X12	FEB 1966..	45·00
X13	AUG 1966...	28·00
X14	NOV 1966...	25·00

1967–68. Ochre cover as Type D. Panes of six phosphor stamps: 24×4d., 6×3d., 6×1d. Wmk Crowns (Nos. 611, 615cca (one side phosphor band), 616a).

X15p	FEB 1967...	10·00

Composition as No. X15p. Wmk Crowns (Nos. 611, 615e (one centre phosphor band), 616a).

X16p	AUG 1967...	7·00
X17p	FEB 1968..	8·00

10s. Booklets with Machin type stamps

XP4 Explorers Series with GPO Cypher

(Des S. Rose)

1968 (25 Mar–Aug). Bright purple cover as T **XP4** (Explorers Series). Pages of six stamps: 24×4d., 6×3d., 6×1d. PVA gum (Nos. 724, 729v, 731v).

XP4	MAY 1968 (Livingstone)........................	4·50
XP5	AUG 1968 (Livingstone)........................	4·50

1968 (16 Sept)–**70.** Yellow-green covers as T **XP4** (Explorers Series) New composition. Pages of six stamps: 12×5d. (with two phosphor bands), 12×4d. (with one centre phosphor band) and pane comprising 4×1d. *se-tenant* with vert pair of 4d. (each with one centre phosphor band). PVA gum (Nos. 725, 732 and 735).

XP6	SEPT 1968 (Scott)..................................	3·00

Change to 4d. bright vermilion (one centre band) but se-tenant pane comprises 1d. with two phosphor bands and 4d. with one left side phosphor band (Nos. 724 and 733/734).

XP7	FEB 1969 (Mary Kingsley) (6.1.69)..........	2·50
XP8	MAY 1969 (Mary Kingsley).....................	3·25
XP9	AUG 1969 (Shackleton)..........................	3·50
XP10	NOV 1969 (Shackleton)..........................	5·00

XP11 Explorers Series with Post Office Corporation Crown Symbol

(Des S. Rose)

*As last but cover changed to T **XP11**.*

XP11	FEB 1970 (Frobisher)..............................	5·00
XP12	NOV 1970 (Captain Cook).......................	6·00

£1 Booklet with Machin type stamps

ZP1

1969 (1 Dec). Stamps for Cooks. T **ZP1** (150×72 mm) with full colour pictorial cover showing Baked, Stuffed Haddock. Contains 12 recipes on interleaving pages and on *se-tenant* labels attached to booklet panes. PVA gum. Stapled.

ZP1	£1 containing panes of 15 stamps (5×3): 15×5d. (No. 735), 30×4d. (No. 733) and pane comprising 6×4d. (three each of Nos. 734 and 734b) *se-tenant* with 6×1d. (No. 724) and 3×5d. (No. 735)......	£225
ZP1a	As last but booklet is sewn with thread instead of being stapled..........................	6·50

II. DECIMAL BOOKLETS, 1971 ONWARDS.

A. Stitched Booklets.

The 25p., 30p., 35p., 45p. and 50p. booklets have pictorial covers (except for the 35p. and 45p.) without the design inscription. This was no longer necessary as the designs and background information were given on the inside of the front cover. Each series was numbered.

10p. Booklets

DN46 British Pillar Box Series

(Des R. Maddox)

1971 (15 Feb–1 June). British Pillar Box Series. Orange-yellow cover as T **DN46**. Panes of four stamps: 2×2p. *se-tenant* vertically with 2×½p. and 2×1p. *se-tenant* vertically with 2×1½p. (Nos. X841l and X844l).
DN46	FEB 1971 (No. 1 1855 type)......................	1·25
DN47	APR 1971 (No. 1 1855 type) (19.3.71).....	1·00
DN48	JUNE 1971 (No. 2 1856 type) (1.6.71)......	1·75

In No. DN47 the pillar box is slightly reduced in size.

1971 (14 July)–**74**. British Pillar Box Series continued. Orange-yellow cover as T **DN46**. Contents unchanged but panes are *se-tenant* horizontally (Nos. X841la and X844m).
DN49	AUG 1971 (No. 2 1856 type) (14.7.71).....	1·50
DN50	OCT 1971 (No. 3 1857–1859 type)	
	(27.8.71)..	1·50
DN51	DEC 1971 (No. 3 1857–1859 type)	
	(6.10.71)...	2·25
DN52	FEB 1972 (No. 4 1866–1879 type)	
	(8.12.71)...	2·25
DN53	APR 1972 (No. 4 1866–1879 type)	
	(24.2.72)...	1·75
DN54	JUNE 1972 (No. 5 1899 type) (12.4.72)...	1·25
DN55	AUG 1972 (No. 5 1899 type) (8.6.72)......	1·50
DN56	OCT 1972 (No. 6 1968 type) (2.8.72).......	1·50
DN57	DEC 1972 (No. 6 1968 type) (30.10.72)...	1·50
DN58	FEB 1973 (No. 7 1936 type) (5.1.73)........	1·50
DN59	APR 1973 (No. 7 1936 type) (2.4.73)........	5·00
DN60	JUNE 1973 (No. 8 1952 type) (18.4.73)...	2·00
DN61	AUG 1973 (No. 8 1952 type) (4.7.73)........	10·00
DN62	OCT 1973 (No. 9 1973 type) (16.8.73).....	1·75
DN63	DEC 1973 (No. 9 1973 type) (12.11.73)....	2·00
DN64	FEB 1974 (No. 9 1973 type) (17.12.73).....	2·25
DN65	APR 1974 (No. 10 1974 type) (22.2.74).....	1·50
DN66	JUNE 1974 (No. 10 1974 type) (23.4.74).	1·50

DN67 Postal Uniforms Series

(Des C. Abbott)

1974 (23 July)–**76**. Postal Uniforms Series. Orange-yellow cover as T **DN67**. Contents unchanged.
DN67	AUG 1974 (No. 1 1793 type)......................	1·00
DN68	OCT 1974 (No. 1 1793 type) (27.8.74).....	1·00
DN69	DEC 1974 (No. 2 1837 type) (25.10.74)...	1·00
DN70	FEB 1975 (No. 2 1837 type) (12.12.74)...	1·00
DN71	APR 1975 (No. 3 1855 type) (26.3.75).....	1·00
DN72	JUNE 1975 (No. 3 1855 type) (21.5.75)...	1·00
DN73	AUG 1975 (No. 3 1855 type) (27.6.75).....	1·00
DN74	OCT 1975 (No. 3 1855 type) (3.10.75).....	50
DN75	JAN 1976 (No. 3 1855 type) (16.3.76)......	50

25p. Booklets

DH39 Veteran Transport Series

(Des D. Gentleman)

1971 (15 Feb). Veteran Transport Series. Dull purple cover as T **DH39**. Panes of six stamps: 5×2½p. with one printed label, 4×½p. with two printed labels, 5×½p. with one printed label (Nos. X841m and X851l/X851m).
DH39	FEB 1971 (No. 1 Knife-board omnibus)..	3·00

DH40

1971 (19 Mar). Issued to publicise the National Postal Museum Exhibition of 80 Years of British Stamp Booklets. Dull purple cover as T **DH40**.
DH40	APR 1971..	3·50

1971 (11 June)–**73**. Dull purple cover as T **DH39**. Veteran Transport Series continued.
DH41	JUNE 1971 (No. 2 B-type omnibus)...........	3·25
DH42	AUG 1971 (No. 2 B-type omnibus)	
	(17.9.71)..	8·00
DH43	OCT 1971 (No. 3 Showman's Engine)	
	(22.11.71)..	8·00
DH44	FEB 1972 (No. 4 Mail Van) (23.12.71).......	4·50
DH45	APR 1972 (No. 4 Mail Van) (13.3.72).........	5·50
DH46	JUNE 1972 (No. 5 Motor Wagonette)	
	(24.4.72)...	4·00
DH47	AUG 1972 (No. 5 Motor Wagonette)	
	(14.6.72)...	8·00
DH48	OCT 1972 (No. 6 Taxi Cab) (17.7.72).........	6·00
DH49	DEC 1972 (No. 6 Taxi Cab) (19.10.72)......	8·00
DH50	DEC 1972 Issue S (No. 6 Taxi Cab)	
	(6.11.72)...	4·50
DH51	FEB 1973 (No. 7 Electric Tramcar)	
	(26.2.73)...	6·00

Nos. DH42/DH51 contain panes showing the perforations omitted between the label and the binding margin.

DH52

1973 (7 June). Dull mauve cover as T **DH52**.
DH52	JUNE 1973...	6·00

No. DH52 contains panes showing the perforations omitted between the label and the binding margin.

30p. Booklets

DQ56 British Birds Series

(Des H. Titcombe)

1971 (15 Feb). British Birds Series. Bright purple cover as T **DQ56**. Panes of six stamps: 2 panes of 5×3p. with one printed label (No. X855l).
DQ56	FEB 1971 (No. 1 Curlew)...........................	2·75

1971 (19 Mar). Bright purple cover as T **DH40**.
DQ57	APR 1971..	3·75

1971 (26 May)–**73**. Bright purple cover as T **DQ56**. British Birds Series continued.

DQ58	JUNE 1971 (No. 2 Lapwing).....................	3·75
DQ59	AUG 1971 (No. 2 Lapwing) (23.7.71)......	3·75
DQ60	OCT 1971 (No. 3 Robin) (1.10.71)...........	3·75
DQ61	DEC 1971 (No. 3 Robin) (10.11.71)........	4·50
DQ62	FEB 1972 (No. 4 Pied Wagtail)	
	(21.12.71)..	3·75
DQ63	APR 1972 (No. 4 Pied Wagtail) (9.2.72)..	3·75
DQ64	JUNE 1972 (No. 5 Kestrel) (12.4.72)........	3·75
DQ65	AUG 1972 (No. 5 Kestrel) (8.6.72)...........	3·75
DQ66	OCT 1972 (No. 6 Black Grouse)	
	(31.7.72)..	4·25
DQ67	DEC 1972 (No. 6 Black Grouse)	
	(30.10.72)..	4·25
DQ68	DEC 1972 Issue S (No. 6 Black Grouse)	
	(6.12.72)..	4·25
DQ69	FEB 1973 (No. 7 Skylark) (29.1.73).........	4·00
DQ70	APR 1973 (No. 7 Skylark) (2.4.73)...........	3·50
DQ71	JUNE 1973 (No. 8 Oystercatcher)	
	(8.5.73)...	4·00
DQ72	AUG 1973 (No. 8 Oystercatcher)	
	(7.6.73)...	5·50
DQ72a	As DQ72 but buff cover (10.8.73)*........	4·50

*   No. DQ72a was printed with a buff cover because of a shortage of the original purple coloured card.

Nos. DQ59/DQ72a contain panes showing the perforations omitted between the label and the binding margin.

1974 (30 Jan). Red cover similar to T **DH52**. Make-up as before but containing panes of 5×3p. (1 centre band) (No. X856) with blank label.

DQ73	SPRING 1974..	3·00

1974 (2 June). Red cover similar to T **DT9**. Make-up as before.

DQ74	JUNE 1974..	4·00

35p. Booklets

DP1 British Coins Series

(Des P Gauld)

1973 (12 Dec)–**74**. British Coins Series. Blue cover as T **DP1**. Panes of six stamps: 2 panes of 5×3½p. with one blank label (No. X858b).

DP1	AUTUMN 1973 (No. 1 Cuthred's Penny).	2·25
DP2	APR 1974 (No. 1 Cuthred's Penny)	
	(10.4.74)...	4·00
DP3	JUNE 1974 (No. 2 Silver Groat) (4.7.74)...	2·50

1974 (23 Oct). Blue cover as T **DT9**. Make-up as before but with No. X859.

DP4	SEPT 1974...	2·50

45p. Booklets

1974 (9 Oct–26 Nov). British Coins Series continued. Yellow-brown cover as T **DP1**. Pages of six stamps: 2 panes of 5×4½p. (No. X865) with one blank label.

DS1	SEPT 1974 (No. 3 Elizabeth Gold	
	Crown)...	3·00
DS2	DEC 1974 (No. 3 Elizabeth Gold Crown)	
	(1.11.74)...	3·00
DS2a	As DS2 but orange-brown cover	
	(26.11.74)*...	20·00

*   No. DS2a was printed with an orange-brown cover because of a shortage of the original yellow-brown card.

50p. Booklets

DT1

(Des Rosalie Southall)

1971 (15 Feb)–**72**. British Flowers Series. Turquoise-green cover as T **DT1**. Panes of six stamps: 6×3p, 4×3p. *se-tenant* horizontally with 2×2½p. (side band), 5×2½p. (centre band) with one printed label and 5×½p. with one printed label (Nos. X841m, X851l, X852l and X855×6).

DT1	FEB 1971 (No. 1 Large Bindweed)...........	5·00
DT2	MAY 1971 (No. 2 Primrose) (24.3.71).......	6·00
DT3	AUG 1971 (No. 3 Honeysuckle)	
	(28.6.71)..	6·00
DT4	NOV 1971 (No. 4 Hop) (17.9.71)..............	6·25
DT5	FEB 1972 (No. 5 Common Violet)	
	(23.12.71)*..	6·25
DT6	MAY 1972 (No. 6 Lords-and-Ladies)	
	(13.3.72)..	6·25
DT7	AUG 1972 (No. 7 Wood Anemone)	
	(31.5.72)..	6·25
DT8	NOV 1972 (No. 8 Deadly Nightshade)	
	(15.9.72)..	5·25

*   Although generally released on 24 December, this booklet was put on sale at the London EC1 Philatelic Counter and also at one other Philatelic Counter on 23 December.

Nos. DT4/DT8 contain panes showing the perforations omitted between the label and the binding margin.

DT9

1973 (19 Jan–June). Turquoise-green cover as T **DT9**.

DT9	FEB 1973..	5·25
DT10	APR 1973 (26.2.73).....................................	7·00
DT11	MAY 1973 (2.4.73).......................................	6·75
DT12	AUG 1973 (14.6.73)....................................	10·50

1973 (14 Nov)–**74**. Moss-green cover similar to T **DT9**. Pages of six stamps: 2 pages of 5×3½p. with one blank label (No. X858b) and 1 page of 5×3p. (centre band) and one blank label (No. X856).

DT13	AUTUMN 1973...	4·50
DT14	MAR 1974 (18.2.74)....................................	3·50

85p. Booklet

1974 (13 Nov). Purple cover similar to T **DT9**.

DW1	Containing 3 pages of 5×4½p. (No. X865) with one blank label and 1 page of 5×3½p. (No. X859) with one blank label...	6·25

No. DW1 is dated SEPT 1974.

SPONSORED AND PRESTIGE BOOKLETS

DX1

(Des J. Wallis)

1972 (24 May). The Story of Wedgwood. Full colour pictorial cover, T **DX1** (150×72 mm). Containing information and illustrations on interleaving panes and on *se-tenant* label attached to booklet panes.

DX1   £1 containing Nos. X841o/X841p, X851n
        and X855n booklet panes...................... 45·00
   Price quoted for No. DX1 is for examples showing the ½p. 1 side band, No. X842, (in pane No. X841p) with full perforations. Examples of the booklet with this ½p. value showing trimmed perforations are priced at £15.

ILLUSTRATIONS. Sponsored and Prestige booklet covers from No. DX2 are illustrated at one-third linear size unless otherwise stated.

DX2

(Des J. Wallis)

1980 (16 Apr). The Story of Wedgwood. Multicoloured cover, T **DX2** (163×97 mm) showing painting Josiah Wedgwood and his Family by George Stubbs. Booklet contains text and illustrations on the labels attached to panes and on interleaving pages.

DX2   £3 containing booklet panes Nos. X849n,
        X849o, X888l and X895l........................... 3·50
   No. DX2 is inscribed January 1980.

DX3

(Des B. Dedman)

1982 (19 May). The Story of Stanley Gibbons. Multicoloured cover, T **DX3** (163×97 mm) showing early envelope design on front and stamp album with text on back. Booklet contains text and illustrations on labels attached to panes and on interleaving pages.

DX3   £4 containing booklet panes Nos. X849p,
        X899m and X907l/X907m....................... 4·50
   No. DX3 is inscribed February 1982.

DX4

(Des B. West)

1983 (14 Sept). The Story of the Royal Mint. Multicoloured cover, T **DX4** (163×97 mm) showing current coins, die and tools. Booklet contains text and illustrations on labels attached to panes and on interleaving pages.

DX4   £4 containing booklet panes Nos.
        X899m×2, X930l and X949l..................... 4·50

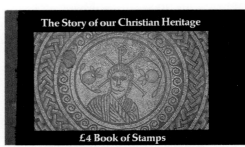

DX5

(Des P. Miles)

1984 (4 Sept). The Story of our Christian Heritage. Multicoloured cover, T **DX5** (163×97 mm) showing mosaic of Christ from Hinton St Mary Roman villa. Booklet contains text and illustrations on labels attached to panes and on interleaving pages.

DX5   £4 containing booklet panes Nos. X886bl,
        X901m×2 and X952l................................ 13·00

DX6

(Des D. Driver)

1985 (8 Jan). The Story of *The Times* (newspaper). Multicoloured cover, T **DX6** (163×95 mm) showing *Waiting for The Times* (painting by Haydon). Booklet contains text and illustrations on labels attached to panes and on interleaving pages.

DX6   £5 containing booklet panes Nos. X864l,
        X900l, X952l and X952m......................... 8·50

DX7

(Des Trickett and Webb Ltd)

1986 (18 Mar). The Story of British Rail. Multicoloured cover, T **DX7** (162×95 mm) showing diesel locomotive. Booklet contains text and illustrations on labels attached to panes and on interleaving pages.
DX7   £5 containing booklet panes Nos. X896l,
        X897m, X952l and X952m....................... 10·00

DX10

(Des Tayburn)

1989 (21 Mar). The Scots Connection. Multicoloured cover, T **DX10** (162×97 mm). Booklet contains text and illustrations on labels attached to the panes and on interleaving pages.
DX10   £5 containing booklet panes Nos. S54l,
        S55l, S62l and S62m............................... 10·00

DX8

(Des Aitken Blakeley Designers)

1987 (3 Mar). The Story of P&O. Multicoloured cover, T **DX8** (162×95 mm) showing the *William Fawcett*. Booklet contains text and illustrations on labels attached to panes and on interleaving pages.
DX8   £5 containing booklet panes Nos. X847m,
        X900l, X900m and X955l.......................... 9·50

DX11

(Des D. Driver)

1990 (20 Mar). London Life. Multicoloured cover, T **DX11** (162×97 mm). Booklet contains text and illustrations on labels attached to the panes and on interleaving pages.
DX11   £5 containing booklet panes Nos. X906m,
        1469n×2 and 1493a................................ 12·50

DX9

(Des The Partners)

1988 (9 Feb). The Story of the *Financial Times* (newspaper). Multicoloured cover, T **DX9** (162×97 mm). Booklet contains text and illustrations on labels attached to the panes and on interleaving pages.
DX9   £5 containing booklet panes Nos. X1005l,
        X1006l, X1009l and X1009m.................... 16·00

DX12

(Des Trickett and Webb Ltd)

1991 (19 Mar). Alias Agatha Christie. Multicoloured cover, T **DX12** (162×97 mm). Booklet contains text and illustrations on labels attached to the panes and on interleaving pages.
DX12   £6 containing booklet panes Nos.
        X1008l×2, X1016l and X1016m.............. 8·50

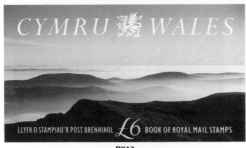

DX13

(Des G. Evernden and J. Gibbs)

1992 (25 Feb). Cymru Wales. Multicoloured cover, T **DX13** (162×97 mm). Booklet contains text and illustrations on labels attached to the panes and on interleaving pages.
DX13   £6 containing booklet panes Nos. 1591a,
                W48l, W49l and W59l............................ 9·00

DX16

(Des Carroll, Dempsey and Thirkell Ltd)

1994 (26 July). Northern Ireland. Multicoloured cover, T **DX16** (162×97 mm). Booklet contains text and illustrations on labels attached to the panes and on interleaving pages.
DX16   £6·04 containing booklet panes Nos. Y1766l,
                1812a and NI70l/NI70m, together with
                a 35p. postal stationery air card............. 10·50

DX14

(Des The Partners)

1992 (27 Oct). Birth Centenary of J. R. R. Tolkien (author). Multicoloured cover, T **DX14** (162×97 mm). Booklet contains text and illustrations on labels attached to the panes and on interleaving pages.
DX14   £6 containing booklet panes Nos. X1011l,
                X1012l and X1017l×2.............................. 9·00

DX17

(Des The Partners)

1995 (25 Apr). Centenary of the National Trust. Multicoloured cover, T **DX17** (162×97 mm). Booklet contains text and illustrations on labels attached to the panes and on interleaving pages.
DX17   £6 containing booklet panes Nos. Y1767l,
                Y1771l, 1869a and NI70n......................... 10·00

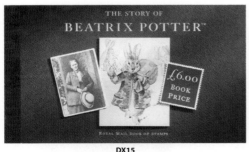

DX15

(Des The Partners)

1993 (10 Aug). The Story of Beatrix Potter. Multicoloured cover, T **DX15** (162×97 mm). Booklet contains text and illustrations on labels attached to the panes and on interleaving pages.
DX15   £5·64 containing booklet panes Nos.
                X1012m, 1451al, 1649b and NI48l.......... 18·00
Although inscribed £6·00 No. DX15 was sold at the face value of its contents, £5·64

DX18

(Des Why Not Associates)

1996 (14 May). European Football Championship. Multicoloured cover, T **DX18** (162×97 mm). Booklet contains text and illustrations on labels attached to the panes and on interleaving pages.
DX18   £6·48 containing booklet panes Nos. Y1775l,
                1925a, 1926a and 1927a......................... 8·50

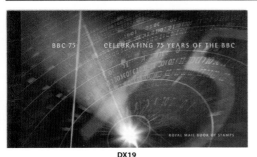

DX19

(Des H. Brown)

1997 (23 Sept). 75th Anniversary of the BBC. Multicoloured cover, T **DX19** (162×97 mm). Booklet contains text and illustrations on labels attached to the panes and on interleaving pages.
DX19   £6·15 containing booklet panes Nos. Y1686l,
           1940ab, 1668l and NI81l............................   10·00

DX20

(Des Dew Gibbons Design Group)

1998 (10 Mar). The Wilding Definitives. Black and gold cover, T **DX20** (162×96 mm). Booklet contains text and illustrations on labels attached to the panes and on interleaving pages.
DX20   £7·49 containing booklet panes Nos.
           2031b/2031c and 2032a/2032b.............   10·50
Folder containing DX20, DX22, DX24 and **MS**2147
cancelled on presentation card...   £150

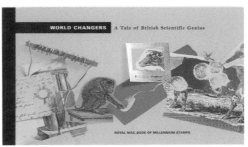

DX21

(Des Roundel Design Group)

1998 (13 Oct). Breaking Barriers. British Speed Record Holders. Multicoloured cover, T **DX21** (161×96 mm). Booklet contains text and illustrations on labels attached to the panes and on interleaving pages.
DX21   £6·16 containing booklet panes Nos. 1665l,
           Y1676al, 2059ac and NI80l......................   17·50

(Des Dew Gibbons Design Group)

1999 (16 Feb). Profile on Print. Multicoloured cover as T **DX20** (162×96 mm). Booklet contains text and illustrations on labels attached to the panes and on interleaving pages.
DX22   £7·54 containing booklet panes Nos. 1667l,
           1671n, 2077l, 2078l and 2079l................   30·00

DX23

(Des Silk Pearce)

1999 (21 Sept). World Changers. Multicoloured cover as T **DX23** (163×96 mm). Booklet contains text and illustrations on labels attached to the panes and on interleaving pages.
DX23   £6·99 containing booklet panes Nos.
           Y1667n, 2072ab, 2080a, 2103ba and
           2104ab..   13·50

(Des Dew Gibbons Design Group)

2000 (15 Feb). Special by Design. Multicoloured cover as T **DX20** (162×96 mm). Booklet contains text and illustrations on labels attached to the panes and on interleaving pages.
DX24   £7·50 containing booklet panes Nos. Y1683l,
           2124dl, 2133al and NI88l........................   25·00

DX25

(Des J. Gibbs)

2000 (4 Aug). Queen Elizabeth the Queen Mother's 100th Birthday. Brownish grey and grey cover as T **DX25** (162×96 mm). Booklet contains text and illustrations on labels attached to the panes and on interleaving pages.
DX25   £7·03 containing booklet panes Nos. 2124m,
           2160a, **MS**2161a and S94l.......................   20·00

DX26

(Des Roundel Design Group)

2000 (18 Sept). A Treasury of Trees. Slate-green and bright green cover as T **DX26** (162×95 mm). Booklet contains text and illustrations on panes and interleaving pages.
DX26   £7 containing booklet panes Nos. 2155a,
           2156a, 2158a, 2159a and W83al.............   17·00

DX27

(Des D. Davis)

2001 (22 Oct). Unseen and Unheard. Centenary of Royal Navy Submarine Service. Black, greenish yellow, new blue and red cover as T **DX27** (162×97 mm). Booklet contains text and illustrations on labels attached to the panes and on interleaving pages.

DX27   £6·76 containing booklet panes Nos.
          2202ab, 2203ab, **MS**2206a and S95l......   25·00

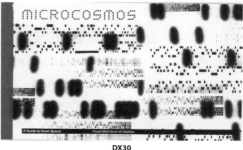

DX30

(Des CDT Design)

2003 (25 Feb). Microcosmos. 50th Anniversary of Discovery of DNA. Multicoloured cover as T **DX30** (164×95 mm). Booklet contains text and illustrations on labels attached to the panes and interleaving pages. Stitched.

DX30   £6·99 containing booklet panes Nos. 1668m,
          2343a, 2345a and NI89l..........................   20·00

DX28

(Des GBH)

2002 (6 Feb). A Gracious Accession. Golden Jubilee of Queen Elizabeth II. Multicoloured cover as T **DX28** (161×96 mm). Booklet contains text and illustrations on labels attached to the panes and interleaving pages.

DX28   £7·29 containing booklet panes Nos. 1664n,
          2253b/2254b and 2258b.........................   30·00

DX31

(Des GBH)

2003 (2 June). A Perfect Coronation. 50th Anniversary of Coronation. Multicoloured cover as T **DX31** (161×96 mm). Booklet contains text and illustrations on labels attached to the panes and on interleaving pages.

DX31   £7·46 containing booklet panes Nos. 1664o,
          2368b/2369b and 2378a.........................   32·00

DX29

(Des CDT Design)

2002 (24 Sept). Across the Universe. Multicoloured cover as T **DX29** (164×95 mm). Booklet contains text and illustrations on labels attached to the panes and interleaving pages. Stitched.

DX29   £6·83 containing booklet panes Nos. 1668m,
          2126ac, **MS**2315a and EN1l....................   32·00

DX32

(Des Kate Stephens)

2004 (16 Mar). Letters by Night A Tribute to the Travelling Post Office. Multicoloured cover as T **DX32** (164×95 mm). Booklet contains text and illustrations on labels attached to the panes and interleaving pages. Stitched.

DX32   £7·44 containing booklet panes Nos. 1668o,
          2392a, 2418a and S109l..........................   20·00

DX33

(Des John and Orna Designs)

2004 (25 May). The Glory of the Garden. Bicentenary of the Royal Horticultural Society. Multicoloured cover as T **DX33** (162×96 mm). Booklet contains text and illustrations on labels attached to the panes and interleaving pages. Stitched.

DX33   £7·23 containing booklet panes Nos. 1668p, 2456a, 2457a and 2463a............................   18·50

DX34

(Des Morgan Radcliffe)

2005 (24 Feb). The Brontë Sisters. 150th Death Anniversary of Charlotte Brontë. Multicoloured cover as T **DX34** (162×96 mm). Booklet contains text and illustrations on panes and interleaving pages. Stitched.

DX34   £7·43 containing booklet panes Nos. 1664p, EN6l, 2518a and 2520a............................   15·00

DX35 White Ensign

(Des Webb & Webb)

2005 (18 Oct). Bicentenary of the Battle of Trafalgar. Black, scarlet and ultramarine cover as T **DX35** (162×96 mm). Booklet contains text and illustrations on labels attached to the panes and interleaving pages. Stitched.

DX35   £7·26 containing booklet panes Nos. 1668q, 2574b/2575b and 2581a............................   16·00

DX36 Plaque showing Clifton Suspension Bridge

(Des Hat-trick Design)

2006 (23 Feb). Birth Bicentenary of Isambard Kingdom Brunel. Grey and grey-black cover as T **DX36** (162×96 mm). Booklet contains text and illustrations on panes and interleaving pages. Stitched.

DX36   £7·40 containing booklet panes Nos. 1668r, 2607a/2608a and 2610a............................   14·00

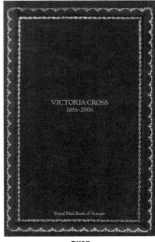

DX37

(Des Atelier Works)

2006 (21 Sept). 150th Anniversary of the Victoria Cross. Blackish-brown and gold cover as T **DX37** (162×96 mm). Booklet contains text and illustrations on panes and interleaving pages. Stitched.

DX37   £7·44 containing booklet panes Nos. 2651l, 2659b, 2660b and 2666a............................   14·00

DX38

(Des R. Warren-Fisher)

2007 (1 Mar). World of Invention. Black, olive-grey and grey cover as T **DX38** (162×95 mm). Booklet contains text and illustrations on panes and interleaving pages. Stitched.

DX38   £7·49 containing booklet panes Nos. S109m, Y1670l, 2721a and 2721b............................   18·00

DY23 Filming Rey (Daisy Ridley) and BB-8 in Desert near Abu Dhabi

(Des Interabang)

2017 (14 Dec). *Star Wars. The Making of the Droids, Aliens and Creatures.*
Multicoloured cover as T **DY23** (162×96 mm). Booklet contains text
and illustrations on panes and interleaving pages. Stitched.
DY23   £15·99 containing booklet panes Nos.
U3150m, 3759c, 3762b and 4008a........   24·50
The contents of No. DY23 have a face value of £14·32.
A limited edition (1977) of this prestige stamp booklet was sold for
£75. It had silver foiling on the cover and was packaged in a silver metal
clamshell..

DY24 *Game of Thrones*

(Des GBH)

2018 (23 Jan). *Game of Thrones.* Multicoloured cover as T **DY24**
(162×96 mm). Booklet contains text and illustrations on panes and
interleaving pages. Stitched.
DY24   £13·95 containing booklet panes Nos. 4033b,
4036b, 4045a and U3072o......................   24·00
The contents of No. DY24 have a face value of £12·99.
A limited edition (2000) of this stamp booklet was issued in a leather
folder and originally sold for £75.

DY25 RAF Roundel and Centenary Emblem

(Des Common Curiosity)

2018 (20 Mar). Centenary of the RAF (Royal Air Force). Multicoloured cover
as T **DY25** (163×96 mm). Booklet contains text and illustrations on
panes and interleaving pages. Stitched.
DY25   £18·69 containing booklet panes Nos.
U3071o, 4058b, 4059b, 4067a and
4071a..   28·00
The contents of No. DY25 have a face value of £18·54
A limited edition (2018) of this stamp booklet with a yellow band at the
left of the front cover was originally sold for £45.

DY26 German Prisoners near Abbeville and Crowds outside
Buckingham Palace

(Des Hat-trick design)

2018 (13 Sept). Centenary of the First World War (5th issue). Multicoloured
cover, as T **DY26** (162×96 mm). Booklet contains text and illustrations
on panes and interleaving pages. Stitched.
DY26   £15·65 containing panes Nos. 3627b,
U3156m, 4133a and 4136a....................   25·00
The contents of No. DY26 have a face value of £14·40.

DY27 Harry Potter

(Des The Chase)

2018 (4 Dec). Harry Potter. Multicoloured cover as T **DY27** (162×96 mm).
Booklet contains text and illustrations on panes and interleaving
pages. Stitched.
DY27   £15·50 containing booklet panes Nos.
U3070o, 4141b, 4142b, 4164a and
4167a..   25·00
The contents of No. DY27 have a face value of £13·97.
A limited edition prestige stamp booklet was originally sold for £45.

DY28 The Head of the Madonna

(Des Kate Stephens)

2019 (13 Feb). 500th Death Anniversary of Leonardo da Vinci (1452–1519,
artist). Multicoloured cover as T **DY28** (163×96 mm). Booklet contains
text and illustrations on panes and interleaving pages. Stitched.
DY28   £13·10 containing booklet panes Nos.
U3072p, 4170b, 4171b and 4175b.........   33·00
The contents of No. DY28 have a face value of £11·64.

DY29 Iron Man

(Des Interabang)

2019 (14 Mar). Marvel. Multicoloured cover as T **DY29** (162×96 mm). Booklet contains text and illustrations on panes and interleaving pages. Stitched.
DY29   £17.45 containing booklet panes Nos.
          U3070p, 4182b, 4185b, 4195a and
          4196a.. 27·00
The contents of No. DY29 have a face value of £15·98.
A limited edition (4995) prestige stamp booklet was originally sold for £64·99. It had a Spider-man front cover and a Spider-man tin presentation case

DY30 Queen Victoria in 1856 (Franz Xavier Winterhalter) and 1890 (Heinrich von Angeli)

2019 (24 May). Birth Bicentenary of Queen Victoria. Multicoloured cover as T **DY30** (162×96 mm). Booklet contains text and illustrations on panes and interleaving pages. Stitched.
DY30   £17·20 containing booklet panes Nos.
          U3071p, 4219b, 4222b and 4226a.......... 50·00
The contents of No. DY30 have a face value of £15·64.

DY31 X-Wing Fighter

2019 (26 Nov). *Star Wars*. The Making of the Vehicles. Multicoloured cover as T **DY31** (162×96 mm). Booklet contains text and illustrations on panes and interleaving pages. Stitched.
DY31   £17·65 containing booklet panes Nos.
          U3072q, 4292b, 4293b, 4306a and
          4309a.. 27·00
The contents of No. DY31 have a face value of £16·08.
A limited edition (1,977) prestige stamp booklet was originally sold for £49·99. It had silver foiling on the front cover and came in an embossed tin case with a Certificate of Authenticity with a lenticular of Han Solo's *Millennium Falcon* in hyperspace.
The three Star Wars booklets from 2015, 2017 and 2019, Nos. DY15, DY23 and DY31, were sold by Royal Mail for £49·44.

DY32 Visions of the Universe.

(Des True North)

2020 (11 Feb). Visions of the Universe. Bicentenary of the Royal Astronomical Society. Multicoloured cover as T **DY32** (162×96 mm). Booklet contains text and illustrations on panes and interleaving pages. Stitched.
DY32   £16·10 containing booklet panes Nos.
          U3070q, U3072r, 4323b and 4324b........ 38·00
The contents of No. DY32 have a face value of £14·82.

DY33 Filming of James Bond

(Des Interabang)

2020 (17 Mar). James Bond. Multicoloured cover as T **DY33** (163×96 mm). Booklet contains text and illustrations on panes and interleaving pages. Stitched.
DY33   £16·99 containing booklet panes Nos.
          U3071q, 4332b, 4336b and 4341a......... 38·00
The contents of No. DY33 had a face value of £15·28.
A limited edition (1,962) prestige stamp booklet waqs originally sold for £64·99. It had a special edition 007 silver foiled front cover inscribed 'BEHIND THE SCENES OF JAMES BOND', and came in a tin display case embossed with the 007 logo.

DY34 Street Party, Manchester

(Des Hat-trick design)

2020 (8 May). 75th Anniversary of the End of the Second World War. Multicoloured cover, 163×96 mm, as T **DY34**. Booklet contains text and illustrations on panes and interleaving pages. Stitched.
DY34   £19·80 containing booklet panes Nos.
          U3072s, 4356b, 4360b and 4365a.......... 39·50
The contents of No. DY34 have a face value of £18·16.

DY35 Queen Band Crest

(Des Baxter & Bailey)

2020 (9 Ju;ly). Queen (rock band). Gold and steel-blue cover, 163×96 mm, as T **DY35**. Booklet contains text and illustrations on panes and interleaving pages. Stitched
DY35   £19·10 containing booklet panes Nos. U3070r,
            4388b, 4392b and 4399a.......................   27·00
    The contents of No. DY35 have a face value of £17·42.

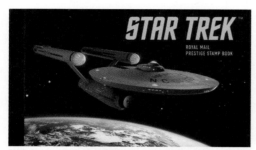

DY36 Starship USS *Enterprise* in Planetary Orbit, *Star Trek* Original Series

(Des Interabang)

2020 (13 Nov). *Star Trek*. Multicoloured cover, 162×96 mm, as T **DY36**. Booklet contains text and illustrations on panes and interleaving pages. Stitched.
DY36   £18·35 containing booklet panes Nos. U3071r,
            4443b, 4449b and 4458a.......................   26·00
    The contents of No. DY36 have a face value of £17·17.
    A limited edition (1996) prestige booklet stamp was originally sold for £75. It had a silver foiled cover front and came in a silver foiled folder with a lenticular printed certificate includinga 3D motion image of the original Star Trek crew.

DY37 *Only Fools and Horses*

(Des Interabang)

2021 (16 Feb). *Only Fools and Horses* (TV Sitcom, 1981–2003) Multicoloured cover as T **DY37** (162×96 mm). Booklet contains text and illustrations on panes and interleaving pages. Stitched.
DY37   £21·70 containing booklet panes Nos. U3075l,
            4477b, 4481b and 4488a.......................   30·00
    The contents of No. DY37 have a face value of £19·77.
    A limited edition (1981) prestige stamp booklet was originally sold for £54·99. It came packaged in Del Boy's briefcase style box and included a certificate of authenticity.

DY38 Onstage at the Ahoy, Rotterdam, Paul McCartney World Tour, 1989

(Des Baxter & Bailey)

2021 (28 May). Paul McCartney. Multicoloured cover, 162×96 mm, as T **DY38**. Booklet contains text and illustrations on panes and interleaving pages. Stitched.
DY38   £20·25 containing booklet panes Nos.
            U3071s, 4517b, 4521b and 4528a..........   30·00
    The contents of No. DY38 have a face value of £18·24.
    A limited edition (1970) prestige stamp booklet was originally sold for £49·99. It has a special edition front cover with a photograph of Paul McCartney taken in 2020 and comes in a matt black folder with a silver foil signature and a certificate of authenticity.

DY39 Black Country near Bilston, from engraving by John Alfred Langford, 1872

(Des Common Curiosity)

2021 (12 Aug). Industrial Revolutions. Multicoloured cover, 162×96 mm, as T **DY39**. Booklet contains text and illustrations on panes and interleaving pages. Stitched.
DY39   £18·03 containing booklet panes Nos. U3072t,
            4555b, 4557b and 4562a.......................   35·00
    The contents of No. DY39 have a face value of £16·38.

DY40 Batman, Wonder Woman and Superman

(Des Interabang)

2021 (17 Sept). DC Collection. Multicoloured cover, 162×95 mm, as T **DY40**. Booklet contains text and illustrations on panes and interleaving pages. Stitched.
DY40   £21·20 containing booklet panes Nos.
            U3075m, 4575b, 4581b, 4591a and
            4593a...   32·00
    The contents of No. DY40 have a face value of £19·58.
    A limited edition (1939) prestige stamp booklet was originally sold for £49·99. It has a special edition front cover and comes in a grey linen box embossed with the official DC logo with a certificate of authenticity.

DY41 The Rolling Stones

(Des Baxter & Bailey)

2022 (20 Jan). The Rolling Stones. Multicoloured cover, 161×95 mm, as T **DY41**.

DY41 £20·85 containing booklet panes Nos.
U3074n, 4614b, 4616b and 4623a.......... 30·00

The contents of No. DY41 have a face value of £18·90.

A limited edition (5000) prestige stamp booklet was originally sold for £49.99. It had a special front cover showing the Rolling Stones tongue and lips logo and came in a flight case style presentation box with a certificate of authenticity.

DY42 Queen Elizabeth II leaving Fiji, February 1977

(Des Kate Stephens)

2022 (4 Feb). Platinum Jubilee. Multicoloured cover, 161×95 mm, as T **DY42**. Booklet contains text and illustrations on panes and interleaving pages. Stitched.

DY42 £19·50 containing booklet panes Nos. U3071t,
3319Bc, 4627b and 4628b....................... 29·00

The contents of No. DY42 have a face value of £17·84.

DY43 Women's Auxiliary Air Force Ground Crew on their way to Service and Repair a Short Stirling Heavy Bomber, 1944

(Des Supple Studio)

2022 (5 May). Unsung Heroes. Women of World War II. Multicoloured cover, 162×100 mm, as T **DY43**. Booklet contains text and illustrations on panes and interleaving pages. Stitched.

DY43 £20·75 containing booklet panes Nos. V4750l,
4661b, 4664b and 4672a......................... 31·00

The contents of No. DY43 have a face value of £19·10.

DY44 Transformers

(Des The Chase)

2022 (1 Sept). Transformers. Multicoloured cover, 163×101 mm, as T **DY44**. Booklet contains text and illustrations on panes and interleaving pages.

DY44 £21·25 containing booklet panes Nos. 4700b,
4704b, 4709a, 4711a and V4841l........... 32·00

The contents of No. DY44 have a face value of £19·58.

A limited edition (1,984) prestige stamp booklet was originally sold for £49.99. It had a special front cover and a bespoke slipcase inspired by the 'Autobot Matrix of Leadership', and was sold with a certificate of authenticity.

DY45

2022 (24 Nov). Tutankhamun. Black, buff and vermilion cover, 163×99 mm, as Type **DY45**. Booklet contains text and illustrations on panes and interleaving pages. Stitched.

DY45 £21·55 containing booket panes Nos. V4845l,
4743b, 4745b and 4752a......................... 32·00

The contents of No. DY45 have a face value of £20·11.

DY46 Wolverine

(Des Interabang)

2023 (16 Feb). X-Men. Multicoloured cover, 163×100 mm, as Type **DY46**. Booklet contains text and illustrations on panes and interleaving pages. Stitched.

DY46 £19·95 containing booklet panes Nos. 4765b,
4766b, 4778a and 4780b......................... 29·00

The contents of No. DY46 have a face value of £18·79.

DY47 *Flying Scotsman* passing Langwith, Settle and Carlisle Line, 14 December 2019

(Des Steers McGillan Eves)

2023 (9 Mar). *Flying Scotsman* (steam locomotive). Multicoloured cover, 162×99 mm, as Type **DY47**. Booklet contains text and illustratations on panes and interleaving pages. Stitched.
DY47   £21·05 containing booklet panes Nos. V4846l,
           4783b, 4787b and 4792a........................   32·00
    The contents of No. DY47 have a face value of £18·40.

B. Folded Booklets.

NOTE: All panes are attached to the covers by the selvedge. Inscribed dates are those shown with the printer's imprint.

Illustrations for 10p., 50p., £1 and £2 booklets are ¾ size; others are ⅔ size.

10p. Booklets

FA1

1976 (10 Mar)–**77**. Cover as T **FA1** printed in dull rose on very pale lavender. Containing booklet pane No. X841r.
FA1   NOV 1975....................................   45
FA2   MAR 1976 (9.6.76).....................................   60
FA3   JUNE 1977 (13.6.77)...............   40

FA4

(Des N. Battershill)

1978 (8 Feb)–**79**. Farm Buildings Series. Bistre-brown and turquoise-blue covers as T **FA4**, containing booklet pane No. X843m.
FA4   Design No. 1, Oast Houses........................   35
FA5   Design No. 2, Buildings in Ulster
              (3.5.78)..   40
FA6   Design No. 3, Buildings in Yorkshire
              (9.8.78)..   35
FA7   Design No. 4, Buildings in Wales
              (25.10.78)..   35
FA8   Design No. 5, Buildings in Scotland
              (10.1.79)..   35
FA9   Design No. 6, Buildings in Sussex
              (4.4.79)..   35
    Nos. FA4/FA5 are inscribed January 1978, No. FA6 July 1978, No. FA7 October 1978, No. FA8 December 1978 and No. FA9 March 1979.

FA10

(Des Hamper and Purssell)

1979 (17 Oct)–**80**. London 1980 International Stamp Exhibition. Red and blue cover as T **FA10** showing Post Office exhibition stand and containing No. X845l.
FA10   Inscr August 1979......................................   30
FA11   Inscr January 1980 (12.1.80)....................   35

50p. Booklets

All booklets were sold at the cover price of 50p. although some contain stamps to a greater value.

FB1

1977 (26 Jan). Cover as T **FB1** printed in maroon and pale blue.
FB1A   containing booklet pane X841s.............   1·50
FB1B   containing booklet pane X841sa...........   1·50

1977 (13 June). Cover as T **FB1**. Printed in chestnut and stone.
FB2A   containing booklet pane X844n.............   2·50
FB2B   containing booklet pane X844na...........   1·50
    Nos. FB1A and FB1B are inscribed March 1976 and Nos. FB2A and FB2B June 1977.

FB3

(Des J. Ireland)

1978 (8 Feb)–**79**. Commercial Vehicles Series. Olive-yellow and grey covers as T **FB3**. A. Containing booklet pane No. X844n. B. Containing booklet pane No. X844na.

		A	B
FB3	Design No. 1, Clement Talbot van..........	2·75	1·75
FB4	Design No. 2, Austin taxi (3.5.78)............	2·75	1·50
FB5	Design No. 3, Morris Royal Mail van		
	(9.8.78)..	2·75	1·50
FB6	Design No. 4, Guy Electric dustcart		
	(25.10.78)..	3·75	1·50
FB7	Design No. 5, Albion van (10.1.79)..........	4·00	3·75
FB8	Design No. 6, Leyland fire engine		
	(4.4.79)..	3·75	3·75

    Nos. FB3/FB4 are inscribed January 1978, No. FB5 July 1978, No. FB6 October 1978, No. FB7 December 1978 and No. FB8 March 1979.

1979 (28 Aug). Contents changed. A. Containing booklet pane No. X849l. B. Containing booklet pane No. X849la.

		A	B
FB9	Design No. 6, Leyland fire engine..........	1·50	1·50

No. FB9 is inscribed August 1979.

FB10

(Des B. Smith)

1979 (3 Oct)–**81**. Veteran Cars Series. Orange-red and reddish lilac covers as T **FB10**. A. Containing booklet pane No. X849l. B. Containing booklet pane No. X849la.

		A	B
FB10	Design No. 1, 1907 Rolls-Royce Silver Ghost...........................	1·50	1·50

No. FB10 is inscribed August 1979.

Contents changed. A. Containing booklet pane No. X849m. B. Containing booklet pane No. X849ma.

FB11	Design No. 2, 1908 Grand Prix Austin (4.2.80)................................	1·50	1·50
FB12	Design No. 3, 1903–1905 Vauxhall (25.6.80)................................	1·50	1·50
FB13	Design No. 4, 1897–1900 Daimler (24.9.80)................................	1·50	1·50

No. FB11 is inscribed January 1980, No. FB 12 May 1980 and No. FB 13 July 1980.

Contents changed. A. Containing No. X841t. B. Containing No.X841ta.

FB14	Design No. 5, 1896 Lanchester (26.1.81)................................	1·50	1·50
FB15	Design No. 6, 1913 Bull-nose Morris (18.3.81)................................	1·75	1·75

Nos. FB14/FB15 are inscribed January 1981.

FB16

(Des R. Downer)

1981 (6 May)–**82**. Follies Series. Brown and orange-brown covers as T **FB16**. A. Containing No. X841t. B. Containing No. X841ta.

		A	B
FB16	Design No. 1, Mugdock Castle, Stirlingshire........................	1·50	1·50

No. FB16 is inscribed January 1981.

Contents changed. A. Containing No. X854l. B. Containing No. X854la.

FB17	Design No. 1, Mugdock Castle, Stirlingshire (26.8.81)................	4·25	7·00
FB18	Design No. 2, Mow Cop Castle, Cheshire–Staffs border (30.9.81).............	4·25	4·25

Nos. FB17/FB18 are inscribed January 1981.

Contents changed. A. Containing No. X841u. B. Containing No. X841ua.

FB19	Design No. 3, Paxton's Tower, Llanarthney, Dyfed (1.2.82).....................	1·75	1·75
FB20	Design No. 4, Temple of the Winds, Mount Stewart, Northern Ireland (6.5.82)................................	1·75	1·75
FB21	Design No. 5, Temple of the Sun, Stourhead, Wilts (11.8.82).......................	1·00	1·75
FB22	Design No. 6, Water Garden, Cliveden, Bucks (6.10.82)................................	1·75	1·75

Nos. FB19/FB22 are inscribed February 1982.

FB23

(Des H. Titcombe)

1983 (16 Feb–26 Oct). Rare Farm Animals Series. Bright green and black covers as T **FB23**. A. Containing booklet pane No. X841u. B. Containing booklet pane No. X841ua.

		A	B
FB23	Design No. 1, Bagot Goat........................	1·75	2·00

Contents changed. Containing No. X845n.

FB24	Design No. 2, Gloucester Old Spot Pig (5.4.83)................................	3·50
	b. Corrected rate...	12·00
FB25	Design No. 3, Toulouse Goose (27.7.83)	3·75
FB26	Design No. 4, Orkney Sheep (26.10.83)..	3·75

No. FB23 is inscribed February 1982 and Nos. FB24/FB26 April 1983. The corrected rate reads, 36p. for 200g instead of 37p. for 200g.

FB27

(Des P. Morter)

1984 (3 Sept)–**85**. Orchids Series. Yellow-green and lilac covers as T **FB27**. Containing booklet pane No. X845p.

FB27	Design No. 1, *Dendrobium nobile* and *Miltonia* hybrid................................	2·50
FB28	Design No. 2, *Cypripedium calceolus* and *Ophrys apifera* (15.1.85)...................	2·50
FB29	Design No. 3, *Bifrenaria* and Vanda tricolor (23.4.85)................................	2·50
FB30	Design No. 4, *Cymbidium* and *Arpophyllum* (23.7.85)...............................	2·50

Nos. FB27/FB30 are inscribed September 1984.

FB31

(Des M. Thierens Design)

1985 (4 Nov). Cover as T **FB31** printed in black and bright scarlet. Containing booklet pane No. X909l.

FB31	Pillar box design..	2·75

No. FB 31 is inscribed November 1985.

FB32

(Des P. Morter)

1986 (20 May–12 Aug). Pond Life Series. Dull blue and emerald covers as T **FB32**. Containing booklet pane No. X909l.

FB32	Design No. 1, Emperor Dragonfly, Four spotted Libellula and Yellow Flag..........	1·75
FB33	Design No. 2. Common Frog, Fennel-leaved Pondweed and Long-stalked Pondweed (29.7.86)................................	2·25
	a. containing booklet pane No. X909la (12.8.86).....................................	2·25

Nos. FB32/FB33a are inscribed November 1985.

FB34

(Des N. Battershill)

1986 (29 July). Roman Britain Series. Brown-ochre and Indian red cover as T **FB34**. Containing booklet pane No. X845q.

FB34	Design No. 1, Hadrian's Wall....................	6·50

No. FB34 is inscribed November 1985.

1986 (20 Oct)–**87**. Pond Life Series continued. Dull blue and emerald covers as T **FB32**. Containing booklet pane No. X845s.

FB35	Design No. 3, Moorhen and Little Grebe....................	3·50
FB36	Design No. 4, Giant Pond and Great Ramshorn Snails (27.1.87).......................	3·50

No. FB36 is inscribed October 1986.

1986 (20 Oct)–**87**. Roman Britain Series continued. Brown ochre and Indian red covers as T **FB34**. Containing booklet pane No. X847l.

FB37	Design No. 2, Roman Theatre of Verulamium, St Albans...........................	2·25
FB38	Design No. 3, Portchester Castle, Hampshire (27.1.87).................................	2·40

No. FB38 is inscribed October 1986.

FB39

(Des Patricia Howes)

1987 (14 Apr)–**88**. Bicentenary of Marylebone Cricket Club Series Brown and dull ultramarine covers as T **FB39**. Containing booklet pane No. X847l.

FB39	Design No. 1, Father Time weather vane...	1·75
FB40	Design No. 2, Ashes urn and embroidered velvet bag (14.7.87)...........	1·75
FB41	Design No. 3, Lord's Pavilion and wrought iron decoration on roof (29.9.87)...	1·75
FB42	Design No. 4, England team badge and new stand at Lord's (26.1.88)...........	1·75

Nos. FB39/FB42 are inscribed October 1986.

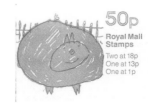

FB43

(Des G. Evernden)

1987 (14 Apr)–**88**. Botanical Gardens Series. Covers as T **FB43**. Containing booklet panes No. X845s (Nos. FB43/FB44) or X845sa (Nos. FB45/FB46).

FB43	Design No. 1 (cover in ultramarine and rosered), Rhododendron, Elizabeth, Bodnant...	3·25
FB44	Design No. 2 (cover in deep ultramarine and cobalt), Gentiana sino-ornata, Edinburgh (14.7.87)............	3·25

FB45	Design No. 3 (cover in dull ultramarine and orange-yellow), Lilium auratum and Mount Stuart (incorrect inscr) (29.9.87)....................	1·75
	a. With corrected spelling Mount Stewart (30.10.87)......................	2·00
FB46	Design No. 4 (cover in dull ultramarine and yellow-orange), Strelitzia reginae, Kew (26.1.88)................................	2·00

Nos. FB43/FB46 are inscribed October 1986.
The panes from Nos. FB45/FB46 have imperforate vertical sides.

FB47

1988 (12 Apr–5 July). London Zoo. Children's Drawings Series. Covers as T **FB47**.

FB47	Pigs design (cover in black and rose) containing booklet pane No. X847l.......	2·00
FB48	Birds design (cover in black and yellow) containing booklet pane No. X845sa...	2·00
FB49	Elephants design (cover in black and grey) containing booklet pane No. X847l (5.7.88)...................................	2·00

Nos. FB47/FB49 are inscribed October 1986.
The pane from No. FB48 has imperforate vertical sides.

FB50

(Des P. Morter)

1988 (5 July). Marine Life Series. Blue and orange-brown cover as T **FB50**. Containing booklet pane No. X845sa.

FB50	Design No. 1, Parasitic Anemone on Common Whelk Shell and Umbrella Jellyfish..	2·00

No. FB50 is inscribed October 1986 and has the vertical sides of the pane imperforate.

FB51

(Des Lynda Gray)

1988 (5 Sept)–**89**. Gilbert and Sullivan Operas Series. Black and red covers as T **FB51**. Containing booklet pane No. X904l.

FB51	Design No. 1, The Yeomen of the Guard. .	5·00
FB52	Design No. 2, The Pirates of Penzance (24.1.89)...	5·00
FB53	Design No. 3, The Mikado (25.4.89).........	5·00

1989 (18 July). Marine Life Series continued. Blue and orange brown cover as T **FB50**. Containing booklet pane No. X904l.

FB54	Design No. 2, Common Hermit Crab, Bladder Wrack and Laver Spire Shell......	5·00

For Design No. 3, see £1 Booklet No. FH17.

FB55

(Des P. Hutton)

1989 (2 Oct)–**90**. Aircraft Series. Turquoise-green and light brown covers as T **FB55**. Containing booklet pane No. X906l.

FB55   Design No. 1, HP42, Armstrong Whitworth Atalanta and de Havilland Dragon Rapide.. 7·50

No. FB55 was incorrectly inscribed Atalanta.

As before, but containing Penny Black Anniversary booklet pane No. 1468l.

FB56   Design No. 2, Vickers Viscount 806 and de Havilland Comet 4 (30.1.90).............. 10·00

1990 (4 Sept)–**91**. Aircraft Series continued. Turquoise-green and light brown covers as T **FB55**. Containing booklet pane No. X911l.

FB57   Design No. 3, BAC 1-11 and VC10........... 10·00
FB58   Design No. 4, BAe ATP, BAe 146 and Aérospatiale–BAC Concorde (25.6.91)... 10·00

FB59

(Des A. Drummond)

1991 (10 Sept)–**92**. Archaeology Series. Covers as T **FB59**. Containing booklet pane No. X925m.

FB59   Design No. 1 (cover in bright blue and lake brown), Sir Arthur Evans at Knossos, Crete... 1·75
       a. Corrected rate (10.91)............................... 2·00
FB60   Design No. 2 (cover in bright blue and yellow), Howard Carter in the Tomb of Tutankhamun (21.1.92)........................... 1·75
FB61   Design No. 3 (cover in bright blue and yellow), Sir Austen Layard at Assyrian site (28.4.92)... 1·50
FB62   Design No. 4 (cover in new blue and yellow), Sir Flinders Petrie surveying the Pyramids and temples of Giza (28.7.92)... 1·75

On the inside front cover of No. FB59 the inland letter rates are shown as 1st class 24p., 35p., 43p., 51p. and 2nd class 18p., 28p., 33p., 39p. These were corrected on No. FB59a to read: 1st class 24p., 36p., 45p., 54p. and 2nd class 18p., 28p., 34p., 41p.

FB63

(Des J. Matthews)

1992 (22 Sept). 1000th Anniversary of Appointment of Sheriffs. Dull blue and scarlet cover as T **FB63**. Containing booklet pane No. X925m.

FB63   Design showing Crest, with Helm and Mantling, and Badge of The Shrievalty Association.. 1·60

FB64

(Des M. Newton)

1993 (9 Feb–6 July). Postal History Series. Covers as T **FB64**. Containing booklet pane No. X925m.

FB64   Design No. 1 (cover in grey-green and greyblack), Airmail postmarks................. 1·50
FB65   Design No. 2 (cover in dull orange and black), Ship mail postmarks (6.4.93)....... 1·50
FB66   Design No. 3 (cover in blue and grey-black), Registered mail postmarks (6.7.93).. 1·50

1993 (1 Nov). Postal History Series continued. Rose-red and grey-black cover as T **FB64** containing booklet pane No. Y1689l.

FB67   Design No. 4, Paid postmarks................. 1·50

FB68

(Des A. Davidson)

1994 (25 Jan–6 Sept). Coaching Inns Series. Covers as T **FB68**. Containing booklet pane No. Y1689l.

FB68   Design No. 1 (cover in myrtle-green and pale myrtle-green), Swan with Two Necks.. 1·50
FB69   Design No. 2 (cover in sepia and buff), Bull and Mouth (26.4.94)...................... 1·50
FB70   Design No. 3 (cover in reddish brown and cinnamon), Golden Cross (6.6.94)... 1·50
FB71   Design No. 4 (cover in black and slate-blue), Pheasant Inn, Wiltshire (6.9.94).... 1·50

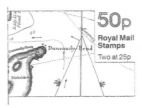

FB72

(Des D. Davis)

1995 (7 Feb–4 Apr). Sea Charts Series. Rosine and black covers as T **FB72**, containing booklet pane No. Y1689l.

FB72   Design No. 1, John o' Groats, 1800.......... 1·50
FB73   Design No. 2, Land's End, 1808 (4.4.95).. 1·50

1995 (6 June–4 Sept). Sea Charts Series continued. Rosine and black covers as T **FB72**, containing booklet pane No. Y1690l.

FB74   Design No. 3, St David's Head, 1812....... 2·00
FB75   Design No. 4, Giant's Causeway, 1828 (4.9.95)... 2·00

65p. Booklet

1976 (14 July). Cover as T **FB1**, but larger (90×49 mm). Printed in turquoise-blue and pale buff. A. Selvedge at left. B. Selvedge at right.

		A	B
FC1	containing 10×6½p. (No. X872)..............	10·00	5·25

No. FC1 is inscribed March 1976.

70p. Booklets

1977 (13 June). Cover as T **FB1**, but larger (90×49 mm). Printed in purple-brown and dull rose. A. Selvedge at left. B. Selvedge at right.

		A	B
FD1	containing 10×7p. (No. X875).................	4·00	4·00

No. FD1 is inscribed June 1977.

FD2

(Des E. Stemp)

1978 (8 Feb)–**79**. Country Crafts Series. Grey-green and red brown covers as T **FD2** (90×49 mm). Containing 10×7p. (No. X875). A. Selvedge at left. B. Selvedge at right.

		A	B
FD2	Design No. 1, Horse shoeing....................	35·00	3·00
FD3	Design No. 2, Thatching (3.5.78)..............	£175	3·00
FD4	Design No. 3, Dry stone walling (9.8.78)......................	£165	3·00
FD5	Design No. 4, Wheel making (25.10.78).	5·75	4·00
FD6	Design No. 5, Wattle fence making (10.1.79)......................	12·00	4·00

Nos. FD2/FD3 are inscribed January 1978, No. FD4 July 1978, No. FD5 October 1978 and No. FD6 December 1978.

FD7

(Des F. Wegner)

1979 (5 Feb). Official opening of Derby Mechanised Letter Office. Pale yellow-green and lilac cover as T **FD7** (90×49 mm). Containing 10×7p. (No. X875). A. Selvedge at left. B. Selvedge at right.

		A	B
FD7	Kedleston Hall............................	5·50	5·50

No. FD7 is inscribed December 1978.

On sale only in the Derby Head Post Office area to promote postcode publicity and also at the Philatelic Bureau, Edinburgh and philatelic sales counters.

1979 (4 Apr). Country Crafts Series continued. Grey-green and red-brown covers as T **FD2** (90×49 mm). containing 10×70p. (No. 875) A. Selvedge at left. B. Selvedge at right.

		A	B
FD8	Design No. 6, Basket making..................	6·00	3·00

No. FD8 is inscribed March 1979.

80p. Booklet

FE1

(Des P. Hutton)

1979 (3 Oct). Military Aircraft Series. Blue and grey cover as T **FE1** (90×49 mm). Containing 10×8p. (No. X879) attached by the selvedge. A. Selvedge at left. B. Selvedge at right.

		A	B
FE1	Design No. 1, BE2B, 1914, and Vickers Gun Bus, 1915............................	2·25	2·25

No. FE1 is inscribed August 1979.

85p. Booklet

1976 (14 July). Cover as T **FB1** but larger (90×49 mm). Printed in light yellow-olive and brownish grey. A. Selvedge at left. B. Selvedge at right.

		A	B
FF1	containing 10×8½p. (No. X881)..............	5·50	7·50

No. FF1 is inscribed March 1976.

90p. Booklets

1977 (13 June). Cover as T **FB1**, but larger (90×49 mm). Printed in deep grey-blue and cobalt. A. Selvedge at left. B. Selvedge at right.

		A	B
FG1	containing 10×9p. (No. X883).................	3·50	5·50

No. FG1 is inscribed June 1977.

FG2

(Des R. Maddox)

1978 (8 Feb)–**79**. British Canals Series. Yellow-olive and new blue covers as T **FG2** (90×49 mm). Containing 10×9p. (No. X883). A. Selvedge at left. B. Selvedge at right.

		A	B
FG2	Design No. 1, Grand Union......................	22·00	4·00
FG3	Design No. 2, Llangollen (3.5.78).............	3·00	£325
FG4	Design No. 3, Kennet & Avon (9.8.78).....	10·00	7·50
FG5	Design No. 4, Caledonian (25.10.78).......	4·25	5·50
FG6	Design No. 5, Regents (10.1.79)...............	10·00	6·25

Nos. FG2/FG3 are inscribed January 1978, No. FG4 July 1978, No. FG5 October 1978 and No. FG6 December 1978.

(Des F. Wegner)

1979 (5 Feb). Official Opening of Derby Mechanised Letter Office. Violet-blue and rose cover as T **FD7** (90×49 mm). Containing 10×9p. (No. X883). A. Selvedge at left. B. Selvedge at right.

		A	B
FG7	Tramway Museum, Crich.........................	7·00	7·00

No. FG7 is inscribed December 1978.

On sale only in the Derby Head Post Office area to promote postcode publicity and also at the Philatelic Bureau, Edinburgh and philatelic sales counters.

1979 (4 Apr). British Canals Series continued. Yellow-olive and new blue cover as T **FG2** containing 10×9p. (No. X883). A. Selvedge at left. B. Selvedge at right.

		A	B
FG8	Design No. 6, Leeds & Liverpool.............	3·00	3·00

No. FG8 is inscribed March 1979.

£1 Booklets

All booklets were sold at the cover price of £1 although some contain stamps to a greater value.

FH1

(Des N. Battershill)

1979 (3 Oct). Industrial Archaeology Series. Red and green cover as T **FH1** (90×49 mm). Containing 10×10p. (No. X887). A. Selvedge at left. B. Selvedge at right.

		A	B
FH1	Design No. 1, Ironbridge, Telford, Salop	2·50	2·50

No. FH1 is inscribed August 1979.

1980 (4 Feb–24 Sept). Military Aircraft Series continued. Blue and grey covers as T **FE1** (90×49 mm). Containing 10×10p. (No. X888). A. Selvedge at left. B. Selvedge at right.

		A	B
FH2	Design No. 2, Sopwith Camel and Vickers Vimy	2·50	2·50
FH3	Design No. 3, Hawker Hart* and Handley Page Heyford (25.6.80)	3·50	3·50
FH4	Design No. 4, Hurricane ans Wellington (24.9.80)	2·50	2·50

* On the booklet cover the aircraft is wrongly identified as a Hawker Fury.
No FH2 is inscribed January 1980, No. FH3 May 1980 and No. FH4 July 1980.

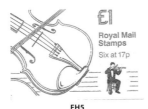

FH5

(Des M. Newton and S. Paine)

1986 (29 July)–**87**. Musical Instruments Series. Scarlet and black covers as T **FH5**. Containing 6×17p. (No. X952).

FH5	Design No 1, Violin	3·00

No. FH5 is inscribed November 1985.

Contents changed. Containing No. X901n.

FH6	Design No. 2, French horn (20.10.86)	3·00
FH7	Design No. 3, Bass clarinet (27.1.87)	3·00

No. FH7 is inscribed October 1986.

FH8

(Des A. Davidson)

1987 (14 Apr)–**88**. Sherlock Holmes Series. Bright scarlet and grey-black covers as T **FH8**. Containing booklet pane No. X901n (Nos. FH8/FH9) or X901na (Nos. FH10/FH11).

FH8	Design No. 1, *A Study in Scarlet*	3·00
FH9	Design No. 2, *The Hound of the Baskervilles* (14.7.87)	3·00
FH10	Design No. 3, *The Adventure of the Speckled Band* (29.9.87)	3·00

FH11	Design No. 4, *The Final Problem* (26.1.88)	3·00

Nos. FH8/FH11 are inscribed October 1986.
The panes from Nos. FH10/FH11 have imperforate vertical sides.

1988 (12 Apr). London Zoo. Children's Drawings Series. Cover as T **FB47** in black and brown. Containing booklet pane No. X901na.

FH12	Bears design	3·00

No. FH12 is inscribed October 1986 and has the vertical sides of the pane imperforate.

FH13

(Des Liz Moyes)

1988 (5 July)–**89**. Charles Dickens Series Orange-red and maroon covers as T **FH13**.

FH13	Designs No. 1, *Oliver Twist*, containing booklet pane No. X901na	3·75
FH14	Design No. 2, *Nicholas Nickleby*, containing booklet pane No. X904m (5.9.88)	3·75
FH15	Design No. 3, *David Copperfield*, containing booklet pane No. X904m (24.1.89)	3·75
FH16	Design No. 4, *Great Expectations*, containing booklet pane No. X1051l (25.4.89)	8·50

No. FH13 is inscribed October 1986 and No. FH16 is inscribed September 1988.
Nos. FH13/FH16 have the vertical sides of the pane imperforate.

1989 (18 July). Marine Life Series continued. Cover as T **FB50** in turquoise-green and scarlet. Containing booklet pane No. X904m.

FH17	Design No. 3, Edible Sea Urchin, Common Starfish and Common Shore Crab	3·75

No. FH17 has the vertical edges of the pane imperforate.

FH18

(Des J. Sancha)

1989 (2 Oct)–**90**. Mills Series. Grey-black and grey-green matt card cover as T **FH18**.

FH18	Design No. 1, Wicken Fen, Ely containing booklet pane No. X960l	4·00

*As T **FH18** but glossy card cover containing Penny Black Anniversary booklet pane No. 1476l printed in litho by Walsall.*

FH19	Design No. 1 (cover in bottle-green and pale green), Wicken Fen, Ely (30.1.90)	9·50

No. FH19 was an experimental printing to test a new cover material. This appears glossy when compared with Nos. FH18 and FH20.

*As T **FH18** but changed to matt card cover containing Penny Black Anniversary booklet pane No. 1469l printed in photo by Harrison.*

FH20	Design No. 2 (cover in grey-black and bright green), Click Mill, Dounby, Orkney (30.1.90)	6·00

1990 (4 Sept)–**91**. Mills Series continued. Covers as T **FH18**. Containing booklet pane No. X911m.

FH21	Design No. 3 (cover printed in light blue and buff) Jack and Jill Mills, Clayton, Sussex	3·00
FH22	Design No. 4 (cover printed in dull blue and bright yellow-green). Howell Mill, Llanddeusant, Anglesey (25.6.91)	3·00

Nos. FH18/FH22 have the vertical edges of the pane imperforate.

FH23

(Des J. Gibbs)

1991 (10 Sept)–**92**. 150th Anniversary of *Punch* Magazine. Magenta and grey-black covers as T **FH23** containing booklet pane No. X927l.

FH23   Design No. 1, Illustrations by Richard
       Doyle and Hoffnung.................................. 2·00
       a. Corrected rate (10.91)........................... 2·00
FH24   Design No. 2, Illustrations by Sir John
       Tenniel and Eric Burgin (21.1.92)............. 2·00
FH25   Design No. 3, Illustrations by Sir John
       Tenniel and Anton (28.4.92)................... 2·00
FH26   Design No. 4, Illustrations by Sir John
       Tenniel and Hewison (28.7.92)................ 2·00

Nos. FH23/FH26 have the vertical edges of the pane imperforate.
No. FH23a has corrected letter rates as No. FB59a.

(Des J. Matthews)

1992 (22 Sept). 1000th Anniversary of Appointment of Sheriffs. Scarlet and dull blue cover as T **FB63** containing booklet pane No. X927l.

FH27   Design as Type **FB63** but elements in
       reverse order... 2·00

No. FH27 has the vertical edges of the pane imperforate.

FH28

(Des J. Lawrence)

1993 (9 Feb–6 July). Educational Institutions Series. Covers as T **FH28** containing booklet pane No. X1050l printed in litho by Walsall.

FH28   Design No. 1 (cover in lake-brown and
       light blue), University of Wales................ 4·00
FH29   Design No. 2 (cover in deep dull green
       and lemon), St Hilda's College, Oxford
       (6.4.93)... 4·00
FH30   Design No. 3 (cover in purple-brown
       and flesh), Marlborough College,
       Wiltshire (6.7.93)..................................... 4·00

1993 (1 Nov). Educational Institutions Series continued. Deep bluish green and lilac cover as T **FH28** containing 4×25p. (No. Y1775) printed in litho by Walsall.

FH31   Design No. 4, Free Church of Scotland
       College, Edinburgh.................................... 3·75

FH32

(Des H. Brockway)

1994 (25 Jan). 20th-century Prime Ministers Series. Brown and pale brown cover as T **FH32** containing 4×25p. (No. Y1775) printed in litho by Walsall.

FH32   Design No. 1, Herbert Asquith................. 1·75

(Des H. Brockway)

1994 (26 Apr–6 Sept). 20th-century Prime Ministers Series continued. Covers as T **FH32**. Containing 4×25p. (No. Y1689) printed in photo by Harrison.

FH33   Design No. 2 (cover in sepia and buff),
       David Lloyd-George.................................. 1·75
FH34   Design No. 3 (cover in greenish blue
       and pale blue), Winston Churchill
       (6.6.94)... 1·75
FH35   Design No. 4 (cover in black and
       yellow-olive), Clement Attlee (6.9.94).... 1·75

FH36

(Des L. Thomas)

1995 (7 Feb–4 Apr). 50th Anniversary of End of Second World War. Covers as T **FH36** containing 4×25p. (No. Y1689) printed in photo by Harrison.

FH36   Design No. 1 (cover in brown-olive and
       brownish black), Violette Szabo (SOE
       agent)... 1·75
FH37   Design No. 2 (cover in red-brown and
       black), Dame Vera Lynn (entertainer)
       (4.4.95)... 1·75

1995 (16 May–4 Sept). 50th Anniversary of End of Second World War Series continued. Covers as T **FH36** containing 4×25p. (No. Y1690) printed in photo by Harrison.

FH38   Design No. 3 (cover in black and
       steel-blue), R. J. Mitchell (designer of
       Spitfire).. 1·75
FH39   Design No. 4 (cover in grey-green and
       black), Archibald McIndoe (plastic
       surgeon) (4.9.95)..................................... 2·00

FH40

1996 (16 Jan). Multicoloured laminated cover as T **FH40**. Stamps printed in litho by Questa.

FH40   containing 4×25p. stamps (No. Y1775).. 4·00

For an initial test period No. FH40 was only available from machines at 12 post offices, five in London and seven in Scotland, in addition to philatelic outlets. Stocks were distributed nationally from May 1996.

1996 (8 July)–**97**. Multicoloured laminated cover as T **FH40**. Stamps printed in litho by Questa.

FH41   containing booklet pane of No. Y1760l.   3·75
       a. Corrected rate (4.2.97)........................... 3·50
       b. Inland rate table at right...................... 3·50

No. FH41 was reissued on 4 February 1997 showing the 200 gram second class rate on the inside cover altered from 47p. to 45p. A further printing issued 5 May 1998 was without the overseas postage rate table.

1998 (1 Dec). Multicoloured laminated cover as T **FH40**. Stamps printed in gravure by Questa.

FH42   containing booklet pane of No. Y1667l.   20·00

1999 (26 Apr). Multicoloured laminated cover as T **FH40**. Stamps printed in gravure by Questa.

FH43   containing booklet pane of No.
       Y1667m... 6·00

2000 (27 Apr)–**01**. Multicoloured laminated cover as T **FH40**. Stamps printed in gravure by Questa.

FH44   containing booklet pane of No. 1664l.... 6·75
       a. containing booklet pane No. 1664la
       (17.4.01)... 7·00

£1·15 Booklets

1981 (26 Jan–18 Mar). Military Aircraft Series continued. Blue and grey covers as T **FE1** (90×49 mm). Containing 10×11½p. (No. X893). A. Selvedge at left. B. Selvedge at right.

		A	B
FI1	Design No. 5, Spitfire and Lancaster.......	3·00	3·00
FI2	Design No. 6, Lightning and Vulcan (18.3.81).................................	3·25	3·00

Nos. FI1/FI2 are inscribed January 1981.

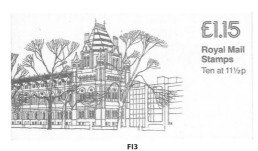

FI3

(Des R. Maddox)

1981 (6 May–30 Sept). Museums Series. Blue and turquoise green covers as T **FI3** (90×49 mm). Containing 10×11½p. (No. X893). A. Selvedge at left. B. Selvedge at right.

		A	B
FI3	Design No. 1, Natural History Museum (British Museum), London......................	3·00	3·00
FI4	Design No. 2, National Museum of Antiquities of Scotland (30.9.81).............	3·00	3·00

Nos. FI3/FI4 are inscribed January 1981.

£1·20 Booklets

1980 (4 Feb–24 Sept). Industrial Archaeology Series continued. Red and green covers as T **FH1** (90×49 mm). Containing 10×12p. (No. X943). A. Selvedge at left. B. Selvedge at right.

		A	B
FJ1	Design No. 2, Beetle Mill, Ireland...........	3·00	3·00
FJ2	Design No. 3, Tin Mines, Cornwall (25.6.80)...............................	3·00	4·00
FJ3	Design No. 4, Bottle Kilns, Gladstone, Stoke-on-Trent (24.9.80)........................	3·00	3·25

No. FJ1 is inscribed January 1980, No. FJ2 May 1980 and No. FJ3 July 1980.

1986 (14 Jan). Pillar box Write Now. Yellow-green and pale red cover as T **FB31** (90×49 mm). Containing 10×12p. (No. X896). A. Selvedge at left. B. Selvedge at right.

		A	B
FJ4	Write Now (Pillar box design) (no imprint date).................................	4·50	4·50

FJ5

(Des R. Maddox)

1986 (29 Apr). National Gallery. Magenta and blue-green cover as T **FJ5** (90×49 mm). Containing 10×12p. (No. X896). A. Selvedge at left. B. Selvedge at right.

		A	B
FJ5	National Gallery design............................	4·25	4·25

No. FJ5 is inscribed November 1985.

FJ6

(Des Trickett and Webb Ltd)

1986 (29 July). Handwriting Bright orange and bright blue cover as T **FJ6** (90×49 mm). Containing 10×12p. (No. X896). A. Selvedge at left. B. Selvedge at right.

		A	B
FJ6	Maybe...	4·25	4·25

No. FJ6 is inscribed November 1985.

£1·25 Booklets

1982 (1 Feb–6 Oct). Museums Series continued. Blue and turquoise-green covers as T **FI3** (90×49 mm). Containing 10×12½p. (No. X898). A. Selvedge at right.

		A	B
FK1	Design No. 3, Ashmolean Museum, Oxford...	2·75	2·75
FK2	Design No. 4, National Museum of Wales, Cardiff (6.5.82).......................	2·75	2·75
FK3	Design No. 5, Ulster Museum, Belfast (11.8.82)......................................	2·75	2·75
FK4	Design No. 6, Castle Museum, York (6.10.82).......................................	2·75	2·75

Nos. FK1/FK4 are inscribed February 1982.

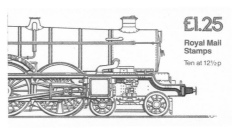

FK5

(Des S. Paine)

1983 (16 Feb–26 Oct). Railway Engines Series. Red and blue-green covers as T **FK5** (90×49 mm). Containing 10×12½p. (No. X898). A. Selvedge at left. B. Selvedge at right.

		A	B
FK5	Design No. 1, GWR *Isambard Kingdom Brunel*.................................	4·00	4·00
FK6	Design No. 2, LMS Class 4P Passenger Tank Engine (5.4.83)........................	4·75	4·75
	a. Corrected rate..	80·00	£125
FK7	Design No. 3, LNER *Mallard* (27.7.83)......	4·00	4·00
FK8	Design No. 4, SR/BR *Clan Line* (26.10.83)...........................	4·00	4·00

No. FK5 is inscribed February 1982 and Nos. FK6/FK8 April 1983. The corrected rate reads 36p. for 200 grams instead of 37p. for 200 grams.

£1·30 Booklets

FL1

(Des J. Gibbs)

1981 (6 May–30 Sept). Postal History Series. Covers as T **FL1** (90×49 mm). Containing No. X894l. A. Selvedge at left. B. Selvedge at right.

		A	B
FL1	Design No. 1, Penny Black (red and black cover)...	3·75	2·75
FL2	Design No. 2, The Downey Head, 1911 (red and green cover) (30.9.81)...............	4·75	16·00

No. FL1 is inscribed April 1981 and No. FL2 September 1981.

FL3

(Des J. Thirsk)

1984 (3 Sept)–**85**. Trams Series. Yellow-orange and purple covers as T **FL3** (90×49 mm). Containing 10×13p. (No. X900). A. Selvedge at left. B. Selvedge at right.

		A	B
FL3	Design No. 1, Swansea/Mumbles Railway Car No. 3.............................	2·75	2·75
FL4	Design No. 2, Glasgow Car No. 927 and Car No. 1194 (15.1.85)......................	3·25	3·25
FL5	Design No. 3, Car No. 717, Blackpool (23.4.85)..	3·25	3·00
FL6	Design No. 4, Car No. 120 and D Class Car, London (23.7.85)............................	2·75	2·75

Nos. FL3/FL6 are inscribed September 1984.

FL7

(Des Anne Morrow)

1986 (20 Oct). Books for Children. Rose-red and lemon cover as T **FL7** (90×49 mm). Containing 10×13p. (No. X900). A. Selvedge at left. B. Selvedge at right.

		A	B
FL7	Teddy bears design....................................	2·75	2·75

FL8

(Des Trickett and Webb Ltd)

1987 (27 Jan). Keep in Touch. Light green and bright blue cover as T **FL8** (90×49 mm). Containing 10×13p. (No. X900). A. Selvedge at left. B. Selvedge at right.

		A	B
FL8	Handclasp and envelope design............	2·75	2·75

No. FL8 is inscribed October 1986.

FL9

(Des Hannah Firmin)

1987 (14 Apr). Ideas for your Garden. Bistre and orange-brown cover as T **FL9** (90×49 mm). Containing 10×13p. stamps (No. X900). A. Selvedge at left. B. Selvedge at right.

		A	B
FL9	Conservatory design.................................	2·75	2·75

No. FL9 is inscribed October 1986.

FL10

(Des Trickett and Webb Ltd)

1987 (14 July). Brighter Writer. Orange and bright reddish violet cover as T **FL10** (90×49 mm). Containing 10×13p. stamps (No. X900). A. Selvedge at left. B. Selvedge at right.

		A	B
FL10	Flower design...	2·75	2·75

No. FL10 is inscribed October 1986.

FL11

(Des E. Stemp)

1987 (29 Sept). Jolly Postman. Pale blue and deep blue cover as T **FL11** (90×49 mm). Containing 10×13p. stamps (No. X900). A. Selvedge at left. B. Selvedge at right.

		A	B
FL11	Boy drawing design...................................	2·75	2·75

No. FL11 is inscribed October 1986.

FL12

(Des E. Hughes)

1988 (26 Jan). Bicentenary of Linnean Society. Blue and claret cover as T **FL12** (90×49 mm). Containing 10×13p. stamps (No. X900). A. Selvedge at left. B. Selvedge at right.

		A	B
FL12	Mermaid, fish and insect (from *Hortus Sanitatis*, 1497)..	3·50	3·50

No. FL12 is inscribed October 1986.

FL13

1988 (12 Apr). Recipe Cards. Brown and green cover as T **FL13** (90×49 mm). Containing 10×13p. stamps (No. X900). A. Selvedge at left. B. Selvedge at right.

		A	B
FL13	Vegetables design......................................	2·75	2·75

No. FL13 is inscribed October 1986.

FL14

(Des Trickett and Webb Ltd)

1988 (5 July). Children's Parties. Blue-green and bright purple cover as T **FL14** (90×49 mm). Containing 10×13p. stamps (No. X900). A. Selvedge at left. B. Selvedge at right.

		A	B
FL14	Balloons and streamers design...............	2·75	2·75

No. FL14 is inscribed October 1986.

£1·40 Booklets

1981 (26 Jan–18 Mar). Industrial Archaeology Series continued. Red and green covers as T **FH1** (90×49 mm). Containing 10×14p. (No. X946). A. Selvedge at left. B. Selvedge at right.

		A	B
FM1	Design No. 5, Preston Mill, Scotland.......	2·75	3·00
FM2	Design No. 6, Talyllyn Railway, Tywyn (18.3.81)..	3·00	2·75

Nos. FM1/FM2 are inscribed January 1981.

FM3

(Des E. Stemp)

1981 (6 May–30 Sept). 19th-century Women's Costume Series. Claret and blue covers as T **FM3** (90×49 mm). Containing 10×14p. (No. X946). A. Selvedge at left. B. Selvedge at right.

		A	B
FM3	Design No. 1, Costume, 1800–1815.......	2·75	2·75
FM4	Design No. 2, Costume, 1815–1830 (30.9.81)..	2·75	2·75

Nos. FM3/FM4 are inscribed January 1981.

FM5

(Des A. Drummond)

1988 (5 Sept). Pocket Planner. Grey-black and yellow cover as T **FM5** (90×49 mm). Containing 10×14p. stamps (No. X903). A. Selvedge at left. B. Selvedge at right.

		A	B
FM5	Legal Charge design................................	2·75	2·75

FM6

(Des Debbie Cook)

1989 (24 Jan). 150th Anniversary of Fox Talbot's Report on the Photographic Process to Royal Society. Reddish orange and black cover as T **FM6** (90×49 mm). Containing 10×14p. stamps (No. X903). A. Selvedge at left. B. Selvedge at right.

		A	B
FM6	Photographs and darkroom equipment..	2·80	2·80

No. FM6 is inscribed September 1988.

£1·43 Booklets

1982 (1 Feb–6 May). Postal History Series continued. Covers as T **FL1** (90×49 mm). Containing No. X899l. A. Selvedge at left. B. Selvedge at right.

		A	B
FN1	Design No. 3, James Chalmers (postal reformer) (orange and turquoise-blue cover)...	3·00	3·00
FN2	Design No. 4, Edmund Dulac (stamp designer) (brown and red cover) (6.5.82)..	3·00	3·00

FN3

(Des J. Gardner)

1982 (12 July). Holiday Postcard Stamp Book Purple and turquoise-blue cover as T **FN3** (90×49 mm). Containing No. X899l. A. Selvedge at left. B. Selvedge at right.

		A	B
FN3	*Golden Hinde* on front, postcard voucher on back..	3·00	3·00

1982 (21 July)–**83**. Postal History Series continued. Covers as T **FL1** (90×49 mm). Containing No. X899l. A. Selvedge at left. B. Selvedge at right.

		A	B
FN4	Design No. 5, Forces Postal Service (grey and violet cover)............................	3·00	3·00
FN5	Design No. 6, The £5 Orange (orange and black cover) (6.10.82)....................	3·00	3·00
FN6	Design No. 7, Postmark History (bright scarlet and deep dull blue cover) (16.2.83)...	3·00	3·00

No. FN1 is inscribed February 1982. Nos. FN2/FN3 May 1982, No. FN4 July 1982, No. FN5 October 1982, No. FN6 November 1982.

For booklet No. FS2 with cover price of £1·45, see £1·60 booklets.

£1·46 Booklets

1983 (5 Apr–26 Oct). Postal History Series continued. Covers as T **FL1** (90×49 mm). A. Containing No. X899n. B. Containing No. X899na.

		A	B
FO1	Design No. 8, Seahorse High Values (blue and green cover)............................	5·50	5·50
	a. Corrected rate................................	48·00	15·00
FO2	Design No. 9, Parcel Post Centenary (turquoise-blue and carmine cover) (27.7.83)...	4·75	4·75
FO3	Design No. 10, Silver Jubilee of Regional Stamps (dull green and reddish violet cover) (26.10.83)...............	4·75	4·75

No. FO1 is inscribed March 1983, No. FO2 May 1983 and No. FO 3 June 1983.
The corrected rate reads 36p. for 200g instead of 37p. for 200g.

£1·50 Booklets

1986 (14 Jan). Pillar box Write Now. Ultramarine and red cover as T **FB31** (90×49 mm). A. Containing No. X897l. B. Containing No. X897la.

		A	B
FP1	Write Now (Pillar box design)..................	3·50	3·50

No. FP1 does not show imprint date.

1986 (29 Apr). National Gallery. Violet and vermilion cover as T **FJ5** (90×49 mm). A. Containing No. X897l. B. Containing No. X897la.

		A	B
FP2	National Gallery design...........................	3·50	3·50

No. FP2 is inscribed November 1985.

1986 (29 July). Handwriting. Blue-green and bright blue cover as T **FJ6** (90×49 mm). A. Containing No. X897l. B. Containing No. X897la.

		A	B
FP3	No...	3·50	3·50

No. FP3 is inscribed November 1985.

£1·54 Booklets

1984 (3 Sept)–**85**. Postal History Series continued. Covers as T **FL1** (90×49 mm). A. Containing No. X901l. B. Containing No. X901la.

		A	B
FQ1	Design No. 11, Old and new Postage Dues (reddish purple and pale blue cover)...	3·00	3·00
FQ2	Design No. 12, Queen Victoria embossed stamps (yellow-green and blue cover) (15.1.85)...........................	3·00	3·00
FQ3	Design No. 13, Queen Victoria surface printed stamps (blue-green and carmine cover) (23.4.85).....................	3·00	3·00
FQ4	Design No. 14, 17th-century mounted and foot messengers (deep brown and orange-red cover) (23.7.85)...................	3·00	3·00

No. FQ1 is inscribed July 1984 and Nos. FQ2/FQ4 are inscribed September 1984.

£1·55 Booklets

1982 (1 Feb–6 Oct). 19th-century Women's Costume Series continued. Claret and blue covers as T **FM3** (90×49 mm). Containing 10×15½p. (No. X948). A. Selvedge at left. B. Selvedge at right.

		A	B
FR1	Design No. 3, Costume, 1830–1850........	2·75	2·75
FR2	Design No. 4, Costume, 1850–1860 (6.5.82)...	2·75	2·75
FR3	Design No. 5, Costume, 1860–1880 (11.8.82)...	3·00	3·00
FR4	Design No. 6, Costume, 1880–1900 (6.10.82)...	2·75	2·75

Nos. FR1/FR4 are inscribed February 1982.

£1·60 Booklets

FS1

(Des Carol Walklin)

1983 (5 Apr). Birthday Box Design. Magenta and red-orange cover as T **FS1** (90×49 mm). Depicting birthday cake and associated items. A. Selvedge at left. B. Selvedge at right.

		A	B
FS1	containing 10×16p. stamps (No. X949) (no imprint date)........................	3·50	3·50
	a. Rates altered and February 1983 imprint date.....................................	60·00	90·00

The converted rate reads 36p. for 200g. instead of 37p. for 200g.

FS2

(Des R. Maddox)

1983 (10 Aug). British Countryside Series. Special Discount Booklet (*sold at £1·45*). Greenish blue and ultramarine cover as T **FS2** (90×49 mm). Containing 10×16p. stamps (No. X949u). A. Selvedge at left. B. Selvedge at right.

		A	B
FS2	Design No. 1, Lyme Regis, Dorset...........	4·75	4·75

Stamps from No. FS2 show a double-lined D printed in blue on the reverse over the gum.
No. FS2 is inscribed April 1983.

1983 (21 Sept). British Countryside Series continued. Dull green on violet cover as T **FS2** (90×49 mm). Containing 10×16p. stamps (No. X949). A. Selvedge at left. B. Selvedge at right.

		A	B
FS3	Design No. 2, Arlington Row, Bibury, Gloucestershire....................................	3·00	3·00

No. FS3 is inscribed April 1983.

FS4

(Des M. Newton)

1984 (14 Feb). Write it Design. Vermilion and ultramarine cover as T **FS4** (90×49 mm). Containing 10×16p. stamps (No. X949). A. Selvedge at left. B. Selvedge at right.

		A	B
FS4	Fountain pen.....................................	3·50	3·50

No. FS4 is inscribed April 1983.

£1·70 Booklets

FT1

1984 (3 Sept). Social Letter Writing Series. Rose and deep claret cover as T **FT1** (90×49 mm). Containing 10×17p. (No. X952). A. Selvedge at left. B. Selvedge at right.

		A	B
FT1	Design No. 1, Love Letters........................	3·50	3·50

No. FT1 is inscribed September 1984.

1985 (5 Mar). Social Letter Writing continued. Special Discount Booklet (*sold at* £1·55). Turquoise-blue and deep claret cover as T **FT1** (90×49 mm). Containing 10×17p. (No. X952u). A. Selvedge at left. B. Selvedge at right.

		A	B
FT2	Design No. 2, Letters abroad..................	3·50	3·50

Stamps from No. FT2 show a double-lined D printed in blue on the reverse over the gum.
No. FT2 is inscribed September 1984.

1985 (9 Apr). Social Letter Writing Series continued. Bright blue and deep claret cover as T **FT1** (90×49 mm). Containing 10×17p. (No. X952). A. Selvedge at left. B. Selvedge at right.

		A	B
FT3	Design No. 3, Fan letters...........................	3·25	3·25

No. FT3 is inscribed September 1984.

FT4

(Des B. Smith)

1985 (30 July). 350 Years of Royal Mail Public Postal Service Special Discount Booklet (*sold at* £1·53). Rosine and bright blue cover T **FT4** (90×60 mm). Containing 10×17p. (No. 1290u) with selvedge at top.

FT4	Datapost Service design...........................	3·75

The stamps from this booklet show double-lined letters D printed on the reverse over the gum.
No. FT4 is inscribed September 1984.

1985 (8 Oct)–**86**. Social Letter Writing Series continued. Black and bright scarlet cover as T **FT1** (90×49 mm). Containing 10×17p. (No. X952). A. Selvedge at left. B. Selvedge at right.

		A	B
FT5	Design No. 4, Write Now (Pillar box).......	3·25	3·25
	a. Revised rates (2nd class (60g) 12p.)		
	(1.86)...	24·00	16·00

1986 (29 Apr). National Gallery. Blue-green and blue cover as T **FJ5** (90×49 mm). Containing 10×17p. (No. X952). A. Selvedge at left. B. Selvedge at right.

		A	B
FT6	National Gallery design...........................	3·50	3·50

No. FT6 is inscribed November 1985.

1986 (29 July). Handwriting. Red and bright blue cover as T **FJ6** (90×49 mm). Containing 10×17p. (No. X952). A. Selvedge at left. B. Selvedge at right.

		A	B
FT7	Yes..	3·50	3·50

No. FT7 is inscribed November 1985.

£1·80 Booklets

1986 (20 Oct). Books for Children. New blue and orange-brown cover as T **FL7**. Containing 10×18p. (No. X955). A. Selvedge at left. B. Selvedge at right.

		A	B
FU1	Rabbits design..	3·75	3·75

1987 (27 Jan). Keep in Touch. Magenta and bright blue cover as T **FL8**. Containing 10×18p. (No. X955). A. Selvedge at left. B. Selvedge at right.

		A	B
FU2	Handclasp and envelope design.............	3·75	3·75

No. FU2 is inscribed October 1986.

1987 (14 Apr). Ideas for your Garden Claret and brown-olive cover as T **FL9** (90×49 mm). Containing 10×18p. stamps (No. X955). A. Selvedge at left. B. Selvedge at right.

		A	B
FU3	Garden path design..................................	3·75	5·00

No. FU3 is inscribed October 1986.

1987 (14 July). Brighter Writer. Turquoise-green and reddish orange cover as T **FL10** (90×49 mm). Containing 10×18p. stamps (No. X955). A. Selvedge at left. B. Selvedge at right.

		A	B
FU4	Berries and leaves design.........................	3·75	3·75

No. FU4 is inscribed October 1986.

1987 (29 Sept). Jolly Postman. Deep blue and claret cover as T **FL11** (90×49 mm). Containing 10×18p. stamps (No. X955). A. Selvedge at left. B. Selvedge at right.

		A	B
FU5	Girl drawing design...................................	3·75	3·75

No. FU5 is inscribed October 1986.

1988 (26 Jan). Bicentenary of Linnean Society. Dull yellow-green and dull claret cover as T **FL12** (90×49 mm). Containing 10×18p. stamps (No. X955). A. Selvedge at left. B. Selvedge at right.

		A	B
FU6	Wolf and birds (from *Hortus Sanitatis*, 1497).....	3·75	3·75
	a. Inside cover text for FL12................	95·00	95·00

No. FU6 is inscribed October 1986.
The inside cover text for FU6a has the special offer of the £1·30 booklet, No. FL12 (4×13p. stamps).

1988 (12 Apr). Recipe Cards. Claret and Indian red cover as T **FL13** (90×49 mm). Containing 10×18p. stamps (No. X955). A. Selvedge at left. B. Selvedge at right.

		A	B
FU7	Fruits, pudding and jam design..............	3·75	3·75

No. FU7 is inscribed October 1986.

1988 (5 July). Children's Parties. Violet and rosine cover as T **FL14** (90×49 mm). Containing 10×18p. stamps (No. X955). A. Selvedge at left. B. Selvedge at right.

		A	B
FU8	Balloons and party hats design..............	3·75	3·75

No. FU8 is inscribed October 1986.

£1·90 Booklets

1988 (5 Sept). Pocket Planner. Yellow-green and magenta cover as T **FM5** (90×49 mm). Containing 10×19p. stamps (No. X956). A. Selvedge at left. B. Selvedge at right.

		A	B
FV1	Marriage Act design..................................	4·50	4·50

1989 (24 Jan). 150th Anniversary of Fox Talbot's Report on the Photographic Process to Royal Society. Emerald and black cover as T **FM6** (90×49 mm). Containing 10×19p. stamps (No. X956). A. Selvedge at left. B. Selvedge at right.

		A	B
FV2	Fox Talbot with camera and Lacock Abbey.........	4·50	4·50

No. FV2 is inscribed September 1988.

£2 Booklets

FW1

(Des Debbie Cook)

1993 (1 Nov)–**94**. Postal Vehicles Series. Covers as T **FW1**. Containing 8×25p. (No. Y1689).

FW1	Design No. 1 (cover in dull vermilion and deep blue), Motorised cycle-carrier	3·25
FW2	Design No. 2 (cover in green and deep violet-blue), Experimental motor mail van (26.4.94)...............	3·25
FW3	Design No. 3 (cover in red and black), Experimental electric mail van, 1932 (6.9.94)......................	3·25

FW3

(Des The Four Hundred)

1995 (7 Feb–4 Apr). Birth Bicentenary of Sir Rowland Hill. Covers as T **FW3**. Containing 8×25p. (No. Y1689).

FW4	Design No. 1 (cover in purple and new blue), Rowland Hill as director of London and Brighton Railway Company	3·25
FW5	Design No. 2 (cover in deep mauve and greenish blue), Rowland Hill and Hazlewood School (4.4.95)......................	3·25

1995 (6 June–4 Sept). Birth Bicentenary of Sir Rowland Hill Series continued. Covers as T **FW3**. Containing 8×25p. (No. Y1690).

FW6	Design No. 3 (cover in deep blue-green and dull orange), Rowland Hill as Secretary to the Post Office.................	3·50
FW7	Design No. 4 (cover in red-brown and orange), Uniform Penny Postage petition and Mulready envelope (4.9.95)	3·50

1996 (16 Jan). Multicoloured laminated cover as T **FH40**. Stamps printed in litho by Questa.

FW8	containing 8×25p. stamps (No. Y1775)..	3·75

For an initial test period No. FW8 was only available from machines at 12 post offices, five in London and seven in Scotland, in addition to philatelic outlets. Stocks were distributed nationally from May 1996.

1996 (8 July)–**97**. Multicoloured laminated cover as T **FH40**. Stamps printed in litho by Questa.

FW9	containing booklet pane of No. Y1772l..	3·75
	a. Corrected rate (4.2.97)............................	3·75
	b. Inland rate table inside at right (5.5.98)	3·75

No. FW9 was reissued on 4 February 1997 showing the 200 gram second class rate on the inside cover altered from 47p. to 45p. A further printing issued 5 May 1998 was without the overseas postage rate table.

1998 (1 Dec). Multicoloured laminated cover as T **FH40**. Stamps printed in gravure by Questa.

FW10	containing booklet pane of No. Y1685l.	20·00

1999 (26 Apr). Multicoloured laminated cover as T **FH40**. Stamps printed in gravure by Questa.

FW11	containing booklet pane of No. Y1682l.	6·50

2000 (27 Apr). Multicoloured laminated cover as T **FH40**. Stamps printed in gravure by Questa.

FW12	containing booklet pane of No. 1664m	8·50

CHRISTMAS BOOKLETS

FX1

(Des J. Matthews)

1978 (15 Nov). Christmas Greetings. Rose-red and sage-green cover T **FX1** (90×49 mm).

FX1	£1·60 containing booklet pane No. X875l........	2·50

No. FX1 is inscribed August 1978.

FX2

(Des P. Sharland)

1979 (14 Nov). Christmas Greetings. Red and green cover as T **FX2** (90×49 mm), showing Christmas cracker.

FX2	£1·80 containing booklet pane No. X879l........	3·00

No. FX2 is inscribed October 1979.

FX3

(Des E. Fraser)

1980 (12 Nov). Christmas. Red and blue cover as T **FX3** (90×49 mm), showing Nativity scene.

FX3	£2·20 containing booklet pane No. X888m.....	3·25

No. FX3 is inscribed September 1980.

FX4

(Des W. Sanderson)

1981 (11 Nov). Christmas. Red and blue cover as T **FX4**, (90×49 mm), showing skating scene.

FX4	£2·55 containing booklet pane No. X893l........	4·25

No. FX4 is inscribed January 1981.

FX5

(Des A. Davidson)

1982 (10 Nov). Christmas. Red and green cover as T **FX5** (90×49 mm), showing Christmas Mummers.
FX5   £2·50 containing booklet pane No. X898l........   5·00
    No. FX5 is inscribed February 1982 and was sold at a discount of 30p. off the face value of the stamps.
    Each stamp in the pane has a blue star printed on the reverse over the gum.

FX6

(Des Barbara Brown)

1983 (9 Nov). Christmas. Brown-lilac and yellow cover as T **FX6** (90×49 mm), showing pantomime scenes.
FX6   £2·20 containing 20×12½p. (No. X898v)..........   4·50
    No. FX6 is inscribed April 1983 and was sold at a discount of 30p. off the face value of the stamps.
    Each stamp in the pane has a double-lined blue star printed on the reverse over the gum.

FX7

(Des Yvonne Gilbert)

1984 (20 Nov). Christmas. Light brown and red-orange cover as T **FX7** (90×60 mm), showing Nativity scene.
FX7   £2·30 containing 20×13p. (No. 1267u)............   5·00
    No. FX7 is inscribed September 1984 and was sold at a discount of 30p. off the face value of the stamps.
    The stamps from this booklet show double-lined blue stars printed on the reverse over the gum.

FX8

(Des A. George)

1985 (19 Nov). Christmas. Bright blue and rose cover as T **FX8** (90×60 mm), showing The Pantomime.
FX8   £2·40 containing 20×12p. (No. 1303u)............   4·50
    The stamps from this booklet show double-lined blue stars printed on the reverse over the gum.

FX9

(Des Lynda Gray)

1986 (2 Dec). Christmas. Red and dull blue-green cover as T **FX9** (90×49 mm), showing Shetland Yule cakes. A. Selvedge at left. B. Selvedge at right.

		A	B
FX9	£1·20 containing 10×13p. (No. X900u)............	4·50	8·00

    No. FX9 is inscribed October 1986 and was sold at a discount of 10p. off the face value of the stamps.
    Each stamp in the pane has a blue star printed on the reverse over the gum.

For 1990 and later Christmas stamps, see Barcode Booklets Section G.

£1·90 Greetings Booklet

FY1

(Des L. Moberly)

1989 (31 Jan). Greetings Stamps. Multicoloured cover as T **FY1** (89×60 mm). Containing booklet pane No. 1423a, including 12 special greetings labels in a block (3×4) at right, attached by the selvedge.
FY1   Greetings design......................................   24·00
    No. FY1 is inscribed September 1988.
    The cover of No. FY 1 shows an overall pattern of elements taken from the stamp designs. Due to the method of production the position of these elements varies from cover to cover.

For Greetings stamps in Barcode booklets, see Barcode Booklets Section F.

III. BARCODE BOOKLETS

These booklets are listed in 11 sections:

SECTION C: G numbers containing Machin stamps with face value

SECTION D: H numbers containing Machin NVI stamps

SECTION E: J numers containing Machin Penny Black Anniversary stamps

SECTION F: KX numbers containing Greetings stamps

SECTION G: LX numbers containing Christmas stamps

SECTION H: M numbers containing self-adhesive NVI definitive stamps

SECTION I: N numbers containing self-adhesive definitive stamps with face value

SECTION J: PM numbers containing both special and definitive self-adhesive NVI stamps

SECTION K: Q numbers containing NVI 'Smiler' stamps in definitive size

SECTION L: R numbers containing stamps with value indicator at upper left

SECTION M: SA numbers containing NVI 'Smiler' stamps and definitive stamps

SECTION N: T numbers containing NVI barcode Machin stamps

These are produced for sale in both post offices and commercial outlets.

NOTE. All panes are attached to the covers by the selvedge. Barcode booklet covers are illustrated at two-thirds linear size, *unless otherwise stated.*

C. Barcode Booklets containing Machin stamps with values shown as T 367.

COVERS. These are all printed in scarlet, lemon and black with the barcode on the reverse. T **GA1** has a clear 'window' to view the contents, T **GB3** is shorter and has a stamp illustration printed on the cover to replace the 'window'. These illustrations show an oblique white line across the bottom right-hand corner of the 'stamp'. Unless otherwise stated all covers were printed by Harrison.

From early 1997 the printer of each booklet is identified by a small capital letter below the barcode on the outside back cover.

52p. Booklet

GA1

1987 (4 Aug). Laminated cover T **GA1** (75×60 mm).
GA1   containing booklet pane No. X900n......   2·25
   No. GA1 is inscribed 20 October 1986.

56p. Booklets

1988 (23 Aug). Laminated cover as T **GA1** (75×56 mm).
GB1   containing booklet pane No. X903l........   3·50

1988 (11 Oct). Laminated cover as T **GA1** (75×56 mm) printed by Walsall.
GB2   containing booklet pane No. X903l........   5·25

GB3 Large Crown

1988 (11 Oct). Laminated cover as T **GB3** (75×48 mm) with stamp printed on the cover in deep blue.
GB3   containing booklet pane No. X903n......   4·00
   No. GB3 is inscribed 5 September 1988 and has the horizontal edges of the pane imperforate.

1989 (24 Jan). Laminated cover as T **GB3** (75×48 mm) with stamp printed on the cover in deep blue by Walsall.
GB4   containing booklet pane No. X903q......   20·00
   No. GB4 is inscribed 5 September 1988 and has the three edges of the pane imperforate.

72p. Booklet

1987 (4 Aug). Laminated cover as T **GA1** (75×60 mm).
GC1   containing booklet pane No. X955m.....   2·25
   No. GC1 is inscribed 20 October 1986.

76p. Booklets

1988 (23 Aug). Laminated cover as T **GA1** (75×56 mm).
GD1   containing booklet pane No. X956l........   4·00

1988 (11 Oct). Laminated cover as T **GA1** (75×56 mm) printed by Walsall.
GD2   containing booklet pane No. X956l........   4·25

1988 (11 Oct). Laminated cover as T **GB3** (75×48 mm) with stamp printed on the cover in bright orange-red.
GD3   containing booklet pane No. X956n......   5·00
   No. GD3 is inscribed 5 September 1988 and has the horizontal edges of the pane imperforate.

1989 (24 Jan). Laminated cover as T **GB3** (75×48 mm) with stamp printed on the cover in bright orange-red by Walsall.
GD4   containing booklet pane No. X956q......   20·00
   No. GD4 is inscribed 5 September 1988 and has the three edges of the pane imperforate.

78p. Booklet

GD4a (As T **GM1** but without '4')

1992 (28 July). Multicoloured laminated cover as T **GD4a** (75×49 mm) with stamp printed on the cover in bright mauve by Walsall.
GD4a   containing 2×39p. stamps (No. X1058)
           (pane No. X1058l with right-hand vert
           pair removed) and pane of 4 airmail
           labels..   2·00
   Stamps in No. GD4a have top or bottom edge imperforate.
   Booklet No. GD4a was produced in connection with a Kellogg's Bran Flakes promotion.

£1·04 Booklet

1987 (4 Aug). Laminated cover as T **GA1** (75×60 mm).
GE1   containing booklet pane No. X971bl.....   10·00
   No. GE1 is inscribed 20 October 1986.

£1·08 Booklets

1988 (23 Aug). Laminated cover as T **GA1** (75×56 mm).
GF1   containing booklet pane No. X973l........   7·00
   a. Postage rates omitted from inside
       back cover..............................   20·00

1988 (11 Oct). Laminated cover as T **GB3** (75×48 mm) with stamp printed on the cover in chestnut.
GF2   containing booklet pane No. X973m.....   20·00
    No. GF2 is inscribed 5 September 1988 and has the horizontal edges of the pane imperforate.

£1·16 Booklets

GG1 Redrawn Crown

1989 (2 Oct). Laminated cover as T **GG1** (75×48 mm) with stamp printed on the cover in deep mauve by Walsall.
GG1   containing booklet pane No. X1054l.....   9·00
    No. GG1 has three edges of the pane imperforate.

1990 (17 Apr). Laminated cover as T **GG1** (75×48 mm) with stamp printed on the cover in deep mauve by Walsall.
GG2   containing booklet pane No. X1055l.....   10·00
    No. GG2 has three edges of the pane imperforate.

£1·20 Booklets

GGA1 (BY AIR MAIL par avion at bottom left)

1998 (5 May). Multicoloured laminated cover as T **GGA1** (75×50 mm) with stamps printed on cover in olive-grey by Walsall. Inscribed For items up to 20g on yellow tab at right.
GGA1   containing 4×30p. (gravure) (No. Y1694) and a pane of 4 airmail labels.....   2·25

GGA2 Create a card Design

1998 (3 Aug). Multicoloured laminated cover as T **GGA2** (75×50 mm) printed by Walsall. Inscribed See inside for offer details on yellow tab at right.
GGA2   containing 4×30p. (gravure) (No. Y1694) and a pane of 4 airmail labels.....   2·25
    This booklet was not placed on philatelic sale until 7 September 1998.

£1·24 Booklet

GH1 Crown on White

1990 (17 Sept). Multicoloured laminated cover as T **GH1** (75×49 mm) with stamp printed on the cover in ultramarine by Walsall.
GH1   containing booklet pane No. X1056l.....   4·00
    No. GH1 has the horizontal edges of the pane imperforate.

£1·30 Booklet

1987 (4 Aug). Laminated cover as T **GA1** (98×60 mm).
GI1   containing booklet pane No. X900o.....   3·25
    No. GI1 is inscribed 20 October 1986.

£1·32 Booklet

GJ1

1991 (16 Sept)–**92**. Multicoloured laminated cover as T **GJ1** (75×49 mm) with stamp printed on the cover in light emerald by Walsall. Inscribed For letters up to 10g on yellow strip at right.
GJ1   containing booklet pane No. X1057l
            and a pane of 4 airmail labels.....   3·50
          a. Inscribed For Worldwide Postcards on
            yellow strip (8.9.92).....   7·00
    Nos. GJ1/GJ1a have the horizontal edges of the pane imperforate.

£1·40 Booklets

1988 (23 Aug). Laminated cover as T **GA1** (97×56 mm).
GK1   containing booklet pane No. X903m.....   8·50

1988 (11 Oct). Laminated cover as T **GA1** (97×56 mm) printed by Questa.
GK2   containing 10×14p. (No. X1007).....   9·50

1988 (11 Oct). Laminated cover as T **GB3** (75×48 mm) with stamp printed on the cover in deep blue.
GK3   containing booklet pane No. X903p.....   5·50
    No. GK3 is inscribed 5 September 1988 and has horizontal edges of the pane imperforate.

1988 (11 Oct). Laminated cover as T **GB3** (75×48 mm) with stamp printed on the cover in deep blue by Questa.
GK4   containing 10×14p. (No. X1007).....   9·50

1993 (1 Nov). Laminated cover as T **GJ1** (76×50 mm) with stamp printed on the cover in yellow by Walsall. Inscribed For Worldwide Postcards on yellow tab at right.
GK5   containing 4×35p. (No. Y1778) and a pane of 4 airmail labels.....   3·25

GK6 (without diagonal white line across corners of stamps)

1995 (16 May). Multicoloured laminated cover as T **GK6** (75×48 mm) with stamps printed on the cover in yellow by Walsall.
GK6   containing 4×35p. (No. Y1778) and a
              pane of 4 airmail labels............................   3·25

1996 (19 Mar). Multicoloured laminated cover as T **GK6** (75×48 mm) without International and showing Olympic symbols on the back. Stamps printed on the cover in yellow by Walsall.
GK7   containing 4×35p. (No. Y1778) and a
              pane of 4 airmail labels............................   3·50

£1·48 Booklets

GL1 (Worldwide Postcard Stamps ranged left without diagonal white lines across corner of stamps)

1996 (8 July). Multicoloured laminated cover as T **GL1** (75×48 mm) showing Olympic symbols on the back. Stamps printed on the cover in bright mauve by Walsall. Inscribed For Worldwide Postcards on yellow tab at right.
GL1   containing 4×37p. (No. Y1779) and a
              pane of 4 airmail labels............................   5·25

1997 (4 Feb). Multicoloured laminated cover as T **GL1** (75×48 mm) without Olympic symbols on the back. Stamps printed on the cover in bright mauve by Walsall. Inscribed For Worldwide Postcards on yellow tab at right.
GL2   containing 4×37p. (No. Y1779) and a
              pane of 4 airmail labels............................   5·25

GL3

1997 (26 Aug)–**98**. Multicoloured laminated cover as T **GL3** (75×48 mm) printed by Walsall. Inscribed For Worldwide Postcards on yellow tab at right.
GL3   containing 4×37p. (gravure) (No.
              Y1703) and a pane of 4 new design
              airmail labels..   3·25
              a. Showing validity notice on inside back
                 cover (5.5.98)..   3·00
No. GL3 has the postage rate table on the inside back cover.

1998 (3 Aug). Multicoloured laminated cover as T **GGA2** (Create a card design) (75×50 mm) printed by Walsall.
GL4   containing 4×37p. (gravure) (No.
              Y1703) and a pane of 4 airmail labels.....   5·00
This booklet was not placed on philatelic sale until 7 September 1998.

£1·52 Booklet

1999 (26 Apr). Multicoloured laminated cover as T **GGA1** (76×50 mm) with stamps printed on cover in ultramarine by Walsall. Inscribed For Worldwide Postcards on yellow tab at right.
GLA1   containing 4×38p. (gravure) (No.
              Y1707) and a pane of 4 airmail labels.....   3·25

£1·56 Booklet

GM1

1991 (16 Sept). Multicoloured laminated cover as T **GM1** (75×49 mm) with stamp printed on the cover in bright mauve by Walsall.
GM1   containing booklet pane No. X1058l
              and a pane of 4 airmail labels..................   5·75
No. GM1 has the horizontal edges of the pane imperforate.

£1·60 Booklet

2000 (27 Apr). Multicoloured laminated cover as T **GGA1** (76×50 mm) with stamps printed on cover in deep azure by Walsall. Inscribed For Worldwide Postcards on yellow tab at right.
GMA1   containing 4×40p. (gravure) (No.
              Y1710) and a pane of 4 airmail labels.....   4·00

£1·64 Worldwide Airmail Stamps Booklets

1993 (1 Nov). Laminated cover as T **GM1** (76×50 mm) with stamp printed on the cover in drab by Walsall. Inscribed For letters up to 10g on yellow tab at right.
GN1   containing 4×41p. (No. Y1780) and a
              pane of 4 airmail labels............................   3·00

1995 (16 May). Multicoloured laminated cover as T **GK6** (75×48 mm) with stamps printed on the cover in drab by Walsall. Inscribed For items up to 10g on yellow tab at right.
GN2   containing 4×41p. (No. Y1780) and a
              pane of 4 airmail labels............................   3·00

1996 (19 Mar). Multicoloured laminated cover as T **GK6** (75×48 mm) without International and showing Olympic symbols on the back. Stamps printed on the cover in drab by Walsall. Inscribed For items up to 10g on yellow tab at right.
GN3   containing 4×41p. (No. Y1780) and a
              pane of 4 airmail labels............................   3·00

£1·80 Booklet

1987 (4 Aug). Laminated cover as T **GA1** (98×60 mm).
GO1   containing booklet pane No. X955n......   4·75
No. GO1 is inscribed 20 October 1986.

£1·90 Booklets

1988 (23 Aug). Laminated cover as T **GA1** (97×56 mm).
GP1   containing booklet pane No. X956n......   6·50

1988 (11 Oct). Laminated cover as T **GA1** (97×56 mm) printed by Questa.
GP2   containing 10×19p. (No. X1013).............   12·50

1988 (11 Oct). Laminated cover as T **GB3** (75×48 mm) with stamp printed on the cover in bright orange-red.
GP3   containing booklet pane No. X956o......   6·50
No. GP3 is inscribed 5 September 1988 and has the horizontal edges of the pane imperforate.

1988 (11 Oct). Laminated cover as T **GB3** (75×48 mm) with stamp printed on the cover in bright orange-red by Questa.
GP4   containing 10×19p. (No. X1013).............   12·50

£2·40 Booklets

1994 (9 Aug). Laminated cover as T **GM1** (75×49 mm) with stamp printed on the cover in dull blue-grey by Walsall. Inscribed items up to 20g on yellow tab at right.

GQ1   containing 4×60p. (No. Y1784) and a pane of 4 airmail labels............................ 4·50

GQ2

1994 (4 Oct). Laminated cover as T **GQ2** (75×49 mm) with stamp printed on the cover in dull blue-grey by Walsall.

GQ2   containing 4×60p. (No. Y1784) and a pane of 4 airmail plus 4 Seasons Greetings labels............................ 4·50

1995 (16 May). Laminated cover as T **GK6** (75×48 mm) with stamps printed on the cover in dull blue-grey by Walsall. Inscribed For items up to 20g on yellow tab at right.

GQ3   containing 4×60p. (No. Y1784) and a pane of 4 airmail labels............................ 4·50

1996 (19 Mar). Multicoloured laminated cover as T **GK6** (75×48 mm) without International and showing Olympic symbols on the back. Stamps printed on the cover in dull grey blue by Walsall. Inscribed For items up to 20g on yellow tab at right.

GQ4   containing 4×60p. (No. Y1784) and a pane of 4 airmail labels............................ 4·50

£2·52 Booklets

1996 (8 July). Multicoloured laminated cover as T **GL1** (75×48 mm) but inscribed Worldwide Airmail Stamps and showing Olympic symbols on the back. Stamps printed on the cover in light emerald by Walsall. Inscribed For items up to 20g on yellow tab at right.

GR1   containing 4×63p. (No. Y1787) and a pane of 4 airmail labels............................ 8·00

1997 (4 Feb). Multicoloured laminated cover as T **GL1** (75×48 mm) without Olympic symbols on the back. Stamps printed on the cover in light emerald by Walsall. Inscribed For items up to 20g on yellow tab at right.

GR2   containing 4×63p. (No. Y1787) and a pane of 4 airmail labels............................ 8·00

1997 (26 Aug). Multicoloured laminated cover as T **GL1** (75×48 mm). Stamps printed on the cover in light emerald by Walsall. Inscribed For items up to 20g on yellow tab at right.

GR3   containing 4×63p. (gravure) (No. Y1732) and a pane of 4 airmail labels..... 5·00

1998 (5 May). Multicoloured laminated cover as T **GGA1** (75×50 mm). Stamps printed on the cover in light emerald by Walsall. Inscribed For items up to 20g on yellow tab at right.

GR4   containing 4×63p. (gravure) (No. Y1732) and a pane of 4 new design airmail labels.......................... 5·00

£2·56 Booklet

1999 (26 Apr). Multicoloured laminated cover as T **GGA1** (75×50 mm). Stamps printed on cover in turquoise-green by Walsall. Inscribed For items up to 20g on yellow tab at right.

GS1   containing 4×64p. (gravure) (No. Y1733) and a pane of 4 airmail labels..... 5·25

£2·60 Booklet

2000 (27 Apr). Multicoloured laminated cover as T **GGA1** (76×50 mm) with stamps printed on cover in greenish blue by Walsall. Inscr For items up to 20g on yellow tab at right.

GT1   containing 4×65p. (gravure) (No. Y1734) and a pane of 4 airmail labels..... 6·00

D. Barcode Booklets containing No Value Indicated stamps with barcodes on the back cover.

Panes of four 2nd Class stamps.

HA1 Redrawn Crown (small)

1989 (22 Aug). Laminated cover as T **HA1** (75×48 mm) with stamp printed on the cover in bright blue by Walsall.

HA1   (56p.) containing booklet pane No. 1449l........ 5·00

No. HA1 has three edges of the pane imperforate.

1989 (28 Nov). Laminated cover as T **HA1** (75×48 mm) with stamp printed on the cover in bright blue by Walsall containing stamps printed in gravure by Harrison.

HA2   (60p.) containing booklet pane No. 1445m..... 22·50

No. HA2 has three edges of the pane imperforate.

HA3 Crown on white

1990 (7 Aug). Multicoloured laminated cover as T **HA3** (75×48 mm) with stamp printed on the cover in deep blue by Walsall.

HA3   (60p.) containing booklet pane No. 1515l........ 5·00

No. HA3 has the horizontal edges of the pane imperforate.

1991 (6 Aug). Multicoloured laminated cover as T **HA3** (75×48 mm) with stamp printed on the cover in bright blue by Walsall (25.9.92). Barcode in black.

HA4   (68p.) containing booklet pane No. 1449m..... 5·00
        a. Barcode printed in blue.......................... 5·00

No. HA4 has the horizontal edges of the pane imperforate and exists with the barcode printed in either black or blue.

HA5 Olympic Symbols

1992 (21 Jan). Multicoloured laminated cover as T **HA5** (75×48 mm) with stamp printed on the cover in bright blue by Walsall.

HA5   (72p.) containing booklet pane No. 1449m..... 5·00

No. HA5 has the horizontal edges of the pane imperforate.

> **PERFORATIONS.** Booklets from No. HA6 show perforations on all edges of the pane and contain stamps with one elliptical hole on each vertical side.

1993 (6 Apr). Multicoloured laminated cover as T **HA3** (75×48 mm) with stamp printed on the cover in bright blue by Walsall.

HA6   (72p.) containing 4×2nd Class stamps (No. 1670)... 5·00

No. HA6 was re-issued on 6 December 1994 showing the inscriptions on the inside of the cover re-arranged.

1993 (7 Sept). Multicoloured laminated cover as T **HA3** (75×48 mm) with stamp printed on the cover in bright blue by Harrison.
HA7   (72p.) containing 4×2nd Class stamps (No.
         1664).. 5·00

HA8 (Second Class Stamps centred) (with diagonal white line across corners of stamps)

1995 (10 Jan). Multicoloured laminated cover as T **HA8** (75×48 mm) with stamps printed on the cover in bright blue by Harrison.
HA8   (76p) containing 4×2nd Class stamps (No.
         1664).. 5·00

1995 (12 Dec). Multicoloured laminated cover as T **HA8** (75×48 mm) with stamps printed on the cover in bright blue by Walsall, but without Pull Open inscription on yellow tab.
HA9   (76p.) containing 4×2nd Class stamps (No.
         1670).. 5·00
No. HA9 was initially sold at 76p, which was increased to 80p. from 8.7.96.

1996 (6 Feb). Multicoloured laminated cover as T **HA8** (75×48 mm) but without Pull Open inscription on yellow tab and showing Olympic symbols on the back. Stamps printed on the cover in bright blue by Walsall.
HA10   (76p.) containing 4×2nd Class stamps (No.
         1670).. 5·00

NOTE. From No. HA11 onwards, the printer of each booklet is identified by a small capital letter below the barcode on the outside back cover.

HA11 (Second Class Stamps ranged left) (without diagonal white line across corners of stamps)

1997 (4 Feb). Multicoloured laminated cover as T **HA11** (75×48 mm). Stamps printed on the cover in bright blue by Walsall.
HA11   (80p.) containing 4×2nd Class stamps (No.
         1670).. 5·00

1997 (26 Aug). Multicoloured laminated cover as T **HA11** (75×48 mm). Stamps printed on the cover in bright blue by Walsall.
HA12   (80p.) containing 4×2nd Class stamps
         (gravure) (No. 1664).................................. 5·00
No. HA12 was re-issued on 5 May 1998 showing the positions of the imprint and the post code notice transposed, and again on 14 March 2000 with changed telephone number and added website address.

Panes of four 1st Class stamps

1989 (22 Aug). Laminated cover as T **HA1** (75×48 mm) with stamp printed on the cover in brownish black by Walsall.
HB1   (76p.) containing booklet pane No. 1450l........ 7·75
No. HB1 has three edges of the pane imperforate.
No. HB1 was initially sold at 76p., which was increased to 80p. from 2.10.89.

1989 (5 Dec). Laminated cover as T **HA1** (75×48 mm) with stamp printed on the cover in brownish black by Walsall containing stamps printed in photo by Harrison.
HB2   (80p.) containing booklet pane No. 1447m..... 24·50
No. HB2 has three edges of the pane imperforate.

1990 (7 Aug). Multicoloured laminated cover as T **HA3** (75×48 mm) with stamp printed on the cover in bright orange-red by Walsall (22.9.92). Barcode in black.
HB3   (80p.) containing booklet pane No. 1516l........ 6·00
         a. containing pane No. 1516cl..................... 10·00
         b. Barcode in blue....................................... 6·00
No. HB3 has the horizontal edges of the pane imperforate.

1992 (21 Jan). Multicoloured laminated cover as T **HA5** (75×48 mm) with stamp printed on the cover in bright orange-red by Walsall.
HB4   (96p.) containing booklet pane No. 1516l........ 6·00
No. HB4 has the horizontal edges of the pane imperforate.

PERFORATIONS. Booklets from No. HB5 show perforations on all edges of the pane.

1993 (6 Apr). Multicoloured laminated cover as T **HA3** (75×48 mm) with stamp printed on the cover in bright orange-red by Harrison.
HB5   (96p.) containing 4×1st Class stamps (No.
         1666).. 6·00

1993 (17 Aug). Multicoloured laminated cover as T **HA3** (76×50 mm) with stamp printed on the cover in bright orange-red by Walsall.
HB6   (96p.) containing 4×1st Class stamps (No.
         1671).. 6·00
No. HB6 was re-issued on 1 November 1993 with changes to the inside cover text.

1994 (27 July). Multicoloured laminated cover as T **HA3** (76×50 mm) with stamp printed on the cover in bright orange-red by Questa.
HB7   (£1·00) containing booklet pane No.
         1671l which includes a label
         commemorating the 300th
         anniversary of the Bank of England........ 6·00

1995 (10 Jan). Multicoloured laminated cover as T **HA8** (75×48 mm) with stamps printed on the cover in bright orange-red by Walsall.
HB8   (£1·00) containing 4×1st Class stamps (No.
         1671).. 6·00

1995 (16 May). Multicoloured laminated cover as T **HA8** (75×48 mm) with stamps printed on the cover in bright orange-red by Walsall.
HB9   (£1·00) containing booklet pane No.
         1671la which includes a label
         commemorating the birth centenary
         of R. J. Mitchell (designer of Spitfire)...... 6·00

1996 (6 Feb–Aug). Multicoloured laminated cover as T **HA8** (75×48 mm) showing Olympic symbols on the back. Stamps printed on the cover in bright orange-red by Walsall.
HB10   (£1·00) containing 4×1st Class stamps (No.
         1671).. 6·00
         a. Without diagonal white line across
         corners of stamps (8.96)........................ 95·00

1996 (16 Apr). Multicoloured laminated cover as T **HA11** (75×48 mm) with stamps printed on the cover in bright orange-red by Walsall. Inscribed Commemorative Label Inside on yellow tab at right.
HB11   (£1·00) containing booklet pane No. 1671la
         (includes label commemorating the
         70th birthday of Queen Elizabeth II)...... 6·00

NOTE. From No. HB12 onwards, the printer of each booklet (with the exception of No. HB19) is identified by a small capital letter below the barcode on the outside back cover.

1997 (4 Feb). Multicoloured laminated cover as T **HA11** (75×48 mm). Stamps printed on the cover in bright orange-red by Walsall.
HB12   (£1·04) containing 4×1st Class stamps (No.
         1671).. 6·00

1997 (12 Feb). Multicoloured laminated cover as T **HA11** (75×48 mm). Stamps printed on the cover in bright orange-red by Walsall. Inscribed Special Label Inside on yellow tab at right.
HB13   (£1·04) containing booklet pane No. 1671la
         (includes label commemorating
         Hong Kong '97 international stamp
         exhibition).. 6·00

1997 (26 Aug). Multicoloured laminated cover as T **HA11** (75×48 mm). Stamps printed on the cover in bright orange-red by Walsall.
HB14   (£1·04) containing 4×1st Class stamps
         (gravure) (No. 1667)................................ 6·00
No. HB14 was re-issued on 5 May 1998 showing the positions of the imprint and the post code notice transposed, on 16 March 1999 with Please note that the First Class rate is no longer valid to Europe added to inside back cover and again on 14 March 2000 with changed telephone number and added website address.

1997 (21 Oct). Multicoloured laminated cover as T **HA11** (75×48 mm). Stamps printed on the cover in bright orange-red by Walsall. Inscribed Commemorative Label Inside on yellow tab at right.

HB15   (£1·04) containing booklet pane No. 1671la (litho) (includes label commemorating Commonwealth Heads of Government Meeting, Edinburgh)................................ 6·25

1998 (14 Nov). Multicoloured laminated cover as T **HA11** (75×48 mm). Stamps printed on the cover in bright orange-red by Walsall. Inscribed Commemorative Label Inside on yellow tab at right.

HB16   (£1·04) containing booklet pane No. 1671la (litho) (includes label commemorating 50th birthday of the Prince of Wales)..... 6·00

1999 (12 May). Multicoloured laminated cover as T **HA11** (75×48 mm). Stamps printed on the cover in bright orange-red by Walsall. Inscribed Commemorative Label Inside on yellow tab at right.

HB17   (£1·04) containing booklet pane No. 1667m (gravure) (includes label commemorating 50th anniversary of Berlin Airlift)................................ 6·00

1999 (1 Oct). Multicoloured laminated cover as T **HA11** (76×50 mm). Stamps printed on the cover in bright orange-red by Walsall. Inscribed Commemorative Label Inside on yellow tab at right.

HB18   (£1·04) containing booklet pane No. 1667m (gravure) (includes label commemorating Rugby World Cup)...... 6·00

2000 (21 Mar). Multicoloured laminated cover as T **HA11** (75×48 mm). Stamps printed on the cover in olive-brown by Walsall with Postman Pat. Inscribed Postman Pat Label Inside on yellow tab at right.

HB19   (£1·04) containing booklet pane No. 2124l (gravure) (includes label commemorating Stamp Show 2000, Earls Court)................ 6·00

2000 (4 Apr). Opening of National Botanic Garden of Wales. Multicoloured laminated cover as T **HA11** (75×48 mm). Stamps printed on the cover in olive-brown by Walsall. Inscribed Botanic Garden Label Inside on yellow tab at right.

HB20   (£1·04) containing booklet pane No. 2124l........ 6·00

Panes of eight 1st Class stamps plus pane of 2 Millennium commemoratives

HBA1

1999 (12 May). Multicoloured laminated cover as T **HBA1** (76×50 mm) showing Millennium and Machin stamps printed by Walsall.

HBA1   (£2·60) containing booklet pane No. 2085a and 8×1st Class stamps (gravure) (No. 1667)................................ 13·50

1999 (21 Sept). Multicoloured laminated cover as T **HBA1** (76×50 mm) showing Millennium and Machin stamps printed by Walsall.

HBA2   (£2·60) containing booklet pane No. 2108a and 8×1st Class stamps (gravure) (No. 1667)................................ 13·50

2000 (26 May). Multicoloured laminated cover as T **HBA1** (76×50 mm) showing Millennium and Machin stamps printed by Walsall.

HBA3   (£2·70) containing booklet pane No. 2126ab and 8×1st Class stamps (gravure) (No. 2124)................................ 13·50

2000 (18 Sept). Multicoloured laminated cover as T **HBA1** (76×50 mm) showing Millennium and Machin stamps printed by Walsall.

HBA4   (£2·70) containing booklet pane No. 2153a and 8×1st Class stamps (gravure) (No. 2124)................................ 13·50

Panes of ten 2nd Class stamps

1989 (22 Aug–2 Oct). Laminated cover as T **HA1** (75×48 mm) with stamp printed on the cover in bright blue by Harrison.

HC1   (£1·40) containing booklet pane No. 1445l........ 10·00
   a. Inside cover with new rates (2.10.89)....... 10·00
Nos. HC1/HC1a have the horizontal edges of the pane imperforate.

1989 (19 Sept). Laminated cover as T **HA1** (75×48 mm) with stamp printed on the cover in bright blue by Questa.

HC2   (£1·40) containing 10×2nd Class stamps (No. 1451).. 10·00
No. HC2 has perforations on all edges of the pane.

1990 (7 Aug). Multicoloured laminated cover as T **HA3** (75×48 mm) with stamp printed on the cover in deep blue by Harrison.

HC3   (£1·50) containing booklet pane No. 1511l...... 10·00
No. HC3 has the horizontal edges of the pane imperforate.

1990 (7 Aug). Multicoloured laminated cover as T **HA3** (75×48 mm) with stamp printed on the cover in deep blue by Questa.

HC4   (£1·50) containing 10×2nd Class stamps (No. 1513).. 10·00
No. HC4 has perforations on all edges of the pane.

1990 (7 Aug). Multicoloured laminated cover as T **HA3** (75×48 mm) with stamp printed on the cover in deep blue by Walsall.

HC5   (£1·50) containing booklet pane No. 1515m..... 10·00
No. HC5 has the horizontal edges of the pane imperforate.

1991 (6 Aug)–**92**. Multicoloured laminated cover as T **HA3** (75×48 mm) with stamp printed on the cover in bright blue by Questa. Barcode in black.

HC6   (£1·70) containing 10×2nd Class stamps (No. 1451).. 10·00
   a. Barcode printed in blue (22.9.92)........... 10·00
No. HC6 has perforations on all edges of the pane.
No. HC6a was sold at £1·80.

1991 (6 Aug)–**92**. Multicoloured laminated cover as T **HA3** (75×48 mm) with stamp printed on the cover in bright blue by Walsall. Barcode in black.

HC7   (£1·70) containing booklet pane No. 1449n....... 10·00
   a. Barcode printed in blue (22.9.92)........... 10·00
No. HC7 has the horizontal edges of the pane imperforate.
No. HC7a was sold at £1·80.

1992 (21 Jan). Multicoloured laminated cover as T **HA5** (75×48 mm) with stamp printed on the cover in bright blue by Walsall.

HC8   (£1·80) containing booklet pane No. 1449n...... 10·00
No. HC8 has the horizontal edges of the pane imperforate.

1992 (31 Mar). Multicoloured laminated cover as T **HA5** (75×48 mm) with stamp printed on the cover in bright blue by Questa.

HC9   (£1·80) containing 10×2nd Class stamps (No. 1451).. 10·00
No. HC9 has perforations on all edges of the pane.

1992 (22 Sept). Multicoloured laminated cover as T **HA3** (75×48 mm) with stamp printed on the cover in bright blue by Harrison.

HC10   (£1·80) containing booklet pane No. 1445l....... 10·00
No. HC10 has the horizontal edges of the pane imperforate.

PERFORATIONS. Nos. HC11/HC22 show perforations on all edges of the pane and contain stamps with one elliptical hole on each vertical side.

1993 (6 Apr). Multicoloured laminated cover as T **HA3** (75×48 mm) with stamp printed on the cover in bright blue by Questa.

HC11   (£1·80) containing 10×2nd Class stamps (No. 1670).. 10·00
No. HC11 was re-issued on 17 August 1993 showing changes to the text on the inside of the cover and again on 6 September 1994 showing further changes.

1993 (1 Nov). Multicoloured laminated cover as T **HA3** (75×48 mm) with stamp printed on the cover in bright blue by Walsall.

HC12   (£1·90) containing 10×2nd Class stamps (No. 1670).. 10·00

1995 (10 Jan). Multicoloured laminated cover as T **HA8** (75×48 mm) with stamps printed on the cover in bright blue by Questa.

HC13   (£1·90) containing 10×2nd Class stamps (No. 1670).. 10·00

1995 (12 Dec). Multicoloured laminated cover as T **HA8** (75×48 mm) with stamps printed on cover in bright blue by Harrison.

HC14   (£1·90) containing 10×2nd Class stamps (No. 1664).. 10·00

1996 (6 Feb). Multicoloured laminated cover as T **HA8** (75×48 mm) showing Olympic symbols on the back. Stamps printed on the cover in bright blue by Harrison.

HC15   (£1·90) containing 10×2nd Class stamps (No. 1664).. 10·00

1996 (6 Feb). Multicoloured laminated cover as T **HA8** (75×48 mm) showing Olympic symbols on the back. Stamps printed on the cover in bright blue by Questa.

HC16   (£1·90) containing 10×2nd Class stamps (No. 1670).. 10·00

NOTE. From No. HC17 onwards, the printer of each booklet is identified by a small capital letter below the barcode on the outside back cover.

1996 (6 Aug). Multicoloured laminated cover as T **HA8** (75×48 mm) but with diagonal white lines across corners of stamps, showing Olympic symbols on the back. Stamps printed on the cover in bright blue by Harrison.
HC17 (£2·00) containing 10×2nd Class stamps (No.
1664)... 10·00

1996 (6 Aug). Multicoloured laminated cover as T **HA11** (75×48 mm) showing Olympic symbols on the back. Stamps printed on the cover in bright blue by Questa.
HC18 (£2·00) containing 10×2nd Class stamps (No.
1670)... 10·00

1997 (4 Feb). Multicoloured laminated cover as T **HA11** (75×48 mm). Stamps printed on the cover in bright blue by Harrison.
HC19 (£2·00) containing 10×2nd Class stamps (No.
1664)... 10·00

1997 (4 Feb). Multicoloured laminated cover as T **HA11** (75×48 mm). Stamps printed on the cover in bright blue by Questa.
HC20 (£2·00) containing 10×2nd Class stamps (No.
1670)... 10·00
No. HC20 was re-issued on 5 May 1998 showing the positions of the imprint and the post code notice transposed.

1998 (5 May). Multicoloured laminated cover as T **HA11** (75×48 mm). Stamps printed on the cover in bright blue by De La Rue.
HC21 (£2·00) containing 10×2nd Class stamps (No.
1664)... 10·00

1998 (1 Dec). Multicoloured laminated cover as T **HA11** (75×48 mm). Stamps printed on the cover in bright blue by Questa.
HC22 (£2·00) containing 10×2nd Class stamps (No.
1664a) (gravure).. 10·00
No. HC22 was re-issued on 14 March 2000 with changed telephone number and added website address.

Panes of ten 1st Class stamps

1989 (22 Aug–2 Oct). Laminated cover as T **HA1** (75×48 mm) with stamp printed on the cover in brownish black by Harrison.
HD1 (£1·90) containing booklet pane No. 1447l........ 13·00
a. Inside cover with new rates (2.10.89)...... 13·00
Nos. HD1/HD1a have the horizontal edges of the pane imperforate.
No. HD1a was sold at £2.

1989 (19 Sept). Laminated cover as T **HA1** (75×48 mm) with stamp printed on the cover in brownish black by Harrison.
HD2 (£1·90) containing 10×1st Class stamps (No.
1452)... 13·00
No. HD2 has perforations on all edges of the pane.

1990 (7 Aug). Multicoloured laminated cover as T **HA3** (75×48 mm) with stamp printed on the cover in bright orange-red by Harrison. Barcode in black.
HD3 (£2·00) containing booklet pane No. 1512l....... 13·00
b. Barcode printed in blue (22.9.92)............ 13·00
No. HD3 has the horizontal edges of the pane imperforate.

1990 (7 Aug)–**92**. Multicoloured laminated cover as T **HA3** (75×48 mm) with stamp printed on the cover in bright orange-red by Questa. Barcode in black.
HD4 (£2·00) containing 10×1st Class stamps (No.
1514)... 13·00
b. Barcode printed in blue (22.9.92)............ 13·00
No. HD4 has perforations on all edges of the pane.

1990 (7 Aug)–**92**. Multicoloured laminated cover as T **HA3** (75×48 mm) with stamp printed on the cover in bright orange-red by Walsall. Barcode in black.
HD5 (£2·00) containing booklet pane No. 1516m..... 13·00
c. Barcode printed in blue (22.9.92)............ 13·00
No. HD5 has the horizontal edges of the pane imperforate.

1992 (21 Jan). Multicoloured laminated cover as T **HA5** (75×48 mm) with stamp printed on the cover in bright orange-red by Harrison.
HD6 (£2·40) containing booklet pane No. 1512l........ 13·00
No. HD6 has the horizontal edges of the pane imperforate.

1992 (21 Jan). Multicoloured laminated cover as T **HA5** (75×48 mm) with stamp printed on the cover in bright orange-red by Walsall.
HD7 (£2·40) containing booklet pane No. 1516m........ 13·00
No. HD7 has the horizontal edges of the pane imperforate.

1993 (9 Feb). Multicoloured laminated cover as T **HA3** (77×44 mm) with advertisement for Greetings Booklet on reverse showing Rupert Bear as in T **KX5**. Stamp printed on the cover in bright orange-red by Walsall.
HD8 (£2·40) containing booklet pane No. 1516m..... 13·00
No. HD8 has the horizontal edges of the pane imperforate.

PERFORATIONS. Nos. HD9/HD53 show perforations on all edges of the pane and contain stamps with one elliptical hole on each vertical side.

1993 (6 Apr). Multicoloured laminated cover as T **HA3** (75×48 mm) with stamp printed on the cover in bright orange-red by Harrison.
HD9 (£2·40) containing 10×1st Class stamps (No.
1666)... 13·00
No. HD9 was re-issued on 17 August 1993 showing changes to the text on the inside of the covers.

1993 (6 Apr). Multicoloured laminated cover as T **HA3** (75×48 mm) with stamp printed on the cover in bright orange-red by Walsall.
HD10 (£2·40) containing 10×1st Class stamps (No.
1671)... 13·00
No. HD10 was re-issued on 17 August 1993 showing changes to the text on the inside of the covers.

1993 (1 Nov). Laminated cover as T **HA3** (75×50 mm) with stamp printed on the cover in bright orange-red by Questa.
HD11 (£2·50) containing 10×1st Class stamps (No.
1671)... 13·00
No. HD11 was re-issued on 4 October 1994 showing changes to the text on the inside of the cover.

1993 (1 Nov). Laminated cover as T **HA3** (75×50 mm) with advertisement for Greetings Booklet on reverse showing Rupert Bear as in T **KX5**. Stamp printed on the cover in bright orange-red by Walsall.
HD12 (£2·50) containing 10×1st Class stamps (No.
1671)... 13·00

1994 (22 Feb). Multicoloured laminated cover as T **HA3** (75×48 mm) with stamp printed on the cover in bright orange-red by Walsall. Inscribed FREE POSTCARDS on yellow tab at right.
HD13 (£2·50) containing 10×1st Class stamps (No.
1671) and additional page giving details of Greetings Stamps postcard offer.. 13·00

1994 (1 July). Multicoloured laminated covers as T **HA3** (76×50 mm) with advertisement for Greetings Booklet on reverse showing Rupert Bear as in T **KX5**. Stamp printed on the cover in bright orange-red by Walsall. Inscribed OPEN NOW Chance to win a kite on yellow tab at right.
HD14 (£2·50) containing 10×1st Class stamps (No.
1671) with Better luck next time. etc on inside back cover................................ 13·00
HD15 (£2·50) containing 10×1st Class stamps (No.
1671) with You've Won! etc on inside back cover.. 13·00
Nos. HD14/HD15 were initially only available from branches of W. H. Smith and Son. They were issued in connection with a competition in which the prizes were Paddington Bear kites.
The booklets were not available from Royal Mail philatelic outlets until 4 October 1994.

HD16

1994 (20 Sept). Multicoloured laminated covers as T **HD16** (76×50 mm) printed by Walsall. Inscribed ORDER YOURS INSIDE on yellow tab at right.
HD16 (£2·50) containing 10×1st Class stamps (No.
1671) with DO NOT OPEN UNTIL.... on front cover... 13·00
HD17 (£2·50) containing 10×1st Class stamps (No.
1671) with KEEP IN TOUCH on front cover.. 13·00
HD18 (£2·50) containing 10×1st Class stamps (No.
1671) with HAPPY BIRTHDAY on front cover.. 13·00
HD19 (£2·50) containing 10×1st Class stamps
(No. 1671) with What's Happenin' Multicoloured on front cover.................. 13·00

1995 (10 Jan). Multicoloured laminated cover as T **HA8** (75×48 mm) with stamps printed on the cover in bright orange-red by Harrison.
HD20   (£2·50) containing 10×1st Class stamps (No.
1666)...   13·00

1995 (10 Jan). Multicoloured laminated cover as T **HA8** (75×48 mm) with stamps printed on the cover in bright orange-red by Questa.
HD21   (£2·50) containing 10×1st Class stamps (No.
1671)...   13·00

1995 (10 Jan). Multicoloured laminated cover as T **HA8** (75×48 mm) with stamps printed on the cover in bright orange-red by Walsall.
HD22   (£2·50) containing 10×1st Class stamps (No.
1671)...   13·00

HD31

1996 (13 May). Multicoloured laminated covers as T **HD31** (76×48 mm) showing woman lighting Olympic torch, printed by Harrison, with each booklet showing a scratch card on the reverse based on different Olympic events.
HD31   (£2·50) containing 10×1st Class stamps (No.
1667) (Shot Put)...   13·00
HD32   (£2·50) containing 10×1st Class stamps (No.
1667) (Hurdles)...   13·00
HD33   (£2·50) containing 10×1st Class stamps (No.
1667) (Archery)..   13·00

HD23

1995 (14 Feb). Multicoloured laminated cover as T **HD23** (76×50 mm) showing card, Thorntons chocolates and box, printed by Walsall. Inscribed DETAILS INSIDE on yellow tab at right.
HD23   (£2·50) containing 10×1st Class stamps (No.
1671)...   13·00

1995 (4 Apr). Multicoloured laminated cover as T **HA8** (76×48 mm) with stamps printed on cover in bright orange-red by Harrison.
HD24   (£2·50) containing 10×1st Class stamps (No.
1667)...   13·00

1995 (24 Apr). Multicoloured laminated cover as T **HA8** (75×48 mm) with stamps printed on cover in bright orange-red by Walsall. Inscribed W H Smith Special Offer on yellow tab at right.
HD25   (£2·50) containing 10×1st Class stamps (No.
1671)...   13·00
No. HD25 was initially only available from W. H. Smith branches and offered 50p. off the purchase of own brand stationery.
The booklet was not placed on philatelic sale until 3 October 1995.

1995 (26 June). Multicoloured laminated cover as T **HA8** (76×48 mm) with stamps printed on cover in bright orange red by Questa. Inscribed Sainsbury's Promotion on yellow tab at right.
HD26   (£2·50) containing 10×1st Class stamps (No.
1671)...   13·00
No. HD26 was initially only available from Sainsbury's branches and offered the chance to win a year's free shopping.
The booklet was not placed on philatelic sale until 5 September 1995.

1995 (4 Sept). Multicoloured laminated cover as T **HD23** (76×48 mm) showing ceramic figures of Benjy Bear and Harry Hedgehog, printed by Harrison.
HD27   (£2·50) containing 10×1st Class stamps (No.
1667)...   13·00

1996 (6 Feb). Multicoloured laminated cover as T **HA8** (76×48 mm) showing Olympic symbols on the back. Stamps printed on the cover in bright orange-red by Walsall.
HD28   (£2·50) containing 10×1st Class stamps (No.
1671)...   13·00

1996 (19 Feb). Multicoloured laminated cover as T **HD23** (76×48 mm) showing Walt Disney World, printed by Harrison.
HD29   (£2·50) containing 10×1st Class stamps (No.
1667)...   13·00

1996 (19 Mar). Multicoloured laminated cover as T **HA8** (76×48 mm) showing Olympic symbols on the back, printed by Harrison.
HD30   (£2·50) containing 10×1st Class stamps (No.
1667)...   13·00

NOTE. From No. HD34 onwards, the printer of each booklet is identified by a small capital letter below the barcode on the outside back cover.

1996 (15 July). Multicoloured laminated cover as T **HA11** (76×48 mm) showing Olympic symbols on the back. Stamps printed on the cover in bright orange-red by Walsall. Inscribed W. H. Smith Offer Inside on yellow tab at right.
HD34   (£2·60) containing 10×1st Class stamps (No.
1671)...   13·00
No. HD34 was initially only available from branches of W. H. Smith and Sons. It was issued in connection with a special offer of AA/OS Leisure Guides.
The booklets were not available from Royal Mail philatelic outlets until 17 September 1996.

1996 (6 Aug). Multicoloured laminated cover as T **HA11** (76×48 mm), but with diagonal white line across corners of stamps and showing Olympic symbols on the back. Stamps printed on the cover in bright orange-red by Harrison.
HD35   (£2·60) containing 10×1st Class stamps (No.
1667)...   13·00

1996 (6 Aug). Multicoloured laminated cover as T **HA11** (76×48 mm) showing Olympic symbols on the back. Stamps printed on the cover in bright orange-red by Walsall.
HD36   (£2·60) containing 10×1st Class stamps (No.
1671)...   13·00

1996 (9 Sept). Multicoloured laminated cover as T **HD31** (76×48 mm) showing iced cakes on front and back, printed by Walsall. Inscribed OPEN FOR DETAILS on yellow tab at right.
HD37   (£2·60) containing 10×1st Class stamps (No.
1671)...   13·00

1996 (7 Oct). Multicoloured laminated cover as T **HA11** (76×48 mm) showing Olympic symbols on the back. Stamps printed on cover in bright orange-red by Walsall. Inscribed Offer Inside on yellow tab at right.
HD38   (£2·60) containing 10×1st Class stamps (No.
1671)...   13·00
No. HD38 was initially only available from ASDA stores and offered £1 off greetings cards. The booklet was not placed on philatelic sale until 13 January 1997.

1997 (4 Feb). Multicoloured laminated cover as T **HA11** (76×48 mm). Stamps printed on the cover in bright orange-red by Harrison.
HD39   (£2·60) containing 10×1st Class stamps (No.
1667)...   13·00

1997 (4 Feb). Multicoloured laminated cover as T **HA11** (76×48 mm). Stamps printed on the cover in bright orange-red by Walsall.
HD40   (£2·60) containing 10×1st Class stamps (No.
1671)...   13·00

1997 (21 Apr). Royal Golden Wedding. Multicoloured laminated cover as T **HA11** (76×48 mm). Stamps printed on the cover in gold by Harrison.
HD41   (£2·60) containing 10×1st Class stamps (No.
1668)...   13·00

1997 (21 Apr). Royal Golden Wedding. Multicoloured laminated cover as T **HA11** (76×48 mm). Stamps printed on the cover in gold by Walsall.
HD42   (£2·60) containing 10×1st Class stamps (No.
1668)...   13·00

1997 (15 Sept). Multicoloured laminated cover as T **HD31** (76×48 mm) showing a tropical beach scene printed by Harrison. Inscr FIRST CLASS TRAVEL on front, and OPEN FOR DETAILS on yellow tab at right.
HD43   (£2·60) containing 10×1st Class stamps (No. 1668).................   13·00

1997 (8 Nov). Multicoloured laminated cover as T **HA11** (76×48 mm). Stamps printed on the cover in bright orange-red by Walsall.
HD44   (£2·60) containing 10×1st Class stamps (gravure) (No. 1667).................   13·00
No. HD44 was re-issued on 5 May 1998 showing the positions of the imprint, which was now vertical, and the post code notice transposed and again on 16 March 1999 with Please note that the First Class rate is no longer valid to Europe added to inside back cover.

HD45

1998 (2 Feb). Multicoloured laminated cover as T **HD45** (76×48 mm) showing Disney illustration printed by De La Rue, with a scratch card on the reverse. Inscribed See reverse for Scratch and Win on yellow tab at right.
HD45   (£2·60) containing 10×1st Class stamps (gravure) (No. 1667).................   13·00

HD46

1998 (27 Apr). Multicoloured laminated cover as T **HD46** (76×48 mm) showing Peugeot 106 printed by De La Rue. Inscribed WIN A PEUGEOT 106 on yellow tab at right.
HD46   (£2·60) containing 10×1st Class stamps (gravure) (No. 1667).................   13·00
No. HD46 was not placed on philatelic sale until 23 June 1998.

1998 (5 May). Multicoloured laminated cover as T **HA11** (76×48 mm). Stamps printed on the cover in bright orange-red by De La Rue.
HD47   (£2·60) containing 10×1st Class stamps (gravure) (No. 1667).................   13·00

1998 (1 July). Multicoloured laminated cover as T **HD46** (76×48 mm) showing JVC Camcorder printed by De La Rue. Inscribed WIN A JVC CAMCORDER on yellow tab at right.
HD48   (£2·60) containing 10×1st Class stamps (gravure) (No. 1667).................   13·00
No. HD48 was not placed on philatelic sale until 27 August 1998.

1998 (3 Aug). Multicoloured laminated cover as T **GGA2** (76×48 mm) inscribed (Create a card design), printed by De La Rue.
HD49   (£2·60) containing 10×1st Class stamps (gravure) (No. 1667).................   13·00
No. HD49 was not placed on philatelic sale until 7 September 1998.

1998 (7 Sept). Multicoloured laminated cover as T **HA11** (75×49 mm), with stamps printed on the cover in bright orange-red by Questa.
HD50   (£2·60) containing 10×1st Class stamps (litho) (No. 1671).................   13·00

1998 (1 Dec). Multicoloured laminated cover as T **HA11** (75×48 mm). Stamps printed on the cover in bright orange-red by Questa.
HD51   (£2·60) containing 10×1st Class stamps (gravure) (No. 1667a).................   13·00
No. HD51 was re-issued on 16 March 1999 with Please note that the First Class rate is no longer valid to Europe added to inside back cover.

2000 (6 Jan). Multicoloured laminated cover as T **HA11** (75×48 mm). Millennium definitives printed on the cover in olive-brown by Questa.
HD52   (£2·60) containing 10×1st Class stamps (gravure) (No. 2124d).................   13·00
No. HD52 was re-issued on 14 March 2000 with a changed telephone number on the inside back cover.

2000 (6 Jan). Multicoloured laminated cover as T **HA11** (75×48 mm). Millennium definitives printed on the cover in olive-brown by Walsall.
HD53   (£2·60) containing 10×1st Class stamps (gravure) (No. 2124).................   13·00
No. HD53 was was re-issued on 14 March 2000 with a changed telephone number on the inside back cover.

Panes of four European Airmail stamps

HF1

1999 (19 Jan). Multicoloured laminated cover as T **HF1** (75×50 mm). Stamps printed on the cover in deep blue by Walsall. Inscribed For items up to 20g on yellow tab at right.
HF1   (£1·20) containing 4×European Airmail stamps (No. 1669) and pane of four airmail labels.................   10·00
No. HF1 was re-issued on 27 April 2000 showing an amended Customer Services telephone number on the inside back cover.

E. Barcode Booklets containing Penny Black Anniversary stamps with barcodes on back cover.

60p. Booklet

JA1

1990 (30 Jan). Laminated cover as T **JA1** (75×48 mm) showing Penny Black Anniversary stamp in bright blue. Containing booklet pane No. 1475l, printed in litho by Walsall.
JA1   containing booklet pane No. 1475l........   3·75
No. JA1 has three edges of the pane imperforate.

80p. Booklets

1990 (30 Jan). Laminated cover as T **JA1** (75×48 mm) showing Penny Black Anniversary stamp in brownish black and cream. Containing booklet pane No. 1476m, printed in litho by Walsall.
JB1   containing booklet pane No. 1476m.....   5·00
No. JB1 has three edges of the pane imperforate.

1990 (17 Apr). Laminated cover as T **JA1** (75×48 mm) showing Penny Black Anniversary stamp printed on the cover in brownish black by Walsall. Containing stamps printed in photo by Harrison.
JB2   containing booklet pane No. 1469r........   4·50
No. JB2 has three edges of the pane imperforate.

£1·50 Booklets

1990 (30 Jan). Laminated cover as T **JA1** (75×48 mm) showing Penny Black Anniversary stamp in bright blue. Containing booklet pane No. 1467l printed in photo by Harrison.
JC1   containing booklet pane No. 1467l........   5·50
No. JC1 has the horizontal edges of the pane imperforate.

1990 (17 Apr). Laminated cover as T **JA1** (75×48 mm) showing Penny Black Anniversary stamp printed on the cover in bright blue, printed in litho by Questa.

JC2 containing 10×15p. (No. 1477).............. 10·00

1990 (12 June). Laminated cover as T **JA1** (75×48 mm) showing Penny Black Anniversary stamp in bright blue. Containing booklet pane No. 1475m, printed in litho by Walsall.

JC3 containing booklet pane No. 1475m..... 6·25

No. JC3 has three edges of the pane imperforate.

£2 Booklets

1990 (30 Jan). Laminated cover as T **JA1** (75×48 mm) showing Penny Black Anniversary stamp in brownish black and cream. Containing booklet pane. No. 1469m, printed in photo by Harrison.

JD1 containing booklet pane No. 1469m..... 6·25

No. JD1 has the horizontal edges of the pane imperforate.

1990 (17 Apr). Laminated cover as T **JA1** (75×48 mm) showing Penny Black Anniversary stamp printed on the cover in brownish black, printed in litho by Questa.

JD2 containing 10×20p. (No. 1478).............. 12·00

1990 (12 June). Laminated cover as T **JA1** (75×48 mm) showing Penny Black Anniversary stamp in brownish black and cream. Containing booklet pane No. 1476n, printed in litho by Walsall.

JD3 containing booklet pane No. 1476n....... 9·00

No. JD3 has three edges of the pane imperforate.

F. Barcode Booklets containing Greetings stamps with barcodes on the back cover.

For first greetings booklet, issued 31 January 1989, see No. FY1 in section B.

£2 Greetings Booklet

KX1 (*Illustration reduced. Actual size 135×85 mm*)

(Des Michael Peters and Partners)

1990 (6 Feb). Greetings Stamps. Scarlet, lemon and black cover as T **KX1** (135×85 mm) by Harrison. Containing booklet pane No. 1483a, and a separate sheet of 12 greetings labels.

KX1 (£2·00) Smile design cut-out showing stamps inside.. 13·50

Greetings Booklets containing No Value Indicated stamps

KX2

(Des T. Meeuwissen)

1991 (5 Feb). Greetings Stamps. Multicoloured laminated cover as T **KX2** (95×69 mm) by Harrison. Containing booklet pane No. 1536a, including 12 special greetings labels in a block (3×4) at right, attached by the selvedge.

KX2 (£2·20) Good Luck charms design........................ 13·50

KX3

(Des Michael Peters and Partners)

1991 (26 Mar)–**92**. Greetings Stamps. Multicoloured laminated cover as T **KX3** (95×69 mm) by Harrison. Containing booklet pane No. 1550a, including 12 special greetings labels in a block (3×4) at right, attached by the selvedge.

KX3 (£2·20) Laughing pillar box design....................... 13·50
a. Amended text to inside back cover (3.3.92)... 13·50

The note on the inside back cover of No. KX3 is headed Greetings Stamps.

In No. KX3a there is no heading but details of the validity of the stamps to European destinations have been added.

KX4

(Des Trickett and Webb)

1992 (28 Jan). Greetings Stamps. Multicoloured laminated cover as T **KX4** (95×69 mm) by Harrison. Containing booklet pane No. 1592a, including 12 special greetings labels in a block (3×4) at right, attached by selvedge.

KX4 (£2·40) Pressed Flowers design............................ 13·50

KX5

(Des Newell and Sorrell)

1993 (2 Feb). Greetings Stamps. Multicoloured laminated cover as T **KX5** (96×60 mm) by Harrison. Containing booklet pane No. 1644a and pane of 20 special greetings labels in a block (5×4), both panes attached by a common gutter margin.
KX5   (£2·40) Children's Characters design.................   13·50

No. KX5 was re-issued on 15 June 1993 with 'Thompson' corrected to 'Thomson' (bottom line at left) and on 17 August 1993 with 'Sorell' corrected to 'Sorrell'.

KX6

(Des Newell and Sorrell)

1994 (1 Feb). Greetings Stamps. Multicoloured cover as T **KX6** (96×60 mm) by Harrison. Containing booklet pane No. 1800a and pane of 20 special greetings labels in a block (5×4), both panes attached by a common gutter margin.
KX6   (£2·50) Children's Characters design.................   13·50

KX7

(Des Newell and Sorrell)

1995 (21 Mar)–**96**. Greetings Stamps. Multicoloured cover as T **KX7** (96×60 mm) by Walsall. Containing booklet pane No. 1858a and pane of 20 special greetings labels in a block (5×4), both panes attached by a common gutter margin. Inscribed Pull Open on yellow strip at right.
KX7   (£2·50) Clown design...   13·50
        a. No inscription on yellow strip (5.2.96)...   14·50

KX8

(Des M. Wolff)

1996 (26 Feb–11 Nov). Greetings Stamps. Multicoloured cover as T **KX8** (96×60 mm) by Walsall. Containing booklet pane No. 1905a and pane of 20 special greetings labels in a block (5×4), both panes attached by a common gutter margin.
KX8   (£2·50) MORE! LOVE design................................   13·50
        a. Containing pane No. 1905pa (11.11.96)   24·00

No. KX8a shows a redesigned inside front cover which omits references to 1996 dates.

KX9

(Des Tutssels)

1997 (6 Jan). Greetings Stamps. 19th-century Flower Paintings. Multicoloured cover as T **KX9** (96×61 mm) by Walsall. Containing booklet pane No. 1955a and pane of 20 special greetings labels in a block (5×4), both panes attached by a common gutter margin.
KX9   (£2·60) *Gentiana acaulis* design...........................   13·50

No. KX9 was re-issued on 16 March 1999 with Please note that the First Class rate is no longer valid to Europe' added to inside front cover.

1997 (3 Feb). Greetings Stamps. 19th-century Flower Paintings. Multicoloured cover as T **KX9** (96×61 mm) by Walsall but with box inscribed WIN A BEAUTIFUL BOUQUET INSTANTLY Multicoloured printed in yellow on red over the flower on the front and with a scratch card on the inside back cover. Inscribed Open now – See if you've won on yellow tab at right. Containing booklet pane No. 1955a and pane of 20 special greetings labels in a block (5×4), both panes attached by a common gutter margin.
KX10   (£2·60) *Gentiana acaulis* design...........................   14·00

KX11

(Des Tutssels)

1998 (5 Jan). Greetings Stamps. 19th-century Flower Paintings. Multicoloured cover as T **KX11** (96×61 mm) by Walsall. Inscribed See reverse for special offer on yellow tab at right. Containing booklet pane No. 1955a and pane of 20 special greetings labels in a block (5×4), both attached by a common gutter margin.
KX11   (£2·60) Chocolate design......................................   14·00

1998 (3 Aug). Greetings Stamps. 19th-century Flower Paintings. Multicoloured cover as T **GGA2** (88×61 mm) printed by Walsall. Containing booklet pane No. 1955a and pane of 20 special greetings labels in a block (5×4), both attached by a common gutter margin.
KX12   (£2·60) Create a card design................................   14·00

No. KX12 was not placed on philatelic sale until 7 September 1998.

G. Barcode Booklets containing Christmas stamps with barcode on the back.

LX1

(Des A. Davidson)

1990 (13 Nov). Christmas. Multicoloured laminated cover as T **LX1** (96×60 mm) by Harrison. Containing booklet pane No. 1526b, attached by the selvedge.
LX1   £3·40 Snowman design.. 5·50

1991 (12 Nov). Multicoloured laminated cover as T **LX1**, but 95×70 mm by Harrison. Containing booklet pane No. 1582b attached by the selvedge.
LX2   £3·60 Holly design... 5·75

LX3

(Des Karen Murray)

1992 (10 Nov). Multicoloured laminated cover as T **LX3** (95×70 mm) by Harrison. Containing booklet pane No. 1634a attached by the selvedge.
LX3   £3·60 Santa Claus and Reindeer design........... 5·75

1993 (9 Nov). Multicoloured laminated covers as T **LX3**, but 95×60 mm by Harrison, each showing Santa Claus and Reindeer. Panes attached by selvedge.
LX4   £2·50 containing 10×25p. stamps (No. 1791).. 5·00
LX5   £3·80 containing 20×19p. stamps (No. 1790).. 6·00
    No. LX4 was only available from Post Offices in the Central TV area and from philatelic outlets.

LX6

(Des Yvonne Gilbert)

1994 (1 Nov). Multicoloured laminated covers as T **LX6** (95×60 mm) by Harrison, showing different Nativity Play props. Panes attached by selvedge.
LX6   £2·50 containing 10×25p. stamps (No. 1844).. 4·00
LX7   £3·80 containing 20×19p. stamps (No. 1843).. 5·50

LX8

(Des K. Lilly)

1995 (30 Oct). Multicoloured laminated covers as T **LX8** (95×60 mm) by Harrison, showing Robins as depicted on the contents. Panes attached by selvedge.
LX8   £2·40 containing 4×60p. stamps (No. 1900)
              plus 4 airmail labels................................... 3·75
LX9   £2·50 containing 10×25p. stamps (No. 1897).. 3·75
LX10 £3·80 containing 20×19p. stamps (No. 1896).. 6·00

LX11

1996 (28 Oct). Multicoloured laminated covers as T **LX11** (95×60 mm) by Harrison, showing scenes from the Nativity as depicted on the contents. Panes attached by selvedge.
LX11 (£2·60) containing 10×1st Class stamps (No.
       1951).. 13·50
LX12 (£4·00) containing 20×2nd Class stamps (No.
       1950).. 19·00

LX13

1997 (27 Oct). Multicoloured laminated covers as T **LX13** (95×60 mm) by Harrison, showing Father Christmas and crackers as depicted on the contents. Panes attached by selvedge.
LX13 (£2·60) containing 10×1st Class stamps (No.
       2007).. 13·50
LX14 (£4·00) containing 20×2nd Class stamps (No.
       2006).. 19·00

LX15

1998 (2 Nov). Multicoloured laminated covers covers as T **LX15** (95×60 mm) by De La Rue, showing Angels as depicted on the contents. Panes attached by selvedge.

| LX15 | £2·60 containing 10×26p. stamps (No. 2065).. | 4·25 |
| LX16 | £4·00 containing 20×20p. stamps (No. 2064).. | 6·25 |

LX17

1999 (2 Nov). Multicoloured laminated covers as T **LX17** (95×70 mm) by De La Rue, showing designs as depicted on the contents. Inscribed Season's Greetings on yellow tab at right. Panes attached by selvedge.

| LX17 | £2·60 containing 10×26p. stamps (No. 2116).. | 4·25 |
| LX18 | £3·80 containing 20×19p. stamps (No. 2115).. | 6·00 |

LX19

2000 (7 Nov). Multicoloured laminated covers as T **LX19** (96×70 mm) by De La Rue, showing designs as depicted on the contents. Inscribed Season's Greetings on yellow tab at right. Panes attached by selvedge.

| LX19 | £2·70 containing 10×1st Class stamps (No. 2171)................................... | 13·50 |
| LX20 | £3·80 containing 20×2nd Class stamps (No. 2170)................................... | 19·00 |

2001 (6 Nov). Self-adhesive booklet containing Nos. 2238a and 2239a, each with a multicoloured header label showing barcode and Royal Mail emblem and further label at foot with telephone numbers, folded to form booklets 119×81 mm by De La Rue.

| LX21 | £3·24 containing 20×1st Class stamps (No. 2239a)................................ | 16·00 |
| LX22 | £4·56 containing 24×2nd Class stamps (No. 2238a)................................ | 22·00 |

Nos. LX21/LX22 show the surplus self-adhesive paper around each stamp retained.

2002 (5 Nov). Self-adhesive booklet containing Nos. 2321a and 2322a, each with a multicoloured header label showing barcode and Royal Mail emblem and further label at foot with telephone numbers, folded to form booklets 105×72 mm by De La Rue.

| LX23 | £3·24 containing 12×1st Class stamps (No. 2322a)................................ | 16·00 |
| LX24 | £4·56 containing 24×2nd Class stamps (No. 2321a)................................ | 22·00 |

No. LX23 was sealed into a cellophane packet which also contained a *Lord of the Rings* game card.

Nos. LX23/LX24 show the surplus self-adhesive paper around each stamp retained.

Notes. From No. LX25 all the booklets in this section have the surplus self-adhesive paper around each stamp removed, *unless otherwise stated*. All self-adhesive booklets containing 2nd Class Christmas stamps from No. LX31 onward have two small notches at the top right tab edge. All self-adhesive booklets containing 1st Class Christmas stamps from No. LX32 onward have a single small notch at the top right tab edge. From No. LX51 all booklets in this section have repeating undulating 'ROYALMAIL' background in two sizes of grey text printed on the front of the backing paper. On Nos. LX51/LX52 the text is upright (Type PB-Up); from No. LX53 onward alternate pairs of lines are inverted (i.e. Types PB-Ls and/or PB-sL, see footnotes) or as noted.

2003 (4 Nov). Self-adhesive booklet containing Nos. 2410a and 2411a, each with a multicoloured header label showing barcode and Royal Mail emblem and further label at foot with telephone numbers, folded to form booklets 106×71 mm by De La Rue.

| LX25 | £3·36 containing 12×1st Class stamps (No. 2411a)................................ | 16·00 |
| LX26 | £4·80 containing 24×2nd Class stamps (No. 2410a)................................ | 22·00 |

2004 (2 Nov). Self-adhesive booklet containing Nos. 2495a and 2496a, each with a multicoloured header label showing barcode and Royal Mail emblem and further label at foot with contact information, folded to form booklets 105×71 mm by De La Rue.

| LX27 | £3·36 containing 12×1st Class stamps (No. 2496a)................................ | 16·00 |
| LX28 | £5·04 containing 24×2nd Class stamps (No. 2495a)................................ | 22·00 |

2005 (1 Nov). Self-adhesive booklet containing Nos. 2582a and 2583a, each with a multicoloured header label showing barcode and Royal Mail emblem and further label at foot with contact information, folded to form booklets 106×71 mm by De La Rue.

| LX29 | £3·60 containing 12×1st Class stamps (No. 2583a)................................ | 16·00 |
| LX30 | £5·04 containing 24×2nd Class stamps (No. 2582a)................................ | 22·00 |

LX31

2006 (7 Nov). Covers as T **LX31** (75×57 mm) by De La Rue. Self-adhesive.
LX31 £2·76 containing 12×2nd Class stamps (No.
2678a).. 13·50
LX32 £3·84 containing 12×1st Class stamps (No.
2679a) (as Type **LX31** but red cover
inscribed 12×1st).................................... 16·00

2007 (6 Nov). Covers as T **LX31** (75×57 mm) by De La Rue. Self-adhesive.
LX33 £2·88 containing 12×2nd Class stamps (No.
2789a).. 13·50
LX34 £4·08 containing 12×1st Class stamps (No.
2790a) (as Type **LX31** but red cover
inscribed 12×1st).................................... 16·00

2008 (4 Nov). Covers as T **LX31** (75×57 mm) by De La Rue. Self-adhesive.
LX35 £3·24 containing 12×2nd Class stamps (No.
2876a).. 13·50
a. Oh YES it is! along right-hand edge of
pane... 13·50
LX36 £4·32 containing 12×1st Class stamps (No.
2877a) (as Type **LX31** but red cover
inscribed 12×1st).................................... 16·00
a. It's behind you! along right-hand edge
of pane.. 16·00
No. LX35 is inscribed Oh NO it isn't! and No. LX36 Abracadabra!, both
along the right-hand edges of the booklet panes.

2009 (3 Nov). Covers as T **LX31** (75×57 mm) by De La Rue. Self-adhesive.
LX37 £3·60 containing 12×2nd class stamps (No.
2991a).. 13·50
LX38 £4·68 containing 12×1st class stamps (No.
2992a) (as Type **LX31** but red cover
inscribed 12×1st).................................... 16·00

LX39 Wallace and Gromit posting Christmas Cards

2010 (2 Nov). Covers as T **LX39** (74×58 mm) by De La Rue. Self-adhesive.
LX39 £3·84 containing 12×2nd class stamps (No.
3128a).. 13·50
LX40 £4·92 containing 12×1st class stamps (No.
3129a) (as Type **LX39** but red cover
inscribed 12×1st).................................... 16·00

2011 (8 Nov). Covers as T **LX31** (74×58 mm) by De La Rue. Self-adhesive.
LX41 £4·32 containing 12×2nd class stamps (No.
3242a).. 13·50
LX42 £5·52 containing 12×1st class stamps (No.
3243a) (as Type **LX31** but red cover
inscribed 12×1st).................................... 16·00

2012 (6 Nov). Covers as T **LX31** (74×58 mm) by Walsall. Self-adhesive.
LX43 £6·00 containing 12×2nd class stamps (No.
3415a).. 13·50
LX44 £7·20 containing 12×1st class stamps (No.
3416a) (as Type **LX31** but red cover
inscribed 12×1st).................................... 16·00

2013 (5 Nov). Covers as T **LX31** (89×66 mm) by Walsall. Self-adhesive.
LX45 £6·00 containing 12×2nd class stamps (No.
3542a).. 13·50
LX46 £7·20 containing 12×1st class stamps (No.
3543a) (as Type **LX31** but red cover
inscribed 12×1st).................................... 16·00

2014 (4 Nov). Covers as T **LX31** (74×58 mm) by Walsall. Self-adhesive.
LX47 £6·36 containing 12×2nd class stamps (No.
3650a).. 13·50
LX48 £7·44 containing 12×1st class stamps (No.
3651a) (as Type **LX31** but red cover
inscribed 12×1st).................................... 16·00

2015 (3 Nov). Covers as T **LX31** (89×65 mm) by ISP Walsall. Self-adhesive.
LX49 (£6·48) containing 12×2nd class stamps (No.
3771a).. 13·50
LX50 (£7·56) containing 12×1st class stamps (No.
3772a) (as Type **LX31** but red cover
inscribed 12×1st).................................... 16·00

LX51

2016 (8 Nov). Covers as T **LX51** (89×65 mm) by ISP Walsall. Self-adhesive
with repeating 'ROYALMAIL' wording (Type PB-Up) printed on the
front of the self-adhesive backing paper.
LX51 (£6·60) containing 12×2nd class stamp (No.
3903a).. 13·50
LX52 (£7·68) containing 12×1st class stamps (No.
3904a) (as Type **LX51** but red cover
inscribed 12×1st).................................... 16·00

2017 (7 Nov). Covers as T **LX51** (89×65 mm). Printed by ISP Walsall. Self-
adhesive with repeating 'ROYALMAIL' wording printed on the front of
the self-adhesive backing paper.
LX53 (£6·72) containing 12×2nd class stamps (No.
4019a).. 13·50
LX54 (£6·72) containing 12×2nd class stamps (No.
4019b).. 13·50
LX55 (£7·80) containing 12×1st class stamps (No.
4020a) (as Type **LX51** but red cover
inscribed 12×1st).................................... 16·00
LX56 (£7·80) containing 12×1st class stamps (No.
4020b) (as Type **LX51** but red cover
inscribed 12×1st).................................... 19·00
Nos. LX54 and LX56 were described by Royal Mail as Reserve stock and,
initially, were only available from Philatelic Bureau, Edinburgh.
No. LX53 exists with the large 'ROYALMAIL' lettering above the small
and with the small above the large in the alternate pairs of lines in the
background text (Types PB-Ls/sL).
Nos. LX54, LX55 and LX56 exist with the large 'ROYALMAIL' lettering
above the small in the alternate pairs of lines in the background text
(Type PB-Ls).

2018 (1 Nov). Covers as T **LX51** (89×65 mm). Printed by ISP Walsall. Self-
adhesive with repeating 'ROYALMAIL' wording printed on the front of
the self-adhesive backing paper.
LX57 (£6·96) containing 12×2nd class stamps (No.
4154a).. 17·00
LX58 (£8·04) containing 12×1st class stamps (No.
4155a) (as Type **LX51** but red cover
inscribed 12×1st).................................... 20·00
Nos. LX57 and LX58 exist with the large 'ROYALMAIL' lettering above the
small in the alternate pairs of lines in the background text (Type PB-Ls).

2019 (5 Nov). Covers as T **LX51** (89×65 mm). Printed by ISP Walsall. Self-
adhesive with repeating 'ROYALMAIL' wording printed on the front of
the self-adhesive backing paper.
LX59 (£7·32) containing 12×2nd class stamps (No.
4283a).. 12·50
LX60 (£8·40) containing 12×1st class stamps (No.
4284a) (as Type **LX51** but red cover
inscribed 12×1st).................................... 17·50
Nos. LX59 exists with the large 'ROYALMAIL' lettering above the small
and with the small above the large in the alternate pairs of lines in the
background text (Type PB-Ls/sL).
No. LX60 exists with the small 'ROYALMAIL' lettering above the large in
the alternate pairs of lines in the background (Type PB-sL).

2020 (3 Nov). Covers as Type **LX51** (89×65 mm). Printed by ISP Walsall. Self-adhesive with repeating 'ROYALMAIL' wording printed on the front of the self-adhesive backing paper.

LX61 (£7·80) containing 12×2nd class stamps (No. 4434a)... 12·50

LX62 (£9·12) containing 12×1st class stamps (No. 4435a) (as Type **LX51** but red cover inscribed '12×1st').......................... 17·50

Nos. LX61 exists with the large 'ROYALMAIL' lettering above the small and with the small above the large in the alternate pairs of lines in the background text (Type PB-Ls/sL).

No. LX62 exists with the small 'ROYALMAIL' lettering above the large in the alternate pairs of lines in the background text (Type PB-sL).

2021 (2 Nov). Covers as T **LX51** (89×65 mm)by ISP Walsall. Self-adhesive with repeating 'ROYALMAIL' wording printed on the front of the self-adhesive backing paper.

LX63 (£7·92) containing 12×2nd class stamps (No. 4606a)... 12·50

LX64 (£10·20) containing 12×1st class stamps (No. 4608a) (as Type **LX51** but red cover inscr '12×1st').......................... 17·50

No. LX63 exists with the large 'ROYALMAIL' lettering above the small and with the small above the large in the alternate pairs of lines in the background text (Types PB-Ls/sL).

No. LX64 exists with the small 'ROYALMAIL' lettering above the large in the alternate pairs of lines in the background text (Type PB-sL).

2023 (3 Nov). Christmas. Covers as T **LX65** (93×69 mm) by ISP Walsall. Self-adhesive with repeating 'ROYALMAIL' wording printed on the front of the self-adhesive backing paper.

LX65 (£5·44) containing eight 2nd class stamps (No. 4732a)... 8·25

LX66 (£7·60) containing eight 1st class stamps (No. 4733a) (as Type LX65 but bluish violet cover inscr '8×1st')................................... 12·00

H. Self-adhesive Barcode Booklets containing No Value Indicated stamps.

NOTES. All booklets in this section have the surplus self-adhesive paper around each stamp removed, *unless otherwise stated*. All 'MB' booklets from No. MB3 onward have a single small notch at the top right tab edge. All 'ME' booklets from No. ME2 onward have two small notches at the top right tab edge. All 'MF' booklets from No. MF3 onward have a single small notch at the top right tab edge.

Containing 6×2nd class stamps

MA1

2001 (29 Jan). Multicoloured cover as T **MA1** (74×56 mm). Stamps on the cover in bright blue printed by Walsall.

MA1 (£1·14) containing 6×2nd Class self-adhesive stamps (No. 2039)........................... 6·50

a. Imperf (containing 2039ab)..................... —

No. MA1 has the surplus self-adhesive paper around each stamp retained.

No. MA1 was re-issued on 1 August 2001 showing Cod Post added to the Ffôn Testun inscription on the back cover.

Containing 6×1st Class stamps

2001 (29 Jan). Multicoloured cover as T **MA1** (74×56 mm). Stamps on the cover in bright orange-red printed by Walsall.

MB1 (£1·62) containing 6×1st Class self-adhesive stamps (No. 2040)........................... 7·50

No. MB1 has the surplus self-adhesive paper around each stamp retained.

No. MB1 was re-issued on 1 August 2001 showing Cod Post added to the Ffôn Testun inscription on the back cover.

MB2

2001 (29 Jan). Multicoloured cover as T **MB2** (74×56 mm). Stamps on the cover in bright orange-red with portrait of Queen Victoria printed by Walsall.

MB2 (£1·62) containing pane No. 2040l (includes label commemorating death centenary of Queen Victoria).................. 11·50

No. MB2 has the surplus self-adhesive paper around each stamp retained.

MB3

2002 (5 June). Gold cover as T **MB3** (74×56 mm) printed by Questa.

MB3 (£1·62) containing 6×1st Class self-adhesive stamps (No. 2295)........................... 7·50

2002 (5 June)–**08**. Gold cover as T **MB3** (74×56 mm) printed by Walsall.

MB4 (£1·62) containing 6×1st Class self-adhesive stamps (No. 2295)........................... 7·50

a. Inside cover with Smilers advertisement (27.1.05)...................... 8·00

b. Back cover with added text about new pricing structure (25.4.06)...................... 8·50

c. Inside cover with To find the correct postcodes for your mail notice (5.6.07).. 7·50

d. Inside cover with commemorative inscription for Machin Anniversary (5.6.07)... 7·50

e. Inside cover with Harry Potter stamps advertisement (28.8.07)...................... 7·50

f. Inside cover with postcode text in English and Welsh (20.9.07).................. 8·00

g. Inside cover with Carry On stamps advertisement (10.6.08)...................... 7·50

No. MB4 was re-issued on 27 January 2005 (No. MB4a) with a Smilers advertisement (showing No. 2262 and photograph of baby) on the inside front cover. It was re-issued again on 26 July 2005 with a different Smilers advertisement (showing No. 2261 and photograph of bride).

No. MB4a was available from Philatelic Bureau, Edinburgh from 27 January 2005, and from general post offices from 22 March 2005.

No. MB4b does not have Smilers advertisement.

The added text on the back cover of No. MB4b reads 'Valid for items up to 60g before 21 August 2006. Under new pricing structure from 21 August 2006 – valid for postal items up to: 240 mm Long; 165 mm Wide; 5 mm Thick; 100g Weight'.

The text on the back cover of Nos. MB4c/MB4g reads 'Valid for items up to: 240 mm Long; 165 mm Wide; 5 mm Thick; 100g Weight'.

No. MB4d has Arnold Machin's signature along the right-hand edge of the booklet pane.

No. MB4g has characters from Carry On films illustrated along the right-hand edge of the booklet pane.

2002 (4 July). Multicoloured cover as T **MA1** (74×56 mm) with stamps on the cover in bright orange-red printed by Questa.

MB5 (£1·62) containing 6×1st Class self-adhesive stamps (No. 2040)..................................... 7·50

No. MB5 was sold at £1·62.

MB6 (The Real Network added below logo)

2003 (27 Mar). Gold cover with multicoloured emblem as T **MB6** (74×56 mm) printed by Walsall.

MB6 (£1·62) containing 6×1st Class self-adhesive stamps (No. 2295)..................................... 7·50

a. Imperf (containing 2295a)....................... —

MB7 (Supporting London 2012)

2004 (15 June). London's bid to host Olympic Games, 2012. Gold cover with multicoloured emblem as T **MB7** (74×56 mm) printed by Walsall.

MB7 (£1·68) containing 6×1st Class self-adhesive stamps (No. 2295)..................................... 8·50

Containing 6×1st Class 'Security' Machins

2009 (31 Mar)–**11**. Gold cover with multicoloured emblem as T **MB3** (74×57 mm) printed by Walsall.

MB8 (£2·16) containing 6×1st Class self-adhesive stamps (No. U2985) (code MSIL) without year code)................................... 15·00

a. Containing No. U3019 (code MSIL with year code) (26.1.10)............................ 10·00

b. containing No. U3019 (code MSIL with year code). Inside cover with inscription and emblem for London 2010 Festival of Stamps (30.3.10)............ 8·75

c. containing No. U3019 (code MSIL with year code) (19.8.10)................................ 7·50

d. containing No. U3019 (code MSIL with year code). Inside front cover advertising the 2012 special stamp programme. Back cover with FSC logo (25.10.11)....................................... 11·50

The e-mail address on the inside front cover of No. MB8 reads www.royalmail.com/Postcodes4free.

No. MB8a has a lower case 'p' in the email address www.royalmail.com/postcodes4free.

No. MB8b has LONDON 2010 FESTIVAL OF STAMPS along the right hand edge of the booklet pane.

Nos. MB8/MB8b are inscribed Walsall Security Printers, UK along the left hand edge of the back cover. This was removed for Nos. MB8c/MB8d.

No. MB8d was previously listed as MB8e.

Year codes for Nos. MB8a/MB8b are MA10, for No. MB8c MA10 or M11L and for No. MB8d M11L.

Containing 6×1st Class Olympic and Paralympic Games stamps

MB9

2012 (5 Jan). Olympic and Paralympic Games, London. Multicoloured cover (75×58 mm) as T **MB9** printed by Walsall.

MB9 (£2·76) containing self-adhesive pane No. 3250a with Paralympic Games stamp at top left... 7·50

MB10 (£2·76) containing self-adhesive pane No. 3250a with Olympic Games stamp at top left... 7·50

The inside cover of No. MB9 is inscribed London's vision is to reach young people all around the world, to connect them with the inspirational power of the Games, so that they are inspired to choose sport.

The inside cover of No. MB10 is inscribed Key dates for London 2012 and dates.

Containing 6×1st Class 'Security' Machins

MB11

2012 (1 Oct). Diamond Jubilee. Slate-blue cover with multicoloured emblem as T **MB11** (74×57 mm) printed by Walsall.

MB11 (£3·60) containing 6×1st Class self-adhesive stamps (No. U3275, code MSND)............ 8·00

MB12

2013 (3 Jan). Red cover with multicoloured emblem as T **MB12** (74×57 mm) printed by Walsall.

MB12 (£3·60) containing 6×1st Class vermilion self-adhesive stamps (No. U3024, code MSIL).. 8·00

No. MB12 re-issued on 31 July 2014 with the Royal Mail telephone numbers on the back cover changed from 08457 740 740 and 08456 000 606 to 03457 740 740 and 03456 000 606.

The price shown for No. MB12 is with either the 08 or 03 telephone numbers.

Year codes for No. MB12 are M12L, M13L or M14L, and with changed telephone numbers M14L or M15L.

Containing 6×1st Class 175th Anniversary of the Penny Black stamps

2015 (6 May). 175th Anniversary of the Penny Black. Red cover with multicoloured emblem as T **MB12** (75×57 mm) printed by ISP Walsall.

MB13 (£3·78) containing 6×1st Class self-adhesive stamps (No. 3709)...................................... 10·00

Containing 6×1st Class Long to Reign Over Us 'Security' Machins

MB14

2015 (9 Sept). Long to Reign Over Us. Lilac cover with multicoloured emblem as T **MB14** (74×58 mm) printed by ISP Walsall.

MB14 (£3·78) containing 6×1st Class self-adhesive stamps (No. U3745, code REIGS)............. 7·75

Year code for No. MB14 is O15R.

'ROYAL MAIL' printed backing paper. From early 2016, Barcode booklets appeared with a repeated undulating 'ROYALMAIL' background in two sizes of grey text printed on the front of the backing paper. Initially the two sizes of grey text were printed upright: Type PB-Up (Printed Backing Upright). In early 2017 the background was changed so that alternate pairs of lines of the repeated 'ROYALMAIL' text were inverted in relation to each other. The pairs of lines can appear with the Large lettering above the small (Type PB-Ls), or with the small above the Large (Type PB-sL). In October 2018 a fourth type appeared on some PM64 booklets. In this type the 'ROYALMAIL' background, in two sizes of grey text, is all inverted (Type PB-Inv).

2016. Long to Reign Over Us. Lilac cover with multicoloured emblem as T **MB14** (74×58 mm) printed ISP Walsall. Repeating 'ROYALMAIL' wording (Type PB-Up) printed on the front of the self-adhesive backing paper

MB15 (£3·78) Containing 6×1st Class self-adhesive stamps (No. U3745, code REIGS)............. 27·00

Year codes for No. MB15 are O15R or O16R.

Note that, where Security Machin booklets' stamps exist with more than one year code, the price shown is for the cheapest version. Where a booklet is known with both Type PB-Ls and Type PB-sL the price noted is for the cheaper of the two, whichever that is. For further details of Security Machin booklets with different year codes and/or different Types of 'ROYALMAIL' printed backing, please refer to the tables later in this listing.

Containing 6×1st Class 175th Anniversary of the Penny Red stamps

2016 (18 Feb). 175th Anniversary of the Penny Red. Red cover with multicoloured emblem as T **MB12** (74×57 mm) printed by ISP Walsall.

MB16 (£3·78) containing 6×1st Class self-adhesive stamps (No. 3806)...................................... 10·00

Containing 6×1st Class 'Security' Machins

MB17

2016 (28 July). Multicoloured cover as T **MB17** (74×57 mm) printed by ISP Walsall. Repeating 'ROYALMAIL' wording (Type PB-Up) printed on the front of the self-adhesive backing paper.

MB17 (£3·84) containing 6×1st Class vermilion self-adhesive stamps (No. U3024, code MSIL).. 8·00

Year code for No. MB17 is M16L.

MB18

2016 (20 Oct). Multicoloured cover as T **MB18** (74×57 mm) printed by ISP Walsall. Repeating 'ROYALMAIL' wording printed on the front of the self-adhesive backing paper.

MB18 (£3·84) containing 6×1st Class bright scarlet self-adhesive stamps (No. U3028, code MSIL) (Type PB-Up)................................. 9·50
a. With alternate pairs of lines in background text inverted (Types PB-Ls/sL).. 10·50

No. MB18a exists with the large 'ROYALMAIL' lettering above the small and with the small above the large in the alternate pairs of lines in the background text.

Year code for No. MB18 is M16L or M18L, and for No. MB18a is M16L, M17L, M18L, M19L or M20L (Types PB-Ls and sL), or M21L (Type PB-sL).

MB19

2017 (5 June). The Machin Definitive. 50th Anniversary. Red cover with multicoloured emblem as T **MB19** (74×57 mm) printed by ISP Walsall. Repeating 'ROYALMAIL' wording (Type PB-Up) printed on the front of the self-adhesive backing paper.

MB19 (£3·90) containing 6×1st Class bright scarlet self-adhesive stamps (No. U3028, code MSIL)...................................... 9·00

Year code for No. MB19 is M17L.

Containing 6×1st Class The Iron Throne stamps

2018 (23 Jan). *Game of Thrones*. Red cover with multicoloured emblem as T **MB19** (74×57 mm) printed by ISP Walsall. Repeating 'ROYALMAIL' wording printed on the front of the self-adhesive backing paper, with alternate pairs of lines inverted.

MB20 (£3·90) containing 6×1st Class self-adhesive stamps (No. 4044)...................................... 8·00

No. MB20 has the large 'ROYALMAIL' lettering above the small (Type PB-Ls) in the alternate pairs of lines in the background text.

Containing 6×1st class (2×Penny Black, 2×Penny Red and 2×Two Pence Blue) stamps

2020 (10 Mar). London 2020 International World Stamp Exhibition. Red cover with multicoloured emblem as T **MB19** (74×57 mm) printed by ISP Walsall. Repeating 'ROYALMAIL' wording printed on the front of the self-adhesive backing paper, with alternate pairs of lines inverted.

MB21 (£4·20) containing self-adhesive pane No. 4331a of 2×Penny Black (No. 3709), 2×2 Pence Blue (No. 4331) and 2×Penny Red (No. 3806) stamps............. 8·00

No. MB21 exists with the large 'ROYALMAIL' lettering above the small and with the small above the large in the alternate pairs of lines in the background text (Type PB-Ls/sL).

Containing 6×1st class Queen (rock band) stamps

2021 (29 Mar). Queen (rock band). Red cover with Multicoloured emblem as Type **MB19** (74×57 mm) printed by ISP Walsall. Repeating 'ROYALMAIL' wording printed on the front of the self-adhesive backing paper, with alternate pairs of lines inverted.

MB22 (£5·10) containing six 1st Class self-adhesive stamps (No. 4502)...................................... 8·00

No. MB22 has the large 'ROYALMAIL' lettering above the small (Type PB-Ls/sL) in the alternate pairs of lines in the background text.

Containing 10×2nd Class stamps

2001 (29 Jan). Multicoloured cover as T **MA1** (74×56 mm). Stamps on the cover in bright blue printed by Questa.

MC1 (£1·90) containing 10×2nd Class self-adhesive stamps (No. 2039)...................................... 10·00

No. MC1 was intended for use in stamp machines.
No. MC1 has the surplus self-adhesive paper around each stamp retained.

Containing 10×1st Class stamps

2001 (29 Jan). Multicoloured cover as T **MA1** (74×56 mm). Stamps on the cover in bright orange-red printed by Questa.

MD1 (£2·70) containing 10×1st Class self-adhesive stamps (No. 2040)...................................... 13·00

No. MD1 was intended for use in stamp machines.
No. MD1 has the surplus self-adhesive paper around each stamp retained.

Containing 12×2nd Class stamps

2001 (29 Jan). Multicoloured cover as T **MA1** (74×56 mm). Stamps on the cover in bright blue printed by Questa.

ME1 (£2·28) containing 12×2nd Class self-adhesive stamps (No. 2039)...................................... 13·00

No. ME1 has the surplus self-adhesive paper around each stamp retained.
No. ME1 was re-issued on 1 August 2001 showing Cod Post added to the Ffôn Testun inscription on the back cover.

2002 (4 July). Blue cover with multicoloured emblem as T **ME2** (74×57 mm) printed by Questa.

ME2 (£2·28) containing 12×2nd Class self-adhesive stamps (No. 2039)...................................... 13·00

ME3 (The Real Network added below logo)

2003 (27 Mar). Blue cover with multicoloured emblem as T **ME3** (74×57 mm) printed by Walsall.

ME3 (£2·28) containing 12×2nd Class self-adhesive stamps (No. 2039)...................................... 13·00

2004 (15 June)–**07**. Blue cover with multicoloured emblem as T **ME2** (74×56 mm) printed by Walsall.

ME4 (£2·52) containing 12×2nd Class self-adhesive stamps (No. 2039)...................................... 13·00
 a. Back cover with added text about new pricing structure (25.4.06)...................... 13·00
 b. Back cover with text about validity (5.6.07).. 13·00

The back cover of No. ME4a has added text as No. MB4b.
The back cover of No. ME4b has text as Nos. MB4c/MB4d.

Containing 12×2nd Class 'Security' Machins

2009 (31 Mar)–**11**. Blue cover with multicoloured emblem as T **ME2** (74×57 mm) printed by Walsall.

ME5 (£3·24) containing 12×2nd Class self-adhesive stamps (No. U2981, code MTIL without year code)...................................... 13·00
 a. Ditto but containing No. U3013 (code MTIL with year code) (2.10)...................... 60·00
 b. Ditto but with printer's imprint removed (19.8.10)...................................... 13·50
 c. Ditto but with FSC logo added (25.10.11).. 14·00

Nos. ME5/ME5a are inscribed Walsall Security Printers Limited, UK along the left-hand edge of the back cover. This was removed for Nos. MB5b/MB5c.
No. ME5c was re-issued on 31 July 2014 with the telephone numbers on the back cover charged from 08 to 03 numbers as for No. MB12.
The price shown for No. ME5c is with either the 08 or 03 telephone numbers.
Year code for No. ME5a is MA10, for No. ME5b MA10 or M11L, for No. ME5c M11L , M12L, M13L or M14L, and for No. ME5c with changed telephone numbers M14L or M15L.

2016. Blue cover with multicoloured emblem as T **ME2** (74×57 mm) printed by Walsall. Repeating 'ROYALMAIL' wording (Type PB-Up) printed on the front of the self-adhesive backing paper

ME6 (£6·48) containing 12×2nd Class self-adhesive stamps (No. U3013, code MTIL with year code)...................................... 25·00

Year codes for No. ME6 are M15L or M16L.

ME2

ME7

2016 (20 Oct). Blue cover with multicoloured emblem as T **ME7** (74×57 mm) printed by ISP Walsall. Repeating 'ROYALMAIL' wording printed on the front of the self-adhesive backing paper.

ME7   (£6·60) containing 12×2nd Class self-adhesive stamps (No. U3013 code MTIL) (Type PB-Up)...................................... 18·00
    a. With alternate pairs of lines in the background text inverted (Types PB-Ls/sL)... 18·00

No. ME7a exists with the large 'ROYALMAIL' lettering above the small and with small above the large in the alternate pairs of lines in the background text.

Year code for No. ME7 is M16L and M18L, and for No. ME7a is M16L (Type PB-sL only), M17L, M18L, M19L, M20L or M21L (Types PB-Ls and sL).

Containing 12×1st Class stamps

2001 (29 Jan). Multicoloured covers as T **MA1** (74×56 mm). Stamps on the covers in bright orange-red printed by Questa (No. MF1) or Walsall (No. MF2).

MF1   (£3·24) containing 12×1st Class self-adhesive stamps (No. 2040) (Questa)....................... 14·50
MF2   containing 12×1st Class self-adhesive stamps (No. 2040) (Walsall)...................... 14·50

Nos. MF1/MF2 has the surplus self-adhesive paper around each stamp retained.

Nos. MF1/MF2 were re-issued on 1 August 2001 showing Cod Post added to the Ffôn Testun inscription on the back covers.

2002 (5 June)–**07**. Gold cover as T **MB3** (74×56 mm) printed by Walsall.

MF3   (£3·24) containing 12×1st Class self-adhesive stamps (No. 2295)................................. 14·50
    a. Back cover with added text about new pricing structure (25.4.06)....................... 15·00
    b. Back cover with text about validity (5.6.07)................................. 14·50

The back cover of No. MF3a has added text as No. MB4b. The back cover of No. MF3b has text as Nos. MB4c/MB4d.

2003 (27 Mar). Gold cover with multicoloured emblem as T **ME3** (74×57 mm) printed by Walsall.

MF4   (£3·24) containing 12×1st Class self-adhesive stamps (No. 2295)................................. 14·50

> Note that, where Security Machin Booklets' stamps exist with more than one year code, the price shown is for the cheapest version. Where a booklet is known with both Type PB-Ls and Type PB-sL the price noted is for the cheaper of the two, whichever that is. For further details of Security Machin booklets with different year code and/or different Types of 'ROYALMAIL' printed backing, please refer to the tables elsewhere in this listing.

Containing 12×1st Class 'Security' Machins

2009 (31 Mar)–**11**. Gold cover with multicoloured emblem as T **MB3** (74×57 mm) printed by Walsall.

MF5   (£4·32) containing 12×1st Class self-adhesive stamps (No. U2986, code MTIL without year code)..................................... 16·00
    a. Ditto but with printer's imprint removed (15.12.09)....................... 17·00
    b. Ditto but containing No. U3020, code MTIL with year code (2.10)....................... 26·00
    c. Ditto but with FSC logo added (25.10.11)................................. 17·00

No. MF5 is inscribed Walsall Security Printers Limited, UK along the left hand edge of the back cover. This was removed for Nos. MF5a/MF5c. Year codes for No. MF5b are MA10 or M11L and for No. MF5c M11L or M12L.

2012 (6 Feb). Diamond Jubilee. Slate-blue cover with multicoloured emblem as T **MB11** (74×57 mm) printed by Walsall.

MF6   (£5·52) containing 12×1st class self-adhesive stamps (No. U3272, code MTND)............ 14·00

2013 (3 Jan). Red cover with multicoloured emblem as T **MB12** (74×57 mm) printed by Walsall.

MF7   (£7·20) containing 12×1st Class vermilion self-adhesive stamps (No. U3025, code MTIL)... 16·00

No. MF7 was re-issued on 31 July 2014 with the telephone numbers on the back cover charged from 08 to 03 numbers as for No. MB12. The price shown for No. ME7 is with either the 08 or 03 telephone numbers.

Year codes for No. MF7 are M12L, M13L or M14L, and with changed telephone numbers M14L or M15L.

2016. Red cover with multicoloured emblem as T **MB12** (74×57 mm) printed by Walsall. Repeating 'ROYALMAIL' wording (Type PB-Up) printed on the front of the self-adhesive backing paper.

MF8   (£7·56) containing 12×1st Class vermilion self-adhesive stamps (No. U3025, code MTIL)... 22·00

Year codes for No. MF8 are M15L or M16L.

2016 (20 Oct). Red cover with multicoloured emblem as T **ME7** (74×57 mm) printed by ISP Walsall. Repeating 'ROYALMAIL' wording printed on the front of the self-adhesive backing paper.

MF9   (£7·68) containing 12×1st Class bright scarlet self-adhesive stamps (No. U3029, code MTIL) (Type PB-Up).................................. 19·00
    a. With alternate pairs of lines in the background text inverted (Types PB-Ls/sL)... 19·00

No. MF9a exists with the large 'ROYALMAIL' lettering above the small and with the small above the large in the alternate pairs of lines in the background text

Year code for No. MF9 is M16L, and for No. MF9a is M16L, M17L, M18L, M19L or M20L (Type PB-Ls and sL), or M21L (Type PB-sL only).

Containing 20×1st Class stamps

MG1

1993 (19 Oct). Multicoloured cover as T **MG1** (91×77 mm) printed by Walsall.

MG1   (£4·80) containing 20×1st Class No. 1789.......... 20·00

No. MG1 has the surplus self-adhesive paper around each stamp retained.

Containing 6×E stamps

2002 (4 July). Multicoloured cover as T **ME2** (74×57 mm) printed by Walsall.

MH1   (£2·22) containing 6×E stamps (No. 2296) and six Airmail labels.. 15·00

The official issue of No. MH1 was without any notch on the tab edge. Some booklets with a single notch at the top right tab edge were manufactured and released in error.

2003 (28 May). Multicoloured cover as T **MB6** (74×57 mm) with The Real Network added below logo printed by Walsall

MH2   (£2·28) containing 6×E stamps (No. 2296) and six Airmail labels.. 15·00

Containing four Europe stamps

MI1 (The Real Network below logo)

2003 (27 Mar). Ultramarine cover with multicoloured emblem as T **MI1** (74×57 mm) printed by Walsall.

MI1   (£2·08) containing 4×Europe 40g self-adhesive stamps (No. 2358) and four Airmail labels.. 10·50

MI2

2004 (15 June). Ultramarine cover with multicoloured emblem as T **MI2** (74×57 mm) printed by Walsall.

| MI2 | (£2·28) containing 4×Europe up to 40 grams self-adhesive stamps (No. 2358) and four Airmail labels...................................... | 10·50 |

2010 (30 Mar). Deep green cover with multicoloured emblem as T **MI2** (74×57 mm) printed by Walsall.

| MI3 | (£2·24) containing 4×Europe up to 20 grams self-adhesive stamps (No. 2357b) and four Airmail labels...................................... | 10·00 |

Containing four Worldwide stamps

2003 (27 Mar). Red cover with multicoloured emblem as T **MI1** (74×57 mm) printed by Walsall.

| MJ1 | (£4·48) containing 4×Worldwide up to 40 grams self-adhesive stamps (No. 2359) and four Airmail labels.............................. | 13·00 |

2004 (15 June). Red cover with multicoloured emblem as T **MI2** (74×57 mm) printed by Walsall.

| MJ2 | (£4·48) containing 4×Worldwide up to 40 grams self-adhesive stamps (No. 2359) and four Airmail labels.............................. | 13·00 |

2010 (30 Mar). Deep mauve cover with multicoloured emblem as T **MI2** (74×57 mm) printed by Walsall.

| MJ3 | (£3·60) containing 4×Worldwide up to 20 grams self-adhesive stamps (No. 2358a) and four Airmail labels................. | 10·00 |

Containing four Worldwide postcard stamps

2004 (1 Apr). Grey-black cover with multicoloured emblem as T **MI2** (74×57 mm) printed by Walsall.

| MJA1 | (£1·72) containing 4×Worldwide postcard self-adhesive stamps (No. 2357a) and four Airmail labels...................................... | 10·50 |

I. Self-adhesive. Barcode Booklets containing stamps with face values.

NOTE. All booklets in this section have the surplus self-adhesive paper around each stamp removed.

£2·52 Booklets

2002 (4 July). Multicoloured cover as T **ME2** (74×57 mm) printed by Walsall.

| NA1 | containing 6×42p. stamps (No. 2297) and six Airmail labels.............................. | 25·00 |

The official issue of No. NA1 was without any notch at the top right tab edge. Some booklets with a single notch at the top right tab edge were manufactured and released in error.

2003 (28 May). Multicoloured cover as T **MB6** (74×57 mm) with The Real Network added below logo printed by Walsall.

| NA2 | containing 6×42p. stamps (No. 2297) and six Airmail labels.............................. | 23·00 |

£4·08 Booklets

2002 (4 July). Multicoloured cover as T **ME2** (74×57 mm) printed by Walsall with the surplus self-adhesive paper removed.

| NB1 | containing 6×68p. stamps (No. 2298) and six Airmail labels.............................. | 26·00 |

The official issue of No. NB1 was without any notch on the tab edge. Some booklets with a single notch at the top right tab edge were manufactured and released in error.

2003 (28 May). Multicoloured cover as T **MB6** (74×57 mm) with The Real Network added below logo printed by Walsall.

| NB2 | containing 6×68p. stamps (No. 2298) and six Airmail labels.............................. | 26·00 |

J. Self-adhesive Barcode Booklets containing No Value Indicated Special or Occasions issues, with Definitive stamps.

NOTE. All booklets in this section have the surplus self-adhesive paper around each stamp removed, *unless otherwise stated*. From No. PM7 onwards the booklets have a single small notch at the top right tab edge.

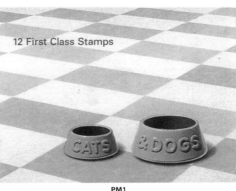

PM1

2001 (13 Feb). Cats and Dogs. Multicoloured cover as T **PM1** (84×64 mm). Printed by Walsall.

| PM1 | (£3·24) containing pane of 12×1st stamps (No. 2187b)... | 25·00 |

No. PM1 has the surplus self-adhesive paper around each stamp retained.

PM2

2001 (17 Apr). Centenary of Royal Navy Submarine Service. Multicoloured cover as T **PM2** (75×57 mm). Printed by Questa.

| PM2 | (£1·62) containing pane No. 2207a..................... | 70·00 |

No. PM2 has the surplus self-adhesive paper around each stamp retained.

2001 (4 Sept). Punch and Judy Show Puppets. Multicoloured cover as T **PM2** (74×57 mm). Printed by Questa.

| PM3 | (£1·62) containing pane No. 2230a..................... | 15·00 |

No. PM3 has the surplus self-adhesive paper around each stamp retained.

2001 (22 Oct). Flags and Ensigns. Multicoloured cover as T **PM2** (74×57 mm). Printed by Questa.

| PM4 | (£1·62) containing pane No. 2208a..................... | 15·00 |

No. PM4 has the surplus self-adhesive paper around each stamp retained.

2002 (2 May). 50th Anniversary of Passenger Jet Aviation. Airliners. Multicoloured cover as T **PM2** (74×57 mm). Printed by Questa.

| PM5 | (£1·62) containing pane No. 2290a..................... | 7·50 |

No. PM5 has the surplus self-adhesive paper around each stamp retained.

2002 (21 May). World Cup Football Championship, Japan and Korea. Multicoloured cover as T **PM2** (74×57 mm). Printed by Walsall.
PM6   (£1·62) containing pane No. 2293a...................   7·50
No. PM6 has the surplus self-adhesive paper around each stamp retained.

PM7

2002 (10 Sept). Bridges of London. Gold cover with multicoloured emblem and stamp illustration as T **PM7** (74×57 mm). Printed by Questa.
PM7   (£1·62) containing pane No. 2314a...................   7·50

2003 (4 Mar). Occasions Greetings Stamps. Gold cover with multicoloured emblem and stamp illustration as T **PM7** (74×57 mm). Printed by Questa.
PM8   (£1·62) containing pane No. 2264ab..................   7·50

PM9 (The Real Network added below logo)

2003 (29 Apr). Extreme Endeavours. Gold cover with multicoloured emblem and stamp illustration as T **PM9** (74×57 mm). Printed by De La Rue.
PM9   (£1·62) containing pane No. 2366a...................   7·50

2003 (15 July). A British Journey. Scotland. Gold cover with multicoloured emblem and stamp illustration as T **PM9** (74×57 mm). Printed by De La Rue.
PM10   (£1·68) containing pane No. 2391a..................   7·50

2003 (18 Sept). Classic Transport Toys. Gold cover with multicoloured emblem and stamp illustration as T **PM7** (74×57 mm). Printed by De La Rue.
PM11   (£1·68) containing pane No. 2403a..................   7·50

2004 (16 Mar). A British Journey. Northern Ireland. Gold cover with multicoloured emblem and stamp illustration as T **PM7** (74×57 mm). Printed by De La Rue.
PM12   (£1·68) containing pane No. 2445a..................   7·50

2004 (13 Apr). Ocean Liners. Gold cover with multicoloured emblem and stamp illustration as T **PM7** (74×57 mm). Printed by De La Rue.
PM13   (£1·68) containing pane No. 2455a..................   7·50

2004 (15 June). A British Journey. Wales. Gold cover with multicoloured emblem and stamp illustration as T **PM7** (74×57 mm). Printed by De La Rue.
PM14   (£1·68) containing pane No. 2472a..................   7·50

PM15

2008 (13 May). Beside the Seaside. Red cover with multicoloured emblem (74×57 mm) as T **PM15**. Printed by Walsall.
PM15   (£2·16) containing pane No. 2848a..................   7·50
No. PM15 has the self-adhesive paper removed from around the 1st class gold stamps only.

Booklets containing four 'Security' Machins* and two commemorative stamps

Unless otherwise stated Nos. PM16–PM32, PM35–PM48, and PM54–PM66 contain 1st Class Machin stamps with source code MCIL. Nos. PM33/PM34 contain 1st Class Diamond Jubilee Machin stamps with source code MCND. Nos. PM49/PM53 contain 1st Class Long to Reign Over Us Machin stamps with source code REIGC. Nos. PM16–PM21 are without a year code, and Nos. PM22–PM35, and PM37–PM83 are year codes, which for the convenience of collectors are noted below along with the appropriate U-number. All have the self-adhesive paper removed from around the Machin stamps only.
*   No. PM36 contains four definitive-size Tardis stamps in place of the usual Machin design.

2009 (10 Mar). Design Classics 1. (Telephone Kiosk and Routemaster Bus). Red cover with multicoloured emblem as T **PM15** (74×57 mm). Printed by Walsall.
PM16   (£2·16) containing pane No. 2911a..................   7·50

2009 (21 Apr). Design Classics 2. (Mini). Red cover with multicoloured emblem as T **PM15** (74×57 mm). Printed by Walsall.
PM17   (£2·34) containing pane No. 2913a..................   7·50

2009 (21 May). 50th Anniversary of NAFAS (National Association of Flower Arrangement Societies). Red cover with multicoloured emblem as T **PM15** (74×57 mm). Printed by Walsall.
PM18   (£2·34) containing pane No. 2942a..................   10·00

2009 (18 Aug). Design Classics 3. (Concorde). Red cover with multicoloured emblem as T **PM15** (74×57 mm). Printed by Walsall.
PM19   (£2·34) containing pane No. 2914a..................   7·50

2009 (17 Sept). Design Classics 4. (Miniskirt). Red cover with multicoloured emblem as T **PM15** (74×57 mm). Printed by Walsall.
PM20   (£2·34) containing pane No. 2915a..................   7·50

2010 (7 Jan). Olympic and Paralympic Games, London (2012) 1 (Judo and Archery). Red cover with multicoloured emblem as T **PM15** (74×57 mm). Printed by Walsall.
PM21   (£2·34) containing pane No. 3020a..................   7·50

2010 (25 Feb). Olympic and Paralympic Games, London (2012) 2 (Track and Basketball). Red cover with multicoloured emblem as T **PM15** (74×57 mm). Printed by Walsall.
PM22   (£2·34) containing pane No. 3022a..................   7·50
Contains Security Machin No. U3016 with year code MA10.

2010 (15 June). Mammals. Red cover with multicoloured emblem as T **PM15** (74×57 mm). Printed by Walsall.
PM23   (£2·46) containing pane No. 3095a..................   11·00
Contains Security Machin No. U3016 with year code MA10.

2010 (27 July). Olympic and Paralympic Games, London (2012) 3 (Rowing and Tennis). Red cover with multicoloured emblem as T **PM15** (74×57 mm). Printed by Walsall.
PM24   (£2·46) containing pane No. 3107a..................   7·50
Contains Security Machin No. U3016 with year code MA10.

2010 (15 Sept). British Design Classics 5. (Spitfire). Red cover with multicoloured emblem as T **PM15** (74×57 mm). Printed by Walsall.
PM25   (£2·46) containing pane No. 2915ba.................   7·50
Contains Security Machin No. U3016 with year code MA10.

2010 (12 Oct). Olympic and Paralympic Games, London (2012) 4 (Football and Cycling). Red cover with multicoloured emblem as T **PM15** (74×57 mm). Printed by Walsall.
PM26   (£2·46) containing pane No. 3108ab.................   7·50
Contains Security Machin No. U3016 with year code MA10.

2011 (11 Jan). F.A.B. The Genius of Gerry Anderson Red cover with multicoloured emblem as T **PM15** (74×57 mm). Printed by Walsall.
PM27 (£2·46) containing pane No. 3143a...................... 7·50
    Contains Security Machin No. U3016 with year code M11L.

2011 (24 Feb). 50th Anniversary of the British Heart Foundation. Red cover with multicoloured emblems as T **PM15** (74×57 mm). Printed by Walsall.
PM28 (£2·46) containing pane No. 3153a...................... 7·50
    Contains Security Machin No. U3016 with year code M11L.

2011 (14 June). Thomas the Tank Engine. Red cover with multicoloured emblem as T **PM15** (74×57 mm). Printed by Walsall.
PM29 (£2·76) containing pane No. 3194a...................... 7·50
    Contains Security Machin No. U3016 with year code M11L.

2011 (27 July). Olympic and Paralympic Games, London (2012) 5 (Wheelchair Rugby and Sailing). Red cover with multicoloured emblem as T **PM15** (74×57 mm). Printed by Walsall.
PM30 (£2·76) containing pane No. 3205a...................... 7·50
    Contains Security Machin No. U3016 with year code M11L.

2011 (23 Aug). Classic Locomotives of England. Red cover with multicoloured emblem as T **PM15** (74×57 mm). Printed by Walsall.
PM31 (£2·76) containing pane No. 3215a...................... 7·50
    Contains Security Machin No. U3016 with year code M11L.

2011 (15 Sept). Olympic and Paralympic Games, London (2012) 6 (Gymnastics and Fencing). Red cover with multicoloured emblem as T **PM15** (74×57 mm). Printed by Walsall.
PM32 (£2·76) containing pane No. 3206ab.................. 7·50
    Contains Security Machin No. U3016 with year code M11L.

2012 (31 May). Diamond Jubilee. Red cover with multicoloured emblem as T **PM15** (74×57 mm). Printed by Walsall.
PM33 (£3·60) containing pane No. 3327a...................... 7·50
    Contains slate-blue Machin No. U3274.

2012 (27 Sept). Classic Locomotives of Scotland. Red cover with multicoloured emblem as T **PM15** (74×57 mm). Printed by Walsall.
PM34 (£3·60) containing pane No. 3407a...................... 7·50
    Contains slate-blue Machin No. U3274.

2013 (9 Jan). 150th Anniversary of the London Underground. Red cover with multicoloured emblem as T **PM15** (74×57 mm). Printed by Walsall.
PM35 (£3·60) containing pane No. 3430a...................... 7·50
    Contains Security Machin No. U3022 with year code M12L.

2013 (26 Mar). 50th Anniversary of *Doctor Who* (TV programme). Red cover with multicoloured emblem as T **PM15** (74×57 mm). Printed by Walsall. Self-adhesive.
PM36 (£3·60) containing Tardis pane No. 3448a.......... 14·00

2013 (9 May). Football Heroes. Red cover with multicoloured emblem as T **PM15** (74×57 mm). Printed by Walsall .
PM37 (£3·60) containing George Best and Bobby
        Moore pane No. 3475a............................ 11·00
    Contains Security Machin No. U3022 with year code M13L.

2013 (18 June). Classic Locomotives of Northern Ireland. Red cover with multicoloured emblem as T **PM15** (75×57 mm). Printed by Walsall.
PM38 (£3·60) containing pane No. 3497a...................... 7·50
    Contains Security Machin No. U3022 with year code M13L.

2013 (11 July). Butterflies. Red cover with Multicoloured emblem as T **PM15** (74×57 mm) Printed by Walsall.
PM39 (£3·60) containing pane No. 3509a...................... 7·50
    Contains Security Machin No. U3022 with year code M13L.

2013 (19 Sept). Royal Mail Transport. By Land and Sea. Red cover with multicoloured emblem as T **PM15** (74×57 mm). Printed by Walsall.
PM40 (£3·60) containing pane No. 3530a...................... 14·00
    Contains Security Machin No. U3022 with year code M13L.

2014 (20 Feb). Football Heroes. Red cover with multicoloured emblem as T **PM15** (74×57 mm). Printed by Walsall.
PM41 (£3·60) containing John Charles and Dave
        Mackay pane No. 3477a.......................... 11·00
    Contains Security Machin No. U3022 with year code M13L.

2014 (15 Apr). Buckingham Palace, London. Red cover with multicoloured emblem as T **PM15** (74×57 mm). Printed by Walsall.
PM42 (£3·72) containing pane No. 3595a...................... 7·50
    Contains Security Machin No. U3022 with year code M14L.

2014 (17 July). Commonwealth Games, Glasgow. Red cover with multicoloured emblem as T **PM15** (74×57 mm). Printed by Walsall.
PM43 (£3·72) containing pane No. 3625a...................... 7·50
    Contains Security Machin No. U3022 with year code M14L.

2014 (18 Aug). Sustainable and Threatened Fish. Red cover with multicoloured emblem as T **PM15** (74×57 mm). Printed by Walsall.
PM44 (£3·72) containing pane No. 3632a...................... 11·00
    Contains Security Machin No. U3022 with year code M14L.

2014 (18 Sept). Classic Locomotives of Wales. Red cover with multicoloured emblem as T **PM15** (74×57 mm). Printed by Walsall.
PM45 (£3·72) containing pane No. 3634a...................... 7·50
    Contains Security Machin No. U3022 with year code M14L.

2015 (6 Jan). Alice in Wonderland. Red cover with multicoloured emblem as T **PM15** (74×57 mm). Printed by ISP Walsall.
PM46 (£3·72) containing pane No. 3668a...................... 12·00
    Contains Security Machin No. U3022 with year code M15L.

2015 (1 Apr). Comedy Greats. Red cover with multicoloured emblem as T **PM15** (74×57 mm). Printed by ISP Walsall.
PM47 (£3·78) containing pane No. 3707a...................... 15·00
    Contains Security Machin No. U3022 with year code M15L.

2015 (18 Aug). Bees. Red cover with multicoloured emblem as T **PM15** (74×57 mm). Printed by ISP Walsall.
PM48 (£3·78) containing pane No. 3743a...................... 7·50
    Contains Security Machin No. U3022 with year code M15L.

2015 (18 Sept). Rugby World Cup. Red cover with multicoloured emblem as T **PM15** (74×57 mm). Printed by ISP Walsall.
PM49 (£3·78) containing pane No. 3756a...................... 12·00
    Contains bright lilac Machin No. U3746 with year code O15R.

'ROYALMAIL' printed backing paper. From No. PM50 all booklets in this section have repeating undulating 'ROYALMAIL' background in two sizes of grey text printed on the front of the backing paper. On Nos. PM50/PM56 the text is upright (Type PB-Up). With the exception of PM64a where the text is all inverted (Type PB-Inv), from No. PM57 onward alternate pairs of lines are inverted (i.e. Type PB-Ls and/or Type PB-sL, see footnotes) or as noted. Where a booklet is known with both Type PB-Ls and Type PB-sL the price noted is for the cheaper of the two, whichever that is.

2016 (21 Apr). 90th Birthday of Queen Elizabeth II (Book I). Red covers with multicoloured emblem as T **PM15** (74×57 mm). Printed by ISP Walsall.
PM50 (£3·84) containing Prince Charles and Queen
        Elizabeth pane No. 3833a....................... 15·00
    Contains bright lilac Machin No. U3746 with year code O16R.

2016 (9 June). 90th Birthday of Queen Elizabeth II (Book II). Red covers with multicoloured emblem as T **PM15** (74×57 mm). Printed by ISP Walsall.
PM51 (£3·84) containing Prince George and Prince
        William pane No. 3835a.......................... 7·50
    Contains bright lilac Machin No. U3746 with year code O16R.

2016 (28 July). 150th Birth Anniversary of Beatrix Potter. Red cover with multicoloured emblem as T **PM15** (74×57 mm). Printed by ISP Walsall.
PM52 (£3·84) containing pane No. 3862a...................... 11·00
    Contains bright lilac Machin No. U3746 with year code O16R.

2016 (16 Aug). Landscape Gardens. Red cover with multicoloured emblem as T **PM15** (74×57 mm). Printed by ISP Walsall.
PM53 (£3·84) containing pane No. 3877a...................... 10·00
    Contains bright lilac Machin No. U3746 with year code O16R.

PM54

2016 (20 Oct). Mr Men and Little Miss (children's books by Roger Hargreaves). Red cover with multicoloured emblem as T **PM54** (74×57 mm). Printed by ISP Walsall.
PM54 (£3·84) containing pane No. 3901a...................... 7·50
    Contains Security Machin No. U3027 with year code M16L.

2017 (15 Feb). Windsor Castle. Red cover with multicoloured emblem as T **PM54** (74×57 mm). Printed by ISP Walsall.

PM55   (£3·84) containing pane No. 3926a.................... 7·50

   Contains Security Machin No. U3027 with year code M17L.

2017 (14 Mar). David Bowie (1947–2016, singer, songwriter and actor). Commemoration. Red cover with multicoloured emblem as T **PM54** (74×57 mm). Printed by ISP Walsall.

PM56   (£3·84) containing pane No. 3934a.................... 7·50

   Contains Security Machin No. U3027 with year code M17L.

2017 (12 Oct). *Star Wars*. Red cover with multicoloured emblems as T **PM54** (74×57 mm). Printed by ISP Walsall.

PM57   (£3·90) containing Maz Kanata and
            Chewbacca pane No. 4015a................... 7·50

PM58   (£3·90) containing BB-8 and R2-D2 pane No.
            4017a... 7·50

   Nos. PM57/PM58 contain Security Machin No. U3027 with year code M17L.

   No. PM57 exists with the large 'ROYALMAIL' lettering above the small and with the small above the large in the alternate pairs of lines in the background text (Types PB-Ls/sL).

   No. PM58 exists with the small 'ROYALMAIL' lettering above the large in the alternate pairs of lines in the background text (Type PB-sL).

2018 (20 Mar). Centenary of the RAF (Royal Air Force). Red cover with multicoloured emblem as T **PM54** (74×57 mm). Printed by ISP Walsall.

PM59   (£3·90) containing Hurricane Mk I and
            Lightning F6 pane No. 4065a................ 7·50

   Contains Security Machin No. U3027 with year code M18L.

   No. PM59 exists with the large 'ROYALMAIL' lettering above the small and with the small above the large in the alternate pairs of lines in the background text (Types PB-Ls/sL).

2018 (11 May). Centenary of the RAF (Royal Air Force). Red cover with multicoloured emblem as T **PM54** (74×57 mm). Printed by ISP Walsall.

PM60   (£4·02) containing Red Arrows Flypast and
            Swan pane No. 4080a......................... 12·50

   Contains Security Machin No. U3027 with year code M18L.

   No. PM60 exists with the large 'ROYALMAIL' lettering above the small and with the small above the large in the alternate pairs of lines in the background text (Types PB-Ls).

   No. PM60 with small 'ROYALMAIL' lettering above large (sL) is also known to exist but appears to only be a tiny part of the overall printing.

2018 (26 June). 50th Anniversary of *Dad's Army* (BBC television sitcom 1968–1977). Red cover with multicoloured emblem as T **PM54** (74×57 mm). Printed by ISP Walsall.

PM61   (£4·02) containing pane No. 4107a.................... 13·00

   Contains Security Machin No. U3027 with year code M18L.

   No. PM61 exists with the small 'ROYALMAIL' lettering above the large in the alternate pairs of lines in the background text (Type PB-sL).

2018 (31 July). Hampton Court Palace. Red cover with multicoloured emblem as T **PM54** (74×57 mm). Printed by ISP Walsall.

PM62   (£4·02) containing pane No. 4116a.................... 25·00

   Contains Security Machin No. U3027 with year code M18L.

   No. PM62 exists with the large 'ROYALMAIL' lettering above the small in the alternate pairs of lines in the background text (Types PB-Ls).

   No. PM62 with small 'ROYALMAIL' lettering above large (sL) is also known to exist but appears to only be a small part of the overall printing.

2018 (13 Sept). Centenary of the First World War. Red cover with multicoloured emblem as T **PM54** (74×57 mm). Printed by ISP Walsall.

PM63   (£4·02) containing pane No. 4139a.................... 15·00

   Contains Security Machin No. U3027 with year code M18L.

   No. PM63 exists with the large 'ROYALMAIL' lettering above the small in the alternate pairs of lines in the background text (Type PB-Ls).

2018 (16 Oct). Harry Potter. Red cover with multicoloured emblem as T **PM54** (74×57 mm). Printed by ISP Walsall.

PM64   (£4·02) containing pane No. 4152a.................... 7·50
      a. With repeating 'ROYALMAIL' lettering
         the same way up but inverted (Type
         PB-Inv)... 20·00

   Contains Security Machin No. U3027 with year code M18L.

   No. PM64 exists with the small 'ROYALMAIL' lettering above the large in the alternate pairs of lines in the background text (Type PB-sL).

   No. PM64a comes from a small part of the overall issue.

2019 (14 Mar). Marvel. Red cover with multicoloured emblem as T **PM54** (74×57 mm). Printed by ISP Walsall.

PM65   (£4·02) containing pane No. 4193a.................... 10·00

   Contains Security Machin No. U3027 with year code M19L.

   No. PM65 exists with the large 'ROYALMAIL' lettering above the small in the alternate pairs of lines in the background text (Type PB-Ls).

2019 (4 Apr). Birds of Prey. Red cover with multicoloured emblem as T **PM54** (74×57 mm). Printed by ISP Walsall.

PM66   (£4·20) containing pane No. 4210a.................... 50·00

   Contains Security Machin No. U3027 with year code M19L.

   No. PM66 exists with the small 'ROYALMAIL' lettering above the large in the alternate pairs of lines in the background text (Type PB-sL).

2019 (6 June). 75th Anniversary of D-Day. Red cover with multicoloured emblem as T **PM54** (74×57 mm). Printed by ISP Walsall.

PM67   (£4·20) containing pane No. 4237a.................... 10·00

   No. PM67 exists with the small 'ROYALMAIL' lettering above the large in the alternate pairs of lines in the background text (Type PB-sL).

   No. PM67 with large 'ROYALMAIL' lettering above small (Ls) is also known to exist but appears to only be a small part of the overall printing.

2019 (3 Sept). Elton John. Red cover with multicoloured emblem as T **PM54** (74×57 mm). Printed by ISP Walsall.

PM68   (£4·20) containing pane No. 4262a.................... 12·95

   Contains Security Machin No. U3027 with year code M19L.

   No. PM68 exists with the large 'ROYALMAIL' lettering above the small and with the small above the large in the alternate pairs of lines in the background text (Types PB-Ls/sL).

2019 (19 Sept). Royal Navy Ships. Red cover with multicoloured emblem as T **PM54** (74×57 mm). Printed by ISP Walsall.

PM69   (£4·20) containing pane No. 4272a.................... 50·00

   No. PM69 exists with the large 'ROYALMAIL' lettering above the small in the alternate pairs of lines in the background text (Type PB-Ls).

2019 (26 Nov). *Star Wars*. Red cover with multicoloured emblem as T **PM54** (74×57 mm). Printed by ISP Walsall.

PM70   (£4·20) containing Poe Dameron and Sith
            Trooper pane No. 4304a...................... 12·00

   Contains Security Machin No. U3027 with year code M19L.

   No. PM70 exists with the large 'ROYALMAIL' lettering above the small and with the small above the large in the alternate pairs of lines in the background text (Types PB-Ls/sL).

2020 (21 Jan). Video Games. Red cover with multicoloured emblem as T **PM54** (74×57 mm). Printed by ISP Walsall.

PM71   (£4·20) containing Tomb Raider pane No.
            4321a... 15·00

   Contains Security Machin No. U3027 with year code M20L.

   No. PM71 exists with the large 'ROYALMAIL' lettering above the small in the alternate pairs of lines in the background text (Type PB-Ls).

2020 (17 Mar). James Bond. Red cover with multicoloured emblem as T **PM54** (74×57 mm). Printed by ISP Walsall.

PM72   (£4·20) containing pane No. 4339a.................... 15·00

   No. PM72 exists with the large 'ROYALMAIL' lettering above the small in the alternate pairs of lines in the background text (Type PB-Ls).

   No. PM72 with small 'ROYALMAIL' lettering above large (sL) is also known to exist but appears to only be a small part of the overall printing.

2020 (28 May). *Coronation Street*. Red cover with multicoloured emblems as T **PM54** (74×57 mm). Printed by ISP Walsall.

PM73   (£4·56) booklet containing pane No. 4378a....... 7·50

   Contains Security Machin No. U3027 with year code M20L.

   No. PM73 exists with the small 'ROYALMAIL' lettering above the large in the alternate pairs of lines in the background text (Type PB-sL).

2020 (9 July). Queen (rock band). Red cover with multicoloured emblem as T **PM54** (74×57 mm). Printed by ISP Walsall.

PM74   (£4·56) booklet containing pane No. 4397a....... 15·00

   Contains Security Machin No. U3027 with year code M20L.

   No. PM74 exists with the large 'ROYALMAIL' lettering above the small and with the small above the large in alternate pairs of lines in the background text (Types PB-Ls/sL).

2020 (18 Aug). *Sherlock*. Red cover with multicoloured emblem as T **PM54** (4×57 mm). Printed by ISP Walsall.

PM75   (£4·56) booklet containing pane No. 4418a....... 10·00

   No. PM75 exists with the small 'ROYALMAIL' lettering above the large in alternate pairs of lines in the background text (Type PB-sL).

2020 (13 Nov). *Star Trek*. Red cover with multicoloured emblem as T **PM54** (7×57 mm). Printed by ISP Walsall.

PM76   (£4·56) booklet containing pane No. 4456a....... 7·50

   No. PM76 exists with the large 'ROYALMAIL' lettering above the small and with the small above the large in the alternate pairs of lines in the background text (Types PB-Ls/sL).

2021 (14 Jan). National Parks. Red cover with multicoloured emblem as T **PM54** (74×57 mm). Printed by ISP Walsall.

PM77   (£5·10) booklet containing pane No. 4474a....... 7·50

   Contains Security Machin No. U3027 with year code M21L.

   No. PM77 exists with the small 'ROYALMAIL' lettering above the large in the alternate pairs of lines in the background text (Types PB-sL).

   No. PM77 with large 'ROYALMAIL' lettering above small (Ls) is also known to exist but appears to only be a tiny part of the overall printing

2021 (16 Feb). *Only Fools and Horses*. Red cover with multicoloured emblem as T **PM54** (74×57 mm). Printed by ISP Walsall

PM78   (£5·10) booklet containing pane No. 4486a.................... 7·50

   Contains Security Machin No. U3027 with year code M21L.

   No. PM78 exists with the small 'ROYALMAIL' lettering above the large in the alternate pairs of lines in the background text (Types PB-sL).

2021 (28 May). Paul McCartney. Red cover with multicoloured emblem as T **PM54** (74×57 mm). Printed by ISP Walsall
PM79　(£5·10) booklet containing pane No. 4526a.......　7·50
　　Contains Security Machin No. U3027 with year code M21L.
　　No. PM79 exists with the small 'ROYALMAIL' lettering above the large in the alternate pairs of lines in the background text (Types PB-sL).

2021 (1 July). Dennis and Gnasher. Red cover with multicoloured emblem as T **PM54** (74×57 mm). Printed by ISP Walsall.
PM80　(£5·10) booklet containing pane No. 4540a.......　7·50
　　Contains Security Machin No. U3027 with year code M21L.
　　No. PM80 exists with the large 'ROYALMAIL' lettering above the small and with the small above the large in alternate pairs of lines in the background text (Types PB-Ls/sL).

2021 (22 July). Wild Coasts. Red cover with multicoloured emblem as T **PM54** (74×57 mm). Printed by ISP Walsall.
PM81　(£5·10) booklet containing pane No. 4553a.......　7·50
　　Contains Security Machin No. U3027 with year code M21L.
　　No. PM81 exists with the small 'ROYALMAIL' lettering above the large in the alternate pairs of lines in the background text (Types PB-sL).

2021 (17 Sept). DC Collection. Red covers with multicoloured emblems as T **PM54** (74×57 mm). Printed by ISP Walsall
PM82　(£5·10) booklet containing Batman and Robin pane No. 4588a...........................　7·50
PM83　(£5·10) booklet containing Wonder Woman pane No. 4590a...........................　7·50
　　Nos. PM81/PM82 contain Security Machin No. U3027 with year code M21L.
　　Nos. PM82/PM83 both exist with the large 'ROYALMAIL' lettering above the small and with the small above the large in alternate pairs of lines in the background text (Types PB-Ls/sL).

K. Self-adhesive Barcode Booklets containing No Value Indicated Smilers stamps in definitive size.

NOTE. Nos. QA1–QA4 and QB1 have the self-adhesive paper removed from around the stamps and have a single notch at the top right tab edge.

Containing six Smilers stamps

QA1

2005 (4 Oct). Gold cover with multicoloured emblem as T **QA1** (74×56 mm) by printed Walsall.
QA1　(£1·80) containing Smilers (1st series) Love pane No. 2567a...........................　9·00

QA2

2006 (17 July). Gold cover with multicoloured emblem as T **QA2** (74×56 mm) printed by Walsall.
QA2　(£1·92) containing Smilers (1st series) Love pane No. 2567a...........................　10·00

2006 (17 Oct). Gold cover with multicoloured emblem as T **QA1** (74×56 mm) printed by Walsall.
QA3　(£1·92) containing Smilers (2nd series) Thank You pane No. 2672a...................　7·50

2008 (28 Feb). Gold cover with multicoloured emblem as T **QA2** (74×56 mm) printed by Walsall.
QA4　(£2·04) containing Smilers (3rd series) pane No. 2819a...........................　30·00

Containing 12 Smilers stamps

2015 (20 Jan). Red cover with multicoloured emblem as T **MB12** (74×57 mm) printed by ISP Walsall.
QB1　(£7·44) containing pane No. 3670a.....................　18·00

L. Self-adhesive Barcode Booklets containing stamps with value indicator at upper left.

NOTE. All booklets in this section have the surplus self-adhesive paper around each stamp removed, *unless otherwise stated*. All RA booklets have two large notches at the top right tab edge, while all RB booklets have a single large notch at the top right tab edge.

RA1

2006 (15 Aug). Blue cover with multicoloured emblem as T **RA1** (74×57 mm) printed by Walsall.
RA1　(£1·48) containing 4×2nd Class Large self-adhesive stamps (No. 2656)....................　6·00

Containing 4×2nd Class Large 'Security' stamps

2009 (31 Mar)–**11**. Blue cover with multicoloured emblem as T **RA1** (74×57 mm) printed by Walsall.
RA2　(£1·68) containing 4×2nd Class Large self-adhesive stamps (No. U2988 code FOYAL without year code)......................　7·50
　　a. Ditto but containing No. U3032 (code MFIL with year code) (8.5.10)................　£100
　　b. Ditto but with printer's imprint removed (22.3.11)....................................　7·50
　　c. Ditto but with FSC logo added (25.10.11)...　7·50
　　Nos. RA2/RA2a are inscribed Walsall Security Printers Limited, UK along the left-hand edge of the back cover. This was removed from Nos. RA2b/RA2c.
　　No. RA2c was re-issued on 31 July 2014 with the telephone numbers on the back cover changed from 08 to 03 numbers as for No. MB12.
　　The price shown for RA2c is with the 08 telephone number. With 03 telephone number £10·00.
　　Year code for No. RA2a is MA10, for No. RA2b MA11 and for No. RA2c MA11, MA12, MA13 or MA14, and with changed telephone numbers MA14 or MA15.

2016. Blue cover with multicoloured emblem as T **RA1** (74×57 mm) printed by ISP Walsall. Repeating 'ROYALMAIL' wording (Type PB-Up) printed on the front of the self-adhesive backing paper
RA3　(£3·00) containing 4×2nd Class Large self-adhesive stamps (No. U3032 code MFIL)..　22·00
　　Year code for No. RA3 is M16L.

RA4

2016 (20 Oct). Blue cover with multicoloured emblem as T **RA4** (74×56 mm) printed by ISP Walsall. Repeating 'ROYALMAIL' wording printed on the front of the self-adhesive backing paper

RA4 (£3·00) Containing 4×2nd Class Large self-adhesive stamps (No. U3032 code MFIL) (Type PB-Up).................................. 12·00

a. With alternate pairs of lines in the background text inverted (Types PB-Ls/sL)... 11·00

No. RA4a exists with the large 'ROYALMAIL' lettering above the small and with the small above the large in the alternate pairs of lines in the background text.

Year code for No. RA4 is M16L, and for No. RA4a is M17L (Type PB-Ls only), M18L or M19L (Types PB-Ls and sL), M20L or M21L (Type PB-sL only).

Note that, where Security Machin Booklets' stamps exist with more than one year code, the price shown is for the cheapest version. Where a booklet is known with both Type PB-Ls and Type PB-sL the price noted is for the cheaper of the two, whichever that is. For further details of Security Machin booklets with different year codes and/or different Types of 'ROYALMAIL' printed backing, please refer to the tableselsewhere in this listing.

Containing 4×1st Class Large stamps

RB1

2006 (15 Aug). Gold cover with multicoloured emblem as T **RB1** (74×57 mm) printed by Walsall.

RB1 (£1·76) containing 4×1st Class Large self-adhesive stamps (No. 2657)..................... 7·50

Containing 4×1st Class Large 'Security' stamps

2009 (31 Mar)–**11** Gold cover with multicoloured emblem as T **RB1** (74×57 mm) printed by Walsall.

RB2 (£2·08) containing 4×1st Class Large self-adhesive stamps (No. U2990 code FOYAL without year code)...................... 11·00

a. Ditto but containing No. U3035 (code MFIL with year code) (8.5.10)................... 20·00

b. Ditto but with printer's imprint removed (22.3.11)..................................... 8·50

c. Ditto but with FSC logo added (25.10.11)....................................... 8·50

No. RB2/RB2a are inscribed Walsall Security Printers Limited, UK along the left-hand edge of the back cover. This was removed for Nos. RB2b/RB2c. Year code for No. RB2a is MA10 and for Nos. RB2b/RB2c MA11.

2012 (25 Apr). Diamond Jubilee. Slate-blue cover with multicoloured emblem as T **RB1** (74×57 mm) printed by Walsall.

RB3 (£3·00) containing 4×1st Class Large self-adhesive stamps (No. U3277, code JUBILFE).. 8·00

RB4

2013 (3 Jan). Red cover with multicoloured emblem as T **RB4** (74×57 mm) printed by Walsall.

RB4 (£3·60) containing 4×1st Class Large vermilion self-adhesive stamps (No. U3037, code MFIL)... 8·50

No. RB4 was re-issued on 31 July 2014 with the telephone numbers on the back cover changed from 08 to 03 numbers as for No. MB12. The price shown for No. RB4 is with either the 08 or 03 telephone numbers.

Year codes for No. RB4 are MA12, MA13 or MA14, and with changed telephone numbers MA14 or MA15.

2016. Red cover with multicoloured emblem as T **RB4** (74×57 mm) printed by ISP Walsall. Repeating 'ROYALMAIL' wording (Type PB-Up) printed on the front of the self-adhesive backing paper

RB5 (£3·80) containing 4×1st Class Large vermilion self-adhesive stamps (No. U3037, code MFIL)... 13·00

Year code for No. RB5 is MA15 or M16L.

RB6

2016 (20 Oct). Red cover with multicoloured emblem as T **RB6** (74×57 mm). Printed by ISP Walsall. Repeating 'ROYALMAIL' wording printed on the front of the self-adhesive backing paper.

RB6 (£3·84) containing 4×1st Class Large bright scarlet self-adhesive stamps (No. U3039, code MFIL) (Type PB-Up)............ 11·00

a. With alternate pairs of lines in the background text inverted (Types PB-Ls/sL)... 11·00

No. RB6a exists with the large 'ROYALMAIL' lettering above the small and with the small above the large in the alternate pairs of lines in the background text.

Year code for No. RB6 is M16L, and for No. RB6a is M17L, M18L (Types PB-Ls and PB-sL), M19L (Type PB-Ls only), M20L or M21L (Type PB-sL only).

Containing six Pricing in Proportion 1st class stamps

2006 (12 Sept)–07. Gold cover with multicoloured emblem as T **MB3** (74×57 mm) printed by Walsall.

RC1	(£1·92) containing 6×1st Class self-adhesive stamps (No. 2655)......................................	7·50
	a. Inside cover with don't just send a stamp advertisement (2.10.06)...............	8·50
	b. Inside cover with To find the correct postcodes for your mail notice (1.2.07).	8·00

Nos. RC1/RC1b has a single small notch at the top right tab edge.

Containing 12 Pricing in Proportion 2nd class stamps

2006 (12 Sept). Blue cover with multicoloured emblem as T **MB3** (74×57 mm) printed by Walsall.

RD1	(£2·76) containing 12×2nd Class self-adhesive stamps (No. 2654)......................................	13·00

Nos. RD1 has two small notches at the top right tab edge.

Containing 12 Pricing in Proportion 1st class stamps

2006 (12 Sept). Gold cover with multicoloured emblem as T **MB3** (74×57 mm) printed by Walsall.

RE1	(£3·84) containing 12×1st Class self-adhesive stamps (No. 2655)......................................	16·00

No. RE1 has a single small notch at the top right tab edge.

M. Self-adhesive Barcode Booklets containing No Value Indicated Smilers stamps in definitive size, with Definitive stamps.

NOTE. Nos. SA1 and SA2 have the surplus self-adhesive paper around each stamp removed and a single small notch at the top right tab edge.

2007 (16 Jan). Gold cover with multicoloured emblem as T **MB3** (74×57 mm) printed by Walsall.

SA1	(£1·92) containing 1st Class Pricing in Proportion Machin and Love stamps pane No. 2693a..	18·00

2008 (15 Jan). Gold cover with multicoloured emblem as T **MB3** (74×57 mm) printed by Walsall.

SA2	(£2·04) containing 1st Class Love and Machin stamps with Be My Valentine label pane No. 2693b..	6·50

N. Self-adhesive Barcode Booklets containing NVI barcode Machin definitive stamps

Containing 4×1st Class Barcoded Security Machin stamps

TB1

2022 (1 Feb). Deep violet cover with multicoloured emblem as T **TB1** (93×68 mm). Printed by ISP Walsall. Repeating 'ROYALMAIL' wording printed on the front of the self-adhesive backing paper.

TB1	(£3·40) Containing 4×1st class Barcoded Security Machin self-adhesive stamps (No. V4507, code 'MFIL')...........................	7·25

No. TB1 exists with the large ROYALMAIL lettering above the small and with the small above the large in the alternate pairs of lines in the background text (Type PB-Ls/sL).

Year code for No. TB1 is 'M22L'.

No. TB1 has a single small notch at the top right tab edge.

Containing 8×2nd Class Barcoded Security Machins stamps

TC1

2022 (1 Feb). Emerald cover with multicoloured emblem as T **TC1** (94×68 mm). Printed by ISP Walsall. Repeating 'ROYALMAIL' wording printed on the front of the self-adhesive backing paper.

TC1	(£5·28) Containing 8×2nd class Barcoded Security Machin self-adhesive stamps (No. V4502, code 'MEIL')...........................	10·00

No. TC1 exists with the small ROYAL MAIL lettering above the large in the alternate pairs of lines in the background text (Type PB-sL).

Year code for No. TC1 is 'M22L'.

No. TC1 has two small notches at the top right tab edge.

Containing 8×1st class Barcoded Security Machins stamps

TD1

2022 (1 Feb). Deep violet cover with multicoloured emblem as T **TD1** (93×68 mm). Printed by ISP Walsall. Repeating 'ROYALMAIL' wording printed on the front of the self-adhesive backing paper.

TD1	(£6·80) Containing 8×1st Class Barcoded Security Machin self-adhesive stamps (No. V4506, code 'MEIL')...........................	15·00

No. TD1 exists with the small ROYAL MAIL lettering above the large in the alternate pairs of lines in the background text (Type PB-sL).

Year code for No. TD1 is 'M22L'.

No. TD1 has a single small notch at the top right tab edge.

Containing 4×2nd Large Barcoded Security Machin stamps

TE1

2022 (1 Feb). Grey-green cover with multicoloured emblem as T **TE1** (93×68 mm). Printed by ISP Walsall. Repeating 'ROYALMAIL' wording printed on the front of the self-adhesive backing paper.
TE1   (£3·84) Containing 4×2nd Large Barcoded
            Security Machin self-adhesive stamps
            (No. V4512, code 'MFIL')............................ 7·75
    No. TE1 exists with the large ROYALMAIL lettering above the small and with the small above the large in the alternate pairs of lines in the background text (Type PB-Ls/sL).
    Year code for No. TE1 is 'M22L'.
    No. TE1 has two large notches at the top right tab edge.

Containing 4×1st Large Barcoded Security Machin stamps

TF1

2022 (1 Feb). Greenish blue cover with multicoloured emblem as T **TF1** (93×69 mm). Printed by ISP Walsall. Repeating 'ROYALMAIL' wording printed on the front of the self-adhesive backing paper.
TF1   (£5·16) Containing 4×1st class Large Barcoded
            Security Machin self-adhesive stamps
            (No. V4516, code 'MFIL')............................ 10·50
    No. TF1 exists with the small ROYAL MAIL lettering above the large in the alternate pairs of lines in the background text (Type PB-sL).
    Year code for No. TF1 is 'M22L'.
    No. TF1 has a single large notch at the top right tab edge.

Where a booklet is known with both Type PB-Ls and Type PB-sL the price noted is for the cheaper of the two, whichever that is.

KING CHARLES III

A. Self-adhesive Barcode Booklets containing NVI barcode definitive stamps

Containing 4 × 1st Class Barcoded Security Definitives

TB2

2023 (4 Apr). Deep violet cover with multicoloured emblem as Type **TB2** (93×68 mm). Printed by Cartor SP. Repeating 'ROYALMAIL' wording printed on the front of the self-adhesive backing paper.
TB2   (£4·40) Containing four 1st class Barcoded
            self-adhesive stamps (No. V5016, code
            'MFIL')... 7·25
    No. TB2 exists with the large ROYALMAIL lettering above the small and with the small above the large in the alternate pairs of lines in the background text (Type PB-sL).
    Year code for No. TB2 is 'M23L'.
    No. TB2 has a single small notch at the top right tab edge and 'KC' at lower right.

Containing 8 × 2nd Class Barcoded Security Definitives

TC2

2023 (4 Apr). Emerald cover with multicoloured emblem as Type **TC2** (94×68 mm). Printed by Cartor SP. Repeating 'ROYALMAIL' wording printed on the front of the self-adhesive backing paper .
TC2   (£6·00) Containing eight 2nd class Barcoded
            Security self-adhesive stamps (No.
            V5010, code 'MEIL')................................ 10·00
    No. TC2 exists with the small ROYAL MAIL lettering above the large in the alternate pairs of lines in the background text (Type PB-sL).
    Year code for No. TC2 is 'M23L'.
    No. TC2 has two small notches at the top right tab edge and 'KC' at lower right.

Containing 8 × 1st class Barcoded Security Definitives

TD2

2023 (4 Apr). Deep violet cover with multicoloured emblem as Type **TD2** (93×68 mm). Printed by ISP Walsall. Repeating 'ROYALMAIL' wording printed on the front of the self-adhesive backing paper.

TD2   (£8·80) Containing eight 1st Class Barcoded
              Security self-adhesive stamps (No.
              V5015, code 'MEIL')..................................... 15·00

    No. TD2 exists with the small ROYAL MAIL lettering above the large in the alternate pairs of lines in the background text (Type PB-sL).

    Year code for No. TD2 is 'M23L'.

    No. TD2 has a single small notch at the top right tab edge and 'KC' at lower right.

Containing 4 × 1st Large Barcoded Security Definitives

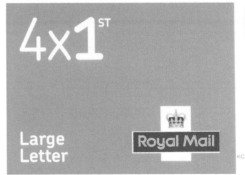

TF2

2023 (4 Apr). Greenish blue cover with multicoloured emblem as Type **TF2** (93×69 mm). Printed by Cartor SP. Repeating 'ROYALMAIL' wording printed on the front of the self-adhesive backing paper.

TF2   (£6·40) Containing 4×1st class Large Barcoded
              Security self-adhesive stamps (No.
              V4518, code 'MFIL').................................... 10·50

    No. TF2 exists with the small ROYAL MAIL lettering above the large in the alternate pairs of lines in the background text (Type PB-sL).

    Year code for No. TF2 is 'M23L'.

    No. TF2 has a single large notch at the top right tab edge and 'KC' at lower right.

> Where a booklet is known with both Type PB-Ls and Type PB-sL the price noted is for the cheaper of the two, whichever that is.

Containing 4 × 2nd Large Barcoded Security Definitives

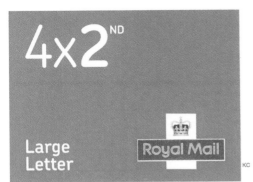

TE2

2023 (4 Apr). Grey-green cover with multicoloured emblem as Type **TE2** (93×68 mm). Printed by Cartor SP. Repeating 'ROYALMAIL' wording printed on the front of the self-adhesive backing paper.

TE2   (£4·60) Containing 4×2nd Large Barcoded
              Security self-adhesive stamps (No.
              V5017, code 'MFIL').................................... 7·75

    No. TE2 exists with the large ROYALMAIL lettering above the small and with the small above the large in the alternate pairs of lines in the background text (Type PB-sL).

    Year code for No. TE2 is 'M23L'.

    No. TE2 has two large notches at the top right tab edge and 'KC' at lower right.

Table A

6 × 1st Long to Reign Over Us retail booklets with self-adhesive Security Machins, with source code and year code.
Printed in gravure by ISP Walsall. With lilac covers as noted below.
Front of the self-adhesive backing paper plain, or with repeating 'ROYALMAIL' wording as noted.

Booklet	Stamp	Booklet description	Backing paper type	Source/year code	
MB14	U3745 1st bright lilac	Lilac cover (Type **MB14**)	Plain	'REIGS' 'O15R'	7·75
MB15	U3745 1st bright lilac	Lilac cover (Type **MB14**)	Type PB-Up Type PB-Up	'REIGS' 'O15R' 'REIGS' 'O16R'	£175 27·00

Table B

6 × 1st retail booklets with self-adhesive Security Machins, with source code (top right), with year code.
Printed in gravure by ISP Walsall. With covers as noted below.
Repeating 'ROYALMAIL' wording printed on the front of the self-adhesive backing paper.
Stamps vermilion or bright scarlet.

Booklet	Stamp	Booklet description	Backing paper type	Source/year code	
MB17	U3024 1st vermilion	Padlock cover, traditional style typeface on outside cover (sharp edges to value indicator) (Type **MB17**)	Type PB-Up	'MSIL' 'M16L'	8·00
MB18	U3028 1st bright scarlet	Padlock cover, new corporate style typeface on outside cover (rounded edges to value indicator) (Type **MB18**), as issued on 20 October 2016	Type PB-Up Type PB-Up	'MSIL' 'M16L' 'MSIL' 'M18L'	9·50 22·00
MB18a	U3028 1st bright scarlet	Cover as **MB18**	Type PB-Ls/sL Type PB-Ls/sL Type PB-Ls/sL Type PB-Ls/sL Type PB-Ls/sL Type PB-sL	'MSIL' 'M16L' 'MSIL' 'M17L' 'MSIL' 'M18L' 'MSIL' 'M19L' 'MSIL' 'M20L' 'MSIL' 'M21L'	18·00 19·00 11·00 12·00 12·00 24·00

Note. The repeating 'ROYALMAIL' wording that is printed on the front of the backing paper where alternate pairs of lines are inverted can exist in two versions, with Large lettering above small (Type PB-Ls), and with small lettering above Large (Type PB-sL). For further information see the notes to the tables listing source and year-code combinations which follow the Security Machin listing. Where a booklet is known with both Type PB-Ls and Type PB-sL the price quoted is for the cheaper of the two versions, whichever that is. Type PB-Up are noted and priced separately.

Table C

12 × 2nd retail booklets with self-adhesive Security Machins, with source code (top right), with year code.
Printed in gravure by ISP Walsall. With blue covers as noted below
Repeating 'ROYALMAIL' wording printed on the front of the self-adhesive backing paper.

Booklet	Stamp	Booklet description	Backing paper type	Source/year code	
ME6	U3013 2nd bright blue	Traditional style typeface on outside cover (sharp edges to value indicator) (Type **ME2**)	Type PB-Up Type PB-Up	'MTIL' 'M15L' 'MTIL' 'M16L'	£100 25·00
ME7	U3013 2nd bright blue	New corporate style typeface on outside cover (rounded edges to value indicator) (Type **ME7**), as issued on 20 October 2016	Type PB-Up Type PB-Up	'MTIL' 'M16L' 'MTIL' 'M18L'	18·00 40·00
ME7a	U3013 2nd bright blue	Cover as **ME7**	Type PB-sL Type PB-Ls/sL Type PB-Ls/sL Type PB-Ls/sL Type PB-Ls/sL Type PB-Ls/sL	'MTIL' 'M16L' 'MTIL' 'M17L' 'MTIL' 'M18L' 'MTIL' 'M19L' 'MTIL' 'M20L' 'MTIL' 'M21L'	40·00 23·00 18·00 18·00 18·00 18·00

Note. The repeating 'ROYALMAIL' wording that is printed on the front of the backing paper where alternate pairs of lines are inverted can exist in two versions, with Large lettering above small (Type PB-Ls), and with small lettering above Large (Type PB-sL). For further information see the notes to the tables listing source and year-code combinations which follow the Security Machin listing. Where a booklet is known with both Type PB-Ls and Type PB-sL the price quoted is for the cheaper of the two versions, whichever that is. Type PB-Up are noted and priced separately.

Table D

12 × 1st retail booklets with self-adhesive Security Machins, with source code (top right), with year code.
Printed in gravure by ISP Walsall. With red covers as noted below.
Repeating 'ROYALMAIL' wording printed on the front of the self-adhesive backing paper.
Stamps vermilion or bright scarlet.

Booklet	Stamp	Booklet description	Backing paper type	Source/year code	
MF8	U3025 1st vermilion	Traditional style typeface on outside cover (sharp edges to value indicator) (Type **MB12**)	Type PB-Up	'MTIL' 'M15L'	£100
			Type PB-Up	'MTIL' 'M16L'	22·00
MF9	U3029 1st bright scarlet	New corporate style typeface on outside cover (rounded edges to value indicator) (Type **ME7**), as issued on 20 October 2016	Type PB-Up	'MTIL' 'M16L'	19·00
MF9a	U3029 1st bright scarlet	Cover as **MF9**	Type PB-Ls/sL	'MTIL' 'M16L'	£110
			Type PB-Ls/sL	'MTIL' 'M17L'	20·00
			Type PB-Ls/sL	'MTIL' 'M18L'	19·00
			Type PB-Ls/sL	'MTIL' 'M19L'	19·00
			Type PB-Ls/sL	'MTIL' 'M20L'	19·00
			Type PB-sL	'MTIL' 'M21L'	19·00

Note. The repeating 'ROYALMAIL' wording that is printed on the front of the backing paper where alternate pairs of lines are inverted can exist in two versions, with Large lettering above small (Type PB-Ls), and with small lettering above Large (Type PB-sL). For further information see the notes to the tables listing source and year-code combinations which follow the Security Machin listing. Where a booklet is known with both Type PB-Ls and Type PB-sL the price quoted is for the cheaper of the two versions, whichever that is. Type PB-Up are noted and priced separately.

Table E

4 x 2nd Large retail booklets with self-adhesive Security Machins, with source code (in front of hair), with year code.
Printed in gravure by ISP Walsall. With blue covers as noted below.
Repeating 'ROYALMAIL' wording printed on the front of the self-adhesive backing paper.

Booklet	Stamp	Booklet description	Backing paper type	Source/year code	
RA3	U3032 2nd bright blue	Traditional style typeface on outside cover (sharp edges to value indicator) (Type **RA1**)	Type PB-Up	'MFIL' 'M16L'	22·00
RA4	U3032 2nd bright blue	New corporate style typeface on outside cover (rounded edges to value indicator) (Type **RA4**), as issued on 20 October 2016	Type PB-Up	'MFIL' 'M16L'	12·00
RA4a	U3032 2nd bright blue	Cover as **RA4**	Type PB-Ls	'MFIL' 'M17L'	30·00
			Type PB-Ls/sL	'MFIL' 'M18L'	27·00
			Type PB-Ls/sL	'MFIL' 'M19L'	11·00
			Type PB-sL	'MFIL' 'M20L'	11·00
			Type PB-sL	'MFIL' 'M21L'	11·00

Note. The repeating 'ROYALMAIL' wording that is printed on the front of the backing paper where alternate pairs of lines are inverted can exist in two versions, with Large lettering above small (Type PB-Ls), and with small lettering above Large (Type PB-sL). For further information see the notes to the tables listing source and year-code combinations which follow the Security Machin listing. Where a booklet is known with both Type PB-Ls and Type PB-sL the price quoted is for the cheaper of the two versions, whichever that is. Type PB-Up are noted and priced separately.

Table F

4 x 1st Large retail booklets with self-adhesive Security Machins, with source code (in front of hair), with year code.
Printed in gravure by ISP Walsall. With red covers as noted below.
Repeating 'ROYALMAIL' wording printed on the front of the self-adhesive backing paper.
Stamps vermilion or bright scarlet.

Booklet	Stamp	Booklet description	Backing paper type	Source/year code	
RB5	U3037 1st vermilion	Traditional style typeface on outside cover (sharp edges to value indicator) (Type **RB4**)	Type PB-Up	'MFIL' 'MA15'	25·00
			Type PB-Up	'MFIL' 'M16L'	15·00
RB6	U3039 1st bright scarlet	New corporate style typeface on outside cover (rounded edges to value indicator) (Type **RB6**), as issued on 20 October 2016	Type PB-Up	'MFIL' 'M16L'	35·00
RB6a	U3039 1st bright scarlet	Cover as **RB6**	Type PB-Ls/sL	'MFIL' 'M17L'	18·00
			Type PB-Ls/sL	'MFIL' 'M18L'	11·00
			Type PB-Ls	'MFIL' 'M19L'	11·00
			Type PB-sL	'MFIL' 'M20L'	11·00
			Type PB-sL	'MFIL' 'M21L'	11·00

Note. The repeating 'ROYALMAIL' wording that is printed on the front of the backing paper where alternate pairs of lines are inverted can exist in two versions, with Large lettering above small (Type PB-Ls), and with small lettering above Large (Type PB-sL). For further information see the notes to the tables listing source and year-code combinations which follow the Security Machin listing. Where a booklet is known with both Type PB-Ls and Type PB-sL the price quoted is for the cheaper of the two versions, whichever that is. Type PB-Up are noted and priced separately.

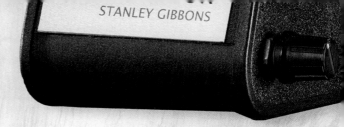

Detectamark Spectrum Watermark Detector

The Stanley Gibbons Detectamark Spectrum makes it easy to discover those hidden rarities. It's simple to use and the versatile colour settings and adjustable light source provide additional help when identifying the more difficult watermarks.

R2570 £164

KEY FEATURES

- Easy to discover hidden rarities
- Unique multiple colour settings
- It's able to detect watermarks on modern stamps printed on thick, chalk surfaced papers with full gum, which other detectors fail to identify
- No chemicals or solvents are used making this a safe, clean and highly effective
- Lightweight and battery operated

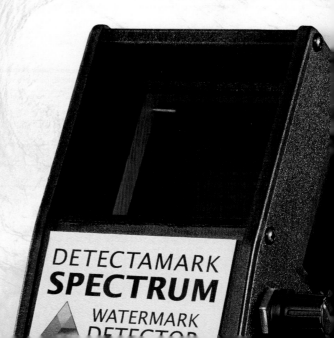

POST OFFICE LABEL SHEETS

At the Stamp Show 2000 International Stamp exhibition visitors could purchase sheets of 10×1st class stamps in the Smiles designs (as Nos. 1550/15559), each stamp having a *se-tenant* label on which the exhibition visitor's picture was printed, the photographs being taken in a booth at the exhibition.

For those unable to visit the exhibition, the same sheet could be purchased from the Philatelic Bureau and from Post Office philatelic outlets with a Stamp Show 2000 label in place of the photograph.

For Christmas 2000, sheets of 20×19p. stamps in the Robin in Pillar Box design (as No. 1896) or 10×1st class Father Christmas with Cracker design (as No. 2007) were available through the Philatelic Bureau, with se-tenant labels as part of a customised service, purchasers supplying their own photographs for reproduction on the se-tenant label.

This service continued under the name Smilers, after the initial set of stamp designs employed, and was also made available at selected post offices. Corporate label panes, allowing commercial and charitable organisations to have their logo or message reproduced on the se-tenant labels were made available through the Bureau from 2000.

From 26 July 2018 it was announced that the Smilers service would be put on hold for an indefinite period.

Label sheets have continued to be offered with a standard greeting or message. These Generic Smilers have been available from the Philatelic Bureau or from philatelic outlets.

In 2015 a new style of sheet was released, entitled, Star Wars Heroes and Villains, comprising ten stamps and labels, this style has since become known as Collectors Sheets and are included in this listing.

As personalised, corporate and generic label sheets could only be purchased at a premium over the face value of the stamps within them, they are not given full listing in this catalogue; neither are individual stamps (with or without their se-tenant label), some of which are identifiable as having come from Label Sheets, due to perforation, phosphor or printing differences.

The list which follows comprises the generic sheets only. Differences between the stamp in the Label Sheets and those of the standard issues are given under the respective listings in this catalogue.

An asterisk (*) in the listing indicates a difference in process, phosphor or perforation from the original design.

Smilers

LS1

2000 (22 May). The Stamp Show 2000. T **LS1**. Gravure Questa. Original selling price £2·95. Perf 15×14.

LS1   10×(1st) Smiles stamps, as Nos. 1550/1559 and attached labels.............. 22·00

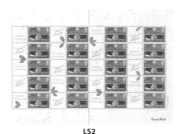

LS2

LS3

2000 (3 Oct)–**01**. Christmas. Types **LS2** and **LS3**. Gravure Questa. Original selling price £3·99 (Nos. LS2/LS2a) and £2·95 (Nos. LS3/LS3a). Perf 15×14.

LS2   20×19p. Robin in Pillar Box stamps, as No. 1896 and attached labels (Imprint Post Office 2000)........................ £125
     a. Imprint Consignia 2001 (9.10.01)............ £600

LS3   10×(1st) Father Christmas with Cracker stamps, as No. 2007 and attached labels (Imprint Post Office 2000)............. £125
     a. Imprint Consignia 2001 (9.10.01)............ £600

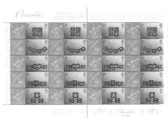

LS4

2001 (5 June). Occasions. T **LS4**. Litho* Questa. Original selling price £5·95. Perf 14×14½.

LS4   20×(1st) Occasions stamps as Nos. 2182/2186 in four vertical columns of five with attached labels......................... £120

2001 (3 July). Smiles As T **LS1** but with greetings shown in attached labels. Litho* Questa. Original selling price £2·95. Perf 14½×14*.

LS5   10×(1st) Smiles stamps, as Nos. 1550/1559 and attached labels............... £160

LS6

2001 (18 Dec). Greetings Cartoons T **LS6**. Litho Questa. Original selling price £2·95. Two phosphor bands. Perf 14½×14 (without* elliptical holes).

LS6   10×(1st) Greetings Cartoons, as Nos. 1905p/1914p and attached labels......... 28·00

LS7

2002 (23 Apr). Occasions Stamps. T **LS7**. Litho Questa. Original selling price £5·95. Perf 14*.

LS7   20×(1st) Occasions stamps as Nos. 2260/2264 in four vertical columns of five with attached labels......................... 60·00

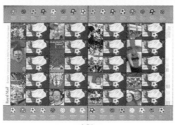

LS8

2002 (21 May). Football World Cup. T **LS8**. Litho* Questa. Original selling price £5·95. Perf 14½×14.
LS8   20×(1st) as bottom right quarter of flag stamp in No. **MS**2292 and attached labels.. 27·00

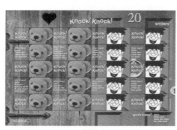

LS9

2002 (1 Oct). Smiles T **LS9**. Litho* Questa. Original selling price £5·95. Perf 15×14.
LS9   10×(1st) Teddy Bear and 10×(1st) Dennis the Menace, as Nos. 1550/1551, each with attached labels... 28·00

LS10

2002 (1 Oct). Christmas. T **LS10**. Litho* Questa. Original selling price £5·95. Perf 14½×14*.
LS10   20×(1st) Father Christmas with Cracker, as No. 2007, with attached greetings labels.. 27·00

LS11

2003 (21 Jan). Flower Paintings. T **LS11**. Litho Questa. Original selling price £5·95. Perf 14½×14 (without* elliptical holes).
LS11   20×(1st) Flowers Greetings Stamps, as Nos. 1955/1964 (two of each design) with floral labels attached....................... 27·00

LS12

2003 (4 Feb). Occasions. T **LS12**. Litho Questa. Original selling price £5·95. Perf 14½×14.
LS12   20×(1st) Tick box Occasions stamps, as Nos. 2337/2342 (four of Nos. 2338 and 2340 and 3 each of the others) with attached labels.. 27·00
          a. Multiple Choice in green..........................
Multiple Choice at top left of sheet is generally in red.
No. LS12a is believed to have come from trial sheets which were put on sale in error.

LS13

2003 (29 July). Crossword Cartoons. T **LS13**. Litho Questa. Original selling price £6·15. Two phosphor bands. Perf 14½×14 (without* elliptical holes).
LS13   20×(1st) Cartoons as Nos. 1905p/1914p with Crossword labels attached.. 27·00

LS14

2003 (30 Sept). Christmas. Winter Robins. T **LS14**. Litho* De La Rue. Original selling price £6·15. Self-adhesive. Perf 14½.
LS14   20×(1st) Winter Robins, as No. 2239 with labels alongside................................ 27·00

LS15

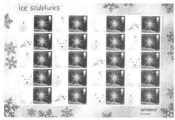

LS16

2003 (4 Nov). Christmas. Types **LS15** and **LS16**. Litho* De La Rue. Original
selling prices £4·20 (2nd) and £6·15 (1st). Self-adhesive. Perf 14½×14.
LS15   20×(2nd) Ice Sculptures as No. 2410
             with labels showing ice sculptures of
             polar fauna alongside.............................. 20·00
LS16   20×(1st) Ice Sculptures as No. 2411
             with labels showing photographs of
             polar fauna alongside.............................. 27·00

LS17

2004 (30 Jan). Hong Kong Stamp Expo. T **LS17**. Litho Walsall. Original
selling price £6·15. Perf 14*.
LS17   20×(1st) Hello greetings stamps, as No.
             2262 with labels alongside...................... 27·00

LS18

2004 (3 Feb). Occasions Entertaining Envelopes T **LS18**. Litho De La Rue.
Original selling price £6·15. Perf 14½×14.
LS18   20×(1st) Entertaining Envelopes
             greetings stamps, as Nos. 2424/2428
             (four of each design) with attached
             labels.. 27·00

LS20

2004 (27 July). Rule Britannia. T **LS20**. Litho* Walsall. Original selling price
£6·15. Perf 14½.
LS20   20×(1st) Union Flag, as T **1517** with
             attached labels.. 27·00

LS21

2004 (2 Nov). Christmas. T **LS21**. Litho* De La Rue. Original selling price
£5·40. Self-adhesive. Perf 14½×14.
LS21   10×(2nd) and 10×(1st) Father
             Christmas, as Nos. 2495/2496 with
             attached labels.. 23·00

LS22

2005 (11 Jan). Farm Animals. T **LS22**. Litho* Walsall. Original selling price
£6·15. Perf 14½.
LS22   20×(1st) Farm Animals, as Nos.
             2502/2511 with attached labels.............. 27·00

LS23

2005 (15 Mar). Centenary of the Magic Circle. T **LS23**. Litho* Walsall.
Original selling price £6·15. Perf 14½×14.
LS23   20×(1st) Spinning Coin, as No. 2525
             with attached labels.................................. 27·00

LS19

2004 (25 May). Royal Horticultural Society. T **LS19**. Litho* Walsall. Original
selling price £6·15. Perf 14½.
LS19   20×(1st) Dahlia, as No. 2457 with
             attached labels.. 27·00

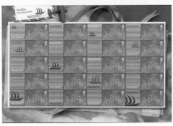

LS24

2005 (21 Apr). Pacific Explorer 2005 World Stamp Expo. T **LS24**. Litho Walsall. Original selling price £6·55. Perf 14*.
LS24 20×(1st) Hello greetings stamps, as No.
   2262 with attached labels........................ 27·00

LS25

2005 (21 June). The White Ensign. T **LS25**. Litho* Cartor. Original selling price £6·55. Perf 14½.
LS25 20×(1st) White Ensign stamps, as T
   1516 with attached labels........................ 27·00

LS26

2005 (15 Sept). Classic ITV. T **LS26**. Litho Walsall. Original selling price £6·55. Perf 14½×14.
LS26 20×(1st) *Emmerdale* stamps, as No.
   2562 with attached labels........................ 27·00
   The original printing of No. LS26 contained errors in some of the labels and was withdrawn prior to issue.

LS27

2005 (1 Nov). Christmas. Christmas Robins. T **LS27**. Litho* Cartor. Original selling price £5·60. Self-adhesive. Perf 14½.
LS27 10×(2nd) and 10×(1st) Robins, as Nos.
   2238/2239 with attached labels............. 23·00

LS28

2006 (10 Jan). A Bear called Paddington. T **LS28**. Litho Cartor. Original selling price £6·55. Self-adhesive*. Perf 14½.
LS28 20×(1st) Paddington Bear, as No. 2592
   with attached labels................................. 27·00

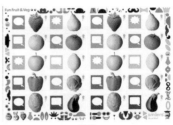

LS29

2006 (7 Mar). Fun Fruit and Veg. T **LS29**. Litho* Cartor. Original selling price £6·55. Self-adhesive. Perf 14½×14.
LS29 20×(1st) Fruit and Vegetables stamps
   as Nos. 2348/2357 with attached
   labels... 27·00

LS30

2006 (25 May). Washington 2006 International Stamp Exhibition. T **LS30**. Litho Cartor. Original selling price £6·95. Perf 14*.
LS30 20×(1st) Hello greetings stamps, as No.
   2262 with attached labels........................ 27·00

LS31

2006 (6 June). World Cup Football Championship, Germany. World Cup Winners T **LS31**. Litho Cartor. Original selling price £6·95. Perf 14½.
LS31 20×(1st) England footballer (1966)
   stamps, as No. 2628 with attached
   labels... 27·00

LS32

2006 (4 July). For Life's Special Moments. T **LS32**. Litho* Cartor. Original selling price £6·95. Self-adhesive. Perf 15×14.
LS32   20×(1st) Smilers stamps as Nos. 2567/2572 (four of Nos. 2568/2569 and three each of the others) with attached labels... 27·00

LS33

2006 (17 Oct). Extra Special Moments. T **LS33**. Litho* Cartor. Original selling price £6·95. Self-adhesive. Perf 15×14.
LS33   20×(1st) Smilers stamps as Nos. 2672/2677 (four of Nos. 2672 and 2677, three each of the others) with attached labels... 27·00

LS34

2006 (7 Nov). Christmas. T **LS34**. Litho* Cartor. Original selling price £6. Self-adhesive. Perf 15×14.
LS34   10×(2nd) and 10×(1st) Christmas as Nos. 2678/2679 with attached labels..... 23·00

LS35

2006 (9 Nov). We Will Remember Them. T **LS35**. Litho* Cartor. Original selling price £6·95. Perf 14½.
LS35   20×(1st) Poppies on barbed wire stems stamps as Type **1941** with attached labels... 27·00

LS36

2006 (14 Nov). Belgica 2006 International Stamp Exhibition, Brussels. T **LS36**. Litho Cartor. Original selling price £6·95. Perf 14*.
LS36   20×(1st) Hello greetings stamps, No. 2262 with attached labels....................... 27·00

LS37

2007 (1 Mar). Glorious Wales. T **LS37**. Litho Cartor. Original selling price £6·95. Self-adhesive*. Perf 15×14 (without* elliptical holes).
LS37   20×(1st) Wales stamps as No. W122 with attached labels................................. 27·00

LS38

2007 (23 Apr). Glorious England. T **LS38**. Litho Cartor. Original selling price £7·35. Self-adhesive*. Perf 15×14 (without* elliptical holes).
LS38   20×(1st) England stamps as No. EN30 with attached labels................................. 27·00
On labels from the original printing Isle of Wight was incorrectly spelled Isle of White. These were recalled before issue but some were released in error. (*Price* £650)

LS39

2007 (17 May). Memories of Wembley Stadium. T **LS39**. Litho* Cartor. Original selling price £7·35. Perf 14½×14.
LS39   20×(1st) stamps as No. 2291 but without WORLD CUP 2002 inscription with attached labels................................. 27·00

LS40

2007 (5 June). 40th Anniversary of the First Machin Definitives. T **LS40**. Litho Cartor. Original selling price £7·35. Phosphor frame*. Perf 14½.
LS40   20×(1st) stamps as T **1984** with
                attached labels... 27·00

LS41

2007 (17 July). Harry Potter. T **LS41**. Litho Walsall. Original selling price £7·35. Self-adhesive*. Perf 15×14.
LS41   20×(1st) stamps as within No. **MS**2757
                four of each design with attached
                labels.. 27·00

LS42

2007 (6 Nov). Christmas. T **LS42**. Litho* Cartor. Original selling price £8·30. Self-adhesive. Perf 15×14.
LS42   8×(2nd), 8×(1st) and 4×78p. Christmas
                as Nos. 2789/2790 and 2793 with
                attached labels... 23·00

LS43

2007 (8 Nov). Letters from the Front. T **LS43**. Litho Cartor. Original selling price £7·35. Perf 14½.
LS43   20×(1st) Soldiers in poppy flower
                stamps as T **2038** with attached labels.. 27·00

LS44

2007 (30 Nov). Glorious Scotland. T **LS44**. Litho Cartor. Original selling price £7·35. Self-adhesive*. Perf 15×14 (without* elliptical holes).
LS44   20×(1st) Scotland stamps as No. S131
                with attached labels.................................... 27·00

LS45

2008 (15 Jan). I wrote to say. T **LS45**. Litho* Cartor. Original selling price £7·35. Self-adhesive. Perf 15×14 (with one elliptical hole in each vert side*).
LS45   20×(1st) Smilers stamps as Nos.
                2568/2570 (eight of No. 2569, six each
                of Nos. 2568 and 2570) with attached
                circular labels.. 27·00

LS46

2008 (11 Mar). Glorious Northern Ireland. T **LS46**. Litho Cartor. Original selling price £7·35. Self-adhesive*. Perf 15×14 (without* elliptical holes).
LS46   20×(1st) Northern Ireland stamps as
                No. NI95 with attached labels................. 27·00

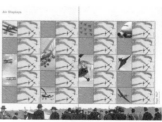

LS47

2008 (17 July). Air Displays. T **LS47**. Litho* Cartor. Original selling price £7·75. Perf 14½×14.
LS47   20×(1st) Red Arrows stamps as No.
                2855 with attached labels....................... 27·00

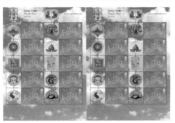

LS48

2008 (5 Aug). Beijing 2008 Olympic Expo. T **LS48**. Litho Cartor. Original selling price £7·75. Perf 14*.

LS48   20×(1st) Hello greetings stamps No. 2262 with attached labels......................   27·00

LS49

2008 (29 Sept). Glorious United Kingdom. T **LS49**. Litho Cartor. Original selling price £7·75. Self-adhesive*. Perf 15×14 (with one elliptical hole in each vertical side).

LS49   5×1st England, 5×(1st) Northern Ireland, 5×(1st) Scotland and 5×(1st) Wales stamps as Nos. EN30, NI95, S131 and W122 with attached labels..............   27·00

LS50

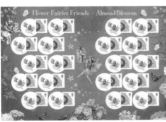

LS51

LS52

LS53

2008 (28 Oct). Smilers for Kids (1st series). Types **LS50/LS53**. Litho* Cartor. Original selling price £7·95 each. Self-adhesive. Perf 15×14 (with one elliptical hole on each vertical side).

LS50   20×(1st) New Baby stamps as No. 2672* with attached circular Peter Rabbit labels..   90·00

LS51   20×(1st) Sunflower stamps No. 2820 with attached circular Almond Blossom fairy labels...................................   90·00

LS52   20×(1st) Balloons stamps No. 2822 with attached circular Mr Men labels.....   90·00

LS53   20×(1st) Balloons stamps No. 2822 with attached circular Noddy labels.......   90·00

No. LS50 contains stamps as No. 2672 but perforated with one elliptical hole on each vertical side.

Sheets as Nos. LS50/LS53 but containing ten stamps and ten labels were sold in packs at £7·95 per pack.

LS54

2008 (4 Nov). Christmas. T **LS54**. Litho* Cartor. Original selling price £8·85. Self-adhesive. Perf 15×14 (with one elliptical hole on each vertical side).

LS54   8×(2nd), 8×(1st) and 4×81p. Christmas as Nos. 2876/2877 and 2881 with attached labels..   23·00

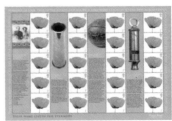

LS55

2008 (6 Nov). We Will Remember. T **LS55**. Litho Cartor. Original selling price £7·75. Perf 14½.

LS55   20×(1st) Soldier's face in poppy flower stamps as No. 2885 with attached labels..   27·00

LS56

2009 (13 Jan). Design Classics. T **LS56**. Litho Cartor. Original selling price £7·75. Perf 14×14½*.
LS56   20×(1st) Mini stamps as No. 2889 with
                 attached labels... 27·00

LS57

2009 (2 Mar). 40th Anniversary of the First Flight of Concorde. T **LS57**. Litho Cartor. Original selling price £7·75. Perf 14×14½*.
LS57   20×(1st) Concorde stamps as No. 2891.. 27·00

LS58

2009 (17 Mar). Castles of Northern Ireland. T **LS58**. Litho Cartor. Original selling price £7·75. Self-adhesive*. Perf 15×14 (with one elliptical hole in each vertical side).
LS58   20×(1st) Northern Ireland stamps as
                 No. NI95 with attached labels................. 27·00

LS59

2009 (23 Apr). Castles of England. T **LS59**. Litho Cartor. Original selling price £8·35. Self-adhesive*. Perf 15×14 (with one elliptical hole in each vertical side).
LS59   20×(1st) As St George's flag stamp
                 from No. **MS**EN50 with attached labels.   27·00

LS60

LS61

LS62

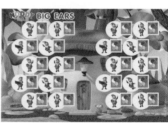

LS63

2009 (30 Apr). Smilers for Kids (2nd series). Types **LS60/LS63**. Litho* Cartor. Original selling price £8·50 each. Self-adhesive. Perf 15×14 (with one elliptical hole in each vertical side).
LS60   20×(1st) Hello stamps as No. 2819 with
                 attached circular Jeremy Fisher labels...   90·00
LS61   20×(1st) Sunflower stamps as No. 2820
                 with attached circular Wild Cherry fairy
                 labels...   90·00
LS62   20×(1st) Balloons stamps as No. 2822
                 with attached circular Little Miss
                 Sunshine labels..   90·00
LS63   20×(1st) Balloons stamps as No. 2822
                 with attached circular Big Ears labels.....   90·00
   Sheets as Nos. LS60/LS63 but containing ten stamps and ten labels were sold in packs at £7·95 per pack.

LS64

2009 (3 Aug). Thaipex 09 International Stamp Exhibition, Bangkok. T **LS64**. Litho Cartor. Original selling price £8·35. Perf 14*.
LS64   20×(1st) Hello greetings stamps as No.
                 2262 with attached labels.........................   27·00

LS65

2009 (18 Aug). Post Boxes. T **LS65**. Litho Cartor. Original selling price £8·35. Perf 14.

LS65   20×(1st) Letter box stamps as No. 2950 with attached labels.................................   27·00

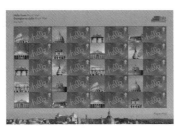

LS66

2009 (21 Oct). Italia 2009 International Stamp Exhibition, Rome. T **LS66**. Litho Cartor. Original selling price £8·35. Perf 14*.

LS66   20×(1st) Hello greetings stamps as No. 2262 with attached labels.......................   27·00

LS67

2009 (3 Nov). Christmas. T **LS67**. Litho* Cartor. Original selling price £9. Self-adhesive. Perf 14½×14 (with one elliptical hole in each vertical side).

LS67   8×(2nd), 8×(1st), 2×56p. and 2×90p. Christmas as Nos. 2991/2992, 2994 and 2996...   23·00

LS68

2009 (30 Nov). Castles of Scotland. T **LS68**. Litho* Cartor. Original selling price £8·35. Self-adhesive*. Perf 15×14 (with one elliptical hole in each vertical side).

LS68   20×(1st)As Scottish flag stamp from No. **MS**S153 with attached labels..........   27·00

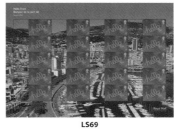

LS69

2009 (4 Dec). MonacoPhil 2009 International Stamp Exhibition, Monaco. T **LS69**. Litho Cartor. Original selling price £8·35. Perf 14*.

LS69   20×(1st) Hello greetings stamps as No. 2262 with attached labels.......................   27·00

LS70

2010 (26 Jan). For all occasions T **LS70**. Litho Cartor. Original selling price £9·70. Self-adhesive*. Perf 14½×14 (with one elliptical hole in each vertical side).

LS70   16×(1st), 2×(Europe up to 20 grams) and 2×(Worldwide up to 20 grams) stamps as within No. **MS**3024 but two of each design with attached labels.......   30·00

LS71

2010 (1 Mar). Castles of Wales. T **LS71**. Litho Cartor. Original selling price £8. Self-adhesive*. Perf 15×14 (with one elliptical hole in each vertical side).

LS71   20×(1st) As Red Dragon stamp from No. **MS**W147 with attached labels.........   27·00

LS72

2010 (8 May). London 2010 Festival of Stamps. T **LS72**. Litho* Cartor. Original selling price £8·50. Self-adhesive. Die-cut Perf 15×14 (with one elliptical hole in each vertical side).

LS72   20×(1st) Hello greetings stamps as No. 2819 with attached labels.......................   27·00

LS73

2010 (8 May). Keep Smiling Ten Years of Smilers T **LS73**. Litho Cartor. Original selling price £10. Self-adhesive*. Die-cut Perf 15×14 (with one elliptical hole in each vertical side).

LS73   3×No. 2821 (1st) Union Jack, one each of Nos. 2572 (1st) Robin in pillar box, No. 2674 (1st) THANK YOU, No. 2693 (1st) LOVE, No. 2822 (1st) Balloons; No. 2823 (1st) Fireworks and also 4×(1st) Birthday cake, 4×(1st) Birthday present, 2×(Europe up to 20 grams) and 2×(Worldwide up to 20 grams) stamps as within No. **MS**3024 with attached labels.. 50·00

LS74

2010 (15 Sept). 70th Anniversary of the Battle of Britain. T **LS74**. Litho Cartor. Original selling price £8·50. Perf 14×14½*.

LS74   20×(1st) Spitfire stamps as No. 2887 with attached labels.................................... 27·00

LS75

2010 (2 Nov). Christmas. T **LS75**. Litho* Cartor. Original selling price £9·30. Self-adhesive. Perf 14½×14 (with one elliptical hole in each vertical side).

LS75   8×(2nd), 8×(1st), 2×60p. and 2×97p. Christmas as Nos. 3128/3134.................. 23·00

LS76

2011 (12 Feb). Indipex International Stamp Exhibition, New Delhi. T **LS76**. Litho* Cartor. Original selling price £8·50. Self-adhesive. Perf 15×14 (with one elliptical hole in each vertical side).

LS76   20×(1st) Union Jack stamps as No. 2821 with attached labels........................ 27·00

LS77

2011 (28 July). Philanippon '11 World Stamp Exhibition, Yokohama. T **LS77**. Litho* Cartor. Original selling price £9·50. Self-adhesive. Die-cut perf 15×14 (with one elliptical hole in each vertical side)

LS77   20×(1st) Hello greetings stamps as No. 2819 with attached labels showing origami models.. 27·00

LS78

2011 (15 Sept). 350th Anniversary of the Postmark. T **LS78**. Litho Cartor. Original selling price £9·50. Self-adhesive*. Die-cut perf 14½×14 (with one elliptical hole in each vertical side).

LS78   20×(1st) Recreation of Crown seal stamps as within No. **MS**3024 with attached labels showing postmarks........ 27·00

LS79

2011 (8 Nov). Christmas. 400th Anniversary of the *King James Bible*. T **LS79**. Litho* Cartor. Original selling price £10·45. Self-adhesive. Die-cut perf 14½×14 (with one elliptical hole in each vertical side).

LS79   8×(2nd), 8×(1st), 2×68p. and 2×£1·10 Christmas stamps as Nos. 3242/3243 and 3246/3247 with attached labels showing verses from the *King James Bible*... 30·00

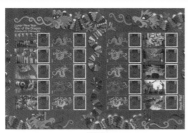

LS80

2012 (20 Jan). Lunar New Year. Year of the Dragon. T **LS80**. Litho* Cartor. Original selling price £9·50. Die-cut perf 15×14 (with one elliptical hole in each vertical side).
LS80   20×(1st) Fireworks self-adhesive greetings stamps as No. 2823 with attached labels........................... 27·00

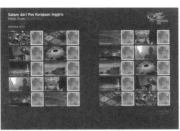

LS81

2012 (18 June). Indonesia 2012 International Stamp Exhibition, Jakarta. T **LS81**. Litho* Cartor. Original selling price £12·50. Self-adhesive. Die-cut perf 15×14 (with one elliptical hole in each vertical side).
LS81   20×(1st) Hello greetings stamps as No. 2819 with attached labels showing images of Indonesia.................................. 27·00

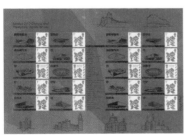

LS82

2012 (27 June). Olympic and Paralympic Games, London. Games Venues. T **LS82**. Litho* Cartor. Self-adhesive. Die-cut perf 14½×14 (with one elliptical hole in each vertical side).
LS82   8×(1st) Olympic Games, 8×(1st) Paralympic Games, 2×Worldwide up to 20 grams Olympic Games and 2×Worldwide up to 20 grams Paralympic Games as Nos. 3250/3253 with attached labels showing Games venues.. 90·00

LS83

2012 (6 Nov). Christmas. Illustrations by Axel Scheffler. T **LS83**. Litho* Cartor. Original selling price £13·10. Self-adhesive. Die-cut perf 14½×14 (with one elliptical hole in each vertical side).
LS83   8×(2nd), 8×(1st), 2×87p. and 2×£1·28 Christmas as Nos. 3415/3416, 3418 and 3420...................... 24·00

LS84

2013 (7 Feb). Lunar New Year. Year of the Snake. T **LS84**. Litho* Cartor. Original selling price £12·50. Self-adhesive. Die-cut perf 15×14 (with one elliptical hole in each vertical side).
LS84   20×(1st) Fireworks stamps as No. 2823 with attached labels showing Chinese decorations.................................. 27·00

LS85

2013 (26 Mar). 50th Anniversary of *Doctor Who* (TV programme). T **LS85**. Litho* Cartor. Original selling price £12. Self-adhesive. Die-cut perf 14½×14 (with one elliptical hole in each vertical side).
LS85   20×(1st) TARDIS stamps as No. 3449 with attached labels showing Cybermen, Daleks, Silurians, Sontarans and The Master.. 27·00

LS86

2013 (10 May). Australia 2013 World Stamp Exhibition, Melbourne. T **LS86**. Litho* Cartor. Original selling price £12·50. Self-adhesive. Die-cut perf 15×14 (with one elliptical hole in each vertical side)
LS86   20×1st Hello greetings stamps as No. 2819 with attached labels showing images of Melbourne............................... 27·00

LS87

2013 (2 Aug). Bangkok 2013 World Stamp Exhibition, Thailand. T **LS87**. Litho* Cartor. Original selling price £12·50. Self-adhesive. Die-cut perf 15×14 (with one elliptical side).

LS87   20×1st Hello greetings stamps as No. 2819 with attached labels showing images of Thailand.................................... 27·00

LS88

2013 (5 Nov). Christmas. Madonna and Child Paintings. T **LS88**. Litho* ISP Cartor. Original selling price £13·62. Self-adhesive. Die-cut perf 14½×15 (with one elliptical hole in each vertical side).

LS88   8×(2nd), 8×(1st), 2×88p. and one each of £1·28 and £1·88 Christmas as Nos. 3542/3543, 3545 and 3547/3548 with attached labels... 40·00

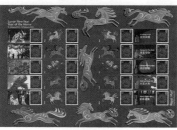

LS89

2013 (10 Dec). Lunar New Year. Year of the Horse. T **LS89**. Litho* ISP Cartor. Original selling price £12·50. Self-adhesive. Die-cut perf 15×14 (with one elliptical hole in each vertical side).

LS89   20×1st Fireworks stamps as No. 2823 with attached labels................................ 27·00

LS90

2014 (4 Nov). Christmas. Illustrations by Andrew Bannecker. T **LS90**. Litho* ISP Cartor. Original selling price £15·20. Self-adhesive. Die-cut perf 14½×15 (with one elliptical hole in each vertical side*).

LS90   8×(2nd), 8×(1st), 2×£1·28 and 2×£1·47 Christmas as Nos. 3650/3651 and 3654/3655 with attached labels............. 25·00

LS91

2014 (19 Nov). Lunar New Year. Year of the Ram. T **LS91**. Litho* ISP Cartor. Original selling price £12·90. Self-adhesive. Die-cut perf 15×14 (with one elliptical hole in each vertical side).

LS91   20×1st Fireworks stamps as No. 2823 with attached labels................................ 27·00

LS92

2014 (1 Dec). Kuala Lumpur 2014 World Stamp Exhibition, Malaysia. T **LS92**. Litho* ISP Cartor. Original selling price £12·90. Self-adhesive. Die-cut perf 15×14 (with one elliptical hole in each vertical side).

LS92   20×1st Hello greetings stamps as No. 2819 with attached labels showing images of Malaysia.................................... 27·00

LS93

2015 (20 Jan). Smilers. T **LS93**. Litho* ISP Cartor. Original selling price £12·90. Self-adhesive. Die-cut perf 14½×14 (with one elliptical hole in each vertical side*).

LS93   20×1st Smilers stamps as Nos. 3670/3677 (3×Nos. 3670, 3672/3673 and 3675, 2×Nos. 3671, 3674 and 3676/3677) with attached labels........... £190

LS94

2015 (6 May). 175th Anniversary of the Penny Black. T **LS94**. Litho* ISP Cartor. Original selling price £13·10. Self-adhesive*. Die-cut perf 14½×14 (with one elliptical hole in each vert side).

LS94   10×(1st) Penny Black and 10×(1st) Two Pence Blue (as within No. **MS**3710) with attached labels................................. 65·00

LS95

2015 (13 May). Europhilex London 2015 Exhibition. T **LS95**. Litho* ISP Cartor. Original selling price £13·10. Self-adhesive. Die-cut perf 15×14 (with one elliptical hole in each vert side).

LS95   20×(1st) Hello greetings stamps as No. 2819 with attached labels........................ 27·00

LS96

2015 (20 Oct). *Star Wars*. Heroes and Villains. T **LS96**. Litho ISP Cartor. Original selling price £6·80. Self-adhesive*. Die-cut perf 14½.

LS96   10×(1st) *Star Wars* stamps as Nos. 3758/3759, each×3, and as Nos. 3761/3762, each×2.................................. 15·00

LS97

2015 (3 Nov). Christmas. T **LS97**. Litho* ISP Cartor. Original selling price £15·96. Self-adhesive. Die-cut perf 14½×15 (with one elliptical hole in each vert side*).

LS97   8×(2nd), 8×(1st) and one each of £1, £1·33, £1·52 and £2·25 Christmas as Nos. 3771/3772 and 3775/3778 with attached labels.. 28·00

LS98

2015 (9 Nov). Lunar New Year. Year of the Monkey. T **LS98**. Litho* ISP Cartor. Original selling price £13·10. Self-adhesive. Die-cut perf 15×14 (with one elliptical hole in each vert side).

LS98   20×(1st) Fireworks greetings stamps as No. 2823 with attached labels................ 27·00

LS99

2016 (18 Feb). 175th Anniversary of the Penny Red. T **LS99**. Litho* ISP Cartor. Original selling price £13·10. Self-adhesive. Die-cut perf 14½×14 (with one elliptical hole in each vert side).

LS99   20×(1st) Penny Red stamps as No. 3806 with attached labels........................ 27·00

LS100

2016 (28 May). New York World Stamp Show. T **LS100**. Litho* ISP Cartor. Original selling price £13·30. Self-adhesive. Die-cut perf 15×14 (with one elliptical hole in each vert side).

LS100   20×(1st) Hello greetings stamps as No. 2819 with attached labels........................ 27·00

LS101

2016 (20 Oct). Mr Men and Little Miss (children's books by Roger Hargreaves). T **LS101**. Litho ISP Cartor. Original selling price £6·90. Self-adhesive*. Die-cut perf 14½.

LS101   10×(1st) Mr Men and Little Miss
                    stamps as Nos. 3891/3900......................   14·00

LS102

2016 (8 Nov). Christmas. T **LS102**. Litho ISP Cartor. Original selling price £16·21. Self-adhesive. Die-cut perf 14½×15 (with one elliptical hole in each vert side*).

LS102   8×(2nd), 8×(1st) and one each
                    of £1·05, £1·33, £1·52 and £2·25
                    Christmas as Nos. 3903/3904 and
                    3907/3910 with attached labels.............   25·00

LS103

2016 (8 Nov). Celebrating 50 Years of Christmas Stamps. T **LS103**. Litho ISP Cartor. Original selling price £12·40. Self-adhesive. Die-cut perf 14½×15 (with one elliptical hole in each vert side*).

LS103   10×(2nd) and 10×(1st) Christmas
                    stamps as Nos. 3903/3904 and
                    3907/3910 with attached labels.............   23·00

LS104

2016 (15 Nov). Lunar New Year. Year of the Rooster. T **LS104**. Litho* ISP Cartor. Original selling price £13·30. Self-adhesive. Die-cut perf 15×14 (with one elliptical hole in each vert side).

LS104   20×(1st) Fireworks greetings stamps as
                    No. 2823 with attached labels................   29·00

LS105

2017 (24 May). Finlandia 2017 European Stamp Exhibition, Tampere. T **LS105**. Litho* ISP Cartor. Original selling price £13·50. Self-adhesive. Die-cut perf 15×14 (with one elliptical hole in each vert side).

LS105   20×(1st) Hello greetings stamps as No.
                    2819 with attached labels......................   27·00

LS106

2017 (12 Oct). *Star Wars*. Droids, Aliens and Creatures. T **LS106**. Litho ISP Cartor. Original selling price £7. Self-adhesive*. Die-cut perf 14½.

LS106   10×(1st) As Nos. 4007/4010, 4011×2,
                    4012/4013 and 4014×2 with attached
                    labels showing film stills..........................   14·00
For Ultimate Collector's Sheet see No. **MS**4014*a* in main section

LS107

2017 (7 Nov). Christmas. T **LS107**. Litho* ISP Cartor. Original selling price £16·40. Self-adhesive. Die-cut perf 14½×15 (with one elliptical hole in each vert side).

LS107   8×(2nd), 8×(1st) and one each
                    of £1·17, £1·40, £1·57 and £2·27
                    Christmas stamps as Nos. 4019/4020
                    and 4023/4026 with attached labels......   32·00

LS108

2017 (7 Nov). Christmas. T **LS108**. Litho* ISP Cartor. Original selling price £12·60. Self-adhesive. Die-cut perf 14½×15 (with one elliptical hole in each vert side).

LS108   10×(2nd) and 10×(1st) Christmas
         stamps as Nos. 4028/4029 with
         attached labels........................... 23·00

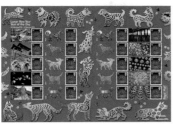

LS109

2017 (16 Nov). Lunar New Year. Year of the Dog. T **LS109**. Litho* ISP Cartor. Original selling price £13·50. Self-adhesive. Die-cut perf 15×14 (with one elliptical hole in each vert side).

LS109   20×(1st) Fireworks greetings stamps as
         No. 2823 with attached labels................. 27·00

LS110

2018 (23 Jan). *Game of Thrones*. T **LS110**. Litho ISP Cartor. Original selling price £7·50. Self-adhesive*. Die-cut perf 14×14½.

LS110   10×(1st) As Nos. 4033/4042..................... 14·00

LS111

2018 (26 June). 50th Anniversary of *Dad's Army* (BBC television sitcom 1968–1977). T **LS111**. Litho ISP Cartor. Original selling price £7·50. Self-adhesive*. Die-cut perf 14×14½*.

LS111   10×(1st) *Dad's Army* stamps as Nos.
         4101/4102, each×5.................................. 30·00

LS112

2018 (16 Oct) Harry Potter T **LS112**. Litho ISP Cartor. Original selling price £7·70. Self-adhesive*. Die-cut perf 14×14½.

LS112   10×(1st) As Nos. 4141/4150 but with
         ten labels....................................... 35·00

LS113

2018 (1 Nov). Christmas. T **LS113**. Litho* ISP Cartor. Original selling price £17·50. Self-adhesive. Die-cut perf 14½×15 (with one elliptical hole in each vert side).

LS113   8×(2nd), 8×(1st) and one each
         of £1·25, £1·45, £1·55 and £2·25
         Christmas stamps as Nos. 4154/4155
         and 4158/4161 with attached labels...... 24·00

LS114

2018 (15 Nov). Lunar New Year. Year of the Pig. T **LS114**. Litho* ISP Cartor. Original selling price £14·40. Self-adhesive. Die-cut perf 15×14 (with one elliptical hole in each vert side).

LS114   20×(1st) Fireworks greetings stamps as
         No. 2823 with attached labels................. 27·00

LS115

2019 (14 Mar). Marvel. T **LS115**. Litho* ISP Cartor. Original selling price £7·70. Self-adhesive*. Die-cut perf 14½.

LS115   10×(1st) As Nos. 4182/4191 but with ten labels.. 14·00

LS118

2019 (5 Nov). Christmas. T **LS118**. Litho* ISP Cartor. Original selling price £18·40. Self-adhesive. Die-cut perf 14½×15.

LS118   8×(2nd), 8×(1st) and one each of £1·35, £1·55, £1·60 and £2·30 Christmas stamps as Nos. 4283/4284 and 4287/4290 with attached labels...... 35·00

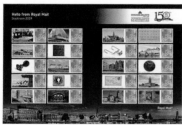

LS116

2019 (29 May). Stockholmia 2019 Exhibition. T **LS116**. Litho* ISP Cartor. Original selling price £15·10. Self-adhesive. Die-cut perf 15×14 (with one elliptical hole in each vert side).

LS116   20×(1st) Hello greetings stamps as No. 2819 with attached labels......................... 27·00

LS119

2019 (18 Nov). Lunar New Year. Year of the Rat. T **LS119**. Litho* ISP Cartor. Original selling price £15·10. Self-adhesive. Die-cut perf 15×14 (with one elliptical hole in each vert side).

LS119   20×(1st) Fireworks greetings stamps as No. 2823 with attached labels................. 27·00

LS117

2019 (10 Oct). *The Gruffalo*. T **LS117**. Litho ISP Cartor. Original selling price £11·50. Self-adhesive*. Die-cut perf 14*.

LS117   3×(1st) Owl, 3×(1st) Mouse, 2×£1·55 Snake, 2×£1·55 Fox (all as within No. **MS**4282) with attached labels................. 25·00

LS120

2019 (26 Nov). *Star Wars*. T **LS120**. Litho ISP Cartor. Original selling price £8·10. Self-adhesive*. Die-cut perf 14½.

LS120   10×(1st) As Nos. 4292/4301 with attached labels... 15·00

LS121

2020 (21 Jan). Video Games. T **LS121**. Litho ISP Cartor. Original selling price £11·40. Self-adhesive*. Die-cut perf 14×14½.
LS121   3×(1st) *Tomb Raider*, 1996, 3×(1st) *Tomb Raider*, 2013, 2×£1·55 *Adventures of Lara Croft*, 1998, 2×£1·55 *Tomb Raider Chronicles*, 2000 (all as within No. **MS**4320) with attached labels.......... 25·00

LS124

2020 (9 July). Queen Album Covers. T **LS124**. Litho ISP Cartor. Original selling price £13·15. Self-adhesive*. Die-cut perf 13 (with one elliptical hole in each vert side)*.
LS124   5×(1st) and 5×£1·63 Queen stamps as Nos. 4388/4389, 4390×2, 4391/4392, 4393×2 and 4394/4395........................... 25·00

LS122

2020 (17 Mar). James Bond. T **LS122**. Litho ISP Cartor. Original selling price £12·60. P 14.
LS122   5×(1st) and 5×£1·60 James Bond stamps Nos. 4332×3, 4333/4336 and 4337×3 with attached labels.................. 35·00

LS125

2020 (9 July). Queen Live. T **LS125**. Litho ISP Cartor. Original selling price £8·80. Self-adhesive*. Die-cut perf 14½×14 (with one elliptical hole on each vert side)
LS125   10×(1st) Queen stamp as No. 4403......... 14·00

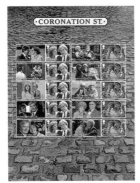

LS123

2020 (26 May). *Coronation Street*. T **LS123**. Litho ISP Cartor. Original selling price £8·80. Self-adhesive*. Perf 14×14½*.
LS123   19×(1st) As Nos. 4371/4372, each×5...... 25·00

LS126

2020 (18 Aug). *Sherlock* T **LS126**. Litho ISP Cartor. Original selling price £11·95. Self-adhesive*. Perf 14*.
LS126   6×(1st), 2×£1·68 as Nos. 4411/4416........ 55·00

LS127

LS130

2020 (3 Nov). Christmas. Stained-glass Windows. T **LS127**. Litho* ISP Cartor. Original selling price £20·60. Self-adhesive. Die-cut perf 14½×15.
LS127   8×(2nd), 8×(1st) and one each
        of £1·45, £1·70, £2·50 and £2·55
        Christmas stamps as Nos. 4434/4435
        and 4438/4441 with attached labels......   £140

2020 (8 Dec). Lunar New Year. Year of the Ox. T **LS129**. Litho* ISP Cartor. Original selling price £16·40. Self-adhesive. Die-cut perf 15×14 (with one elliptical hole in each vert side)
LS130   20×(1st) Fireworks greetings stamps as
        No. 2823 with attached labels................   27·00

LS128

LS131

2020 (3 Nov). James Bond: *No Time to Die*. T **LS128**. Litho* ISP Cartor. Original selling price £8·80. Self-adhesive. Die-cut perf 14×14½.
LS128   10×(1st) As Type **3430** with attached
        labels...   14·00

2021 (16 Feb). *Only Fools and Horses* (TV sitcom, 1981–2003). T **LS131**. Litho ISP Cartor. Original selling price £9·60. Self-adhesive*. Die-cut perf 14×14½.
LS131   10×(1st) *Only Fools and Horses* stamps
        as Types **3558/3559**, each×5..................   14·00

LS129

LS132

2020 (13 Nov). *Star Trek*. T **LS129**. Litho ISP Cartor. Original selling price £8·70. Self-adhesive*. Die-cut perf 14½.
LS129   10×(1st) Star Trek Captains stamps as
        Nos. 4443/4444×3 and 4445/4448.........   14·00

2021 (28 May). Paul McCartney. Album Covers. T **LS132**. Litho ISP Cartor. Original selling price £13. Perf 14.
LS132   6×(1st) and 4×£1·70 Paul McCartney
        stamps as Nos. 4517/4518×2 and
        4519/4524 with attached labels.............   18·00

LS133

2021 (1 July). Dennis and Gnasher. T **LS133**. Litho* ISP Cartor. Original
selling price £9·70. Self-adhesive. Die-cut perf 14½.
LS133   10×(1st) Dennis and Gnasher stamps
as Types **3614/3615**, each×5, with
attached labels showing *Beano*
characters..   14·00

LS134

2021 (22 July). Wild Coasts. T **LS134**. Litho ISP Cartor. Original selling price
£9·70. Self-adhesive*. Die-cut perf 14½
LS134   10×(1st) Wild Coasts stamps as Nos.
4542/4551 with attached labels
showing coastal wildlife...........................   14·00

LS135

2021 (17 Sept). DC Collection. Batman. T **LS135**. Litho ISP Cartor. Original
selling price £11·40. Self-adhesive*. Die-cut perf 14½
LS135   12×(1st) DC Collection stamps as Nos.
4575/4586 with attached labels..............   16·00

LS136

2021 (2 Nov). Christmas. Nativity Illustrations by Joseph Cocco. T **LS136**.
Litho* ISP Cartor. Original selling price £21·75. Self-adhesive. Die-cut
perf 14½×15 (with one elliptical hole in each vert side*).
LS136   8×(2nd), 8×(1st) and two each of
£1·70 and £2·55 Christmas stamps as
Nos. 4606, 4608 and 4611/4612 with
attached labels...   30·00

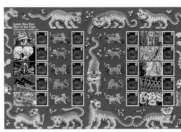

LS137

2021 (8 Dec). Lunar New Year. Year of the Tiger. T **LS137**. Litho* ISP Cartor.
Original selling price £18·20. Self-adhesive. Die-cut perf 14½×14 (with
one elliptical hole in each vert side)
LS137   20×(1st) Fireworks greetings stamps as
No. 2823 with attached labels.................   27·00

LS138

2022 (20 Jan). The Rolling Stones, Hyde Park 1969 and 2013. T **LS138**.
Litho ISP Cartor. Original selling price £11·50. Self-adhesive*. Die-
cut perf 14
LS138   4×(1st) and 4×£1.70 Rolling Stones
stamps as Nos. 4614/4621 with
attached labels showing scenes from
1969 and 2013 concerts in Hyde Park....   17·00

LS139

2022 (20 Jan). The Rolling Stones on Tour. T **LS139**. Litho ISP Cartor. Original selling price £11·50. Self-adhesive*. Die-cut perf 14

LS139   4×(1st) and 4×£1·70 Rolling Stones stamps as Nos. 4614/4621 with attached labels showing the band on tour... 17·00

LS140

2022 (19 Feb). London 2022 International Stamp Exhibition. T **LS140**. Litho* ISP Cartor. Original selling price £18·20. Self-adhesive. Die-cut perf 15×14 (with one elliptical hole in each vert side)

LS140   20×(1st) Hello greetings stamps as No. 2819 with labels depicting the 'Mail Rail' subterranean railway system used to transport London mail from 1927 to 2003.. 27·00

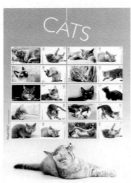

LS141

2022 (9 June). Cats. T **LS141**. Litho ISP Cartor. Original selling price £15·20. Self-adhesive*. Die-cut perf 14

LS141   2×(2nd), 4×(1st), 2×£1·85, 2×£2·55 Cats stamps as Nos. 4676/4683 with attached labels showing photographs of cats... 22·00

LS142

2022 (1 July). Pride. T **LS142**. Litho ISP Cartor. Original selling price £12·40. Self-adhesive*. Die-cut perf 14.

LS142   4×(1st), 4×£1·85 Pride stamps as Nos. 4684/4691 with attached labels showing LGBTQ flags................................ 17·50

LS143

2022 (1 Sept). Transformers. T **LS143**. Litho ISP Cartor. Original selling price £12·40. Self-adhesive*. Die-cut perf 14

LS143   4×(1st), 4×£1·85 Transformers stamps as Nos. 4700/4707 with attached labels showing Transformers................... 17·50

LS144

2022 (19 Oct). Aardman Classics. T **LS144**. Litho ISP Cartor. Original selling price £13·25. Self-adhesive*. Die cut-perf 13½×14

LS144   2×(2nd), 2×(1st), 2×£1·85, 2×£2·55 Aardman stamps as Nos. 4723/4730 with attached labels showing Aardman characters.................................. 19·00

LS145

2022 (3 Nov). Christmas. Nativity Illustrations by Katie Ponder. T **LS145**. Litho* ISP Cartor. Original selling price £23·05. Self-adhesive. Die-cut perf 14½×14*

LS145   8×(2nd), 8×(1st) and two each of £1·85 and £2·55 Christmas stamps as Nos. 4732/4733 and 4736/4737 with attached labels.. 32·00

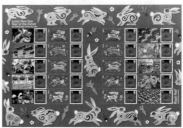

LS146

2022 (8 Dec). Lunar New Year. Year of the Rabbit. T **LS146**. Litho* ISP Cartor. Original selling price £20·20. Self-adhesive. Die-cut perf 14½×14 (with one elliptical hole in each vert side)

LS146   20×(1st) Fireworks greetings stamps as No. 2823 with attached labels.................. 28·00

LS147

2023 (12 Jan). Iron Maiden. Concerts. T **LS147**. Litho ISP Cartor. Original selling price £12·40. Self-adhesive*. Die-cut perf 14

LS147   4×(1st) and 4×£1.84 Iron Maiden stamps as Nos. 4756/4763 with attached labels showing scenes from various concerts.. 17·50

LS148

2023 (12 Jan). Iron Maiden. Eddie. T **LS148**. Litho ISP Cartor. Original selling price £12·40. Self-adhesive*. Die-cut perf 14

LS148   4×(1st) and 4×£1.84 Iron Maiden stamps as Nos. 4756/4763 with attached labels showing 'Eddie' artwork.. 17·50

LS149

2023 (16 Feb). X-Men. T **LS149**. Litho ISP Cartor. Original selling price £10·99. Self-adhesive*. Die-cut perf 14.

LS149   6×(2nd) and 6×(1st) X-Men stamps as Nos. 4765/4776 with attached labels showing X-Men... 15·00

ROYAL MAIL 'COMMEMORATIVE SHEETS'

The following Royal Mail commemorative sheets were sold at a significant premium over the face value of the stamps:

1.4.2008	100 Years of the Territorial Army. 10×1st Union Flag stamps with labels
24.7.2008	The London 1908 Olympic Games. 10×1st Union Flag stamps with labels
14.11.2008	60th Birthday of Prince Charles. 10×1st Wales self-adhesive stamps with labels
21.7.2009	40th Anniversary of Moon Landing. 10×1st Union Flag stamps with labels
18.9.2009	Big Ben 10×1st Union Flag stamps with labels
7.10.2009	800th Anniversary of the University of Cambridge. 10×1st Fireworks stamps (as T **1993**) with labels
22.10.2009	Olympic and Paralympic Games (I). The Journey Begins 10×1st as Types **2192/2201** with labels
18.5.2010	Halley's Comet 10×1st Union Flag stamps with labels
8.7.2010	Grand Prix 10×1st Union Flag stamps with labels
27.7.2010	Olympic and Paralympic Games (II). One Aim 10×1st as Types **2290/2299** with labels
10.8.2010	Tenth Anniversary of the London Eye. 10×1st Union Flag stamps with labels
28.10.2010	Remembrance. The National Memorial Arboretum. 10×1st Poppies on Barbed Wire Stem stamps (as T **2112**)
30.3.2011	50th Anniversary of the E-Type Jaguar. 10×1st Union Flag stamps with labels
10.6.2011	90th Birthday of Prince Philip. 10×1st self-adhesive Union Flag stamps with labels
27.7.2011	Olympic and Paralympic Games (III). High Hopes. 10×1st as Types **2383/2392** with labels
10.4.2012	Centenary of the Sinking of the *Titanic*. 10×1st As Crown seal stamp from No. **MS**3024 with labels
1.5.2012	50th Anniversary of the First James Bond Film. 10×1st Union Flag stamps with labels
5.10.2012	40th Anniversary of the Last Goon Show. 10×1st Union Flag stamps with labels
8.11.2012	150th Anniversary of Notts County Football Club. 10×1st Fireworks stamps with labels
16.4.2013	60th Anniversary of Launch of Royal Yacht *Britannia*. 10×1st Union Flag stamps with labels
1.5.2013	Birth Bicentenary of David Livingstone (explorer and medical missionary) 10×1st Scottish Flag stamps (as within No. **MS**S153) and labels
19.9.2013	150th Birth Anniversary of Bertram Mackennal 10×1st As Crown Seal stamps from No. **MS**3024 with labels
25.2.2014	Middlesex County Cricket Club 10×1st Fireworks stamps with labels
25.3.2014	By Sea, By Land. 350th Anniversary of the Royal Marines 10×1st Union Flag stamps with labels
16.10.2014	50th Anniversary of Donald Campbell's Water and Land Speed Records. 10×1st Union Flag with labels
11.11.2014	Christmas Truce. 10×1st Poppies on Barbed Wire Stems stamps as T **2588** with labels
18.3.2015	The Post Office Rifles during the Great War. 10×1st Union Flag stamps with labels
24.4.2015	Birth Bicentenary of Anthony Trollope. 10×1st Union Flag stamps with labels
20.8.2015	The Gurkhas Celebrating 200 Years of Service 1815–2015. 10×1st Union Flag stamps with labels
17.9.2015	Animals of the First World War 1914–1918. 10×1st Union Flag stamps with labels
12.1.2016	The Duke of Edinburgh's Award Diamond Anniversary 10×1st Union Flag stamps with labels
25.4.2016	ANZAC. 10×1st Poppies on Barbed Wire Stems stamps as T **2588** with labels
14.10.2016	950th Anniversary of the Battle of Hastings. 10×1st England Flag stamps as T **EN6** with labels
13.6.2017	HRH The Princess Royal 30th Anniversary. 10×1st Union Flag stamps with labels
30.6.2017	Canada Celebrating 150 Years. 10×1st Fireworks stamps with labels
13.9.2017	Opening of The Postal Museum. 10×1st (4×Penny Black as T **2848**, 3×Two Pence Blue as T **2938**, 3×Penny Red as T **2937**) all with labels
1.6.2018	150th Anniversary of the Trades Union Congress. 10×1st Royalty Seal stamps with labels
10.10.2018	United for Wildlife. 10×1st Royalty seal stamps with labels

This index gives an easy reference to the inscriptions and designs of the Special Stamps 1953 to April 2021. Where a complete set shares an inscription or type of design, then only the catalogue number of the first stamp is given in addition to separate entries for stamps depicting popular thematic subjects. Paintings, inventions, etc., are indexed under the name of the artist or inventor, where this is shown on the stamp.

1. £.s.d. ISSUES 1953–70

Miniature Sheet Design Index

Stanley Gibbons receives, on a regular basis, enquiries concerning the allocation of SG Numbers to some of individual stamps included in Miniature Sheets. Stamps which are available from more than one source, usually from counter sheets in addition to the Miniature sheet, are allocated numbers.

From this flow of enquiries a decision was made, as part of the review of the design index, to include a new section identifying all the Miniature Sheets issued for GB. These are listed numerically by SG Number, alphabetically by title of sheet and finally (alphabetically) by the individual stamps printed within the MS.

Numerically by SG Number

**Alphabetically by the individual stamps
printed within the MS.**

We may have a new look, but at the heart of everything we do, it's still all about stamps.

Our dedicated shop team are here to help with all philatelic enquiries, from fulfilling everyday lists and new GB issues to recommending the best albums and stamp accessories to suit your collection.

Call on +44 (0)20 7557 4436 or email them at shop@stanleygibbons.com

STANLEY GIBBONS
THE HOME OF STAMP COLLECT

Subscribe & Save Money

on the cover price*

The Stanley Gibbons Auction House has been operating philatelic auctions since 1901.

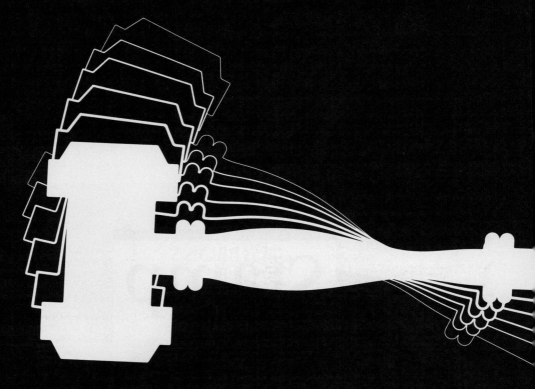

STANLEY GIBBONS
AUCTIONS

The Stanley Gibbons Auction House has been operating philatelic auctions since 1901. Following the refurbishment of our auction room, and the continuing increase of instructions from third parties, we are looking for national and international agents who may be interested in working with our recognised and trusted brand as we continue to expand our global reach.

We offer uncapped commission, and our unrivalled team of in-house experts ensure maximum realisation from our lots.

If you would be interested in working with us please email our Head of Auctions, Tom Hazell at thazell@stanleygibbons.com

 @StanleyGibbons   /StanleyGibbonsGroup    @StanleyGibbons

Stanley Gibbons
Stamp Catalogues

STAMPS OF THE WORLD
Volume 4 | *Jersey – New Republic*

2023 Edition
Simplified Stamp Catalogue

COMMONWEALTH & BRITISH EMPIRE STAMPS 1840-1970

2023 Edition
Stamp Catalogue

We have catalogues to suit every aspect of stamp collecting

Our catalogues cover stamps issued from across the globe - from the Penny Black to the latest issues. Whether you're a specialist in a certain reign or a thematic collector, we should have something to suit your needs. All catalogues include the famous SG numbering system, making it as easy as possible to find the stamp you're looking for.

Commonwealth & British Empire Stamps 1840–1970 (125th edition, 2023)

King George VI (9th edition, 2018)

Commonwealth Country Catalogues

Australia with Australian States & Dependencies (12th edition, 2022)

Bangladesh, Pakistan & Sri Lanka (3rd edition, 2015)

Brunei, Malaysia & Singapore (5th edition, 2017)

Canada (7th edition, 2020)

Cyprus, Gibraltar & Malta (5th edition, 2019)

East Africa with Egypt & Sudan (4th edition, 2018)

Eastern Pacific (3rd edition, 2015)

Falkland Islands (8th edition, 2019)

Hong Kong (6th edition, 2018)

India (including Convention & Feudatory States) (6th edition, 2023)

Indian Ocean (4th edition, 2022)

Ireland (7th edition, 2019)

Leeward Islands (3rd edition, 2017)

New Zealand & Dependencies (7th edition, 2022)

Northern Caribbean, Bahamas & Bermuda (4th edition, 2016)

St Helena & Dependencies (6th edition, 2017)

West Africa (2nd edition, 2012)

Western Pacific (4th edition, 2017)

Windward Islands & Barbados (3rd edition, 2015)

Stamps of the World 2023

Volume 1	Abu Dhabi – Charkhari
Volume 2	Chile – Georgia
Volume 3	German Commands – Jasdan
Volume 4	Jersey – New Republic
Volume 5	New South Wales – Singapore
Volume 6	Sirmoor – Zululand

Great Britain Catalogues

2023 Collect British Stamps (74th edition, 2023)

2022 Channel Islands & Isle of Man (31st edition, 2022)

2022 GB Concise (37th edition, 2022)

Great Britain Specialised

Volume 1	Queen Victoria, Part 1 Line-engraved and Embossed Issues (1st edition, 2020)
Volume 2	King Edward VII to King George VI (14th edition, 2015)
Volume 3	Queen Elizabeth II Pre-decimal issues (13th edition, 2019)
Volume 4	Queen Elizabeth II Decimal Definitive Issues – Part 1 (10th edition, 2008)
	Queen Elizabeth II Decimal Definitive Issues – Part 2 (10th edition, 2010)

Foreign Countries

Arabia (1st edition, 2016)

Austria and Hungary (8th edition 2014)

Belgium & Luxembourg (1st edition, 2015)

China (12th edition, 2018)

Czech Republic and Slovakia (1st edition, 2017)

Denmark and Norway (1st edition, 2018)

Finland and Sweden (1st edition, 2017)

France, Andorra and Monaco (1st edition, 2015)

French Colonies (1st edition, 2016)

Germany (13th edition, 2019)

Italy and Colonies (1st edition, 2022)

Middle East (1st edition, 2018)

Netherlands & Colonies (1st edition, 2017)

North East Africa (2nd edition, 2017)

Poland (2nd edition, 2023)

Portugal and Colonies (1st edition, 2022)

Southern Balkans (1st edition, 2019)

Spain and Colonies (1st edition, 2019)

Switzerland (1st edition, 2019)

United States of America (8th edition, 2015)

STANLEY GIBBONS
THE HOME OF STAMP COLLECTING

BY APPOINTMENT TO
HER MAJESTY THE QUEEN
PHILATELISTS
STANLEY GIBBONS LTD
LONDON

STANLEY GIBBONS | 399 Strand | London | WC2R 0LX
www.stanleygibbons.com

 @StanleyGibbons   /StanleyGibbonsGroup   @StanleyGibbons

Are You **THINKING** of **SELLING?**

This is How The Stamp Trade Works

Philatelic Expert Lets You into his *Selling Secrets* so you can benefit from a *totally different* (and New) Selling Experience

1 **If You want to learn** how the stamp trade works, please read on… When I was 15, I did. I wondered if there was some secret source of supply? So, I bought my 1st stamp mixture, (wholesale I thought), broke it into 50 smaller units, advertised it in Stamp Magazine 'Classifieds', and waited for the orders to

ANDREW PROMOTING PHILATELY ON THE ALAN TITCHMARSH SHOW ITV

About The Author ▶ Andrew found his Father's stamps at the age of 10. A year later at Senior School he immediately joined the School Stamp Club. He 'specialised'(!) in British, but soon was interested in Queen Victoria which he could not afford. The 2nd to last boy wearing short trousers in his school year, he religiously bought Post Office New Issues on Tuesdays with his pocket money. He soon found that he enjoyed swapping / trading stamps as much as collecting them. Aged 19, eschewing University he quickly found a philatelic career in London, leading to creating his own companies in stamps. Andrew has authored many internationally published Stamp 'Tips' articles, appearing on Local Radio and National TV promoting Philately with Alan Titchmarsh. Andrew's area of expertise is unusual – in so far as his grounding in collecting and wide philatelic knowledge has given him a deep understanding of Philately. He has studied Philately for the past 51 years, in combination with Commerce and Marketing Expertise, enabling him to create synergies in 'lifetime' interlinked Stamp Selling Systems, selling unit-priced stamps through to handling collections & Rarities up to £700,000 each. Today Andrew is fortunate to be co-owner with his Wife, of Universal Philatelic Auctions (aka UPA) – the Largest No Buyer's Premium Reducing-Estimate System Stamp Auction in the World, creating records selling stamps to 2,261 different bidders from 54 different countries 'in his international auctions. Andrew stopped collecting stamps aged 18 reasoning that his enjoyment of stamps would be in handling them and selling them… He loves working in stamps and looks forward to each philatelic day

REQUEST MY 'TOP TIPS OF THE TRADE' FREE BOOKLET

roll in… I'm still waiting, 51 years later !...

Wrong Offer ✗   *Wrong Price* ✗   *Wrong Place* ✗
(naïve seller) ✔ = 😟 *me but I was only 15 at the time!*

2 **Three years later,** attending my first public stamp auctions I wondered how some bidders seemed to buy everything, paying the highest price? It didn't occur to me that they were probably Auction Bidding Agents, paid by absent (dealer) bidders to represent them. I wondered why two collectors sitting side by side muttered to each other **"he's a dealer"** as if that justified him paying the highest price…

…but did it really? What was the real reason? How could a Dealer pay a higher price than a Collector? It doesn't make sense, does it? Collectors are customers. Customers usually pay the highest price, unless… for a Collector, this was…

Wrong Presentation ✗   *Wrong Place* ✗
therefore Wrong Price ✗

3 **Fast-forward 48 years later** to a British Empire collection, lot #1 in an International Stamp Auction – Estimated at £3,000, but we were the highest bidder at £21,000 – **YES** – some 7×higher. Including Buyer's Premium in the extraordinary sum of £4,788 we actually paid GBP£25,788= upon a £3,000 estimate… **however,** we broke it down into sets, singles, mini-collections etc. We made a profit. Some might say it found its price. Others may say:

Wrong Estimate ✗ *Wrong Presentation* ✗
Wrong Structure ✗ *Wrong Protection of Price* ✗

– *Lucky for the seller that 2 well-heeled bidders saw the potential value that day* or it could have been given away… the seller could easily have lost out couldn't he? or she?

So, by un-peeling the layers of obfuscation, hopefully we can all agree:
The Secret is Simple –
it's **ALL ABOUT : TIMING**

Plus the 3 Philatelic 'P's –
<u>Presentation</u>✔ Place ✔ and Price ✔

4 **Understanding the problem…** I always remember the car trade had their own little 'bible' – *Glass's Guide*. I've no idea, I've not even looked – in this internet-dominated world, it may even have disappeared. Well, there was an insider Stamp Trade publication for Stamp Dealers called *"The Stamp Wholesaler"*. There was nothing that special about it – and you would not have learnt much or found massively reduced prices by subscribing then – **BUT** – it was a forum, a paper focal point, a last 'bastion' in this on-line transparent world that we inhabit… whereby dealers (and auctioneers) can try and communicate with each other. I published my own articles there…

More recently in print, I discussed the outcome of my 10 years' simple research, asking dealers and auctioneers 'what is your biggest problem?'

To a man, (why are we almost all men), they replied – **"my biggest problem is stock, if I can get more of the right stock I can sell it easily"**

Strange that, nobody ever asked me the same question back – because my answer would have been entirely different (and I don't treat it as a problem) – **I seek to satisfy more collector clients than any other stamp auction**

This is the reason why my company has such massive advertising. This is the reason why we spend up to 8% of turnover – up to £200,000 per annum in marketing costs. (Most dealers don't even sell £200K per annum).

5 **Why is that?** Because, as the world revolved **the Stamp Market**, imperceptibly **Changed**, and incrementally –**Massively**

So, although few will tell you this,

it's clearly evident that the problem for most Sellers of Stamps today is no longer absent stock – but **absent collectors in the place they choose to sell their stamps in.** Simply put, other Dealers, Auctions, Stamp Fairs have not invested in marketing to have a strong Customer-core. To be fair, this is not true of all – but it is true of most – so that a former competitor had 800 bidders in a recent auction. In my most recent 18,933 lots UPA 80th Auction we had 1,893 different bidders from 51 different countries, 95% of whom were Collectors. Some other well-advertised auctions only have 200 bidders (a high percentage of whom are dealers – so that, essentially they are Dealer-dominated auctions) – so that when you sell through them – you're paying up to 18% (including VAT) seller's commission and the buyer is paying up to 25% **and** more in Buyer's Premium, credit card fees, on-line bidding fee, delivery and insurance etc… **AND all of that so that your stamps may be sold, wait for it – TO DEALERS (and some collectors),** but Dealers, that naturally must make a profit to survive…

6 Now, let's examine the cost implications – Example: Your stamp collection sells in public auction for £800. Upon a 25% buyer's premium, the dealer pays £1,000 and it could be more. He breaks it into £2,000+ selling price (much lower and he'll go out of business). The auction charges you a seller's commission of up to 18% (VAT included) upon the £800 sale price. This is GBP£144. Therefore you receive approaching £656 – which is approximately 33% of the dealer's £2,000+/- retail selling price - **BUT… now that we have identified the problem…**

Isn't the Solution Staring us Right in The Face ?

7 Why Pay an Auction to Sell to Dealers: **Sell to Collectors instead?** In our example with buyer's premium, sellers commission, lotting fees, extra credit card charges, VAT and even insurance - you're already being charged in different ways up to 40% of the selling price to sell, possibly or probably, **to the wrong person.**

Why not direct that 40% cost you're paying to sell to Collectors instead? Sounds good, so why hasn't this been done before ?

WE CAN SAFELY COLLECT YOUR STAMPS NOW

Contact UPA: 01451 861 111

8 Truth is, it Has been done before…Sometimes the 'old' ways are the best ways aren't they? But in today's enthusiasm to obscure the obvious so that money may be taken, almost surreptitiously, in numerous different ways, (without us apparently noticing until we see the cheque in our pocket) – the transparent 'seller pays' has been deliberately 'obscured' – so much so that, **amazingly,** the latest 2017 European Auction Selling Legislation just introduced – now requires auctions that charge 'buyer's premiums' **to warn the buyer in advance.** Just imagine going into the petrol station, and being warned that the price you're paying to put fuel in you tank is not the real price, you have

to pay a premium! Obviously, there would be an uproar…

9 How can you cut out the middleman and sell to Collectors instead? Well, I can think of two ways. 1). **DIY** - Do It Yourself selling on eBay. That may be fine for lower grade material – but, would you risk auctioning relatively unprotected rare material on eBay ? We don't and we're professionals, so we should know what we're doing. Or 2). Cut out the extra middle-man. **Use my company UPA, which reaches collectors instead.** Here's how it works: Continuing from our previous **Example**:

The auction sold your stamps to a dealer for £1,000 – but You received circa £656

UPA sells them to collectors for you for up to £2,000 – even after 40% commission you receive up to £1,200. Up to £544 more. Now that's amazing, isn't it?

10 Sounds Good Andrew, but Can You 'Deliver'? Obviously, nothing is as simple as that, and as we auction stamps to collectors some collections may 'break' to the example £2,000+/- but the stamps may be sold for more or less – especially as we reserve all lots at 20% below, (Estimate £2,000 = £1,600 reserve) and not everything sells first or even 2nd time so prices may come down… Naturally, it's not that straightforward for a dealer either – he may sell at a discount to 'move' stock **OR**, like many dealers he may be sitting on the same unsold stamps, that you see time and time again, in dealer's stocks years later and still at the same unattractive prices… So, I think it is more reasonable for you to expect up to 36% to 50% more, indirectly or directly via my **Collector's Secret Weapon:** Universal Philatelic Auctions, which moves material more quickly, by incrementally reducing estimate (and reserve) price in a structured selling system…

Request Your Next FREE Catalogue NOW

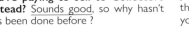

11 Q.) What is the Collector's 'Secret Weapon'?

A.) It's called the Unique UPA Reducing Estimate System... ★★★

This is a rather long explanation, I don't want to bore you, but 20 years ago, when my wife and I set up Universal Philatelic Auctions I detected that the stamp trade's biggest problem then was not what sold – *but what didn't sell*... So, because I didn't want to try to keep on offering the same either unsaleable or overpriced stock I created the unique UPA Reducing Estimate (and reserve) Selling System. Simply put, if a lot doesn't sell in the 1st auction we reduce the estimate (and reserve) by 11% and unlike other dealers and auctions **WE TELL YOU – 'US'** = once unsold. If unsold after the following auction we **reduce by a further 12%** and **WE TELL YOU 'US2'**, if unsold after a 3rd UPA auction we reduce by a further 13% and **WE TELL YOU 'US3'** and so on till the lot finds its price, is sold or virtually given away... ✔

12 Any Scientist will tell you that combinations of ingredients can produce powerful results. So we created the unique combination of my UPA Reducing Estimate System, married (in stone), with UPA's fair 'NO BUYER'S Premium' policy, PLUS each lot carries my total 'no quibble' guarantee – this formula is the reason why within the span of 4 auctions (one year)… 90%-95% of lots broken from a collection have sold. This Unique Philatelic Selling System **Formula** is the reason why we are the largest stamp auction in the UK today with more than 2,250 different regular bidders. 🧠

In Hindsight Dealers warned me 20 years ago that my idea wouldn't work. 20 years later I think I've proven that it does. (Reader: Please Request a complimentary UPA catalogue – using the contact details further below)

13 OK, Cut to the Chase Andrew, what's the offer? All of my Selling Systems are based upon **selling to Collectors Globally**, so that 95% of stamps sold by UPA are sold directly to Collectors. If you wish to benefit by up to 50% or more, depending upon your

circumstance and type of material, by cutting out the middleman – then this offer may be for you. Generally 'time' is the enemy in our lives, and for most dealers not being able to sell stock. Now is the time to let 'time' do the 'heavy-lifting' and consider making 'time' work for you, so that at UPA you can make time your friend. 👍

14 AND the SMALL PRINT? Some lots are too small in value for us to offer this system. Other lots may not be suited to selling in this manner (e.g. surplus mint British decimal stamps best used for postage) – especially if the market is heavily compromised by stock overhang in specific areas. Some Collectors will not wish to use time and systems to leverage price, others will want to agree a specific price and know that they are paid precisely this amount. No client is treated like a number and no client is forced like a square peg into a round hole. ☀

15 OK, What Do I Do Next?

a). You contact UPA to discuss with Andrew or a highly-qualified Auction Valuer/Describer what you have to dispose of and your options bearing in mind your specific interests / requirements

b). If you wish, get a 2nd opinion, but investigate what type of auction / dealer you are dealing with. Is it a Dealer's auction with relatively few collectors? Can you see where / how the Dealer sells? If you can't easily see any pricelists or high quality selling catalogues – that Dealer may sell your stamps to other dealers…

c). **Finally** you ask U P A to collect your stamps, insure in transit for an estimated replacement retail value… ☎ 🖥🚚

16 What Happens then? A member of my Team telephones/ e-mails you to confirm safe receipt. 'Overnight' valuations, unless simple, are rare. Valuing stamp collections that have taken tens of years to create takes time. Depending upon your priorities / timescale I, or an experienced member of my Team will contact you to discuss your requirements and the options available to you for the sale of your collection. Provided only that you feel well-informed and comfortable do we agree strategy 🖩 🤝

17 How Strong is the Stamp and Cover Market? Everybody knows that the strongest areas are GB and British Empire. Post-Independence / QEII material sells but if hinged at considerable discount. Mint hinged material pre 1952 is regarded as the industry 'norm' and therefore desirable – but genuine never-hinged commands a premium. Europe sells but at reduced levels, Americas is good, as generally is Asia but the 'heat' has come off China which is still good – and Russia which can still be good. East Europe is weaker. Overall, Rarities throughout can command their own price levels and real Postal History has good demand.

18 What Should I Do Next? Discuss your collection with U P A. Contact Andrew or an experienced member of his Team now… 🖥☎

19 Guarantee: I want You to be absolutely Sure So If You're not sure we'll transport and return your stamps for FREE up to £200 in actual shipping cost at our expense. It sounds generous (and it is), but it's far less than the cost of driving 100+ miles each way and 3 to 6 hours in your home valuing your stamps ☺

20 My Double Cast Iron Guarantee: We can do a better job valuing your stamps in our office than in your home. If you don't agree I'll pay you an extra £50 for you to pay somebody trusted to open the boxes and put your albums back, in the same place, on the shelf they came from. ☺☺

21 Act NOW: Contact Andrew

or an experienced member of his Team using the on-line selling form at our website, by fax, telephone or by mail. We'll work harder for you not to regret the decision to sell all or part of your collection… ☎🖥

Andrew McGavin, Philatelic Expert, Author, Managing Director Universal Philatelic Auctions UPA

UNIVERSAL PHILATELIC AUCTIONS GBCon23
4 The Old Coalyard, West End, Northleach, Glos. GL54 3HE UK
Tel: 01451 861111 • Fax: 01451 861297

www.upastampauctions.co.uk • info@upastampauctions.co.uk